THE ATOMIC ENERGY DESKBOOK

JOHN F. HOGERTON
Consultant to Arthur D. Little, Inc.
Cambridge, Massachusetts

Consultant

EDWARD A. MASON
Associate Professor of Nuclear Engineering
Massachusetts Institute of Technology
Cambridge, Massachusetts

Associates

HOWARD T. PHELAN
Arthur D. Little, Inc.
Cambridge, Massachusetts

ROBERT TUMBLESON
Oberlin School of Commerce
Oberlin, Ohio

Prepared under the auspices of the Division of Technical Information, U. S. Atomic Energy Commission

REINHOLD PUBLISHING CORPORATION, NEW YORK
CHAPMAN & HALL, LTD., LONDON

DEDICATION

This book is dedicated with affection and respect to the memory of the late Alberto F. Thompson, and to the contributions he made to the field of science communication, first as head of the U. S. Atomic Energy Commission's technical information program from 1946 to 1956 and, subsequently, as director of science information for the National Science Foundation.

Library of Congress Catalog Card Number 63-13445

Printed in the United States of America

FOREWORD

The sheer magnitude and complexity of the national nuclear energy effort make difficult the task of anyone seeking a better understanding of the scientific and technical developments involved and the administrative environment in which they take place. Responsible citizenship requires the layman to acquire a grasp of nuclear matters if he is to pass intelligent judgments on pressing domestic and international issues. The active participants in nuclear enterprise —scientists, engineers, and administrators—also need to broaden their vistas, to become better acquainted with areas outside their particular specialties. It has been with the needs of both the interested layman and the busy specialist in mind that the U. S. Atomic Energy Commission has sponsored the preparation of this Deskbook.

Glenn T. Seaborg
Chairman
U. S. Atomic Energy Commission

INTRODUCTORY STATEMENT

Progress in science and technology depends on the communication of information. In no field is this more true than in atomic energy. For this is a field in which scientists and engineers of many different disciplines are engaged, in which the time gap between laboratory research and engineering development is short, and in which legal and regulatory factors are often interwoven with technical and economic factors. Therefore the pattern of communication is complex.

We hope that The Atomic Energy Deskbook, in bringing together in one volume many of the information ingredients involved, will prove to be a useful contribution to the literature of the atomic energy industry and thereby aid communication in this important field.

RAYMOND STEVENS
Chairman,
Arthur D. Little, Inc.

AUTHOR'S PREFACE

The Atomic Energy Deskbook presents information on the background and status of atomic energy development, and on the framework of law and policy within which work in this field is conducted. Combining features of a dictionary and an encyclopedia, it contains more than one thousand alphabetically arranged entries ranging from brief definitions of terms to journal-length articles on major topics. It deals mainly with work being done in the United States on peaceful uses of atomic energy, but information is also given on military applications and there are entries on foreign atomic energy programs.

The Deskbook is designed to be useful to businessmen and students as well as scientists and engineers. Its orientation is toward subjects of industrial importance. Subjects considered to be of peripheral interest to industry are discussed in broad terms or omitted altogether.

TREATMENT

The major subjects covered by the Deskbook are treated at several levels of detail. Take, for example, development work on nuclear reactors for civilian nuclear power use. There is a general entry, titled *nuclear power development, U. S.*, which presents general programmatic information and is mainly intended to orient readers who are not close to this subject. There is a series of major entries dealing with the different types of power reactors under development—*pressurized water reactors, boiling water reactors, sodium graphite reactors,* etc. These discuss the concepts involved and summarize the development work being done. There are also brief entries on individual reactor projects completed or in progress as of mid-1962—*Dresden Nuclear Power Station, Elk River Plant,* etc. Finally, there are entries that cut across reactor lines. For example, the longest entry in the Deskbook, *nuclear power economics,* deals generally with the economic status of nuclear power development. Similarly, there are general entries on *reactor materials, fuel element fabrication, fuel reprocessing,* and *radioactive waste disposal,* and also on major reactor components, such as *pumps, valves,* and *pressure vessels.*

The purpose in fragmenting a subject such as nuclear power into a number of separate entries, rather than presenting it in a chapter or series of chapters, as in a conventional text, is to permit quick reference to specific topics. The Deskbook can be likened to a "briefing book" in which an attempt has been made to array in one-two-three order essential facts on particular subjects.

ARRANGEMENT

The Deskbook entries are alphabetically arranged. To minimize duplication of subject matter, the entries are liberally cross-referenced. The cross-referencing is done by setting the appropriate words in bold-face type. In most cases the exact entry title is given as the cross-reference, but in some cases key words are used. For example, entries on *alpha particle* and *gamma ray* may be cross-referenced as follows:

. . . some **alpha** and **gamma** activity persists . . .

As a general rule, entries on specific reactors, plants, laboratories and the like, appear under the proper name thereof—e.g., *Enrico Fermi Atomic Power Plant, Savannah River Plant,* and *E. O. Lawrence Radiation Laboratory.*

HOW TO USE THE DESKBOOK

Preceding the first entry is a partial list of contents which serves to show the headings under which major subjects are covered. In most instances, the entries listed lead the reader by cross-references to related material.

Appendix A lists all Deskbook entries together with numerous cross-references and thus constitutes a detailed index.

It is hoped that the reader will quickly find that he can turn directly to the topic he wants to look up without having to consult the index in Appendix A.

An important feature of the Deskbook is Appendix B which lists selected reading references for major subjects.

METHOD OF PREPARATION

The Deskbook was prepared under a contract between Arthur D. Little, Inc., and the U. S. Atomic Energy Commission. It has been compiled largely from published sources of information. The material was reviewed in draft form by expert reviewers on the staff of the U. S. Atomic Energy Commission and its contractor organizations. Work on the Deskbook manuscript began in 1959 and was completed early in 1962. Prior to publication, the major areas of programmatic information were reviewed and updated to reflect developments as of mid-1962.

CONTRIBUTORS

Edward A. Mason, Associate Professor of Nuclear Engineering, Massachusetts Institute of Technology, served as technical consultant for the Deskbook and additionally made substantive contributions to particular subject entries.

Howard T. Phelan of Arthur D. Little, Inc., made significant contributions to Deskbook material, both of a substantive and an editorial nature.

Robert Tumbleson, formerly director of science information, National Science Foundation, brought together much of the information from which the Deskbook was written and helped work out the method of presentation used.

ACKNOWLEDGMENTS

Many individuals acted as reviewers for the Deskbook. Their comments contributed greatly to the balance and quality of the information presented, and their interest and help is very much appreciated.

Staff members of the Division of Technical Information, U. S. Atomic Energy Commission, gave invaluable general advice and assistance, notably James D. Cape and J. William Young. Dr. Charles W. Shilling, formerly Deputy Director of the Division of Biology and Medicine, U. S. Atomic Energy Commission and Irving Kaplan of Massachusetts Institute of Technology were consulted on particular subject areas.

Many research organizations and industrial concerns furnished photographs or other illustrative material for use in the Deskbook and additional assistance along this line was received from *Nucleonics,* which kindly made available its extensive file of illustrations.

Particular thanks are due Miss E. Maeve McCann of the Arthur D. Little staff, who handled the many problems involved in shepherding the Deskbook through the sequence of manuscript preparation, illustration, review, reworking, indexing, proofreading and assembly.

JOHN F. HOGERTON

Cambridge, Massachusetts
February, 1963

CONTENTS

(*See Appendix A for complete listing*)

A-BOMB

A shorthand expression for a nuclear weapon, usually connoting a device whose explosive energy derives solely from nuclear **fission.** (See **weapons**)

ABSORPTION

In context with **nuclear reactions,** a process in which an elementary particle (neutron, proton or other) is absorbed and retained by an atomic nucleus. The process raises the energy state of the absorbing nucleus, and correspondingly, in many cases results in the emission of a photon.

In the case of nonfissionable nuclides, absorption **cross section** is synonymous with **capture** cross section; in the case of fissionable nuclides, the absorption cross section is the sum of the capture and fission cross sections.

ACCELERATORS. See **particle accelerators.**

ACCESS PERMIT

A permit issued by the U.S. Atomic Energy Commission authorizing the holder, after appropriate security approval and access authorizations, to obtain **Restricted Data** useful for civilian applications of atomic energy in the business, trade or profession of the applicant. Access Permits are issued to business firms, self-employed individuals, schools, associations, and federal, state and local governmental bodies.

The Civilian Access Permit Program established under the Atomic Energy Act of 1954, provides for two types of permits: (1) authorization for access to Confidential Restricted Data ("LX"); and (2) authorization for access to Confidential and Secret Restricted Data ("QX").

A charge is made under the program for each access authorization (security clearance) requested, except for employees of nonprofit educational institutions. Present charges are $385 for "QX" and $15 for "LX". Charges are also made for consultations, documents, abstract journals, and literature searches requested by the permit holder.

As of June 30, 1961, 933 permits were in effect. The peak number of outstanding permits was reached in August, 1958, when active permits totaled 1432. The decline since then has resulted from the increasing amount of information that has been declassified.

ACCOUNTABILITY FOR SOURCE AND SPECIAL NUCLEAR MATERIALS

For control purposes the U.S. Atomic Energy Commission has established a system of accountability for **source materials,*** **special nuclear materials,**** and, from time to time, other materials that are of special significance. Materials subject to accountability are referred to collectively as "SS" materials.

The AEC accountability system requires the measuring and recording of SS materials transfers from one station to another to establish how much SS material should be on hand, and periodic inventory checks to determine how much actually is on hand. The system is

* Presently defined to include normal uranium, depleted uranium, and thorium.

** Presently defined to include plutonium, uranium-233, and enriched uranium.

designed to detect losses and to identify where they are occurring so that corrective action may be taken. The inherent lack of absolute precision in measurement techniques necessitates treating accountability measurements statistically.

The AEC has established an **Advisory Committee for Standard Reference Materials and Methods of Measurement;** and, related thereto, a series of standard samples of enriched uranium and plutonium has been developed jointly by the AEC, the National Bureau of Standards, and others, as an aid in measurement calibration.

Regulations governing material control procedures of AEC contractors are prepared by the Division of Nuclear Materials Management and are set forth in the AEC Manual. Regulations governing accountability procedures of AEC licensees are published in the Code of Federal Regulations.* The AEC's field staff is responsible for implementing the regulations including: (1) establishing detailed material control procedures; (2) establishing SS stations; (3) surveying SS stations; (4) investigating and correcting deficiencies in accountability methods and procedures.

Two checks on the effectiveness of material control procedures are the "Book-Physical Inventory Difference" (B-PID) and the "Shipper-Receiver Difference" (S/R). The former term is defined as that amount by which the SS material determined by inventory to be on hand differs from that which transfer records indicate should be on hand. The latter term is defined as that amount by which the quantity of SS material measured by the shipping station differs from the amount measured by a receiving station. B-PID's and S/R's can stem from measurement uncertainties, process losses, or thefts, or can reflect gross errors, i.e., mistakes in reading or recording data. Statistical techniques are an aid in evaluating whether or not B-PID's or S/R's are of such magnitude as to warrant investigation. If so, the first step is normally to recheck inventory records and related measurement data. If the difference is still unresolved, a new inventory may be taken. If serious discrepancies remain and the cognizant AEC Operations Office suspects theft or diversion, the Federal Bureau of Investigation and AEC headquarters are notified.

The foregoing relates to SS materials within or under the jurisdiction of the United States. The problem of SS materials accountability also arises in international relationships. (See **international control of atomic energy**)

* *Cf.* 10 CFR 40, "Control of Source Materials"; 10 CFR 70, "Special Nuclear Material."

ACTIVATION

In nuclear physics, the process of inducing radioactivity. (See **induced radioactivity**)

ACTIVATION ANALYSIS

A method of chemical and/or isotopic analysis based on identifying radioactive nuclides formed when a sample is subjected to neutron bombardment, either in a nuclear reactor or by exposure to an external neutron source; also called neutron activation analysis. The method takes advantage of the fact that the radionuclides formed have characteristic half-lives and radiation energies. The method is sensitive enough to be applied to submicroscopic amounts of material. In some cases it can detect concentration of one part in 10^{12}, and hence is especially useful for trace or impurity analysis. Its major advantage over other analytical techniques is that it usually allows identification of elements without chemical separation; however, in some applications chemical separation of the reaction products is required to screen out interfering radioactivity. (See Fig. 1.)

While neutrons are the particles most often used in activation analysis, charged particles (protons, deuterons or alpha particles) are sometimes used. (See **neutron sources**)

ACTIVITY

Commonly used as a shorthand expression for **radioactivity.** Also, the intensity or strength, usually expressed as the number of disintegrations per second (i.e., in **curies**), of a radioactive source.

Fig. 1. Archeological application of activation analysis. Here scientist scrapes a few particles from a Mayan bowl. By neutron activation analysis of this minute sample, trace impurities can be detected and identified and then compared with those associated with other archeological specimens found in same geographical region. In this fashion articles made in the region can be differentiated from articles brought into it from other regions. (*Courtesy of Brookhaven National Laboratory*)

ACUTE EXPOSURE, TO IONIZING RADIATION

A term used in reference to a single large dose of ionizing radiation or to a series of substantial doses in a short interval of time, as differentiated from **chronic exposure.** (See **biological effects of ionizing radiation**)

ACUTE RADIATION SYNDROME

A collective term for the symptoms of severe radiation illness, which in humans usually become manifest following acute exposure to 300 or more **rems** of ionizing radiation. (See **biological effects of ionizing radiation**)

ADIABATIC COMPRESSION

A technique used in some experimental controlled-**fusion** devices for raising the temperature of the fuel **plasma.** In adiabatic compression, the plasma is heated by gradually increasing the strength of the magnetic field used for the confinement thereof. It is thus distinct from **shock heating,** which involves a very rapid increase in field strength.

ADSORPTION

Adhesion of a substance to the surface of another substance, as in the adsorption of ions by resins in ion exchange processes; not to be confused with absorption.

ADVANCED ENGINEERING TEST REACTOR (ETR-II)

A large, high-flux, general-purpose **test reactor** under construction at the National Reactor Testing Station. This facility, expected to cost $28 million to build, exclusive of test loop facilities, will furnish neutron fluxes of the order of 10^{15} neutrons per square centimeter per second. The core will have a cloverleaf configuration for maximum experimental capacity. *Type:* Tank reactor. *Power rating:*

~ 250 megawatts (thermal). *Fuel:* Modified MTR fuel elements. *Coolant:* H_2O. *Moderator:* H_2O. *Reflector:* Beryllium. *Designer:* Phillips Petroleum Company (conceptual design) and Ebasco Services, Inc. (architect-engineer). *Construction contractor:* The Fluor Co., Ltd. *Start-up:* Scheduled for **1964**.

ADVANCED EPITHERMAL THORIUM REACTOR (AETR) CONCEPT

An advanced concept for a sodium-cooled power reactor based on: (1) operation with neutrons in the high epithermal energy range (1000 to 100,000 electron volts); (2) use of graphite or beryllium as moderator; (3) use of a uranium-thorium fuel mixture. Should graphite be selected as the moderator, the AETR concept would in effect represent an extension of the sodium-graphite reactor (SGR) concept. The expected advantages of the AETR relative to the SGR concept are as follows:

1. Operation in the high-epithermal neutron range opens up the possibility of breeding on the U^{233}—Th^{232}—U^{233} cycle in a sodium environment. One reason is that U^{233} has a higher **eta** value for high-epithermal range neutrons than U^{235} or Pu^{239}. Another is that neutron absorption losses would be sharply reduced, due to the fact that most materials, including fission products, have much lower neutron capture cross sections for high-epithermal range neutrons than for thermal neutrons.

2. Operation in the high-epithermal neutron range reduces the amount of moderator required in the reactor, resulting in higher power densities and more compact core structures.

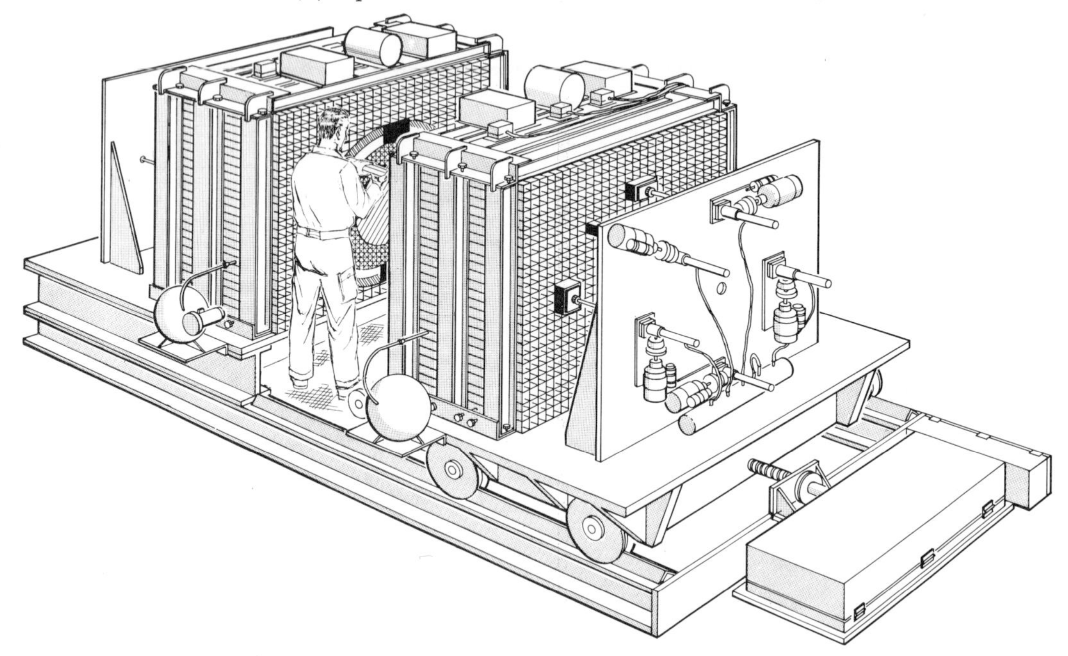

Fig. 2. Sketch of critical experiment facility built for research on Advanced Epithermal Thorium Reactor (AETR) Concept. (*Courtesy of Atomics International*)

In sum, the AETR concept offers the prospect of achieving lower fuel cycle and capital costs relative to the SGR concept, while retaining many of the basic characteristics of that concept, including the capability of high temperature operation in a low-pressure system. (See **sodium-graphite reactors**)

The AETR concept is presently at an early stage of development in the laboratories of Atomics International, a division of North American Aviation, Inc. A five-year research and development program sponsored by Southwestern Atomic Energy Associates, an organization representing 15 private electric utilities,* was initiated by Atomics International in 1958. The program is essentially a study of the feasibility of the AETR concept and has been budgeted at ~ $5 million. Preliminary conceptual design studies have been completed and a critical experiment facility was placed in operation late in 1960. U.S. Atomic Energy Commission participation in the program has been limited to providing uranium-233 and other special materials needed for the critical experiments.

A decision on whether or not to build a demonstration reactor awaits the outcome of the present exploratory program. Ebasco Services, Inc. has been retained by Southwestern Atomic Energy Associates to advise on aspects of engineering feasibility.

ADVISORY COMMITTEE FOR BIOLOGY AND MEDICINE

An *ad hoc* (nonstatutory) advisory committee to the U.S. Atomic Energy Commission which reviews AEC programs and makes policy recommendations in the fields of biological and medical research and health. The Committee was formed in 1947. Membership listed in Appendix D.

ADVISORY COMMITTEE FOR STANDARD REFERENCE MATERIALS AND METHODS OF MEASUREMENT

An *ad hoc* (nonstatutory) advisory committee to the U.S. Atomic Energy Commission which evaluates and recommends means for providing standard reference materials (e.g., certified chemical and isotopic standards for uranium and plutonium) and approved methods of measurement of materials of special importance to atomic energy activities. The Committee was originally established in 1956 as the Committee for Uranium Isotopic Standards, and was reconstituted under its present name in 1958. Membership listed in Appendix D.

* The companies represented are: Arkansas Power and Light Company, Arkansas-Missouri Power Company, Central Louisiana Electric Company, the Empire District Electric Company (Missouri), Gulf States Utilities Company (Texas), Kansas Gas and Electric Company, the Kansas Power and Light Company, Louisiana Power and Light Company, Mississippi Power and Light Company, Missouri Public Service Company, New Orleans Public Service Inc., Oklahoma Gas and Electric Company, Public Service Company of Oklahoma, Southwestern Electric Power Company (Louisiana), and Western Light and Telephone Company (Missouri).

ADVISORY COMMITTEE OF STATE OFFICIALS

An *ad hoc* (nonstatutory) advisory committee to the U.S. Atomic Energy Commission established in 1955 for consultation on AEC regulatory activities in the field of public health and safety, and broadened in membership in 1960 for consultation on cooperation between the federal and state governments in regulating atomic energy activities. The broadening of the Committee's scope followed enactment of Public Law 86-373, which amended the Atomic Energy Act of 1954 by adding a section on federal-state cooperation. (See **legislation, federal**; also, **state activities in the atomic energy field**) Membership listed in Appendix D.

ADVISORY COMMITTEE ON ISOTOPE AND RADIATION DEVELOPMENT

An *ad hoc* (nonstatutory) advisory committee to the U.S. Atomic Energy Commission formed in 1958 for consultation on means of encouraging industrial uses of radioisotopes and radiation. Membership listed in Appendix D.

ADVISORY COMMITTEE ON MEDICAL USES OF ISOTOPES

An *ad hoc* (nonstatutory) advisory committee to the U.S. Atomic Energy Commission formed in 1958 for consultation on policies and standards for the regulation and licensing of medical uses of radioisotopes in humans. Membership listed in Appendix D.

ADVISORY COMMITTEE ON REACTOR PHYSICS

An *ad hoc* (nonstatutory) advisory committee to the U.S. Atomic Energy Commission formed to review and consult on the general "state of the art" of reactor physics information needed for the evaluation and development of reactor concepts and the design and construction of reactor installations. Membership listed in Appendix D.

ADVISORY COMMITTEE ON REACTOR SAFEGUARDS (ACRS)

A statutory * advisory committee to the U.S. Atomic Energy Commission established to review safety studies and facility license applications referred to it and make reports thereon, advise the Commission with regard to the hazards of proposed or existing reactor facilities and the adequacy of proposed reactor safety standards, and to perform other such duties as the Commission may request. (See **Atomic Energy Commission—Licensing and Regulatory Procedure**)

Members are appointed by the Commission for a term of four years each. One member is elected by the Committee as its Chairman and holds that post for one year. Membership listed in Appendix D.

ADVISORY COMMITTEE ON TECHNICAL INFORMATION

An *ad hoc* (non-statutory) advisory committee to the U.S. Atomic Energy Commission formed in 1949 for consultation on the planning and execution of the AEC's technical information program. Membership listed in Appendix D.

AEC. See **Atomic Energy Commission.**

AERIAL MONITORING

The use of low-flying aircraft carrying a scintillation counter or other sensitive radiation detection equipment to locate or survey ground radioactivity. Aerial monitoring has been widely used in **uranium exploration** as a means of locating radioactive anomalies and thereby identifying areas that warrant prospecting. Another application is in surveying the level of radiation contamination in areas in which **radioactive fallout** has occurred.

Aerial monitoring should not be confused with air monitors which are ground-based instruments used to monitor airborne radioactivity.

* A nonstatutory advisory committee prior to September, 1957. Given statutory status by a 1957 amendment (Public Law 85–256) to the Atomic Energy Act of 1954.

AEROJET-GENERAL NUCLEONICS REACTORS (AGN SERIES)

Trade name of a line of small nuclear reactors developed and manufactured by Aerojet Nucleonics Corporation of San Ramon, California. Through 1960, 19 AGN units had been supplied or were scheduled for delivery to laboratories in the United States and abroad, mainly for use in student training. *Type:* Solid homogeneous reactors in tank or pool-type installations. *Power ratings:* AGN-201 series, 0.1 watt (thermal). AGN-201M series, 5 watts. AGN-211 series, 15 watts. AGN-201P series, 20 watts. *Fuel:* Discs containing uranium dioxide of 20% isotopic enrichment mixed with polyethylene. *Coolant:* None required. *Moderator:* Polyethylene. *Reflector:* Graphite. *Neutron flux:* Of the order of 10^6n/cm^{2}sec (thermal).

For a listing of AGN reactor installations and general background information, see **research and training reactors.**

AEROSOL

A general term for a dispersion of finely divided solid or liquid particles in a gaseous medium, e.g., smoke, fog, mist or suspended dust. The characteristics of aerosols are studied in connection with **radioactive fallout**, health hazards in uranium mining and processing, radioactive waste disposal, etc.

AFGHANISTAN

A member of the **International Atomic Energy Agency** (IAEA). No significant atomic energy activity has been reported beyond the fact that Afghanistan is one of a number of

Fig. 3. Instruction in the operation of AGN Reactors at Aerojet-General Nucleonics' plant. (*Courtesy of Aerojet-General Corporation*)

nations receiving technical assistance from the IAEA.

AGN SERIES. See **Aerojet-General Nucleonics Reactors.**

AGREEMENTS FOR COOPERATION

Agreements between the United States and other governments or international organizations covering cooperation in specific areas of atomic energy activity. They are of three general types—research, research and power, and mutual defense—and cover the communication of Restricted Data, the distribution of special nuclear material, and the export of production and utilization facilities. Tables 1A and 1B summarize the agreements in force as of October 19, 1961.

Background. During World War II there was cooperation among the United States, the United Kingdom and Canada in the development of military applications of atomic energy and in the procurement of uranium for the common defense. The basis for this cooperation was the Quebec Agreement of August, 1943. The postwar enactment of the U.S. Atomic Energy Act of 1946, which prohibited the exchange of classified information with other nations in the fields of military and industrial uses of atomic energy, required redefinition of the relations between the three allies in the atomic energy field. A *modus vivendi* agreement, reached in 1948, continued the joint ore procurement program but modified other areas of cooperation in the light of the restrictions of the 1946 Act.

Several other agreements were entered into during and after World War II with friendly nations in the area of uranium exploration and procurement.

In 1951, an amendment to the 1946 Act enabled the United States to engage in limited

TABLE 1A. U.S. AGREEMENTS FOR COOPERATION
RESEARCH AND POWER
(October 19, 1961)

Cumulative Numbers Countries	*Agreements*	*Country*	*Scope of Exchange*	*Termination Date*
1	1	Argentina	Research [2]	July 28, 1962
2	2	Australia [1]	Research and power	May 27, 1967
3	3	Austria	Research	Jan. 24, 1970
4	4	Belgium [1]	Research and power [2]	July 31, 1965
5	5	Brazil	Research [2]	Aug. 2, 1962
6	6	Canada [1]	Research and power [2]	July 13, 1980
7	7	China, Republic of	Research [2]	July 17, 1962
8	8	Costa Rica	Research	July 7, 1966
9	9	Cuba	Research	Oct. 9, 1962
10	10	Denmark	Research [2]	Sept. 7, 1968
11	11	Dominican Republic	Research	Dec. 20, 1961
12	12	Ecuador	Research	Feb. 5, 1963
13	13	France	Research and power [2]	Nov. 20, 1966
14	14	Germany, Federal Republic of	Research and power [2]	Aug. 7, 1967
	15	West Berlin, city of	Research	July 31, 1962
15	16	Greece	Research [2]	Aug. 3, 1962
16	17	Guatemala	Research	Apr. 21, 1962
17	18	Indonesia	Research	Sept. 20, 1965
18	19	Iran	Research	Apr. 26, 1964
19	20	Ireland	Research	July 9, 1963
20	21	Israel	Research [2]	July 11, 1962
21	22	Italy	Research and power	Apr. 14, 1978
22	23	Japan	Research and power [2]	Dec. 4, 1968
23	24	Korea, Republic of	Research [2]	Feb. 2, 1966
24	25	Netherlands [1]	Research and power [2]	Aug. 7, 1967
25	26	Nicaragua	Research	Mar. 6, 1963
26	27	Norway	Research and power	June 2, 1967
27	28	Philippines	Research [2]	July 26, 1963
28	29	Portugal	Research [2]	July 20, 1962
29	30	South Africa	Research and power	Aug. 21, 1967
30	31	Spain	Research and power	Feb. 11, 1968
31	32	Sweden	Research [2]	June 1, 1968
32	33	Switzerland	Research	July 17, 1965
	34	Switzerland [1]	Power [2]	Jan. 28, 1967
33	35	Thailand	Research [2]	Mar. 11, 1963
34	36	Turkey	Research	June 9, 1965
35	37	United Kingdom [1]	Research and power [2]	July 20, 1965
36	38	Venezuela	Research and power	Feb. 8, 1970
37	39	Vietnam	Research	June 30, 1964

[1] Classified agreements.
[2] Denotes agreement has been amended.

TABLE 1B. U.S. AGREEMENTS FOR COOPERATION SPECIAL AND MUTUAL DEFENSE AGREEMENTS (October 19, 1961)

Special Agreements:	
1. European Atomic Energy Joint Nuclear Power Program Community (EURATOM)	Feb. 18, 1959
2. European Atomic Energy Additional Agreement Community (EURATOM)	July 25, 1960
3. International Atomic Energy Supply of Materials, etc. Agency (IAEA)	Aug. 7, 1959
Mutual Defense Purposes Agreements:	
1. Australia [1]	Aug. 14, 1957
2. Canada [1]	July 27, 1959
3. France	July 20, 1959
4. France [1]	Oct. 9, 1961
5. Germany, Federal Republic of [1]	July 27, 1959
6. Greece [1]	Aug. 11, 1959
7. Italy [1]	May 24, 1961
8. Netherlands [1]	July 27, 1959
9. Turkey [1]	July 27, 1959
10. United Kingdom [1]	Aug. 4, 1958
(Amendment to United Kingdom Agreement) [1]	July 20, 1959

[1] Classified agreements.

exchange of classified information with other nations. This amendment led to information-exchange agreements with Canada and several other friendly nations supplying raw materials to the United States.

In an address before the United Nations General Assembly on December 8, 1953, President Eisenhower made his historic "Atoms for Peace" proposal, which in part called for increased international cooperation in research and development relating to constructive atomic energy applications and for the establishment of an International Atomic Energy Agency. The following year the 1946 Act was superseded by the Atomic Energy Act of 1954, which provided a framework for a broadened international cooperation program. The several types of agreements that have been entered into under the revised Act, together with the general statutory provisions controlling these agreements, are briefly described in the paragraphs which follow.

Statutory Provisions. The 1954 Act requires that an Agreement for Cooperation be in force before the communication of **restricted data**, the export of **production** or **utilization facilities**, or the distribution of **special nuclear material** to another country can take place. In a similar vein, the Act prohibits persons or organizations from engaging directly or indirectly in the production of special nuclear material outside the United States except under an Agreement for Cooperation or upon a specific authorization by the U.S. Atomic Energy Commission.

The Act sets forth the terms under which the AEC may communicate restricted data to other nations in areas of technology relating to the refining, purification, and subsequent treatment of **source material**, civilian reactor development, the production of special nuclear material, health and safety, industrial and other applications of atomic energy for peaceful purposes, and research and development relating to these areas. It similarly establishes terms under which the Department of Defense, with the assistance of the AEC, may cooperate with other nations or regional defense organizations and communicate restricted data in connection with certain military aspects of atomic energy, namely, the development of defense plans; the training of personnel in the employment of and defense against atomic weapons; the evaluation of the capabilities of potential enemies in the employment of atomic weapons; and the development of compatible delivery systems for atomic weapons.

The Act also provides that the President may authorize cooperation in the military aspects of atomic energy with another nation to exchange restricted data concerning atomic weapons provided "communication of such restricted data to that nation is necessary to improve its atomic weapon design, development, or fabrication capability and provided that nation has made substantial progress in the development of atomic weapons." The President may also authorize cooperation with another nation to communicate or exchange with that nation restricted data concerning research, development, or design of military reactors.

Before any Agreement for Cooperation either for civilian uses or for mutual defense programs can become effective, there must be compliance with the following general provisions of the Act:

1. The AEC or the Department of Defense, as the case may be, must have submitted to the President a proposed agreement incorporating:

 a. The terms, conditions, duration, nature and scope of the cooperation;
 b. A guaranty by the cooperating party that requisite security safeguards and standards will be maintained;
 c. A guaranty by the cooperating party that any material transferred pursuant to the agreement, except in the case of those agreements for cooperation arranged pursuant to subsection 91c, will not be used for any military purpose;
 d. A guaranty by the cooperating party that any material or restricted data provided pursuant to the agreement will not be transferred by that party to unauthorized persons, or beyond the jurisdiction of the cooperating party, except as specified in the agreement for cooperation.

2. The President must have approved and authorized the execution of the proposed agreement and made a determination in writing that performance thereof will promote, and will not constitute an unreasonable risk to, the common defense and security;

3. The proposed agreement, together with the President's approval and determination, must be before the Joint Congressional Committee on Atomic Energy for a period of 30 days, if an agreement for cooperation in civil uses, or 60 days if an agreement for mutual defense purposes. The waiting period for civil uses agreements, however, may be waived by the JCAE.

Research Agreements. The majority of the bilateral agreements now in force (see Table 1A) are limited to cooperation in the field of atomic energy research for peaceful purposes. These agreements are characterized by the following provisions:

1. The term of the agreements is, in general, five years.

2. They provide for exchange of unclassified information relating to research reactors and their applications; health and safety problems relating thereto; and the broad field of radioisotope usage. (No classified information is exchanged under these agreements.)

3. Most research agreements provide for the leasing of a specified quantity of uranium enriched in the uranium-235 isotope. Generally, in cases where the agreement contains comprehensive control and safeguard provisions, uranium enriched to a maximum of 90% U^{235} may be leased or sold for use in research or materials testing reactors or in reactor experiments capable of operating with a fuel loading not in excess of 8 kilograms. In cases where comprehensive control and safeguard provisions are not contained in the agreement, the lease arrangements are limited to uranium of a maximum enrichment of 20% containing from six to a maximum of 15 kilograms of U^{235}, depending upon the specific requirements of the user.

4. Except in the early research agreements which provided only for lease, they require that the enriched uranium be reprocessed in AEC facilities or in a facility approved by the AEC.

5. They provide for the sale of reactor materials which may not be available commercially, other than special nuclear materials; for example, heavy water.

6. They may provide for the transfer of small quantities of special nuclear material for research purposes other than fueling. The maximum amounts are 100 grams of contained U^{235}; 10 grams of U^{233}; 250 grams of plutonium in the form of neutron sources or foils; and 10 grams of plutonium in other forms.

7. They contain additional provisions satisfying U.S. statutory requirements (see above).

On reaching the expiration date, research agreements may be extended or allowed to expire, depending on whether or not the cooperating country can satisfy its continuing requirements through the **International Atomic Energy Agency.**

Research and Power Agreements. Bilateral agreements that provide for cooperation in the nuclear power field as well as in atomic research fall into three categories:

1. Special arrangements exist with the United Kingdom, Canada, and Belgium. The Agreements for Cooperation with these countries were the first to be negotiated after enactment of the 1954 Act in recognition of the prior contributions each had made to the U.S. program. The agreements were tailored to individual requirements and, in each case, provided for exchange of information on civilian power reactors and related technology. The agreements with Canada and Belgium provided for the sale of uranium-235 for use in reactors. No maximum amount was specified, however the agreements stipulated that transfer during any year was subject to availability and, further, that the total quantity of "weapon quality" (i.e., high enrichment) material transferred should not be of military significance. Each of these agreements has been amended one or more times since they first became effective on July 21, 1955.

2. At a later stage in the U.S. program, agreements were concluded with some countries providing for information exchange and for the sale of enriched uranium for specified research and power reactor projects. The maximum amount typically specified for transfer over a ten-year term is 500 kilograms of contained uranium-235 in uranium enriched up to 20%. Many of the agreements provide that a portion of the 500 kilograms maximum can be made available in highly enriched form (up to 90%) for use in research or materials testing reactors or reactor experiments capable of operating with a fuel loading not in excess of 8 kilograms. The agreements give the United States a first option to purchase special nuclear material that is produced from this material and which is not to be used by the cooperating country in its own civilian program. Also, the reprocessing of the U.S.-supplied material must be done in AEC facilities or in a facility approved by the AEC. As of October 19, 1961, agreements of this kind were in force with Australia, the Netherlands, Norway, the Union of South Africa, Spain, and Switzerland.

3. Agreements with some countries (as of October 19, 1961, France, Germany, Italy, Japan, and Venezuela) now provide for the sale of larger quantities of uranium enriched up to 20%. Here the amounts are based on broad program requirements, rather than being keyed to specific projects. The terms of these agreements are otherwise similar to those noted in the preceding paragraph.

AGRICULTURAL APPLICATIONS OF ATOMIC ENERGY

Atomic energy contributions to the field of agriculture stem principally from the use of radioisotopes as tracers and from experiments conducted with ionizing radiation. The U.S. Atomic Energy Commission supports some applied research on agricultural problems but its major programs in this field are in the category of basic research. National laboratories, universities and agricultural research stations participate in these programs. The information presented here relates to the use of radioisotopes and ionizing radiation in plant, insect and animal studies. Research on the use of ionizing radiation in extending the storage life of foodstuffs is covered under a separate heading. (See **food preservation**)

Plant Studies. Research is conducted on plant genetics, plant physiology and biochemistry, and plant pathology. Following are notes on major areas of effort:

Radiation Genetics. Ionizing radiation can be used to induce genetic mutations in plant species and thereby short-cut the natural mutation process. Extensive experimental programs have been undertaken in which nuclear reactors and other radiation sources have been used to irradiate seeds of various common U.S. plant species. This work is contributing to improved understanding of plant genetics and to date has created at least two new plant varieties which have been made available for agricultural production. One is a variety of navy bean, which has been found to result in 30%

higher crop yields than the parent variety; the other is a variety of peanut exhibiting improved crop-yield and disease-resistance characteristics. Ionizing radiation is also used to produce somatic mutations in plants which can be propagated with cuttings or grafts, and to achieve genetic rearrangement by chromosome fragmentation. Beneficial results from the latter have included an early and late-ripening variety of peach and disease-resistant strains of wheat, oats and flax.

Photosynthesis. The use of radioisotopes as tracers has done much to advance man's understanding of the process by which living plants use the green pigment (chlorophyll) in their leaves to absorb energy from light rays and thereby convert carbon dioxide and water into sugar and starch and other food substances. The first major breakthrough in decades of research on this subject occurred in the late fifties when experiments with carbon-14 enabled scientists to trace the carbon-dioxide fixation phase of photosynthesis. More recently, a complex technique developed at the E. O. Lawrence Radiation Laboratory involving the use of oxygen-18 as a tracer has begun to clarify the water-decomposition phase of the process. Additional research on photosynthesis is being conducted at the subcellular level by isolating the microscopic substances (chloroplasts) which contain the chlorophyll, and studying them in experiments which are free of the complex side reactions normally present in plant systems.

Fig. 4. Research on photosynthesis. Here leaf is simultaneously exposed to radioactive carbon dioxide and bright light. After brief period of exposure, leaf will be digested and distribution of carbon-14 measured. (*Courtesy of E. O. Lawrence Radiation Laboratory*)

Other Plant Metabolism Studies. Metabolism, which can be defined as the sum total of all chemical reactions taking place in an organism, is widely studied, with photosynthesis perhaps the most heavily researched metabolic process. Other specific metabolic phenomena

Fig. 5. Top, "Gamma Garden." When the area is clear, a cobalt-60 source is raised into position in the pipe by remote control. This facility is used to study radiation-induced mutations in various plant species. Left, special greenhouse in which plants can be fed with nutrients labeled with a radioisotope (tracer experiments) or continuously exposed to a radioactive atmosphere (mutation experiments). Right, dahlia plant with a mixture of red and white petals is an example of a radiation-induced mutation. (*Courtesy of Brookhaven National Laboratory (top, right) and Argonne National Laboratory (left)*)

being studied by tracer techniques include the breakdown of carbohydrates and the synthesis of fatty acids.

Nutrient Studies. Radioisotopes of phosphorus, calcium, and zinc have been used to study the uptake of nutrients from the soil and have thrown considerable light on soil fertilization procedures. Much research has also been done on the mechanisms of nutrient uptake. Here a significant finding has been that many inorganic and organic nutrients are taken up by plant leaves as well as by the root structure—an unexpected result that has led to mounting interest in the possibility of "foliar feeding" by means of nutrient sprays.

Other. Other major areas of plant research include studies of substances, such as the auxin group of plant hormones, which play a key role in plant growth; studies of plant growth regulators and herbicides; research on plant diseases and fungicides; and research on soil properties, such as density and water content.

Insect Studies. The major areas of research on insects are the following:

Biological Studies. Radioisotopes have been used to "tag" various household, agricultural, and forest insects and thereby determine their range of travel and also the effectiveness of insect control programs.

Insect Sterilization. Ionizing radiation can be used to sterilize insects and thereby eliminate pest populations. In 1955, the Department of Agriculture demonstrated the feasibility of eliminating the screwworm fly by sterilization in experiments conducted on the island of Curacao in the Netherlands West Indies. The technique used was to release male flies which had been rendered sexually sterile by irradiation and hence could produce no offspring. The success of these experiments led to the application of the same technique in the southeastern section of the United States. This program started in 1957 and promises to be completely effective.

Insect Destruction. Direct destruction of insects by application of a lethal radiation dose has been proposed for use in reducing insect damage to stored grain, clothing, wood products, and some processed foodstuffs; however, this has not as yet been demonstrated. Experiments indicate that high radiation doses are required—$\sim$ 65,000 roentgens in the case of rice weevils—and a mobile fission-product source capable of supplying such dosages is currently in the planning stage.

Insecticides. Radioactive tracers are being used to study and improve insecticide performance.

Farm Animal Studies. The major areas of research on farm animals are the following:

Animal Nutrients. Various radioisotopes are used in studying the metabolism of nutrient elements important in animal feeding. Examples are the use of sulfur-35 in determining the effectiveness of inorganic sulfur in poultry feed; and the use of calcium-45 to study the contribution of calcium to embryonic development in fertile poultry eggs.

Biochemistry of Body Processes. Here extensive tracer research has been conducted on the role of certain microorganisms in milk production; on the effect of ambient temperatures on the body processes of cattle; on the role of thyroid hormones in chickens; etc.

AIR BURST

The detonation of a nuclear weapon at an altitude below 100,000 feet but at sufficient height that the **fireball** does not come into contact with the earth's surface (land or water). (See **weapons phenomenology**)

AIR FORCE NUCLEAR ENGINEERING TEST REACTOR (NETR)

A 10,000-kilowatt pool-type **test reactor** in stand-by status at Wright Air Development Center, Dayton, Ohio. It is owned by the U.S. Air Force and was originally intended to be used to test the effects of radiation on materials and equipment components of interest to the Air Force. Completed in 1961, its use at this writing is uncertain, due to cancellation of the **Aircraft Nuclear Propulsion Program.** The contractors for the installation were Maxon Construction Company and Allis-Chalmers Manufacturing Company.

AIR SAMPLERS AND MONITORS

Instruments for the detection and measurement of airborne radioactivity. Air samplers consist of a collection mechanism (usually a filter or an electrostatic precipitator) through which air samples are drawn. The radioactive deposits thus collected *in situ* are then taken to a laboratory for measurement. Air monitors consist of air samplers with a built-in radiation counter and/or a recording or alarm device to provide immediate information *in situ*.

Applications include: (1) Monitoring reactor installations for the escape of particulate or gaseous radioactivity, as from a ruptured fuel element, or for radioactivity induced in dust particles present in the atmosphere; (2) monitoring laboratories or plants in which radioactive materials are handled; (3) monitoring uranium mines or mills to detect excessive concentrations of uranium dusts or radioactive daughter products (radon) from the decay of radium; (4) detection of **radioactive fallout** from weapons tests; and (5) measurement of **background** radioactivity from natural sources.

Some air monitors are permanently installed and operate continuously; others are portable or semiportable and designed for spot surveys. Some detect or measure total radioactivity, others are designed to discriminate between **gamma** and **beta** activity, and still others measure only **alpha** activity.

AIRCRAFT CARRIER, NUCLEAR. See **Naval Reactors Program;** U.S.S. ***Enterprise.***

AIRCRAFT NUCLEAR PROPULSION FACILITY

A government-owned reactor development laboratory located at Evendale, Ohio. *Operating contractor:* General Electric Company (Aircraft Nuclear Propulsion Department ANPD). *AEC investment:* * ~ $10 million (for equipment only; the basic plant is the property of the U.S. Air Force). The Evendale laboratory was established under the **Aircraft Nuclear Propulsion Program,** and concentrated on the development of direct-cycle reactor systems for military aircraft propulsion. The peak employment was ~ 3000. When the ANP Program was canceled early in 1961, the laboratory's program was sharply curtailed and redirected toward research on high-temperature materials for high-performance reactor systems for civilian applications.

* Excludes investment in related facilities at the National Reactor Testing Station.

AIRCRAFT NUCLEAR PROPULSION (ANP) PROGRAM

A recently terminated program of research and development on nuclear propulsion systems for manned aircraft.** From 1946, when an exploratory study was initiated, to March, 1961, when development work was brought to a halt, in the neighborhood of $1 billion was spent in this program. Over most of this period the effort was jointly directed by the U.S. Air Force and the U.S. Atomic Energy Commission through an interagency group, the Aircraft Nuclear Propulsion Office (ANPO), headquartered in the AEC's Division of Reactor Development. The Air Force bore the responsibility for application aspects of the program and for the development of non-nuclear components; the AEC was responsible for reactor development and related nuclear technology. The Navy participated in the program and was represented in ANPO.

The conceptual advantages of nuclear-powered aircraft, all of which stem from the extreme compactness of nuclear fuel as an energy source, are: (1) greatly extended cruising range in terms of distance, time or a combination of the two; (2) payload capability independent of range; and (3) unlimited capability for low-altitude penetration of target area.

The achievement of a practical nuclear propulsion system for manned aircraft involves many difficult problems including:

1. The development of compact reactors having extremely high power-to-weight ratios

** For information on the nuclear propulsion of unmanned aircraft, space vehicles, etc., see **Pluto Project** (ramjet propulsion of missiles), and **Rover Project** (rocket propulsion of space vehicles). Also see **SNAP Program.**

and capable of operation at full power for 100 or more hours. To achieve the desired power-to-weight ratios requires operation at temperatures and power densities well beyond the range of civilian power reactor technology, which in turn means pushing reactor materials well beyond conventional limits.

2. The design of compact radiation shielding of minimum weight and optimum weight distribution.

3. The design of airframes to accommodate unprecedented weight distributions and landing loads. Unlike conventional aircraft, the weight of fuel consumed during flight is negligible.

4. Comprehensive environmental testing of materials and components used in aircraft systems (seals, lubricants, insulating materials, transistors, etc.) to determine the effect of radiation on equipment performance and lifetime.

5. Development of facilities and techniques for ground handling, including provision for remote maintenance.

6. Analysis of operational safety.

From 1951, there were two approaches to the development of nuclear power for manned aircraft—the direct cycle and the indirect cycle. These cycles are described later in this discussion.

Objectives. The first definite objective set for the ANP Program was to demonstrate a proof-of-principle, direct-cycle nuclear propulsion system in a modified conventional aircraft (B-36) by the late fifties. Plans for the "X-6 flying testbed" program, formalized in 1952, were criticized by the Secretary of Defense on the grounds that such a demonstration would have no military value. In 1953 the flying testbed program was canceled and the funding of the ANP Program was cut back under budget pressure. A second definite objective was set in 1955 following renewed military interest in the program. At that time an Air Force weapon system requirement was established for a high-performance airplane that would cruise at subsonic speed under nuclear power but attack at supersonic speed under chemical power. Ground testing of a prototype propulsion system was tentatively scheduled for 1959 and development work was accelerated. A year later (1956) the high-performance objective was canceled as technically infeasible and the funding of the ANP Program was again cut back.

A third definite objective was defined by the DOD early in 1960 in connection with an Air Force requirement for the "CAMAL" * weapon system for the Strategic Air Command. That objective was to develop a nuclear propulsion system capable of powering an aircraft in the 500,000-pound weight class at high subsonic speed (0.8 to 0.9 Mach range) at an altitude of 35,000 feet with a potential power plant life of 1000 hours. Ground testing of developmental equipment was tentatively scheduled for 1962 with the expectation that flight testing of an actual power plant could begin in the mid-sixties. Work proceeded essentially on this basis on both direct- and indirect-cycle systems through 1960.

In the meantime the ANP Program continued to be subject to policy debate and budget pressure. When the budget message of the outgoing Eisenhower administration was submitted to the Congress, it contained a recommendation that one of the two lines of propulsion engine development be canceled. Subsequently, in March, 1961, President Kennedy submitted a special defense message to the Congress which contained the recommendation that both lines of engine development, together with all airframe development, be canceled on the grounds that "the possibility of achieving a militarily useful aircraft in the foreseeable future is still very remote." In making the recommendation, President Kennedy proposed that related scientific work on high-temperature materials and high-performance reactors be continued under AEC direction within the framework of the AEC's broad reactor development objectives. Pursuant to this recommendation, the AEC and the Air Force issued cancellation notices to their ANP prime contractors. In April, 1961, the AEC announced plans for a program of high-temperature ma-

* Continuous Airborne Missile Launching and Low-Level Penetration System.

terials and high-performance reactor development to be carried out by the contractors who had been engaged in the nuclear phases of the ANP Program (see below).

Early History. In May, 1946, the Air Force contracted with Fairchild Engine & Airplane Company to explore the feasibility of nuclear-powered aircraft. The study, known as the NEPA Project (from Nuclear Energy for the Propulsion of Aircraft), was conducted in facilities at Oak Ridge, Tennessee.

In 1948, an independent evaluation was made for the AEC by Massachusetts Institute of Technology. The findings, published in the so-called "Lexington Report," were that aircraft nuclear propulsion appeared feasible in principle, but that it would probably take 15 years of intensive effort, especially in basic reactor studies and materials research, to achieve a practical system.

In November, 1949, the AEC initiated a program of research at Oak Ridge National Laboratory with emphasis on high-temperature reactor concepts and radiation shielding problems (see below).

By 1951, it was felt that sufficient progress had been made to warrant starting engine development. In May of that year the NEPA Project was accordingly terminated.

Direct-Cycle Engine Development. Early in 1951 the General Electric Company was selected as the prime contractor for a reactor-engine development program. Work began in the spring and by early fall the decision had been made to base the development on a direct-cycle system utilizing a high-temperature air-cooled reactor. In such a system air enters the compressor section of a jet engine, is heated by passing through the reactor, and is then exhausted through a jet nozzle.

The development work centered in government-owned laboratories (known as the Aircraft Nuclear Propulsion Facility) located adjacent to a General Electric plant in Evendale, Ohio, and in test facilities at the National Reactor Testing Station. A series of ground-based reactor experiments was conducted at the latter site to study the performance of high-temperature fuel elements and other key materials, and to gain experience with the operation of a reactor in a jet engine system. The experiments, designated Heat Transfer Reactor Experiments-1, -2 and -3, can be summarized as follows:

1. HRTE-1 was moderated with water and fueled with nickel-chromium-uranium dioxide fuel elements.* The reactor operated in conjunction with a single J-47 jet engine at power levels up to 18.5 megawatts. Tests were conducted with this system during 1956, including full-power runs for periods of time in excess of 100 hours at fuel temperatures up to 180°F and core exit temperatures in the neighborhood of 1300°F.

2. HRTE-2 was a rebuilt version of HRTE-1 with mechanical modifications to permit testing more advanced fuel elements and other materials. It began intermittent test operation in 1957.

3. HRTE-3 employed a solid high-temperature moderator (zirconium-hydride), and fuel elements similar to those used in HRTE-1. The reactor operated in conjunction with two J-47 jet engines at power levels up to about 32 megawatts. Tests were conducted with this system from late 1959 through most of 1960, including full power runs in excess of 100 hours at fuel temperatures up to 1900°F and core exit temperatures somewhat above 1600°F.

At the time of cancellation of the ANP Program, a reactor experiment known as the Advanced Core Test (ACT) was in the planning stage.

Indirect-Cycle Engine Development. In 1951 Pratt & Whitney Aircraft Corporation was brought into the ANP Program to develop an indirect-cycle engine, i.e., one in which an intermediate fluid is used to transfer heat from the reactor to the working fluid (air). Several reactor concepts were studied, namely: (1) a system using solid fuel elements and supercritical water as coolant (1951-1953); (2) a circulating-fuel system of the molten salt type being developed by Oak Ridge National Laboratory (1953-1957); and

* Consisting of a dispersion of fully enriched uranium dioxide in a nickel-chromium matrix, clad with nickel-chromium alloy.

(3) a system using solid fuel elements and liquid lithium as coolant (1955-1961).* In 1958, the decision was made to base a reactor development program on the latter concept on the grounds that it offered the greatest long-range potential for a high-performance nuclear-powered aircraft. The development work centered in a government-owned facility, the Connecticut Aircraft Nuclear Engine Laboratory (CANEL),** at Middleton, Connecticut. At the time of cancellation of the ANP Program, plans were being drawn for the construction of reactor test facilities at the National Reactor Testing Station.

Supporting R&D. Early in the Oak Ridge National Laboratory research program, experimental work began on the **molten salt reactor** concept. This work culminated in a fluid-fuel molten salt reactor experiment, known as the Aircraft Reactor Experiment (ARE), which was successfully operated in 1954 and then dismantled. ORNL worked closely with Pratt & Whitney during the reactor evaluation phase of the indirect-cycle engine development program (see above), and subsequently provided technical support to both the indirect-cycle and the direct-cycle engine programs.

ORNL made major contributions to the ANP Program through its research on radia-

Fig. 6. Tower Shielding Reactor Facility used for radiation shielding studies for ANP Program. (*Courtesy of Oak Ridge National Laboratory*)

* This concept is now the basis for development of a compact reactor for use in electric rocket propulsion systems for space vehicles (see reference to SNAP-50 under **SNAP Progam).**

** Now known as the **Connecticut Advanced Nuclear Engineering Laboratory.**

tion shielding, especially in developing the theory and design of "divided shields," i.e., two-part shielding systems consisting of a thick shield around the reactor to protect the crew and equipment against direct radiation plus a relatively thin shield surrounding the crew quarters to protect against air scattering effects. Such a system serves to distribute the weight of shielding material as well as to reduce weight requirements. In connection with its research on divided shields and other aspects of the shielding problem, ORNL built and operated a novel experimental facility to study air scattering and other phenomena. This facility, known as the Tower Shielding Reactor (TSR-1, -2) consisted essentially of a tank-type research reactor suspended (during operation) from four 320-foot steel columns. TSR-1, rated at 500 kilowatts (thermal), was used from 1954 to 1958 and then dismantled. TSR-2, rated at 5000 kilowatts (thermal), began operation in 1960.

Fig. 7. Connecticut Aircraft Nuclear Engine Laboratory (CANEL), Middletown, Conn. (*Courtesy of Pratt & Whitney Aircraft Corp.*)

Airframe Development. In 1951 the Air Force contracted with Convair Division of General Dynamics Corporation to study application and airframe design problems. Air Force requirements were redefined at several stages of the ANP Program (see earlier discussion). Preliminary design of an airframe for a development aircraft (the NX-2) was completed. In the course of its work, Convair conducted extensive environmental studies, including both shielding and radiation effects measurements. This work was conducted in facilities at Fort Worth, Texas. Two test reactors were employed—one a pool-type installation, known as the **Ground Test Reactor** (GTR); the other a tank-type installation known as the **Aircraft Shield Test Reactor** (ASTR). Additional measurements were made with the ASTR installed in a modified B-36 airplane and serving as a radiation source during actual flight operations.

In 1955, the Air Force contracted with Lockheed Aircraft Corporation to design an airframe for a high-performance aircraft in conjunction with the Pratt & Whitney indirect-cycle engine development. With the decision the following year to abandon the high-performance aircraft objective this assignment was canceled. Lockheed subsequently planned an experimental program in the area of radiation effects on aircraft components and materials to be conducted in a special test reactor and related facilities at Dawsonville, Georgia (see **Radiation Effects Reactor**). The ANP Program was canceled before significant results could be obtained from this work.

ANP Funding. Following is a summary of funding of the ANP Program from 1946 through mid-1960:

ANP FUNDING ($ MILLION) [1, 2]

	R&D	*Capital Costs*	*Total*
AEC	401.3	38.0	439.3
U.S. Air Force	390.1	127.1	517.2
U.S. Navy	14.4	—	14.4
Totals	$805.8	$165.1	$970.9

[1] Air Force and Navy expenditures in FY 1959 and 1960 are estimates.
[2] AEC data taken from AEC Annual Report for 1960. Air Force and Navy data taken from testimony presented to Joint Congressional Committee on Atomic Energy in July, 1959.

The following breakdown of AEC research and development expenditures affords an indication of the distribution of the nuclear effort:

	$ Million	*%*
Direct-cycle system	220.4	55
Indirect-cycle system	156.7	39
Other R&D	24.2	6
	$401.3	100%

AIRCRAFT REACTOR EXPERIMENT (ARE). See Aircraft Nuclear Propulsion Program.

AIRCRAFT SHIELD TEST REACTOR (ASTR)

A portable, special-purpose **test reactor** formerly operated by the Convair Division of General Dynamics Corporation, Forth Worth, Texas, under contract to the U.S. Air Force, and now in stand-by status. It was designed for radiation shielding experiments in support of the development of airframes for nuclear-propelled aircraft (see **Aircraft Nuclear Propulsion Program**). It has been operated in an airplane as well as on the ground. *Type:* Tank reactor. *Power rating:* 3000 kilowatts (thermal). *Fuel:* Modified MTR-type fuel elements. *Coolant:* H_2O. *Moderator:* H_2O. *Start-up:* 1954. Operation discontinued in 1961.

ALBANIA

A member of the **International Atomic Energy Agency** and a minor participant in the **Joint Institute for Nuclear Research** at Dubna in the U.S.S.R.

ALBEDO

The name of an experimental apparatus used in the early fifties at the Livermore Branch of the E. O. Lawrence Radiation Laboratory for research on controlled **fusion.** Albedo was developed to study the use of a radiofrequency field to enhance confinement of the fuel **plasma.** The radiofrequency field applied was in resonance with the gyromagnetic frequency of the plasma ions, and appreciable trapping of ions resulted. Although the work showed promise, it was abandoned because of problems arising from penetration of the field into the plasma at moderately high density. (See **magnetic mirror systems**)

ALICE (Adiabatic Low-Energy Injection and Capture Experiment)

The name of an experimental apparatus now being built at the E. O. Lawrence Radiation Laboratory for research on controlled **fusion.** In this experiment a beam of neutral deuterium atoms of 15-20 Kev energy is injected into a magnetic mirror geometry (see **magnetic mirror systems**). Collisions with other atoms or with other ions result in ionization of the injected atoms. The magnetic field is constant during the period of atom injection and plasma containment thus permitting the plasma to approach an equilibrium state. The magnetic field may then be increased to move the plasma further from the walls by **adiabatic compression.** This also increases the temperature somewhat.

ALPHA ACTIVITY

The emission of **alpha particles** from unstable atomic nuclei. (See **alpha decay**)

ALPHA DECAY

Radioactive decay of an unstable atomic nucleus by emission of an **alpha particle**, resulting in a daughter product with an atomic weight four units less than that of the parent and an atomic number two units less than that of the parent. (See **beta decay, radioactivity**)

ALPHA PARTICLE (α)

A positively charged subatomic particle consisting of two **protons** and two **neutrons** and hence identical with the nucleus of a helium atom. Alpha particles, **beta particles** and **gamma rays** are the basic forms of **radioactivity.**

Alpha particles are spontaneously emitted by some naturally radioactive elements, generally those with atomic weights above 200; uranium and radium, for example, are alpha emitters. Alpha particles can induce nuclear transformations by the alpha-neutron reaction, e.g.:

$$_4Be^9 + {_2He^4} \longrightarrow {_6C^{12}} + {_0n^1}$$

This reaction is commonly used to supply neutrons for laboratory experiments, radium or polonium usually serving as the alpha source. Alpha particles are produced by some nuclear transformations, such as the neutron-alpha reaction for the production of tritium from lithium-6:

$$_3Li^6 + {_0n^1} \longrightarrow {_1H^3} + {_2He^4}$$

(See **alpha decay, nuclear reactions)**

Alpha particles were discovered by the British physicist, Ernest Rutherford. They have a mass of 4.00279 atomic mass units (6.44×10^{-24} gram); and a positive electric charge of 9.6050×10^{-10} electrostatic unit, which is twice that of the negatively charged electron. As emitted, alpha particles characteristically have sharply defined energies in the range of 4-10 Mev, and velocities about one-twentieth of that of light. They have high specific ionization power and correspondingly low penetrating power; they are usually absorbed by a single thickness of paper, equivalent to a path of 5 to 7 centimeters in air. They thus cannot penetrate the skin. For this reason, the health hazard associated with alpha emitters stems from the danger of ingestion, rather than from external exposure. Some alpha emitters, such as refined uranium, can be safely handled with straightforward precautions against ingestion or inhalation. Other alpha emitters, notably polonium and plutonium, have biochemical properties which make them extremely toxic to man; they are usually handled in glove boxes, i.e., hermetically sealed enclosures with rubber-glove attachments for handling purposes. Still other alpha emitters are hazardous because of the properties of their daughter products. Radium, for example, decays to radon, which is an intense gamma emitter and also a gas and therefore a potential inhalation hazard.

Being electrically charged, alpha particles can readily be accelerated to high energies by means of **particle accelerators** and are commonly used in studying nuclear phenomena.

ALTERNATING GRADIENT SYNCHROTRON (AGS)

An advanced type of **particle accelerator** being used to supply beams of extremely high-energy protons (25-35 Bev). An AGS machine is essentially a **proton synchrotron** in which

Fig. 8. (See caption on facing page for details.)

Fig. 8. Brookhaven Alternating Gradient Proton Synchrotron. Top left, aerial view of earthen shielding embankment overlying tunnel containing the magnet ring. Small building in left foreground houses the injection system; target building, laboratories and office are at center. Brookhaven Graphite Research Reactor installation seen at upper right. Bottom left, view inside the AGS tunnel showing one of 12 radio-frequency accelerating stations. Above, linear accelerator used in injection system of Brookhaven Alternating Gradient Proton Synchrotron. (*Courtesy of Brookhaven National Laboratory*)

successive segments of the magnetic field have opposite polarity—hence the term "alternating gradient." This arrangement serves to focus the protons into a narrower and denser beam than in a conventional proton synchrotron—a phenomenon known as "strong focusing." In addition to reducing the size of the beam aperture (and hence the volume of the vacuum system), strong focusing reduces the size and weight of the magnet required. The net effort is to permit the attainment of particle energies well beyond the maximum practical range of conventional proton synchrotrons.

Two AGS machines have been built to date, one at Brookhaven National Laboratory and the other at the European Organization for Nuclear Research (CERN) in Geneva, Switzerland. The two machines are comparable in size and design, and began operation within a year of each other (1959 in the case of the CERN unit, and 1960 in the case of the Brookhaven unit). There follows a brief description of the Brookhaven AGS Machine (see Fig. 8):

1. Injector system: Protons are produced by ionization of hydrogen gas in a **Cockroft-Walton machine** and accelerated therein to an energy of 750 Kev. The exit beam is then accelerated to an energy of 50 Mev in a **linear accelerator** prior to injection into the vacuum chamber of the AGS Machine proper.

2. AGS system: The particles travel around in a ring-shaped track approximately half a mile in circumference (diameter: 842.9 feet). 240 magnet sections are spaced at intervals around the ring, as are 12 radio-frequency acceleration stations. The particles gain approximately 96 Kev in a single orbit around the track, so that some 250,000 orbits are made in reaching an energy level of 25 Bev. The system operates in pulse fashion. To compensate for relativistic increase of particle mass at increasing particle energy, the strength of the magnetic field and the frequency of the acceleration impulses increase in a synchronized manner during the acceleration cycle. (See discussion under **cyclotron, proton synchrotron**)

3. Beam delivery: Provision is made to bend the accelerated beam to strike a target inserted into the vacuum chamber. Alternatively, the beam can be deflected out of the chamber and directed to strike targets in external experimental setups.

4. Cost: The Brookhaven AGS Machine was completed in 1960 at a cost of approximately $31 million.

ALUMINUM

Element No. 13 (symbol, Al; atomic weight, 26.98), used as a protective coating for fuel elements, and as a fuel alloying or diluent material. Aluminum has a low thermal neutron cross section (~ 0.2 barn) and is resistant to corrosion in air and water at moderate temperatures. It is a relatively low-cost material and is easily fabricated. These properties account for its use as the fuel cladding or canning material in many research and high-flux test reactors and in the production reactors at Hanford and Savannah River. It is also used in these reactors as a structural material. Aluminum **cermets,** referred to as "APM" or "SAP" alloys, are under development for use in certain power reactors (see **organic cooled reactors**). Aluminum cannot be used in unalloyed form in power reactors due to the fact that it has poor mechanical strength at elevated temperatures.

Uranium-aluminum alloys and dispersions of uranium compounds in aluminum have been tested as possible fuel materials for use in power reactors and have shown good dimensional stability under irradiation and thermal cycling. Plutonium-aluminum alloys and dispersions are also of current interest as possible reactor fuel materials. (See **reactor materials**)

AMERICAN NUCLEAR SOCIETY (ANS)

A professional society founded in 1954 and made up of scientists and engineers of various disciplines who have a common interest in atomic energy and its applications. ANS holds national meetings in June and December of each year, the proceedings of which are published in a semiannual *Transactions*. Other publications include a monthly scientific journal, *Journal of Nuclear Science and Engineering,* and a monthly newsletter, *Nuclear News*.

ANS membership, as of the spring of 1961, totaled approximately 4000, and included more than 270 overseas members from 33 different countries. Following is a breakdown of the membership by discipline: engineering, 48%; physics, 32%; chemistry, 9%; metallurgy, 4%; mathematics, 2%; life sciences, 2%; other, 3%.

The following men have served as presidents of ANS:

W. H. Zinn	1955-56
C. Rogers McCullough	1956-57
Leland J. Haworth	1957-58
Chauncey Starr	1958-59
A. M. Weinberg	1959-60
M. C. Leverett	1960-61
W. B. Lewis	1961-62
Manson Benedict	1962-63

AMERICIUM

Element No. 95 (symbol, Am), first identified in 1944 by G. T. Seaborg, R. A. James and L. D. Morgan at the E. O. Lawrence Radiation Laboratory. The discovery was the result of the bombardment of plutonium-239 with reactor neutrons, the reactions being as follows:

$$_{94}Pu^{239} + {_0n^1} \longrightarrow {_{94}Pu^{240}} + \gamma$$

$$_{94}Pu^{240} + {_0n^1} \longrightarrow {_{94}Pu^{241}} + \gamma$$

$$_{94}Pu^{241} \xrightarrow{\beta-} {_{95}Am^{241}}$$

Americium is one of the eleven **transuranium elements** discovered in the past two decades.

Americium occurs as an intermediate product in the production of **curium-242,** which is of interest as an energy source for small auxiliary power units. (See **SNAP Program**)

AMES LABORATORY

A U.S. Atomic Energy Commission research center at Ames, Iowa. *Operating contractor:* Institute for Atomic Research, Iowa State University. *Director:* Frank H. Spedding. *AEC investment in plant and equipment:* $14 million.* *Staff:* ~ 250 scientists and engineers, plus ~ 200 supporting personnel.

---

* Includes facilities authorized or under construction as of June 30, 1960. Not adjusted for depreciation.

Major areas of effort of Ames Laboratory proper include research on the properties of rare earth elements and compounds; development of alloys and ceramics for reactor applications; and research on pyrometallurgical **fuel reprocessing** techniques. This work centers in three buildings constructed and equipped with AEC funds on land leased from the University. A research reactor facility is under construction (see **Ames Laboratory Research Reactor**). Additionally, and largely in its own facilities, the Institute for Atomic Research conducts a range of fundamental investigations in solid-state physics, high-energy physics, radiochemistry, plant physiology and other fields.

Ames Laboratory is an outgrowth of activity undertaken by the University during World War II. In collaboration with the Metallurgical Laboratory of the University of Chicago, a group at Ames developed and piloted the methods used during the **Manhattan Project** for the production of reactor-grade uranium and, while industrial facilities were being built, supplied 1000 tons of metal from semi-works apparatus.

AMES LABORATORY RESEARCH REACTOR (ALRR)

A 5000-kilowatt (thermal) heavy water-moderated tank reactor scheduled to begin operation in 1963 at Ames Laboratory. The reactor was supplied by AMF Atomic, Inc. (See **research and training reactors**)

AMEX PROCESS

One of several processes used in uranium mills to recover uranium from acid **leach liquors.** The Amex process (from *am*ine *ex*traction) is based on **solvent extraction** techniques. The solvents employed are organic solutions of high molecular weight alkyl amines, such as trilauryl or trisooctyl amine.

There are several process variations. In one, uranium is stripped from the solvent into a dilute sodium carbonate solution, from which it is in turn precipitated by the addition of ammonia. The resulting ammonium diuranate [$(NH_4)_2U_2O_7$] is separated by filtration and then dried, yielding **"yellow cake."** Sodium chloride solutions may be used in place of sodium carbonate in the stripping step; alternatively, the uranium may be precipitated directly from the organic phase by mixing with an aqueous slurry of magnesium oxide. The Amex process was developed at Oak Ridge National Laboratory and is in use at several U.S. uranium mills. See **uranium milling** for background information. For information on related processes, see **Dapex process, DDPA process.**

AMMONIUM DIURANATE

A compound of uranium formed as an intermediate product in several processes leading to uranium dioxide (UO_2) or trioxide (UO_3). (See **uranium milling, uranium dioxide**)

ANTIPARTICLES

In nuclear physics, a term most often used for **elementary particles** that differ from each other only in having electric charges (or magnetic moment) of opposite sign. The first antiparticle to be discovered was the **positron** (1932) which has the same mass and spin as the electron and a charge equal in magnitude to that of the electron, but opposite in sign. The antiproton was observed in 1955 as one of the products of high-energy nuclear reactions induced by 6.2-Bev protons from the Bevatron at the E. O. Lawrence Radiation Laboratory. To a neutral particle, such as a neutron, there corresponds an antiparticle which differs from it only in having a magnetic moment of the opposite sign. Thus, in the experiments which led to the detection of the antiproton, the antineutron was also found. **Mesons** of different types (mu, pi, and K) have been known to occur with both signs of charge, corresponding to particle and antiparticle. The **hyperons** presumably also have antiparticles.

A particle and an antiparticle have the very important property of undergoing mutual annihilation, the products being electromagnetic quanta. For example, a positron and electron at rest can annihilate each other with the production of two gamma rays, each with energy 0.511 Mev, corresponding to the rest mass of an electron or positron. A particle-antiparticle pair can also be formed by the interaction between an atomic nucleus and electromagnetic radiation of sufficiently high energy. This process, called **pair production,** is important in the absorption of highly energetic electromagnetic radiation by matter.

ANTIPROTON. See **antiparticles.**

APM ALLOYS

A term for aluminum powder metallurgy materials under development for fuel element cladding applications. (See **organic cooled reactors)**

APPROPRIATIONS. See **Atomic Energy Commission —Financial Data.**

AQUEOUS HOMOGENEOUS REACTORS

Any nuclear reactor fueled and moderated with a homogeneous mixture (solution or slurry) of fissionable material and water. A distinction should be made between circulating and noncirculating aqueous homogeneous systems. Circulating systems, discussed herein, have been under development for use in nuclear power applications. Noncirculating systems are used in research reactors of the "water boiler" type, which are discussed separately. (See **research and training reactors)**

In a circulating system, the water in the fuel mixture serves as heat-transport medium as well as moderator. As is shown in Fig. **9**, the fuel stream is circulated in a closed pressurized loop, referred to as the primary loop. The loop contains a critical region (core) wherein the heat is produced, and a heat exchanger (steam generator), wherein the fuel steam transfers heat to cooling water, thereby generating steam for electrical power production. The geometry of the components of the

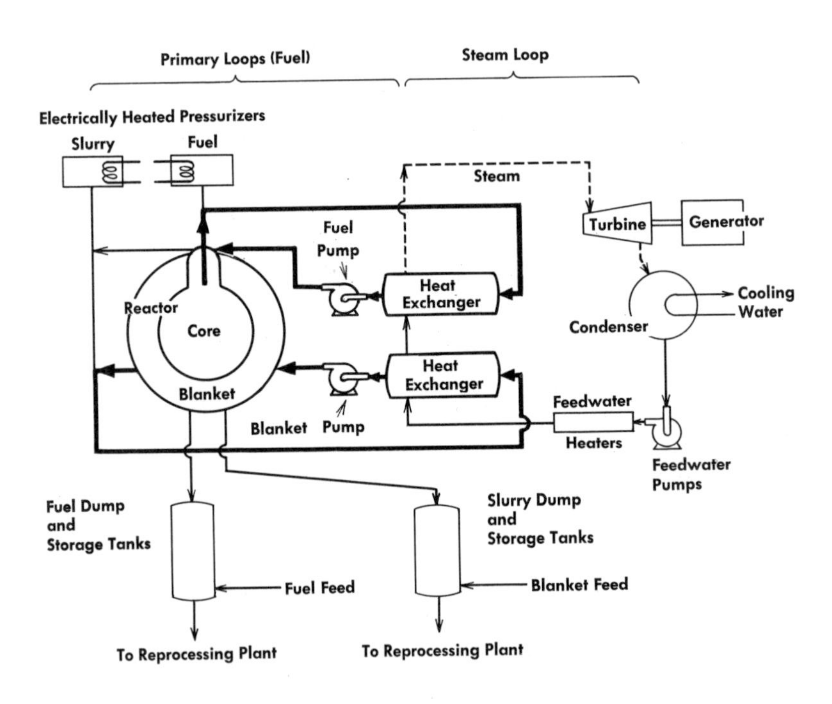

Fig. 9. Simplified flow diagram of two-region aqueous homogeneous reactor plant.

loop, including the interconnecting piping, is such that a critical mass of fuel exists only in the core section.

Status. Experience with the operation of circulating aqueous homogeneous reactor systems has been gained in small-scale reactor experiments conducted at Oak Ridge National Laboratory and Los Alamos Scientific Laboratory (see Table 1). On two occasions industrial groups announced plans to build demonstration aqueous homogeneous plants but in each case the project was canceled. (See **Pennsylvania Advanced Reactor Project, Wolverine Electric Cooperative Reactor Project**)

In 1959, following a review of its over-all civilian power reactor development program, the U.S. Atomic Energy Commission concluded that none of the fluid fuel concepts then being studied * showed promise of meeting short-term objectives. This finding led to a decision to concentrate on the concept that appeared to offer the best long-range promise as a thermal breeder. Subsequent evaluation indicated that the aqueous homogeneous concept offered the best breeding potential in terms of annual fuel yield, with the molten salt and liquid metal fuel concepts ranking second and third, respectively. However, the engineering problems associated with the aqueous homogeneous concept appeared formidable and, on balance, it was decided to discontinue this line of development on completion of certain experiments in 1961. Work on the liquid metal fuel concept was terminated in 1960. The molten salt concept thus emerged as the basis for future fluid fuel power reactor development.

General Considerations. The major considerations that originally sparked interest in the aqueous homogeneous concept for power applications are as follows:

1. As in any fluid fuel concept, there is a promise of lower fuel cycle costs than in solid fuel systems, due to such factors as elimination of the expense of fuel element fabrication; elimination of radiation damage as a limiting factor in fuel burn-up; and simplification of spent fuel reprocessing.

2. Excellent neutron economy, due to the absence of need for neutron-absorbing structural materials in the reactor core; and the possibility of continuously removing fission product poisons from the circulating fuel stream.

3. Excellent control characteristics, including a strong negative temperature coefficient of reactivity; and the possibility of controlling the reactor essentially by regulating the concentration of fissionable material in the fuel stream, thereby eliminating the need for control rods.

Some of the major problems found to be associated with the concept are:

1. The extreme difficulty of engineering an equipment system capable of handling the intensely radioactive fuel stream with long-term integrity. There are three principal factors: First, the primary loop must operate at high pressure ($\sim$ 2000 psi) to achieve high enough temperatures for power generation.** Second, the system must be designed to withstand corrosion and/or erosion by the circulating fuel stream.† Third, the entire primary loop must be massively shielded and all maintenance tasks carried out by remote techniques.

2. The difficulty of keeping the fissionable material properly distributed in the aqueous medium. In the case of fuel solutions, the problem arises from a tendency for fissionable material to precipitate out of solution and/or undergo phase separation at elevated temperatures. In the case of fuel slurries, the problem is one of keeping the solid particles in proper suspension, which requires maintaining

* Fluid fuel concepts under development at the time of the review included the aqueous homogeneous concept, the **molten salt** concept, the molten plutonium concept (see **Los Alamos Molten Plutonium Experiment No. 1)**, and the **Liquid Metal Fuel Reactor Concept.**

** The high vapor pressure of water makes it impractical to design aqueous homogeneous reactors to operate at temperatures higher than about 600°F, which limits the thermal conversion efficiency that can be achieved in power generation. Corrosion considerations also act to limit the operating temperature.

† Aqueous fuel solutions are extremely corrosive. Aqueous fuel slurries are less corrosive but more erosive.

turbulent flow. Both problems create difficulties in the hydrodynamic design of the system.

3. Problems introduced by the radiolytic dissociation of water, which occurs at a faster rate in aqueous homogeneous reactors than in solid fuel reactors due to the fact that, being intimately mixed with the fissionable material, the water is exposed to fission recoil fragments. The addition of certain chemicals to the fuel stream has been found to be effective in catalyzing the recombination of the resulting radiolytic gases, but adds to the complexity of the chemical system. Copper sulfate is used for this purpose in the case of uranyl sulfate solutions.

TABLE 1. AQUEOUS HOMOGENEOUS POWER REACTOR EXPERIMENTS

Name	*Location*	*Fuel*	*Rated Power (kilowatts thermal)*	*Start-up*	*Shutdown*
HRE-I [1]	Oak Ridge National Lab.	Light water solution of uranyl sulfate	1000	1952	1954
LAPRE-1 [2]	Los Alamos Scientific Lab.	Light water solution of uranyl phosphate	2000	1956	1956
HRE-II [1]	Oak Ridge National Lab.	Heavy water solution of uranyl sulfate	5000	1957	1961
LAPRE-2 [2]	Los Alamos Scientific Lab.	Light water solution of uranyl phosphate	800-1000	1959	1959

[1] See Homogeneous Reactor Experiments.
[2] See Los Alamos Power Reactor Experiments.

Considerations of Thermal Breeding. Consideration of the potential of aqueous homogeneous reactors as thermal breeders brings additional factors into focus. These relate principally to the need for an extremely refined neutron economy for good breeding efficiency:

1. A two-region heavy-water system appears to be necessary (or at least very desirable) for thermal breeding. Choice of a two-region system stems from the questionable practicality of building a one-region core of the size that would be required to reduce neutron leakage to an acceptably low level. Choice of heavy water stems from the fact that ordinary water would absorb too many neutrons, due to the high thermal neutron cross section of hydrogen.

2. A two-region system would have a uranium mixture in the core and a thorium mixture in the blanket region.* The preferred core medium is a dilute aqueous uranyl sulfate solution ($\sim$ 6 grams U/liter), which is less subject to phase separation at elevated temperatures than a concentrated solution. No suitable soluble thorium salt exists, hence the choice of blanket medium is restricted to an aqueous slurry of thorium oxide or other insoluble thorium compound.

3. Whereas stainless steel or titanium can be used as the container material in the primary loop, neutron absorption considerations dictate that the core tank be fabricated of zirconium alloy.** Unfortunately, zirconium

* The optimum fuel cycle for a thermal breeder is the uranium-233—thorium-232—uranium-233 cycle, i.e., the use of uranium-233 as fuel and thorium as fertile material, resulting in the breeding of additional uranium-233. A uranium-235—thorium—uranium-233 "chain" may also be used, however U^{235} has a lower eta value for thermal neutrons than U^{233} (2.07) *vs.* an estimated 2.29 neutrons/fission), so that this system is usually considered only as a means of obtaining the U^{233} needed to start the more efficient U^{233} cycle.

** Zirconium has a thermal neutron cross section of $\sim$0.2 barn *vs.* $\sim$2.5 barns for stainless steel and 5.6 barns for titanium. Zircaloy-2 is presently the preferred alloy. Zirconium-columbium alloys show promise.

corrodes excessively when exposed to fuel solutions undergoing a high rate of fission, which limits the allowable power density in the core and hence the power output of the reactor.

Status. Aqueous homogeneous thermal breeders are at too incomplete a stage of development to permit defining plant characteristics or evaluating capital and operating costs.

ARGENTINA

The Comision Nacional de Energia Atomica (CNEA), Buenos Aires, is responsible for atomic energy matters. Research facilities include a low-power research and training reactor of the **Argonaut** type built by CNEA personnel and fueled with uranium of 20% enrichment leased from the United States. In 1960 Argentina received a foreign equipment grant from the United States for cobalt-60 teletherapy units for agricultural research and medical therapy, and for a medical research laboratory at the University of Buenos Aires.

Uranium mining operations are conducted on a limited scale, principally in the Malargue area of Mendoza Province, and in Salta Province, where new significant deposits have recently been discovered. A semi-works facility for processing ore is located at Malargue and a full-scale plant is planned. A survey of prospects for nuclear power application in Argentina was undertaken in 1960.

Argentina is a member of the **International Atomic Energy Agency** and the **Inter-American Nuclear Energy Commission,** and has a research-type **Agreement for Cooperation** with the United States.

ARGONAUT REACTOR (CP-11)

A small training reactor at Argonne National Laboratory. The Argonaut design (from Argonne Naught Power Reactor) was developed by the ANL staff with an eye to university requirements for a flexible low-power reactor for student training and physics experiments. The installation at ANL, formally known as the Argonne Nuclear Assembly for University Training, is primarily used in the program of ANL's International Institute of Nuclear Science and Engineering. *Type:* Graphite/water reactor. *Power:* Usually operates at power levels in the range, 1-100 watts (thermal). Can be operated at levels up to 10 kilowatts. *Fuel:* Aluminum-clad plates containing a dispersion of U_3O_8 of 20% isotopic enrichment in an aluminum matrix. *Coolant:* H_2O. *Moderator:* Graphite and H_2O. *Neutron flux:* $\sim 5 \times 10^{11} n/cm^2$ sec (maximum thermal). *Start-up:* 1957. (See **research and training reactors**)

ARGONNE CANCER RESEARCH HOSPITAL

A U.S. Atomic Energy Commission medical research and treatment center in Chicago, Illinois. *Operating contractor:* University of Chicago. *Director:* Leon O. Jacobson. *AEC investment in plant and equipment:* $\sim$ $5 million. *Staff:* $\sim$ 50 scientists, plus $\sim$ 150 supporting personnel.

The hospital specializes in the application of radiation techniques to cancer research and therapy. It also conducts a range of fundamental investigations, including study of the mechanisms of red blood cell production, and research on the role of the blood, pituitary, spleen and other body organs and hormones in protecting individuals from radiation damage or assisting in recovery from radiation exposure. The hospital is equipped with a 2200-curie cobalt-60 teletherapy unit, a 50-Mev linear accelerator, and a 2-Mev Van de Graaff generator.

ARGONNE FAST SOURCE REACTOR (AFSR)

A small special-purpose **test reactor** operated by Argonne National Laboratory at the National Reactor Testing Station. AFSR has a near-minimum critical mass and operates in the fast portion of the neutron spectrum. It is used as a source of fast neutrons for studies of special equipment for fast breeder reactors. *Power rating:* 1 kilowatt (thermal). *Fuel:* Highly enriched uranium. *Coolant:* Air. *Moderator:* None. *Reflector:* Depleted uranium.

Designer: Argonne National Laboratory. *Start-up:* 1959.

ARGONNE LOW POWER REACTOR. See **SL-1.**

ARGONNE NATIONAL LABORATORY (ANL)

A major U.S. Atomic Energy Commission research center, situated on a 3700-acre tract of land in Du Page County, Illinois, 25 miles southwest of Chicago. (Post Office address: Argonne, Illinois.) *Operating contractor:* University of Chicago. *Director:* Albert V. Crewe * *AEC investment in plant and equipment:* ~ $200 million,** exclusive of supplementary facilities operated by ANL at the National Reactor Testing Station. *Staff:* ~ 850 scientists and engineers, plus some 2750 supporting personnel.

The Laboratory's program includes fundamental and applied research and engineering development in a variety of fields. While the basic orientation of much of the Laboratory's effort has traditionally been reactor development, there has been increasing emphasis in recent years on high-energy physics and other basic research.

Argonne is an outgrowth of the wartime Metallurgical Laboratory, which was organized by the University of Chicago in connection with the **Manhattan Project.** Including the wartime accomplishments, the work it has done in the reactor field includes: (1) demonstration of the first nuclear chain-reaction (see **Chicago Pile No. 1**); (2) basic design, in collaboration with E. I. duPont de Nemours & Co., of the plutonium production reactors at Hanford and Savannah River; (3) basic design, in collaboration with Bettis Laboratory, of the prototype reactor for the submarine, *Nautilus;* (4) development of basic technology of fast breeder reactors (see **Experimental Breeder Nos. 1 & 2, Transient Reactor Test Experiment**); (5) development of basic technology of **boiling water reactors** (see **Borax Experiments,** and **Experimental Boiling Water Reactor**); (6) basic work on the safety characteristics of water-cooled reactors (see **Special Power Excursion Reactor Test Program**); (7) design, in collaboration with Oak Ridge National Laboratory, of the first high-flux materials testing reactor (see **Materials Testing Reactor**); (8) design of the forerunner of a line of heavy water-moderated, tank-type research reactors (see **Argonne Research Reactor**); and (9) design of the forerunner of a line of low-power research and training reactors. (See **Argonaut**)

Along with its reactor development programs, Argonne has done extensive research and development in the field of spent fuel reprocessing. It worked jointly with Oak Ridge National Laboratory in the development of the original solvent extraction method for uranium-plutonium separation and decontamination (see **Redox process**); and more recently, has pioneered work on nonaqueous reprocessing processes based on **fluoride volatility** and **pyrometallurgical processes.**

As noted above, Argonne has become increasingly active in high-energy physics. A major current project in this field is the design and construction of a 10-15-Bev proton synchrotron, expected to be completed in 1961 (Zero Gradient Synchrotron). Another major field of activity is biomedical research, clinical aspects of which are coordinated with the **Argonne Cancer Research Hospital.**

Specialized experimental facilities at the ANL site include: *Reactors:* The Argonne Research Reactor, and **JANUS** (a test reactor for biological studies). For information on other experimental reactor facilities operated by ANL, see **National Reactor Testing Station.** *Accelerators:* A 60-inch cyclotron, Van de Graaff and Cockroft-Walton accelerators, in addition to the Zero Gradient Synchrotron (see above). *Other:* A bent-crystal gamma-ray spectrometer; special facilities for fabricating plutonium-bearing fuel elements; extensive chemical engineering semi-works; high-speed electronic computers; and controlled-atmosphere greenhouses. Much of the electrical power required by the Laboratory is supplied

* Succeeded Norman Hilberry, who retired on November 1, 1961.

** Includes facilities authorized or under construction as of June 30, 1960. Not adjusted for depreciation.

by the Experimental Boiling Water Reactor, which is a prototype nuclear power plant with a rated output of 5000 megawatts (electrical) located on the ANL site.

Argonne conducts the **International Institute of Nuclear Science and Technology.** Also, the Laboratory maintains active cooperation with 31 midwestern university and industrial research institutions, thereby serving as a regional atomic energy research and training center. The participating institutions are: Battelle Memorial Institute, Carnegie Institute of Technology, Case Institute of Technology, Illinois Institute of Technology, Indiana University, Iowa State University of Science and Technology, Kansas State College, Loyola University (Chicago, Illinois), Marquette University, Mayo Foundation, Michigan College of Mining and Technology, Michigan State University of Agriculture and Applied Science, Northwestern University, Ohio State University, Oklahoma State University of Agriculture and Applied Science, Purdue University, St. Louis University, State University of Iowa, University of Chicago, University of Cincinnati, University of Illinois, University of Kansas, University of Michigan, University of Minnesota, University of Missouri, University of Nebraska, University of Notre Dame, University of Wisconsin, Washington University (St. Louis, Missouri), Wayne University, and Western Reserve University.

ARGONNE RESEARCH REACTOR (CP-5)

A heavy water-moderated research reactor at Argonne National Laboratory. It was designed by the ANL staff and is used for general experimentation and radioisotope production. *Type:* Tank reactor. *Power rating:* 5000 kilowatts (thermal). *Fuel:* Tubular fuel elements fabricated of an alloy of highly enriched uranium and aluminum and clad with

Fig. 10. Building housing the Argonne Research Reactor (CP-5). (*Courtesy of Argonne National Laboratory*)

aluminum. *Coolant:* D_2O. *Moderator:* D_2O. *Reflector:* Graphite. *Start-up:* **1954**. *Neutron flux:* Of the order of 10^{13}n/cm^{2}sec (maximum thermal). (See **research and training reactors**)

ARMOUR RESEARCH REACTOR (ARR)

A 50-kilowatt (thermal) water boiler-type research reactor used by Armour Research Foundation of Chicago, Illinois, for contract research programs. It was supplied by Atomics International and began operation in **1956**. (See **research and training reactors**)

ARMY NUCLEAR POWER PROGRAM

A reactor development program geared to the land-based nuclear power requirements of the Department of Defense (DOD). The Army acts as agent for DOD in this activity. The program is jointly funded by the U.S. Atomic Energy Commission and DOD and is administered by a joint AEC-Army group headquartered in AEC's Division of Reactor Development. (See **Atomic Energy Commission**)

The program involves the development of a family of stationary,* portable,** and mobile † nuclear power plants with capacities ranging from 200 or 300 kilowatts to 10 or more megawatts (electrical). Present or potential military uses for such plants include:

1. Supply of electricity and heat (for space heating) to military bases at remote locations where the delivery of conventional fuels poses unusual logistic problems and/or entails excessive cost.
2. Supply of emergency power to localities cut off from normal power supplies, i.e., bombed cities, disaster areas, and the like.
3. Special tactical uses, e.g., the propulsion of military land vehicles.

The development criteria vary with the application, however the following notes relating to portable plants for use in remote locations are indicative of the special considerations involved:

1. The plant components must be reasonably compact and lightweight to facilitate air transport.
2. A premium is placed on factory preassembly to permit rapid field erection and disassembly.
3. The plants must have a high degree of reliability in operation under extreme environmental conditions. The equipment must therefore be rugged and dependable, and the engineering design as simple as possible.
4. The number of operating and maintenance personnel must be kept to a minimum to ease logistic problems.
5. The cost of power must be competitive or nearly competitive with that from alternative energy sources, taking into account the logistic factors involved.

The program was initiated in **1954**. The projects undertaken to date are listed in Table 1. (Details will be found in separate entries on the individual projects.) The project designations indicated in Table 1 derive from the following code:

1. The initial capital letter denotes the type of plant, i.e., "S" for stationary, "P" for portable, and "M" for mobile (see earlier definitions).
2. The second capital letter denotes the size of the plant. "L" stands for low power (0.1-1.0 electrical megawatt). "M" stands for medium power (1-10 electrical megawatts). "H" stands for high power (10 or more electrical megawatts). §
3. The first arabic numeral indicates the order of initiation of projects with the same two-letter designation.
4. The final capital letter, if any, indicates the order of initiation of field plants of a specific type. The absence of a final letter denotes a prototype or pilot model.

---

* Permanent installation.

** Components preassembled for rapid field erection and packaged for air transport. Plant can be relocated.

† Plant can be moved intact, or virtually intact; may or may not operate in transit.

§ The highest power considered to be within the scope of the Army Nuclear Power Program is 40 megawatts (electrical).

TABLE 1. ARMY NUCLEAR POWER PROGRAM
(1961)

Project	*Reactor Type*	*Location*	*Prime Contractor*	*Electrical Output (MWe)*	*Space Heating (MWt)*	*Start-up*
Stationary Plants:						
SM-1	Pressurized water	Fort Belvoir, Va.	Alco Products Inc.	1.855	—	1957
SL-1	Boiling water	National Reactor Testing Station	Argonne National Lab.[1]	0.2	0.4	1958
SM-1A *	Pressurized water	Fort Greeley, Alaska	Peter Kiewit Sons Co. Reactor Contractor: Alco Products, Inc.	1.640	11.15	1961
SM-2	Pressurized water	(Design only)	Alco Products, Inc.	(6.0)	—	—
Portable Plants:						
PM-2A *	Pressurized water	Camp Century, Greenland	Alco Products, Inc.	1.5	0.293	1960
PM-1	Pressurized water	Sundance Air Force Station, Wyo.	The Martin Co.	1.0	2.0	1962
PM-3A *	Pressurized water	McMurdo Sound, Antarctica	The Martin Co.	1.5	—	1962
PL-1	Boiling water	(Design only)	Combustion Engineering, Inc.	(0.3)	(0.4)	—
PL-2	Boiling water	(Design only)	Combustion Engineering, Inc.	(1.0)	(0.4)	—
PL-3	Pressurized water	Byrd Station, Antarctica	Allis-Chalmers Manufacturing Co.	1.0	0.440	(1963)
Mobile Plants:						
ML-1	Gas-cooled	National Reactor Testing Station	Aerojet-General Corp.	0.4	—	1961
ML-1A *	Gas-cooled	(To be trailer-mounted)	To be selected	0.3–0.5	—	—
MH-1A *	Pressurized water	(To be barge-mounted)	The Martin Co.	10.0	—	—
R&D Projects:						
Gas-Cooled Reactor Experiment	Gas-cooled	National Reactor Testing Station	Aerojet-General Corp.	—	—	1959
Gas Turbine Test Facility *	—	Fort Belvoir, Va.	Aerojet-General Corp.	0.4	—	1960
Military Compact Reactor Project	Liquid-metal-cooled	(Development project)	United Nuclear Corp. and General Motors Corp.	(3.0)	—	—

* Department of Defense project.
[1] Designer.

Fig. 11. Army nuclear power projects. Left, SM-1 at Fort Belvoir, Va., prototype stationary power plant. This plant, completed in 1957, has a rating of 1855 kilowatts. Top, cutaway drawing of ML-1, 400-kilowatt prototype mobile plant. Right, one of several subassemblies of PM-1, 1500-kilowatt prototype portable plant, seen being loaded for shipment to site. *(Courtesy of Alco Products, Inc. (SM-1), Aerojet General Nucleonics (ML-1), The Martin Co. (PM-1)*

As Table 1 shows, the emphasis of the Army Nuclear Power Program has been on adapting existing pressurized and boiling water reactor technology to meet land-based military requirements. The first major departure from this pattern was the initiation of a gas-cooled reactor program based on the use of nitrogen in a closed direct-cycle power-generating system, which is an original concept involving basic reactor and gas turbine development.* The Military Compact Reactor Project now involves basic development work on a liquid metal-cooled reactor system.

* **Gas-cooled reactors** under development for civilian power applications are based on an indirect-cycle system. Until 1960 a direct-cycle gas-cooled system was under development for the **Aircraft Nuclear Propulsion Program,** but the coolant was air and the cycle was open.

AEC research and development expenditures under the Army Nuclear Power Program totaled approximately **$45** million through **FY** 1961, exclusive of capital costs. The distribution of effort is shown by the following breakdown:

	% of Total
Pressurized water reactor development	21
Boiling water reactor development	9
Gas-cooled reactor development	60
Other studies and development	10
	100

ARMY PACKAGE POWER PLANTS. See **Army Nuclear Power Program.**

ASTRON PROGRAM

One of several lines of U.S. research on controlled **fusion** (see **thermonuclear power).** The Astron concept, keyed to the use of a cylindrical sheet of high-energy electrons for **plasma** confinement and heating, was proposed in 1953 by N. C. Christofilos, then at Brookhaven National Laboratory. The concept underwent theoretical study for three years before a group was set up at the Livermore Branch of the E. O. Lawrence Radiation Laboratory to develop the Astron experimental program. The group, directed by Christofilos, accounts for approximately 25% of the total Livermore effort in the controlled fusion field.

Concept. Relativistic (i.e., very high energy) electrons are injected into an evacuated cylindrical chamber in the presence of an externally applied magnetic field, so that they execute circular orbits. As more and more electrons are introduced they effectively form a cylindrical sheet, known as the "E-layer." This layer serves the following purposes.

1. It creates its own magnetic field which, acting upon the externally applied field, results in lines of magnetic force that close in upon themselves. Given a sufficiently dense electron layer, the resulting magnetic "bottle" is one within which a plasma can, in principle, be adequately confined (see Fig. 12).

2. Its high-energy electrons interact with neutral atoms of injected fuel **(deuterium** and/or **tritium),** ionizing them. These ions form a plasma trapped immediately by the system of closed magnetic field lines.

3. The electrons in the plasma gain energy from the E-layer electrons as a result of collisions, and part of this energy is then transferred to the ions. It is hoped that the temperature of the ions can in this manner be increased to the point where thermonuclear reactions take place at an appreciable rate.

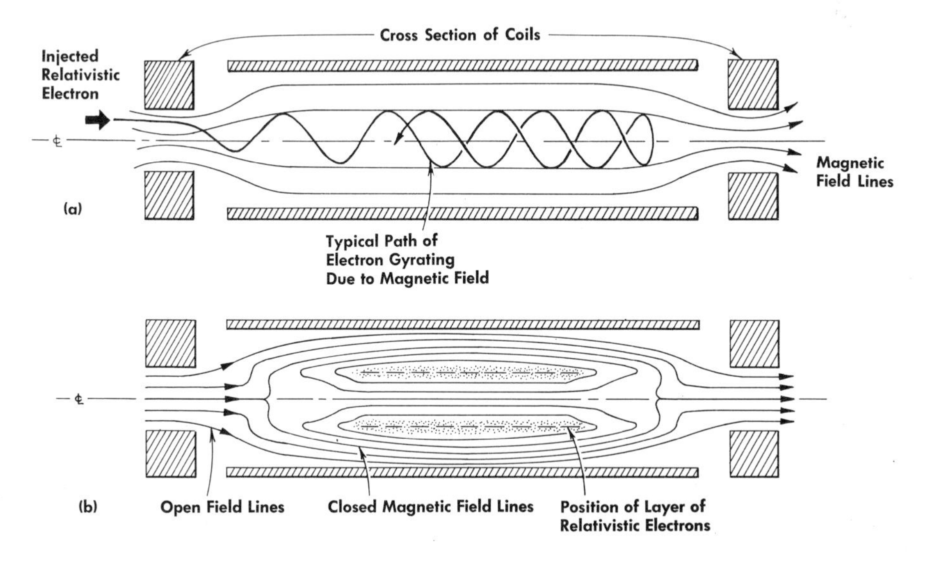

Fig. 12. Principle of Astron concept.

Concurrent with (3), the plasma tends to lose energy as the ions diffuse gradually through the "walls" of the magnetic bottle and ultimately escape confinement. In principle, however, given a sufficiently dense E-layer, the energy gain will exceed the loss and the plasma can be brought up to the **ignition temperature** of the fusion system.

Program. The experimental work conducted to date has been mainly devoted to resolving uncertainties with regard to the formation and stability of the E-layer, in hopes that E-layers of the requisite density for a practical system can be achieved.

An experimental model based on the Astron principle, using a 750-Kev electron beam, and also a pulsed electron gun have been constructed and operated with encouraging results. The electron gun is capable of producing a beam of 1-Mev energy at a peak current of 100 amperes for pulses of one microsecond duration. A modified accelerator will be used to increase the energy and current of the electron gun to 4 Mev and 200 amperes. A further increase of electron beam energy to 5 Mev is planned in order that advanced electron injection techniques may be tested.

Fig. 13. General view of Astron apparatus at the Livermore Branch of the E. O. Lawrence Radiation Laboratory. (*Courtesy of the E. O. Lawrence Radiation Laboratory*)

ATOM

A particle of matter indivisible by chemical means and hence the fundamental building block of chemical elements. From a chemical standpoint, there are as many different species of atoms as there are different chemical elements—103 at present. Atoms of the same chemical element often differ markedly in their nuclear properties, however, so that from a nuclear standpoint there is a considerably larger number of atomic species. (See **nuclide**)

It is postulated that an atom consists of a dense, positively charged nucleus around which orbit one or more negatively charged electrons.

In the case of hydrogen, the lightest atom, the nucleus consists of a single **proton;** all other nuclei contain two or more protons and one or more **neutrons.** The number of electrons surrounding the nucleus of a neutral atom is the same as the number of protons contained in the nucleus of that atom; it is referred to as the "atomic number" (symbol, A) and establishes the atom's chemical identity. The sum of the protons and neutrons contained in the nucleus is referred to as the "mass number" (symbol, Z). Atoms that have the same atomic number but different mass numbers are called "isotopes"; it is this difference which has given rise to the use of the term "nuclide" referenced above.

ATOMIC BATTERIES. See **nuclear batteries.**

ATOMIC BOMB

A term generally taken to mean any type of nuclear weapon (see **weapons).** In the technical literature, "atomic bomb" has been largely replaced by "nuclear weapon," much as "atomic pile," has largely been replaced by "nuclear reactor."

ATOMIC BOMB CASUALTY COMMISSION (ABCC)

A research group engaged in case history studies of the long-term biological effects of the nuclear attacks on Hiroshima and Nagasaki during World War II. The ABCC is directed by the National Research Council of the National Academy of Sciences, but it is principally supported by the U.S. Atomic Energy Commission. It is located in Japan and has the active cooperation of the Japanese Government.

ATOMIC CLOCK

Any of several types of devices utilizing the constant vibration or oscillation frequency of a crystal, molecule, or atomic nucleus for measurement of time intervals. The precision of modern atomic clocks is of the order of one part per billion for short periods.

An atomic clock based upon the natural oscillation of the cesium atom is in use as a time standard at the U.S. Naval Observatory.

ATOMIC ENERGY

Energy released from atomic nuclei by **nuclear reactions** (notably **fission** or **fusion)** or by radioactive decay processes (see **radioactivity).** The terms "atomic energy" and "nuclear energy" are used synonymously.

ATOMIC ENERGY ACT OF 1946

The original U.S. atomic energy law, sometimes referred to as the McMahon Act, which established the civilian U.S. Atomic Energy Commission as the agency responsible for national atomic energy matters. The 1946 Act (Public Law 79-585) was superseded by the Atomic Energy Act of 1954. See **legislation, federal.**

ATOMIC ENERGY ACT OF 1954

Public Law 83-703, which superseded the Atomic Energy Act of 1946 and, as amended, constitutes the basic atomic energy law of the United States. See **legislation, federal.**

ATOMIC ENERGY COMMISSION (AEC)

An independent office of the federal government with broad statutory responsibility for U.S. atomic energy matters. The AEC was established by the Atomic Energy Act of 1946 (Public Law 79-585) as the successor agency to the Manhattan Engineer District, U.S. War Department. The transfer of responsibility became effective on January 1, 1947. The basic statute under which the AEC now operates is the Atomic Energy Act of 1954 (Public Law 83-703) as amended (see **legislation, federal).** Headquarters of the AEC are located at Germantown, Maryland, approximately 27 miles northwest of Washington, D.C.

Functions. The AEC combines in a single agency the responsibilities of an operating, "promotional" and regulatory body. Its functions and the major program activities associated therewith, can be outlined as follows:

1. Maximizing the contribution of atomic energy to the national defense and security:

   a. Procurement of adequate stocks of raw materials, notably uranium. (See **uranium mining, uranium milling**; also see **thorium production technology**)

   b. Production of basic atomic energy materials, notably fissionable materials. (See **uranium refining and conversion, uranium enrichment, plutonium**; also see **deuterium**)

   c. Development, fabrication, and storage of nuclear **weapons.**

   d. Development of military reactor applications. (See **Army Nuclear Power Program, Naval Reactors Program**; **Pluto Project**; also see **Aircraft Nuclear Propulsion Program**)

   e. Control of classified atomic energy information. (See **classification–declassification**)

   f. Technical support of U.S. efforts toward achieving **international control of atomic energy.**

2. Maximizing the contribution of atomic energy to scientific and industrial progress.

   a. Conducting and sponsoring basic research in the atomic energy sciences.

   b. Development of peaceful uses of atomic energy, notably

      (1) Reactors for electrical power generation. (See **nuclear power development, U.S.**)

      (2) Other civilian reactor applications. (See **Maritime Reactors Program, process heat applications for reactors**; **Rover Project**)

      (3) Applications of radioisotopes and radiation. (See **radioisotopes in industry, agricultural applications of atomic energy, medical aspects of atomic energy, radiation applications in chemical industry, food preservation, cold sterilization of pharmaceuticals,** etc.)

      (4) Peaceful uses of nuclear explosives. (See **Plowshare Program**)

   c. Dissemination of scientific and technical information. (See **Atomic Energy Commission—information services**)

   d. International cooperation. (See **Agreements for Cooperation**)

   e. Education and training programs. (See **education and training**)

3. Protecting the public from potential atomic energy hazards.*

   a. Through licensing and regulatory activities. (See **licenses**)

   b. Through research on the biological effects of radiation, contributing to improved radiation protection standards. (See **medical aspects of atomic energy**)

   c. Through monitoring of radioactive fallout. (See **radioactive fallout**)

Organization. The Commission proper is composed of five members appointed by the President by and with the advice and consent of the Senate. The terms are now set at five years, and are staggered so that one term expires each calendar year.** One member, designated by the President as Chairman, serves as the official spokesman for the Commission and, traditionally, has also served as personal adviser to the President on atomic energy matters and as a member of the National Security Council. Compensation for Commissioners is at the rate of $22,000 per annum except for the Chairman, who receives $22,500 per annum. Table 1 lists past and present Commissioners and indicates which have served as Chairman or acting Chairman.

---

* Exclusive of Civil Defense aspects.

** Appointments are for a shorter period when made to fill an uncompleted term.

TABLE 1. PAST AND PRESENT MEMBERS U.S. ATOMIC ENERGY COMMISSION (1946–1961)

Name	*Professional Background*	*Period(s) Served*	
		From	*To*
Sumner T. Pike [2]	Businessman and financier	10/31/46	6/30/50; term expired
		(2nd term) 7/19/50	12/15/51; resigned
David E. Lilienthal [1]	Lawyer	11/1/46	2/15/50; resigned
Robert F. Bacher	Physicist	11/1/46	5/10/49; resigned
William W. Waymack	Editor	11/5/46	12/21/48; resigned
Lewis L. Strauss	Investment banker	11/12/46	4/15/50; resigned later served again (see below)
Gordon E. Dean [3]	Lawyer	5/29/49	6/30/50; term expired
		(2nd term) 6/30/50	6/30/53; term expired
Henry D. Smyth	Physicist	5/30/49	6/30/50; term expired
		(2nd term) 6/30/50	6/30/51; term expired
		(3rd term) 6/28/51	9/30/54; resigned
Thomas E. Murray	Engineer	5/9/50	6/30/50; term expired
		(2nd term) 7/2/50	6/30/52; term expired
		(3rd term) 6/30/52	6/30/57; term expired
T. Keith Glennan	Educator	10/2/50	11/1/52; resigned
Eugene M. Zuckert	Lawyer	2/25/52	6/30/54; term expired
Lewis L. Strauss [4]	Investment banker	7/2/53	6/30/58; term expired
Joseph Cambell	Accountant	7/27/53	11/30/54; resigned
Willard F. Libby [5]	Chemist	10/5/54	6/30/56; term expired
		(2nd term) 6/26/56	6/30/59; resigned
John von Neumann	Mathematician	3/15/55	2/8/57; deceased
Harold S. Vance	Industrialist	10/31/55	8/31/59; deceased
John S. Graham [7]	Lawyer	9/12/57	6/30/59; term expired
		(2nd term) 6/30/59	Term will expire 6/30/64
John F. Floberg	Lawyer	10/1/57	6/23/60; resigned
John A. McCone [6]	Engineer	7/14/58	1/20/61; resigned
John H. Williams	Physicist	8/13/59	6/30/60; resigned
Robert E. Wilson	Chemical engineer	3/22/60	6/30/60; term expired
		(2nd term) 6/30/60	Term will expire 6/30/65
Loren K. Olson	Lawyer	6/23/60	Term expired 6/30/62
Glenn T. Seaborg [8]	Chemist	3/1/61	Term will expire 6/30/63
Leland J. Haworth	Physicist	6/22/61	Term will expire 6/30/66

[1] Chairman 10/28/46–2/15/50.
[2] Acting Chairman 2/16/50–7/10/50.
[3] Chairman 7/11/50–6/30/53.
[4] Chairman 7/2/53–6/30/58.
[5] Acting Chairman 7/1/58–7/13/58.
[6] Chairman 7/14/58–1/20/61.
[7] Acting Chairman 1/21/61–2/28/61.
[8] Chairman 3/1/61–present.

The AEC staff which numbers approximately 6800 is located at Headquarters and in operations and area offices throughout the United States and in liaison offices in several foreign countries. The general pattern of organization, as of August 1961, is shown in Fig. 14. The General Manager is responsible for the operating and "promotional" activities while the regulatory program is under the direction of the Director of Regulation. More detailed information on the AEC organization and functions may be found in the AEC publication, "Functional Organization of the U.S. Atomic Energy Commission."

Advisory Bodies. For information on advisory bodies established by statute see **Joint Committee on Atomic Energy, General Advisory Committee, Advisory Committee on**

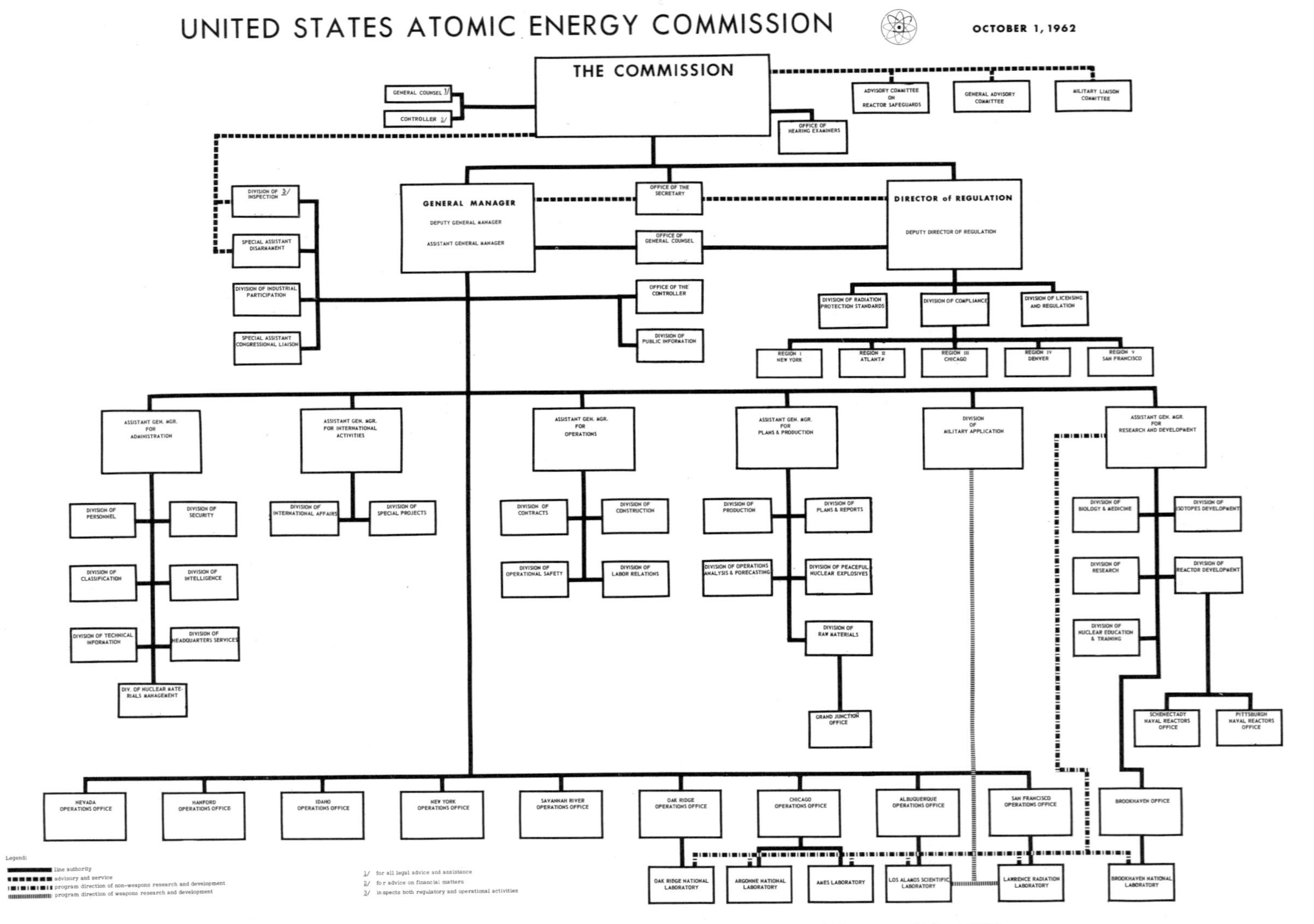

Fig. 14. Organization of the U.S. Atomic Energy Commission, October, 1962. (*Courtesy U.S. AEC*)

Reactor Safeguards, Patent Compensation Board, and **Atomic Energy Labor-Management Relations Panel.**

For information on other advisory bodies appointed by the AEC on essentially an *ad hoc* basis, see **Advisory Committee for Biology and Medicine, Historical Advisory Committee, Advisory Committee on Technical Information, Advisory Committee on Isotope and Radiation Development, Advisory Committee on Medical Uses of Isotopes, Plowshare Advisory Committee, Advisory Committee on Reactor Physics, Advisory Committee for Standard Reference Materials and Methods of Measurement, Advisory Committee of State Officials, Committee of Senior Reviewers, Nuclear Cross Section Advisory Group, Patent Advisory Panel, Personnel Security Review Board,** and **Stack Gas Problem Working Group.**

Operating Philosophy. The statute governing the AEC's operations includes as one of several policy directives that of "(strengthening) free competition in private enterprise." In consonance with this directive, it is AEC's stated policy not to use government-owned facilities whenever private industry can provide, under reasonable terms, the same service or product. Similarly, the AEC has followed the practice, originally established by the Manhattan Engineer District, of contracting with academic or research institutions and industrial concerns to design, construct and operate its facilities.* Thus in contrast with the approximately 6800 persons on AEC's own payroll, an estimated 105,000 persons are currently employed by AEC contractor organizations, exclusive of construction labor.

Other Information. See **Atomic Energy Commission—Facilities, Atomic Energy Commission—Financial Data, Atomic Energy Commission—Information Services, Atomic Energy Commission—Licensing and Regulatory Procedure, Atomic Energy Commission—Rules and Regulations, Education and Training Programs, AEC, Licenses, AEC,** and **Manhattan Project.**

ATOMIC ENERGY COMMISSION—FACILITIES

As of June 30, 1961, AEC's investment in plant and equipment, including plant projects authorized in Public Law 87-315 approved September 26, 1961, amounted to approximately $8.4 billion on a non-depreciated basis (see **Atomic Energy Commission—Financial Data**). Of this total, approximately $0.5 billion represents equity in uncompleted facilities, and approximately $0.7 billion relates to projects authorized but not started. Thus, AEC's mid-1961 equity in completed facilities was approximately $7.2 billion. Table 1 lists individual AEC facilities.

* Only two small AEC laboratories are staffed with AEC personnel, namely, the **Health and Safety Laboratory** and the **New Brunswick Laboratory.**

TABLE 1. SUMMARY OF AEC-OWNED PLANT AND EQUIPMENT
(Investment "At Cost" as of June 30, 1960)

	Principal Function	*Location*	*Operating Contractor*	*AEC Investment* [1] *($ millions)*
RESEARCH AND DEVELOPMENT FACILITIES: [2]				
Ames Laboratory	Research center	Ames, Iowa	Iowa State University	10.0
Argonne Cancer Research Hospital	Medical research	Chicago, Ill.	University of Chicago	4.8
Argonne National Laboratory	Research center	Lemont, Ill.	University of Chicago	142.1
Atomics International (reactor and research facilities)	Power reactor development	Canoga Park and Santa Susanna, Calif.	Atomics International	21.0

TABLE 1. SUMMARY OF AEC-OWNED PLANT AND EQUIPMENT (*Continued*)
(Investment "At Cost" as of June 30, 1960)

	Principal Function	*Location*	*Operating Contractor*	*AEC Investment* [1] *($ millions)*
RESEARCH AND DEVELOPMENT FACILITIES: [2]				
Bettis Atomic Power Laboratory	Naval reactor development	Pittsburgh, Pa.	Westinghouse Electric Corp.	48.5 [3]
Brookhaven National Laboratory	Research center	Upton, N.Y.	Associated Universities, Inc.	109.7
California Institute of Technology (research facilities)	Research	Pasadena, Calif.	California Institute of Technology	2.0
Carnegie Institute of Technology (accelerator)	Research	Pittsburgh, Pa.	Carnegie Institute of Technology	1.3
Columbia University (accelerator)	Research	New York, N.Y.	Columbia University	2.0
Combustion Engineering (naval reactor facilities)	Naval reactor development	Windsor, Conn.	Combustion Engineering Co.	14.4
Connecticut Aircraft Nuclear Engine Laboratory [13]	Aircraft reactor development [13]	Middletown, Conn.	Pratt & Whitney Div., United Aircraft	5.4 [4]
E. O. Lawrence Radiation Laboratory, Berkeley Branch	Research center	Berkeley, Calif.	University of California	42.4
E. O. Lawrence Radiation Laboratory, Livermore Branch	Weapons research	Livermore, Calif.	University of California	87.0
Experimental Gas-cooled Reactor	Reactor development	Oak Ridge, Tenn.	Union Carbide Nuclear Co.	0.4
General Electric	Research	Lockland, Ohio	General Electric Co.	11.1 [4, 5]
Harvard University (accelerator)	Research	Cambridge, Mass.	Harvard University	5.0
Health and Safety Laboratory	Industrial hygiene	New York, N.Y	(New York Op. Office, AEC)	n.a. [6]
Hiroshima Research Facility	Radiation effects	Hiroshima, Japan	National Academy of Sciences	2.1
Knolls Atomic Power Laboratory	Naval reactor development	Schenectady and West Milton, N.Y.	General Electric Co.	80.3 [7]
Los Alamos Scientific Laboratory	Research center	Los Alamos, N.M.	University of California	159.9
National Reactor Testing Station	Reactor experimentation and testing	Idaho Falls, Idaho	Phillips Petroleum Co. and others	238.8
New Brunswick Laboratory	Analytical laboratory	New Brunswick, N.J.	(Oak Ridge Op. Office, AEC)	2.1
New York University (computer facility)	Research	New York, N.Y.	New York University	1.6
Oak Ridge Institute of Nuclear Studies	Research and training	Oak Ridge, Tenn.	Oak Ridge Institute of Nuclear Studies	3.6
Oak Ridge National Laboratory	Research center	Oak Ridge, Tenn.	Union Carbide Nuclear Co.	161.6
PM-1 (Army Package Power Reactor 2)	Demonstration reactor	Sundance, Wyo.	The Martin Co.	0.4

TABLE 1. SUMMARY OF AEC-OWNED PLANT AND EQUIPMENT (*Continued*)
(Investment "At Cost" as of June 30, 1960)

	Principal Function	*Location*	*Operating Contractor*	*AEC Investment* [1] *($ millions)*
RESEARCH AND DEVELOPMENT FACILITIES: [2]				
Princeton University (accelerator, Model C-Stellarator, research facilities)	Research	Princeton, N.J.	Princeton University and University of Pennsylvania	20.6
Puerto Rico Nuclear Center	Research and training	Mayaguez, Puerto Rico	University of Puerto Rico	4.2
Raw Materials Development Laboratory	Research on ore processes	Winchester, Mass.	National Lead Company of Ohio	1.3
Sandia Laboratory	Weapons engineering	Albuquerque, N.M., and Livermore, Calif., and Tonopah, Nev.	Sandia Corp.	93.5
Stanford University Linear Electron Accelerator	Research	Palo Alto, Calif.	Stanford University	0.3
University of California at Los Angeles Atomic Energy Project	Medical research	Los Angeles, Calif.	University of California at Los Angeles	1.3
University of Minnesota (accelerator)	Research	Minneapolis, Minn.	University of Minnesota	1.9
University of Notre Dame (research facilities)	Radiation research	Notre Dame, Ind.	University of Notre Dame	0.3
University of Rochester Atomic Energy Project	Medical research	Rochester, N.Y.	University of Rochester	5.6
University of Tennessee (agricultural research facility)	Agricultural research	Oak Ridge, Tenn.	University of Tennessee	1.4
Yale University (accelerators)	Research	New Haven, Conn.	Yale University	2.3
POWER DEMONSTRATION REACTORS:				
Shippingport Atomic Power Station	Power demonstration	Shippingport, Pa.	Duquesne Power and Light Co.	49.2
Boiling Nuclear Superheat Reactor (BONUS)	Power demonstration	Punta Higuera, P.R.	Puerto Rico Water Resources Authority	3.6
Piqua Organic Moderated Reactor	Power demonstration	Piqua, Ohio	City of Piqua	6.3
Hallam Nuclear Power Facility	Power demonstration	Hallam, Neb.	Consumers Public Power District	25.6
Rural Cooperative Power Association Reactor	Power demonstration	Elk River, Minn.	Rural Cooperative Power Association	8.1
PRODUCTION FACILITIES:				
Boron Plant [8]	Boron-10 production	Niagara Falls, N.Y.	Olin Mathieson Chemical Corp.	7.5
Feed Materials Plant	Uranium refining and conversion	Weldon Spring, Mo.	Mallinckrodt Chemical Works	58.0
Feed Materials Production Center	Uranium refining, conversion and fabrication	Fernald, Ohio	National Lead Company of Ohio	112.5

TABLE 1. SUMMARY OF AEC-OWNED PLANT AND EQUIPMENT (*Continued*)
(Investment "At Cost" as of June 30, 1960)

	Principal Function	*Location*	*Operating Contractor*	*AEC Investment*[1] *($ millions)*
PRODUCTION FACILITIES: (*Continued*)				
Grand Junction Facilities	Uranium sampling, etc.	Grand Junction, Colo.	Lucius Pitkin, Inc.	4.7
Hanford Works	Plutonium production	Hanford, Wash.	General Electric Co. (HAPO)	932.9
Huntington Pilot Plant	Nickel production	Huntington, W.Va.	International Nickel Co.	4.7
Iowa Ordnance Plant	Operations relating to weapons	Burlington, Iowa	Mason and Hanger	32.4 [9]
Kansas City Plant	Operation relating to weapons	Kansas City, Mo.	Bendix Aviation Corp.	33.5 [10]
Monticello ore processing plant [11]	Uranium milling	Monticello, Utah	—	4.4
Mound Laboratory	Production and research relating to weapons	Miamisburg, Ohio	Monsanto Chemical Co.	31.7
Oak Ridge Gaseous Diffusion Plant	Uranium-235 production	Oak Ridge, Tenn.	Union Carbide Nuclear Co.	840.7
Oak Ridge fabrication and development	Operations relating to weapons	Oak Ridge, Tenn.	Union Carbide Nuclear Co.	387.2
Paducah Gaseous Diffusion Plant and Feed Materials Plant	Uranium-235 production	Paducah, Ky.	Union Carbide Nuclear Co.	782.7
Pantex Plant	Operations relating to weapons	Amarillo, Tex.	Mason and Hanger	26.5 [9]
Pinellas Plant	Operations relating to weapons	Pinellas, Fla.	General Electric Co.	11.8
Portsmouth Gaseous Diffusion Plant and Feed Materials Plant	Uranium-235 production	Portsmouth, Ohio	Goodyear Atomic Corp.	763.3
Rocky Flats Plant	Operations relating to weapons	Boulder, Colo.	Dow Chemical Co.	75.7
Savannah River Plant	Plutonium production	Aiken, S.C.	E.I. duPont de Nemours & Co.	1,269.9
South Albuquerque Works	Operations relating to weapons	Albuquerque, N.M.	ACF Industries, Inc.	23.4
Sylvania	Fuel and canning preparation	Hicksville, N.Y.	Sylvania Electric Products, Inc.	2.0
WEAPONS TESTING AND STORAGE FACILITIES:				
Nevada Test Site	Weapons testing	Mercury, Nev.	Reynolds Electric Engineering Co., University of California and Lawrence Radiation Laboratory	45.1
Salton Sea Test Base	Non-nuclear ballistic tests	Salton Sea, Calif.	Sandia Corp.	7.0
Tonopah Test Range	Non-nuclear ballistic tests	Tonopah, Nev.	Sandia Corp.; Reynolds Electrical and Engineering Co.	0.9
Weapons storage facilities	Weapons stockpile storage	—	—	185.5 [12]

TABLE 1. SUMMARY OF AEC-OWNED PLANT AND EQUIPMENT (*Continued*)
(Investment "At Cost" as of June 30, 1960)

	Principal Function	*Location*	*Operating Contractor*	*AEC Investment*[1] *($ millions)*
COMMUNITY OPERATIONS AND SERVICES:				
Los Alamos	Operation of the community	New Mexico	The Zia Co.	128.6
	Operation of Los Alamos Hospital	New Mexico	Los Alamos Medical Center, Inc.	2.9
Monticello	Services to the community	Utah	Lucius Pitkin, Inc.	0.3
Oak Ridge	Services to the community	Tennessee	—	20.2
Richland	Services to the community	Washington	General Electric Co. (HAPO)	2.7
OTHER:				
AEC Headquarters Building	Offices	Germantown, Md.	—	17.8
Other	Miscellaneous	—	—	51.1
			Total:	$7,245.6

[1] Includes only completed plant and equipment as of June 30, 1961.
[2] Includes power reactor experiments and prototypes, but not power reactors built under AEC's Power Demonstration Reactor Program.
[3] AEC has a related investment of $58.4 million in test facilities at the National Reactor Testing Station. This is included in the investment figure shown for NRTS.
[4] Equipment only.
[5] AEC has a related investment of $37.4 million in test facilities at the National Reactor Testing Station. This is included in the investment figure shown for NRTS.
[6] Not itemized but included in the total.
[7] Includes $38.0 million in related test facilities at West Milton site.
[8] In standby status.
[9] Basic plant owned by U.S. Army.
[10] Basic plant owned by U.S. Navy.
[11] Shut down in December 1959.
[12] Approval given in August 1961 to turn these facilities over to the Department of Defense.
[13] In 1962 this facility became known as the Connecticut Advanced Nuclear Engineering Laboratory, and was assigned other functions.

ATOMIC ENERGY COMMISSION—FINANCIAL DATA *

The U.S. Atomic Energy Commission annually includes a detailed financial analysis of its operations as part of its annual report to the U.S. Congress.** Data given in the 1961 report form the basis for the accompanying exhibits.

Appropriations. Table 1 summarizes the funding of the government atomic energy program since its inception. The cumulative appropriation comes to more than **$27** billion (more accurately **$27,386,900,000**).

* The financial data given here include AEC Fiscal Year 1961 information. Elsewhere in this book, the AEC financial information given is largely on the basis of Fiscal Year 1960 information.

** Available at nominal cost from the Superintendent of Public Documents, U.S. Government Printing Office.

TABLE 1. FUNDING OF U.S. GOVERNMENT ATOMIC ENERGY PROGRAM [1] (Through FY 1961)

	Amount ($ millions)	
Appropriation Expenditures		
National Defense Research Council	$ .5	
Office of Scientific Research and Development	14.6	
War Department (including Manhattan Engineer District)	2,218.3	
		$ 2,233.4
Atomic Energy Commission		
Fiscal years prior to 1952	2,705.8	
Fiscal year 1952	1,669.4	
Fiscal year 1953	1,812.7	
Fiscal year 1954	1,930.5	
Fiscal year 1955	1,861.8	
Fiscal year 1956	1,633.5	
Fiscal year 1957	1,931.5	
Fiscal year 1958	2,268.0	
Fiscal year 1959	2,541.2	
Fiscal year 1960	2,622.8	
Fiscal year 1961	2,713.5	
Total payments through fiscal year 1961-net		$23,690.7
		$25,924.1
Unexpended balance of funds in U.S. Treasury at close of fiscal year 1961		1,462.8
		$27,386.9

[1] Exclusive of postwar funding of government agencies other than AEC; hence does not reflect the activities of the Department of Defense, National Aeronautics and Space Administration, U.S. Maritime Administration, etc.

AEC Operating Costs. Table 2 shows a breakdown of AEC operating costs for fiscal year 1961, exclusive of expenditures for new plant and equipment. Nearly three-quarters of the approximately $2.7 billion in operating costs related to production activities, namely, the procurement of raw materials (mainly uranium ores and concentrates), the production of nuclear materials (notably uranium-235 and plutonium), and the development and fabrication of atomic weapons.

TABLE 2. AEC FY 1961 OPERATING COSTS [1]

	Amount ($ millions)		% of Total
Production			
Procurement of raw materials	$636.8		
Production of nuclear materials	732.5		
Weapons development and fabrication	515.5		
		$1,884.9	72.0%
Reactor Development			
Civilian nuclear power	$102.3		
Naval propulsion	93.4		
Aircraft propulsion	71.1		
Missile and space propulsion	48.2		
Auxiliary power sources (SNAP Project)	17.2		
Army reactors	13.5		
Merchant ships	5.3		
General research and development [2] *	86.1		
		$ 437.3	16.7
Research			
Physical sciences [3]	$154.1		
Life sciences [4]	53.9		
Peaceful use of thermonuclear explosives (Plowshare Program)	7.3		
Isotope development	3.7		
		$ 218.9	8.4
Other			
Community operations (net cost)	$ 4.5		
Sales of materials and services (net return)	(2.4)		
Education and training	8.9		
AEC administrative expense	57.4		
Security investigations	6.5		
Other costs	8.2		
Other income	(8.3)		
Special items	(3.7)		
		$ 71.1	2.9
	Total [5]	$2,612.2	100.0%

[1] Extracted from AEC 1961 Annual Financial Report. Columns do not always match totals due to rounding off. Tabulation does not include capital expenditures.

* See p. 47 for notes.

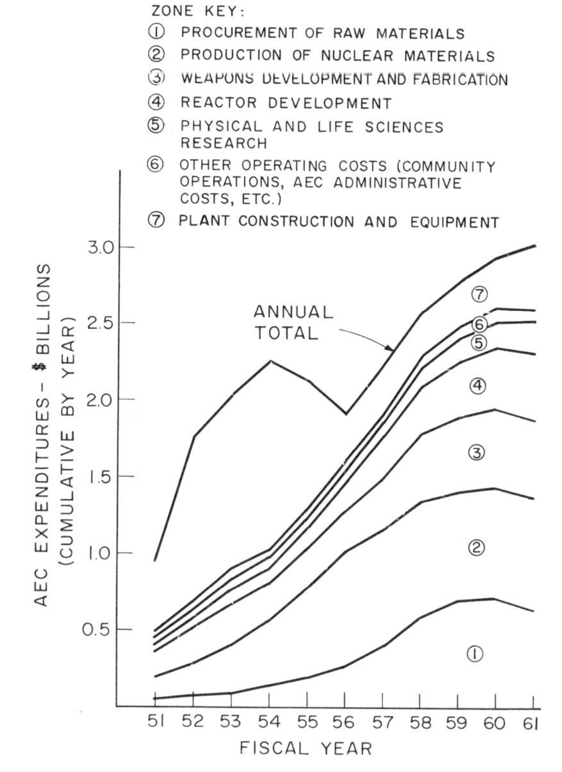

Fig. 15. Annual AEC expenditures, fiscal years 1951-61.

Trends in AEC Expenditures. Fig. 15 shows the trend in the annual operating and capital expenditures of the AEC over the eleven-year period, fiscal year 1951 through fiscal year 1961. The sharp rise in capital expenditures from 1951 through 1954 reflects a major expansion in AEC production facilities that took place over those years. That expansion largely accounts for the fact that the costs of nuclear materials production increased by a factor of approximately five between fiscal year 1952 and fiscal year 1961 (note zone 2 of chart).

AEC Reactor Development Costs. Table 3 shows a breakdown of AEC's cumulative reactor development costs for research and development through the fiscal year 1961 and

TABLE 3. BREAKDOWN OF AEC REACTOR DEVELOPMENT COSTS [1, 2]
(Cumulative through FY 1961)

	Research and Development Costs		*Capital Investment* [3]	
	$ millions	*%*	*$ millions*	*%*
Civilian nuclear power [4]	$ 457.1	18.6%	$ 181.9	23.2%
Naval reactors	650.3	26.4	238.0	30.3
Aircraft reactors [5]	472.4	19.0	54.1	6.9
Rocket propulsion (Rover Project)	74.2	3.0	28.9	3.7
Ramjet propulsion (Pluto Project)	57.9	2.4	10.7	1.4
Auxiliary power sources (SNAP Project)	41.7	1.7	6.5	0.9
Army reactors	45.4	1.8	12.3	1.5
Merchant ship reactors	13.8	0.6	20.4	2.6
General research and development	650.8	26.5	231.3	29.5
Totals	$2,463.6	100.0%	$ 784.1	100.0%

[1] Excerpted from AEC 1961 Annual Financial Report.
[2] Includes AEC depreciation but does not include funding by other Federal agencies.
[3] Includes only construction costs incurred. Additional construction authorized is not included.
[4] Does not include costs of private organizations participating in the Power Demonstration Reactor Program.
[5] The Aircraft Nuclear Propulsion Program was discontinued in 1961.

[2] Breakdown:

Fuels and materials	$ 19.7 million
Engineering physics and advanced reactor concepts	33.1
Reactor safety	12.1
Fuel elements separation systems	6.6
Radioactive waste storage and disposal systems	2.5
Reactor components	2.7
Miscellaneous	9.4
	$ 86.1 million

[3] Breakdown:

High energy physics	$ 47.5 million
Fusion power research	30.1
Chemical properties and reactions	25.2
Nuclear structure and neutron physics	19.8
Metallurgy and materials research	15.3
Systems and materials chemistry	5.3
Computer research and development	3.5
Physical and chemical methods of isotope separation	1.9
Other physical research	5.5
	$154.1 million

[4] Breakdown:

Somatic effects of radiation	$ 14.0 million
Radiation genetics	4.1
Molecular and cellular level studies	9.6
Environmental radiation studies	8.6
Radiological and health physics and instrumentation	4.3
Cancer research	5.1
Other	8.2
	$ 53.9 million

[5] Includes depreciation allowance of $287 million.

the AEC investment in completed plant and equipment and construction work in progress as of June 30, 1961. It should be stressed that this breakdown merely shows the distribution of program costs. The percentage figures should not be construed to be an index of the technical effort that has gone into each particular line of development since work conducted along one line often directly benefits another; civilian nuclear power development, for example, has made extensive use of work done under the Naval Reactors Program.

For additional information on AEC civilian nuclear power development costs, see **nuclear power development, U.S.** Similarly, see **Naval Reactors Program, Aircraft Nuclear Propulsion Program,** and **Army Nuclear Power Program.**

AEC Equity in Plant and Equipment. Fig. 16 shows cumulative figures for the period,

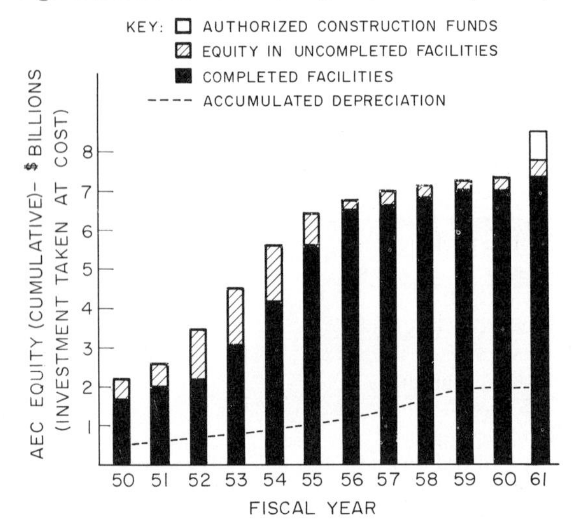

Fig. 16. AEC equity in plant and equipment.

fiscal year 1950 through fiscal year 1961. As of June 30, 1961 (i.e., the close of fiscal year 1961), the cumulative equity, figured at the original cost of the facilities, was approximately $7.7 billion (more accurately $7,664,-736,000). Adding authorized but as yet unexpended construction funds, brings this total to approximately $8.4 billion. Accumulated depreciation through fiscal year 1961 totaled approximately $2.2 billion, so that on a depreciated basis, AEC's equity as of June 30, 1961, was $5.5 billion; or $6.2 billion, counting authorized construction funds.

Table 4 shows a breakdown of the $7.7 billion figure. Three-quarters of it is seen to relate to production facilities.

TABLE 4. AEC EQUITY IN COMPLETED PLANT AND EQUIPMENT [1, 2]
(As of June 30, 1961)

		Amount ($ millions)	*% of Total*
Production			
Raw materials facilities	$ 4.0		
Feed materials facilities	269.7		
Gaseous diffusion plants	2,344.8		
Production reactors and separation areas	1,597.7		
Weapons production and storage facilities	837.8		
Heavy water production facilities	163.4		
Other production facilities	236.2		
		$5,453.6	75.7%
Research and Development			
Laboratories	$ 917.0		
Reactors	359.4		
Accelerators	128.8		
Other research facilities	29.8		
		$1,435.0	19.9
Communities		77.8	1.1
Other		235.5	3.3
	Total	$7,201.9	100.0%

[1] Investment figured at original cost, i.e., without depreciation. Authorized but unexpended construction not included. Source: AEC 1961 Annual Financial Report.
[2] Columns do not always match totals due to rounding off.

For a list of particular facilities and their cost, see **Atomic Energy Commission—Facilities.**

ATOMIC ENERGY COMMISSION—INFORMATION SERVICES *

General Information. The AEC issues an annual report ** to the Congress which con-

* The services described relate to unclassified atomic energy information. The AEC also furnishes classified atomic energy information services to properly cleared government agencies and their contractors and to holders of AEC **Access Permits.**

** Formerly a semiannual report.

tains a general review of its activities on a calendar-year basis. The report is submitted late in January and copies can be purchased usually in February from the Superintendent of Documents, U.S. Government Printing Office, Washington 25, D.C. The AEC through its Division of Public Information issues frequent press releases on its current activities.

Nuclear Science Abstracts (NSA): AEC's Division of Technical Information issues this semimonthly journal which abstracts and indexes all available publications relating to nuclear science and technology. Current NSA coverage exceeds 30,000 entries per year. Copies of NSA are available from the Superintendent of Documents, U.S. Government Printing Office, Washington 25, D.C. at an annual subscription rate (postpaid) of $22.00, domestic; and $27.50, foreign. The NSA indexes, cumulated quarterly, are available from the same source; the annual subscription rate being $15.00, domestic; and $17.50, foreign. Multi-volume indexes are issued periodically.

Technical Progress Reviews. The Division of Technical Information also publishes a series of quarterly journals reviewing developments in specific fields of nuclear technology. These reviews, prepared under contract by authorities in the fields covered, are written for technical and management readers. The series presently consists of four journals:

Nuclear Safety, prepared by Oak Ridge National Laboratory, is designed to be read by reactor designers, builders, and operators; regulatory, public health, and safety personnel; and others concerned with nuclear safety and related fields. Subjects covered include research on safety problems; safety criteria; nuclear incidents; and radiation monitoring and decontamination techniques. In addition, the journal highlights activities of AEC's Hazards Evaluation Branch and Advisory Committee on Reactor Safeguards, and reviews recent safeguards reports.

Power Reactor Technology, prepared by General Nuclear Engineering Corporation, is oriented toward the reactor engineer. It covers recent developments in the technology of civilian reactors and their applications; including new concepts, design innovations, and operating experience.

Reactor Materials, prepared by Battelle Memorial Institute, covers developments in the field of solid reactor materials, including fuel, moderator, cladding, and structural materials; nuclear poisons; and special fabrication techniques.

Reactor Fuel Processing, prepared by Argonne National Laboratory, covers all aspects of fuel processing, including the processing of raw and feed materials, spent fuel reprocessing, and radioactive waste disposal.

These journals are available from the Superintendent of Documents, U.S. Government Printing Office, Washington 25, D.C. The annual subscription rate for each is $2.00, domestic, and $2.50, foreign.

Technical Reports. Scientists and engineers engaged in AEC sponsored work annually publish approximately 2000 technical articles in professional and trade journals. In addition, about 6000 technical reports are issued each year covering current unclassified work or work that has been declassified. The reports are abstracted in NSA and may be purchased from the following sources:

1. Some, especially topical and summary reports, proceedings of symposia, and other compilations, are available from the Office of Technical Services (OTS), U.S. Department of Commerce, Washington 25, D.C. OTS also sells microfilm and photostat copies of reports, and provides a reference section.
2. Other reports (full size) are sold through the Superintendent of Documents, U.S. Government Printing Office, Washington 25, D.C.
3. Reports, in microcard form, are available from Microcard Editions, 901 26th Street, N.W., Washington 7, D.C., or in microprint form from the Readex Microprint Corporation, 115 University Place, New York 3, New York.

Technical Books and Monographs. The Division of Technical Information sponsors the preparation of various books and monographs on atomic subjects. These are published and distributed by arrangement with commercial publishing houses. Notable examples are Samuel Glasstone's "Sourcebook on Atomic Energy," and "The Reactor Handbook," a four-volume compilation of reactor technology. These and other titles will be found listed in Appendix B which summarizes general sources of atomic energy information.

Bibliographies. The Division of Technical Information compiles various bibliographies of atomic energy literature which may be purchased from the Office of Technical Services, U.S. Department of Commerce, Washington 25, D.C. It also offers a literature searching service for those who wish to have bibliographies (annotated or otherwise) prepared on particular atomic energy topics. Inquiries regarding this service, which is billed at the rate of $6.00 per hour, should be addressed to U.S. Atomic Energy Commission, Division of Technical Information Extension, P. O. Box 62, Oak Ridge, Tennessee.

Translations. The Division of Technical Information annually sponsors about 600 translations of foreign articles and reports on atomic energy subjects. These are abstracted in NSA and may be purchased from the Office of Technical Services, U.S. Department of Commerce, Washington 25, D.C. Photocopies may also be obtained from OTS or from the Special Libraries Association Translation Pool maintained at the John Crerar Public Library, 86 East Randolph Street, Chicago 1, Illinois.

Depository Libraries. Comprehensive collections of the AEC literature described under the above headings are on file in depository libraries currently maintained in 86 U.S. cities and in 85 foreign countries. See Appendix C for listings.

Films. More than 90 general-interest 16-mm sound films on atomic energy subjects, and a like number of technical films are made available by AEC on a short-term loan basis for educational or other noncommercial purposes. Film libraries are maintained at the following AEC offices:

Albuquerque Operations Office			Albuquerque, N.M.
Chicago	"	"	Argonne, Ill.
Grand Junction	"	"	Grand Junction, Colo.
Hanford	"	"	Richland, Wash.
Idaho	"	"	Idaho Falls, Ida.
New York	"	"	New York, N.Y.
Oak Ridge	"	"	Oak Ridge, Tenn.
San Francisco	"	"	Berkeley, Calif.
Savannah River	"	"	Aiken, S.C.
Headquarters			Washington 25, D.C.

For catalogs giving detailed information and description of films, write to the USAEC Division of Technical Information Extension (Educational Materials Section), P. O. Box 62, Oak Ridge, Tennessee.

Domestic Exhibits. The AEC has 22 traveling exhibits available without charge for not-for-profit showings under sponsorship of local clubs, fairs, libraries, and schools. Trained demonstrators accompany some units, while others are shipped and displayed without an attendant. The exhibits employ varying formats and sizes to meet a variety of audiences and display conditions. During 1961, exhibits in use included:

1. "You and the Atom": a large exhibit suitable for display at state fairs and in major population centers. This exhibit requires approximately 5000 square feet of display space and features manned demonstrations of nuclear power plant principles; radioisotope principles and techniques; and the use of "mechanical hands" for remote handling of radioactive materials.

2. "Your Stake in the Atom": a new exhibit housed in a 50-foot diameter exogeodesic "Exhibidome." The Exhibidome is essentially a nylon canopy supported by aluminum ribs. Its walls are lined with a variety of animated displays highlighting the history of atomic energy research and development and illustrating present and future applications. On the stage of the Exhibidome demonstrators present supplementary material and a wide-screen motion picture is shown. While the Exhibidome is on display in an area, an accompanying demonstration exhibit makes the

rounds of neighboring high schools, and exhibits of current atomic energy literature are shown in local libraries.

3. "ATOMS AT WORK": a scaled-down version of "YOU AND THE ATOM" housed in a self-propelled, walk-through van. It is used to serve small communities and suburban neighborhoods.

4. "THIS ATOMIC WORLD": an exhibit tailored for high schools. Trained demonstrators, equipped with animated demonstration equipment, visit a different school each day. They present at least one assembly demonstration before the entire student body, then spend the remainder of the school day meeting with science classes and answering questions of students and teachers.

5. "ATOMS IN ACTION": an unmanned exhibit consisting of self-explanatory panels and freestanding models designed for use at small fairs, schools, and clubs. It is shipped as a package for erection and display by the sponsoring organization. It requires approximately 60 lineal feet of display space.

A permanent atomic energy exhibit is maintained at the American Museum of Atomic Energy in Oak Ridge, Tennessee. This exhibit comprises some 12,000 square feet of displays, demonstrations, and audience-actuated devices. As with the traveling exhibits, admission to the Museum is free. The Museum also serves as the home base for construction, scheduling, and maintenance of the traveling exhibits; for the training of exhibits managers and demonstrators; and for the Museum Division of the **Oak Ridge Institute of Nuclear Studies** (ORINS), which operates the Domestic Exhibits Program for the AEC.

Organizations interested in sponsoring an atomic energy exhibit, or an organized group visit to the Museum, should write: Extension Department, Museum Division, Oak Ridge Institute of Nuclear Studies, P. O. Box 117, Oak Ridge, Tennessee.

Educational Materials. Selections of atomic energy literature and literature references are supplied upon request to students, teachers, and the general public. Inquiries should specify topics of primary interest and inquirer's occupational concern, and should be addressed to the USAEC Division of Technical Information Extension (Educational Materials Section), P. O. Box 62, Oak Ridge, Tennessee.

International Exhibits. The AEC from time to time presents scientific exhibits abroad. Major exhibits have been held in Argentina, Egypt, Brazil, India, Italy, Japan,

Fig. 17. Examples of AEC exhibits. Top, "exhibidome" of domestic traveling exhibit. Center, panel truck used to transport demonstration apparatus for high school exhibit. Bottom, the AEC's Latin American Exhibit at Rio de Janiero, May 3—June 4, 1961, presented in cooperation with the Brazilian Comissao Nacional de Energia Nuclear.

Lebanon, Pakistan, Peru, and Switzerland. Such exhibits characteristically include demonstration and training programs utilizing an operating training reactor and a gamma irradiation facility; a series of classroom seminars and lectures; an orientation film; and various instrument, equipment and other displays. The International Exhibits Program is directed by the AEC's Division of Special Projects.

ATOMIC ENERGY COMMISSION—LICENSING AND REGULATORY PROCEDURE

The Atomic Energy Act of 1954, as amended, provides the legal basis for the U.S. Atomic Energy Commission's regulation of civilian atomic energy activity. This regulation is implemented by requiring a license for each of the following purposes (see **Licenses, AEC**): *

1. To receive, possess, use, and transfer **special nuclear material.**
2. To transfer, deliver, receive, possess, import, or export **source materials** after removal from the place of deposit in nature.
3. To transfer, receive, manufacture, produce, acquire, own, possess, import, or export **by-product material.**
4. For construction and operation of **production** and **utilization facilities.**
5. For individuals to manipulate the controls of various classes of utilization or production facilities.

More detailed information on the requirement for a license in any particular case may be found in Title 10 of the Code of Federal Regulations. (See **Atomic Energy Commission—Rules and Regulations**)

By-Product Materials Licensing Procedure. An illustration of the AEC's licensing procedure is that for by-product materials. The procedure is as follows:

1. The applicant submits the detailed information required on AEC's form "Application for Byproduct Material License" to the Division of Licensing and Regulation. The applicant is afforded an opportunity to modify, clarify, or expand deficient applications by amendment.
2. The L&R technical staff reviews each application and in some instances conducts an independent investigation of the proposal. If after review the staff determines that the activities described in the application can be conducted safely, a "By-product Material License" is issued.
3. If the application does not contain sufficient information to determine that the activity can be conducted safely a letter of denial is issued.
4. A public hearing on the application will be held at the request of the applicant or any person whose interest may be affected.

To illustrate the most complex of the AEC's licensing responsibilities, the following outline of the procedures which are followed in processing a license for a power and test reactor facility is given.

Power and Test Reactor Licensing Procedure.

Construction Permit. The basic application including preliminary safeguards report is submitted by the applicant to the Division of Licensing and Regulation (L&R). Copies of the application are filed in the Commission's public document room, located at 1717 H Street, NW, Washington, D.C., and sent to the Advisory Committee on Reactor Safeguards (ACRS), the Division of Compliance, and officials of the state and local area in which the facility is to be located. Notice of the receipt is filed with the Federal Register and sent to the Joint Committee on Atomic Energy. The same procedure is followed as amendments to the application are received.

The application is subjected to administrative review and a hazards evaluation by L&R staff members. When necessary, L&R has the application reviewed by consultants to obtain the best possible advice with respect to certain aspects involved in a hazards evaluation. After L&R has completed its review and obtained as part of the application all the information which appears necessary to form a basis for action, a staff hazards analysis is prepared and sent to the ACRS.

* There are special cases where licenses are not required.

The ACRS meets with the Commission's staff and its consultants and with representatives of the applicant. When it has collected sufficient information upon which to formulate its advice, the Committee sends a report to the Commission.

A public hearing is held pursuant to the requirements of the Act. Persons whose interest may be affected are afforded an opportunity to intervene in the proceeding. At the hearing the AEC staff submits for the record the application and such amendments as may have been filed. Testimony is given by the applicant on whom the burden of proof rests. Independently, AEC staff members testify concerning the safety aspects of the reactor and the applicant's technical and financial qualifications to construct the reactor. If there are interveners, the testimony of the interveners' witnesses is taken. Subsequently, proposed findings and conclusions and a proposed construction permit are submitted to the examiner.

If after reviewing the hearing record, the examiner finds that there is reasonable assurance that a facility of the general type proposed can be constructed and operated at the proposed location without undue risk to the health and safety of the public he renders an intermediate decision authorizing the issuance of a construction permit. The intermediate decision becomes final on a specified date (not less than 20 days after the decision date) unless a party files a petition for review of decision or the Commission on its own motion undertakes to review the examiner's intermediate decision. After the intermediate decision becomes final, L&R issues the construction permit. The construction permit for a power reactor is a provisional permit in that it authorizes construction, but not operation of the reactor —it takes into account that the AEC has not been furnished all the technical information required to complete an analysis on operational safety but that there is reasonable assurance that the omitted information will be supplied.

Operating License. After the applicant submits the remainder of the required technical information, including proposed technical specifications and operating and emergency procedures, a similar procedure is followed—the information is reviewed and a hazards summary analysis is prepared by the AEC technical staff and provided to the ACRS, and public hearing is held to determine whether the reactor, as finally designed and constructed, can be operated without undue risk to the public health and safety.

In some cases a provisional operating license is issued (limited by regulation to a period of 18 months) and another hearing is held for conversion of such a license to a full-term license authorizing operation at the designed conditions.

Appealment. Appealment of adverse determinations is provided for through Commission reviews and access to the U.S. Court of Appeals, which has been provided for in the Atomic Energy Act.

ATOMIC ENERGY COMMISSION—RULES AND REGULATIONS

The regulatory material issued by AEC is originally published in the Federal Register and is codified under Title 10 of the Code of Federal Regulations (10 CFR).

All regulations published through February 27, 1962, have been issued under one of the following Parts of Title 10:

Part	1	Statement of organization, delegations, and general information
Part	2	Rules of practice
Part	4	Criteria and procedures for determining eligibility for security clearance
Part	5	Procurement policy
Part	6	Security policies and practices relating to labor-management relations
Part	7	Advisory Boards
Part	8	Interpretations
Part	9	Public Records
Part	10	Criteria and procedures for determining eligibility for access to restricted data or defense information within industry
Part	20	Standards for protection against radiation
Part	25	Permits for access to restricted data
Part	30	Licensing of byproduct material
Part	31	Radiation safety requirements for radiographic operations

Part 37 Radioisotope Research Support Program
Part 40 Licensing of source material
Part 50 Licensing of production and utilization facilities
Part 55 Operators' licenses
Part 60 Domestic uranium program
Part 70 Special nuclear material
Part 71 Regulation to protect against accidental conditions of criticality in the shipment of special nuclear material
Part 80 General rules of procedure on applications for the determination of reasonable royalty fee, just compensation, or the grant of an award for patents, inventions or discoveries
Part 81 Standard specifications for the granting of patent licenses
Part 83 Waiver of patent rights
Part 95 Safeguarding of restricted data
Part 110 Unclassified activities in foreign atomic energy programs
Part 115 Procedures for review of certain nuclear reactors exempted from licensing requirements
Part 130 Priorities regulation
Part 140 Financial protection requirements and indemnity agreements

For information on AEC policies and procedures in major areas of regulatory responsibility, see appropriate subject entries, i.e., **licenses; patents; insurance and indemnification against atomic risks;** etc. Also see **Atomic Energy Commission—Licensing and Regulatory Procedure.**

ATOMIC ENERGY LABOR-MANAGEMENT RELATIONS PANEL

A body established to assist the parties in adjusting labor-management disputes that imperil the government's atomic energy program and which have not been solved through normal processes of collective bargaining and mediation. Members of the Panel are designated by the President. Membership listed in Appendix D.

ATOMIC EXPLOSIVES, PEACEFUL USES OF. See **Plowshare Program.**

ATOMIC POWER. See **nuclear power development.**

ATOMIC INDUSTRIAL FORUM (AIF)

A nonprofit membership association formed to encourage private initiative in the development of peaceful uses of atomic energy and in the growth of atomic industry. Major activities of the Forum are as follows:

1. Meetings: The Forum holds an annual atomic energy conference usually accompanied by an industrial exhibit. It also holds meetings from time to time on specific topics of current interest, many of these taking the form of panel discussions or seminars.

2. Committees: Through the mechanism of standing committees or *ad hoc* working groups, the Forum studies and reports on specific problems affecting the U.S. atomic energy industry. Standing committees have been established in such subject areas as Contract Practices, Insurance and Indemnity, Mining and Milling, Patents, and Public Understanding. Problem areas that have recently been studied by *ad hoc* groups include national atomic policy, reactor safety, space applications of atomic energy, uranium-235 costs and pricing, private ownership of nuclear fuel, AEC regulatory organization, and workmen's compensation. The Forum has additionally sponsored university studies of the domestic and international aspects of insurance and indemnity.

3. Publications: In addition to publishing the proceedings of its conferences and reports of its study groups, the Forum publishes a monthly news summary and analysis (*Forum Memo to Members*); an annual report; and a periodic tabulation of U.S. nuclear power projects. It also issues special publications from time to time, recent examples being a survey and forecast of the growth of the U.S. atomic energy industry, and an illustrated survey of world-wide atomic industrial activity.

4. Other: The Forum maintains a library, including a comprehensive collection of unclassified U.S. Atomic Energy Commission literature; and provides reference services.

The Forum was established in April, 1953.

The formation of such an organization had been informally suggested the preceding fall by T. Keith Glennan, then a member of the U.S. Atomic Energy Commission, and was spearheaded by Walker L. Cisler of the Detroit Edison Company. The following individuals have served as President of the Forum:

April 1953-September 1956	Walker L. Cisler
September 1956-November 1958	Alfred Iddles
November 1958-December 1960	Francis K. McCune
December 1960-December 1962	Charles H. Weaver

The Executive Manager, since the inception of the organization, has been Charles Robbins. Forum offices are in New York City.

As of 1960, the Forum had some 430 organizational and 1700 individual members. Membership is open to foreign nationals and, as of 1960, included organizations or individuals from 21 countries. Following is a breakdown of the Forum's organizational membership:

Field	*U.S.*	*Foreign*	*Total*
Manufacturing, mining and processing	30%	6%	36%
Electric power	12	2	14
Engineering services	7	2	9
Insurance	5	<1	6
Law	5	<1	5
Finance	3	1	4
Academic and other nonprofit institutions	12	4	16
Government agencies	2	2	4
Other	4	2	6
Total	80%	20%	100%

ATOMIC MASS (A)

The mass of a neutral atom of a nuclide. It is usually expressed in atomic mass units. The atomic mass unit (amu) is defined as exactly one-sixteenth of the mass of a neutral atom of the most abundant isotope of oxygen, oxygen-16; 1 amu $= 1.657 \times 10^{-24}$ gram, and is equivalent in energy to 931 Mev. The atomic masses of the different nuclides are very close to integers in value; the integer closest to the atomic mass of a given nuclide is called the mass number of that nuclide, and is usually denoted by the symbol, A.

ATOMIC NUMBER (Z)

The number of **protons** contained within the nucleus of an atom. A neutral atom contains a corresponding number of **electrons** and, since these determine its chemical properties, the atomic number establishes the atom's chemical identity. To date 103 different chemical elements have been identified and so atomic numbers presently range from 1 (hydrogen) to 103 (lawrencium).* See **mass number.**

ATOMIC POWER. See **nuclear power development.**

ATOMIC POWER PROJECTS, TABULATIONS OF. See **nuclear power development;** also see **boiling water reactors, fast breeder reactors, heavy water-moderated power reactors, pressurized water reactors.**

ATOMIC POWERED AIRCRAFT. See **Aircraft Nuclear Propulsion Program.**

ATOMIC POWERED MISSILES. See **Pluto Project.**

ATOMIC POWERED ROCKETS. See **rocket propulsion (nuclear), Rover Project, SNAP Program.**

ATOMIC POWERED SHIPS. See **Naval Reactors Program, Maritime Reactors Program.**

ATOMIC REACTOR. See **reactor (nuclear).**

ATOMIC WEAPONS. See **weapons.**

ATOMS FOR PEACE AWARD

An award given in recognition of outstanding achievement by individuals throughout the world in fields related to the peaceful uses of atomic energy. The awards consisting of $75,000 each and a gold medal were made possible through the establishment of a $1,000,000 grant by the Ford Motor Company in 1955

* Proposed name for element whose discovery was announced April 12, 1961, by scientists of the E. O. Lawrence Radiation Laboratory.

as a memorial to Henry and Edsel Ford. Recipients have been:

1959—Leon Szilard and Eugene P. Wigner (joint award)
1960—Walter H. Zinn and Alvin M. Weinberg (joint award)
1961—Sir John Cockcroft

See **Fermi Award, Lawrence Memorial Award.**

ATTENUATION

In radiation shielding, attenuation refers to the reduction in intensity of radiation due to **scattering** and **absorption** as it passes through matter. In this usage, attenuation is strictly a function of the nature of the radiation and the scattering and absorption coefficients of the material traversed. More generally, radiation is also subject to geometric attenuation which results from the distribution of non-collimated radiation (i.e., radiation not confined to a beam of constant diameter) over larger and larger areas as the distance from the radiation source increases.

AUSTRALIA

Agencies. AAEC (Australian Atomic Energy Commission), Coogee, New South Wales, is the official government agency responsible for atomic energy matters. AINSE (Australian Institute of Nuclear Science and Engineering) is a joint agency of the AAEC and the ten Australian universities whose purpose is to support and coordinate university research and training activity.

International Relationships. Member of the **International Atomic Energy Agency.** Comprehensive **Agreement for Cooperation** with the United States.

Research Center. The AAEC Research Establishment is located 25 miles south of Sydney at Lucas Heights, N.S.W. Its experimental facilities include a heavy water-moderated tank-type research reactor (HIFAR), which operates at a power level of 10,000 kilowatts (thermal), and a 10-kilowatt (thermal) UTR-model research and training reactor (Moata). HIFAR was built by Head-Wrightson Limited (U.K.) and has been in operation since 1958. Moata (named after the aboriginal word for "firesticks") was supplied by the Atomic Energy Division of American Standard Radiator and Sanitary Corp. (U.S.) and began operation in 1961.

Production Activity. Uranium mines and mills are operated near Mt. Isa, Queensland; in the Northern Territory; and in South Australia at Radium Hill. Current production is over 1000 tons of uranium oxide (U_3O_8) per year.

Energy Economy. Australia's electrical power capacity is about 5000 megawatts, four-fifths of it coal-fired and the rest hydroelectric. Coal reserves are large and there is considerable undeveloped hydroelectric potential.

Nuclear Power Program. There is interest in nuclear power development for use in some locations; however, no nuclear power projects have been initiated to date.

AUSTRIA

Agencies. Österreichische Beratende Regierungsflommission Für Fragen Der Atomenergie, Vienna, is the official advisory commission to the Austrian Government on atomic energy matters. Austrian Federal Chancellory, Section V, Department 10c, Vienna, is a branch of the government responsible for coordination of external affairs relating to atomic energy, including Austria's participation in the activities of the OECD (see below). Österreichische Studiengesellschaft Für Atomenergie (SGAE), Vienna, is a corporation, 51% owned by the government and 49% by private interests, charged with implementation of Austria's atomic energy program.

International Relationships. Member of the **International Atomic Energy Agency** and the **European Nuclear Energy Agency.** Research-type **Agreement for Cooperation** with the United States.

Research Centers. The Austrian Research Reactor Center, located at Seibersdorf, 18 miles southeast of Vienna, and operated by SGAE, is Austria's principal atomic energy research establishment. Facilities include ASTRA, a tank-in-pool-type research reactor which operates at a power level of 5000 kilowatts (thermal) but is designed to permit future service at higher power as a materials testing facility. ASTRA was supplied by AMF Atomics (U.S.) and began operation in 1960. The United States contributed $350,000 toward the construction of ASTRA under its program of Foreign Research Reactor Grants. Atominstitut Der Österreichischen Hochschulen, Vienna, is a research and training institution whose facilities include a Triga Mark II reactor supplied by General Atomic (U.S.) and designed to operate at a power level of 100 kilowatts (thermal).

Nuclear Production. No significant deposits of uranium are known. Experiments are in progress (see below) to determine the economic feasibility of constructing a plant for the production of heavy water.

Energy Economy. Austria's electric power capacity is approximately 4000 megawatts, nearly three-quarters of it hydroelectric. There is considerable undeveloped hydroelectric potential.

Industry Notes. Österreichische Stickstoffwerke A.G. (Austrian Nitrogen Works Co.), Linz, a nationalized enterprise, is operating pilot facilities with a view toward constructing a full-scale heavy water production plant, and is also interested in undertaking uranium processing and fabrication. The Austro-Chematon Nuclear Fuel Company, Ltd., Linz, has recently been organized to enter the field of nuclear fuel production. This is a venture of the Austrian chemical firm, Stickstoffwerke, A.G., in association with German and Anglo-Canadian interests, respectively, Degussa and Rio Tinto Management Services, Ltd.

AUTOCATALYTIC

A term applied to a power reactor whose reactivity increases as the power level increases; for example, a reactor with a **positive temperature coefficient.** Reactors that employ a coolant whose effect on reactivity as a neutron absorber outweighs its positive contribution as a neutron moderator may become autocatalytic in the event of displacement or loss of coolant from the reactor core.

AUTORADIOGRAPHY

A radiographic technique in which an internal, rather than an external radiation source, is used; thus an autoradiograph is, in effect, a self x-ray picture. The technique involves incorporating a radioactive tracer into the specimen under study. It is usually applied in research on life processes, as in studying the manner in which a particular chemical element or compound localizes in plant or animal cells and tissues; but is also applicable in other ways, as in examining flaws in a casting.

Fig. 18. Autoradiograph of leaf of coleus plant fed with nutrient containing radioactive phosphorus. (*Courtesy of Brookhaven National Laboratory*)

An autoradiograph is prepared by placing the test specimen (into which a radioactive tracer has been introduced) in contact with a photographic emulsion, working either in a dark room or under safelight conditions. It is kept in contact by pressure and stored for an exposure period of hours to days, and then the specimen is removed and the film developed. Radiation emanating from the tracer passes through the emulsion and sensitizes silver bromide granules, which are reduced to metallic silver by the developer solution. A pattern of silver grains deposits on the film, showing how the tracer is distributed (see Fig. 18).

AUTUNITE

Hydrated calcium uranyl phosphate—a secondary mineral, usually lemon yellow or green in color, found in the presence of other uranium minerals, especially where oxidation of the primary deposit has occurred. Autunite occurs in sedimentary deposits in the Spokane area of Washington, and in vein deposits in the Front Range of Colorado and the Marysvale district of Utah; however it is not an important source of U.S. uranium production at the present time. (See **uranium deposits and reserves**)

AUXILIARY POWER UNITS, NUCLEAR. See **SNAP Program.**

B

BACKGROUND

Natural **background radiation.** Also, the level of radiation, from whatever source, above which a phenomenon must manifest itself to be measured; sometimes referred to as "noise."

BACKGROUND RADIATION (natural)

Ionizing radiation that is a natural part of man's environment. The sources are **cosmic rays** and **natural radioactivity,** the latter including naturally radioactive substances present in the air, the earth's crust and the body. Background radiation varies in intensity from locality to locality, depending on altitude and other factors. Representative values are given in the accompanying table.

BACKGROUND RADIATION

Source	*Exposure (millirems per year)*
Cosmic rays (sea level)	30 [1]
Natural radioactivity	
External [2]	100
Internal [3]	50
Total	180

[1] Compares with 70 millirems at 5000 feet elevation.

[2] From uranium, thorium and associated decay products in the earth's crust or atmosphere.

[3] From potassium-40, radium and its decay products, and carbon-14 in the body.

USS *BAINBRIDGE* (DLG(N)25)

The third nuclear-powered Naval surface ship. A guided-missile destroyer (frigate size), *Bainbridge* displaces about 7900 tons and is powered by twin D2G pressurized water re-

Fig. 19. Launching of *USS Bainbridge* at Quincy, Mass. on April 15, 1961. (*Official U.S. Navy photograph*)

actors designed by Knolls Atomic Power Laboratory (KAPL). The ship, constructed by the Shipbuilding Division of Bethlehem Steel Company, was launched on April 15, 1961, and is scheduled for sea trials in mid-1962.

An additional nuclear-powered destroyer has been authorized. (See **Naval Reactors Program**)

BARN

A measure of the probability that a given nuclear reaction or interaction will occur; more specifically, the unit for expressing **cross-section** values for reactions between particular nuclides and particular incident particles of particular energies. In physical terms, the barn is a unit of area; 1 barn $= 1 \times 10^{-24}$ square centimeter.

BASE LOAD

In electric power generation, that part of the total load carried by a power generating unit which is continuous as distinct from that part which fluctuates widely as the total system load changes from hour to hour or seasonally. (See **load factor, capacity factor**)

BATTELLE RESEARCH REACTOR (BRR)

A 2000-kilowatt (thermal) pool-type research reactor used by Battelle Memorial Institute for contract research programs. It was supplied by AMF Atomics Inc. to BMI specifications and is located, together with other BMI nuclear facilities, at West Jefferson, Ohio. It has been in operation since 1956. (See **research and training reactors**)

BELGIUM

Agencies. Commissariat á l'Energie Atomique (CEA), Brussels, is the official government agency responsible for atomic energy matters. Centre d'Etudes de l'Energie Nucléaire (CEN), Brussels, is a quasi-official organization sponsored jointly by government, industry, and universities, whose function is to sponsor research and operate the research center at Mol (see below).

International Relationships. Member of the **International Atomic Energy Agency** (IAEA), the European Atomic Energy Community **(Euratom)**, the **European Nuclear Energy Agency** (ENEA), and the European Organization for Nuclear Research **(CERN)**. Comprehensive **Agreement for Cooperation** with the United States.

Fig. 20. The BR-3 power reactor installation at Mol. This is an 11.5-megawatt (electrical) pressurized water installation supplied by Westinghouse Electric Corporation (U.S.) with the participation of Belgonucléaire and Bureau d'Etudes Nucléaires. (*Courtesy of Centre d'Etudes de l'Energie Nucléaire, Belgium*)

Research Center. Mol Laboratory, 50 miles northeast of Brussels, is a diversified atomic energy research center operated by CEN. Its experimental facilities include two reactors: BR-1, a graphite-moderated, air-cooled research reactor fueled with natural uranium, operates at a power level of 4000 kilowatts (thermal). It was designed by the laboratory staff and has been in operation since 1956. BR-2, a light water-moderated tank-type materials testing reactor fueled with enriched uranium, operates at a power level of 50,000 kilowatts (thermal). It was designed by Nuclear Development Corporation of America * and CEN and began operation in 1961.

* Now part of United Nuclear Corporation.

A prototype power reactor is also located at Mol (see BR-3 below) and near the laboratory is the site of a pilot fuel reprocessing facility being constructed under the auspices of the European Nuclear Energy Agency. (See **Eurochemic**)

Production Activity. Union Minière du Haut Katanga, a Belgian company, produced uranium ore and concentrate at Shinkolobwe in Katanga Province, Republic of the Congo, before this facility was closed in 1960. The Shinkolobwe deposit was a major source of uranium for the United States during the wartime **Manhattan Project** and in postwar years. Société Générale Métallurgique de Hoboken, operates a uranium refining plant at Olen, Belgium, with a capacity of 600 tons per year of orange oxide (UO_3). A pilot metal reduction facility with a capacity of 50 tons per year is also in operation at Olen.

Fig. 21. The BR-1 research reactor at Mol. This is a graphite-moderated, air-cooled reactor designed by the Mol staff. (*Courtesy of Centre d'Etudes de l'Energie Nucléaire, Belgium*)

Energy Economy. The capacity of Belgium's electric power generating plant is about 4000 megawatts, almost all of which is coal-fired. In recent years Belgium has imported coal in amounts equivalent to as much as 10 or 15% of its energy requirements, and increasing imports have been predicted. However, at this writing virtually all of the country's current requirements are being met by stockpiles and domestic production, which is currently at the level of 30 million metric tons per year. Belgium has very limited hydroelectric resources.

Nuclear Power Program. Belgium is actively pursuing nuclear power development as a means of stabilizing its energy economy and forestalling projected increases in coal imports. Tentative plans for nuclear power plant construction are as follows: 500 megawatts (electrical) by 1967 and 1500 megawatts by 1975. Following is the status of specific projects:

BR-3: This is a 11.5-megawatt prototype power reactor of the pressurized water type which was placed in operation at Mol in 1962. It was supplied by Westinghouse Electric Corporation. Belgonucléaire and BEN (see below) participated in the project.

Centrale Nucléaire Franco-Belge des Ardennes: This is a 242-megawatt (electrical) nuclear power station of the pressurized water type scheduled to be placed in operation in 1965 at Chooz (Givet) in the French Ardennes near the Franco-Belgian border. The plant is being financed by Société d'Energie Nucléaire Franco-Belge des Ardennes (SENA), which is a joint (50-50) venture of the French national utility company, Electricité de France, and the Belgian utility syndicate, Centre et Sud (see below). The project is to be carried out under the terms of the **U.S.-Euratom Joint Program.** A contract was awarded in 1960 to Westinghouse Electric Company and its licensees, Framatom (in **France)** and Atelièrs des Constructions Electriques de Charleroi (in Belgium), for this project.

Project CNB (Centrale Nucléaire Belge): This project now in the planning stage, contemplates construction of a 300-megawatt plant of unspecified type at Dessel, Belgium by the late sixties.

Belgian interests are known to favor fast breeder power reactors for the country's long-term nuclear power program and development work has been in progress looking toward the construction of a nuclear power plant of this type by the late sixties; however, no specific project plans along this line have yet been reported.

A study of reactors for ship propulsion is in progress.

Industry Notes. See Table 1.

TABLE 1. PARTIAL LISTING OF BELGIAN INDUSTRY ACTIVE IN ATOMIC ENERGY

Firm or Group	*Notes*
Groupement Professionnel de l'Industrie Nucléaire (Brussels)	Industry association analogous to the U.S. Atomic Industrial Forum.
ACEC (Atelièrs des Constructions Electriques de Charleroi) (Charleroi)	Reactor component manufacturer. Licensee of Westinghouse Electric Corporation.
Belchim (Société Belge de Chimie Nucléaire) (Brussels)	Corporation representing Belgian interests in the **Eurochemic** fuel reprocessing project at Mol.
Belgonucléaire (Société Belge pour l'Industrie Nucléaire) (Brussels)	Syndicate formed to supply reactors and reactor components and pursue other commercial objectives in the nuclear field.
BEN (Bureau d'Etudes Nucléaires) (Brussels)	Architect-engineering firm established by five engineering interests to offer services in the nuclear field.
Société Belge Centre et Sud (Brussels)	Corporation representing Belgian utility interests in SENA.
CNRM (Centre National des Recherches Métallurgiques) (Liege and Hainaut)	Private nonprofit research organization emphasizing metallurgy and ceramics.
Cockerill-Ougrée (Seraing)	Engineering and manufacturing concern. Principal sponsor of nuclear ship propulsion study.
MMN (Métallurgie et Mécanique Nucléaires) (Brussels-Mol)	Corporation established to manufacture fuel elements and other reactor core components. Major participants are Fabrique Nationale d'Armes de Guerre and Société Métallurgique de Hoboken.
NDA-Europe (Brussels)	European subsidiary of Nuclear Development Corporation of America. Provides consulting services and conducts development and manufacturing operations. Participants include Belgonucléaire and Société Générale des Minerais.
SENA (Société d'Energie Nucléaire Franco-Belge des Ardennes) (Paris)	Company jointly established by Electricité de France and Société Belge Centre et Sud to operate the Centrale Nucléaire Franco-Belge des Ardennes nuclear power station.
SYCA (Syndicat d'Etude des Centrales Atomiques) (Brussels)	Syndicate of private electric utilities and related interests established to coordinate nuclear power plans.

BERKELIUM

Element No. 97 (symbol, Bk), first identified in 1949 by S. G. Thompson, A. Ghiorso and G. T. Seaborg at the E. O. Lawrence Radiation Laboratory. The discovery followed particle accelerator experiments in which **americium-241** was bombarded with high-energy alpha particles. Berkelium is one of the eleven **trans-uranium elements** discovered in the past two decades. The reaction which led to the discovery of berkelium was:

$$_{95}Am^{241} + {_2}He^4 \longrightarrow {_{97}}Bk^{243} + 2{_0}n^1$$

BERYL

Synonym for beryllium aluminum silicate ($Be_3Al_2Si_6O_{18}$). (See **beryllium)**

BERYLLIA

Beryllium oxide (BeO). (See **beryllium)**

BERYLLIUM

Element No. 4 (symbol, Be; atomic weight, 9.013), used as a reactor moderator or reflector, and as a fuel element cladding or diluent material. Its advantages include a low thermal neutron cross section ($\sim$ 0.1 barn), a high melting point ($\sim$ 2340°F), and good mechanical strength. Its disadvantages are high cost, low ductility, relatively poor corrosion resistance, and toxicity. Beryllium oxide (beryllia) and beryllium carbide are compounds of beryllium of particular interest in high-temperature reactor applications. (See **reactor materials)**

The bombardment of beryllium with alpha particles from radioactive substances such as radium or polonium provides a convenient source of neutrons for oil-well logging, laboratory experiments, etc.

Production. Beryllium is produced commercially from ore deposits of **beryl**—a beryllium aluminum silicate mineral. The beryllium content of commercial-grade ore usually runs about 5% but may be as low as 3.5%. Although some domestic ore is available, mainly as a by-product of feldspar mining, the bulk of the beryllium produced in the United States comes from ores supplied by Argentina, Brazil, India and South Africa. In recent years ore imports have averaged about 6000 tons per year, and domestic ore production about 600 tons per year. Less than half of this tonnage has been processed, the balance being held in stockpiles.

The steps involved in the production of reactor-grade beryllium from ore are as follows (see Fig. 22): (1) The ore is prepared for subsequent treatment by crushing, grinding, arc melting and quenching operations. (2) It is then digested in sulfuric acid, yielding a solution of beryllium sulfate ($BeSO_4$). (3) Impurities are removed by successive precipitation-filtration operations. (4) The purified beryllium sulfate may then be crystallized and the crystals ignited to yield commercial-grade beryllium oxide (BeO); more generally, however, it is converted to beryllium fluoride (BeF_2) by precipitation as beryllium hydroxide and subsequent treatment with hydrofluoric acid in the presence of ammonium fluoride. (5) The beryllium fluoride is mixed with magnesium and charged to a graphite-lined furnace wherein it is reduced by a thermite-type reaction to beryllium metal. The product from the furnace is commercial-grade "pebble" beryllium (98% pure). (6) Reactor-grade beryllium (99+% pure) is obtained by remelting the pebble material in the presence of fluxing agents—usually calcium and beryllium fluorides. (7) The product material is cast into ingots, which are then ground to a fine powder. (8) The powder is fabricated into reactor components by conventional powder metallurgical techniques.

Suppliers. The two major U.S. suppliers of beryllium products are the Beryllium Corporation (Reading, Pennsylvania) and the Brush Beryllium Company (Elmore, Ohio). In 1956, the AEC contracted with each for the fixed-price production over a five-year period of 500,000 pounds of reactor-grade beryllium metal, a figure subsequently re-

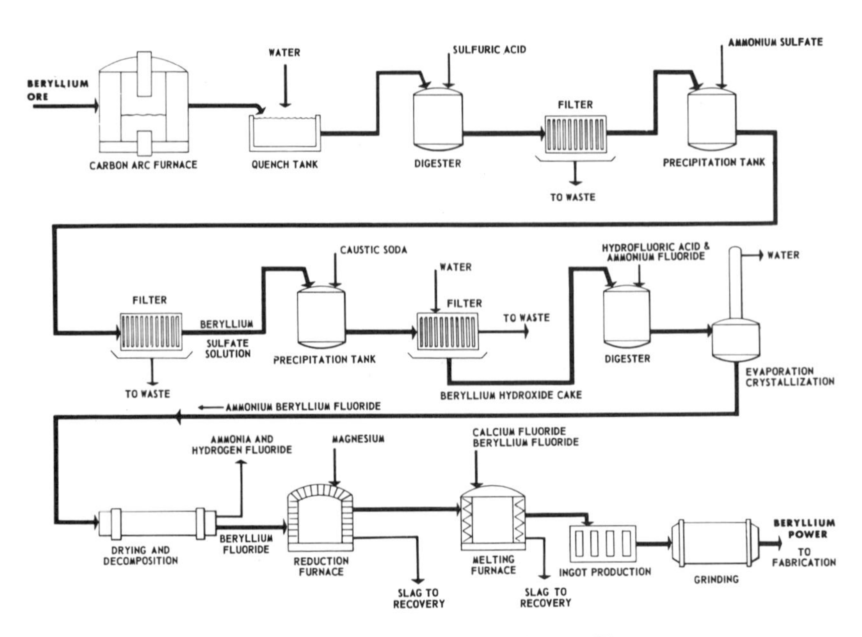

Fig. 22. Production of reactor-grade beryllium.

duced to 37,500 pounds per year. The average cost of this metal in ingot form is $47 per pound.

Toxicity. Exposure to beryllium can cause "berylliosis," or beryllium poisoning. The principal hazard is inhalation of dusts, leading to acute or chronic pneumonitis, but skin lesions from body contact have also been observed. These effects may not manifest themselves for considerable periods of time after exposure has taken place. Also, there is some evidence of an allergy process in that some individuals appear to be particularly susceptible to beryllium poisoning. A number of cases of beryllium poisoning occurred during early production operations; however once the problem was diagnosed it proved possible to control it by straightforward plant safety measures—principally the use of equipment enclosures and other precautions against the release of dusts or fumes, and improved ventillation of plant areas.

BETA ACTIVITY

The emission of **beta particles** from unstable atomic nuclei. (See **beta decay)**

BETA DECAY

Radioactive decay of an unstable atomic nucleus by emission of a **beta particle,** resulting in a daughter product with essentially the same atomic weight as the parent but an atomic number one unit greater than that of the parent. See **alpha decay, radioactivity.**

Beta decay is accounted for by postulating the disintegration of a neutron in the nucleus into a proton, an electron and a neutrino. The electron and neutrino are emitted from the nucleus; the proton remains in the nucleus. The results are no appreciable change in atomic mass (since the electron and neutrino have negligible mass) but a definite change in the chemical properties of the atom (since the nucleus now contains a proton where it formerly contained a neutron and, hence, moves up one unit in the scale of **atomic numbers).**

Beta decay is a common mode of disintegration, both in natural radioactive substances and in those in which radioactivity has been induced artificially, and may occur concurrently with other disintegration processes. Where it occurs as the sole disintegration process, the radioactive substance is referred to as a "pure beta" emitter, a familiar example being strontium-90.

The following equation illustrates beta decay:

$$_{93}\mathrm{Np}^{239} \xrightarrow{2.3\text{ days}} {}_{94}\mathrm{Pu}^{239} + {}_{-1}\beta^{0}$$

This will be recognized as a step in the production of **plutonium** from uranium-238.

BETA FACTOR

In controlled fusion, the ratio of the plasma **kinetic pressure** to the **magnetic pressure.** If beta is less than one, the magnetic field has a chance to contain the plasma providing there are no instabilities. If beta is larger than one, there is no possible chance of containment.

BETA GAGE. See **gages.**

BETA PARTICLE (β)

A negatively charged elementary subatomic particle identical to an electron. Beta particles, **alpha particles** and **gamma rays** are the basic forms of radioactivity. Beta particles are emitted by many natural and artificial radionuclides, a phenomenon accounted for by the decay of a neutron into a proton, a beta particle and a neutrino. (They are not orbital electrons displaced from the extranuclear atom structure.) There are some "pure beta" emitters, such as strontium-90; in general, however, radionuclides which undergo **beta decay** also emit gamma rays.

Beta particles have a mass equivalent to approximately one two-thousandth of a hydrogen atom, and a negative electric charge of 4.802×10^{-10} electrostatic units, which is half that of the positively charged alpha particle. Unlike alpha particles, beta particles are emitted in a continuous spectrum of energy values up to a maximum value for any particular radionuclide. Beta radiation is somewhat more penetrating than alpha radiation and has correspondingly lower specific ionization power. Beta particles are usually absorbed by a thin pane of glass or foil of aluminum. External exposure to high-intensity beta radia-deceleration of energetic beta particles is ac-tion can cause serious skin burns. Also, the companied by the generation of x-rays, a phenomenon known as bremsstrahlung.

Beta-emitting radionuclides are widely used in devices for industrial quality control. (See **radioisotopes in industry; gages)**

BETATRON

A type of **particle accelerator** used to supply beams of high-energy electrons (up to ~ 300 Mev). The betatron accelerates electrons by magnetic induction. It consists essentially of a doughnut-shaped evacuated glass tube placed between the poles of a strong electromagnet. Electrons, previously energized by electrostatic means, are injected into the tube and the magnetic field strength is progressively increased. In effect, the electron beam acts as the secondary of a transformer; as alternating current is fed into the magnet coil, an electrical potential is induced which acts to accelerate the electrons. Since the electrons are moving in a magnetic field, they describe a circular path. Due to the fact that their relativistic mass increases as they speed up, their tendency is to spiral outward; however, this tendency is compensated for by the rising magnetic field so that, if the system is properly operated, they can be kept in a fixed circular orbit. Upon reaching maximum energy (which corresponds to the point of maximum field strength), the beam is deflected from the tube and the cycle is repeated.

The betatron concept was proposed as early as 1928 but was first reduced to practice by D. W. Kerst (U.S.) in 1940. The largest betatron built to date is at the University of Illinois. This unit, also built by Kerst, accelerates electrons up to energies of 300 Mev.

The term "betatron" should not be confused with "Bevatron," which is the name given a large proton synchrotron at the E. O. Lawrence Radiation Laboratory.

BETTIS ATOMIC POWER LABORATORY

A U.S. Atomic Energy Commission power reactor development center, principally for Naval reactor programs, near Pittsburgh,

Pennsylvania. *Operating contractor:* Westinghouse Electric Corporation. *General Manager:* Philip N. Ross. *AEC investment in plant and equipment:* ~ $57 million.* *Staff:* ~ 1000 scientists and engineers, plus ~ 2900 supporting personnel.

The principal site of the Laboratory is Bettis Field at West Miflin, Pennsylvania, a former airfield named in honor of aviation pioneer Cyrus Bettis. The Laboratory additionally operates reactor development and test facilities at the Naval Reactors Facility of the National Reactor Testing Station.

The Laboratory was established in the winter of 1948 and is organized into project groups with supporting technical and service departments. Apart from carrying the responsibility for the **Shippingport Atomic Power Station,** the first large-scale civilian atomic power plant built in the United States, it has worked entirely on Naval reactor programs. Except for studies of advanced reactor systems, all of its research and development work has involved pressurized water reactor technology. The Naval reactor systems it has developed include: (1) The prototype system (S1W) used in the *Nautilus* submarine (Argonne National Laboratory collaborated on the basic design); (2) The Submarine Fleet Reactor (S3W/S4W) used in submarines of the *Skate* class; (3) The High-Speed Submarine Reactor (S5W) used in attack submarines of the *Skipjack* and *Thresher* classes and in Polaris missile submarines of the *George Washington* class; (4) The Large Ship Reactor (A2W) used in large surface vessels (the aircraft carrier, *Enterprise,* is powered by 8 A2W units and the cruiser, *Long Beach,* is powered by 2 A2W units); and (5) A single-reactor plant (D1W) for use in destroyers. For background information, see **Naval Reactors Program.**

In the course of its pressurized reactor development work, Bettis has made a number of basic contributions to power reactor technology, notably: (1) pioneering work on the use of zirconium as a reactor material, including development of special alloys (zircaloys); (2) pioneering work on the use of uranium dioxide (UO_2) as a reactor fuel; (3) the development of canned pumps and other special equipment components for water-cooled power reactors; (4) the development of basic computational codes used in the design of pressurized water reactor systems.

* Includes facilities authorized or under construction as of June 30, 1960. Not adjusted for depreciation.

BEV

Shorthand expression for billion **electron volts;** may be written bev, or Bev. In international usage, Bev is usually replaced by **Gev.**

BEVATRON

A 6.2-Bev proton synchrotron at the E. O. Lawrence Radiation Laboratory. (See **proton synchrotron** for description)

BILATERAL AGREEMENTS. See **Agreements for Cooperation.**

BINDING ENERGY

The energy that would be needed to separate an atom of atomic number Z and mass number A into Z protons and (A-Z) neutrons. It is the energy equivalent of the difference between the sum of the masses of the Z protons and the (A-Z) neutrons and the mass of the atom. Except for the lightest nuclides, the binding energy is approximately equal to (8 A) Mev, and the binding energy per particle is approximately 8 Mev. The concept of binding energy can be illustrated by means of the simplest complex atom, deuterium, which may be regarded as made up of one proton and one neutron. The mass difference is, in amu:

$$\underset{\text{(proton)}}{1.008142} + \underset{\text{(neutron)}}{1.008982} - \underset{\text{(deuterium atom)}}{2.014732} = \underset{\text{(difference)}}{0.002392}$$

The binding energy is the energy equivalent of this difference, or 0.002392 amu × 931.16 Mev/amu = 2.227 Mev; for energies equal to or greater than 2.227 Mev, the deuterium atom is disintegrated into a neutron and a proton.

It is also possible to speak of the binding energy of a single neutron or proton; the former is the energy needed to remove a single neutron from a nucleus; the latter is the energy needed to remove a proton.

BIOLOGICAL EFFECTS OF IONIZING RADIATION

Radiation acts on biological tissue at the molecular level and therefore primarily on the cell and its constituents, or on the surrounding oxygenated aqueous media. Thus, exposure to ionizing radiation may result in changes in the highly organized molecular system within the cell, or in destruction of certain cellular elements, which leads to altered function or death of the cell. These changes are brought about by the physical process of **ionization** and may be due to highly reactive chemical intermediates liberated within the cell.

Radiation consisting of charged particles (such as alpha and beta particles) causes ionization directly. Other types of ionizing radiation (namely neutrons, gamma rays and x-rays) indirectly induce ionization. In either case the amount of ionization depends on the kind, quantity and energy of the incident radiation, and on the characteristics of the tissue. It follows that three of the basic factors that act to determine biological effects are (1) the nature of the radiation, (2) the amount of radiation absorbed (i.e., the absorbed dose), and (3) the portion of the body affected. Other basic factors are (4) the time interval over which exposure occurs, (5) whether the radiation emanates from an external source (external exposure) or from within the body (internal exposure), (6) the sensitivity of the organ receiving the dose, and (7) the age of the individual. To simplify discussion, the following presentation refers to levels of radiation exposure, rather than to amounts of dose absorbed. (See **radiation dose** for information on dose terminology and units)

Chronic Exposure. The human body is continuously exposed to small amounts of ionizing radiation due to **background radiation,** i.e., radiation and radioactivity naturally present in man's environment. Over a generation (taken as 30 years) the accumulated radiation exposure from natural sources (both external and internal) is in the general range, 4.3 to 5.5 **roentgens.** The average exposure rate is 0.02 milliroentgen per hour (mr/hr). Experience to date indicates that frequent or even more or less continuous exposure of adults to levels of radiation one hundred times higher than the natural level, i.e., ~ 2 mr/hr, may be incurred over a period of many years without apparent effect. However, chronic exposure to levels several thousand times the natural level, i.e., above 40 to 50 mr/hr, can over a period of years result in serious injury. Possible types of injury include:

1. Leukopenia (decrease in white blood corpuscle count).
2. Anemia (decrease in red blood corpuscle count).
3. Detrimental changes in tissue structure.
4. Leukemia (a disease of the blood-forming tissues, characterized by an abnormal and persistent increase in the white corpuscle count and in the amount of bone marrow, with enlargement of the spleen and lymph glands—sometimes referred to as cancer of the blood).
5. Malignant tumors.
6. Cataracts (opacities of the lens of the eye).
7. Increases in the average rate of genetic mutation.

Experiments with small animals indicate that excessive chronic exposure may result in some reduction in life expectancy without the occurrence of any of the above injuries. This indication is supported by the following statistics: *

	Average Age at Death
U.S. population over age 25	65.6 years
Physicians who have not employed x-ray machines or other radiation sources in the practice of their profession	65.7 years
Specialists, such as dermatologists, who have employed radiation sources	63.3 years
Radiologists (x-ray specialists) who can be expected to have received life-time exposure ranging from slight to 1000 or more roentgens	60.5 years

* Source: 1956 report by the National Research Council, National Academy of Sciences.

It should be added that all chronic radiation effects are essentially indistinguishable from pathological conditions normally present in the population due to other causes. Much of the present knowledge of such effects is therefore necessarily inferred from statistical information.

Acute Exposure. Exposure to a single large dose of radiation, or to a series of substantial doses in a short interval of time, is referred to as acute exposure. Acute exposure of the whole body, apart from contributing to the inherently delayed effects noted above, can result in the various more-or-less immediate and dis-

TABLE 1. EFFECTS OF ACUTE WHOLE-BODY RADIATION EXPOSURE [1]
(Units are roentgens)

0–25r	*25–100r*	*100–200r*	*200–300r*	*300–600r*	*600 or more*
No detectable clinical effects.	Slight transient decrease in white blood corpuscle count.	Nausea and fatigue, with possible vomiting above 125r.	Nausea and vomiting on first day.	Nausea, vomiting and diarrhea in first few hours.	Nausea, vomiting and diarrhea in first few hours.
Delayed effects may occur.	Disabling sickness not common; exposed individual should be able to proceed with usual duties.	Decrease in white blood corpuscle count with delayed recovery.	Latent period up to two weeks or perhaps longer.	Latent period with no definite symptoms, perhaps as long as one week.	Short latent period with no definite symptoms in some cases during the first week.
	Delayed effects possible, but serious effects on average individual very improbable.	Delayed effects may shorten life expectancy on the order of one per cent.	Following latent period symptoms appear but are not severe; loss of appetite, and general malaise, sore throat, pallor diarrhea, and moderate emaciation. Also livid spots may appear on the skin due to effusion of the blood (purpura).	Epilation, loss of appetite, general malaise, and fever during second week, followed by hemorrhage, purpura, inflammation of mouth and throat, diarrhea, and emaciation in the third week.	Diarrhea, hemorrhage, purpura, inflammation of mouth and throat, fever toward end of first week.
			Recovery likely in about 3 months unless complicated by poor previous health, superimposed injuries or infections.	Some deaths in 2 to 6 weeks. Possible eventual death of 50% of the exposed individuals for about 450 roentgens.[2]	Rapid emaciation and death as early as the second week with possible eventual death of up to 100% of exposed individuals.

[1] Adapted from "The Effects of Nuclear Weapons," U.S. Government Printing Office, 1957.
[2] See median lethal dose.

cernible clinical effects indicated in Table 1. With reference to Table 1, the effects indicated for exposures in the range, 100-300 roentgens, are collectively referred to as "radiation sickness." Those described for exposures exceeding 300 roentgens are often referred to by the term, "acute radiation syndrome."

Acute exposure of portions of the body can cause local effects which may or may not be accompanied by systemic effects, depending upon the level of exposure and the portion of the body affected. Possible local effects include reddening (erythema), scaling (desquamation), or ulceration of the skin; and, in the case of gonad exposure, temporary or permanent sterility.

Linear and Threshold Concepts. While not accepted as a supportable differentiation by experts in the field, biological effects of radiation are sometimes referred to as having either a "linear" or a "threshold" characteristic. A given effect is said to have a linear characteristic if each increment of exposure, however small, adds inexorably to the ultimate result; there is, in other words, no repair of the damage done. This is believed to be true in the case of at least two types of chronic effect, namely, genetic damage and shortening of the life span. An effect is said to have a threshold characteristic if it only materializes when the dose or dose rate exceeds a general threshold level. Such appears to be the case with some clinical manifestations of acute exposure; however, there is insufficient data, particularly at low exposure levels, to be conclusive.

Genetic Damage. A distinction commonly made in reference to the biological effects of radiation is that between "somatic" and "genetic" effects. The term somatic covers all effects which manifest themselves during the individual's lifetime; it thus includes all of the acute effects discussed above, and also all of the chronic effects save for genetic damage.

By way of introduction to the topic of genetic damage, it should be recalled that hereditary traits are passed down from generation to generation by the transmission of hereditary units, called genes. These are strung together in the human system in tiny threads of genetic material, called chromosomes, which exist as similar but not identical pairs. Each of the some hundred million cells in an adult normally contains 46 chromosomes, half having characteristics inherited from the mother and half having characteristics inherited from the father. The process of cell division (by means of which the human body develops and maintains itself) involves gene duplication. In general perfect duplicates are formed; however some genetic changes may occur during the process—a phenomenon known as mutation.

Mutations may be of thermal or chemical origin, or they may be induced by ionizing radiation. They may result in death of the cell (lethal mutation), or simply in altered cell characteristics (sub-lethal mutation). In the latter event the altered characteristic is preserved through subsequent cell division and, if it be associated with a sperm or egg cell, may be transmitted to successive generations. While some mutations are beneficial, most tend to be harmful in their effects on subsequent generations which may include shortened life span, reduced progeny, and in some cases gross physical abnormality. While mutation phenomena are exceedingly complex, and some compensation factors exist, it holds generally true that genetic damage is proportionate to the rate at which mutations occur; hence any factor which adds to the natural rate is definitely undesirable from a genetic standpoint. In this connection, roughly 4 to 5% of all live births in the United States have defects of a mental or physical nature, approximately half of which (i.e., 2% of total live births) are genetic in origin and appear before sexual maturity.

As has been brought out, the accumulated radiation exposure received by an individual from natural sources over a 30-year period is about 5 roentgens. It is of interest to compare this level of exposure with that associated with non-natural ("man-made") radiation, of which there are three principal sources: (1) medical x-rays, (2) **radioactive fallout** from nuclear weapon tests, and (3) civilian atomic energy development:

1. According to present estimates, the av-

erage 30-year gonadal exposure due to medical x-rays is 3-4 roentgens;

2. An estimate made several years ago placed the average 30-year exposure due to radioactive fallout at about 0.2 roentgen assuming continuation of the 1955 pattern of weapon testing. Actually, the fission yield from weapon tests was larger in the three subsequent years, and then fell essentially to zero from October, 1958 to September, 1961, the period of the recent three-power test moratorium (see **weapons testing**). Political uncertainties make it impossible at this time to develop a meaningful 30-year forecast of radiation exposure due to fallout; however, the estimate given above at least serves to indicate the experienced order of magnitude of this source of exposure, i.e., fractions of a roentgen, rather than tens of roentgens.

3. Probably the most meaningful figure that can be cited for possible exposure of the general population due to civilian atomic energy development (nuclear power, etc.) is the "safe practice" limit allowed by the current **Radiation Protection Guide,** which is an average 30-year gonadal dose of 5 rems (see **radiation protection standards and regulations**). For present purposes, this can be taken as roughly equivalent to an accumulated gonadal exposure of 5 roentgens (see **radiation dose**). Actually only those segments of the population living in the vicinity of an atomic energy installation would be subject to this source of exposure; hence the application of the 5-roentgen figure to the total population overstates, rather than understates, the possible genetic consequences.

Geneticists speak of the "doubling dose," which is defined as the amount of man-made radiation required to produce, during a given period, the same number of mutations as result from natural causes. Clearly if ionizing radiation were the only cause of mutations, the doubling dose would be numerically the same as the dose from natural radioactivity, i.e., about 5 roentgens over a 30-year period. Reflecting the fact that ionizing radiation is only one of several causes of mutations (see above), most geneticists place the 30-year doubling dose between 30 and 80 roentgens. On this basis, geneticists generally make the following recommendations with regard to exposure of the population to man-made radiation: (1) that such exposure be kept as low as possible; (2) that the average exposure over the reproductive lifetime (conception to age 30) be kept within an upper limit of 10 rems.

In the latter connection, it is of interest to note that the above estimates closely approach this recommended limit:

Source of Man-made Radiation	*Population Estimated Exposure*
Medical x-rays	3–4 rems
Radioactive fallout	<1 rems
Civilian atomic energy development	5 rems [1]
Total	8–10 rems

[1] Conservative upper limit.

BIOLOGICAL HALF-LIFE

The time required for a biological system to eliminate, by natural processes, half the amount of a substance that has been either produced or absorbed by it. Natural processes include elimination by way of urine, feces, exhalation and perspiration. See **effective half-life.**

BIOLOGICAL SHIELD

A shield used to protect personnel from exposure to the radiation emitted by intense radiation sources such as nuclear reactors or particle accelerators, as distinct from thermal shield. (See **shielding**)

BISMUTH

Element No. 83 (symbol, Bi; atomic weight, 209.00), studied as a possible working fluid for use in high-temperature reactor systems (see **Liquid Metal Fuel Reactor Concept**). Bismuth has a low thermal neutron cross section (~ 0.03 barn), a relatively low melting point (520°F) and good thermal conductivity. The principal problems associated with its use in reactor systems arise from corrosion and mass transfer phenomena, which make containment difficult; and from the formation, by neutron capture in bismuth, of polonium, an alpha-emitting metal of considerable toxicity.

BISMUTH PHOSPHATE PROCESS

A precipitation process used during the **Manhattan Project** and until 1956 for the recovery and decontamination of plutonium from irradiated uranium fuel elements (see **fuel reprocessing**). The operations were: (1) acid dissolution of the fuel elements; (2) coprecipitation of the plutonium with bismuth phosphate ($BiPO_4$); (3) decontamination of the plutonium (i.e., removal of radioactive fission products) by a series of oxidation and reduction steps involving successive dissolution and precipitation operations. Final decontamination was effected by coprecipitation of plutonium with lanthanum fluoride. The process was operated in batch fashion and did not recover uranium, which remained in solution in step (2) and was sent to underground radioactive waste storage tanks. The bismuth phosphate process became obsolete with the postwar development of solvent extraction techniques that recover uranium as well as plutonium and operate in continuous fashion (see **Redox** and **Purex**). Two large-scale plants operated during the Manhattan Project at the Hanford Works have been dismantled and converted to other use.

BLACK OXIDE. Uranous uranyl oxide (U_3O_8).

BLANKET

A layer of **fertile material** usually placed external to the core of a **breeder** (or a converter) reactor; the fertile material captures neutrons which leak from the core and is transformed into fissionable material by subsequent **beta decay.** A reactor containing a core and a blanket is generally referred to as a two-region system.

In the special case of a reactor employing a **seed core,** the blanket is not external to the core.

BODEGA BAY ATOMIC PARK

A large-scale nuclear power plant of the direct-cycle **boiling water** type, planned for construction on the Pacific coast, 50 miles north of San Francisco. The plant, which will have a power rating of 325,000 kilowatts and is expected to be completed in 1965, is being wholly financed by Pacific Gas and Electric Company. General Electric Company is supplying the reactor.

The Bodega plant represents the first U.S. nuclear power project in the 300-megawatt size range. Based on operation at 90% **capacity factor,** Pacific Gas & Electric Company has estimated that the plant will generate power at a cost slightly below 6 mills per kilowatt-hour, a level of performance matching that of comparable oil-fired power stations in the San Francisco area. (See **nuclear power economics** for general information on power costs)

Particulars of the Bodega plant are as follows:

Power: 325 megawatts (gross electrical). *Fuel:* Slightly enriched uranium ($\sim$ 2.0% U^{235}) in the form of uranium dioxide (UO_2). *Fuel element design:* A single fuel element consists of an assembly of thin stainless steel tubes loaded with UO_2 pellets. *Fuel inventory:* 70.1 metric tons of uranium dioxide. *Steam conditions:* Saturated steam at 1000 pounds pressure and 544°F. *Containment:* Vapor suppression system. *Cost:* Capital cost estimated at $61 million. *Dates:* Start of construction in the fall of 1962. Full power operation scheduled for December, 1965. *Notes:* The reactor, of advanced design, will employ an internal steam separator.

BODY BURDEN

The amount of a given radionuclide, usually measured in micrograms, present in the body. The term is used in connection with internal exposure to ionizing radiation. (See **maximum permissible concentration**)

BOILING NUCLEAR SUPERHEAT REACTOR (BONUS)

A small nuclear power plant of the direct-cycle **boiling water** type (with integral nuclear superheating) near Rincon, Puerto Rico. The project is being carried out under the "second round" of the U.S. Atomic Energy Commission's Power Demonstration Reactor Program. The AEC is financing the cost of reactor construction and related research and development. The Puerto Rico Water Resources Authority is providing the site and the electrical portion of the plant; and will operate the plant and distribute the power produced, making payment to the AEC for the steam used. *Reactor designer:* General Nuclear Engineering Corporation, a subsidiary of Combustion Engineering Company. *Architect–engineer:* Jackson and Moreland, Inc. *Construction contractor:* Maxon Construction Company. The following notes reflect the status of the project as of mid-1962:

Power: 16.3 megawatts (electrical). *Fuel:* The fuel for the boiler section of the core will be slightly enriched uranium (2.4% U^{235}) in the form of uranium dioxide (UO_2) pellets. That for the superheater section will be uranium of 3.3% enrichment in the form of UO_2 pellets. *Fuel element design:* The boiler fuel elements will consist of assemblies of thin Zircaloy-2 tubes loaded with UO_2 pellets. The superheater fuel elements will be similar but will have stainless steel cladding in place of Zircaloy-2. *Steam conditions:* Steam will leave the superheater section of the core at 900 pounds pressure and 900-950°F. *Thermal conversion efficiency:* 32.6%. *Control materials:* Boron-steel control rods. *Containment:* Steel sphere 190 feet in diameter. *Construction cost:* Estimated at $12.8 million, exclusive of research and development. For other project costs, see Table 3 under **nuclear power development.** *Dates:* Project authorized in January, 1960. Construction started in August, 1960. Operation scheduled to start early in 1963.

BOILING REACTOR EXPERIMENTS (BORAX I-V)

A series of reactor experiments conducted to study the feasibility and operating characteristics of **boiling water reactors.** Five experimental reactors have been built and operated to date under this program, which has been conducted by Argonne National Laboratory at the National Reactor Testing Station.

The BORAX experiments have been largely concerned with the effect of "steam void" formation on the control characteristics of boiling water reactor systems. An increase in the operating temperature of a boiling water reactor is accompanied by the formation of additional steam in the reactor core. This additional steam effectively displaces (or "voids") water from the core. Since water is a more effective neutron moderator than steam, the formation of steam voids tends to reduce the reactivity of the system, i.e., to slow down the reaction.* The system thus has a "negative temperature coefficient." In the event, therefore, that excess reactivity is added to the system (as by withdrawing control rods), the reaction will at first tend to speed up but then as the temperature increases will tend to slow down as the negative temperature coefficient takes effect. Reactor designers use the term "void coefficient" to express the relationship between the amount of reactivity added and the amount of steam formed.

Under normal operating conditions the void coefficient automatically limits the power level attainable in a boiling water reactor, and thus constitutes a built-in control mechanism. However, as in many feed-back control systems, it also introduces the possibility of instability under abnormal conditions. In general the BORAX experiments have established the fact that boiling water reactor systems are inherently stable over a range of operating conditions. Instabilities were only observed when the amount of reactivity being compensated by steam voids exceeded substantial limits.** Then the normal power fluctuations gave way to distinct and divergent power oscillations—a phenomenon known as "chugging."

BORAX-I was the first boiling water reactor. After a long series of experiments which successfully demonstrated the technical feasi-

---

* This is a deliberately simplified statement of a complex phenomenon.

** The reactivity added to a BORAX system by control-rod movement *after* criticality has been achieved is referred to as "reactivity compensated by steam." In nonpressurized power-excursion experiments instabilities were found to develop in the BORAX-I apparatus when the reactivity compensated by steam exceeded 1.5 or 1.6% of the effective coefficient of reactivity (k_{eff}). In excursion experiments conducted at 135 pounds pressure in the same apparatus, the corresponding value was ~2% k_{eff}.

bility and inherent stability (under normal conditions) of this reactor concept, BORAX-I was subjected to an extreme power excursion experiment which involved the spring-actuated ejection of a control rod. Although the ejection of the rod took only a fifth of a second, so rapid was the power excursion that the reactor power reached a peak value of ~ 19,000 megawatts before the rod had been completely removed. The total nuclear energy release during the excursion, which was of less than a tenth of a second's duration overall, has been estimated at 135 megawatt-seconds. The peak pressure in the reactor vessel is estimated to have reached at least 6000 psi and may have exceeded 10,000 psi. The physical effects included partial melt-down of the core and explosive rupture of the (thin-walled) reactor tank. There was relatively little damage to reactor equipment located outside the reactor tank, nor was there significant radioactive contamination beyond the immediate vicinity of the reactor installation. High-speed motion pictures of the event indicated that the nuclear reaction "turned itself off" at an early stage in the explosion. (A flash of light of 0.003 second duration was recorded as the reactor power level reached its peak but was extinguished before any ejected steam or debris appeared above the top of the reactor tank). Thus, the experiment dramatically confirmed the self-quenching characteristic of steam void formation which had been observed in the earlier less-violent power excursions.

BORAX-II was set up near the BORAX-I site and used some of the BORAX-I parts. It had about twice the core volume of BORAX-I and was equipped with a heavier pressure vessel to permit higher pressure operation. It was used to extend the study of natural-circulation boiling water parameters, including observation of the response of the reactor system to sudden closing of the main steam valve and sudden opening of the safety pressure relief valves.

BORAX-III was similar in most respects to BORAX-II but had fuel elements of heavier construction and was equipped with a turbine-generator. Its main purpose was to study the performance of a boiling water reactor when operated as an integral component of an electric power generating system. (It was thus the first boiling water reactor to demonstrate the generation of electric power.) BORAX-III was found to operate stably over a broad range of operating pressures (from atmospheric to 300 psi).

In 1956 the BORAX-III facility was equipped with a new core and became known as BORAX-IV. The fuel elements in the new core consisted of pellets of a urania-thoria mixture bonded with lead and clad with aluminum. BORAX-IV has been used to obtain more detailed information particularly about stability

NOTES ON BORAX EXPERIMENTS

	BORAX-I	BORAX-II	BORAX-III	BORAX-IV	BORAX-V
Start-up	1953	1954	1955	1957	1962
Rated heat output (megawatts-thermal)	1.2	6.4	12.0	20.5	20
Turbine-generator	no	no	yes	yes	yes
Fuel	U-Al	U-Al	U-Al	UO_2-ThO_2	UO_2
Uranium enrichment	~90% U^{235}	~90% U^{235}	~90% U^{235}	fully enriched	boiling zone—5 and 10% superheater zone—~93%
Pressure (psi)	135	300	300	300	600
Power density (tkw/liter of core)	10	27	27	36	n.a.
Reactivity compensated by steam (% k_{eff})	2.0	3.1	2.0	5.5	n.a.

and safety of boiling waters needed for power reactor design purposes, and to study the performance of the oxide fuel elements.

BORAX-V, which began operation in 1962, will be used for further development of the boiling water reactor art with particular emphasis on nuclear superheating. Plans call for testing three cores: (1) a straight boiling core, (2) a boiling core with a peripherally located superheater section, and (3) a boiling core with a centrally located superheater section. The boiling zone is fueled with slightly enriched uranium in the form of UO_2 pellets in stainless steel cladding; the superheater zone will be fueled with highly enriched uranium in the form of UO_2 dispersed in stainless steel plates clad with stainless steel.

BOILING SULFUR REACTOR CONCEPT

In 1958 the U.S. Atomic Energy Commission accepted a proposal from Aerojet General Nucleonics to explore the feasibility of the use of boiling sulfur as reactor coolant and working fluid in a high-temperature direct-cycle power system. A series of corrosion and heat-transfer experiments was undertaken but the program was terminated in mid-1960 due to unacceptable corrosion rates—~ 10-20 mils penetration per year—in the alloys considered most promising for such a system.

BOILING WATER REACTORS

A type of power reactor that employs ordinary water (H_2O) * as coolant and moderator and allows bulk boiling in the core, so that steam is generated in the primary reactor vessel. The latter feature distinguishes boiling water reactors from **pressurized water reactors.**

Boiling water plants are usually classified by the manner in which the reactor is connected to the steam turbine. Installations in which the steam passes directly from the reactor vessel to the turbine are referred to as "direct-cycle" plants (Fig. 23). If an intermediate heat exchanger is used, so that it is secondary steam which operates the turbine, they are referred to as "indirect-cycle" plants (Fig. 23). There are also "dual-cycle" plants (Fig. 23) in which some of the steam used to run the turbine comes directly from the reactor and some is generated in a secondary heat exchanger. Any of these schemes may employ natural convection and/or forced circulation

* Heavy water (D_2O) has been considered as a coolant for boiling reactor systems and is in fact used in Norway's **Halden Project;** however, the term "boiling water reactor" usually connotes an H_2O system and is so treated herein.

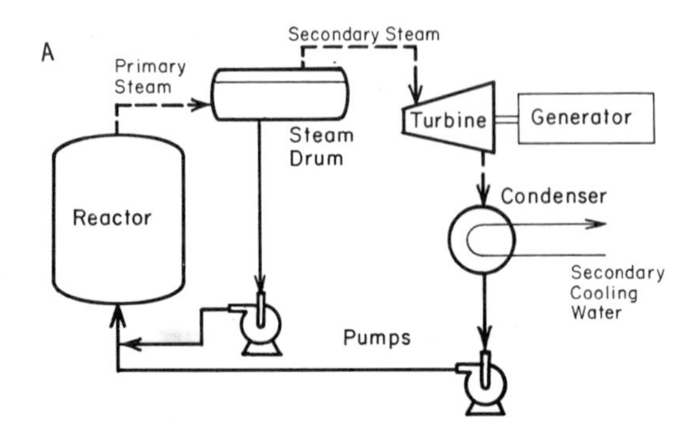

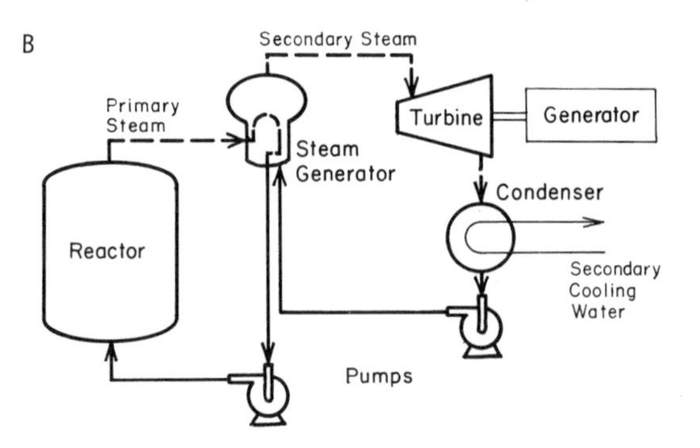

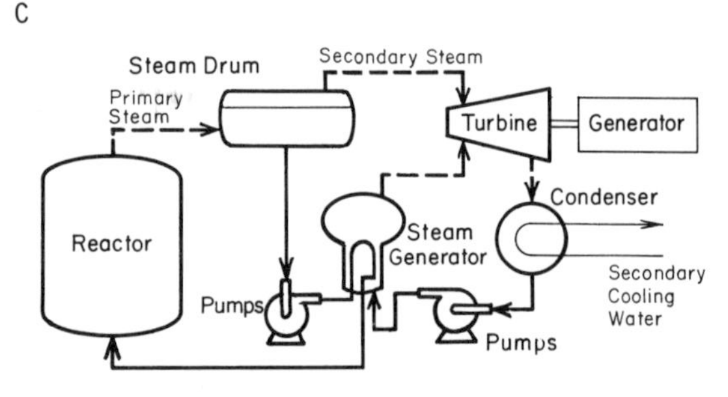

Fig. 23. Boiling water reactor concepts. (A) Direct cycle; (B) Indirect cycle; (C) Dual cycle. (Feed-water heaters and coolant purification equipment not shown.)

of the coolant. The direct and dual-cycle schemes require that entrained water be separated before the reactor-produced steam is fed to the turbine.

The basic feasibility of the boiling water concept was first demonstrated by Argonne National Laboratory's BORAX-I experiment in 1953 (see **Boiling Reactor Experiments**). The first prototype boiling water power plant was placed in operation in 1956 (see **Experimental Boiling Water Reactor**). The first large-scale boiling water plant was placed in operation in 1959 (see **Dresden Nuclear Power Station**). To date more civilian nuclear power projects have been based on the boiling water concept than on any other single-power reactor concept. A list of such projects and of related reactor experiments is given in Table 1. There has also been activity in boiling water reactor development under the **Army Nuclear Power, Maritime Reactors,** and **SNAP Programs.**

Of the approximately $476 million spent by the U.S. Atomic Energy Commission on civilian reactor research and development through mid-1960, $40 million ($\sim$ 8%) related specifically to boiling water programs.* In addition, the boiling water concept has benefited directly or indirectly from much of the considerably larger research and development effort that has been focused on pressurized water reactors, the two technologies being closely related.

General Considerations. The strong points usually cited for boiling water reactors are:

1. The technology of water-cooled reactors is at an advanced stage of development relative to that of other U.S. power reactor concepts.

2. Boiling water reactors operate at lower pressures than pressurized water reactors, permitting somewhat lighter construction of the primary system. The reason is that the operating pressure is the vapor pressure of water at the operating temperature; there is no excess pressure as there is in a pressurized system.

3. The direct-cycle scheme has an attractive simplicity from an engineering standpoint, an important feature being elimination of the need for an external steam generator.

4. Direct-cycle boiling water plants can achieve higher thermal conversion efficiencies than pressurized water plants at a given operating temperature, due to elimination of the intermediate heat-transfer step.

5. Boiling water reactors have been found to be stable in operation over a wide range of operating conditions.

6. Boiling water reactors share with pressurized water reactors the advantages of the use of ordinary water, namely, the fact that water has good heat transfer properties, is an effective neutron moderator, and can be maintained at high purity at low cost. Also, there is a long background of experience in the use of water as a heat exchange medium.

The major limitations of boiling water reactors are:

1. As is true of all H_2O-moderated systems, their neutron economy is such that they cannot operate on normal (non-enriched) uranium, and cannot serve as breeders.

2. The ceiling operating temperature of a straight boiling water system is $\sim$ 600-650°F, which limits the thermal conversion efficiency attainable in a non-superheated plant. (The temperature ceiling of the reactor can be raised by nuclear superheating, and the thermal efficiency of the plant can be improved by nuclear or conventional superheating.)

3. Boiling water reactors operate at lower power densities than pressurized water reactors, due basically to the fact that a given volume of boiling water (i.e., a mixture of steam and water) cannot carry away as much heat as the same volume of nonboiling water. The lower operating pressure of boiling water reactors is a contributing factor. Lower power densities result in a larger core size and higher fuel inventory charges for a given power output.

4. The physical size of the core is limited by the size of pressure vessel that can be fabricated and transported. In combination with (3) above, this limitation acts to restrict the

* These figures are exclusive of capital costs. Source: AEC Annual Report for 1960.

TABLE 1. CIVILIAN NUCLEAR POWER PROJECTS—BOILING-WATER REACTORS [1]
(Including BORAX Experiments)

Name of Plant or Project	*Type*	*Location*	*Reactor Designer*	*Rated Power Output (megawatts electrical)*	*Start-up*
U.S. Locations:					
Boiling Reactor Experiment No. 1 (BORAX-I)	(Experimental Facility)	National Reactor Testing Station	Argonne National Lab.	—	1953
Boiling Reactor Experiment No. 2 (BORAX-II)	(Experimental Facility)	National Reactor Testing Station	Argonne National Lab.	—	1954
Boiling Reactor Experiment No. 3 (BORAX-III)	(Experimental Facility)	National Reactor Testing Station	Argonne National Lab.	nominal	1955
Experimental Boiling Water Reactor (EBWR)	Direct-cycle	Lemont, Illinois	Argonne National Lab.	5	1956
Boiling Reactor Experiment No. 4 (BORAX-IV)	(Experimental Facility)	National Reactor Testing Station	Argonne National Lab.	nominal	1957
Vallecitos Boiling Water Reactor (VBWR)	Direct-cycle	Pleasanton, Cal.	General Electric	5.2	1957
Dresden Nuclear Power Station (Commonwealth Edison)	Dual-cycle	Morris, Ill.	General Electric	180	1959
Boiling Reactor Experiment No. 5 (BORAX-V)	(Experimental Facility)	National Reactor Testing Station	Argonne National Lab.	nominal	1962
Elk River Plant (Rural Coop. Power Association)	Indirect-cycle with coal-fired superheater	Elk River, Minn.	Allis-Chalmers	22 [2]	(1962)
Pathfinder Plant (Northern States Power)	Direct-cycle with integral nuclear superheating	Sioux Falls, S.D.	Allis-Chalmers	62	(1963)
Humboldt Bay Power Plant (Pacific Gas & Electric)	Direct-cycle	Eureka, Cal.	General Electric	48.5	(1962)
Consumers Power Company Project	Direct-cycle	Big Rock Point, Mich.	General Electric	50	(1962)
La Crosse Boiling Water Reactor	Modified direct-cycle	La Crosse, Wisconsin	Allis-Chalmers	50	(1964–5)
Boiling Nuclear Superheat Reactor (BONUS)	Direct-cycle with integral nuclear superheating	Rincon, Puerto Rico	General Nuclear Eng. Corp.	16	(1963)
Bodega Bay Atomic Park	Direct-cycle	Bodega Bay, Calif.	General Electric	325	(1965)
Foreign Locations:					
RWE Project		West **Germany**	General Electric	16	1961
JPDR Project		**Japan**	General Electric	12.5	(1962)
Project ENSI (SENN)	Dual-cycle	**Italy**	General Electric	150	(1963)

[1] For information on military boiling water reactors, see **Army Nuclear Power Program**.
[2] Includes power from conventional superheater.
Note: For cost information on U.S. reactors listed, see Table 3, nuclear power development.

power output that can be achieved from a boiling water system. At one time it was thought that the "ceiling" might be ~ 300 megawatts (electrical); it now appears, however, that outputs as high as 400-500 megawatts can be obtained from a single reactor unit.

5. Boiling water reactors are not inherently responsive to load changes in a power generating system, i.e., to changes in steam demand (see discussion below).

6. Equipment surfaces exposed to the coolant must be clad with stainless steel or other corrosion-resistant alloys.

Special Considerations. An important factor in the design and operation of boiling water reactors is the effect of steam voids on the reactivity of the system. Reference here is to the fact that as steam bubbles form, they displace (or "void") water from the core. Since steam is a less effective neutron moderator than water, the effect of an increase in steam voids is a loss in reactivity. This can result either from an increase in the operating temperature or a decrease in the operating pressure.* While the "void coefficient" serves within limits as a built-in safety mechanism against power surges (see discussion under **Boiling Reactor Experiments**), it also has certain undesirable effects which should be noted:

1. It may limit the power level attainable.

2. It tends to set up an axial power distribution in the core, with the highest power at the bottom (where there are fewest steam voids) and the lowest power at the top. This is usually compensated for by introducing the control rods through the bottom of the reactor vessel, rather than through the top.

3. It complicates the operation of a boiling water power plant by reason of the fact that it is "load resistant," rather than load responsive, in its effect. In other words, the reactor's natural tendency is to slow down, rather than speed up, when called upon to increase its steam output to meet a demand for greater electrical output. In the operation of direct and indirect cycle systems this tendency must be overruled by control rod adjustments. Dual-cycle systems minimize the problem by initially absorbing changes in steam demand by manipulation of the flow of steam from the secondary steam generator.

The magnitude of the void coefficient is a function of the ratio of water to fuel in the reactor core. For large-scale boiling water installations employing oxide fuel, a water-to-fuel ratio of about two is thought to be optimal at the present time.

There has been some concern over the possibility that in direct and dual-cycle systems there might be sufficient entrainment of radioactive particles in the steam from the reactor to cause serious radioactive contamination of the steam turbine. There has been virtually no indication of turbine contamination in the several boiling water plants run to date, however long-term operating results are needed to provide a definitive answer to this question.

Plant Characteristics. See Table 2.

Design Trends. Various efforts are being made to increase the power density of boiling water reactors. One possible route is to increase the pressure from the present level of about 1000 pounds up to 1500 pounds (see Table 2). Another is to work toward a more even power distribution in the reactor core, thereby flattening undesirable temperature peaks. By these and other approaches it is expected that power densities in the neighborhood of 60 thermal kilowatts per liter will be reached in the relatively near future.

Another basic development objective is to increase the temperature of the steam produced by boiling water reactors and thereby attain higher thermal conversion efficiencies in power generation. Increasing the operating pressure from 1000 to 1500 pounds would of itself go a long way to improving steam temperature since an operating pressure of 1500 pounds corresponds to an exit coolant temperature of 595°F (*vs.* 545°F at 1000 pounds). An alternative (or possibly supplementary approach) is the use of superheating. Development work is in progress on nuclear superheating schemes, which essentially involve routing steam back through a superheater section of

* As when the reactor is suddenly called on to supply more steam to the steam turbine.

TABLE 2. SOME CHARACTERISTICS OF BOILING WATER POWER PLANTS

System Parameters:	*Recent Design* [1] (Dual-cycle)	*Projection* [2] (Direct-cycle)
Reactor pressure	1015 psi	1400 psi
Primary steam conditions	950 psi, 540°F	1400 psi, 585°F
Secondary steam conditions	460 psi, 460°F	—
Thermal conversion efficiency	29%	30%
Power density	29 tkw/liter	50 tkw/liter
Specific power	13.2 tkw/kg U	
Fuel:		
Enrichment	1.5% U-235	
Form	uranium dioxide	
Cladding material	Zircaloy-2	
Maximum surface temperature	585°F	
Average burnup	11,000 MWD/metric ton U	19,000 MWD/metric ton U

[1] Based on an optimized design of a non-superheated 200-megawatt (electrical) plant prepared under AEC auspices in the fall of 1959. Source: TID-8516, Part I.
[2] Projection for a non-superheated 300-megawatt (electrical) plant placed in operation in 1967-8, assuming success of development work now in progress. Source: TID-8516, Part II.

the core before allowing it to leave the reactor. Work is also being done on steam-cooled reactors for use as separate superheaters. Also, the use of conventional coal or oil-fired superheaters is being evaluated.

The fuel technology of boiling water reactors is quite similar to that of pressurized water reactors. (See remark on fuel and fuel cladding developments in the entry on **pressurized water reactors**)

Other current boiling water reactor development activity includes: efforts to simplify the engineering design of indirect-cycle systems; study of the relative merits of internal *vs.* external steam separation; study of the economics of natural convection *vs.* forced circulation; and study of new **containment** techniques.

Economics. See **nuclear power economics.**

BOLIVIA

The Comision Boliviana de Energia Nuclear, La Paz, a dependent agency of the Comision Nacional de Coordinacion and Planeamiento, was established in 1960 to promote peaceful uses of atomic energy. Bolivia is a member of the **Inter-American Nuclear Energy Commission.**

BONUS. See **Boiling Nuclear Superheat Reactor.**

BORAL

An aluminum-clad mixture of boron carbide and aluminum (35 to 50% B_4C) developed for use in thermal neutron shielding applications and sometimes used as a reactor control material. Boral has excellent thermal neutron absorption properties, good thermal conductivity, and is resistant to corrosion in air or water at moderate temperatures. It is now available commercially, usually in sheet form. (See **boron**)

BORAX EXPERIMENTS. See **Boiling Reactor Experiments.**

BORON

Element No. 5 (symbol, B; atomic weight, 10.82), used as a reactor control material (either in control rods or as a **solution** or **burnable poison**); in lightweight thermal neutron shielding; and as the sensing element in certain neutron detection instruments. These applications are based on the fact that boron has a high cross section for thermal neutron capture (755 barns for the natural isotopic mixture). In the pure state the element has a melting point in the neighborhood of 4200°F, and among elementary materials, it is second only to diamonds in hardness. It is used in reactor control rods in various forms, including boron-stainless steel alloys; boron carbide—either in the form of pellets or as a dispersion in a stainless steel or zirconium matrix—and **boral,** an aluminum boron alloy (see **reactor materials**). All of these forms are available commercially.

As found in nature, boron is a mixture of two stable isotopes, B^{10} (18.8%) and B^{11} (81.2%). It is the former isotope which gives the element its excellent neutron absorption properties (cross section of B^{10}: 4010 barns). The more abundant B^{11} has a low thermal neutron cross section ($\sim$ 0.05 barn) and has attracted some speculative interest as a possible moderator for thermal reactor systems. Gram amounts of boron highly enriched in B^{10} ($>$ 92%) have long been available from Oak Ridge National Laboratory for use in physical research and in an experimental technique of cancer treatment known as neutron capture therapy. Larger quantities of boron assaying up to 92% B^{10} have been produced at the U.S. Atomic Energy Commission's **Boron Plant,** now in stand-by status near Niagara Falls, New York. An inventory of this material is available to industry and can be purchased through the AEC channels. It can be supplied either as elemental boron, potassium fluoroborate, or dimethylether boron trifluoride.

The cost varies with the boron-10 concentration. Current prices, exclusive of packaging and handling costs, range as follows:

Form	*Price Range*
Elemental boron	\$3.10–\$8.60/gram
Potassium fluoroborate	\$1.25–\$5.65/gram
Boron trifluoride complex	\$0.85–\$5.30/gram

BORON PLANT

A U.S. Atomic Energy Commission facility for the production of boron enriched in the boron-10 isotope, located at Model City, near Niagara Falls, New York; currently maintained in stand-by status. *Stand-by contractor:* Olin Mathieson Chemical Company. *AEC investment in plant and equipment:* $\sim$ \$4 million. (Other AEC facilities located on the same site bring the total to $\sim$ \$8 million.)

The boron plant was engineered by Singmaster and Breyer, and was operated by Hooker Electrochemical Company from 1954 up until the time it was placed in stand-by status. It was designed to produce $\sim$ 1 kilogram per day of boron metal of 92% B-10 content. Its principal components are a bromine trifluoride distillation facility (for isotope separation) and an electrolysis facility (for converting the product to metal form).

BRAZIL

Agencies. Comissao Nacional de Energia Nuclear (CNEN), Rio de Janeiro, coordinates Brazilian activity in the atomic energy field which is conducted on a decentralized basis at various university and other research institutes.

International Relationships. Brazil is a member of the **International Atomic Energy Agency** and the **Inter-American Nuclear Energy Commission,** and has a research-type **Agreement for Cooperation** with the United States.

Research and Training Centers. Research and training in the physical and life sciences centers at the Instituto de Fisica Atomica of the University of São Paulo, and the Instituto de Pesquisas Radioactivas of the University of Minas Gerais. Research and training in the medical uses of radioisotopes centers at the Laboratorio de Isotopes of the School of Medicine of the University of São Paulo, and the Instituto de Biofisica in Rio. Training in nuclear engineering is given at the Instituto Tecnologico de Aeronautica at San José de Campos. Research on the ultracentrifuge method of uranium isotope separation is in progress at the Instituto de Pesquisas Tecnicas at São Paulo. Two research reactors are currently in operation in Brazil. One is a 5-megawatt (thermal) pool reactor (Babcock & Wilcox) installed at the University of São Paulo with the aid of $350,000 Foreign Research Reactor Grant from the U.S. The other is a 30-kilowatt (thermal) Triga Mark II reactor (General Atomic) at the University of Minas Gerais.

Nuclear Material Production. No commercial-grade deposits of uranium have been located to date, however several tons of uranium concentrate have been recovered at high cost from submarginal sources. Brazil has extensive deposits of thorium in monazite sands in the State of Espiritu Santo.

Energy Economy. Brazil has significant amounts of undeveloped hydro potential. Coal reserves are large but are of low grade and are mostly in the southern part of the country. Petroleum production currently meets only a fraction of national requirements even though petroleum potential reserves are great.

Nuclear Power Program. A large-scale (150-200 megawatts electrical) nuclear power plant is planned for construction on the Mambucaba River between Rio de Janeiro and São Paulo. Completion is tentatively scheduled for 1966. The project is being directed by CNEN. Kennedy and Donkin (U.K.) and Internuclear Corp. (U.S.) have been retained as consultants. The CNEN is reported to be conducting location studies for a smaller (20-30 megawatts) nuclear power unit.

BREEDER REACTOR

Two conflicting definitions are in common use: (1) a nuclear reactor that produces more fissionable material than it consumes; (2) a nuclear reactor that produces the same species of fissionable material as it consumes, regardless of the net gain or loss. Those who favor the former definition use the term "converter" to refer to any reactor producing less fissionable materials than it consumes. Those who favor the latter definition regard as a converter any reactor producing a different species of fissionable material than it consumes. The former definition is used in this book.

Of importance to the **neutron economy** of a breeder reactor is the breeding ratio, which is defined as the number of new fissionable atoms produced per atom of the fissionable species consumed. The breeding ratio is given by (η-1-l), where η (eta) is the number of neutrons emitted per neutron absorbed in the fissionable material, and l is the number of neutrons lost by parasitic (nonfission) absorption or leakage per neutron absorbed in the fissionable material. The value of eta depends on the fissionable material and on the energy of the neutrons causing fission; some values of η-1 are:

	Thermal Neutrons	*Fast Neutrons* (as in a typical fast reactor)
U^{235}	1.07	1.18
U^{223}	1.28	1.42
Pu^{239}	1.10	1.74

The fact that η-1 is greater than unity indicates that more fissionable material can be produced than is consumed, provided neutron losses can be kept low enough so that η-1-l (the breeding ratio) is greater than unity. The most promising possibilities are: (1) the breeding of plutonium-239 in a fast reactor fueled with plutonium-239 and containing a **blanket** of uranium-238 (see **fast breeder reactors**); (2) the breeding of uranium-233 in a **thermal reactor** fueled with uranium-233 and containing a blanket of thorium-232 (see **aqueous homogeneous reactors, molten salt reactors**).

The practical effectiveness of a breeder reactor is described by the expression, **doubling time,** i.e., the time required to achieve (by successive cycles of operation) a net doubling of the amount of fissionable material in the core loading of a breeder reactor. Doubling times for breeder systems as presently conceived are of the order of fifteen or so years.

Breeding, in the sense of a net gain of fissionable material, was first accomplished in the **Experimental Breeder Reactor No. 1** (EBR-1) at the National Reactor Testing Station in 1952. The **Enrico Fermi Atomic Power Plant** is designed to be the first large-scale breeder reactor. EBR-1, its successor EBR-II, and Fermi are all fast breeders. No thermal breeder reactor has been built to date.

Breeding has an important bearing on the efficiency of utilization of nuclear fuel resources in nuclear power generation. (See **energy statistics, U.S.**)

BREEDING GAIN

The net increase in the number of fissionable atoms in a **breeder reactor** per fissionable atom consumed; it is equal to the **breeding ratio** minus one.

BREEDING RATIO

The number of new fissionable atoms produced in a **breeder reactor** per fissionable atom consumed in the reactor.

BREMSSTRAHLUNG

Electromagnetic radiation that is produced when a fast-moving electron undergoes a sudden change in velocity as it approaches a positively charged atomic nucleus and is deflected by it (literally: "braking radiation"). Technically speaking, bremsstrahlung includes all electromagnetic radiation due to acceleration and deceleration of charged particles in the electric fields of nuclei. For example, ordinary x-rays from an x-ray tube are bremsstrahlung. Bremsstrahlung is mostly in the x-ray and ultraviolet regions of the frequency spectrum.

Bremsstrahlung is a complicating factor in the handling of beta-emitting radioisotopes (see radiation **shielding**) and in the operation and use of electron **accelerators.** Also, it is one of the principal sources of energy loss from systems built to achieve controlled-fusion reactions. (See **thermonuclear power**)

BROOKHAVEN GRAPHITE RESEARCH REACTOR (BGRR)

A large, graphite-moderated, air-cooled research reactor at Brookhaven National Laboratory. It was designed by the BNL staff and is used for general experimentation and radioisotope production. Originally fueled with natural uranium, it was converted in 1957-1958 to an enriched fuel loading. *Type:* Graphite reactor. *Power rating:* 20,000 thermal kilowatts. *Fuel:* Aluminum-clad fuel elements fabricated of highly enriched uranium-aluminum alloy. *Coolant:* Air. *Moderator:* Graphite. *Neutron flux:* Of the order of 10^{13} n/cm^2 sec (maximum thermal). *Start-up:* 1950. (See **research and training reactors**) (Fig. 24)

BROOKHAVEN HIGH FLUX-BEAM RESEARCH REACTOR (HFBR)

A high-flux research reactor under construction at Brookhaven National Laboratory. It is to be used for general nuclear research activities requiring high neutron fluxes. Combustion Engineering Company is the principal contractor; the basic nuclear design was developed by the BNL staff. *Type:* Tank reactor. *Power rating:* 40,000 thermal kilowatts. *Fuel:* MTR-type fuel elements. *Coolant:* D_2O. *Moderator:* D_2O. *Neutron flux:* Of the order of 10^{15} n/cm^2 sec (maximum thermal). *Start-up:* Scheduled for 1963. (See **research and training reactors**)

BROOKHAVEN MEDICAL RESEARCH REACTOR (MRR)

A nuclear reactor at Brookhaven National Laboratory used for **neutron capture therapy** experiments, biomedical research, and related activities. The MRR facility, which includes a 48-bed hospital and supporting laboratory facilities, represents an investment of approximately $6.5 million and is the first reactor to have been designed exclusively for medical research. The reactor was designed by the BNL staff and constructed by Daystrom, Inc. *Type:* Tank reactor. *Power rating:* Steady-state operation, 3000 thermal kilowatts. Levels of 5000 kilowatts are permissible for 10-minute periods. *Fuel:* MTR-type fuel elements. *Coolant:* H_2O. *Moderator:* H_2O. *Neutron flux:* Of the order of 10^{13} n/cm^2 sec (maximum thermal). *Start-up:* 1959. (See **research and training reactors**)

Fig. 24. Brookhaven Graphite Research Reactor. Top left, building housing the reactor and associated "hot" laboratories. Top right, loading face of the reactor. Bottom left, research equipment positioned at beam ports of the west face of the reactor.

BROOKHAVEN NATIONAL LABORATORY (BNL)

A major U.S. Atomic Energy Commission research center situated on a 6750-acre tract of land near Upton, Long Island, 70 miles east of New York City. *Operating contractor:* Associated Universities, Inc. *Director:* Maurice Goldhaber.* *AEC investment in plant and equipment:* ~ $133 million.** *Staff:* ~ 440 scientists and engineers, and ~ 1400 supporting personnel.

The laboratory has traditionally been oriented toward basic research but also conducts extensive applied research and development programs. Some principal areas of activity are:

1. Physics: Theoretical and experimental studies of atomic structure and of the properties of nuclear particles and their binding energies. BNL accelerator and reactor facilities contribute importantly to this work, which has led to the discovery of the meson-hyperon formation process known as "associated production," and to the identification of several new members of the growing family of "strange particles."

* Succeeded Leland Haworth when the latter was appointed a member of the U.S. Atomic Energy Commission.

** Includes facilities authorized or under construction as of June 30, 1960. Not adjusted for depreciation.

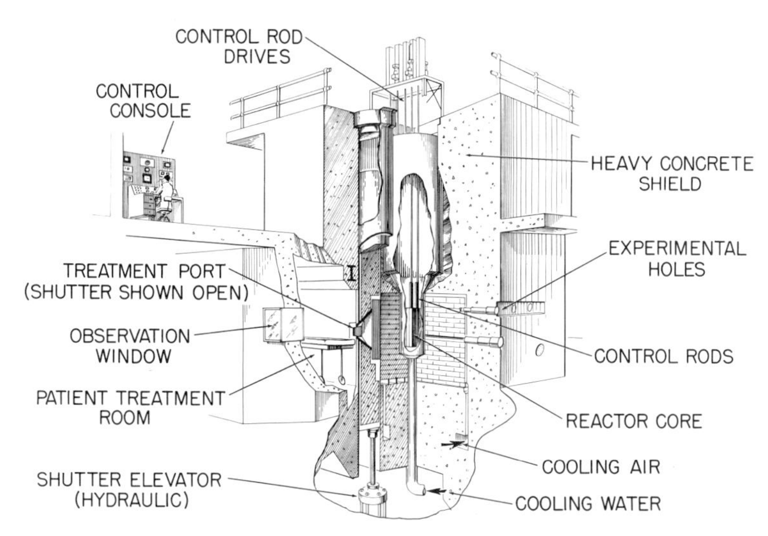

Fig. 25. Cutaway of Brookhaven Medical Research Reactor. (*Courtesy of Brookhaven National Laboratory*)

2. Chemistry: Tracer studies; research on the chemical effects of radiation; studies of molecular and crystal structure; identification of nuclear reaction products (in support of particle physics experiments).

3. Nuclear technology: Development work on high-temperature reactor systems and components (see **Liquid Metal Fuel Reactor Concept**); research on radioactive waste disposal techniques, including a clay-fixation process for high-level waste storage; research on industrial applications of high intensity ionizing radiation; general reactor physics studies.

4. Biology: Studies of the genetic effects of radiation; research in biochemistry, biophysics, and plant and animal physiology.

5. Medical research: research on neutron

Fig. 26. Medical Research Center at Brookhaven National Laboratory. The cylindrical structure next to the stack houses the Brookhaven Medical Research Reactor. Main laboratory building at left; 48-bed hospital at right. (*Courtesy of Brookhaven National Laboratory*)

capture techniques for brain tumor and other therapy; studies of the role of trace elements in metabolic and other life processes; studies of the effects of radiation in antibody production; development of tracer techniques for medical research and diagnostic appliances.

Major experimental facilities at BNL include: (1) *Accelerators:* Two large proton synchrotrons, namely, the 3-Bev **Cosmotron** and the 30-Bev **Alternating Gradient Synchrotron**; a 60-inch cyclotron and several other accelerators. (2) *Reactors:* **The Brookhaven Graphite Research Reactor,** and the **Brookhaven Medical Research Reactor.** A third major reactor facility, the **Brookhaven High-Flux-Beam Research Reactor** is under construction. (3) *Other:* An extensive "hot" laboratory; a recently completed high-intensity radiation development laboratory equipped with radionuclide and spent-fuel-element radiation sources; a medical research center which includes a 45-bed hospital; a 10-acre field equipped with a central gamma source; a high-speed digital computer; and a meteorological tower facility.

Brookhaven was established in **1947** as a regional atomic energy research and training center. It has been operated since its inception by Associated Universities, Inc., a non-profit educational corporation representing the following **9** northeastern universities: Columbia, Cornell, Harvard, Johns Hopkins, Massachusetts Institute of Technology, Pennsylvania, Princeton, Rochester, and Yale. AUI is governed by a Board of Trustees made up of one scientist and one administrative officer from each of these institutions.

BROWN OXIDE. Uranium dioxide (UO_2).

BUBBLE CHAMBER

A device for studying the movement and interaction of energetic charged particles by means of observation of tracks made by the particles as they move through a superheated liquid (as distinct from a supersaturated gas, as in a **cloud chamber**). The tracks in a bubble chamber are gas bubbles which form along the path of the moving particles. Superheated

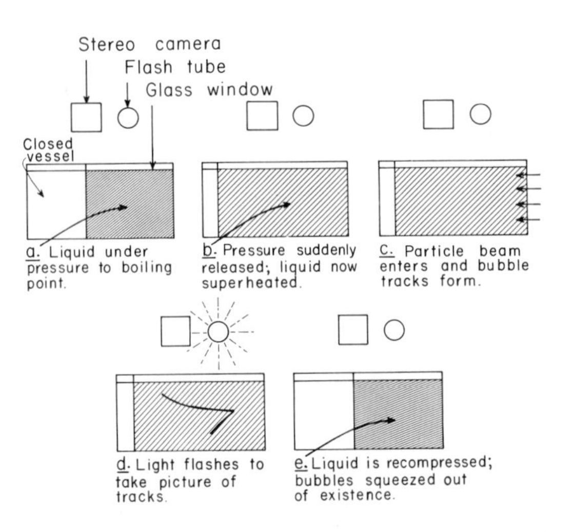

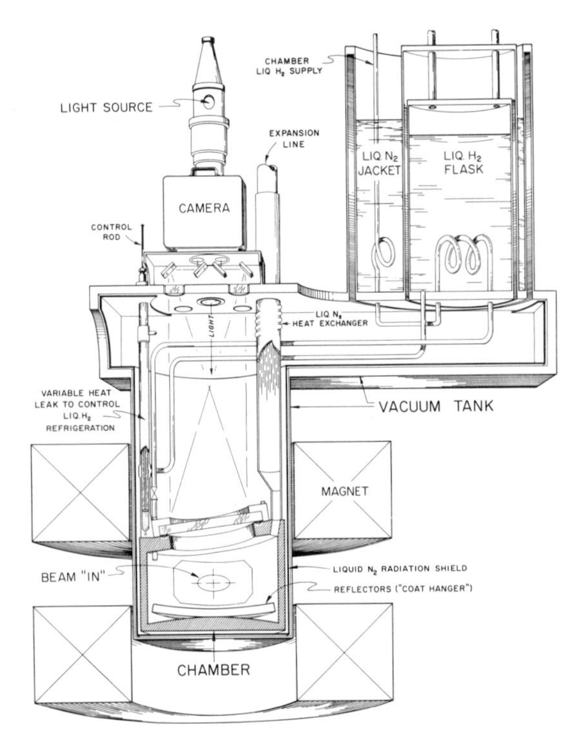

Fig. 27. Bubble chamber. Above, operating cycle. Right, diagram showing equipment arrangement. (*Courtesy of E. O. Lawrence Radiation Laboratory*)

conditions in the liquid medium are achieved intermittently but on a very fast cycle (fractions of a second) by successively lowering and raising the pressure in the chamber in pulse fashion. As in the operation of cloud chambers, study of sequential photographs of these tracks permits analysis of the nuclear events taking place.

The bubble chamber was invented in 1952 by Donald A. Glaser, then working at the University of Michigan. For his invention and subsequent development of the bubble chamber, Dr. Glaser, now on the staff of the E. O. Lawrence Radiation Laboratory at Berkeley, received the 1960 Nobel physics award.

The original bubble chamber used diethyl ether as the liquid medium. The medium most frequently used is liquid hydrogen, which, having essentially one kind of atom, simplifies the interpretation of particle collisions. Bubble chamber technology has made very rapid strides. The largest unit in operation, located at Berkeley, has a chamber 72 inches long, 23 inches wide and 15 inches deep. The operating pressure is in the range, 5-6 atmospheres, and the temperature is in the range, 26-28°K. (See Fig. 27 for operating principles and design features.)

BUFFALO, UNIVERSITY OF—RESEARCH REACTOR

A 1000-kilowatt (thermal) pool-type research reactor operated as part of the University's Nuclear Research Center in Buffalo, New York. The reactor was supplied by AMF Atomics, Inc. and began operation in 1961. (See **research and training reactors**)

BULGARIA

A Committee for the Peaceful Uses of Atomic Energy, reporting to the Council of Ministers, is responsible for atomic energy matters. A national nuclear research center is being established in Sofia. The facilities include a 2000-kilowatt (thermal) tank-type research reactor purchased from the U.S.S.R. Since World War II uranium deposits north of Sofia have been mined, partly concentrated, and shipped to the U.S.S.R. There is considerable interest in radioisotope applications but no nuclear power plans have been reported. Bulgaria is a member of the **International Atomic Energy Agency,** and participates in the **Joint Institute for Nuclear Research** at Dubna in the U.S.S.R.

BULK SHIELDING REACTOR (BSR-1, -2)

A pool-type **test reactor** at Oak Ridge National Laboratory used for radiation shielding studies and other specialized experimentation. *Type:* Pool reactor (the first ever built). *Power rating:* 1000 thermal kilowatts. *Fuel:* Two alternative cores. BSR-1 consists of MTR-type fuel elements. BSR-2 consists of stainless steel-clad fuel plates containing a dispersion of fully enriched uranium dioxide in a stainless steel matrix. *Coolant:* H_2O. *Moderator:* H_2O. *Reflector:* Beryllium oxide (removable). *Neutron flux:* Of the order of 10^{13} n/cm^{2}sec.

BURMA

An Atomic Energy Center has been established as part of the Union of Burma Applied Research Institute (UBARI) at Rangoon. The emphasis to date has been on training programs and on staffing and equipping a laboratory for the utilization of radioisotopes in research and development projects. Technical assistance in this activity, as well as in the general UBARI program, is being furnished by the Armour Research Foundation under a contract funded by the United States Government. Burma is a member of the **International Atomic Energy Agency.**

BURNABLE POISON

In a nuclear reactor, a **poison** incorporated in the fuel or fuel cladding that gradually "burns off" under neutron irradiation and thereby compensates for the loss of **reactivity** which inherently occurs as fuel is consumed and fission products accumulate. The use of burnable poisons reduces the number of mechanical controls required and hence the cost of the control system. It is at the same time a means of increasing the amount of **excess reactivity** that can safely be built into a reactor and thereby lengthening the operating life of the fuel loading.

Materials selected for use as burnable poisons usually have a neutron capture cross section four or five times that of the fissionable component of the fuel. For example, **boron,** having a stable isotope with a thermal neutron cross section of 4010 **barns,** is often used in conjunction with uranium-235, which has a thermal neutron cross section of 694 barns. Materials with extremely high thermal neutron cross sections cannot be used as burnable poisons since they would burn off too quickly. Materials with cross sections less than or too close to that of the fissionable nuclide with which they are to be associated would be ineffective since they would burn off too slowly.

BURN-OUT

In certain experimental devices for research on controlled **fusion,** specifically those in which high energy atomic or molecular ions are injected into a high-vacuum reactor chamber, the presence of residual air or other neutral gases interferes with the achievement of desired reaction conditions. Whereas this problem of "background interference" could be partially solved by resorting to ultra high-vacuum techniques, a more practical solution, though involving initial plasma loss, is to take advantage of the fact that the injected high-energy ions will rapidly reduce the density of neutral particles by **charge exchange** and simple ionization (removal of electrons from neutral particles with the formation of ion pairs). Once the rate of ionization of neutral particles in the plasma can be made greater than the rate at which neutral particles enter, a phenomenon called burn-out takes place. There will be a rapid decrease in the neutral particle density once the burn-out point has been passed. (See **Molecular Ion Ignition Program)**

BURN-UP

A measure of the consumption of a given material in a nuclear reactor, and hence of the cumulative radiation exposure to which the material has been subjected. The term can be applied to fuel, control materials, burnable poisons, or other materials used in the core of a reactor, but is most often used in reference to fuel.

Fuel burn-up may be expressed in terms of the total energy extracted from the fuel during its lifetime in the reactor, or it may be expressed in terms of the percentage of fuel consumed over that period. In the former case, the units usually are megawatt-days of heat per metric ton (2200 pounds) of fuel charged to the reactor. (The abbreviation is MWD/tonne, usually written MWD/ton.) In the latter case there are two common usages: some authorities use percentage values based only on atoms consumed by fission; others use values based on all fissionable atoms consumed, whether by fission or by nonfission **capture.** In all cases treated herein, fuel is taken to include fissionable and fertile material. (See **reactor, nuclear)**

Approximate relations between fuel burn-up expressed as a percentage and fuel burn-up expressed in terms of energy output are as follows:

Fission only
1% burn-up = 9000 MWD/metric ton
Fission—non-fission capture (assuming **thermal neutrons)**
1% burn-up = 8200 MWD/metric ton (U^{233})
= 7600 MWD/metric ton (U^{235})
= 6400 MWD/metric ton (Pu^{239})

The differences in the latter values are due to differences in the relative amount of non-fission capture.

High burn-up is desirable in power reactors for long core life and to reduce **fuel reprocessing** and refabrication costs (see **nuclear**

power economics). Two major factors act to limit the burn-up that can be achieved before fuel replacement is necessary: (1) loss of reactivity due to depletion of fissionable material and to the accumulation of fission-product **poisons** and (2) radiation damage to **fuel elements**. In general, radiation damage is the controlling factor in reactors fueled with normal or slightly enriched uranium metal, and loss in reactivity is the controlling factor in reactors fueled with normal or slightly enriched uranium oxide.

From a purely metallurgical standpoint, slightly enriched uranium oxide has shown adequate stability to radiation damage at burn-ups approaching 30,000 MWD/ton, and tests indicate that burn-ups of the order of 50,000 to 60,000 MWD/ton may be possible at some time in the future. Taking into account reactivity effects and also allowing for statistical probabilities of fuel element failure, reactor designers are currently specifying average burn-up values in the neighborhood of 14 or 15,000 MWD/ton for slightly enriched uranium oxide cores. By way of comparison, corresponding values for normal or slightly enriched uranium metal or metal alloys are in the neighborhood of 3000 MWD/ton.

BY-PRODUCT MATERIAL

As defined in federal atomic energy law, any radioactive material, other than a **source** or **special nuclear material**, formed in the process of producing or utilizing source or special nuclear material. Reactor-produced radioisotopes and fission products are thus classed as by-product materials.

C

CADMIUM

Element No. 48 (symbol, Cd; atomic weight, 112.41), used as a neutron-absorbing material in reactor control rods. Cadmium has the highest thermal-neutron cross section (2550 barns) of any of the elements commonly used in control rod applications, however its effectiveness falls off sharply in the epithermal (intermediate) neutron range with the result that it is not as effective across the neutron spectrum as are natural **boron** or **hafnium.** In the pure state, cadmium is a soft, toxic metal with a relatively low melting point (610°F). It is used in the pure state in some control rod applications and in such cases is usually sheathed in (or plated on) aluminum or stainless steel for structural reinforcement. In other applications it is alloyed with elements, such as silver and indium, which are more effective neutron absorbers in the intermediate and higher neutron energy ranges. (See **reactor materials)**

CALCIUM

Element No. 20 (symbol, Ca; atomic weight 40.08), of interest in the nuclear field in two non-related ways: (1) high-purity calcium (produced at U.S. Government facilities) is used as the reduction agent in converting enriched uranium tetrafluoride to massive metal (see **uranium refining and conversion,** and in reduction of thorium tetrafluoride to thorium (see **thorium production technology).** (2) The artificially produced radioisotope, calcium-45 (a 160-day beta emitter), has been used extensively in agricultural research to study the mechanism and rate of fertilizer uptake under various conditions of plant cultivation, and in biological research to study mechanisms of bone growth and milk and egg formation. These latter uses stem from the fact that calcium, an essential element in various life processes, occurs in nature as a mixture of stable isotopes and therefore lends itself readily to radioisotopic tracer techniques.

CALIFORNIUM

Element No. 98 (symbol, Cf), first identified in 1950 by S. G. Thompson, K. Street, A. Ghiorso and G. T. Seaborg at the E. O. Lawrence Radiation Laboratory. The discovery followed particle acceleration experiments in which curium-242 was bombarded with high-energy alpha particles. Californium is one of the eleven **transuranium elements** discovered in the past two decades. One of its isotopes, 55-day californium-254, undergoes spontaneous fission and is believed by astrophysicists to account for the characteristic decrease in light intensity observed in supernovae. The production reaction which allowed the discovery of californium was:

$$_{96}Cm^{242} + {}_{2}He^{4} \longrightarrow {}_{98}Cf^{245} + {}_{0}n^{1}$$

CALUTRON

A high-current **mass spectrometer** originally developed for the large-scale separation of uranium isotopes during the wartime Manhattan Project (see **electromagnetic separation).** Several of the original calutron units are now operated by Oak Ridge National Laboratory for the separation of the stable isotopes of many elements for research purposes. The name is derived from *Cal*ifornia *U*niversity Cyclo*tron*.

CAMBRIDGE ELECTRON ACCELERATOR (CEA)

A 6.0-Bev **electron synchrotron** at Cambridge, Massachusetts, built under AEC sponsorship as a joint project of Harvard University and Massachusetts Institute of Technology.

CANADA

Agencies. The Atomic Energy Control Board (AECB), Ottawa, is responsible for regulatory matters relating to atomic energy development and application. Atomic Energy of Canada, Limited (AECL), Ottawa, is a government-owned corporation responsible for the national atomic energy research and development program. Eldorado Mining and Refining Limited, Ottawa, is a government-owned corporation responsible for the management of government-owned uranium deposits; for the development of processes for the conversion of uranium concentrates into marketable products (e.g., high-purity uranium trioxide); for the operation of the Port Hope Refinery (see below); and for the administration of government contracts for the sale of uranium. The Hydroelectric Power Commission of Ontario, Toronto, which is owned by the Government of Ontario and supplies most of the electrical power requirements of that province, is collaborating with AECL in the development of nuclear power.

International Relationship. Member of the **International Atomic Energy Agency,** associate member of the **European Nuclear Energy Agency,** and member of the tripartite **Combined Development Agency.** Comprehensive **Agreement for Cooperation** with the United States. Under the Colombo Plan, Canada contributed to the cost of construction of the Canada-India Reactor at Trombay, **India,** which was designed and built under Canadian technical direction. Recently signed an agreement with **Euratom** for joint research and development of heavy water-moderated power reactors.

Research Centers. The Chalk River Project, 130 miles west of Ottawa, is AECL's principal research center. Facilities include five reactors, all but one of which (PTR) are fueled with natural uranium and moderated with heavy water. ZEEP, completed in 1945 and the first reactor built outside the United States, is a low-power unit used for lattice measurements. NRX, completed in 1947, is a high-flux tank-type research reactor which operates at a power level of 42,000 kilowatts (thermal). NRU, a reactor of improved design, completed in 1957, operates at a power level of 200,000 kilowatts (thermal). ZED-2, completed in 1960, is another low-power unit used for lattice measurements and physics research. PTR, completed in 1957, is a small pool-type test reactor fueled with enriched uranium which operates at a power level of 100 watts (thermal). Chalk River is a major producer of radioisotopes, notably cobalt-60, which are distributed along with associated equipment such as teletherapy devices, by AECL's Commercial Products Division in Ottawa.

AECL is constructing a reactor testing center, to be known as the Whiteshell Nuclear Research Establishment, at a site on the Winnipeg River 60 miles northeast of Winnipeg, Manitoba. The first reactor installation will be the OTR (see below).

Production Activity. Canadian reserves of economically recoverable uranium are estimated at 300,000 tons, expressed as U_3O_8. Annual production of U_3O_8 reached a peak of nearly 16,000 tons in 1959 but has since tapered off due to a stretch-out of the procurement program of the United States and the United Kingdom. The principal producing areas have been in the Blind River region of southern Ontario; the Bancroft area of eastern Ontario; the Beaverlodge area of Saskatchewan (Lake Athabasca); and the Great Bear Lake district of the Northwest Territories (Port Radium). While private mining interests account for the bulk of production (notably the holdings of Rio Algom Uranium Mines Ltd., and Denison Mines Ltd., in the Blind River district, and those of Gunnar Mines, Ltd., in the Beaverlodge area), one-eighth of Canadian production comes from the Beaver-

Fig. 28. The Chalk River Project. Above, general view of the establishment. Left, the NRU materials testing reactor, a heavy water moderated tank reactor designed to operate at a power level of 200,000 kilowatts (thermal). (*Courtesy of Atomic Energy of Canada, Ltd.*)

lodge holdings of the government-owned company, Eldorado Mining and Refining, Ltd. There is some by-product production of thorium, Canadian reserves of which are estimated at 200,000 tons. Concentrates from mills located in the producing areas are refined at the Port Hope Refinery of Eldorado Mining and Refining, Ltd., which produced high-purity uranium trioxide and uranium metal.

Nuclear Power Program. Canada is committed to the development of nuclear power as an alternative energy source for use in present or future load centers remote from conventional energy sources. AECL's program is largely keyed to the use of natural uranium fuel in combination with heavy water moderation. Three development activities are in progress along this line.

Fig. 29. Model of 200-megawatt (electrical) Douglas Point Nuclear Plant Station under construction in Ontario. (*Courtesy of Atomic Energy of Canada, Ltd.*)

Uranium fuel elements are fabricated by AMF Atomics (Canada) Ltd. at Port Hope, Ontario, and by Canadian General Electric Company, Ltd., at Peterborough, Ontario. Reactor-grade graphite is produced in moderate quantities by the Electrometallurgical Company, a division of Union Carbide (Canada) Ltd.

Energy Economy. Canada's electric power capacity is about 20,000 megawatts, more than 90% of it hydroelectric. Canada has considerable undeveloped hydro potential and abundant supplies of coal, gas, and oil; however, these energy reserves are mainly at long distances from demand centers. Recent construction of transcontinental pipelines is making oil and gas more readily available, but most of the fuel carried by these pipelines is being used for residential or transportation purposes.

NPD-2, a prototype power reactor with a rated output of 20 megawatts (electrical), was completed in 1962 at Rolphton, Ontario (near Chalk River). This unit was designed by AECL and Canadian General Electric Company, Ltd., the construction contractor. It is operated by Hydroelectric Power Commission of Ontario.

CANDU, a large-scale version of NPD-2, is under construction near Douglas Point, Ontario, at what will be known as the Douglas Point Nuclear Power Station. Designed by AECL, CANDU (from Canadian Deuterium Uranium) will have a rated output of 200 megawatts (electrical). The fuel will be in the form of uranium oxide clad in zircaloy. A pressure-tube type of reactor configuration is being used, and the design provides for refueling during reactor operation. Capital costs are estimated at $80 million. Start-up is scheduled for 1964.

Development work is in progress on the use of organic cooling in combination with heavy water moderation. A small-scale reactor experiment, known as OTR, is being undertaken by Canadian General Electric Company Ltd., under contract to AECL. OTR (for Organic-Test Reactor) is to be constructed at the Whiteshell Nuclear Research Establishment in Manitoba.

Industry Association. The Canadian Nuclear Association, an organization similar to the U.S. Atomic Industrial Forum, was established in 1960 with offices in Toronto.

CANEL. See **Connecticut Advanced Nuclear Engineering Laboratory.**

CANNED PUMPS

A type of centrifugal pump in which the rotor windings, drive shaft and impeller are enclosed in an hermetically sealed casing to prevent leakage. Canned pumps, originally developed under the Naval Reactors Program, are widely used as coolant circulators in power reactor systems. (See **pumps)**

CAPACITY FACTOR

In electric power generation, the ratio of the average load on an electrical generating plant or system over a period of time (usually one year) to the rated capacity **(name-plate rating)** of the installed generating equipment; also referred to as plant factor. The capacity factor has an important bearing on the power costs associated with a nuclear plant investment (see **nuclear power economics).** For a related term see **load factor.**

CAPTURE

In relation to nuclear phenomena, a process in which an atomic nucleus absorbs an additional elementary particle, e.g., a neutron or a proton. If a neutron is captured, the **mass number** of the nucleus increases by one unit and a different isotope results; if a proton is captured, both the mass number and the **atomic number** increase by one unit and a different chemical element results. (See **neutron capture, radiative capture)**

CARBIDE FUEL ELEMENTS. See **fuel element fabrication.**

CARBON DIOXIDE

Used as coolant in certain **gas-cooled reactors.**

CARBON-14

A radioactive isotope of carbon, widely used in tracer experiments. It is also of interest as a means of dating archeological artifacts and geological specimens, and as a constituent of **radioactive fallout** from nuclear weapon tests.

A 5568-year beta emitter, carbon-14 is formed as the result of neutron interaction with nitrogen:

$$_7N^{14} + {}_0n^1 \longrightarrow {}_6C^{14} + {}_1p^1$$

Carbon-14 is produced artificially in nuclear reactors, usually by the irradiation of beryllium nitride pellets, the beryllium serving essentially as an inert carrier. The irradiated pellets are then treated chemically to separate the product from the carrier. Carbon-14 is available in several grades (i.e., different **specific activities)** through U.S. Atomic Energy Commission distribution channels, or can be obtained in the form of **labeled compounds** from commercial suppliers. Its uses range, by way of illustration, from studies of the mechanism of life processes, such as photosynthesis and cell metabolism, to investigations of the causes of carbon deposits in internal combustion engines.

Carbon-14 is also formed naturally as the result of cosmic ray bombardment of the atmosphere and is present in atmospheric carbon dioxide in fixed (i.e., equilibrium) concentrations. Advantage of this latter fact is taken in an ingenious archeological geological dating technique developed by Willard F. Libby *et al.* The techniques can be explained as follows: When a plant or animal dies it ceases to take up carbon dioxide, so that, from the moment of death, the amount of carbon-14 present in its system will begin to diminish at a rate fixed by that isotope's decay half life (given above). The concentration of the decaying carbon-14 relative to that of the stable carbon-12 isotope present in the plant or animal's system will decline accordingly. Thus if one measures the proportion of carbon-14 to carbon-12 in, for example, bone fossils removed from an archeological excavation, one can by correlation obtain an estimate of their age.

CARBONATE-LEACH PROCESS

A method of **uranium milling** in which alkaline reagents, rather than acids, are employed to leach the uranium from the ore. Alkaline leaching is generally used in treating lime-rich ores that would consume excessive quantities of reagents if acid leaching were employed. Also, corrosion problems are less severe and hence the cost of materials of construction tends to be lower than in acid-leach installations.

Following are the basic steps typically involved in the carbonate-leach process when treating uranium ores with low vanadium values: (1) After grinding, the ore is contacted with a hot solution of sodium carbonate and bicarbonate in a carefully controlled leaching operation. (2) The leach solution is clarified by filtration, and sodium hydroxide is added to precipitate the uranium as impure sodium diuranate ($Na_2U_2O_7$). (3) The sodium diuranate is recovered as a wet cake by filtration and dried by calcination.

Where vanadium values are high enough to warrant recovery, the conditions of the precipitation step are controlled to remove the uranium selectively before removing the vanadium. There are many other process variations. In some cases sufficient impurities are present to require dissolution and reprecipitation prior to the final calcination step. Also there are alternatives to conventional precipitation, in-

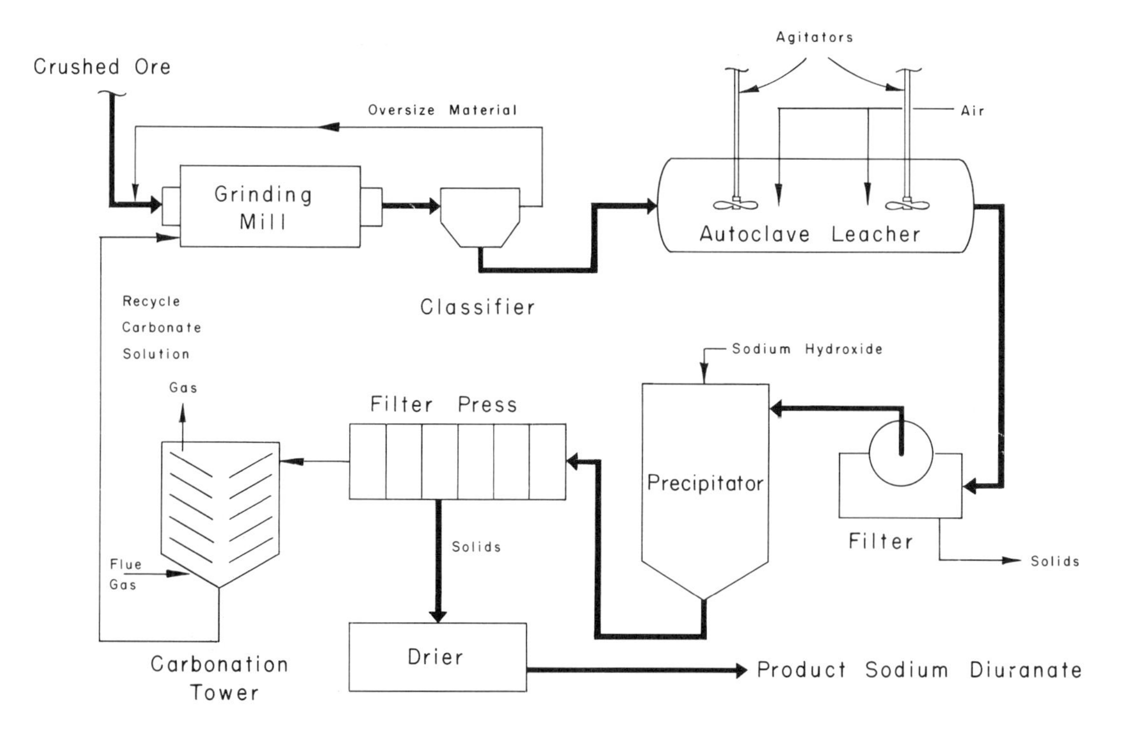

Fig. 30. Simplified flow diagram—carbonate-leach process.

cluding a technique of catalytic reduction of the carbonate complex with hydrogen, yielding a precipitate of uranium dioxide.

The carbonate treatment process is used in a number of U.S. uranium mills.

CARNOTITE

Hydrated potassium uranyl vanadate—a secondary mineral, canary yellow in color, generally found in scattered deposits forming irregular "lenses," or "tables," in sandstone beds. Carnotite-bearing ores, once mined primarily for their vanadium content, today constitute one of the principal U.S. sources of uranium production. Important deposits are widely distributed in the Colorado Plateau region of Colorado, Utah, Arizona and New Mexico; and in the Black Hills area of South Dakota and Wyoming. (See **uranium deposits and reserves**)

CAROLINAS-VIRGINIA TUBE REACTOR (CVTR)

A nuclear power project being conducted under the "third round" of the U.S. Atomic Energy Commission's Power Demonstration Reactor Program, involving the construction of a small prototype plant of the pressurized heavy-water type (see **heavy water-moderated power reactors**). The plant, at Parr Shoals, South Carolina, is owned by Carolinas-Virginia Nuclear Power Associates, an organization of four southern electric utilities.* The AEC is making a financial contribution of $13.9 million for research and development and will waive its normal charge for special nuclear materials for the first five years of operation (corresponding to a financial contribution of $1.2 million). The reactor contractor is Westinghouse Electric Corporation; the architect-engineer, Stone and Webster Engineering Corporation.

The CVTR reactor is fueled with slightly enriched uranium; however, natural uranium may be used in future large-scale installations of this type. The following notes reflect the status of the project as of mid-1962:

Power: 17 megawatts (net electrical), of which 1.5 megawatts represents the contribution of a conventional superheater. *Fuel:* Slightly enriched uranium (2% U^{235}) in the form of uranium dioxide (UO_2) pellets. *Fuel cladding:* zircaloy tubes. *Fuel inventory:* 3410 kilograms of UO_2. *Coolant:* Heavy water at 1500 pounds pressure; inlet temperature, 505°F; outlet temperature, 574°F. *Steam conditions* (from superheater): Superheated steam at 415 pounds, 725°F. *Thermal conversion efficiency:* 28.1%. *Control materials:* Ordinary and borated stainless steel control rods. *Containment:* Steel-lined concrete enclosure. *Construction cost:* Estimated at $17.7 million, exclusive of research and development. For other project costs see Table 3 under **nuclear power development.** *Dates:* Construction started in June, 1960. Startup scheduled for late 1962.

* Duke Power Company, Carolina Power & Light Company, South Carolina Electric & Gas Company, and Virginia Electric and Power Company.

CARRIER-FREE

A term used in reference to a preparation of a radioactive isotope for use in a tracer experiment, to indicate that the preparation is essentially free from stable isotopes of the same element.

CASTILE

Code designation for depleted uranium.

CATARACTS

Cataracts, i.e., opacities of the lens of the eye, are among the delayed biological effects that have been observed among survivors of the nuclear attacks on Hiroshima and Nagasaki who were within 3000 feet of ground zero at the time of the detonations. They are attributed to exposure to the "prompt nuclear radiation," i.e., to the gamma rays and neutrons released more or less at the instant of detonation. Since fast neutrons are known to be particularly effective in inducing cataract formation, the neutron component of the prompt radiation is believed to have been the principal factor.

A few instances of cataract formation have been reported among scientists who worked extensively with cyclotrons during the mid-thirties.

CENTRIFUGE PROCESS.
See **gas centrifuge process.**

CERAMICS

A term ordinarily taken to mean a class of clay, feldspar or silicon-based materials that become refractory and heat-resistant after oven firing (baking); but commonly used in the nuclear field to refer to metallic oxides, carbides and the like. Thus, reactor fuel elements fabricated of uranium dioxide (UO_2) are generally classed as "ceramic" fuel elements.

Ceramics are of interest in the nuclear field in several ways. (1) As a fuel material uranium dioxide is more resistant to radiation damage and can be used at higher temperatures and under higher burn-up conditions than uranium metal or most uranium alloys. The same applies to uranium carbide. (2) Beryllium oxide shows promise as a moderator or reflector for high-temperature reactor systems. (3) Crucibles fabricated of refractory materials such as magnesium oxide are used in various metallurgical processes.

CERENKOV RADIATION

Visible light emitted when charged particles pass through a transparent medium (e.g., water) with a velocity exceeding the velocity of light in the medium. Cerenkov radiation, discovered by the Russian physicist P. A. Cerenkov in 1934, manifests itself as a bluish-white glow. It accounts for the luminescence from the core of a pool-type research reactor, and from freshly irradiated fuel elements stored in water. (Fig. 31)

CERIUM

Element No. 58 (symbol, Ce; atomic weight, 140.13), the most abundant of the **rare earth elements.** Several isotopes of cerium are formed as fission products. The most significant is cerium-144, a short-lived (290-day half-life) beta emitter which decays to praesodymium-144, an intensive beta and gamma emitter (17-minute half-life). Cerium isotopes and their decay products account for as much as three-quarters of the beta activity and one-third of the gamma activity given off by fission product wastes during the first year of decay and hence are an important factor in the problems associated with the handling and reprocessing of irradiated fuels. They are also an important factor in **radioactive fallout** from nuclear weapon tests.

Cerium-144 is of interest as an energy source for small auxiliary power units for space applications (see **SNAP program).** It is also a potentially useful source of beta radiation for medical and industrial applications. It is one of several radionuclides available in kilocurie quantities from Multicurie Fission Products Pilot Plant at Oak Ridge.

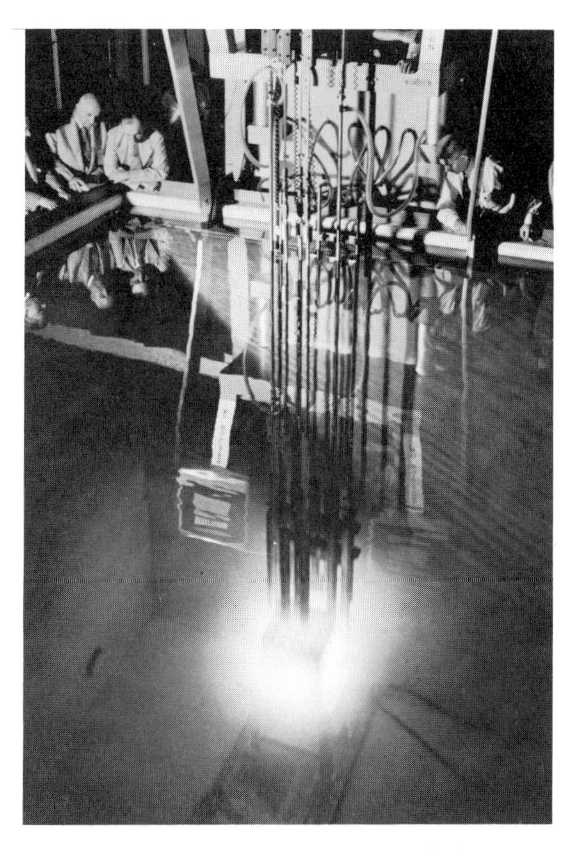

Fig. 31. Cerenkov radiation observed during operation of a pool reactor, Oak Ridge National Laboratory. (*Courtesy of USAEC*)

Elemental cerium is of interest in the nuclear field as an additive to glass to prevent darkening due to radiation exposure.

CERMET

Any ceramic to which a metal binder has been added, usually for improved thermal conductivity, shock resistance, and other "metallic" properties.

CERN (EUROPEAN ORGANIZATION FOR NUCLEAR RESEARCH)

A European center for basic research, principally in the field of high-energy physics, located in Geneva, Switzerland. The sponsoring countries are Belgium, Denmark, France, West Germany, Greece, Italy, the Netherlands, Norway, Sweden, Switzerland, the United Kingdom, and Yugoslavia. Experimental facilities at CERN (for Conseil Européen pour la Recherche Nucléaire) include a 25-30 Bev proton synchrotron, completed in 1960, which is one of the two largest particle accelerators constructed to date. (The other is Brookhaven National Laboratory's **Alternating Gradient Synchrotron.)**

CESIUM-137

A radioactive isotope of cesium, formed in high yield as a product of nuclear fission (see **fission products).** Cesium-137 emits beta particles and 0.66-Mev gamma rays and has a radioactive half-life of 26.6 years. It transforms by **beta decay** into barium-137.

Because of its high fission yield (5%, figured on a 200% base) and long half-life, cesium-137 is one of the most important factors in the long-term storage of radioactive wastes from fuel reprocessing operations (see **radioactive waste disposal).** For example, after three years' radioactive decay, cesium-137, together with its daughter product barium-137 accounts for 15% of the total activity of such wastes, and after 30 years' decay it accounts for 49% of the activity. The only fission product of comparable importance in long-term radioactive waste storage is strontium-90.

Cesium-137 is of interest in a positive context as a source of gamma radiation for industrial **radiography** and medical **teletherapy.** Small radiocesium sources are widely used in the former application, and several kilocurie sources have been supplied for use in the latter. Other applications include use in nuclear batteries (see **SNAP program)** and use in large-scale radiation applications such as food preservation (see **radiation sources).**

Cesium-137 is produced in amounts up to 4,000,000 curies per year by the Multicurie Fission Products Pilot Plant, at Oak Ridge, which receives shipments of cesium-containing material recovered from radioactive wastes at the AEC Hanford Works and processes it into the form of cesium borosilicate. The current price schedule (effective March 20, 1962) is: $1.00 per curie for amounts up to 20,000 curies; $0.75 per curie for amounts in the range 20-100,000 curies; and $0.50 per curie for amounts above 100,000 curies.

Cesium-137 is normally distributed as a chloride salt with a **specific activity** of 20-30 curies per gram. Large sources are normally hermetically sealed in welded stainless steel containers.

CEYLON

Formulation of legislation and plans to promote peaceful uses of atomic energy has been undertaken by a Committee on Atomic Energy under the National Planning Council. Research and training in medical uses of radioisotopes is carried out at the University of Ceylon, and a cobalt-60 teletherapy unit is to be installed at the Cancer Institute, Maharagama, under a Colombo Plan grant. Ceylon is a member of the **International Atomic Energy Agency.**

CHAIN REACTION

A reaction in which one of the agents necessary to the reaction is itself produced by the reaction and can cause further reactions. In the chain reaction based on nuclear fission, a neutron induces a nucleus to undergo fission; this process releases neutrons which have the capacity to cause more fissions to occur. (See **fission, nuclear**)

CHAMBER OF COMMERCE, U.S.

The Chamber has a Committee on Commercial Uses of Atomic Energy which studies problems affecting the development and exploitation of peaceful uses of atomic energy and helps develop Chamber policies and programs with regard thereto. The Committee, which holds several meetings each year, is composed of 30 to 40 individuals drawn principally from industrial organizations active in the U.S. atomic energy industry.

CHARGE EXCHANGE

In an ionized gas, or **plasma,** a collision between a singly charged positive ion and a neutral particle which results in the transfer of an electron, and hence in the neutralization of the ion and the ionization of the neutral particle. The difference between charge exchange and simple ionization is that no neutralization occurs in the latter process. (Ionization is an event in which an electron is dislodged from a neutral atom by some energetic particle or proton.) Charge exchange is an important factor in high-energy ion injection systems for controlled **fusion.** (See **Molecular Ion Ignition Program,** also **burnout**)

CHARGED PARTICLES

Elementary particles that carry an electric charge, e.g., electrons and protons, as well as mesons of various types, and hyperons. The ionized nuclei of some light elements are also referred to as charged particles: the deuteron, triton, and alpha particle are especially important because, on being given high energies in **particle accelerators,** they can be used to induce nuclear reactions.

CHARIOT PROJECT

A study to determine the feasibility of using nuclear explosives for the excavation of a harbor in northwest Alaska; part of the U.S. Atomic Energy Commission's program of research and development on peaceful uses of nuclear explosives (Plowshare Program).

The site being studied is in the Ogotoruk Creek area between Cape Thompson and Cape Seppings. The tentative plan is to excavate a channel with a basin at the end, accomplishing the primary excavation by means of four 20-kiloton nuclear explosions and one 200-kiloton nuclear explosion. The project would provide considerable data on the basic phenomenology of underground nuclear explosives and thereby contribute to the general objectives of the AEC's Plowshare Program.

The study is being conducted by the Livermore Branch of the E. O. Lawrence Radiation Laboratory. The AEC in collaboration with other government agencies, has conducted extensive bioenvironmental and engineering surveys of the proposed site and its environs to obtain data needed for an evaluation of safety and conservation aspects of the undertaking. (See **Plowshare Program** for background information)

CHELATION

A chemical process by which certain organic compounds are able to incorporate inorganic ions into complex molecular structures, called chelates.

Chelation is a mechanism of interest in some solvent extraction processes for uranium refining and reactor **fuel reprocessing.** It is also of interest as a possible therapeutic method for removing harmful radioactive materials, such as plutonium, from the body.

CHEMICAL APPLICATIONS OF RADIATION. See **radiation applications in the chemical industry.**

CHICAGO PILE NO. 1 (CP-1)

The first demonstration of a self-sustaining chain reaction based on nuclear fission, and hence the first nuclear reactor. CP-1 was built as part of the wartime **Manhattan Project** under the direction of the late Enrico Fermi in a squash court under the West Stands of Stagg Field at the University of Chicago. Criticality was achieved at 3:25 P.M. on December 2, 1942, the date generally accepted as marking the beginning of the era of atomic energy development.

CP-1 was essentially an assembly of natural uranium and graphite bricks. At the time of the experiment only 6 tons of uranium metal were available and it was necessary to complete the assembly with 34 tons of uranium oxide; 385 tons of graphite were used. Critical conditions were achieved somewhat sooner than anticipated, so that the reactor assembly, which had been expected to be spherical, took the shape of an obloid spheroid somewhat flattened at the top. Cadmium strips were used to control the chain-reacting system. No provision was made for radiation shielding or cooling. The reactor was operated at a power level of only half a watt, with brief intervals at 200 watts. In the spring of 1943, CP-1 was dismantled and reconstructed at Palos Park, outside of Chicago (see **Chicago Pile No. 2**). The cost of construction CP-1 has been estimated at $1.5 million.

The method of construction of CP-1—i.e., of "piling up" successive layers of moderator and fuel—gave rise to the name, "atomic pile." This term has been largely replaced by "nuclear reactor."

Those who were present at the time CP-1 first went critical were: H. M. Agnew, S. K. Allison, H. L. Anderson, H. M. Barton, T. Brill, R. F. Christy, A. H. Compton, E. Fermi, R. J. Fox, S. A. Fox, D. K. Froman, A. C. Graves, C. H. Greenewalt, N. Hilberry, D. L. Hill, W. H. Hinch, W. R. Kanne, P. G. Koontz, H. E. Kubitschek, H. V. Lichtenberger, Mrs. L. Woods Marshall, G. Miller, G. Monk, Jr., H. W. Newson, R. G. Nobles, W. E. Nyer, W. P. Overbeck, H. J. Parsons, L. Sayvetz, G. S. Pawlicki, L. Seren, L. A. Slotin, F. H. Spedding, W. J. Strum, L. Szilard, A. Watenburg, R. J. Watts, G. L. Weil, E. P. Wigner, M. Wilkening, V. C. Wilson, and W. H. Zinn.

CHICAGO PILE NO. 2 (CP-2)

Reconstructed version of **Chicago Pile No. 1** with radiation shielding and improved controls provided to permit routine operation at a power level of 2 kilowatts (thermal), and with improved experimental facilities. CP-2 was installed in 1943 at the wartime site of Argonne National Laboratory. It was dismantled in 1954.

CHICAGO PILE NO. 3 (CP-3)

The first heavy water-moderated nuclear reactor, built in 1944 at the wartime site of Argonne National Laboratory for experimentation in support of the **Manhattan Project.** As originally built, CP-3 was fueled with natural uranium and operated at a power level of 300 kilowatts (thermal). In 1950, CP-3 was fueled with enriched uranium. It was dismantled in 1955.

CHILE

Radioisotope training and research laboratories have been established at the University of Chile in Santiago and Catholic University in Valparaiso with the aid of a U.S. foreign equipment grant. Chile is a member of the **International Atomic Energy Agency** and the **Inter-American Nuclear Energy Commission,** and has a research-type **Agreement for Cooperation** with the United States.

CHINA, COMMUNIST

Little information has been published on atomic energy activities of the Chinese People's Republic (CPR). An Institute for Atomic Energy has been established in Peking under the jurisdiction of the CPR Academy of Science. Its experimental facilities include a heavy water-moderated research reactor that operates at power levels up to 10,000 kilowatts (thermal) and a cyclotron, both supplied by the U.S.S.R. The Institute is believed to have no connection with production or military programs.

The CPR signed a cooperative agreement

with the U.S.S.R. in 1955 which provided for the furnishing of the research reactor and cyclotron mentioned above and also for technical assistance, including the training of Chinese technicians in the U.S.S.R. In 1956, the CPR became a member of the **Joint Institute for Nuclear Research** at Dubna.

CHINA, NATIONALIST

The Atomic Energy Council, Taipei, is an advisory agency for atomic energy matters. An Institute of Nuclear Science has been established by the Ministry of Education at National Tsing Hua University, Hsinchu. The facilities include radioisotope laboratories, a 3-Mev Van de Graaff accelerator supplied by High Voltage Engineering Corporation, and a 1000-kilowatt (thermal) pool-type research reactor supplied by the General Electric Company. The United States contributed $350,000 toward the cost of the latter under its program of Foreign Research Reactor Grants.

Only minor deposits of uranium have been found to date. There is interest in the possibility of building a nuclear power station by 1968, by which time new power-generating capacity (over and above that already planned) is expected to be required. Taiwan Power Company is conducting studies and plans to reach a decision on a nuclear project in 1963. Taiwan is a member of the **International Atomic Energy Agency** and has a research-type **Agreement for Cooperation** with the United States.

CHLORINE-36

A radioisotope of chlorine used extensively in biological and agricultural tracer experiments. A pure beta emitter with a radioactive half-life of the order of 10^5 years, chlorine-36 is produced in reactors by neutron absorption in the natural chlorine element.

CHRONIC EXPOSURE, TO IONIZING RADIATION

Continuous or intermittent exposure to small amounts of ionizing radiation over a long period of time, as differentiated from **acute exposure.** (See **biological effects of ionizing radiation**)

CHUGACH ELECTRIC ASSOCIATION PROJECT

A nuclear power project proposed at an early stage of the "second round" of the U.S. Atomic Energy Commission's Power Demonstration Reactor Program but canceled before negotiations were completed. The project contemplated the construction at Anchorage, Alaska of a novel sodium-cooled, heavy water-moderated power reactor with a rated capacity of 10 megawatts (electrical). The reactor was to have been developed and designed by Nuclear Development Corporation of America,* and operated by the Chugach Electric Association, a publicly owned cooperative serving the Anchorage area. The decision to cancel the project was made by the AEC in 1959 on the basis that the technical complexity of the proposed reactor mitigated against building a first-of-a-kind installation at a remote location.

CIVIL EFFECTS TEST OPERATIONS

Operations conducted by the U.S. Atomic Energy Commission with the participation of civil defense agencies for the purpose of obtaining data on civil defense aspects of the effects of nuclear weapons.

CIVILIAN NUCLEAR POWER PROGRAM. See nuclear power development, U.S.

CLADDING

A protective enclosure or coating for reactor fuel materials to prevent corrosion or erosion by the reactor coolant, and to contain radioactive fission products, i.e., to keep them from entering and thereby contaminating the coolant stream. (See **fuel element fabrication**)

---

* Now part of United Nuclear Corporation.

CLASSIFICATION—DECLASSIFICATION

Three basic forms of classified information are dealt with by the U.S. Atomic Energy Commission:

1. Restricted Data.
2. Formerly Restricted Data.
3. Other Defense Information.

All information subject to security classification in the United States is categorized as DEFENSE INFORMATION under Executive Order 10501. Congress took note, however, of the special sensitivity of atomic energy information and created, in the Atomic Energy Act of 1946 and again in the Act of 1954, a special category of Defense Information known as RESTRICTED DATA, defined in the latter Act as:

"all data concerning (a) the design, manufacture, or utilization of atomic weapons, (b) the production of **special nuclear material,** or (c) the use of special nuclear material in the production of energy, but not including data declassified or removed from the Restricted Data category pursuant to Section 142."

Section 142 of the 1954 Act makes it possible for the Commission and the Department of Defense to jointly determine that Restricted Data, which they jointly determine relates primarily to the military utilization of atomic weapons can be adequately safeguarded as defense information. Such information is then removed by the Commission from the Restricted Data category and remains classified as Defense Information. However, the provision is made that it, like Restricted Data, cannot be made available to other nations or groups of nations with whom the United States does not have an **Agreement for Cooperation.** To distinguish this form of defense information from all other Defense Information, the markings FORMERLY RESTRICED DATA was devised.

Information relating to the lines of activity noted above in the definition of Restricted Data is "born classified" unless it falls within the area of data declassified by the Commission in accordance with another part of Section 142. Classified documents and other items can only be removed from security restrictions by specific declassification action. (See further discussion.)

The security classifications used are "Top Secret," "Secret," or "Confidential," depending on the sensitivity of the information. The phrase "Official Use Only" (OUO) is sometimes used for administrative control of information; it is not a security classification.

AEC Classification Policy. AEC harmonizes its classification policy in some areas with that of the United Kingdom and Canada. The broad principles are embodied in a "Classification Policy Guide," which is prepared with the assistance of an advisory committee (see **Committee of Senior Reviewers),** and is revised as circumstances warrant. The general guide is supplemented by a series of detailed guides dealing with major programs and even particular establishments.

Over the years a number of major areas of research and development activity have been removed from all security restrictions. Following are notable examples:

Unclassified Area	*When Removed from Restricted Data Category*
Research reactor technology	1955
Civilian power reactor technology	1956
Controlled fusion research	1958
Chemical technology	1960 *

* In 1960 the AEC completely removed restrictions from all chemical engineering activity relating to atomic energy except in the production of military materials. This was in the nature of an incremental step since much of this activity had already been declassified.

As matters stand, civilian atomic energy research and development is virtually free of security restrictions. Some information that is generated in military application programs and would be useful in civilian development is necessarily restricted; however, even in this area much of the basic technology is either unclassified or declassifiable when divorced from its military context.

Declassification Procedure. As was noted above, information that has once been classified can only be removed from security restrictions by specific declassification action. Thus, when the AEC removes a major area of activity from the Restricted Data category, all classified documents relating thereto must be individually put through a declassification process. In other words the act of removing an area from the Restricted Data category does not of itself declassify the existing literature in that area; it merely means that the existing literature can be declassified if review shows that it contains no information relating to other areas still classified. At the same time, information generated *after* the removal of its particular area from security restrictions is, by definition, unclassified.

Designated individuals at major AEC sites have limited authority in certain circumstances to declassify documents that originated at their respective sites. In the main, however, declassification authority is centralized within the AEC headquarters organization. The declassification process normally entails successive or simultaneous review by (a) the Division of Classification at headquarters or its Declassification Branch at Oak Ridge and (b) the AEC Office of Assistant General Counsel for Patents. In making its determination, the Declassification Branch may ask for the recommendation of a responsible reviewer, i.e., a technical expert familiar with the particular area of activity and with the AEC classification policy. The purpose of the patents review is to protect AEC interests by ensuring, in the case of a technical document, that a patent application, if warranted, can be filed before the document is placed in the public domain (see **patents**). Unless a patents clearance is obtained by the time a technical document is declassified, the declassified document is held for "Official Use Only" and cannot be given open publication until cleared. When a document is declassified, it is so stamped (with or without deletions) and all holders of copies of the document are notified of the action. Also, via *Nuclear Science Abstracts*, general notification is made of the action. The declassification process normally takes three to four weeks, starting from the time the document is submitted. Patent problems or a difference of opinion between the Declassification Branch and the Responsible Reviewer can extent this period considerably. In cases difficult to resolve, a member of the **Committee of Senior Reviewers** is sometimes called upon to express an opinion.

Through 1960, AEC had declassified a cumulative total of some 360,000 documents, including nearly 5000 patent applications.

CLOUD CHAMBER

A device for studying the movement and interaction of energetic charged particles by means of observation of tracks made by the particles as they move through a supersaturated vapor. The tracks result from the fact that the particles ionize atoms of vapor along their path, which in turn cause condensation resulting in a visible vapor trail not unlike that of a high-flying airplane. By studying photographs of track patterns, it is possible to deduce considerable information with regard to particle identity and energy and thereby determine the nature of reactions resulting from particle collisions. Analysis is aided by placing the cloud chamber in a magnetic field, which serves to bend the path of the charged particles. The observed degree of curvature and the density of the track throw additional light on particle energy.

Cloud chambers are used extensively in high-energy physics research to study nuclear events induced by **particle accelerators.** Two general types of chambers have been developed: (1) Chambers in which a supersaturated atmosphere is achieved intermittently by adiabatic expansion. Operating cycles are of the order of one or two minutes. (2) Chambers in which diffusive vapor transfer induced by a top-to-bottom temperature differential continuously maintains supersaturated conditions in a center zone.

Cloud chambers are also referred to as Wilson chambers, after the British physicist C. T. R. Wilson, who discovered the underlying principles in 1896. (See **bubble chamber**)

COBALT-60

A radioactive isotope of cobalt, produced by irradiating the natural element in a nuclear reactor. Cobalt-60 is formed by the neutron-gamma reaction:

$$_{27}Co^{59} + _{0}n^{1} = _{27}Co^{60} + \gamma$$

Cobalt-60 emits 1.33 and 1.17-Mev gamma rays and has a radioactive half-life of 5.2 years, transforming by **beta decay** into nickel-60. It is widely used as a source of gamma radiation for medical **teletherapy** and industrial **radiography,** and also for general research on radiation applications.

Cobalt-60 is commercially available in metal form with **specific activities** up to ~ 100 curies per gram. Current prices (without encapsulation) range from $2.00-6.00 per curie, depending on the specific activity and also on the quantity ordered. Cobalt-60 is produced and distributed on a scale of hundreds of thousands of curies per year in the United States, Canada, and several other countries. The U.S. Atomic Energy Commission discontinued routine cobalt-60 production and distribution in May, 1960, pursuant to its policy of withdrawing from the sale of products or services available at reasonable cost from private industry. As of that time, the AEC had sold a total of some 800,000 curies of cobalt-60, accounting, on a curie basis for nearly 75% of all AEC radioisotope sales.

Cobalt-60 teletherapy sources range in size from 30-3000 curies, with the average about 1500 curies (see **medical aspects of atomic energy**). Sources ranging in size up to 60,000 curies are used for research on radiation applications which may lead to requirements for megacurie amounts. (See **radiation sources)**

COCKCROFT-WALTON MACHINE

A type of **particle accelerator** used to produce beams of charged particles having energies up to several Mev. Acceleration is achieved by the direct application of a direct-current voltage to a beam of ions traveling down a straight insulated tube. The voltage is generated by a voltage multiplier system consisting essentially of a number of condenser pairs connected through switching devices (rectifier tubes) to a high-voltage transformer.

Fig. 32. Cockcroft-Walton machine at Los Alamos. (*Courtesy of Los Alamos Scientific Laboratory*)

The Cockcroft-Walton machine is named after the British physicists, J. D. Cockcroft and E. T. S. Walton, who used this means to produce proton beams for the first experiments with induced nuclear reactions, conducted at Cambridge, England, in the early thirties. Numerous accelerators of this type are in use in laboratories around the world, and they are also used in the injection systems of high-energy particle accelerators such as **proton synchrotrons.**

COFFINITE

Hydrated uranium silicate—a primary uranium mineral, black in color, found in sandstone in finely disseminated deposits; often intermixed with **uraninite.** Coffinite ores are an important source of U.S. uranium production. Major deposits are in the Big Indian Wash district of Utah, the Grants-Laguna area of New Mexico, and the Wind River Basin in Wyoming. (See **uranium deposits and reserves)**

COLD STERILIZATION OF PHARMACEUTICALS

The use of high-intensity ionizing radiation, in lieu of heat, to sterilize pharmaceutical products such as drugs and medical supplies; currently applied commercially in the manufacture of certain medical sutures. The basis for cold sterilization is the ability of ionizing radiation to destroy living organisms. The radiation may be supplied by radiation machines or by radionuclide sources.

Advantages. Ordinarily, pharmaceutical products requiring sterilization are heat-sterilized prior to packaging and then packaged and sealed under aseptic conditions. The use of penetrating ionizing radiation permits sterilization after packaging, obviating the need for maintaining aseptic conditions during and immediately prior to the packaging operation and, by the same token, avoiding the possibility that contamination may occur in the interim. It also affords greater latitude in the selection of packaging materials. Another and related advantage of cold sterilization is that it lends itself to continuous operation, whereas conventional methods usually require batch operation. When applicable to heat-sensitive products, cold sterilization offers a process control advantage. In the case of sutures, for example, when heat is used the temperature must be controlled within a few degrees, whereas when radiation is used the sterilization dose can be exceeded by as much as 40% without damaging the product.

Disadvantages. Radiation is presently a more expensive means of sterilization than heat. The cost difference tends to be balanced and may be offset by the savings made possible by streamlining the packaging operation; however, in an existing plant this in turn may require major changes in plant equipment and layout. The economic balance thus tends to be unfavorable to cold sterilization except where a high-volume output of a high-cost commodity is involved and there is reasonable assurance of a stable market for the product. The last-mentioned condition is the exception rather than the rule in the research-intensive pharmaceuticals industry.

The use of cold sterilization is presently ruled out in many applications by undesirable side effects, which in the case of drugs range from slight changes in color to impairment of therapeutic value. Examples of drugs that have shown relatively minor adverse effects (color changes and some loss of potency) include penicillin, streptomycin and certain other antibiotics. Examples of drugs that have shown major adverse effects (marked loss of potency) include vitamin B-12, atropine sulfate and insulin.

Applications. The first known commercial application of cold sterilization was by the Upjohn Company, who in 1955 successfully used the technique to sterilize small "single-use" capsules of ophthalmic ointments. The manufacture of these products was subsequently discontinued when it was found that they could not compete with large "multi-use" tubes for the consumer market. The principal use of cold sterilization at the present time is in the manufacture of certain medical sutures, an application pioneered by the Ethicon Company, a division of Johnson and Johnson. Radiation machines are used as the radiation source.

COLLAPSIBLE CLADDING

Fuel element **cladding** which is nonrigid—i.e., which depends on the fuel material for structural strength. See discussion under **pressurized water reactors.**

COLOMBIA

The Instituto de Asuntos Nucleares (IAN), Bogotá, is the government agency responsible for atomic energy matters. IAN is conducting a minerals exploration program and plans to initiate a program of research in the physical and life sciences. Colombia is a member of the **International Atomic Energy Agency** and the **Inter-American Nuclear Energy Commission.**

COLUMBIUM

Element No. 41 (symbol, Cb; atomic weight, 92.91), also known as niobium (symbol, Nb). It is sometimes used in low concentrations as an alloying material to improve the corrosion resistance and radiation stability of uranium fuels; however, its usefulness in this application is limited by the fact that it has an appreciable thermal neutron absorption cross section (1.1 barns), and is an expensive material ($45-80 per pound).

COLUMBUS

A generic name for experimental devices of the linear "pinch" type built at Los Alamos Scientific Laboratory for research on controlled **fusion.** Columbus I, built in 1954 and later modified, and Columbus II built in 1956, were used for early research on fast, unstabilized pinch-confinement of fuel **plasma** in a straight-tube configuration. A series of devices designated Columbus S1-S5 has been used to study techniques for achieving a stabilized pinch in a straight tube, and for related research on **plasma diagnostics.** (See **Pinch Program)**

COLUMN ION-EXCHANGE PROCESS

One of several processes used in uranium mills for the recovery of uranium from acid **leach liquors.** It is based on conventional **ion-exchange** techniques. Anion-exchange resins in fixed beds **(packed columns)** are employed. To prevent fouling of the resin beds the leach liquor must be clarified before entering the ion-exchange system. As the clear liquor passes through the columns the uranium preferentially adsorbs on the resin surfaces. Once a given bed becomes saturated, it is successively (1) flushed with water to displace the uranium liquor into the next column for adsorption, (2) backwashed with water so that the upflow of water expands the bed and washes out the finely divided solids which were filtered out in the resin bed during the adsorption cycle, and (3) contacted with a solution of ammonium nitrate or sodium chloride which strips ("elutes") the uranium away from the resin surfaces. The uranium-bearing solution is then piped to a series of tanks where ammonia is introduced to precipitate the uranium as ammonium diuranate $[(NH_4)_2U_2O_7]$. The final steps are filtration and drying, yielding **"yellow cake."**

While the column ion-exchange process is in use at several U.S. uranium mills, the majority of mills employing ion exchange for uranium recovery use a newer technique, known as the **resin-in-pulp process,** which eliminates the leach liquor clarification step. (See **uranium milling** for background information)

COMBINED DEVELOPMENT AGENCY (CDA)

A raw materials procurement agency established by Canada, the United Kingdom, and the United States during World War II. CDA now coordinates the procurement of uranium ores and/or mill concentrates from **Australia, Portugal** and **South Africa.**

COMMITTEE OF SENIOR REVIEWERS

An *ad hoc* (nonstatutory) committee to the U.S. Atomic Energy Commission which makes recommendations with respect to rules and guides for the control of scientific and technical information, and as a group or individually provides general consultation on matters of classification and declassification. The committee consists of six members appointed for five-year terms on a rotating basis. Membership listed in Appendix D.

COMPOUND NUCLEUS

An excited nucleus formed as an intermediate stage in a **nuclear reaction.** The incident or bombarding particle is captured by the target nucleus, forming a compound nucleus, which then disintegrates into the product nucleus and one or more emitted particles. It is now thought that many, though not all, nuclear reactions proceed through a compound nucleus stage.

COMPUTERS

Two types of modern, high-speed computers have proved highly useful in atomic energy programs—digital computers and analog computers.

Digital Computers. These deal with discrete numerical quantities and are able to solve difficult mathematical problems by the repeated application of the elementary arithmetic operations. In some cases the solution may require tens or hundreds of thousands of computations, although the number must, of course, be finite.

Some digital computers are also frequently used for performing certain types of logical operations which might be involved, for example, in the design and testing of complicated electronic circuits or, for that matter, in the detection and location of .faulty circuits or breakdowns that may develop in the computer itself.

The principal components of a digital computer consist of a memory, an arithmetic unit, a control, an input, and an output.

The memory unit, which may have a capacity in large machines of several hundred thousand digits, is used to store information frequently needed or to store partial results which will be reincorporated into a computation at a later stage.

Input units may be activated by means of punched cards or magnetic tape, and the output may be obtained in printed form, on punched cards, on magnetic or punched tape, or it may be photographed from an oscilloscope screen or special output tube. In the larger machines, control is automatically provided by means of a detailed plan for the computation, called a program, which provides instructions for the sequence of routines to be followed in arriving at the solution.

Fig. 33. High-speed computer at Los Alamos. It is known as MANIAC-II (acronym for Mathematical Analyzer, Numerical Integrator and Computer). (*Courtesy of Los Alamos Scientific Laboratory*)

Since many problems encountered in a laboratory or in a commercial or industrial operation are similar and recur frequently over a period of time, libraries of pre-coded programs and sub-programs are maintained at large computing centers. Such pre-coded programs might include routines for such things as sorting, or statistical analysis.

All major AEC research centers, including the national laboratories, have high-speed computing centers. Several computers have been designated and developed specifically for use at AEC research centers. Among these are the **LARC, MANIAC, GEORGE,** and **ORACLE.**

Among the problems in nuclear science and engineering for which digital computers may be used are those involving neutron diffusion, shielding, and calculation of reactor parameters.

Analog Computing Machines. These deal with continuous, as opposed to discrete, quantities which may be represented, for example, by voltages. In many machines of this type direct-current voltages, which vary with time, are used to represent the variables. Thus, only one independent variable is permitted; all others are functions of time. Operations that can be performed with standard machines include (1) multiplication of a variable by a constant factor, (2) addition of two or more variables, (3) integration or differentiation of a variable, (4) multiplication of two or more variables, and (5) representation of other functions of a variable.

Analog computers are often used to obtain the solution of systems of ordinary differential equations. They may also be used as a process control instrument, by utilizing the computer output to activate switches. Analog computers have been used to simulate the kinetic behavior of nuclear reactors to assist in training reactor operators.

COMPTON EFFECT. See **gamma rays.**

CONCENTRATE, URANIUM

A term commonly used in reference to the product of a uranium mill. Uranium concentrates typically assay 65-85% uranium expressed as U_3O_8. They are usually in the form of "orange oxide" (UO_3), "black oxide" (U_3O_8), or sodium diuranate ($Na_2U_2O_7$). They contain various chemical impurities, which are subsequently removed during refining operations. (See **uranium milling**)

CONFINEMENT. See **plasma confinement.**

CONNECTICUT ADVANCED NUCLEAR ENGINEERING LABORATORY (CANEL)

A government-owned reactor development laboratory, located in Middleton, Connecticut; formerly known as the Connecticut Aircraft Nuclear Engine Laboratory. *Operating contractor:* Pratt and Whitney Division of United Aircraft Corporation. *AEC investment:* $5 million (for equipment only; the basic plant is the property of the U.S. Air Force).

CANEL was established under the **Aircraft Nuclear Propulsion Program,** and until 1961, concentrated on the development of indirect-cycle reactor systems for military aircraft applications. The peak employment was 1600.

When the ANP program was canceled early in 1961, the CANEL program was redirected toward the development of high-temperature, high-performance reactor systems for civilian power applications. In 1962 CANEL was assigned reponsibility for the development of a lithium-cooled reactor concept for use in electric propulsion systems for space vehicles (see reference to SNAP-50 under **SNAP Program).** A major portion of CANEL's work under the Aircraft Nuclear Propulsion Program was devoted to this reactor concept.

CONSTRUCTION PERMIT, AEC. See **licenses; Atomic Energy Commission—Licensing and Regulatory Procedure.**

CONSUMERS POWER COMPANY PROJECT

A nuclear power plant of the direct-cycle **boiling water** type at Big Rock Point near Charlevoix, Michigan. The project is being carried out by Consumers Power Company under the "third round" of the U.S. Atomic Energy Commission's Power Demonstration Reactor Program. Consumers Power, who will own and operate the plant, is financing the cost of construction. The AEC is contributing approximately $4 million for research and development, and has waived its normal use charge for nuclear fuel for the first five years of operation (corresponding to a financial contribution of $1.7 million). The prime contractor is Bechtel Corporation. General Electric

Fig. 34. Consumers Power Company's Big Rock Point nuclear power plant, near Charlevoix, Mich., as it looked in final stages of construction. (*Courtesy of General Electric Co.*)

Company is designing the reactor and will supply the principal components.

The reactor is designed to operate at high-power densities relative to other boiling water installations. It is expected that the first core will achieve a power density of 45 thermal kilowatts per liter of core volume, and that subsequent cores will achieve power densities of 60 tkw/liter. The following notes reflect the status of the project as of mid-1962:

Power: 48 megawatts (net electrical) in initial operation. (75 megawatts target performance.) *Fuel:* Slightly enriched uranium (3.2% U^{235}) in the form of uranium dioxide (UO_2) pellets. *Steam conditions:* Reactor steam at 1,000 pounds pressure and 546°F. *Thermal conversion efficiency:* 31%. *Construction cost:* Estimated at $27.6 million, exclusive of research and development. For other project costs, see Table 3 under **nuclear power development.** *Dates:* Proposal submitted to AEC in December, 1957. Construction started in June, 1960. Preliminary operation targeted for late 1962.

CONSUMERS PUBLIC POWER DISTRICT OF NEBRASKA. See **Hallam Nuclear Power Facility.**

CONTAINMENT

In reactor technology, the provision of a gas-tight shell or other enclosure around a nuclear reactor to contain radioactive vapors that would otherwise be released to the atmosphere in the event of a major reactor accident. Containment is presently a prerequisite for power reactors located in all but remote locations. The cost of containment varies with the type and size of reactor. In large-scale civilian nuclear power plants containment provisions presently account for 5 or 6% of the total cost of the plant construction.

The design of a vapor container involves a calculation of the maximum possible energy release in the event of a reactor accident, including (1) the initial nuclear energy release, (2) the release of chemical energy in the event of a **metal-water reaction**; and (3) release of the energy stored in the reactor coolant. Conventional containers are designed to withstand the full pressure that would be exerted by that maximum energy release and also to withstand possible shrapnel effects of flying debris. The applicable design standard is the ASTM Code for unfired pressure vessels.

The type of container most commonly used is a spherical or hemispherical steel shell. By way of example, the container installed in the 180-megawatt Dresden Nuclear Power Sta-

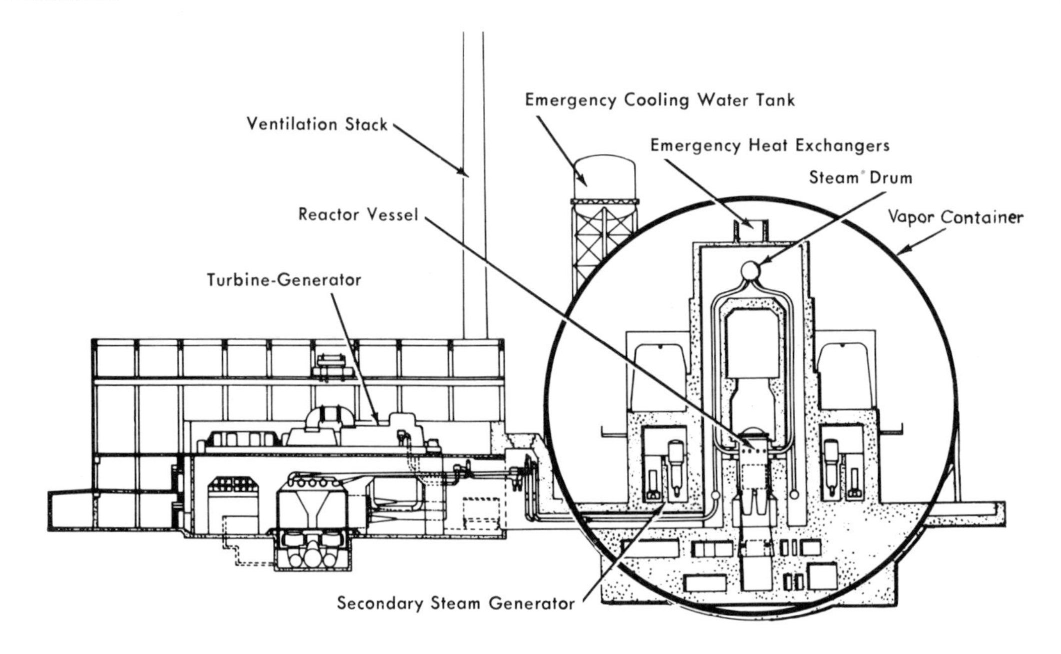

Fig. 35. Layout of Dresden Nuclear Power Station showing general arrangement of reactor equipment in spherical containment vessel. (Reprinted from "Boiling Water Reactors," Addison-Wesley Publishing Co., 1958.)

Fig. 36. Double-door air-lock system in gas-tight building housing the Argonne Research Reactor. Similar air-lock systems are used in power-reactor containment vessels. (*Courtesy of Argonne National Laboratory*)

tion is a spherical vessel 190 feet in diameter, the bottom of which is set 40 feet below ground level. The container is fabricated of steel plate, 1¼ inches thick at the top and 1.4 inches thick at ground level, and is designed to withstand a pressure of approximately 15 psig. Access for personnel and equipment is provided by three pressure locks, each of which has two doors in series with an interlocking arrangement that assures that one door is closed at all times.

Various means are being studied to reduce the cost of containment. One system recently approved by the U.S. Atomic Energy Commission's Advisory Committee on Reactor Safeguards for installation at the Humboldt Bay Power Station is known as vapor suppression. In this design, the reactor vessel is enclosed in a small containment tank ("dry well"), which is connected by a large pipe conduit to an underground water-filled tank ("wet well"). In the event of a major accident, the radioactive vapors would vent into the wet well and most of the radioactivity would be absorbed by the water. This permits housing the reactor installation in a more or less conventional building.*

A nonconventional containment system that has been proposed but not yet approved for use is known as the "burp" system, so-called because the vapor container would contain a vent mechanism designed to relieve the initial pressure pulse. This system is based on calculations which indicate that a shock wave travels ahead of the radioactive vapor so that little or no radioactivity is associated with the initial pressure pulse. Use of what amounts to a pressure relief valve would serve to permit lighter and cheaper construction of the vapor container.

A vapor container notable for its conservative design is that installed in the **Indian Point Station.** Here the container has been massively shielded with concrete. The purpose of this provision is to ensure safe radiation levels immediately outside the vapor container even in the event of a major accident, thereby assuring the continuity of other plant operations which might in future be conducted at the same site.

In the present stage of power reactor development, incomplete knowledge of the phenomenology of reactor accidents necessitates a conservative approach to all features of reactor design related in any way to the safety of civilian nuclear power plants.

To improve existing knowledge, the AEC is sponsoring research on a number of subjects relating to the design of containment systems. These subjects include the dynamic and static rupture of pressure vessels; blast transmission; blast and earthquake loading of containers; the mechanics of penetration and fragmentation; and methods for leak testing.

CONTAMINATION

As used in the atomic energy field, the term implies radioactive contamination, i.e., the unwanted deposition or presence of radioactive matter. (See **decontamination)**

* There are, however, special ventilation requirements.

CONTROL MATERIALS

In a nuclear reactor, materials used as a means of controlling the reactivity of the system (see **reactor control).** Materials used for this purpose have a high cross section for neutron absorption and hence can be regarded as **poisons** that are introduced into the system in a deliberate and controlled manner. They may be introduced via control rods or in the form of **burnable** or **solution poisons.** For information on control rod materials, see **reactor materials.**

CONTROL ROD

A rod containing a material of high neutron absorption cross section used in controlling the reactivity of a nuclear reactor (see **reactor control).** There are three functional classes of control rod—regulating rods, used for fine adjustments; shim rods, used for coarse adjustments; and safety or scram rods, used for rapid or emergency reactor shutdown. For information on control rod materials, see **reactor materials;** and, on actuating mechanisms, see **control rod drives.** (Also see **burnable poison, solution poison)**

CONTROL ROD DRIVES

Mechanisms used to actuate the movement of **control rods** in a nuclear reactor. Control rod functions governing the design of drive mechanisms may be briefly stated as follows:

1. Regulating rods: Used to compensate for transient reactivity changes, thereby maintaining a constant power level; also used to assist in making a change in power level. Rapid and precise movement in response to instrument signals is desired in most power reactor systems. Movement is usually automatically controlled.

2. Shim rods: Used to compensate for large gradual changes of reactivity that cannot be handled by regulating rods; also used in reactor start-up. Speed of withdrawal of movement is limited so that withdrawal at maximum rate will not endanger the reactor.

3. Safety or scram rods: Used for rapid or emergency reactor shutdown. Rapid and dependable movement is essential. Drive mechanisms are designed on a "fail-safe" basis with provision for gravity, spring-actuated, hydraulic, or pneumatic acceleration.

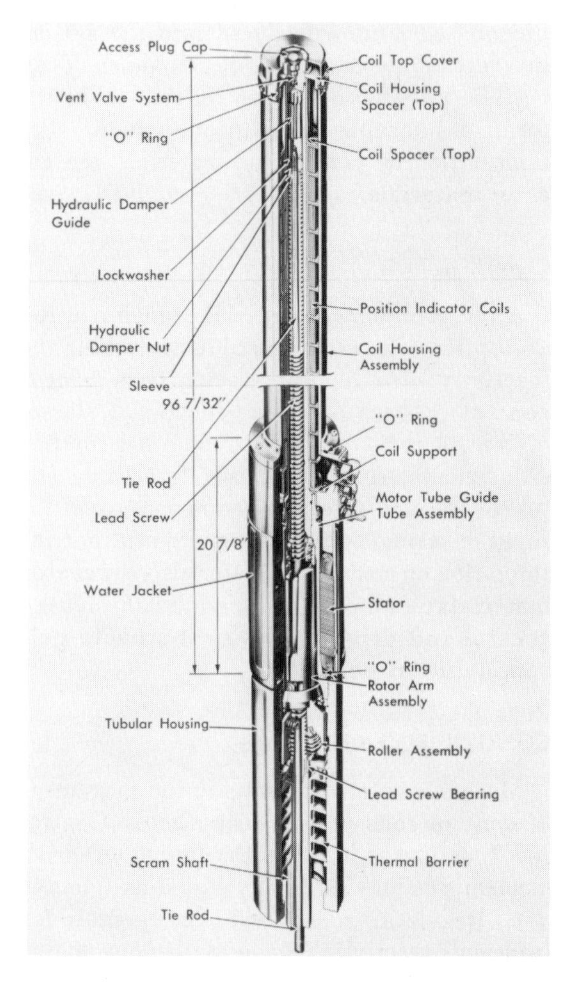

Fig. 37. Ball-and-screw control rod drive of the type used in the Shippingport Atomic Power Station. (Reprinted from "The Shippingport Pressurized Water Reactor," Addison-Wesley Publishing Co., 1958.)

In the latter connection, regulating and shim-rod drive mechanisms usually also have provisions for some form of fast insertion into the reactor.

Various types of control rod drive mechanism have been developed for us in power reactors. Examples are:

1. Rack-and-pinion drive: A motor-driven gear device. This type of drive is top-mounted and, when disengaged, the rod drops into the reactor by gravity action. Safety-rod drives are equipped with a spring mechanism for initial acceleration. The Enrico Fermi Atomic Power Plant employs rack-and-pinion drives.

2. Ball-and-screw drive: A motor-driven device employing a rotating screw and ball-nut mechanism. This type of drive is also top-mounted and contains an electromagnetic disconnect device so that the rod can be dropped by gravity into the reactor. The regulating and shim rods in the Hallam Nuclear Power Facility employ ball-and-screw drives. They are also used in the Shippingport Atomic Power Station (see Fig. 37).

3. Chain-and-sprocket drive: In this type of device, the rod is suspended from a counterweighted electromagnetic mechanism that is moved up and down by means of a link chain actuated by a motor-driven sprocket. Again the drive is top-mounted with the electromagnet acting as a disconnect device to permit the rod to drop into the reactor by gravity. The safety rods in the Hallam Nuclear Power Facility employ chain-and-sprocket drives.

4. Hydraulic drive: An hydraulic piston-type device with detents along the path of travel to control rod position. In the event of loss of hydraulic pressure, the rod is scrammed by compressed air. This type of drive can be top or bottom-mounted. The Dresden Nuclear Power Station employs bottom-mounted hydraulic drives.

5. Magnetic-jack drive: This type of device is essentially a lifting magnet consisting of a fixed and a traveling armature in combination with stationary electromagnet coils. By energizing particular coils the rod moves in fixed increments. Again the drive is top-mounted and, by cutting off the flow of current to the coils, the rod drops into the reactor by gravity. The Yankee Atomic Electric Station employs magnetic-jack drives.

6. Harmonic drive: A recently developed type of control rod-drive mechanism that operates by the controlled elastic deflection of one or more parts of the drive assembly.

The first four types of drive mechanism noted above require the use of some sort of shaft seal; the latter two types are designed as hermetically sealed units.

The number of control rods employed in a power reactor varies considerably, depending upon the control characteristics of the reactor and the design of the particular control systems. The Enrico Fermi Atomic Power Plant, a 94-megawatt fast breeder reactor, has 10 control rods; the Dresden Nuclear Power Station, a 180-megawatt boiling water reactor, has 80 control rods. Costs of control rod drives also vary considerably but generally fall in the range of $20-30,000 per drive.

CONTROLLED FUSION. See **fusion (nuclear).**

CONVERSION RATIO

The number of fissionable atoms produced in a "converter" reactor per fissionable atom consumed. The term is sometimes used synonymously with **breeding ratio.** (See **breeder reactor)**

CONVERTER REACTOR. See **breeder reactor.**

COOLANT

In a nuclear reactor, a fluid used to remove heat from the core or other parts of the reactor in which heat is generated (e.g., the thermal shield). The fluid used to remove heat from the core is referred to as the reactor coolant. In pressurized water and boiling water reactors, the reactor coolant also serves as **moderator.** In fluid fuel reactors, in which the fuel is circulated through the core, the circulating fuel stream serves as the coolant.

In power reactor technology, the terms "primary reactor coolant" and "secondary coolant" are commonly used. The first refers to the fluid which cools the reactor core; the second refers to the working fluid (usually water) used in converting the heat to electricity. A third term, "intermediate coolant," refers to the use of an intermediate heat-exchange medium, as in sodium-cooled power reactors (see **sodium-graphite reactors, fast breeder reactors).**

For information on coolants used in civilian power reactors, see **reactor materials.** Also see **heat exchangers.**

CORE, REACTOR

The central region of a nuclear reactor containing the fuel and, where applicable, the **moderator.** Various configurations are possible. In a pressurized water reactor, for example, the core typically consists of an assembly of **fuel elements** held in a fixed position by grid plates and supports and equipped with channels for the flow of coolant, the movement of control rods, and the insertion of neutron-sensing devices and other control instrumentation. In an aqueous homogeneous reactor, by way of contrast, the core consists essentially of an externally cooled and instrumented spherical vessel containing a critical fuel solution and equipped with inlet and outlet ports through which the fuel is circulated.

CORE SUPPORTS

Structural devices used to support the core of a nuclear reactor employing solid **fuel elements.** In a water-cooled reactor, for example, the core supports typically consist of upper and lower grid plates that respectively align and support the fuel elements and are fastened to the reactor vessel or otherwise braced by structural members.

CORPUSCULAR RADIATION

Radiation consisting of subatomic particles (electrons, protons, deuterons, neutrons, etc.) as distinguished from energy waves **(electromagnetic radiation).**

The term should not be confused with corpuscular emission, which refers specifically to secondary charged particles (usually electrons) associated with the passage of gamma or x-rays through air.

COSMIC-RAY SHOWER

A downward shower of secondary **cosmic ray** particles attributed to events associated with a single primary cosmic ray. The majority of the secondary cosmic rays in a shower are due to a continual interchange of energy between the gamma rays and the electrons passing through the atmosphere. The cosmic gamma rays are absorbed by **pair production** in which a positive electron and a negative electron are produced. The electrons, on the other hand, produce gamma rays when they collide with the nuclei of the atmosphere. Thus, a single primary cosmic ray multiplies into thousands of much lower energy rays as it passes down to the earth's surface.

COSMIC RAYS

Radiation that stems directly or indirectly from sources outside the earth's atmosphere and which, by its presence and through ionization, contributes to the **natural radioactivity** of man's environment.

A distinction is made between primary and secondary cosmic radiation. Primary cosmic rays originate outside the earth's atmosphere and consist mainly of protons, alpha particles and atomic nuclei. Secondary cosmic rays are produced by interaction between primary cosmic radiation and atomic nuclei in the earth's atmosphere or in the earth itself. They consist mainly of mesons, protons, neutrons, electrons, and gamma rays. Most primary cosmic radiation is absorbed in the upper portion of the earth's atmosphere, so that the cosmic radiation observed at or near the earth's surface is mainly due to secondary cosmic rays.

Some constituents of cosmic radiation, especially of primary cosmic rays, have extremely high energies (10^{10} to 10^{17} Mev) and hence high penetrating power (many feet of rock or other dense matter). Due, however, to the absorption of primary cosmic rays in the upper portion of the earth's atmosphere and to attenuation of secondary cosmic rays, the level of cosmic radiation falls off sharply as one approaches the earth's surface. At the latitude of New York City, for example, the intensity (measured as ions per cubic centimeter per second) at 40,000 feet above sea level is 19 times that at 10,000 feet above sea level. This explains why **background radiation** tends to be higher at higher elevations.

COSMOTRON

A 3.0-Bev **proton synchrotron** at Brookhaven National Laboratory.

COSTA RICA

The Comision Nacional Sobre Energia Atomica, San José, established under the University of Costa Rica, is the authority for atomic energy matters. Plans call for establishing an atomic energy training and research center at the University, to be equipped with a radioisotope laboratory and a small research reactor. Costa Rica is a member of the **Inter-American Nuclear Energy Commission.** A research-type **Agreement for Cooperation** with the United States was signed in 1960.

COSTS OF NUCLEAR POWER. See **nuclear power economics.**

COUNTER

A device for the detection and measurement of ionizing **radiation.** There are two principal classes of such devices. One counts the number of ionization events induced in a gas volume (see **Geiger counter,** pulse-type **ionization chamber; proportional counter).** The other counts the number of light flashes induced in phosphors (see **scintillation counter).** Also see **ratemeter, scaler.**

Solid-state devices employing semiconductor materials constitute a third class of radiation counters.

CRITICAL EXPERIMENT

An experiment, usually conducted in connection with the design of a nuclear reactor, in which portions of the reactor **core** are assembled gradually until a **critical mass** has

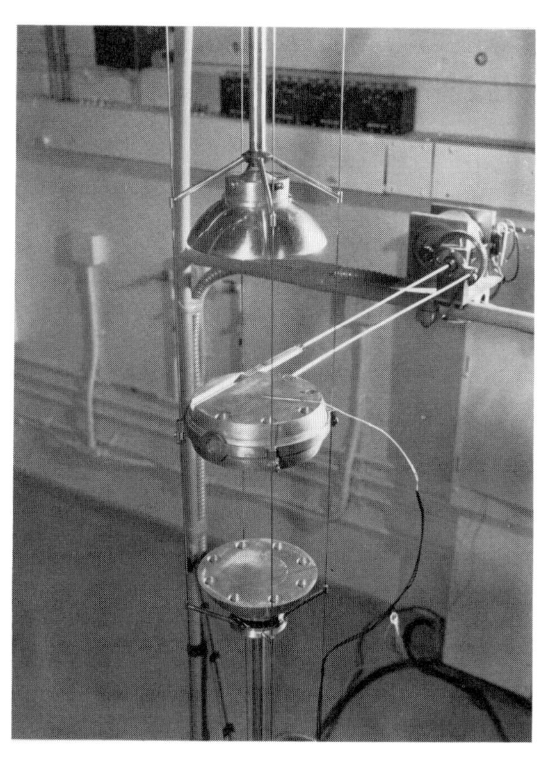

Fig. 38. Critical experiment facilities. Top, Zero Power Reactor III at the National Reactor Testing Station. Right, Jezebel apparatus at Los Alamos Scientific Laboratory. (*Courtesy of Argonne National Laboratory (ZPR-III) and Los Alamos Scientific Laboratory (Jezebel)*)

been reached and a self-sustaining chain reaction is attained. Its purpose is to determine the **critical size** of the reactor core and/or other reactor characteristics, such as neutron flux distributions and control features; and to test design calculations. Critical experiments are performed at very low (practically zero) power and therefore provision for heat removal is not usually required.

CRITICAL MASS

(1) A sufficient mass of a given **fissionable material** to achieve a self-sustaining chain reaction. The amount depends on the fissionable species involved, its concentration and purity, the geometry of the assembly, and the matter surrounding it. (2) The inventory of fissionable material in a nuclear reactor of **critical size.**

CRITICAL SIZE

The minimum size of core and reflector required for a given nuclear reactor to maintain a chain reaction. By increasing the size of the reactor core and reflector the relative loss of neutrons by leakage is reduced. This is a result of the fact that neutron production varies directly with the volume, whereas leakage varies directly with the surface area. The size is increased until the rate of production of neutrons by fission just balances the consumption of neutrons by absorption (in all reactor materials) and leakage. When the core and reflector are large enough so that this balance is achieved without the presence of control **poisons,** the critical size has been achieved.

In reactor design, calculations of critical size are usually confirmed by conducting a **critical experiment.**

CRITICAL TEMPERATURE. See **ignition temperature.**

CRITICALITY FACTOR

In nuclear reactor theory, a quantity which describes the degree to which a chain-reacting system can sustain operation. The value depends on the size and composition of the chain-reacting system. When its value is unity, the system can sustain a chain reaction, and is critical; when it is greater than unity, the system is supercritical, or divergent; and when it is smaller than unity, the system is subcritical and the chain reaction is not self-sustaining. (See **multiplication factor** and **reactivity**)

CRITICALITY INCIDENTS

In 18 years of large-scale atomic energy research and development in the United States (1943 through 1960) there were 11 criticality incidents, i.e., instances in which a supercritical fission chain reaction was inadvertently set in motion, resulting in momentarily uncontrolled release of ionizing radiation. In three of the instances, the individual nearest the apparatus received a fatal radiation dose.

CROSSLINKING

In chemical technology, the linking together of discrete long-chain molecules (linear polymers) into a continuous molecular network by means of transverse bonds. Crosslinking improves the physical properties of some plastics and similar materials; for example the vulcanization of rubber is a crosslinking process. Crosslinking is normally done by chemical means; however it can also be brought about by the application of high-intensity ionizing radiation. The latter technique has been reduced to commercial practice in the manufacture of crosslinked polyethylene. (See **radiation applications in the chemical industry)**

CROSS SECTION

A direct measure of the number of times a given **nuclear reaction** will occur when a particular nuclide is exposed to a given number of incident particles; hence a reaction probability constant for the particular set of conditions. Cross sections are expressed as the effective target area presented by a single atomic nucleus of the target material; and values are given in barns (symbol, D), a term coined in analogy to the expression, "hitting the broad side of a barn." A barn is defined as an effective target area of 10^{-24} square centimeter.

Nuclear cross-section values (symbol σ) for a given nuclide vary with the particular reaction **(capture, scattering,** fission, etc.) and are a function of the energy of the bombarding particles. In many cases the cross-section values peak within a particular energy range or ranges, a phenomenon known as **resonance.** Other terms that should be noted are "macroscopic cross section," which is a cross-section value for a unit volume or mass of target material, and "total cross section," which is the sum of the cross sections for all reactions that may be induced in the target material by the particular bombarding particles. Cross-section values are determined experimentally by observing the number of reactions that occur under controlled conditions. Such measurements constitute an important branch of experimental nuclear physics. A committee known as the Nuclear Cross Sections Advisory Group, makes a continuing review of the cross-section measurement program sponsored by the U.S. Atomic Energy Commission and advises on the need for cross-section information in the AEC's various research and development activities.

Of particular importance in nuclear reactor design are cross-section values for neutron **capture.** Neutron-capture characteristics have an important bearing on the selection and specification of materials used in reactors, especially **thermal reactors,** and detailed cross-section information is needed in order to calculate reaction rates and thereby determine the **neutron economy** of a given reactor design. See accompanying Table 1 for representative thermal neutron capture cross sections for a number of nuclides of interest to reactor designers.

CRUISER, NUCLEAR. See **Naval Reactors Program;** U.S.S. ***Long Beach.***

TABLE 1. SOME THERMAL NEUTRON ABSORPTION CROSS SECTIONS

Element or Nuclide	*Reactor Use or Significance of Material Containing the Element or Nuclide*						*Cross Section (barns) for the Element or Nuclide*
	Fuel Cladding or Other Fuel-Element Use	*Moderator*	*Coolant*	*Control Poison*	*Fission-Product Poison*	*Structural*	
Aluminum	x					x	0.330
Beryllium	x	x					0.010
Bismuth	x (fuel solv.)						0.032
Boron				x			755.
Boron-10				x			3848.
Cadmium				x			2550.
Carbon	x (carbide fuels)	x (graphite)					0.003
Chromium	x (stainless steel)					x (stainless steel)	2.9
Columbium	x (fuel alloys)						1.1
Deuterium		x (D_2O)	x (D_2O)				0.00046
Europium				x			4600.
Gadolinium							46,000.
Hafnium				x			105.
Helium			x				0.007
Hydrogen		x (water)	x (water)				0.330
Iron	x (stainless steel)					x (stainless steel)	2.53
Magnesium	x						0.063
Molybdenum	x (fuel alloys)						2.5
Nickel	x (stainless steel)					x (stainless steel)	4.6
Nitrogen			x (air)				1.88
Oxygen	x (oxide fuels)	x (water)	x (water, air)				0.00019
Samarium-149					x		66,000.
Sodium			x				0.505
Titanium						x	5.6
Xenon-135					x		2,720,000.
Yttrium		x (hydride)					1.28
Zirconium	x					x	0.180

CRYOGENIC COILS

Low-temperature magnet coils proposed for use in experimental controlled-**fusion** systems to reduce the power input required for magnetic confinement of the fuel **plasma** (i.e., ionized gas). The reduction in magnet power stems from improved (i.e., lowered) electrical resistivity at lower temperatures. For example, the copper magnetic coils in the experimental device known as **Alice** are cooled to liquid nitrogen temperature (78°K) in order to reduce their electrical resistance.

The magnet power may be reduced to a minimum by taking advantage of the phenomenon of superconductivity, i.e., the fact that the electrical resistance of metals becomes substantially zero at temperatures within a very few degrees of absolute zero. Coils operated in the range between liquid hydrogen temperatures (20°K) and liquid helium temperatures (4°K) have been considered. One problem that has been encountered is that the normal resistance of some metals tends to reappear when the magnetic field reaches moderate values. This problem has been overcome through the discovery of new alloys (e.g., an alloy of niobium and tin, Nb_3Sn) whose low resistance at low temperatures does not tend to increase appreciably in a strong magnetic field. Sodium and aluminum also appear promising.

CUBA

The Comision de Energia Nuclear de Cuba, Havana, is the agency responsible for atomic energy matters. The principal activity has been in training and research in the medical uses of radioisotopes. Cuba is a member of the **International Atomic Energy Agency** and the **Inter-American Nuclear Energy Commission,** and signed a research-type **Agreement for Cooperation** with the United States in 1957.

CUBE ROOT LAW

A theorem used to predict the blast effects of explosives. As an approximation, such effects increase in magnitude or intensity in ratio to the cube root of the energy released. For example, if a 1-kiloton nuclear weapon produces a certain blast effect 1 mile from the point of detonation, a 1-megaton device would be expected to produce the same effect 10 miles from the point of detonation.

CURIE

(1) The basic unit of radioactivity, equal to 3.7×10^{10} atomic disintegrations per second. (2) An amount of radionuclide having an activity of 1 curie.

The unit was named after Marie Curie and approximates the activity associated with 1 gram of radium.

CURIUM

Element No. 96 (symbol, Cm), first identified in 1944 by G. T. Seaborg, R. A. Jones, L. O. Margain and A. Ghiorso at the E. O. Lawrence Radiation Laboratory. The discovery followed particle accelerator experiments in which plutonium-239 was bombarded with high-energy alpha particles. Named for Pierre and Marie Curie, curium is one of eleven **transuranium elements** discovered in the past two decades.

Curium-242 is of interest as an energy source for small auxiliary power units for space applications. (See **SNAP Program)**

CUSPED GEOMETRY

A general term for cusp-shaped magnetic fields, which are of interest in connection with the problem of achieving stable confinement of an ionized gas, or **plasma,** in controlled-**fusion** research. In a cusp-shaped confinement field, the lines of magnetic force curve everywhere away from the plasma (see Fig. 39), a configuration which, in principle, should lend stability to the confinement system (see **plasma stability**), and also result in a lowered external magnetic field requirement.

Theoretical studies of cusped geometry were

conducted at New York University in the mid-fifties; * however, progress then being made along other lines of plasma confinement acted to reduce the incentive to undertake experimental work on cusp systems. This picture has recently changed due to growing concern with the problem of **cyclotron radiation** losses encountered in other confinement systems. In cusp or other **diamagnetic plasma** systems such losses would only be expected to occur at the surface of the plasma. This expectation has sparked widespread interest in cusp experimentation.

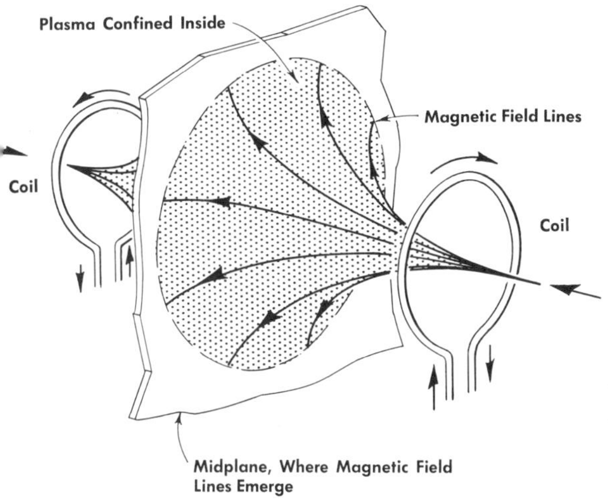

Fig. 39. Simple cusp configuration.

CYCLOTRON

A type of **particle accelerator** used to produce beams of proton, deuterons or alpha particles of moderately high energy (of the order of tens of Mev). The first cyclotron was built in 1931 by the late E. O. Lawrence and coworkers at the University of California. For the invention and subsequent development of the cyclotron Dr. Lawrence received the 1939 Nobel physics award.

The essential parts of a conventional cyclotron are an electromagnet, a vacuum chamber between its poles, and two accelerating electrodes connected to a source of alternating voltage.

The operation begins when an ion source produces nuclear particles at the center of the accelerating chamber. Electrons emitted from a heated wire in the ion source knock electrons from the atoms of entering gas, permitting the positively (+) charged nuclei to float up into the space between the two accelerating electrodes (called "dees"). Depending upon whether hydrogen, heavy hydrogen or helium gas is used, the particles obtained for acceleration are protons, deuterons, or alpha particles.

Between the dees, the particles are under the influence of two powerful forces: the magnetic field and the rapidly alternating electrical charge fed to the dees by the oscillator. The positively (+) charged particles are attracted to the negatively (−) charged dee, the attraction speeding them up. The magnetic field pulls the particles in a semicircular path back to the space between the dees. Meanwhile, the charge on the dees has reversed, and the particles are repelled by the (+) charged dee and attracted to the opposite dee, now (−) charged.

Fig. 40. Sixty-inch cyclotron at Argonne. (*Courtesy of Argonne National Laboratory*)

* They were also studies somewhat earlier, but for a different purpose at the time, at Los Alamos Scientific Laboratory (see **picket fence**).

This process is repeated, the particles gaining speed and energy and traveling in ever widening circles until they near the outer edge of the dees. Here they are drawn out of the chamber by the deflector, and emerge as a beam of high-energy particles.

Conventional cyclotrons are limited in the particle energies they can reach, by the relativistic mass effect. As was predicted in Einstein's special theory of relativity (see **relativity**) a particle gains mass as its energy increases. A conventional cyclotron has no means for compensating for this effect, so that as critical limits are exceeded, the particles get out of phase with the oscillator and the efficiency of the acceleration system falls off rapidly. In the case of the 60-inch cyclotron at the E. O. Lawrence Radiation Laboratory, the limits are about 12 Mev in the case of protons; 24 Mev in the case of deuterons; and 48 Mev in the case of alpha particles. In other, more complicated, accelerator designs, compensation is provided by progressively decreasing the frequency of the oscillator (see **synchrocyclotron**), or by progressively increasing the strength of the magnetic field (see **electron synchrotron**).

CYCLOTRON FREQUENCY

With reference to an ionized gas, or **plasma**, held in magnetic confinement (as in controlled-**fusion** experiments), the natural frequency at which the ions or the electrons of the plasma rotate about the axial lines of magnetic force (see **cyclotron resonance heating**). Since the cyclotron frequency of a particle depends inversely upon its mass, electrons in a particular plasma have a much higher cyclotron frequency than ions.

CYCLOTRON RADIATION

Electromagnetic radiation caused by the centripetal acceleration of charged particles moving along a curved path; also known as synchrotron radiation. Cyclotron radiation, along with bremsstrahlung, is a problem in controlled-**fusion** research, in that it carries energy away from the **plasma** (i.e., ionized gas) in which fusion reactions occur.

Whereas all gyrating charged particles emit cyclotron radiation, only that of electrons is significant under conditions of immediate interest. For electrons, the rate of energy loss may be so large as to greatly exceed that resulting from the emission of bremsstrahlung from the given plasma. The problem of cyclotron radiation has increased interest in experimental cusp machines for the development of a **diamagnetic plasma.** (See **cusped geometry**)

CYCLOTRON RESONANCE HEATING

A method for increasing the energy of fuel **plasma** ions in controlled-**fusion** research. The method is analogous to that used to accelerate charged particles in certain **particle accelerators,** notably the **betatron.** It involves superimposing an alternating magnetic field on the static magnetic field used for plasma confinement. This is done by passing a radiofrequency current through a coil concentric with that producing the static, axial field. The alternating magnetic field, if of the same frequency as the rotating plasma ions, creates an electric field which is in phase with the ions. The "in phase," or resonant, condition allows the ions to be continuously excited by the electric field, thereby continuously gaining energy.

Cyclotron resonance heating is practical for plasma densities below $\sim 10^{12}$ or 10^{13} particles/cm^3. At greater densities, a new phenomenon, that of **ion cyclotron waves** occurs, and the single particle resonance heating method no longer applies.

CZECHOSLOVAKIA

Agencies. The Czechoslovak Academy of Science, Prague, has over-all cognizance over scientific matters, and, through its Institute of Nuclear Physics (see below) administers the national atomic energy program. The Czechoslovak Commission for Atomic Energy, Prague, is responsible for nuclear power development. OMNIA, Prague, is a state agency recently established to control the import and export of nuclear materials and equipment.

International Relationships. Member of the **International Atomic Energy Agency.** Technical assistance agreement with the U.S.S.R. Participant in the **Joint Institute for Nuclear Research** at Dubna in the U.S.S.R.

Research Center. The Institute of Nuclear Physics of the Czechoslovak Academy of Sciences is located at Rez, near Prague. The facilities include a 2000-kilowatt (thermal) pool-type research reactor supplied by the U.S.S.R.

Production Activity. Czechoslovakia has developed rich deposits of uranium, notably the pitchblende ores of the Jachymov region. By agreement with the U.S.S.R., these resources and others, less rich, have been exploited by a Soviet organization, Jachymovske Doly. Uranium processing facilities and facilities for heavy water production are reportedly under developmnet.

Energy Economy. Czechoslovakia's present electric power capacity is about 5000 megawatts, most of it coal-fired. There are substantial supplies of coal and lignite; however supplementary energy sources are believed to be required to sustain the desired rate of industry expansion.

Nuclear Power Program. Czechoslovakia is reportedly planning to build ten nuclear power stations with an aggregate capacity of 5000 megawatts by 1970. The first station is nearing completion at Bohunice, Slovakia. The reactor is heavy-water-moderated, gas-cooled and fueled with natural uranium (mined in Czechoslovakia and processed in the U.S.S.R.). The station is rated at 150 megawatts (electrical) and was designed and built by Soviet engineers. A second nuclear power station was scheduled for completion at Ziar in the Uah Valley in 1962.

D

DAMAGE CRITERIA

With reference to nuclear weapons, the amounts of blast pressure, thermal radiation, and ionizing radiation required to produce specified levels of damage. (See **weapons effects**)

DANA HEAVY WATER PLANT

One of two postwar production facilities built to supply heavy water for use as moderator in the plutonium production reactors at Savannah River. (The other is part of the Savannah River Plant.) The Dana Plant was constructed on an ordnance site at Newport, Indiana (near Dana), and operated by E. I. duPont de Nemours & Co. The basic process employed was **dual-temperature chemical exchange.** The plant represented an investment of approximately $99 million. It was placed in stand-by status in 1957, and in July, 1959, ownership was transferred from the U.S. Atomic Energy Commission to the U.S. Army Chemical Corps to permit modification of the facilities for other use. (See **deuterium** for background information)

DANGER COEFFICIENT

A number expressing the relative poisoning effect of a material in a nuclear reactor. The poisoning effect is caused by parasitic absorption of neutrons by the material and depends on the material's neutron absorption cross section, the amount present, and its location in the reactor. The danger coefficient is used to estimate the loss in **reactivity** that would be incurred by having the material in the reactor.

DAPEX PROCESS

One of the several processes used in uranium mills for the recovery of uranium from acid **leach liquors;** also known as the EHPA process. The Dapex process (from *di*alkyl *p*hosphate *ex*traction) is based on **solvent extraction** techniques. The solvent employed is a kerosene solution of an organic derivative of phosphoric acid—usually, di-2-ethylhexyl phosphoric acid (EHPA) and tributyl phosphate (TBP). After extraction, the uranium is stripped from the solvent into a dilute sodium carbonate solution, from which it is in turn precipitated by the addition of ammonia. The resulting ammonium diuranate $[(NH_4)_2U_2O_7]$ is separated by filtration and then dried, yielding "yellow cake." The Dapex process was developed at Oak Ridge National Laboratory and is in use in several U.S. uranium mills. See **uranium milling** for background information. Also see **Amex process, DDPA process.**

DAREX PROCESS

A technique of **"head-end"** treatment being developed for the reprocessing of stainless steel-clad fuel elements from power reactors; specifically, a process for dissolving such fuel elements preparatory to solvent extraction (see **fuel reprocessing).** Darex is applicable to integral dissolution of cladding and fuel or as a decladding step. The reagent used is dilute aqua regia, a mixture of nitric and hydrochloric acids.

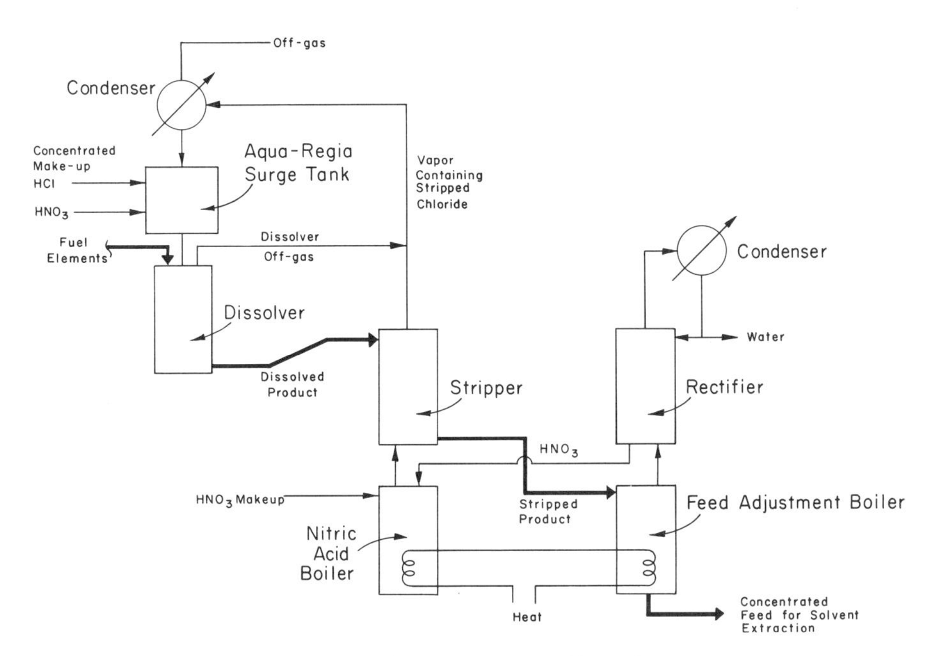

Fig. 41. Simplified flow diagram—Darex Process.

The dissolver product enters a stripping column in which it is freed of chloride ions by countercurrent flow of nitric acid vapor. It then passes into a feed-adjustment boiler wherein sufficient nitric acid and water are removed to achieve a desired ratio of metallic nitrate ions to nitric acid. The resulting concentrated nitrate solution can then be adjusted by simple dilution to provide a suitable feed stream for solvent extraction. Apart from minor off-gas losses, the hydrochloric acid and the excess nitric acid consumed in the process are recovered for reuse.

DAUGHTER PROCESS

The nuclide remaining after the radioactive decay of an atomic nucleus. In alpha particle emission, the daughter product has an atomic number Z of two units less and an atomic mass number A of four units less than the original nuclide. In beta emission (i.e., the emission of an electron from the nucleus), the daughter product has the same atomic mass number while the atomic number is one unit greater than the original.

In positron emission, a nuclear proton is converted into a neutron giving the daughter product an atomic number one less than the original, and keeping the atomic mass number the same. The capture of an atomic electron by the nucleus (K-capture) produces the same daughter product as does positron emission.

DCX SYSTEM (DIRECT-CURRENT EXPERIMENT SYSTEM)

DCX-1 was built in 1957 at Oak Ridge National Laboratory as part of the **Molecular Ion Ignition Program** of research on controlled **fusion.** DCX-1 was designed to test the basic feasibility of trapping a high-energy molecular ion beam in a magnetic field, and the ability of high-current arcs to dissociate a large fraction of that beam.

In the DCX-1 machine, hot **plasma** (i.e., ionized gas) is accumulated in a magnetic containment system by injection of a continuous stream of molecular ions, which are dissociated into atomic ions by a carbon arc located within the magnetic field. Achievement of high plasma densities has been hampered by **charge exchange** phenomena.

DCX-2, a multiple-pass molecular ion injection device, was under construction.

DDPA PROCESS

One of the several processes developed for use in uranium mills for the recovery of uranium from acid **leach liquors.** The DDPA process (from *d*o*d*ecyl *p*hosphoric *a*cid) was developed jointly by the Dow Chemical Company and the Bureau of Mines. It is based on **solvent extraction** techniques, and is similar to the **Dapex process,** except that it employs a different organophosphorous acid solvent. See **uranium milling** for background information. Also see **Amex process.**

DECAY (radioactive)

The process or processes of nuclear disintegration by which a radioactive (i.e., unstable) atom seeks stability. (See **radioactivity)**

DECAY CONSTANT

The fraction of the number of atoms present in a sample of a radioactive substance which undergo disintegration in unit time; hence an expression of the rate of radioactive decay of that substance. (See radioactive **half-life)**

As the term implies, decay constants are independent of temperature, pressure or other environmental conditions.

DECAY COOLING

The storage of irradiated fuel elements to allow for radioactive decay of short-lived radioisotopes prior to initiating **fuel reprocessing** operations. The period of time required depends on the particular fuel, its irradiation history, and the method of reprocessing to be employed.

Where only partial decontamination is contemplated, as in "closed-cycle" reprocessing, the determining factor is the importance placed on recovering bred fissionable material. In the case of irradiated uranium-238, time must be allowed for neptunium-239 to decay to plutonium-239. In the case of irradiated thorium, the consideration is the decay of protoactinium-233 to uranium-233. Since the half-lives for these decay processes are 2.33 and 27.4 days, respectively, thorium requires the longer cooling period.

Where a high degree of decontamination is required in order to permit direct handling of the recovered materials ("open-cycle" reprocessing), other factors become operative. One is the desirability of allowing time for the decay of 8.14-day iodine-131 and 5.27-day xenon-133 in order to limit the amount of radioactive gases given off during fuel dissolution. Another is the need to allow time for the gross activity to subside to avoid radiation-induced degradation of organic solvents used in certain reprocessing systems. Still another is the presence in irradiated uranium fuels of uranium-237, a 6.75-day gamma emitter, which would contaminate the recovered uranium if it were not allowed to decay before starting the recovery process. The latter factor will probably determine the cooling period for highly enriched uranium fuels and for slightly enriched uranium fuels that undergo **burn-up** of more than 1% in power reactor applications. Decay cooling periods of from 90-180 days can be anticipated for such fuels in an open fuel cycle.

DECAY CURVE

A curve in which the quantity, or alternatively the radiation intensity, of a radioactive material is plotted against the time.

If the quantity is plotted on a logarithmic scale, the curve for any particular radioactive isotope becomes a straight line, from which the **decay constant** (λ) and the radioactive **half-life** (T) may be easily calculated. In the case of a mixture of radioactive substances, the graph is not a straight line, but a combination of such lines, each having its own slope. It is frequently possible to determine the decay constants for all the materials present by analysis of the total curve.

DECLASSIFICATION. See **classification-declassification.**

DECONTAMINATION

1. The removal of radioactive contaminants from buildings, instruments, and equipment to reduce or eliminate potential hazards to personnel. Building areas in which the possibility of significant radioactive contamination exists are usually provided with easily removable paints and coverings, which are stripped from the walls and floors during decontamination. Final reduction to acceptable levels of radioactivity at the surfaces of walls, ceilings and floors due to absorbed materials is frequently accomplished by applying multiple coats of paint. Decontamination of equipment is usually accomplished by repeated flushing with detergents and acids containing cleaning solutions. Careful vacuum cleaning and washing are employed on instrumentation. Equipment too radioactive for decontamination is usually disposed of by burial.

2. The removal of fission products from irradiated nuclear fuel in **fuel reprocessing** operation.

(See **decontamination factor)**

DECONTAMINATION FACTOR

In **fuel reprocessing,** a measure of the completeness of removal of radioactive fission-product contaminants from the recovered fissionable materials. More generally, a measure of the efficiency of the removal of radioactive contaminants in any decontamination operation, whether relating to materials or facilities. Numerically, a decontamination factor represents the ratio of fission product concentration, or activity, before the decontamination operation to that after the decontamination operation.

In "closed-cycle" reactor fuel systems, reprocessing serves merely to remove gross fission product poisons from the irradiated fuel, which is returned to the reactor without direct contact by man. Here decontamination factors of 10 to 100 are usually adequate, i.e., it suffices to reduce the fission-product activity to one-tenth to one-hundredth of its initial value. In "open-cycle" reactor fuel systems, direct contact with the recovered fissionable material is a requirement; hence high decontamination factors must be realized. In such applications a common specification is that the amount of radioactivity contributed by residual fission-product contaminants be no greater than that of the fissionable isotopes in equilibrium with their daughter products. This specification usually requires decontamination factors of the order of 10^6 to 10^8.

DECOUPLING. See **weapons test detection.**

DELAYED FALLOUT. See **radioactive fallout.**

DELAYED NEUTRONS

Neutrons emitted by excited nuclei among the fission products in a nuclear reactor, so called because they appear at appreciable time intervals (seconds or minutes) after fission has occurred, as opposed to **prompt neutrons.** Although less than 1% of the neutrons emitted in fission are delayed, they are important in the control of nuclear reactors because they afford a time-margin of safety following small reactivity changes during which control or safety rods can be set in motion. (See **reactor control)**

The delayed neutrons accompany fission fall into five major groups, each of which is characterized by a definite rate of decay. The same five groups accompany the fission of uranium-233, uranium-235, and plutonium-239 (see Table).

CHARACTERISTICS OF DELAYED FISSION NEUTRONS IN THERMAL FISSION
FRACTION OF FISSION NEUTRONS DELAYED

Half-life (sec)	U^{233}	U^{235}	Pu^{239}	*Energy (Mev)*
0.43	1.8×10^{-4}	8.5×10^{-4}	4.0×10^{-4}	0.40
1.52	6.2×10^{-4}	24.1×10^{-4}	10.5×10^{-4}	0.67
4.51	8.6×10^{-4}	21.3×10^{-4}	11.2×10^{-4}	0.41
22.0	5.8×10^{-4}	16.6×10^{-4}	9.4×10^{-4}	0.57
55.6	1.8×10^{-4}	2.5×10^{-4}	1.2×10^{-4}	0.25
Total	0.0024	0.0073	0.0036	

DENMARK

Agency. The Danish Atomic Energy Commission, Copenhagen, is the official government agency responsible for atomic energy matters.

International Relationships. Member of **International Atomic Energy Agency,** the **European Nuclear Energy Agency,** and the European Organization for Nuclear Research **(CERN).** Research-type **Agreement for Cooperation** with the United States.

Research Center. The Risø Research Establishment at Risø, 20 miles west of Copenhagen, is the principal research center of the Danish AEC. Its experimental equipment includes three reactors. DR-1, a small research reactor of the water-boiler type, supplied by Atomics International, operates at a power level of 2000 watts (thermal). DR-2, a tank-type materials testing reactor supplied by Foster-Wheeler Corporation, operates at a power level of 5000 kilowatts (thermal). DR-3, a heavy water-moderated tank-type materials testing reactor supplied by Head-Wrightson Processes Ltd. (U.K.), operates at a power level of 10,000 kilowatts (thermal).

Production Activity. None.

Energy Economy. Denmark's electric power capacity is about 2000 megawatts, all of it thermal and 90% of it dependent on imported fuel. There are no hydroelectric resources.

Nuclear Power Program. Two nuclear power studies are in progress, both under the auspices of DANATOM (see below). One (Project Alpha) is a study of pressurized water reactors for marine (tanker) propulsion. The other (Project Beta) is a study of the economic feasibility of constructing a large-scale nuclear power plant of the gas-cooled graphite-moderated type.

Industry Notes. DANATOM, Copenhagen, is an organization formed by some 40 Danish industrial firms to promote the establishment and growth of nuclear industry in Denmark. ISOTOPCENTRALEN, Copenhagen, is an organization established by the Danish Academy of Technical Sciences to promote the development of applications for isotopes.

General Note. Denmark, through its Theoretical Physics Institute at Copenhagen, has long been a leading contributor in the field of nuclear physics.

DENSITY GAGES. See **gages.**

DEPLETED URANIUM

Uranium containing less than the natural abundance (0.71%) of the uranium-235 isotope. Highly depleted uranium is discharged as a "waste" from **uranium enrichment** plants. It is useful as a **blanket** material in plutonium-breeding reactors. It is also available for sale to licensed U.S. firms for non-nuclear use, such as the manufacture of pigments. Following is the current AEC price list (effective July 1, 1962) for depleted uranium as uranium hexafluoride (UF6), f.o.b. Paducah, Kentucky.

Weight Fraction U-235	*Charge per kg Contained Uranium*
0.0022 up to 0.0038 (if unspecified assay)	$ 2.50
0.0022 up to 0.0038 (user specifies assay)	3.00
0.0040	3.70
0.0050	8.90
0.0060	15.35
0.0070	22.60

DESTROYER, NUCLEAR. See **Naval Reactors Program;** U.S.S. ***Bainbridge.***

DETECTION OF NUCLEAR EXPLOSIONS. See **weapons test detection.**

DEUTERIUM

A stable, naturally occurring hydrogen isotope (symbol, D) having twice the mass of the hydrogen atom and often referred to as "heavy hydrogen." Deuterium is of interest in the nuclear field in three unrelated ways: (1) In the form of "heavy water" (D_2O), it is the most effective material available for neutron moderation in reactors, being second only to hydrogen in its ability to slow down neutrons by elastic collisions and having a significantly lower cross section for thermal-neutron capture. Heavy water is the moderator used in the plutonium production reactors at Savannah River and in research reactors of the type represented by the Argonne Research Reactor (CP-5). Also, several power reactor concepts currently under development are based on heavy water moderation (see **heavy water-moderated power reactors, reactor materials**). (2) Deuterium is a prospective fuel for one of which has as yet been found to be superior over the entire range of concentration involved, i.e., from the starting concentration of 0.015% to the desired production concentration, which is 99.7% or higher.

During the Manhattan Project, catalytic steam-hydrogen exchange and **water distillation** were used to supply partially concentrated material for final concentration by **electrolysis**, a method long used for heavy water production in Norway. Three water distillation

Fig. 42. Night view of heavy water production facilities at the U.S. Atomic Energy Commission's Savannah River Plant. (*Courtesy of E. I. duPont de Nemours & Co.*)

the generation of power by controlled thermonuclear reactions, assuming that this method of power generation is found to be feasible (see **thermonuclear power**). (3) Deuterium, while not as readily detected as its artificially produced radioactive sister isotope, **tritium**, is used in many tracer experiments as a means of following the behavior of the hydrogen element or hydrogen-bearing compounds in complex chemical or biochemical systems.

Production. The natural abundance of deuterium in the hydrogen element is approximately one part in 6500 (0.015%). Various isotope separation processes have been used or studied for use in concentrating deuterium, no

plants, located at midwestern ordnance sites and operated by E. I. duPont de Nemours & Co., fed material of about 90% concentration to an electrolysis facility (adjoining one of the plants), which produced 1.2 tons per year of heavy water product. An integrated steam-hydrogen exchange/electrolysis plant located at Trail, British Columbia, and operated by Consolidated Mining and Smelting Company, produced 0.5 ton per year of heavy water product. In this case the concentration of the material fed to electrolysis was only about 2%. The midwestern facilities were shut down shortly before the close of World War II and later dismantled. The facilities at Trail continued in operation until 1955 to permit studies of process refinements.

With the postwar expansion of the U.S. Atomic Energy Commission's plutonium production network and the selection of heavy water as the moderator for the Savannah River reactors, it became necessary to provide large-scale heavy water production facilities. For this purpose it was decided to use a **dual-temperature chemical exchange** system as the basic process and water distillation and electrolysis for the intermediate and final concentration stages. Two large government-owned plants were built and operated by duPont, one (known as the Dana Plant) at Newport, Indiana, and the other at Savannah River. By 1957, heavy water requirements were well in hand and the Dana Plant was placed in stand-by status. (It has subsequently been transferred to the Army Chemical Corps for conversion to other use.) All current requirements are met by the Savannah River facility, the full capacity of which is approximately 400 tons of heavy water per year (D_2O concentration, 99.75%).

Cost and Availability. Deuterium gas and deuterium oxide (D_2O) are available from commercial companies in research quantities. Heavy water assaying 99.75 D_2O can be purchased in minimum quantities of 125 pounds or more from AEC's Savannah River Operations Office at a price of $28 per pound, f.o.b. Savannah River Plant.

DEUTERIUM OXIDE

D_2O, commonly referred to as "heavy water." (See **deuterium)**

DEUTERON

The nucleus of **deuterium** ("heavy hydrogen"), consisting of one proton and one neutron.

DIAMAGNETIC PLASMA

In context with research on controlled **fusion,** an ionized gas, or **plasma,** which is bounded by a magnetic field, but contains no magnetic field within it. Theoretical studies have indicated that such a plasma should not suffer loss of energy in the form of **cyclotron radiation,** except in the form of a surface effect at the boundary between the plasma and the magnetic confinement field. (See **cusped geometry)**

DIFFUSION BARRIER

A microporous, thin-walled material used as the separative membrane in the **gaseous diffusion** process for uranium isotope separation.

DIPHENYL

An organic compound (C_6H_5—C_6H_5), also referred to as biphenyl, present in varying degree in the organic mixtures used in **organic cooled reactors.** (See **terphenyl)**

DIRECT CYCLE

A term applied to a power reactor system in which the reactor coolant also serves as the working fluid in the power or propulsion machinery. An example is a direct-cycle **boiling water reactor** in which steam generated in the reactor is fed directly to a steam turbine. (See **indirect cycle)**

DIRECT ENERGY CONVERSION

The generation of electricity from an energy source in a manner that does not involve transference of energy to a working fluid. Direct conversion methods are characterized by an absence of moving parts and, relatedly, by the fact that they usually produce direct, rather than alternating, current. Direct conversion methods applicable to nuclear energy sources (nuclear reactors and radionuclides) are **thermoelectric conversion** and **thermionic conversion. Magnetohydrodynamic conversion,** which is potentially applicable to reactor systems, employs a working fluid but does not involve moving parts and in that sense is sometimes regarded as a direct conversion method. **Fuel cells** are direct conversion devices applicable to chemical energy sources.

DIRECT MAINTENANCE

The use of decontamination and direct contact procedures, rather than remote manipulation, in performing maintenance tasks in facilities where large-scale quantities of radioactive materials are handled, e.g., **fuel reprocessing** plants. Where direct maintenance techniques are to be used, the plant facilities are generally arranged in cells to permit isolation of the equipment in need of repair; the cell surfaces are generally lined with stainless steel or coated with specific materials to facilitate decontamination; and provisions for introducing decontamination solutions are built in. Before maintenance personnel can enter the trouble area, the equipment in the cell must be emptied and thoroughly flushed out and the cell surfaces washed down. From a week to a month may be required to achieve sufficient decontamination to permit major maintenance tasks to be performed.

Direct maintenance is used at the Idaho Chemical Processing Plant and the Oak Ridge Metal Recovery Plant. The larger reprocessing facilities at Hanford and Savannah River are equipped for **remote maintenance** for replacement of equipment in need of repair.

DISINTEGRATION (radioactive)

Synonymous with radioactive **decay.**

DISPERSION-TYPE FUEL ELEMENT

A **fuel element** in which a fissionable material is dispersed in a metal, ceramic or graphite matrix. The matrix material serves as diluent and may also serve a moderating function. Dispersion-type fuel elements are being developed for use in high-temperature power reactors. The dispersion concept has several interesting features: (1) By using as the matrix material the same material that is used for cladding, the problems of achieving good thermal bonding and compatibility between fuel and cladding materials can be minimized. (2) Radiation damage caused by recoil of fission fragments is highly localized. (3) In the case of oxide or other ceramic dispersions in a metal or graphite matrix, the superior thermal conductivity of the matrix material results in better heat transfer than can be achieved with a massive ceramic fuel. (4) Where the matrix material serves a moderating function, the fact that there is an essentially homogeneous distribution of fissionable and moderator particles within the fuel element is advantageous from a reactor physics standpoint.

DISPOSAL OF RADIOACTIVE WASTES. See **radioactive waste disposal.**

DIVERTOR

A component of a **stellarator** system whose principal function is to remove impurities. A divertor consists essentially of a chamber into which the outer lines of magnetic flux can be tangentially diverted by means of an auxiliary magnetic coil. High-energy plasma particles that reach the outermost lines of flux find their way into the divertor wherein their energy is transferred to heat by striking collector plates. The cooled particles, together with impurities dislodged from the collector plates, are pumped out of the apparatus. The divertor thus serves to prevent high-energy plasma particles from striking the walls of the stellarator tube and thereby introducing impurities into the main system. Tests of such devices have proved successful in reducing the undesirable effect of impurities on plasma temperature.

DOLLAR

In reactor theory, a unit of **reactivity.** One dollar is the amount of reactivity due to **delayed neutrons.**

DOMINICAN REPUBLIC

The Comision Nacional de Investigaciones Atomicas, Santo Domingo, is the agency responsible for atomic energy matters. The Dominican Republic is a member of the **International Atomic Energy Agency** and the **Inter-American Nuclear Energy Commission,** and has a research-type **Agreement for Cooperation** with the United States.

DOSE FRACTIONATION

In radiotherapy, the administering of a given quantity of ionizing radiation in small doses at daily or longer intervals.

DOSE, OF IONIZING RADIATION. See **radiation dose.**

DOSE RATE METER

Any instrument which measures ionizing radiation dose rate. (See **dosimeter)**

DOSIMETER

An instrument that measures **radiation dose.** Dosimeters (dose meters) are routinely used as an aid in controlling radiation exposure of workers in laboratories and plants where radioactive materials are handled, and are also used extensively in connection with radiation therapy and radiation experiments.

Fig. 43. Dosimeters. Above, film badge. Below, pocket dosimeter. (*Courtesy of Nucleonics*)

Dosimeters used for the former purpose—called personnel dosimeters—are of two principal types: pocket dosimeters and **film badges.** Pocket dosimeters are miniaturized radiation instruments (commonly electroscope-type **ionization chambers)** which provide an instantaneous dose reading and thus afford an immediate indication of excessive radiation levels. Some are equipped with an alarm mechanism that is triggered when a predetermined cumulative dose level has been reached. Film badges provide an after-the-fact dose measurement and are used primarily to maintain long-term records of radiation exposure. Examples of personnel dosimeters are shown in the above illustration.

DOUBLING DOSE (of ionizing radiation)

A term used by geneticists and defined as the amount of artificially produced ionizing radiation required to cause, during a given period, the same number of mutations as result from natural causes. Artificially produced radiation includes medical x-rays, radioactive fallout from weapons tests, and increases in background radiation levels stemming from civilian atomic energy development activities. (See **biological effects of ionizing radiation)**

DOUBLING TIME

In the long-term (multi-cycle) operation of a **breeder reactor** system, the period of time required to achieve a net doubling of the inventory of fissionable material present in the system, usually expressed in years. Doubling time is mainly a function of the **breeding gain** achieved in the reactor and the **specific power** at which the reactor operates. It also depends on losses incurred in the **fuel cycle;** hence factors which act to determine the number of times a given quantity of fuel must be recycled (e.g., fuel **burn-up),** and recovery efficiencies in fuel reprocessing, conversion, and fabrication must also be considered in arriving at estimates of a practical doubling interval.

Estimates of practical doubling times for fast and thermal breeder systems are in the general range, 10-20 years.

DRAGON PROJECT

The construction and operation of an experimental high-temperature gas-cooled power reactor at the Winfrith Heath site of the United Kingdom Atomic Energy Authority. The project is being conducted under the auspices of the Organization for Economic Cooperation and Development (OECD) through its **European Nuclear Energy Agency.** Participating countries and their contribution toward the estimated capital cost of $38 million are as follows:

United Kingdom	$12 million
Euratom	$12 million
Other OECD members	$14 million

Construction began in 1960.

Information-exchange agreements are in effect between the Dragon Project and the U.S. **Experimental Gas-Cooled Reactor** and **High-Temperature Gas-Cooled Reactor** projects.

DRESDEN NUCLEAR POWER STATION

A large-scale nuclear power plant of the dual-cycle **boiling water** type located at the junction of the Kankakee and Des Plaines Rivers near Morris, Illinois. The plant, built for development and demonstration purposes, is owned and operated by the Commonwealth Edison Company. The Nuclear Power Group, an organization of private utility and engineering interests,* helped finance the project and contributed research and development assistance. The plant was supplied by General Electric Company under a fixed-price turn-key contract with performance warranties. Bechtel Corporation served as architect-engineer-constructor.

Major construction work started at the Dresden site in June, 1957. The reactor first went critical in October, 1959 and first reached full power in June, 1960. Early experience showed the reactor to have extremely favorable operating characteristics and indicated that its potential capacity is appreciably higher than its present rated output. A temporary setback occurred late in 1960, when evidence of severe stress-corrosion in control rod mechanisms required that the reactor be shut down for replacement of control rod drive tubes. The following notes relate to the initial core loading:

Power: 184 megawatts (net electrical). *Fuel:* Slightly enriched uranium (1.5% U^{235}) in the form of uranium dioxide (UO_2). *Fuel element design:* A single fuel element consists of an assembly of thin zircaloy-2 tubes loaded with UO_2 pellets. *Fuel inventory:* $\sim$ 60 tons of uranium dioxide. *Coolant:* Ordinary water at 1020 pounds pressure; inlet temperature 505°F; outlet, 545°F. *Steam conditions:* Primary steam (from steam drum) is at 1015 pounds pressure and 546°F; secondary steam (from steam generator) is at 500 pounds pressure and 469°F. *Thermal conversion efficiency:* 28.7%. *Control materials:* 80 boron-steel control rods; reservoir of boron solution used as an emergency control system. *Containment:* Steel sphere, 190 feet in diameter. *Cost:* The turn-key contract price for the plant was $45 million, of which $30 million was borne and has been capitalized by Commonwealth Edison and $15 million was contributed by the Nuclear Power Group and has been written off as research and development expense. An additional $6 million for overhead and site costs was borne by Commonwealth Edison, bringing the total known cost to $51 million. The actual cost experience has not been published.

DUAL-CYCLE BOILING WATER REACTOR

A type of boiling water reactor in which part of the steam used to run the steam-turbine is generated in the reactor core and part is generated in an external heat exchanger. A dual-cycle system thus represents a combination of the **direct-cycle** and **indirect-cycle** modes of operation. (See **boiling water reactors)**

* American Electric Power Service Corporation, Bechtel Corporation, Central Illinois Light Company, Commonwealth Edison Company, Illinois Power Company, Kansas City Power & Light Company, Pacific Gas & Electric Company, and Union Electric Company.

Fig. 44. Dresden Nuclear Power Station near Chicago, Ill. Above, general plant view. Below, cutaway showing equipment arrangement. This Commonwealth Edison Plant is powered by a 180-megawatt dual-cycle boiling water reactor. (*Courtesy of General Electric Co.*)

DUAL-PURPOSE REACTOR

A production reactor which is also designed and equipped for the efficient utilization of the by-product heat, either in space or process heating or electric power generation. Heat from the plutonium production reactors at the Hanford Works has been used to supply steam for building heating; however that was done largely for demonstration purposes and the reactors were not designed with this service in mind. A new plutonium production reactor currently under construction at Hanford is designed to operate as a true dual-purpose facility; however at this writing funds have not been appropriated for installation of heat utilization equipment.

It should be noted that most power reactors produce some new fissionable materials in the course of generating electric power; however, they are not considered to be dual-purpose reactors since their design is optimized for power production and the fissionable material they produce as a by-product is usually inferior to that produced in production reactors due to the long irradiation exposure of the fuel and consequent build-up of undesirable heavy isotopes. The United Kingdom's Calder Hall reactors are an exception, since they are true dual-purpose units. (See **United Kingdom**)

DUAL-TEMPERATURE CHEMICAL EXCHANGE

A method of isotope separation based on the use of temperature differentials in conjunction with classical chemical exchange between gaseous and liquid media. Several dual-temperature chemical exchange systems have been studied for application to **deuterium** concentration (i.e., heavy water production), including steam-hydrogen, ammonia-hydrogen and hydrogen sulfide-water. Of these, the H_2S—H_2O system has the advantage that it does not require the use of a catalyst and can therefore be operated in conventional gas-liquid contacting equipment.

A multistage process based on the H_2S—H_2O system is currently used for the primary concentration of deuterium in the heavy water production facilities at Savannah River. This process, certain patent rights to which have been assigned to J. Spevack, can be described as follows (see Fig. 45): (1) Water containing the natural complement of deuterium (one part in 6500 of the hydrogen element) is contacted with a countercurrent flow of hydrogen sulfide vapor in a low-temperature (80°F) tower. As the two streams mix in passing, the water phase becomes richer in deuterium and the vapor phase correspondingly poorer in that isotope. (2) Part of the enriched water stream is piped to the next stage in the system

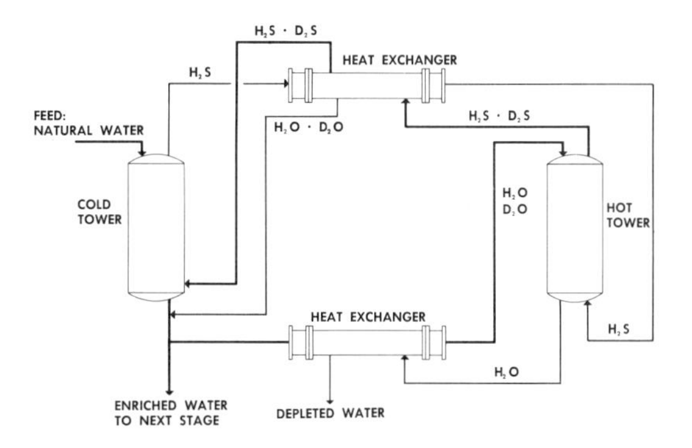

Fig. 45. Production of heavy water by the dual-temperature chemical exchange process.

where step (1) is repeated, and thence to the next stage, etc. (3) The other part of the enriched water stream flows into a high-temperature tower (212°F) wherein it is contacted with the depleted hydrogen sulfide vapor. Here the reverse action occurs, the hydrogen sulfide gaining deuterium and the water losing it. (4) The restored hydrogen sulfide is returned to the low-temperature tower to repeat the cycle. The depleted water from the feed stage is discharged from the plant. The process is thus characterized by a net up-flow of water that becomes progressively richer in deuterium as it reaches successive stages, each of which is served by a closed-cycle hydrogen sulfide loop.

For further information on U.S. heavy water production, see **deuterium.**

DYNAMITRON

Trade name for a type of electron accelerator manufactured by Radiation Dynamics, Inc. for use in research and for industrial radiation applications. The dynamitron converts low-voltage alternating current to high-voltage direct current by means of a cascade of series-connected rectifiers driven in parallel by a radio-frequency oscillator. It delivers a substantial beam current at energies up to 6 Mev.

DYSPROSIUM

Element No. 66 (symbol, Dy; atomic weight, 162.46), a **rare earth** with a high thermal neutron absorption cross section ($\sim$ 1000 barns), of interest for use as a neutron-absorbing material in reactor control rods.

E

E. O. LAWRENCE RADIATION LABORATORY

A major U.S. Atomic Energy Commission research center with branches at Berkeley and Livermore, California. *Operating contractor:* University of California. *Director:* Edwin M. McMillan. *AEC investment in plant and equipment* (Berkeley branch only—see separate entry on Livermore branch): ~ $63 million.* *Staff* (Berkeley): ~ 700 scientists and engineers, and ~ 1500 supporting personnel.

The laboratory is named in honor of its founder, the late Ernest Orlando Lawrence, recipient of the 1939 Nobel Prize in physics for his invention of the cyclotron and other pioneering work in the particle accelerator field. Lawrence established the laboratory in 1936, with the support of the University of California and private sources. The Radiation Laboratory (or "Rad Lab"), as it was then known, played a major role in the **Manhattan Project,** including development of the **electromagnetic separation** process for uranium isotope separation, and the discovery of and early chemical research on plutonium. Since the war, the laboratory has been operated as an AEC research center and was given its present name following Lawrence's death in 1958.

Fig. 46. Nuclear Chemistry Building at the E. O. Lawrence Radiation Laboratory overlooking San Francisco Bay. (*Courtesy of E. O. Lawrence Radiation Laboratory*)

Major areas of activity are noted in the paragraphs following:

High Energy Physics. The laboratory is most closely identified with the development and use of particle accelerators. Major accelerators developed and in use at Berkeley include a 60-inch cyclotron, a 184-inch synchrocyclotron, a 6.2-Bev **proton synchrotron** known as the Bevatron, and a heavy-ion **linear accelerator** ("Hilac"). A novel 88-inch spiral ridge cyclotron is under development. The laboratory has also made contributions in the design of

* Includes facilities authorized or under construction as of June 30, 1960. Not adjusted for depreciation.

related experimental apparatus as reflected in its 72-inch **bubble chamber.**

Among the results of accelerator research at Berkeley are the discovery and/or first artificial production of several "strange particles," including the pi-meson and the antiproton.

Chemistry. Extensive research has been conducted on new nuclear species produced by particle bombardment in the cyclotron and heavy-ion accelerator. New chemical elements first isolated and identified at Berkeley include elements 93 (neptunium), 94 (plutonium), 95 (americium), 96 (curium), 97 (berkelium), 98 (californium), 101 (mendelevium) and 103 (suggested name, lawrencium). Also, scientists from Berkeley participated in the discovery of all other transuranium elements discovered in the past two decades, namely, elements 99 (einsteinium), 100 (fermium) and 102 (tentative name, nobelium).

Biology and Medicine. An important area of research in biochemistry has been study of the process of photosynthesis. Important areas of biomedical research, in which there is close cooperation between the laboratory and the University of California's Donner and Crocker Laboratories and Donner Pavilion Metabolic Ward, include study of the mechanism of cancer induction and control, the hormonal control of diabetes, and certain biological effects of radiation.

In addition, the laboratory works closely with the Livermore branch (see below) in controlled fusion research and other fields of atomic development.

E. O. LAWRENCE RADIATION LABORATORY, LIVERMORE BRANCH

A branch of the E. O. Lawrence Radiation Laboratory (see above entry). *Director:* John S. Foster, Jr. *AEC investment in plant and equipment:* ~ $84 million.* *Staff:* ~ 930 scientists and engineers, and ~ 2700 supporting personnel.

Fig. 47. The Livermore branch of the E. O. Lawrence Radiation Laboratory. (*Courtesy of Lee B. Davenport, Jr., Oakland, Calif.*)

The Livermore branch was established in 1950 in connection with the development of a classified particle accelerator project (MTA Project) then being conducted jointly by the E. O. Lawrence Radiation Laboratory and California Research and Development Corporation and later terminated. In 1952 Livermore was given the assignment of developing new and improved types of nuclear weapons, which shortly became and continues to be its major function. In recent years it has become engaged in several other areas of research and development. Following are notes on these activities:

1. Ramjet propulsion: Livermore is conducting research and development on high-

* Includes facilities authorized or under construction as of June 30, 1960. Not adjusted for depreciation. Excludes facilities operated by Livermore at the Nevada Test Site.

temperature, air-cooled reactor systems for this application (see **Pluto Project).**

2. Controlled fusion: Livermore is one of the principal centers of U.S. research looking to the ultimate development of thermonuclear power. Its activities include work on **magnetic mirror** and **pinch** systems, the **Astron Program,** and related theoretical and diagnostic studies.

3. Peaceful uses of nuclear explosives: Livermore is one of the two major centers of U.S. research in this area, the other being Los Alamos Scientific Laboratory. (See **Plowshare Program)**

Specialized research and experimental facilities at Livermore include the **Livermore Pool-Type Reactor,** a Van de Graaff generator, a high-speed computer of advanced design (the LARC), facilities for studying the phenomenology of explosions, and various controlled-fusion research apparatus.

EARLY FALLOUT. See **radioactive fallout.**

ECONOMICS OF NUCLEAR POWER. See **nuclear power economics.**

ECUADOR

The Comision Nacional de Energia Atomica, Quito, is the agency responsible for atomic energy matters. Interest at present centers in radioisotope applications. A radioisotope laboratory for biomedical research has been established at the Escuela Politecnica Nacional in Quito with the aid of a foreign equipment grant from the United States. Ecuador is a member of the **International Atomic Energy Agency** and the **Inter-American Nuclear Energy Commission,** and has a research-type **Agreement for Cooperation** with the United States.

EDUCATION AND TRAINING PROGRAMS, AEC

Faculty Training. Since 1956 the AEC has sponsored summer faculty training courses in radiation biology. Through 1960 more than 100 high school teachers and approximately 150 college teachers had taken this training. Over the same period the AEC, jointly with the American Society for Engineering Education, has sponsored a series of summer institutes treating recent developments in nuclear science and technology. Through 1960 nearly 600 faculty members representing more than 150 separate educational institutions had participated in this program. In 1960, the AEC, jointly with the National Science Foundation, sponsored three institutes dealing with radioisotope techniques and applications. These were attended by nearly 100 faculty members from 75 separate educational institutions.

Fellowships. The AEC awards fellowships to U.S. students for graduation training in subjects relating to atomic energy development. This program is administered under contract by the **Oak Ridge Institute of Nuclear Studies** (ORINS). Fellowships awarded through 1960 are summarized in Table 1. The AEC additionally sponsors fellowships for foreign students (see below).

TABLE 1. AEC FELLOWSHIP PROGRAM FOR U.S. STUDENTS

Field of Graduate Study	*Year Program was Initiated*	*No. of Fellowships Awarded through 1960*
Life Sciences		
Industrial medicine	1950	60
Industrial hygiene	1950	54
Health physics	1950	>500
Advanced health physics	1959	10
Physical Sciences		
Nuclear science and technology	1957	523

Grants and Loans. The AEC makes grants to educational institutions for the purchase of specialized equipment, such as subcritical assemblies and radiation detection instruments, useful in general atomic energy courses in the life and physical sciences and in instruction in radioisotope technique. It also makes available on loan, for the same purpose, various atomic energy materials, such as radionuclide sources and enriched uranium samples.

Specialized Training Courses. The AEC sponsors a number of specialized training courses for graduate and undergraduate scientists and engineers from the United States and abroad (see listing under Foreign Students below). The AEC recently initiated a series of courses to provide training in health physics and related orientation in AEC licensing regulations to State employees preparing to assume regulatory responsibility (see **state activities in the atomic energy field**). Additionally, various major AEC contractors have arrangements whereby their employees can receive graduate, undergraduate or vocational training in atomic energy subjects.

Vocational Training Courses. Courses designed to provide industrial technicians with basic training in radiation safety, radioisotope technique, and nuclear power plant operation and maintenance have been developed under AEC contract by Stanford Research Institute and are being offered in various vocational schools.

Foreign Students. As part of its effort to encourage international cooperation in atomic energy development, the AEC sponsors fellowships and provides specialized training opportunities for foreign students.

The fellowships are for study in the United States and are handled through the **International Atomic Energy Agency** (IAEA), i.e., the AEC sponsors them but the selection of applicants and other administrative details are handled by IAEA. For the past several years the AEC has annually provided for approximately 120 one-year IAEA followship awards.

The following specialized training courses sponsored by the AEC are open to foreign as well as U.S. students, and in some instances were primarily established for the former:

1. **Oak Ridge Institute of Nuclear Studies:** Two-week courses in basic radioisotope technique; radioisotope techniques in industry; and radioisotope techniques in research.

2. **International Institute of Nuclear Science and Technology** (Argonne National Laboratory): One-year curricula in reactor science and technology; engineering research and development training; physical sciences research; life sciences research; and engineering, administration and operation of nuclear facilities. From 1955 through 1959, Argonne provided basic training at what was then known as the International School of Nuclear Science and Engineering. In 1960 the curriculum was upgraded for more advanced instruction, and the present institute was established.

3. **Oak Ridge National Laboratory:** A one-year course in reactor operation supervision and a one-year course in reactor hazards evaluation.

4. **Puerto Rico Nuclear Center:** A four-week course in basic radioisotope technique, a 4-week course in radiation safety techniques, 1-year curricula in nuclear science and engineering, applications of nuclear science to agriculture and biology, nuclear medicine, and radiological physics. All course instruction is in Spanish and English.

5. AEC **Health and Safety Laboratory:** A six-week course in radiochemical analysis technique with particular reference to the monitoring of radioactive fallout.

6. **Shippingport Atomic Power Station:** Four-month courses affording training in various aspects of nuclear power plant operation and maintenance.

Through 1960 more than 1000 students from some 60 foreign countries had attended one or another of these training programs.

The AEC additionally makes arrangements for foreign students to receive on-the-job training at national laboratories and other centers of nuclear activity. These arrangements are handled on an individual basis. Some 700 assignments were made in 1960 alone.

EDUCATOR REACTORS

Trade name of a line of small nuclear reactors of the graphite/water type manufactured by AMF Atomics, a division of American Machine and Foundry, for student training programs. (See **research and training reactors**)

EFFECTIVE HALF-LIFE

The time required for the activity of a radioactive substance absorbed in a biological system to lose half its intensity. The effective half-life is a function not only of the rate of radioactive decay of the substance but also of the rate at which the substance is eliminated from the system. It is defined by the expression,

$$\text{Effective half-life} = \frac{T_{biol} \times T_{rad}}{T_{biol} + T_{rad}}$$

where T_{biol} is the **biological half-life,** and T_{rad} is radioactive **half-life.**

EINSTEINIUM

Element No. 99 (symbol, Es), formed by the interaction of nitrogen nuclei with uranium-238 and by other processes usually involving multiple neutron capture. The discovery of einsteinium (and **fermium)** was announced in 1954, following radiochemical analysis of coral debris from a thermonuclear weapon test conducted in 1952 at the Eniwetok Proving Grounds in the Marshall Islands, and represented a collaborative effort of scientists from Argonne National Laboratory, E. O. Lawrence Radiation Laboratory, and Los Alamos Scientific Laboratory. The element was formed as a result of the successive instantaneous capture of many neutrons by uranium-238. The product heavy uranium isotopes decayed into isotopes of einsteinium and fermium by the emission of negative beta particles. Einsteinium is one of the eleven **transuranium elements** discovered in the past two decades.

ELASTIC SCATTERING

A type of nuclear reaction in which an incident particle is deflected by a nucleus with no energy change except the exchange of kinetic energy between them. (See **scattering**)

ELECTRIC UTILITY STATISTICS, U.S. See **nuclear power economics.**

ELECTROLYSIS (for deuterium concentration)

The application of electrolysis to **deuterium** concentration (i.e., heavy water production) stems from the fact that ordinary water molecules (H_2O) dissociate somewhat more rapidly than do heavy water molecules (D_2O). Thus, if water is charged to an electrolytic cell, the deuterium complement of the hydrogen that is produced at the anode will be significantly lower than that of the hydrogen remaining in the water. By passing water through a number of electrolytic cells connected in series, progressive enrichment of its deuterium content can thus be attained. The electrolytic production of heavy water from natural water feedstock tends to be uneconomic, on other than a by-product basis, due to excessive electric power consumption and high equipment costs. The process lends itself better to the final stages of heavy water concentration where the volume of water handled is small.

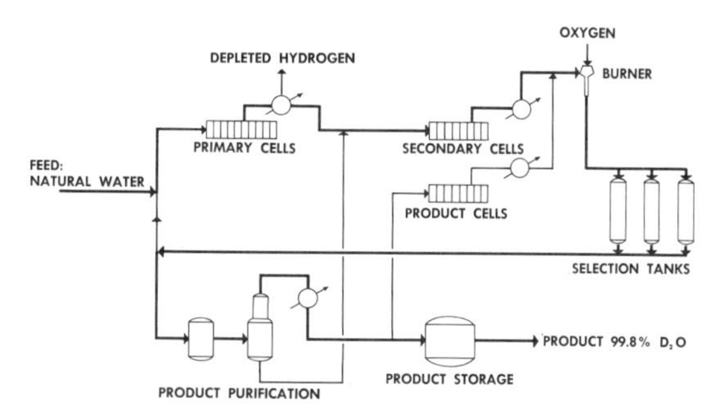

Fig. 48. Production of heavy water by electrolysis.

Prior to the Manhattan Project the only heavy water available in any quantity was produced electrolytically by the Norsk Hydro Company at Rjukan, Norway, in conjunction with the production of electrolytic hydrogen for ammonia synthesis. During the period of enemy occupation of Norway in World War II, this plant was raided by an allied commando team to cut off the supply of heavy water to the Axis Powers.

During the Manhattan Project, electrolysis was used by the United States for the latter stages of deuterium separation and the process has been similarly used in postwar U.S. heavy water production operations. (See **deuterium**)

ELECTROMAGNETIC RADIATION

Electromagnetic and corpuscular radiation are general terms used to distinguish radiation consisting of energy waves of zero rest mass (electromagnetic) from that consisting of particles of finite rest mass (corpuscular). Electromagnetic radiation is classified according to wave length approximately as follows:

Type	*Wave Length*
Gamma rays	~0.01 to 0.5 angstrom [1]
X-rays	~0.01 to 500 angstroms
Ultraviolet	200 to 400 angstroms
Visible light	4000 to 7700 angstroms
Infrared	7700 angstroms to 1 millimeter
Microwaves [2]	0.22 millimeter to several meters
Radio waves	several millimeters to 30 kilometers

[1] Angstrom = one hundred-millionth of a centimeter.
[2] Also called Hertzian waves.

See **radiation** for additional information.

ELECTROMAGNETIC SEPARATION

A method of isotope separation based on the principle of the **mass spectrograph.** In electromagnetic separation an ionized gas, pro-

Fig. 49. Collection chamber being moved into position into one of the original Y-12 calutrons, now used for stable isotope separation. (*Courtesy of Oak Ridge National Laboratory*)

duced by electron bombardment or thermionic emission, is accelerated by an electrical system and the resulting beam is projected into a magnetic field. On entering the magnetic field the ions are deflected into a curved path, the degree of deflection (angle of curvature) being a function of their mass. Separation is accomplished by means of collection slots placed in the ion path. The entire process takes place under high vacuum conditions and operates in cyclic (noncontinuous) fashion. Thus, while the method permits substantial separation of an isotope mixture in a single operation, the quantity of material that can be processed in a single machine is inherently small.

Electromagnetic separation was one of these major processes used by the United States during the **Manhattan Project** for the production of uranium-235.* The equipment units, known as **calutrons,** were developed at the Radiation Laboratory of the University of California (now the E. O. Lawrence Radiation Laboratory). A large plant, known by the code designation Y-12, was built at Oak Ridge, Tennessee, and operated by Tennessee Eastman Corporation. The plant operated successfully but was shut down shortly after the war, gaseous diffusion having been found to be the more economic method. Much of the Y-12 equipment has since been dismantled and the buildings put to other use; however some calutron units were retained to supply small quantities of various stable isotopes for research purposes and are still in service for this purpose.

ELECTRON

An elementary particle carrying one unit of negative electric charge (defined as 4.8025×10^{-10} electrostatic unit) and having a mass at rest equal to 1/1838th that of the hydrogen atom. Electrons in motion through a conductor constitute electricity, a flow of 6.24 billion electrons per second being equal to one ampere of current. Also, electrons determine the chemical behavior of the elements.

In the latter connection, a neutral atom may be described as consisting of a positively charged nucleus and a balancing number of orbital (extranuclear) electrons, i.e., one electron for every positively charged **proton** contained in the nucleus. The number is different for each chemical element (see **atomic number**).

When one or more of the orbital electrons are displaced, the atom takes on a positive charge, i.e., it becomes a positive ion. Conversely, when an atom gains one or more orbital electrons it takes on a negative charge and becomes a negative ion. The process of ion formation can be induced in various ways (see **ionization**).

High-energy electrons are emitted from the nuclei of some unstable (i.e., radioactive) atoms—a process attributed to the decay of a **neutron** into a proton, an electron and a neutrino. Such electrons are called **beta particles.**

An elementary particle exists which has the same mass as an electron but carries an opposite electric charge; it is the **positron.**

ELECTRON CAPTURE

A process of nuclear decay in which an atomic nucleus captures one of its external electrons. Usually an electron in the "K" shell of the atom will be captured by the nucleus; hence, this process is sometimes referred to as "K capture."

Because capture of the K electron by the nucleus will leave the product atom with one electron missing from the K shell, an electron from a higher energy level shell will move into the K shell and simultaneously emit a gamma ray of discrete energy.

ELECTRON SYNCHROTRON

A type of **particle accelerator** used to accelerate electrons to very high energies (up to several Bev). The main feature of synchrotrons is that particles are energized by accelerating them around a circular path of essentially constant radius.

Synchrotrons employ the same basic ac-

* The others were **gaseous diffusion** and **thermal diffusion process.**

celeration concept used in cyclotrons to accelerate positively charged particles; however they differ from the cyclotron principle in that provision is made for compensating for the relativistic increase in particle mass at high particle energies. (See discussion under **cyclotron**) This is done by increasing the magnetic field during a portion of the acceleration cycle, thereby synchronizing particle travel with the frequency of a constant-frequency electrical driving force. In physical terms, the increase in magnetic field strength is accomplished by a phased rate of discharge of current from condensers into the winding of the electromagnet.

In the operation of most electron synchrotrons, the electrons are preaccelerated by transformer action (see **betatron**) prior to acceleration by the radio-frequency system. After acceleration and upon reaching maximum energy they are made to spiral inward to strike a metal target, thereby producing high-energy x-rays for use in research.

The largest electron synchrotrons in the United States, all owned by the U.S. Atomic Energy Commission, are:

1. A 1.5-Bev unit, costing about $1.3 million, at California Institute of Technology.
2. A 1.2-Bev unit, costing about $1.3 million, at Cornell University.
3. A 6.0-Bev unit at Cambridge, Massachusetts, as a joint project of Harvard University and Massachusetts Institute of Technology. This machine, known as the Cambridge Electron Accelerator (CEA), cost approximately $11.5 million.

Other U.S. electron synchrotrons operate at lower energies (up to several hundred Mev).

ELECTRON VOLT (ev)

The amount of energy gained by a particle of unit electric charge when accelerated by an electrostatic potential of 1 volt; equal to 1.6020×10^{-12} erg. Electron-volt units are the basic measure used in nuclear physics to express the energy, and indirectly the velocity, of accelerated particles. For convenience, values are commonly expressed in terms of Kev (1,000 ev), Mev (1,000,000 ev) or Bev (1,000,000,000 ev). An alternative expression for the last is **Gev.**

ELECTROPHORESIS

A process in which an electric potential is used to cause movement of colloidal particles toward the anode (anaphoresis) or the cathode (cataphoresis). Electrophoresis has been studied as a means of applying a protective coating to reactor fuel elements, especially those in which the fuel is in pellet form. Also, electrophoresis has found application in biological research.

ELECTROREFINING

One of several **pyrometallurgical** techniques of interest for possible use in **fuel reprocessing.** Electrorefining involves high-temperature electrolysis in fused salt media. After mechanical decladding, "spent" uranium fuel is charged to a graphite basket immersed in a fused halide salt electrolyte maintained at a temperature of about 1000°C. The uranium serves as the anode. The cathode is generally manganese, a metal that forms a low-melting alloy with uranium. During electrolysis the uranium passes through the electrolyte and deposits on the cathode, forming a molten magnesium-uranium alloy. This is withdrawn and the magnesium removed by vacuum distillation. Noble metal fission products (including zirconium, niobium and ruthenium) remain as a sludge at the anode. Rare gases are vented from the anode. Active metal fission products accumulate in the electrolyte. By adjustment of the process conditions, plutonium can be made to remain in the electrolyte for later recovery by volatilization.

In common with all pyrometallurgical reprocessing techniques presently under development, electrorefining does not achieve complete enough fission-product removal to permit direct-contact handling of the recovered uranium, and hence is limited to "closed-cycle" reactor fuel systems. The **decontamination**

factors that have been achieved in laboratory tests are of the order of 300 to 500. Uranium recovery in these tests has been as high as 98%.

Research on electrorefining originated at Knolls Atomic Power Laboratory. Atomics International Division of North American Aviation Company has investigated the applicability of the technique to irradiated thorium, and Los Alamos Scientific Laboratory has conducted similar investigations of plutonium-alloy fuels.

ELECTROSCOPE. See **ionization chamber.**

ELEMENTARY PARTICLES

In nuclear physics, a general term used to include the various kinds of particles of which all matter and radiation are composed. Originally applied to the electron and proton, the term has been extended to include the neutron, neutrino, the **antiparticles** (e.g., the positron, antiproton, and antineutron) and the so-called **strange particles** (e.g., mu-mesons, K-mesons and hyperons). The term "fundamental particles" is often used synonymously with elementary particles.

The basic problem of nuclear physics is the identification and classification of the elementary particles and elucidation of their role in the behavior of matter. An elementary particle was thought to have a unique set of intrinsic properties and an independent and permanent existence; but it is now known that some of the particles can decay into one or more other particles, and that particles can undergo **pair production** or pair annihilation.

ELK RIVER PLANT

A small government-owned nuclear power plant of the indirect-cycle **boiling water** type (with separate coal-fired superheater) at Elk River, Minnesota. The project is being carried out under the "second round" of the U.S. Atomic Energy Commission's Power Demonstration Reactor Program. The AEC is financing the cost of reactor construction and related research and development. The Rural Cooperative Power Association is providing the site and financing the electrical portion of the plant; it will operate the plant and distribute the power produced, making payment to the AEC for the steam used. Allis-Chalmers Manufacturing Company is the prime contractor for the reactor,* with Sargent and Lundy, Inc. serving as architect-engineer and Maxon Construction Company as builder. The

Fig. 50. The Elk River plant. (*Courtesy of Allis-Chalmers Manufacturing Co.*)

* The contract was originally awarded to the Nuclear Products—ERCO Division of ACF Industries, which division was later acquired by Allis-Chalmers Manufacturing Company.

following notes reflect the status of the project as of mid-1962:

Power: 22 megawatts (net electrical) of which 7 megawatts derive from the energy supplied by the coal-fired superheater. Provision has been made for possible future operation at more than 50% higher power output. *Fuel:* Fully enriched uranium and thorium in the form of a mixture of uranium dioxide (UO_2) and thorium dioxide (THO_2) pellets. *Fuel element design:* A single fuel element consists of an assembly of thin stainless steel tubes loaded with fuel pellets. *Fuel inventory:* 195 kilograms of fully enriched uranium and 4200 kilograms of thorium. *Steam conditions:* Steam leaves the reactor at 922 pounds pressure and 536°F, and leaves the superheater at 612 pounds pressure and 825°F. *Thermal conversion efficiency:* 30.2%. *Control materials:* Boron-steel control rods; burnable poison incorporated in fuel elements. *Construction costs:* Estimated at $10.9 million, exclusive of research and development. For other project costs, see Table 3 under **nuclear power development.** *Dates:* Construction started in August, 1958 and was substantially complete by the fall of 1961. Repairs, necessitated by defects in some of the fuel elements and cracks in the pressure vessel cladding, forced postponement of the scheduled start-up date to late 1962.

EL SALVADOR

The Comision de Energia Atomica de El Salvador, San Salvador, is the agency responsible for atomic energy matters. Interest at present centers in medical and agricultural applications of radioisotopes, and related training programs. El Salvador is a member of the **International Atomic Energy Agency** and the **Inter-American Nuclear Energy Commission.**

EMPIRE STATE ATOMIC DEVELOPMENT ASSOCIATES (ESADA)

A nonprofit membership corporation formed by the seven principal investor-owned electric utilities * in New York State for the joint

* The sponsoring companies are: Niagara Mohawk Power Corporation, Long Island Lighting Company, New York State Electric & Gas Corporation, Consolidated Edison Company of New York, Inc., Rochester Gas and Electric Corporation, Orange and Rockland Utilities, Inc., Central Hudson Gas & Electric Corporation.

Fig. 51. ESADA nuclear superheat project. At left, the existing Vallecitos Boiling Water Reactor (VBWR) at General Electric Company's Laboratory in Pleasanton, California. At right, artist's sketch of the new ESADA Vallecitos Experimental Superheat Reactor (EVSR), which will operate in conjunction with VBWR. (*Courtesy of General Electric Co.*)

sponsorship of research and development on nuclear power systems. ESADA has entered into cooperative arrangements with reactor manufacturers for the following three development programs:

1. Design and testing of components, including fuel elements, suitable for use in a large-scale high-temperature gas-cooled reactor (see **gas-cooled reactors)**. The cost of this program, to be conducted by General Atomic Division of General Dynamics Corporation, is estimated at $8.7 million, of which $4.5 million will be borne by ESADA.

2. Construction and operation of a test reactor facility * to study the performance of fuel elements suitable for use in a large-scale nuclear superheat reactor (see **boiling water reactors)**. The estimated construction cost of the test reactor, which will be rated at 15 megawatts (thermal), is $8 million. This program is to be conducted by the General Electric Company. ESADA will bear $5.75 million of the total cost.

3. Development work on an improved fuel (uranium carbide) for a high-performance **sodium-graphite reactor.** ESADA has awarded a $1.44 million contract for this work to Atomics International, a division of North American Aviation, Inc.

The programs are scheduled to be completed in 1963 and are expected to provide the sponsoring utilities with a basis for reaching a decision on the construction of a 300-500 megawatt (electrical) nuclear power station, tentatively planned for installation at an upper New York State location on a 1968 completion timetable.

ENERGY STATISTICS, U.S.

General Energy Pattern. Table 1 shows the approximate pattern of energy consumption in the United States:

TABLE 1. PATTERN OF U.S. ENERGY CONSUMPTION

Source Breakdown [1]		*Use Breakdown* [2]	
Coal	28.0%	Electric power generation	18%
Petroleum	37.0%	Heat for manufacturing operations	25%
Natural gas	30.8%	Propulsion and locomotion	22%
Water power	4.2%	Residential and commercial heating	30%
		Other, including losses	5%
	100%		100%

[1] Source: Bureau of Mines data in 1959 "Minerals Yearbook."
[2] Source: Based on data in National Planning Association report, "Nuclear Energy and the U.S. Fuel Economy," July, 1958.

As is seen, nearly 96% of the total energy consumed currently comes from three fossil fuels —coal, petroleum and natural gas.

Fossil Fuels. The total amount of fossil fuels consumed in the United States through 1958 has been estimated at 1.39 Q units.** Future fossil fuel consumption is projected in Table 2, assuming, for estimating purposes, no use of nuclear or other nonconventional energy sources:

TABLE 2. PROJECTION OF U.S. FOSSIL FUEL CONSUMPTION [1]

	Projected Consumption, Q units	
Period	*During Period*	*Cumulative from January 1, 1959*
1959–1980	1.34	1.34
1981–2000	2.47	3.81
2001–2020	4.66	8.47
2021–2040	8.45	16.92
2040–2057	11.65	28.57

[1] Source: AEC report, "Fossil Fuels in the Future," October, 1960 (TID-8209). The projections beyond 2000 are based on an assumption of 3% annual growth. All projections assume no use of nuclear or other nonconventional energy sources.

Thus, if conventional energy sources were to continue to carry the total load of U.S. energy requirements, as much fossil fuel would be consumed in the 20-year period, 1959-1980, as was consumed in the prior span of U.S. history.

* Located at General Electric's Vallecitos Laboratory, near Pleasanton, California, and operated in conjunction with the existing **Vallecitos Boiling Water Reactor** (VBWR).

** A Q unit = one quintillion (1×10^{18}) British thermal units (Btu) of heat.

Total U.S. reserves (proven and inferred) of fossil fuels, as of January 1, 1959, are estimated to be equivalent to 28.57 Q units (see Table 3), and hence are just sufficient to meet projected U.S. requirements through the year 2057 (see above)—again assuming no use of nonconventional energy sources and also assuming no export-import imbalance. Two points should be made in this connection. The first is that, as is shown in Table 3, only 5.57 Q (or approximately 20% of the estimated reserves) are in the "low cost" category, i.e., available at production costs no higher than 25% above 1958 cost levels. The balance reserves are contingent on appreciable increases in production costs. All other things equal, the impact of such increases in production costs would not be felt until the beginning of the twenty-first century, since there are sufficient low-cost reserves to cover projected fossil fuel requirements until that time (see Fig. 52). In actual practice—and this is the second point that should be made—the impact can be expected to be felt earlier in some areas of energy usage due to the fact that reserves of petroleum and natural gas are currently being depleted at a disproportionate rate. This point

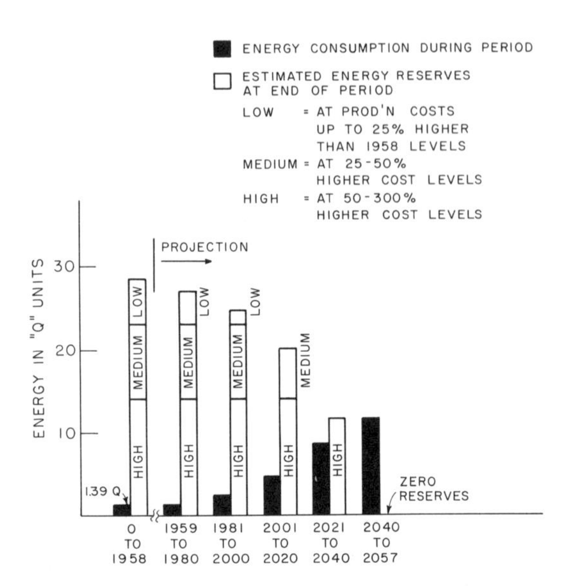

Fig. 52. Projected U.S. fossil fuel depletion (assuming no use of nuclear or other non-conventional energy sources).

TABLE 3. ESTIMATED U.S. RESERVES OF FOSSIL FUELS [1]
(January 1, 1959)

Fuel	*Reserves* [2]							
	Low Cost		*Medium Cost*		*High Cost*		*Total*	
Coal and lignite								
billions of short tons	235		285		426		946	
energy equivalence (Q) [3]		5.06		6.14		9.18		20.38
Petroleum from crude oil [4]								
billions of barrels	64		57		46		167	
energy of equivalence (Q)		0.34		0.32		0.26		0.92
Natural gas								
trillions of cubic feet	160		220		472		852	
energy equivalence (Q)		0.17		0.23		0.49		0.89
Petroleum from								
oil shale and tar sands	—		400		700		1100	
billions of barrels		—		2.32		4.06		6.38
Totals, Q		5.57		9.01		13.99		28.57
% of Total		19.5		31.5		49.0		100%

[1] Estimates taken from AEC report, "Fossil Fuels in the Future," October 1960 (TID-8209). They include known deposits and deposits inferred from geological data, but yet to be discovered.
[2] Low cost = recoverable at real costs up to 25% higher than 1958 levels. Medium cost = recoverable at real costs 25% to 50% higher than 1958 levels. High cost = recoverable at real costs 50% to 300% higher than 1958 levels.
[3] 1 Q = 1 quintillion (1×10^{18}) Btu. Conversion factors used as follows: 1 short ton of coal = 26.2×10^6 Btu. 1 barrel of liquid hydrocarbons, oil shale or tar sand = 5.8×10^6 Btu. 1 cubic foot of natural gas = 1.1×10^3 Btu..
[4] Includes liquid hydrocarbons from natural gas fields.

is clearly shown by comparison made in Table 4.

Table 4. Comparison of U.S. Fossil Fuel Reserves and Consumption

Fuel	Contribution to Reserves[1]		Contribution to Consumption[2] (%)
	Total Reserves (%)	Low cost reserves (%)	
Coal	71.4	91	29
Petroleum (from crude oil)	3.2	6	39
Natural gas	3.1	3	32
Petroleum (from oil shales and tar sands)	22.3	—	—
	100%	100%	100%

[1] From Table 3.
[2] From Table 1, discounting water power.

On a national basis, the generation of electric power in coal-fired power stations will thus be one of the last areas of energy usage to feel the impact of energy cost increases arising from depletion effects.*

Nuclear Fuels. Table 5 summarizes information on U.S. reserves of uranium and thorium. (For more details see **uranium deposits and reserves, thorium deposits and reserves.**) In order to relate these tonnage estimates to energy potential, it is necessary to make certain assumptions bearing on the efficiency of fuel utilization in nuclear power generation. The principal factors involved are:

1. The amount of new fissionable material formed in reactor operation. This can be expressed in terms of the "regeneration ratio," which is defined as the number of fissionable atoms produced per fission event.
2. Whether or not the bred fissionable material (plutonium or uranium-233) is recycled.
3. The **burn-up** achieved during reactor operation, which is usually expressed as the number of megawatt-days of heat produced per metric ton of fuel. (The higher the burn-up, the fewer times fuel must be recycled and hence the smaller the recycling losses.)
4. Losses during processing and fabrication operations.

* Transportation and labor cost factors are another matter.

Table 5. Estimated U.S. Resources of Uranium and Thorium[1, 2]

	Reasonably Assured *	Possible Additional	Total
Uranium (short tons U_3O_8):			
Low cost[3]	240,000	400,000	640,000
Medium cost[4]	400,000	200,000	600,000
High cost[5]	5,000,000	100,000	5,100,000
Total	5,640,000	700,000	6,340,000
Thorium (short tons ThO_2):			
Recoverable at $5/lb ThO_2	100,000 **	400,000	500,000

* Measured, indicated and inferred.
** Largely inferred.
[1] The uranium estimates deposits are based on an AEC report, "Energy from Uranium and Coal Reserves," May, 1960 (TID-8207). The figure of 5,000,000 tons for high cost deposits is included as an indication of the amount of uranium that might prove recoverable with future technology from low-grade sources, principally Chattanooga shales. However, the recovery of uranium from such sources is likely to cost more than $30 per pound U_3O_8, perhaps $50 per pound U_3O_8.
[2] The thorium estimates are from the AEC Division of Raw Materials.
[3] Recoverable at $8–10 per pound U_3O_8.
[4] Recoverable at $16–20 per pound U_3O_8.
[5] Recoverable at $24–30 per pound U_3O_8.

The following energy conversion factors serve to establish broad limits for estimating purposes:

Energy Conversion Factor (Q units per million short tons of initial uranium)	Assumptions
44	Regeneration ratio of 1.4, which is believed achievable in a highly efficient **breeder reactor.** Recycling of bred fissionable material. Burn-up of 15,000 MWD/ton. Losses of 1% of fuel inventory per cycle of operation.
0.64	Regeneration ratio of 0.8 which is representative of current performance in nonbreeder civilian power reactors. Other assumptions as above.

The first energy conversion factor sets an approximate upper limit for the amount of energy recoverable from uranium reserves; hence it should only be used for long-range estimating purposes. The second energy conversion factor sets an approximate lower limit for short-term estimating purposes. Applying the long-range factor to the tonnage estimates in Table 6 yields the following approximation of the maximum energy potential of U.S. nuclear fuel deposits recoverable at a cost of about $50 per pound U_3O_8:

TABLE 6. ENERGY POTENTIAL OF U.S. NUCLEAR FUELS IN Q UNITS [1, 2]

Resources	*Reasonably Assured*	*Possible Additional*	*Total*
Uranium			
Low cost	9	15	24
Medium cost	15	8	23
High cost	187	4	191
Sub total	211	27	238
Thorium			
Low cost only	4	15	19
Total	215	42	257

[1] Before applying the energy conversion factor, the tonnage estimates in Table 5 were first adjusted to put them on the basis of uranium and thorium metal.
[2] To simplify the computation, the energy conversion factor used for uranium has also been used for thorium. This would normally somewhat overstate the energy potential of the thorium reserves but has not here because of rounding of the Q values obtained.

Thus U.S. reserves of low-cost nuclear fuels are estimated to represent roughly eight times the energy potential of U.S. reserves of low-cost fossil fuels. U.S. reserves of nuclear fuels recoverable at costs within 500% of present-day cost levels are estimated to represent roughly nine times the energy potential of comparably defined U.S. reserves of fossil fuels.

General. The availability of the indicated amount of energy from uranium and thorium deposits can be looked at in two ways.

The first and perhaps most obvious is that it extends the period during which the United States can meet its energy requirements with its own energy resources, perhaps by 80 years. (As was brought out earlier, the estimated 28 Q of fossil fuels appear sufficient to meet projected requirements until the mid-twenty-first century. Given a continuation of the assumed post-2000 growth rate of 3% per annum, the estimated 257 Q of nuclear fuels would defer the date of fuel exhaustion from 2057 to about 2140.)

Secondly, the availability of nuclear energy gives needed flexibility to the U.S. energy economy. The use of nuclear fuels in parallel with fossil fuels will extend the period of availability of the latter, and, at some sacrifice in the ultimate date of fuel exhaustion, will facilitate the use of the latter as chemical raw materials.

It is clear in any event that energy sources other than fossil or nuclear fuels must be developed in due course. One possibility, outside the scope of this book, is the exploitation of solar energy. Another, discussed under separate heading, is the achievement and harnessing of controlled fusion reactions (see **thermonuclear power**). Either would open up virtually inexhaustible energy supplies.

For information on related topics, see **energy statistics, world** and **nuclear power economics.**

ENERGY STATISTICS, WORLD

Tables 1 and 2 show a projection of world fossil fuel consumption and an estimate of world fossil fuel reserves. As in the preceding

TABLE 1. PROJECTION OF WORLD FOSSIL FUEL CONSUMPTION [1]
(assuming no use of nuclear or other nonconventional energy sources)

Period	*Projected Consumption, Q Units*	
	During Period	*Cumulative from January 1, 1959* [2]
1959–1980	3.75	3.75
1981–2000	7.90	11.65
2001–2020	18.35	30.00
2021–2040	41.02	71.02
2041–2052	40.00	111.02

[1] Source: AEC report, "Fossil Fuels in the Future," October, 1960 (TID-8209). The projections beyond 2000 are based on an assumption of 4% annual growth.
[2] Total fossil fuel consumption through 1958 has been estimated at 3.70 Q.

TABLE 2. ESTIMATED WORLD RESERVES OF FOSSIL FUELS [1]
(January 1, 1959)

Fuel	*Reserves* [2]			
	Low Cost	*Medium Cost*	*High Cost*	*Total*
Coal and lignite				
billions of short tons	681	825	1241	2747
energy equivalence (Q) [3]	15.27	18.49	27.81	61.57
Petroleum from crude oil [4]				
billions of barrels	553	271	270	1094
energy equivalence (Q)	3.21	1.57	1.57	6.35
Natural gas				
millions of cubic feet	715	1030	2905	4650
energy equivalence (Q)	0.74	1.07	3.01	4.82
Petroleum from oil shales and tar sands				
billions of barrels	negl.	2400	4200	6600
energy equivalence (Q)	negl.	13.92	24.36	38.28
Totals, Q	19.22	35.05	56.75	111.02
% of Total	17.3	31.6	51.1	100%

[1] Estimates taken from AEC report, "Fossil Fuels in the Future," October, 1960 (TID-8209). They include known deposits and deposits inferred from geological data, but not yet discovered.
[2] Low cost = recoverable at real costs up to 25% higher than 1958 levels. Medium cost = recoverable at real costs 25% to 50% higher than 1958 levels. High cost = recoverable at real costs 50% to 300% higher than 1958 levels.
[3] 1 Q = 1 quintillion (1×10^{18}) Btu. Conversion factors used as follows: 1 short ton of coal = 21.2×10^6 Btu. 1 barrel of liquid hydrocarbons, oil shale or tar sand = 5.8×10^6 Btu. 1 cubic foot of natural gas = 1.1×10^3 Btu.
[4] Includes liquid hydrocarbons from natural gas fields.

analysis of the U.S. energy economy (see **energy statistics, U.S.**), if one assumes no use of nuclear or other nonconventional energy sources, the estimated reserves are in the aggregate sufficient to meet projected requirements until the mid-twenty-first century.

Information on foreign uranium and thorium reserves at given production cost levels is incomplete and in the case of the communist bloc countries is virtually nonexistent.

Reasonable assured free world reserves of uranium reported to be recoverable at $8-10 per pound U_3O_8 (i.e., low-cost material) amount to approximately 1 million tons and represent a maximum energy potential of about 40 Q units.* Potentially recoverable medium-cost material ($16-20 per pound U_3O_8) amounts to approximately 3 million tons, or about 120 Q. Total reserves, including high-cost material ($24-30 per pound), appear to be in excess of 5 million tons, or 200 Q. Additional possible discoveries may increase this figure to an excess of 7 million tons, or 300 Q.

Similarly estimated reserves of low-cost thorium amount to about 600,000 tons (about 26 Q), and additional possible reserves may be nearly 1 million tons, or 44 Q. Thus, the total energy potential of free-world nuclear fuels is estimated to exceed 370 Q, which figure can be compared with an estimated 111 Q for the fossil fuel reserves of the free world and communist-bloc countries combined.

* See discussion of energy conversion factors under **energy statistics, U.S.**

ENGINEERING TEST REACTOR (ETR)

A large, general-purpose **test reactor** located at the National Reactor Testing Station and used primarily to study the effects of radiation on fuel, moderator and structural materials of interest to power reactor designers. The principal contractor for the ETR installation was Kaiser Engineers, with the General Electric Company responsible for the nuclear design of the reactor. The construction cost, including supporting experimental facilities, was ~ \$15.7 million. The ETR is operated for the U.S. Atomic Energy Commission by Phillips Petroleum Company. *Type:* Tank reactor. *Power rating:* 175,000 thermal kilowatts. *Fuel:* MTR-type fuel elements. *Coolant:* H_2O. *Moderator:* H_2O. *Reflector:* Beryllium. *Neutron flux:* Average thermal-neutron flux, ~ 4×10^{14} n/cm^2 sec. Average fast-neutron flux, ~ 1.5×10^{15} n/cm^2 sec. *Start-up:* 1957. (Figs. 53-54)

ENGLAND. See **United Kingdom.**

ENIWETOK PROVING GROUNDS

A U.S. Atomic Energy Commission facility for testing large-scale nuclear weapons, located in the Marshall Islands and encompassing Eniwetok and Bikini Atolls. When in progress, tests are conducted under the scientific direction of the sponsoring laboratory (either Los Alamos Scientific Laboratory or the Livermore branch of the E. O. Lawrence

Fig. 53. Engineering Test Reactor (ETR). Above, model showing general arrangement of the reactor. Left, view of the radiation shield above the reactor tank. Water-filled canal in background is used to store fuel elements after removal from the reactor. (*Courtesy of Phillips Petroleum Co.*)

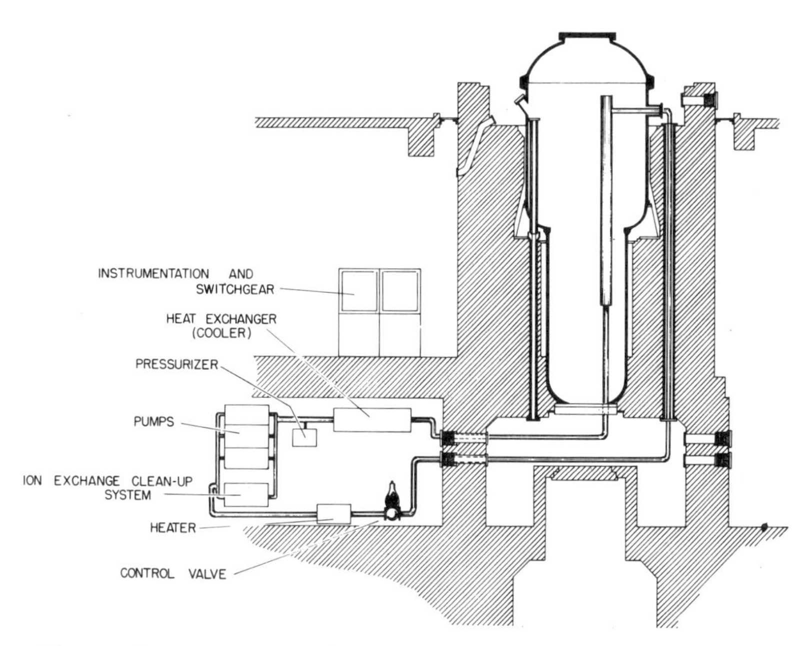

Fig. 54. Components of typical "in-pile" loop used in the Engineering Test Reactor. (*Courtesy of Phillips Petroleum Co.*)

Radiation Laboratory). Facilities at the proving grounds, representing an AEC investment of ~ $36 million, are maintained during test programs by an AEC contractor (Holmes and Narver, Inc.), who also furnishes technical support to the test operations.

In 1960, the proving grounds were made available to be used as terminal facilities of the Pacific Missile Range; however, the arrangement provides for AEC access to the facility when needed.

ENRICHED URANIUM

Uranium containing more than the natural abundance (0.71%) of the U^{235} isotope. (See **uranium enrichment**)

ENRICO FERMI ATOMIC POWER PLANT

A nuclear power plant of the **fast breeder** type located on the shore of Lake Erie at Lagoona Beach, near Monroe, Michigan. The project, undertaken largely at the initiative of the Detroit Edison Company, is being financed under the terms of the "first round" of the U.S. Atomic Energy Commission's Power Demonstration Reactor Program. The reactor is owned and is to be operated by the Power Reactor Development Company (PRDC), an organization formed by some 21 utility and manufacturing interests.* The electrical portion of the plant is owned and is to be operated by Detroit Edison Company, who will purchase the steam from PDRC. The AEC is contributing approximately $3.6 million for research and development, and has waived its normal use charges for the nuclear fuel material for the first five years of operation, equivalent to an additional financial contribution of $3.7 million. Atomic Power Development Associates (APDA), a nonprofit technical

* Allis-Chalmers Manufacturing, Babcock & Wilcox, Burroughs Corporation, Central Hudson Gas & Electric, Cincinnati Gas & Electric, Columbus & Southern Ohio Electric, Combustion Engineering, Consumers Power Co., Delaware Power & Light, Detroit Edison, Fruehauf Trailer Corp., Holley Carburetor Co., Iowa-Illinois Gas & Electric, Long Island Lighting, Philadelphia Electric, Potomac Electric Power, Rochester Gas & Electric, Southern Services, Inc., The Toledo Edison Company, Westinghouse Electric, Wisconsin Electric Power.

organization formed and supported by some 42 utility, manufacturing and engineering interests, designed the reactor and is responsible for the underlying research and development program. Commonwealth Associates, Inc. served as architect-engineer, and United Engineers and Constructors, Inc. as construction contractor.

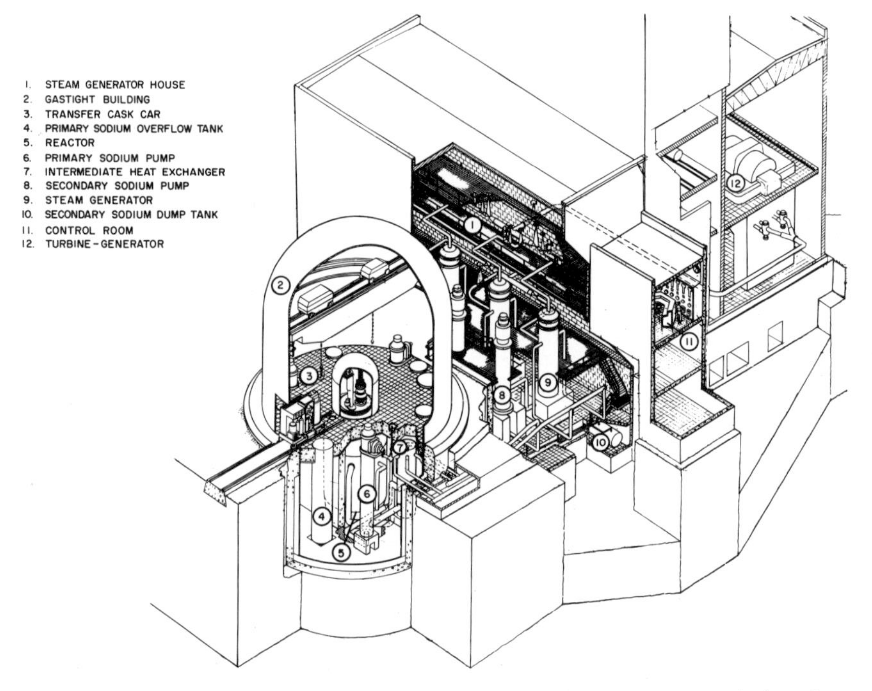

Fig. 55. Layout of Enrico Fermi Atomic Power Plant. (*Courtesy of Atomic Power Development Associates*)

The objective of the Fermi plant is to establish the feasibility of the use of a fast breeder reactor in a power system, and thereby prepare the way for the further development of this potentially low-cost nuclear power concept. It complements the **Experimental Breeder Reactor** projects of the AEC.

Construction of the Enrico Fermi plant began on August 8, 1956, following issuance of a provisional construction permit by AEC. Later that same month (August 31) three AFL-CIO labor unions * petitioned to have the permit set aside on the grounds that certain prerequisite conditions, relating to the safety of the reactor and the financial qualifications of the applicant, had not been met. On December 11, 1958, after holding public hearings, the AEC reconfirmed the construction permit with some modifications. On June 10, 1960, acting on an appeal from the petitioners, a three-man panel of the U.S. Court of Appeals, District of Columbia, set aside the AEC permit on the basis that there was insufficient proof that the reactor could be operated without undue risk to public health and safety. A Justice Department request for a rehearing by the full nine-member Court of Appeals was denied. The AEC and PDRC then appealed the decision to the U.S. Supreme Court.

Apart from the specifics of the PRDC case, two general issues were involved, namely, AEC's authority to grant a provisional construction permit before a final safety review has been made, and AEC's policy with regard to the location of demonstration power reactors. The latter issue was raised by an opinion of the Court of Appeals panel that the

* United Automobile Workers, United Paper Workers, and the International Union of Electrical, Radio and Machine Workers.

AEC must have "compelling reasons" to approve the location of experimental reactors near large population centers.

In June, **1961**, the Supreme Court, by a **7** to **2** majority, upheld the construction permit and the AEC's authority to have issued it.

The following notes reflect the status of the project as of mid-**1962** and relate to the initial core loading:

Power: 60.9 megawatts (electrical). *Fuel:* Enriched uranium (25.6% U^{235}) in the form of uranium-molybdenum alloy (10 weight % Mo) pins. *Blanket:* Depleted (0.36% U^{235}) uranium metal rods. *Cladding material:* stainless steel. *Fuel inventory:* 445 kilograms U^{235} in the core; 45,155 kilograms depleted uranium in the blanket. *Primary coolant:* Sodium at 80 psig; inlet temperature, 550°F; outlet temperature, 800°F. *Intermediate coolant:* Sodium at 8 psig; temperature at steam generator inlet, 750°F. *Steam conditions:* Superheated steam at 600 pounds, 742°F. *Thermal conversion efficiency:* 31.3%. *Control materials:* 10 boron-carbide control rods. *Containment:* Cylindrical steel tank, 72 feet in diameter. *Construction cost:* Estimated at $57.5 million, exclusive of research and development. For other project costs, see Table 3 under **nuclear power development.** *Dates:* Start of construction, August, 1956. Start of operation scheduled for late 1962 or early 1963.

USS *ENTERPRISE* (CVA(N)65)

The second nuclear-powered Naval surface ship. An aircraft carrier and the largest Naval vessel ever constructed, *Enterprise* displaces **86,500** tons and is powered by eight A2W pressurized water reactors. The reactor plant was designed by Bettis Atomic Power Laboratory. The ship, constructed by Newport News Shipbuilding and Drydock Company, was launched on September **24**, **1960**, and commissioned on November **25**, **1961**.

No additional nuclear-powered aircraft carriers had been authorized through **1961**. (See **Naval Reactors Program)**

ENTROPY TRAPPING

A technique being studied at Los Alamos Scientific Laboratory for improving plasma confinement in controlled-**fusion** devices employing **magnetic mirrors.** By providing for ion reflection at the interface between the magnetic field and the plasma, the pattern of ion movement tends to be randomized. This acts to prevent ions from escaping laterally through the magnetic mirrors. The name, entropy trapping, derives from the fact that the increase in randomness of ion movement corresponds to an increase in the entropy of the plasma system.

ENVIRONMENTAL SURVEY

A survey of the **background radiation** and ecological characteristics of the environs prior to the start-up of a nuclear reactor or other facility, test, or experiment which might be expected to alter the radiation environment. Such surveys establish datum conditions against which to compare radiation background measurements routinely made during the operation of the facility or experiment. (See **radiation monitoring)**

In the case of site selection for a nuclear power plant or other reactor facility to be operated at high power levels, environmental surveys include analyses of the seismological, meteorological and hydrological properties of the proposed location, and of the population density and other characteristics of the environs. (See **Atomic Energy Commission—Licensing and Regulatory Procedure.** Also see discussion of land and land rights under **nuclear power economics)**

EPILATION

The temporary or permanent loss of hair, which is a symptom of acute radiation exposure. (See **biological effects of ionizing radiation)**

EPITHERMAL NEUTRONS. See **intermediate neutrons.**

EPITHERMAL REACTOR. See **intermediate reactor, Advanced Epithermal Thorium Reactor.**

ERYTHEMA

An abnormal redness of the skin, due to an excess of blood in the capillaries. One of the symptoms of acute radiation exposure. (See **biological effects of ionizing radiation**)

ETA

In a nuclear reactor, the number of neutrons emitted by a fissionable material per neutron absorbed therein. The symbol for eta is η. (See **breeder reactor** for values for the primary fissionable nuclides)

EURATOM (EUROPEAN ATOMIC ENERGY COMMUNITY)

A supranational organization formed by Belgium, France, West Germany, Italy, Luxembourg, and the Netherlands to "create conditions necessary for the speedy establishment and growth of nuclear industries" in the six countries. Euratom was organized under the Brussels Treaty, signed in Rome in the spring of 1957, and came into existence on January 1, 1958. Its headquarters are in Brussels.

Organization. Euratom is affiliated (and may be merged) with the European Economic Community (Common Market) and the European Coal and Steel Community. The three Communities operate within a common intergovernmental framework. Matters of political policy come under the Council of Ministers. Legislative apparatus is provided by the European Parliamentary Assembly, located in Strasbourg. Judicial questions are adjudicated by the Court of Justice located in Luxembourg.

The Euratom organization is headed by a five-member Commission and consists of an executive secretariat plus a number of program divisions with responsibilities in the following areas: research and training; economic and industrial affairs; supply of materials; safeguards and controls; health protection; information dissemination; foreign relations; and administration and finance. A Scientific and Technical Committee serves the Commission in an advisory capacity.

Research. A $215 million budget was established for research and training through 1962. Designed to supplement existing activity in the member countries, the Euratom program provides for research and reactor physics, materials, and design; controlled fusion; radioisotope applications; and radiation technology. Part of the program is being conducted in Community (i.e., joint) research centers with direct participation of the Euratom staff. Euratom has negotiated agreements with Italy, the Netherlands and West Germany for the use of existing facilities at Ispra, Petten and Karlsruhe, respectively, for this purpose; moreover it has established a Central Measurement Bureau at Belgium's Mol Laboratory. Other Euratom-sponsored research is being conducted under contracts with private or governmental research establishments within the Community, and under agreements with nations or international organizations outside the Community. Program arrangements to date include:

1. A program of cooperation with the United States in nuclear power development (see **U.S.-Euratom Joint Program**), for which Euratom has budgeted $50 million.

2. A program of cooperation with Canada in the development of natural-uranium heavy water-moderated power reactors ($5 million).

3. A contract with KEMA in the Netherlands in support of the study, design and construction of a fluid-bed power reactor ($1.4 million).

4. A program of research on organic cooled power reactors (ORGEL Project), for which $6 million has been budgeted. Tentative plans call for the construction of a 50-megawatt (thermal) organic-cooled heavy water-moderated experimental power reactor, known as ESSOR, which is expected to be located at Ispra. Contracts have been awarded to two industry groups in the Community for design studies, and to the French CEA for materials research and heat transfer studies.

5. A contract with the French CEA for controlled-fusion research ($5.8 million).

6. Contributions to the European Nuclear

Energy Agency's **Dragon Project** ($12 million) and **Halden Project** ($1 million).

7. Allocation of some $32 million for contributions to nuclear power plant construction projects in France (the French-Belgian SENA Project), Italy (the SIMEA Project), West Germany and the Netherlands.

International Agreements. Euratom has an Agreement for Cooperation with the United States covering the above-mentioned **U.S.-Euratom Joint Program,** and an additional agreement providing for the supply of specified quantities of special nuclear materials for use in other Euratom activities. (See above for references to other international agreements.)

Nuclear Power Timetable. The indications are that between 3000 and 4000 megawatts of nuclear power capacity will be in operation in the Community by 1967 (see individual country entries). In a report published in 1960, a Euratom study group made an informal estimate that the total will be of the order of 40,000 megawatts by 1980.

Supply Agency. On June 1, 1960, Euratom established a Supply Agency to handle the procurement of special nuclear materials, and to maintain accounting and inventory control in connection therewith. Under the procedures adopted, producers or consumers in the Community are free to negotiate directly for the sale or purchase of uranium ore or other source materials so long as the terms are consistent with general policies set up by the Agency; however, all **special nuclear material** must be procured through the Agency.

Other. Euratom has established basic health and safety standards for atomic energy activities in the Community. A convention governing control of atomic energy materials has been adopted (see **international control of atomic energy**), and a convention governing third-party liability is in an advanced stage of negotiation (see **insurance and indemnification against atomic energy risks**). In line with the general common-market objective of the member countries, Euratom is working to create a common market for the sale of nuclear products and services within the Community, i.e., the elimination of tariffs, import/export quotas, or other artificial trade barriers.

EUROCHEMIC (EUROPEAN COMPANY FOR THE CHEMICAL PROCESSING OF IRRADIATED FUEL)

A joint stock company organized under the auspices of the **Organization for Economic Cooperation and Development** (OECD) for the purpose of constructing and operating fuel reprocessing facilities to serve nuclear reactors in Western Europe. Of the original capitalization ($21.5 million) 20% was subscribed by private organizations and the balance by governmental and public agencies. The participating countries and their stock holdings (public and private) are: Austria (5%), Belgium (11%), Denmark (5.5%), France (17%), West Germany (17%), Italy (11%), the Netherlands (7.5%), Norway (5%), Portugal (1.5%), Sweden (8%), Switzerland (7.5%), and Turkey (4%). Eurochemic receives broad policy direction from a General Assembly on which all shareholders are represented, and is administered by a 16-member Board of Directors appointed by the General Assembly. Representatives of Euratom and of OECD's **European Nuclear Energy Agency** (ENEA) sit with the Board in an advisory capacity.

Eurochemic's first reprocessing facility will be located near Mol, Belgium, and is scheduled to be in service by 1964. This plant will use a solvent extraction process similar to the U.S. Purex process and is designed to accommodate a variety of fuel compositions, including uranium-aluminum and uranium-molybdenum fuel alloys and uranium dioxide fuel pellets in aluminum, magnesium, zircaloy or stainless steel cladding. The design capacity is 350 kilograms per day of natural uranium or 200-250 kilograms per day of slightly enriched uranium (up to 5% U^{235} content). The plant is to be equipped with two dissolvers, one to handle natural and low enrichment material (up to 1.6% U^{235} content) and the other to handle material of higher enrichment (limit unspecified).

Site preparation began in 1960. Completion

of construction is scheduled for mid-1963 and will be followed by one year of trial operation before actual reprocessing is undertaken. The major contractor is Saint Gobain of France. The estimated cost of construction and five years' operation, originally placed at $21.5 million, was revised upward to $30.5 million after completion of preliminary design in 1961.

Planning for the Eurochemic project has been under the technical direction of ENEA with consultative assistance from the United Kingdom and the United States.

EUROPEAN-AMERICAN NUCLEAR DATA COMMITTEE

An advisory and coordinating group of representatives of the United States, United Kingdom, Canada, Organization for Economic Cooperation and Development (OECD), and the European Atomic Energy Community (Euratom). The Committee is concerned with coordinating measurements of nuclear **cross sections** and other basic nuclear data, and the precommercial development of laboratory instruments and techniques.

EUROPEAN ATOMIC ENERGY SOCIETY (EAES)

A society of the atomic energy commissions of thirteen Western European countries formed to promote cooperation in atomic energy research. The member countries are Austria, Belgium, Denmark, France, West Germany, Italy, the Netherlands, Norway, Portugal, Spain, Sweden, Switzerland, and the United Kingdom.

Not to be confused with the **European Nuclear Energy Agency.**

EUROPEAN NUCLEAR ENERGY AGENCY (ENEA)

A special agency of the **Organization for Economic Cooperation and Development** (OECD) established in 1958 and charged with implementing OECD's program in the atomic energy field.

Background. In 1956 an *ad hoc* study committee of the OEEC (now OECD) recommended that the organization take the following actions:

1. Foster joint technical projects as a means of making maximum utilization of the resources available for atomic energy development.
2. Establish suitable controls to ensure that nuclear materials earmarked for peaceful uses would not be diverted to military uses.
3. Promote trade in nuclear materials, products and services by eliminating, insofar as possible, artificial trade barriers.
4. Take steps to harmonize national legislation, especially in regard to indemnification against risks, and standards for health and safety protection.

These recommendations were approved by OECD's Council of Ministers, and in 1957 a permanent Steering Committee on Nuclear Energy was established to guide OECD's activities in the atomic energy field. In turn, on February 1, 1958, the European Nuclear Energy Agency was established within the framework of the OECD to implement the organization's program under the policy guidance of the Steering Committee.

Organization. The accompanying table lists the membership of the ENEA. The ENEA functions primarily through the mechanism of joint study or working groups composed of individuals from interested member nations. When a joint project is undertaken (see below), a joint Board of Management is ap-

MEMBERSHIP OF EUROPEAN NUCLEAR ENERGY AGENCY

Members:	
Austria [2, 3]	Luxembourg [1, 3]
Belgium [1, 2, 3]	Netherlands [1, 2, 3]
Denmark [2, 3]	Norway [2, 3]
France [1, 2, 3]	Portugal [2]
West Germany [1, 2, 3]	Sweden [2, 3]
Greece	Switzerland [2, 3]
Iceland	Turkey [2]
Ireland	United Kingdom [3]
Italy [1, 2, 3]	
Associates:	
Canada	
United States	

[1] Member of Euratom.
[2] Eurochemic Shareholder.
[3] Participant in Dragon and Halden Projects.

pointed for the particular activity. A small permanent staff (secretariat), located at OECD headquarters in Paris, coordinates and lends support to the joint activities under the policy direction of the OECD Steering Committee.

Program. Major program activities of the ENEA to date are as follows:

1. Joint construction and operation of a pilot facility for reprocessing irradiated fuel from Western European research, test and developmental power reactors. (See **Eurochemic**)
2. Joint construction and operation of an experimental high-temperature gas-cooled power reactor. (See **Dragon Project**)
3. Joint operation of an experimental boiling water power reactor. (See **Halden Project**)
4. A convention establishing procedures for the control of nuclear materials has been signed by the member governments. (See **international control of atomic energy**)
5. A convention covering indemnification of third parties and related questions of liability and insurance has been signed by most member countries. (See **insurance and indemnification against atomic energy risks**)

Additional subject areas assigned to study or work groups include cooperation in reactor development, cooperation in the exchange and compilation of nuclear data, nuclear ship propulsion, heavy water production, food irradiation, health and safety, training, and international trade.

EUROPIUM

Element No. 63 (symbol, Eu; atomic weight, 152.0), a **rare earth** with a high thermal neutron absorption cross section (~ 4600 barns); of interest for use as a neutron-absorbing material in reactor control rods. (See **reactor materials**)

EUTECTIC

A general term for a mixture of two or more solid materials which has the lowest possible melting point, i.e., a lower melting point than is achieved by other formulations of the same materials.

EXCESS REACTIVITY

When a nuclear reactor is loaded with more fuel than is required to achieve criticality it is said to have excess **reactivity.** The reason for so loading a reactor is to provide a means of compensating for factors that act to lower the reactivity of the system once it is in operation, e.g., fuel **burn-up,** the accumulation of fission-product **poisons,** and xenon build-up following reactor shutdown (see **xenon poisoning).** In the case of research and materials and engineering test reactors, an additional requirement for excess reactivity is the demand for neutrons for experiments. In the case of power reactors, especially those designed for propulsion applications, added excess reactivity may be required to extend the life of the core. Whenever excess reactivity is built into a reactor, the control system must be scaled up accordingly, since otherwise the system would be supercritical. This may be done by providing extra control rod capacity and/or by incorporating burnable poisons in the fuel. (See **reactor control)**

EXCLUSION AREA, REACTOR. See **nuclear power economics.**

EXPERIMENTAL BERYLLIUM OXIDE REACTOR. See **Maritime Gas-Cooled Reactor Project.**

EXPERIMENTAL BOILING WATER REACTOR (EBWR)

A small government-owned nuclear power plant of the direct-cycle **boiling water** type located at Argonne National Laboratory, EBWR was designed and is operated by the ANL staff. It serves principally as an experimental facility. It has been particularly useful in establishing that a direct-cycle boiling water reactor system can be operated without serious radioactive contamination of the steam turbine; and in providing information on the

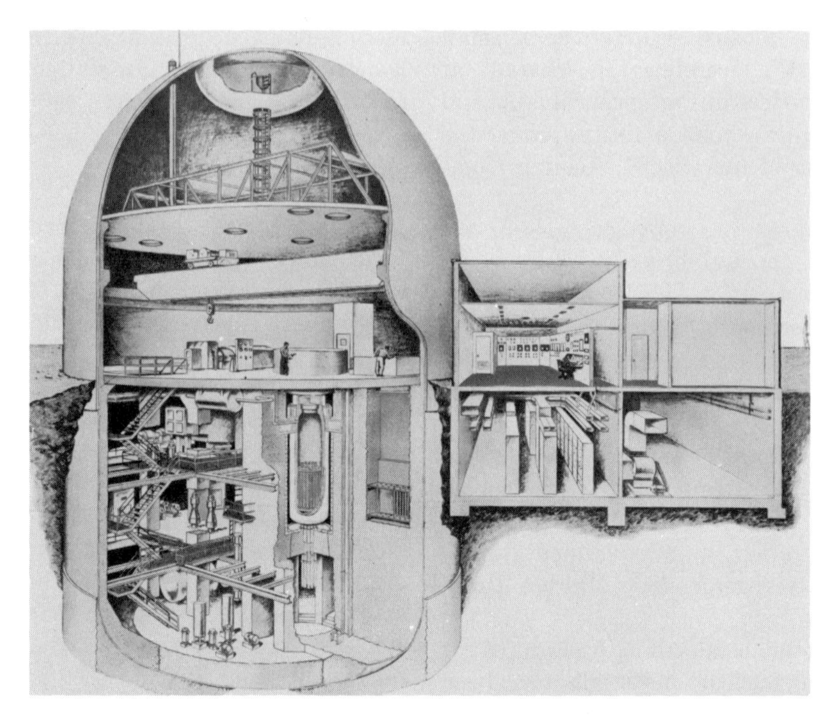

Fig. 56. Cutaway of the Experimental Boiling Water Reactor (EBWR). The reactor vessel and bottom-drive control rods are seen at left center. (*Courtesy of Argonne National Laboratory*)

design and operating characteristics of high-power-density cores under natural-circulation conditions. In the latter connection, EBWR as originally designed was successfully operated at three times its original rated heat output of 20 megawatts (thermal), and was recently modified to achieve a heat output approaching 100 megawatts (thermal). (Its electrical output continues to be fixed at 5 megawatts, which is the capacity of its **turbine-generator**.) Following is a summary of plant particulars:

Power: 4.5 megawatts (net electrical). (See above remarks on reactor heat output.) *Fuel:* Ternary uranium alloy (5% Zr, 1.5% Cb) in plate-type fuel elements clad with zircaloy-2. Both normal and slightly enriched uranium (1.44% U^{235}) are used; also fully enriched UO_2 rods have been used as spikes. *Steam conditions:* Steam leaves the reactor at 600 pounds pressure and 489°F. *Thermal conversion efficiency:* 20.5%. *Control materials:* 5 hafnium and 4 boron-steel control rods; provision to inject boric acid into the coolant stream for emergency shutdown. *Containment:* Steel tank, 80 feet in diameter and 119 feet high, with hemispherically shaped top. *Cost:* Cost of construction of the original facility reported at $5.0 million, exclusive of research and development costs. Cost of plant alternations to achieve 100-megawatt heat output estimated at $2.0 million. *Dates:* Construction started in May, 1955. Reactor first critical in December, 1956. Full power operation reached same month. Plant alterations for high power operation were completed in January, 1962, and operations were resumed in the spring of 1962.

EXPERIMENTAL BREEDER REACTOR NO. I (EBR-I)

An experimental **fast breeder reactor** located at the National Reactor Testing Station. EBR-I was designed and is operated by Argonne National Laboratory. The architect-engineer was The Austin Company; Bechtel Corporation was the construction contractor. Operations, which began in 1951 and are continuing, have served to demonstrate the feasibility of operating a fast reactor system with a net breeding gain,* and to explore the control

* The highest **breeding gain** achieved with uranium fuel: 1.00 ± 0.04.

characteristics and operating performance of such a system. Also, during early trial runs in December, 1951, EBR-I was the first reactor to demonstrate the production of electrical power, albeit in token amounts.

EBR-I has operated on three enriched uranium cores: Mark I, from August 1951 to January 1954; Mark II, from March 1954 to November 1955; and Mark III, from November 1957 to late 1961. A plutonium core (Mark IV) was placed in service in the spring of 1962.

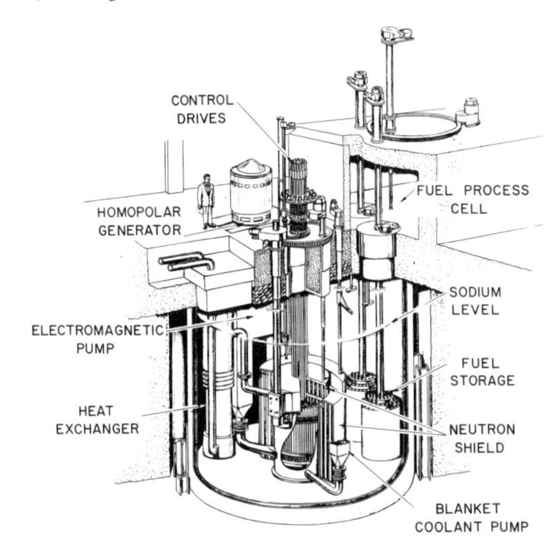

Fig. 57. Diagram of Experimental Breeder Reactor No. 2 (EBR-2). (*Courtesy of Nucleonics*)

During routine operation EBR-I has at all times shown stable operating characteristics. The only anomalies that have been observed have occurred at low coolant flow rates during start-up periods. These first became manifest during operation of the Mark I core. When the Mark II core was installed, a series of experiments was conducted to study the stability of the system under extreme conditions, i.e., with deliberate power oscillations and drastically reduced, even zero, coolant flow rates. Under these conditions the system was found to develop a prompt **positive temperature coefficient,** and in one experiment a delay in scramming the reactor resulted in melt down of the central portion of the core. Analysis of the experimental data led to the conclusion that the runaway was due to an increase in reactivity caused by thermal distortion of the core.* A positive aspect of the experiment was that, in melting down, the core lost criticality, i.e., it "failed safe."

Following the melt down, which occurred in June, 1955, an 8-month cooling period was allowed before the work of removing the Mark II core was started. Installation of the Mark III core, designed for greater rigidity to minimize distortion, was completed in December, 1957. Reactor kinetics experiments demonstrated that this core had a prompt **negative temperature coefficient.**

Following is a summary of EBR-I particulars reflecting the Mark IV core loading:

Power: 1000 kilowatts (thermal). Nominal electrical output (170 kilowatts). *Fuel:* 35 kilograms of plutonium in the form of plutonium—1.25 weight % aluminum alloy, clad with zircaloy. *Primary coolant:* Sodium-potassium eutectic at nominal pressure, inlet temperature, 442°F; outlet temperature 600°F. *Secondary coolant:* sodium-potassium eutectic; temperature at steam generator inlet, 583°F. *Control materials:* 12 stainless steel-jacketed natural uranium control rods. *Containment:* none. *Cost:* Capital cost of original installation reported at $1.4 million. *Dates:* Operation on Mark IV core started in the spring of 1962.

EXPERIMENTAL BREEDER REACTOR NO. II (EBR-II)

An experimental **fast breeder** power reactor located at the National Reactor Testing Station. EBR-II was designed and is operated by Argonne National Laboratory. The architect-engineer was H. K. Ferguson Company.

The primary purpose of EBR-II is to determine the feasibility of using a fast breeder reactor in a power system. Particular emphasis will be placed on determining the feasibility of recycling partially decontaminated fuel and, to this end, EBR-II is being equipped with **pyrometallurgical** reprocessing and fuel refabrication facilities. The reactor is fueled initially on enriched uranium, but ultimately will be fueled with plutonium.

* Fast reactor systems are sensitive to reactivity changes due to the fact that prompt neutrons have a very short lifetime in an unmoderated environment. (See **reactor control**)

The following notes reflect the status of the project as of mid-1962:

Power: 165 megawatts (net electrical). *Fuel:* enriched uranium (49% U^{235}) in the form of uranium-**fissium** alloy pins. *Blanket:* depleted uranium (0.22% U^{235}) metal rods. *Cladding material:* Stainless steel. *Fuel inventory:* 170 kilograms of U^{235} in the core, 28,100 kilograms of depleted uranium in the blanket. *Primary coolant:* Sodium at 60 psi; inlet temperature, 700°F; outlet temperature, 900°F. *Intermediate coolant:* Sodium at 60 psi; temperature at steam generator inlet, 880°F. *Steam conditions:* Superheated steam at 1250 pounds, 850°F. *Thermal conversion efficiency:* 34%. *Control materials:* 12 control rods and 2 safety rods. *Cost:* Initial capital investment estimated at $33.8 million, including fuel reprocessing and refabrication facilities. *Dates:* Construction started in December, 1957. Preliminary operation started in February, 1962; power operation scheduled for late fall of 1962.

EXPERIMENTAL GAS-COOLED REACTOR (EGCR)

An experimental gas-cooled nuclear power facility under construction at Oak Ridge, Tennessee. The reactor was designed under contract to the U.S. Atomic Energy Commission by Kaiser Engineers and the Allis-Chalmers Manufacturing Company. H. K. Ferguson Company is the construction contractor. The facility will be operated for the AEC by the Tennessee Valley Authority. The first civilian gas-cooled power reactor to be built in the United States, EGCR will be used to obtain experience with fuel elements, coolants and other reactor materials of interest to the AEC's **gas-cooled reactor** development program. The electrical power produced will be used by other Oak Ridge installations. The following notes reflect the status of the project as of mid-1962:

Power: 22 megawatts (net electrical). *Fuel:* Slightly enriched uranium (2.55% U^{235}) in the form of uranium dioxide (UO_2) pellets. *Fuel element design:* A single fuel element consists of a cluster of stainless steel tubes loaded with UO_2 pellets. *Coolant:* Helium at ~ 300 pounds pressure; inlet temperature 510°F; outlet temperature 1050°F. *Steam conditions:* Superheated steam at 1300 pounds pressure and 902°F. *Thermal conversion efficiency:* 28.6%. *Cost.* Construction cost estimated at $36.5 million. *Dates:* Construction started in August, 1959. The plant is expected to begin preliminary operation early in 1964.

EXPERIMENTAL ORGANIC-COOLED REACTOR (EOCR)

A government-owned test reactor at the National Reactor Testing Station in Idaho. The purpose of EOCR is to test various coolants, fuel elements, and operating conditions of interest in the development of improved **organic-cooled reactors.** The conceptual design was developed under contract by Phillips Petroleum Company, who operate the facility. The Fluor Corporation was the architect-engineer, and C. F. Braun and Company the construction contractor.

EOCR operates at power levels up to 40 megawatts (thermal). It is not equipped for steam generation or electric power production. The facility is designed to permit a range of operating conditions, including maximum fuel surface temperatures up to 850°F, and is equipped with several test loops.

The following notes are based on 1961 information:

Power: 40 megawatts (thermal). *Fuel:* Enriched uranium in the form of a dispersion of uranium dioxide (UO_2) in a stainless steel matrix. *Fuel element design:* A single fuel element consists of two subassemblies of stainless steel-clad fuel plates contained in a stainless steel sheath. *Coolant:* Santowax-R at 150 psi. *Construction Cost:* Estimated at $7.8 million, exclusive of test loops.

EXPLORATION. See **uranium exploration.**

EXPONENTIAL EXPERIMENT

An experiment in which an external neutron source is used to simulate critical conditions in a subcritical assembly of fissionable material and moderator, usually conducted to obtain information needed for the design of a nuclear reactor. In such an experiment, the **neutron density** decreases exponentially with distance in a given direction from the neutron source; hence the term "exponential." Exponential experiments afford a means of approximating certain parameters of a new reactor design, including the **critical size** of the core, more cheaply and easily than in a **critical experiment.**

EXPORT-IMPORT BANK

Under policy announced in October, 1956, the Export-Import Bank will make loans for the construction of nuclear power plants to countries having **Agreements for Cooperation** with the United States in the atomic energy field. Governments or private interests requesting such financial assistance must furnish information relating to the technical and economic feasibility of the proposed project; the availability of nuclear fuel; the availability of funds to defray local currency costs; and ability to service the dollar debt involved. The loans apply only to equipment, materials, initial fuel loadings, and technical services purchased in the United States. The bank will also consider loan applications from countries which plan to obtain equipment and materials under the auspices of the **International Atomic Energy Agency.**

EXPOSURE (of nuclear fuel)

The cumulative amount of radiation exposure to which fuel has been subjected in a nuclear reactor, usually expressed in terms of the thermal energy produced by the reactor per ton of fuel initially present. The unit is **megawatt-days per ton.** (See **burn-up**)

EXPOSURE DOSE, OF GAMMA OR X-RAYS. See **radiation dose.**

F

FALLOUT. See **radioactive fallout.**

FALSE NEUTRONS. See **nonthermonuclear neutrons.**

FAST BREEDER REACTORS

(1) Broadly speaking, any reactor that operates with neutrons in the fact energy range (> 0.1 Mev) and achieves a **breeding gain,** i.e., produces more fissionable material than it consumes. The optimum fuel cycle for a fast breeder is the plutonium-239—uranium-238—plutonium-239 cycle,* as opposed to the uranium-233—thorium-232—uranium-233 cycle used in **thermal breeders** (see **breeder reactors**). (2) A type of power reactor, based on the fast breeder principle, being developed for central station use. The information which follows deals with the fast breeder power reactor concept.

Fast breeder power reactors employ only slightly diluted fissionable material as fuel in a compact unmoderated core and hence operate at extremely high power densities relative to other types of power reactor. The core is surrounded by a blanket of fertile material. Figure 58 illustrates the design concept upon which most development work is currently based. The reactor coolant, liquid sodium,** is made temporarily radioactive by neutron

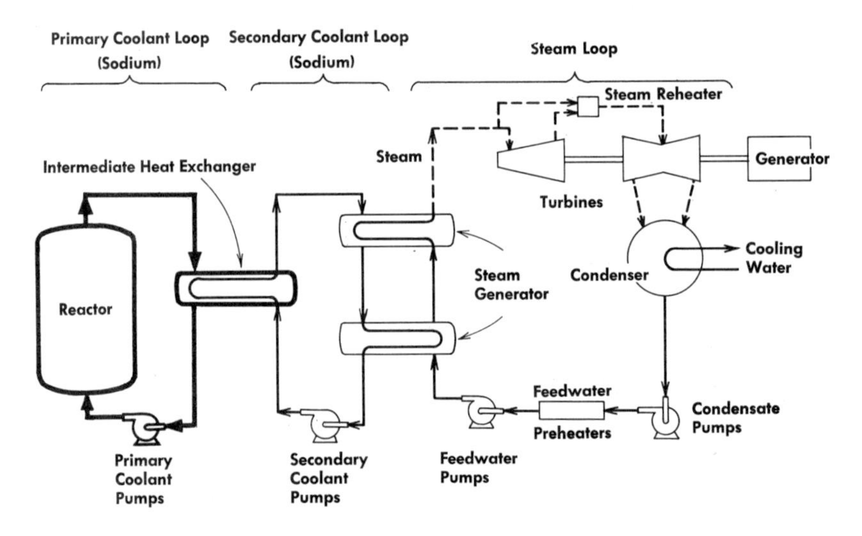

Fig. 58. Simplified flow diagram of fast breeder reactor plant.

* I.e., the use of plutonium as fuel and depleted uranium (essentially uranium-238) as fertile material, resulting in the breeding of additional plutonium. A uranium-235—uranium-238—plutonium-239 "chain" may also be used; however U^{235} has a lower **eta** value for fast neutrons than Pu-239 (~2.2 vs. ~2.7), so that this system is usually considered only as a means of obtaining the plutonium needed to start the more efficient plutonium cycle.

** One of the reasons for the use of sodium is that it is a poor neutron moderator; hence it does not interfere with the maintenance of the desired fast neutron environment. This consideration rules out the use of water and other moderative coolants.

Fig. 59. Construction views of fast breeder reactor installations. Top, Experimental Breeder Reactor No. 2 and associated fuel reprocessing facilities at the National Reactor Testing Station. Bottom, the Enrico Fermi Atomic Power Plant at Lagoona Beach, Michigan. (*Courtesy of the USAEC (top), Detroit Edison Co. (bottom)*)

activation as it passes through the core and is circulated in a closed loop, referred to as the primary loop. To avoid using a radioactive fluid for steam generation, an intermediate heat exchange medium (nonradioactive sodium) is employed. Two heat exchangers are thus required. In the first, referred to as the intermediate heat exchanger, the radioactive sodium transfers heat to nonradioactive sodium. In the second, referred to as the secondary heat exchanger or steam generator, the nonradioactive sodium transfers heat to water, thereby generating steam for power generation.

The feasibility of a fast breeder system was first demonstrated by the successful operation of the **Experimental Breeder Reactor No. I** at the National Reactor Testing Station in December, 1951. A prototype power reactor, **Experimental Breeder Reactor No. II,** was recently installed at an adjoining site and began operation in 1962. A large-scale power plant, the **Enrico Fermi Atomic Power Plant,** located near Monroe, Michigan, is scheduled to be placed in operation late in 1962, or early in 1963. These fast breeder reactor projects, together with related reactor experiments, are listed in the accompanying table.

FAST BREEDER REACTOR PROJECTS AND RELATED EXPERIMENTAL PROGRAMS

Name of Plant or Project	*Location*	*Reactor Designer*	*Rated Power Output (megawatts electrical)*	*Start-up*	*Notes*
Reactor Projects:					
Experimental Breeder Reactor No. I (EBR-I)	National Reactor Testing Station	Argonne National Lab.	nominal	1951	First demonstration of the generation of electricity from heat produced in a nuclear reactor
Experimental Breeder Reactor No. II (EBR-II)	National Reactor Testing Station	Argonne National Lab.	16.5	1962	Equipped with pyrometallurgical reprocessing loop
Enrico Fermi Atomic Power Plant Detroit Edison *et al.*	Monroe, Michigan	Atomic Power Development Associates	60	(1962–1963)	
Experimental Programs:					
Los Alamos Fast Reactor ("Clementine")	Los Alamos, N.M.	Los Alamos Scientific Laboratory	—	1946	First fast reactor
Transient Reactor Test (TREAT) **Experiment**	National Reactor Testing Station	Argonne National Lab.	—	1959	Simulation of power surges in fast reactor system
Zero Power Reactor No. 3 (ZPR-III)	National Reactor Testing Station	Argonne National Lab.	—		Fast reactor physics experiments
Argonne Fast Source Reactor (AFSR)	National Reactor Testing Station	Argonne National Lab.	—	1959	Studies of the physics of fast reactor systems
Los Alamos Molten Plutonium Reactor Experiment (LAMPRE-1)	Los Alamos, N.M.	Los Alamos Scientific Laboratory	—	1961	Test of feasibility of molten plutonium alloy fuel

Note: For cost information on EBR-II and Enrico Fermi, see Table 3 under **nuclear power development.**

Of the approximately $476 million spent by the U.S. Atomic Energy Commission for civilian reactor research and development through mid-1960, $111 million was applied to sodium-cooled reactors and, of this, about half related specifically to fast breeder programs.* In this latter work, much of which has been conducted by Argonne National Laboratory, extensive use has been made of sodium technology developed under other AEC programs, notably the Sodium Intermediate Reactor (SIR) Project (see **Naval Reactors Program**), the **sodium-graphite reactors** program, and general AEC-sponsored research and development on sodium-handling equipment components. Also there has been technical liaison with fast breeder development work in progress at the **United Kingdom's** Dounreay Experimental Reactor Establishment.

General Considerations. The idea of operating power reactors on a breeding basis, i.e., with a net gain in fissionable material, is of course extremely attractive from the standpoint that it assures greater utilization of fertile material resources than is achieved in **converter reactors.** Some believe that the world's supplies of uranium and thorium will not sustain long term exploitation of nuclear power on any other basis; however expert opinion is divided on this point.

The above comment applies to power breeders in general. The strong points usually cited for the sodium-cooled fast-breeder concept in particular are as follows:

1. It offers the prospect, once fully developed, of extremely low fuel costs. One reason is the net gain in plutonium, for which the AEC allows a credit (see **nuclear power economics**). This helps defray, and may ultimately offset, the costs of the fuel cycle (fuel element fabrication, reprocessing, AEC use charges, etc.). Another reason is the possibility of achieving low spent fuel reprocessing costs through pyrometallurgical techniques (see item 5 below).

2. Sodium has a high boiling point (1638°F), which permits operation at high temperature with a low-pressure system.

3. Sodium has excellent heat transfer properties which, combined with its high-temperature capability, permit achieving high thermal conversion efficiencies in power generation.

4. Fast breeder reactors can be designed for large power outputs due to their extremely high power densities; to the excellent heat transfer characteristics of sodium; and to the absence of reactor pressure vessel limitations.

5. Operation in the fast neutron spectrum has several advantages ** which stem from the fact that most materials, including fission products, have low capture cross sections for fast neutrons. One advantage is that neutron absorption considerations do not restrict the choice or amount of structural materials used in the reactor core. A second advantage is that very little **excess reactivity** is needed to compensate for fission-product build-up, which minimizes the requirement for control poisons. A third advantage (closely related to the second) is that the loss in the reactivity of the core due to fission product build-up does not limit fuel burn-up, so that the allowable burn-up is strictly a function of the ability of the fuel elements to withstand radiation damage. A fourth advantage is that the system has a sufficient tolerance for fission products to permit the use of crude fuel reprocessing methods, i.e., methods which do not achieve complete fission product removal. This makes it feasible to employ **pyrometallurgical processes** which, in combination with special techniques for refabricating the fuel, represent a potentially low-cost solution to the problem of fuel reprocessing.†

The major limitations or problems presently associated with sodium-cooled fast breeder reactors are as follows:

1. They are at an early stage of develop-

* These figures are exclusive of capital costs. Source: AEC.

** Relative to operation with neutrons in the thermal energy range.

† Conventional reprocessing techniques must be applied periodically to avoid excessive accumulation of certain fission product nuclides not removed by pyrometallurgical methods; also, the "by-product" plutonium must be processed in a conventional manner.

ment. This is particularly true of their fuel element technology, which is currently characterized by high, rather than by low, costs.

2. Distortion of the core of a sodium-cooled fast reactor has on one occasion triggered power oscillation sufficient to cause fuel elements to melt. There is evidence that this can be avoided by proper core design. (See discussion under **Experimental Breeder Reactor No. I.**) It should be added that extreme conditions leading to core meltdown would not necessarily pose a safety problem, since the core can be (and is) designed to "fail safe," i.e., to forestall the accumulation of a critical mass of molten fuel.

3. The radioactivity induced in sodium by neutron activation * is a disadvantage in two respects. One, noted earlier, is the need to use an intermediate heat exchange system to avoid handling radioactive sodium in the steam generator. The other disadvantage is the need to wait for the radioactivity to decay before maintenance work can be done on the primary sodium system following reactor shutdown. Normally a 10-day waiting period is required; however, in an emergency, access can be had to some of the primary sodium equipment five days after shutdown.

4. The design of the steam generator is complicated by the fact that sodium undergoes a violently exothermic chemical reaction on contact with water in the presence of air. One design approach is to use double-wall tube construction in the steam generator (see **sodium-graphite reactors**). To avoid the expense of double-wall construction, the designers of the Enrico Fermi plant have developed a steam generator with "once-through" flow and hence simplified internals.

5. While not corrosive to most metals, sodium reacts with many impurities which may be introduced into the reactor system, notably oxygen. This is a complicating factor in the design of the system and also in maintenance work since it means that equipment in which sodium is handled must be blanketed with inert gas.

Plant Characteristics. See Table.

Notes on Development Problems. The most critical problem is that of developing

SOME CHARACTERISTICS OF FAST BREEDER PLANTS

	Recent Design [1]	Projection [2]
System Parameters:		
Pressure in primary loop	atmospheric	
Primary coolant outlet temperature	900°F	
Intermediate coolant outlet temperature	850°F	
Steam conditions	850 psi, 780°F	Essentially
Thermal conversion efficiency	34.2%	the
Power density	770 tkw/liter	same
Specific power	950 tkw/kg U	
Fuel:		
Enrichment	93% U^{235}	plutonium/depleted uranium
Form	uranium-molybdenum alloy (10 wt. %Mo)	bulk plutonium oxide/ uranium oxide
Cladding material	stainless steel	stainless steel
Maximum surface temperature	1000°F	
Average burn-up	15,000 MWD/metric ton U	50,000 MWD/metric ton U-Pu

[1] Based on an optimized design of a 150-megawatt (electrical) plant prepared under AEC auspices in the fall of 1959. Source: TID-8516, Part I.
[2] Projected for a 300-megawatt (electrical) plant placed in operation in 1967–1968, assuming success of development work now in progress. Source: TID-8516, Part II.

* Activation occurs by the neutron-gamma reaction, resulting in the formation of sodium-24, a gamma emitter with a radioactive half-life of 15 hours. Sodium-24 decays to magnesium-24, which is stable.

low cost-high burn-up fuel elements. The present uranium-molybdenum alloy elements have high fabrication costs and limited burn-up capability. Work being done to improve this situation includes: study of higher burn-up fuel materials, notably uranium dioxide and plutonium oxide; study of simplified fuel element designs and fabrication techniques; and continued development of pyrometallurgical reprocessing methods and remote refabrication techniques.

Other major areas of research and development activity include studies of the physics of fast reactors; evaluation of alternative system designs; development of improved sodium equipment components; and study of engineering design simplifications. In general this work is aimed at improved understanding of the safety and control characteristics of fast breeder power reactors, and reductions in the capital cost of such reactors.

Economics. See **nuclear power economics.**

FAST BURST REACTOR (FBR)

A special-purpose **test reactor** at Oak Ridge National Laboratory. Its function is to supply microsecond-pulses of fast neutrons (essentially free of moderation) for use in biomedical research. The reactor, which is unmoderated and unshielded, is housed in a building in a remote location. It was designed by the ORNL staff and supplied by United Nuclear Corporation (NDA).

FAST FISSION

Fission caused by **fast neutrons.** Some nuclides, such as uranium-238 and thorium-232 do not undergo fission when bombarded with thermal (slow) neutrons, but can be fissioned by neutrons with energies of about 0.1 Mev or more (fast neutrons). In **heterogeneous reactors** fueled with natural or slightly enriched uranium or containing thorium, fission neutrons, which have an average energy of 2 Mev, can cause fast fission of uranium-238 or thorium-232. The energy released by fast fission can have a significant effect on power reactor output. It is also of significance in the field of nuclear **weapons.**

FAST FISSION EFFECT

The contribution of **fast fission** to neutron production in a nuclear reactor.

FAST NEUTRONS

Neutrons that have energies greater than some arbitrary limit; in reactor physics and engineering this limit is usually taken to be about 100,000 ev. (See **neutron)**

FAST REACTOR

A nuclear reactor in which the fission chain reaction is sustained primarily by **fast neutrons.** Fast reactors contain no **moderator** and inherently require enriched fuel. They are of interest primarily because of their favorable **neutron economy,** which results from a combination of two factors: One is that the number of neutrons released per neutron absorbed in fissionable material is somewhat larger when fission is caused by fast neutrons than when it is caused by **thermal neutrons.** The other is that the probability of neutron loss due to capture by structural materials and impurities is lower in fast neutron systems than in thermal neutron systems (see **resonance absorption).** The former consideration is the basis for interest in fast systems fueled with plutonium for **breeder reactor** applications. The latter consideration is advantageous from a design standpoint, since it permits latitude in the selection and specification of structural materials; and it is advantageous from an operating standpoint, since it means that a greater equilibrium build-up of fission products can be tolerated in fast reactors than in thermal reactors.

FEDAL INSTRUMENTS

In power reactor installations, instruments for the detection of fuel element failures. The term, FEDAL, is an acronym for *f*ailed *e*lement *d*etection *a*nd *l*ocation.

FEDERAL RADIATION COUNCIL (FRC)

A statutory committee of U.S. Government officials established to advise the President on radiation matters, guide all federal agencies in the formulation of radiation-protection standards, and provides for cooperation between the federal government and the states in the radiation protection field. The FRC was created by an Executive Order dated August 14, 1959, and was given statutory status later the same year by an amendment to the U.S. Atomic Energy Act. Its membership consists of the Secretary of Health, Education, and Welfare; the Chairman of the Atomic Energy Commission; the Secretaries of Defense, Commerce and Labor; or their designees, together with such other members as the President may appoint. The Chairman is designated by the President from among the membership. The President's Special Assistant for Science and Technology is authorized to attend meetings of the Council. The law states that "the Council shall consult qualified scientists and experts in radiation matters, including the President of the National Academy of Sciences, the Chairman of the **National Committee on Radiation Protection and Measurements,** and qualified experts in . . . biology and medicine and . . . health physics."

In its first report, "Background Material for the Development of Radiation Protection Standards" dated May 13, 1960, the FRC introduced the terms "radiation protection guide" and "radioactivity concentration guide" to replace **maximum permissible dose** and **maximum permissible concentration,** which are the terms presently used by the National Committee on Radiation Protection and Measurements (NCRP) and other authorities; however, the exposure limits specified in the report are in essential agreement with current NCRP recommendations. (See **radiation protection standards and regulations)**

FEED MATERIALS

Refined uranium or thorium metal or compounds suitable for use in fabricating reactor fuel elements or as feed to uranium enrichment facilities. The term is used to differentiate these materials from "raw materials" (uranium and thorium ores and crude concentrates). (See **uranium refining and conversion)**

FEED MATERIALS PRODUCTION CENTER (FMPC)

A U.S. Atomic Energy Commission production facility for the refining of uranium and the preparation and/or fabrication of **feed materials,** located on a 1050-acre tract of land at Fernald, Ohio, 14 miles northwest of Cincinnati. *Operating contractor:* National Lead Company of Ohio, a subsidiary of National Lead Co. *AEC investment in plant and equipment:* $118 million.* *Employment:* ~ 2500.

The FMPC was placed in operation in 1953 and has since undergone expansion. It is a fully integrated feed materials production complex. The principal production facilities are as follows (see **uranium refining and conversion** for background):

1. Sampling Plant: Incoming raw material, consisting of crude uranium concentrates from domestic and foreign uranium mills, plus some foreign ore fractions, is received, dried, ground classified, and sampled.

2. Ore Refinery: Uranium is extracted and purified by a solvent extraction process and calcined to produce "orange oxide" (UO_3). This may be shipped to one of the **gaseous diffusion** plants as feedstock for uranium-235 production, or it may be further processed at FMPC to reduce the uranium to metal for use in plutonium production. (Steps 3, 4 and 5 below.)

3. Green Salt Plant: Orange oxide is converted to green salt (UF_4) by a continuous process involving reduction with hydrogen and hydrofluorination of the resulting UO_2 with anhydrous hydrogen fluoride.

4. Metal Production Plant: Green salt is

* Includes facilities authorized or under construction as of June 30, 1960. Not adjusted for depreciation.

reduced to massive uranium metal by reaction with ground magnesium in a thermite-type process, and then vacuum-cast into ingots.

5. Metal Fabrication Plant: Uranium ingots are rolled into rods, which are straightened and cut into short slugs. These in turn are machined smooth and shipped to plutonium production facilities for canning and use as fuel elements in plutonium production reactors.

There are, in addition, two other important facilities:

1. Hexafluoride Reduction Plant: Here depleted uranium received from gaseous diffusion plants is converted into green salt. This represents an intermediate step in the reclaiming of depleted uranium as metal for use in weapons applications or as reactor blanket material. The conversion is accomplished by a one-step hydrogen reduction process.

2. Scrap Plant: This is a facility for recovering uranium from scrap materials generated at FMPC or other AEC installations. The operations include grinding, acid dissolution, ammonia precipitation, filtration, and calcination.

Auxiliary facilities include a unit to recover nitric acid for reuse in the refining step; a facility to store the magnesium used in the metal reduction step; and assorted plant services (boiler plant, electric substation, warehouses, etc.). There are, in addition, certain auxiliary technical facilities—principally, a works control laboratory and semi-works facilities for piloting purposes.

The architect-engineer for the original FMPC installation was Catalytic Construction Company, and the construction contractor was George A. Fuller Company. Singmaster & Breyer and Maxon Construction Company were the contractors for a subsequent expansion program.

Another feed materials production facility is operated by Mallinckrodt Chemical Works at Weldom Spring, Missouri. (See **Weldon Spring Plant**)

FERMI ATOMIC POWER PLANT. See **Enrico Fermi Atomic Power Plant.**

FERMI AWARD

An award, honoring the late Enrico Fermi, established in 1956 by the Atomic Energy Commission, pursuant to Section 157b of the 1954 Atomic Energy Act, for especially meritorious contributions on an international basis to the development, use or control of atomic energy. The award is made on the recommendation of AEC's General Advisory Committee with the approval of the President. It consists of a medal, citation, and up to $50,000 which may be given to a single individual or divided among two or more individuals. It may or may not be awarded annually.

Recipients of the award have been:

1956	John von Neumann
1957	E. O. Lawrence
1958	Eugene P. Wigner
1959	Glenn T. Seaborg
1961	Hans A. Bethe
1962	Edward Teller

See **Atoms for Peace Award, Lawrence Memorial Award)**

FERMIUM

Element No. 100 (symbol, Fm), formed by the interaction of oxygen ions with uranium-238 and by other processes usually involving multiple neutron capture. The discovery of fermium (and **einsteinium)** was announced in 1954, following radiochemical analysis of coral debris from a thermonuclear weapon test conducted in 1952 at the Eniwetok Proving Grounds in the Marshall Islands, and represented a collaborative effort of scientists from Argonne National Laboratory, E. O. Lawrence Radiation Laboratory, and Los Alamos Scientific Laboratory. The element was formed as a result of the successive instantaneous capture of many neutrons by uranium-238. The product heavy uranium isotopes decayed into isotopes of fermium and einsteinium by the emission of negative beta particles. Fermium is one of the eleven **transuranium elements** discovered in the past two decades.

FERTILE MATERIAL

A material that can be transformed into a **fissionable material.** The two principal fertile nuclides are uranium-238 and thorium-232 which respectively form plutonium-239 and uranium-233 (both fissionable by **thermal neutrons)** by a process of **neutron capture** and **beta decay** (see **uranium).** The transformation of fertile material into fissionable material occurs in converter or **breeder reactors** and is an important factor in nuclear power **fuel cycles.**

FILM BADGE

A type of personnel **dosimeter;** specifically a badge containing a pack of sensitive photographic film, worn by atomic energy workers to provide a record of radiation exposure. Radiation acts to darken film. By comparing the film pack with control specimens of like material exposed to known amounts of radiation, an approximate determination can be made of the radiation dose that has been received by the wearer. Film badges are normally issued for a period of one month, at the end of which time they are collected, processed, and the exposure data recorded. In some locations they are issued more frequently; also, any visitor to an atomic energy laboratory or plant is routinely issued a film badge.

Film badges usually contain a window to facilitate measurement of beta radiation. The film pack usually consists of films of differing sensitivity, or employs filters, to permit discrimination between beta and gamma exposure. Special films or filters may be provided for measurement of neutron exposure.

FINLAND

Agency. The Finnish Atomic Energy Commission, reporting to the Ministry of Commerce and Industry, is the official agency responsible for atomic matters.

International Relationships. Member of the **International Atomic Energy Agency.**

Research Center. The Institute of Technology, University of Helsinki, is engaged in nuclear research and is equipped with a 100-kilowatt (thermal) TRIGA Mark II research and training reactor supplied by General Atomic (U.S.). Arrangements for obtaining the reactor and the fuel with which to operate it were made through the International Atomic Energy Agency.

Production Activity. Uranium mining is in progress north of Joensuu by Atomienergia Oy (see below). Known ore reserves are about 200,000 tons containing 400 tons U_3O_8. A 100-ton per day ore processing plant began operation in 1960.

Energy Economy. Finland's electric power capacity is about 2000 megawatts, most of it hydroelectric. There are essentially no deposits of fossil fuels.

Industry Notes. Atomienergia Oy, Helsinki, is a consortium of five northern Finnish pulp and paper companies active in the uranium production operations noted above and interested in the use of process heat reactors to furnish steam for pulp and paper manufacture. Viomayhdistys Ydin (Ydin Nuclear Power Association) Helsinki, is a consortium of some 20 southern Finnish pulp and paper companies with general interest in the industrial applications of atomic energy, including nuclear power. Atomivoima Oy, Helsinki, a subsidiary of Ab Granblom Oy, is a potential builder and operator of nuclear power facilities.

FIREBALL

The luminous sphere of hot gases formed by a nuclear explosion. (See **weapons phenomenology)** (Fig. 60)

FISSION (nuclear)

The splitting of a heavy nucleus into two parts (see **fission products),** accompanied by the release of approximately 200 Mev of energy and two or more neutrons. The term is most commonly used in context with uranium-235, plutonium-239 or uranium-233—the principal nuclides which undergo fission upon capture of a **thermal neutron** (see **fissionable**

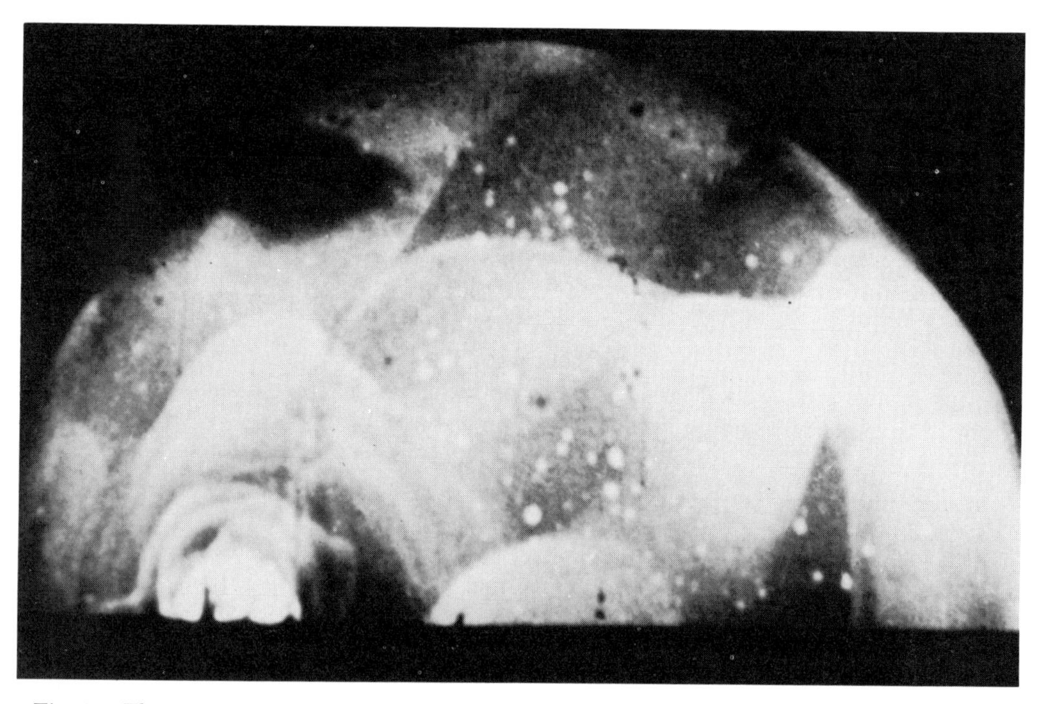

Fig. 60. Three-mile diameter fireball produced by detonation of a megaton-range thermonuclear device ("Mike shot," Eniwetok Proving Grounds, October 31, 1952). (*Courtesy of Edgerton, Germerhausen & Grier, Inc.*)

materials). Fission can be induced in these and other nuclides, notably uranium-238, by **fast neutrons** (see **fast fission**). It can also be induced by photons (photofission) and charged particles, and in some nuclides can occur spontaneously (spontaneous fission).

In the case of uranium-235, the energy released in fission caused by a thermal neutron is distributed approximately as follows:

Type of Energy	*Mev*
Kinetic energy of fission products	168
Kinetic energy of fission neutrons	5
Instantaneous gamma-ray energy	5
Beta particles from fission product decay	7
Gamma rays from fission product decay	6
Neutrinos from fission product decay	10
Total	201

In a nuclear reactor, about 90% of the total energy released (mainly that due to the kinetic energy of fission products) manifests itself as heat at or near the point of fission, i.e., within the fuel. An additional 5%, representing some of the gamma and fast neutron energy, is converted to heat in the moderator, coolant, structural parts, or radiation shield. The balance 5%, namely, the neutrino energy, is irrecoverable.

The magnitude of the energy released by thermal neutron fission of uranium-235 can be expressed as follows:

Approximate:

> The fission of all of the atoms in a gram of U^{235} would yield about 23,000 kilowatt-hours (or approximately 1 megawatt-day) of thermal energy (heat).

More exact:

> 1 megawatt-day of thermal energy equals 2.70×10^{21} fissions.

The discovery of nuclear fission was made in January, 1939, and resulted from the interpretation by L. Meitner and O. R. Frisch of experiments conducted by the German chemists, O. Hahn and F. Strassman. Word of the discovery was brought to the United States by N. Bohr, whose report at a conference on theoretical physics held in Washington, D. C. on January 26 of that year set in motion the chain of events which led to the wartime atomic bomb project and subsequent atomic energy developments. (See **Manhattan Project**)

FISSION PRODUCTS

Any of the primary fragments resulting from the fission of heavy nuclei, together with their radioactive decay products. About 200 different stable and radioactive nuclides have been identified as fission products. These range in mass from 72 to about 160 and represent variant forms (isotopes) of some 35 different chemical elements, ranging from atomic number 30 (zinc) to 74 (gadolinium). The yield of fission products in fission caused by thermal neutrons follow a twin-peaked statistical distribution pattern (see Fig. 61) which is only slightly different for the three primary fissionable materials (uranium-233, plutonium-239, and uranium-235). The maximum yield of any particular nuclide is about 6% (figured on a 200% base), and the highest probabilities in the case of uranium-235 fission, are those nuclides with a mass of 97 or 138.

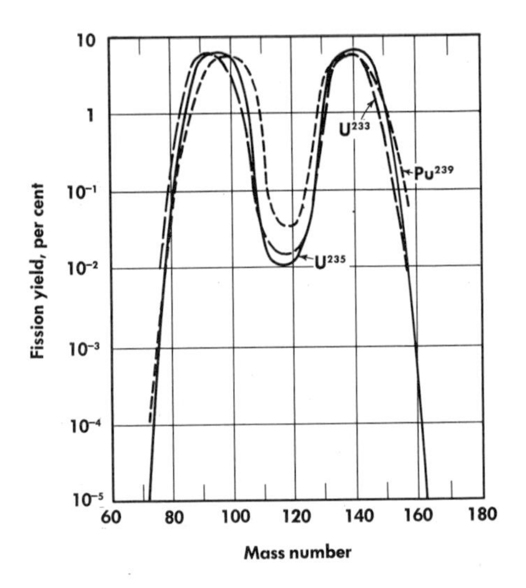

Fig. 61. Distribution of fission product nuclides.

In Reactor Operation. Fission products are important in the reactor field in a number of ways: (1) Fission-product recoil effects contribute to radiation damage in fuel elements during reactor operation and thus are one of the factors that act to limit the length of time fuel can be allowed to remain under irradiation. (2) Fission products in general—and xenon-135 and samarium-149 in particular—are classed as reactor **poisons** since they absorb neutrons wastefully. The rate at which they accumulate has an important bearing on the "**reactivity** lifetime" of the core. (3) Xenon build-up following reactor shutdown is a factor influencing reactor design and/or start-up procedures (see **xenon poisoning**). (4) Fission products account for most of the radioactivity associated with irradiated fuel as it leaves the reactor and for virtually all of the radioactivity contained in the wastes from fuel reprocessing operations. They are thus responsible for most of the complications arising therefrom. (See **decay cooling, fuel reprocessing, radioactive waste disposal**)

In Radioactive Fallout. Fission products account for most of the radioactivity associated with **radioactive fallout** from nuclear weapon tests. The particular nuclide of most concern, because of its yield and biological effects, is **strontium-90.** Other nuclides of biological importance include strontium-89, yttrium-91, zirconium-95 (and its daughter niobium-95), iodine-131, cesium-137 (and its daughter barium-137), barium-140 (and its daughter lanthanum-140), cerium-143 (and its daughter praesodymium-143), cerium-144 (and its daughter praesodymium-144), and neodymium (and its daughter promethium-147).

Applications. Fission products are of interest as possible sources of high-intensity radiation for various industrial applications, either as semi-refined mixtures or as individually separated nuclides (see **radiation sources**). The possible applications, most of which are in an early stage of research, include the **cold sterilization** of drugs and medical supplies, **food preservation,** and the use of radiation as a process variable in chemical manufacture (see **radiation applications in the chemical industry**). Other applications exist for specific fission product nuclides. Thus, cerium-144 is used in some medical teletherapy units (see

medical aspects of atomic energy); and cerium-144 and strontium-90 are of interest as energy sources for small auxiliary power units. (See **SNAP Program**)

Processing: Partly in anticipation of radiation applications and partly in connection with radioactive waste disposal problems, a good deal of research has been done on methods of selectively removing individual fission products from the wastes from fuel reprocessing operations. (See **Multicurie Fission Products Pilot Plant**)

FISSION PRODUCTS DEVELOPMENT LABORATORY (FPDL). See Multicurie Fission Products Pilot Plant.

FISSION YIELD (of nuclear weapons)

The amount of energy released by **fission** (as distinct from that released by **fusion**). (See **yield**)

FISSIONABLE MATERIAL

A material that will undergo nuclear fission. The term is usually restricted to materials that readily undergo fission when bombarded with **thermal neutrons**—principally, uranium-235, plutonium-239 and uranium-233.

FISSIUM

(1) An equilibrium mixture of fission products in reactor fuel that has undergone successive cycles of irradiation and pyrometallurgical reprocessing. The usual constituents are molybdenum, ruthenium, technetium, rhodium, zirconium, and palladium. Certain of these have been found to improve the stability of uranium and uranium-plutonium fuel alloys under fast-neutron irradiation and as the result various synthetic fissium mixes are being studied as possible additives to fuel alloys used in fast reactor systems. (2) The term is also applied to laboratory preparations used to simulate fission product mixtures for experimental purposes.

FIXED-FIELD ALTERNATING GRADIENT SYNCHROTRON (FFAG)

A proposed high-energy high-current **particle accelerator** the principles and feasibility of which are being studied by several laboratories under U.S. Atomic Energy Commission sponsorship, including Midwestern Universities Research Association (MURA), Brookhaven National Laboratory, California Institute of Technology, and Oak Ridge National Laboratory. Notable features of the FFAG concept are as follows:

1. It incorporates the strong focusing principle used in **alternating gradient synchrotrons.**
2. Unlike alternating gradient or other existing synchrotrons, it is based on a fixed, instead of a time-rising, magnetic field. This represents an effort to provide for continuous (nonpulse) operation.
3. Some proposals contemplate the incorporation, in a single machine, of two counterflowing particle beams which, on attaining maximum energy, would be made to collide. This is seen as a means of studying extremely high-energy reaction phenomena.

Both theoretical and experimental studies are in progress to test various aspects of the FFAG concept and to establish a sound design basis for a large-scale machine. Rough estimates indicate that the construction of a 15-Bev "clashing beam" FFAG machine for proton acceleration, together with associated laboratories and service facilities, would involve an investment in excess of $200 million.

FLORIDA WEST COAST REACTOR PROJECT

A recently terminated power reactor development program based on an advanced concept for a gas-cooled natural uranium power reactor. The essential features of the concept studied are as follows:

1. Fuel: uranium dioxide clad with beryllium (see below)
2. Moderator: heavy water
3. Coolant: carbon dioxide at 500 psi in pressure tubes fabricated of a zirconium alloy.

The objective was a reactor system capable of operating at temperatures of ~ 1000°F with average fuel burn-ups of ~ 4000 MWD per metric ton U. Comparable figures for a conventional, i.e., graphite-moderated, gas-cooled natural uranium reactor are 725°F and 3000 MWD per metric ton U. (See **gas-cooled reactors**)

The program was undertaken as part of the "third round" of the U.S. Atomic Energy Commission's Power Demonstration Reactor Program by two electric utility interests—the Florida West Coast Nuclear Group * and the East Central Nuclear Group ** with financial assistance from the AEC. The reactor development work was performed by General Nuclear Engineering Corporation.† American Electric and Power Company was to have provided architect-engineer services for a 50-megawatt (electrical) demonstration reactor provisionally planned for construction near Tampa, Florida.

The initial emphasis of the project was placed on conducting research and development necessary to determine the feasibility of building the demonstration plant. Work began in 1959 based on the use of stainless steel-clad fuel elements. In August, 1960, it was announced that beryllium was to be substituted for stainless steel to improve the neutron economy of the system and that an additional one or two years of research would be needed to develop the necessary beryllium cladding technology. In the spring of 1961, the sponsoring utilities concluded that there were too many technical and economic uncertainties to warrant entering into a firm commitment for plant construction, and the project was accordingly terminated by the AEC.

FLUID FUEL REACTOR

A nuclear reactor in which the fuel is a fluid. The **water boiler** type of research reactor is an example of a fluid fuel system. Other fluid fuel systems have been studied or are under development for use in nuclear power applications. (See **aqueous homogenous reactor, molten salt reactors,** and **Liquid Metal Fuel Reactor Concept)**

The interest in fluid fuel systems for power applications stems in part from a desire to avoid problems associated with the use of solid **fuel elements.** These include the cost of fabricating solid fuel elements and their susceptibility to structural damage during irradiation. Also, the use of a fluid fuel facilitates the removal of fission product **poisons** during reactor operation, and simplifies **fuel reprocessing.** The principal disadvantage of most fluid fuels is that they introduce severe corrosion and/or mass transfer problems. (See further discussion under **nuclear power development, U.S.)**

FLUIDIZED BED REACTOR. See **Liquid Fluidized Bed Reactor Concept.**

FLUORIDE VOLATILITY PROCESSES

Any of several nonaqueous **fuel reprocessing** techniques currently under development based on the volatility of uranium hexafluoride (UF_6). The decontamination factors achieved are comparable to those obtained by aqueous (solvent extraction) techniques. The potential advantages, relative to aqueous techniques, are threefold: (1) Appreciably smaller volumes of radioactive wastes are expected to be generated, facilitating the problem of radioactive waste storage and/or disposal. (2) Uranium can be recovered in the hexafluoride form and hence can either be fed directly into gaseous diffusion facilities for upgrading, or readily converted to metal or other form for re-use as reactor fuel. (The product of aqueous reprocessing is uranyl nitrate, which must go through several additional steps prior to reuse.) (3) It is easier to maintain subcritical conditions in nonaqueous media—a factor that is important in the reprocessing of highly enriched fuels. A disadvantage of fluoride volatility processing is that expensive materials of construction

* Composed of Florida Power Corporation and Tampa Electric Company.

** Representing 14 southeastern and midwestern electric utilities.

† A subsidiary of Combustion Engineering Company.

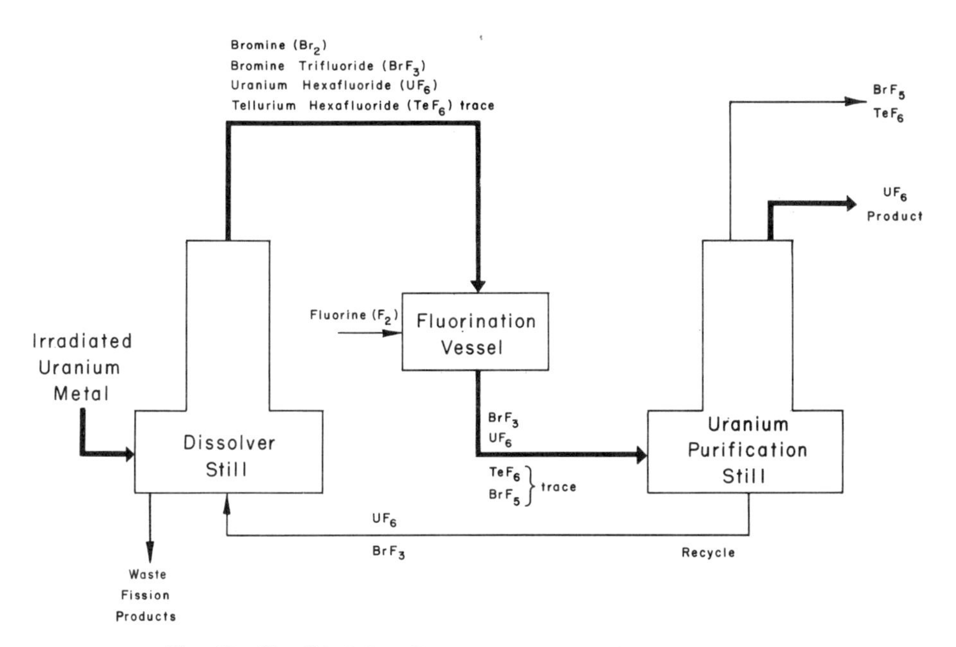

Fig. 62. Simplified flow diagram of the bromine trifluoride process.

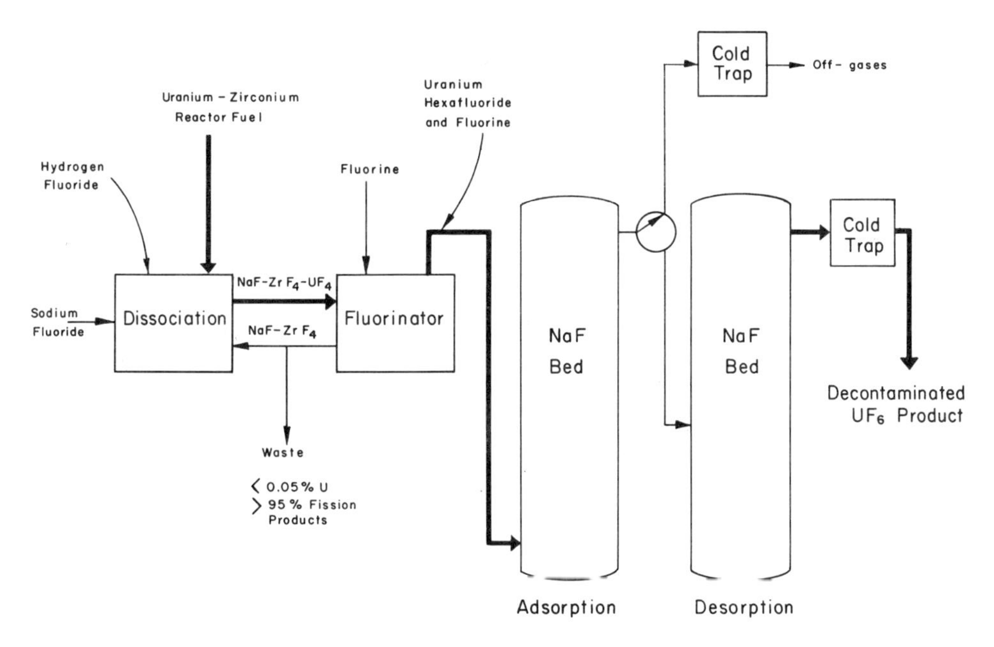

Fig. 63. Simplified flow diagram of fused salt-fluoride volatility process.

must be used to contain the highly corrosive reagents employed. Also, the methods so far developed are limited to uranium recovery. Both methods described below have been successfully tested on a limited scale in "hot" pilot-plant runs.

Low-Alloy Processes. One line of process development aims at the reprocessing of normal or slightly enriched fuels of low alloy content clad with aluminum, zirconium or zircaloy. Here the basic process steps are: (1) The irradiated fuel is dissolved in bromine trifluoride (BrF_3). (2) Uranium hexafluoride and the more volatile fission-product fluorides formed in the dissolution step are removed by volatilization. (3) The uranium hexafluoride is decontaminated by distillation. The plutonium present in the fuel must at present be recovered by supplementary operations.

High-Alloy Processes. A second line of development aims at the reprocessing of highly enriched fuels of high alloy content clad with zirconium or stainless steel. The processes involved are sometimes referred to as fused salt-fluoride volatility processes. The basic steps are: (1) The irradiated fuel is dissolved by contacting with hydrogen fluoride gas (HF) dispersed in a molten mixture of sodium and zirconium fluorides (NaF-ZrF_4) or other suitable fused salt media. Uranium goes into solution during this step as UF_4. (2) The UF_4 is fluorinated to UF_6 using bromine tetrafluoride (BrF_4), chlorine trifluoride (ClF_3), fluorine (F_2), or other suitable fluorination agent. The UF_6 and the more volatile fission-product fluorides are removed by volatilization. (3) The UF_6 is then decontaminated by distillation or, alternatively, by a technique involving selective adsorption on sodium fluoride and subsequent desorption.

FOOD AND AGRICULTURE ORGANIZATION (FAO)

A specialized agency of the United Nations whose atomic energy interests include the use of radioisotopes in agricultural research and the preservation of food by irradiation.

FOOD PRESERVATION

Reference here is to the use of high-intensity **ionizing radiation** as a means of preserving perishable foodstuffs. This application, potentially of major importance, is based on the ability of ionizing radiation to destroy or inhibit the growth of microorganisms that cause food spoilage.

At present two distinct but complementary food irradiation objectives are being pursued in the United States: (1) The use of high-dose irradiation to sterilize perishable foodstuffs so that they can be stored for extended periods of time (months) without refrigeration. Research toward this objective, of potential military logistic value, is being sponsored by the Quartermaster Corps of the U.S. Army. (2) The use of low-dose irradiation to pasteurize perishable foodstuffs so that they can be handled for limited periods without refrigeration and/or so that their refrigerated shelf life can be extended, in either case facilitating the distribution and marketing of commercial food products. Research toward this objective is being sponsored by the U.S. Atomic Energy Commission.

Food Sterilization. True sterilization of food involves the complete destruction of microorganisms associated therewith, and requires massive radiation doses—of the order of 3-5 million **rads.** The application of such doses has been found to accomplish the desired sterilization action in various foodstuffs but generally induces off-flavor effects or other undesirable side reactions, especially in meats. In essence, the problem of radiation sterilization is one of developing irradiation techniques which (1) achieve the desired sterilization action without compromising the wholesomeness or nutritional value of the food, and (2) have acceptable processing costs.

The Quartermaster Corps, in collaboration with the Office of the Surgeon General of the U.S. Army (wholesomeness aspects) and in liaison with the U.S. Atomic Energy Commission, initiated a major effort in food irradiation in 1954. While the emphasis was placed on sterilization, some funds were also devoted to research on less-than-sterilizing doses. The research was conducted under contract by various universities and research institutes and by private industry, and involved a broad spectrum of investigations, including microbiological, chemical and physiological studies of more than 100 different foodstuffs. Plans were developed for the construction of a food irradiation pilot plant at Stockton, California; however in 1959 this project was canceled on the basis that further research was needed before undertaking pilot-scale operations. To advance this work, the decision was made to install an irradiation facility at the research headquarters of the Quartermaster Corps in Natick, Massachusetts, where supporting laboratories were already available. The irradiation facility, which will be equipped with a 1.0-megacurie cobalt-60 source and a 24-Mev linear electron accelerator, is scheduled to be completed by late 1962.

1. Inhibition of sprouting in certain vegetables, notably potatoes and onions: 10-12,000 rads.

2. Deinfestation of foods in bulk, notably grain: 20-30,000 rads.

3. Pasteurization of foods, by which is meant inhibition of spoilage by temporary inactivation of microorganisms: < 1,000,000 rads.

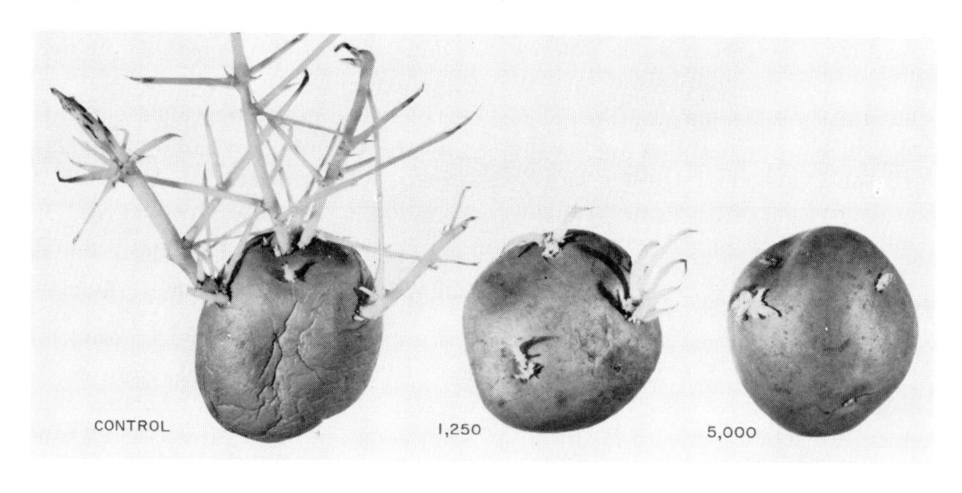

Fig. 64. Effect of high-intensity ionizing radiation in inhibiting the sprouting of potatoes. Samples which received the indicated roentgen doses of gamma irradiation are seen here after eight months of storage. The control sample (top left) was not irradiated. (*Courtesy of Nucleonics*)

In March, 1960, the responsibilities of the Quartermaster Corps in the food irradiation field were redefined and essentially limited to high-dose treatment for military logistic purposes. Research on low-dose treatment, which had been found to offer the greater promise for commercial food preservation applications, was made the responsibility of the AEC.

Food Pasteurization. The range of possible low-dose applications of food irradiation is as follows:

It will be noted that these dose levels are well below those involved in food sterilization. In general, the side effects induced by such "mild" irradiation have been found to be minimal; however extensive and detailed research on biochemical and other factors is required to assure the safety and acceptability of foodstuffs so treated. In essence, the problem in food pasteurization is one of developing irradiation techniques which (1) achieve the desired preservation action in a reproducible fashion, (2) can be shown to result in products that are wholesome and acceptable to the consumer, and (3) are of economic benefit, either on the basis of a direct-cost comparison with other preservation methods * and/or by enabling improvements to be made in food distribution and marketing practice. Minimizing the radiation dose may prove to be another important aspect of the problem of developing successful pasteurization techniques.

As noted above, the U.S. Atomic Energy Commission assumed responsibility for research on food pasteurization in 1960. The AEC program in this field comes under the cognizance of the Division of Isotope Development and the Division of Biology and Medicine. A committee of technical experts, organized at the AEC's request by the American Institute of Biological Sciences, acts in an advisory capacity. There is close liaison with the Quartermaster Corps and the Office of the Surgeon General, U.S. Army. Also, through an Interdepartmental Committee on Radiation Preservation of Foods, there is effective interchange with the Food and Drug Administration and other interested government agencies.

The emphasis of the program is presently placed on the following two classes of food, which being highly perishable are promising subjects for investigation:

1. Fish—specifically clams, haddock, crab, shrimp and flounder.

2. Fruit, including strawberries, grapes, citrus products, tomatoes and peaches.

Preliminary studies of the technical and economic feasibility of "radio-pasteurization" of these two classes of foods have been conducted under AEC contracts by Massachusetts Institute of Technology and Stanford Research Institute, respectively. These studies, in combination with information developed by past Quartermaster Corps experiments, have provided a basis of programming specific research investigations.

As a related activity, Brookhaven National Laboratory has been engaged in the design of special facilities for low-dose food irradiation. The first design, based on a 25,000-curie cobalt-60 source, was completed in 1960. As of mid-1962, three cobalt-60 food irradiation facilities had been built. The first, located at Massachusetts Institute of Technology, is for the joint use of the Institute and the U.S. Department of Interior's Technological Laboratory (Gloucester, Massachusetts). The second is located at the University of California (Davis). The third is installed at the University of Washington.

The Brookhaven program includes an evaluation of the use of radiation machines, e.g., **linear accelerators,** for low-dose food irradiation. (See **radiation sources)**

* These include drying, salting, canning, freezing and freezedrying.

FORATOM (FORUM ATOMIQUE EUROPEEN)

An organization formed in 1960 by atomic industry associations of the six **Euratom** countries and open to membership applications from representative atomic industry associations in other countries. Offices are in Paris.

FORD NUCLEAR REACTOR (FNR)

A 1000-kilowatt (thermal) pool-type research reactor at the University of Michigan, Ann Arbor, Michigan, and operated as part of the University's Phoenix Memorial Project. It was supplied by Babcock & Wilcox Company and began operation in 1957. (See **research and testing reactors)**

FOSSIL FUELS. See **energy statistics, U.S.; energy statistics, world.**

FRACTIONAL CRYSTALLIZATION

One of several **pyrometallurgical** techniques of interest for possible use in **fuel reprocessing** in closed-cycle reactor fuel systems. It involves dissolving the irradiated fuel in a metal solvent and then precipitating the contained uranium as an intermetallic compound by distilling off the solvent metal. Only partial removal of fission products is achieved.

In the Hermex process, under development at Oak Ridge National Laboratory, mercury is the solvent metal. Zinc is the solvent in the Pyrozinc process being investigated at Argonne National Laboratory. The use of cadmium as a solvent is also being studied at Argonne. Nuclear Metals, Inc. has undertaken studies on crystallization processes in general.

Zone melting may be considered a type of fractional crystallization process in which no solvent is added.

FRANCE

Agencies. CEA (Commissariat à l'Energie Atomique), Paris, is the official government agency responsible for atomic matters. EDF (Electricité de France), the state-owned electric utility network, cooperates with CEA in nuclear power development and is responsible for the planning, construction and operation of nuclear power stations.

International Relationships. Member of the **International Atomic Energy Agency,** the European Atomic Energy Community **(Euratom),** the **European Nuclear Energy Agency,** and the European Organization for Nuclear Research **(CERN).** Comprehensive **Agreement for Cooperation** with the United States. Cooperative agreement signed in 1960 with the U.S.S.R. for exchange of information and joint research in controlled fusion, high-energy physics and radiation applications.

Research Centers. Centre d'Etudes Nucléaire de Saclay (CENS), at Saclay, 20 miles southwest of Paris, is CEA's largest research center. Its experimental facilities include a 3.5 Bev synchrotron and two reactors: EL-2, a heavy water-moderated research reactor fueled with natural uranium, which operates at a power level of 2000 kilowatts (thermal), and EL-3, a heavy water-moderated materials testing reactor fueled with slightly enriched uranium, which operates at a power level of 15,000 kilowatts (thermal).

Fontenay-aux-Roses (CENFAR), on the outskirts of Paris, is a nuclear technology center operated by CEA, whose facilities include three research reactors: ZOE (EL-1), France's first reactor, a small heavy water-moderated unit fueled with natural uranium, operates at a power level of 150 kilowatts (thermal) and has been in service since 1948. TRITON, a recently completed pool-type research reactor, operates at a power level of 1200 kilowatts (thermal). MINERVE, a low-power unit is used to test the purity of materials and for physics research.

Centre d'Etudes Nucléaires de Grenoble (CENG), at Grenoble, is a nuclear research center operated by CEA in close collaboration with the University of Grenoble. Its experimental facilities include MELUSINE, a pool-type research reactor which operates at a power level of 1200 kilowatts (thermal), and a second research reactor, SILOE, is under construction.

Centre d'Etudes Nucléaires de Cadarache (CENC), at Cadarache, 50 miles east of Avignon, is CEA's newest research center. As of 1961, three reactors were under construction at this site: PEGASE, a 30,000-kilowatt (thermal) light water-moderated and cooled tank reactor is to be used to test nuclear fuels. RAPSODIE, a sodium-cooled fast breeder reactor, is to be used for fast neutron irradiation work and studies of plutonium breeding. The third reactor under construction at Cadarache is a prototype submarine propulsion unit of the pressurized water type.

Production Activity. France is one of four countries known to be engaged in the production of nuclear weapons, the others being the United States, the United Kingdom and the U.S.S.R.

Raw materials production comes under CEA's Division of Production. At present, essentially all uranium ore supplies come from metropolitan France, the principal mining locations being at Margnac, Bois Noir, l'Escarpière and La Chapelle-Largeau. Reserves in metropolitan France are estimated at 25-30,000 tons of contained uranium, expressed as U_3O_8, with potential reserves totaling an additional 50,000 tons. In addition, major deposits have been discovered in Gabon Republic, Africa, which are expected to furnish 600 tons of uranium per year, after 1962. Uranium ore is processed in four mills, located at Bessines, Forez, L'Escarpière, and Gueugnon. These facilities have a total capacity in excess of 1 million tons of ore per year.

Mill concentrates and rich ore fractions are refined and reduced to metal at Le Bouchet, 30 miles southeast of Paris, and at Malvési, near Narbonne. Production of uranium metal is at the rate of 1200 tons per year and is expected to reach 1800 tons per year after 1962. Several hundred tons per year of thorium oxide are also produced in these facilities from Madagascar ores.

Plutonium is produced at a large plant at Marcoule, 17 miles northwest of Avignon. The facilities include three air-cooled graphite-moderated plutonium production reactors (G-1, -2, -3) and a chemical separations plant of the solvent-extraction type, together with auxiliary installations such as graphite machining facilities. The plutonium production rate is reported to be in the neighborhood of 100 kilograms per year.

Pilot gaseous diffusion facilities for the separation of uranium isotopes have been in operation since 1958. A full-scale gaseous diffusion plant for uranium-235 production is under construction at Drôme, south of Pierrelatte near the hydroelectric development at Donzère.

High-purity graphite for the production reactors at Marcoule and for power reactors is produced by the Pechiney Company at Chedde. Plans have been formulated for the commercial production of heavy water (see below).

Energy Economy. France's electric power capacity is about 20,000 megawatts, about equally divided between hydroelectric and thermal stations. France is a net importer of fuel, her imports of coal currently amounting to 10-20% of annual requirements and those of oil amounting to 90-95% of annual requirements. Most oil imports come from the Middle East, but this is changing with the development of oil fields in the French Sahara. Limited hydroelectric expansion is in progress. Large natural gas deposits have recently been discovered at Lacq in the Pyrenees.

Nuclear Power Program. France looks to nuclear power as a means of stabilizing her energy economy and reducing dependence on fuel imports. With approximately 120 megawatts (electrical) of nuclear power capacity operational now (see below), France expects to have some 850 megawatts in operation by 1965. Following are notes on specific installations or projects:

The G-2 and G-3 plutonium-production reactors at Marcoule each have auxiliary power generation facilities rated at 30 megawatts net electrical output.

EDF-1, located at Avoine near Chinon, is an improved version of G-3, optimized for power production. Built as a project of Electricité de France and completed in 1960, it has a net electrical output of 63 megawatts.

EDF-2, an improved and larger version of EDF-1, is under construction at Avoine. It is scheduled to be in operation in 1963 and is designed for a net electrical output of 167 megawatts.

EDF-3, another unit in the same series, is planned for completion at Avoine in 1965 and will have a net electrical output in the range, 250-320 megawatts.

Centrale Nucléaire Franco-Belge des Ardennes: This is a 242-megawatt (electrical) nuclear power station of the pressurized water type scheduled to be placed in operation in 1965 at Chooz (Givet) in the French Ardennes, near the Franco-Belgian border. The plant is being financed by Société d'Energie Nucléaire Franco-Belge des Ardennes (SENA), which is a joint (50-50) venture of the French national utility company, Electricité de France and the Belgian utility syndicate, Centre et Sud. This project is to be carried out under the terms of the **U.S.-Euratom Joint Nuclear Power Program.** A contract was awarded in 1960 to Westinghouse Electric Company and its licensees, Framatom (in France) and Ateliers des Constructions Electriques de Charleroi (in Belgium), for this project.

EL-4, under construction south of Morlaix in Brittany, is a prototype heavy water-moderated gas-cooled power reactor which will operate on natural uranium and is designed for a net electrical output of 80 megawatts. It is scheduled to be operational in the mid-sixties.

As has been indicated in the earlier notes, France is also active in the development of reactors for nuclear ship propulsion, and in research on thermonuclear power (controlled fusion).

Industry Notes. See table.

PARTIAL LISTING OF FRENCH INDUSTRY ACTIVE IN ATOMIC ENERGY

Firm or Group	*Notes*
ATEN (Association Technique pour la Production & l'Utilisation de l'Energie Nucléaire) (Paris)	Industry association similar to the U.S. Atomic Industrial Forum.
AUXI-ATOME (Société Auxiliaire pour l'Energie Atomique) (Paris)	Syndicate formed to supply auxiliary nuclear equipment and instruments.
BREVATOME (Société Française pour la Gestion des Brevets d'Application Nucléaire) (Paris)	Association for coordinating patent rights in various areas of the nuclear field.
CARATOM (Compagnie d'Applications & de Recherches Atomiques) (Bonneuil-sur-Marne)	Syndicate formed to supply nuclear instruments and related apparatus.
CICAF (Compagnie Industrielle des Combustibles Atomiques Frittés) (Corbeville)	Syndicate formed for the manufacture of sintered ceramic fuels.
CLAA (Centre Lyonnais d'Applications Atomiques) (Lyon)	Association of companies interested in radiation applications, now operating an experimental food irradiation facility at Dagneux, near Lyon.
COFINATOME (Compagnie de Financement de l'Industrie Atomique) (Paris)	Syndicate formed to finance medium and small-scale enterprises in the nuclear energy field.
CONSERVATOM (Lyon)	Association of companies interested in food preservation and other radiation applications.
DYNATOM (Le Plessis-Robinson)	Syndicate formed for reactor construction, with emphasis on sodium-graphite and organic cooled power reactors and solution-type research reactors.
FRAMATOME (Société Franco-Americaine de Constructions Atomiques) (Puteaux)	Reactor design and manufacturing syndicate. Licensee of Westinghouse Electric Corporation.
FRANCE-ATOME (Paris)	Syndicate formed to undertake industrial-scale ventures in the nuclear field. Designed and constructed the G-2 and G-3 reactors under contract to CEA.
"G3A" (Groupement Atomique Alsacienne Atlantique) (Le Plessis-Robinson)	Syndicate formed to supply nuclear and non-nuclear components of nuclear power plants.
INDATOM (Groupement pour l'Industrie Atomique (Paris)	Reactor design and manufacturing syndicate.
PROPATOM (Paris)	Association of three largest French shipyards for coordination in the field of nuclear propulsion.
SATNUC (Société pour les Applications Techniques dans le Domaine de l'Energie Nucléaire) (Paris)	Association of firms interested in atomic energy applications in the chemical industry.
SCUMRA (Société Centrale de l'Uranium et des Minerais et Métaux Radioactifs) (Paris)	Syndicate for uranium prospecting and processing.
SENA (Société d'Energie Nucléaire Franco-Belge des Ardennes) (Paris)	Corporation formed by France's EDF (50%) and Belgium's Centre et Sud (50%) to construct and operate the Centrale Nucléaire Franco-Belge des Ardennes nuclear power station.
SERATOM (Société d'Etudes & des Recherches Atomiques) (Paris)	Syndicate of engineering firms.

PARTIAL LISTING OF FRENCH INDUSTRY
ACTIVE IN ATOMIC ENERGY, *Continued*

Firm or Group	*Notes*
SICN (Société Industrielle des Combustibles Nucléaires) (Annecy)	Syndicate for the fabrication of fuel elements, especially of the pellet type.
SIMO (Société Industrielle des Minerais de l'Ouest) (Paris)	Joint subsidiary of Kuhlman and CEA formed to operate France's uranium mills at l'Escarpière, Bessines, and Forez.
SOD (Société d'Etudes pour l'Obtention du Deuterium) (Paris)	Syndicate formed by CEA and private interests for the production of heavy water by means other than liquefaction.
SODERN (Société Anonyme d'Etudes & Realisations Nucléaires) (Suresnes)	Syndicate formed for the manufacture of electronic devices used in the production or utilization of nuclear energy.
SRTI (Société de Recherches Techniques & Industrielles) (Paris)	Syndicate formed for studies and experiments on uranium isotope separation.
SRU (Société de Raffinage d'Uranium) (Paris)	Organization formed by CEA and private interests to uranium refinery at Malvési.
SUD-ATOME (Paris)	Syndicate of southern shipyards and other interests formed to study nuclear propulsion systems for tankers.
TRANSNUCLEAIRE (Compagnie pour le Transport des Combustibles Nucléaires & d'Isotopes Radioactifs) (Lyon)	Syndicate of freight forwarders formed to conduct studies and provide services in connection with the handling, warehousing, and transporting of radioactive materials.
TRANSPORTATOME (Paris)	Association concerned with the transportation of radioactive materials.
USSI (Société de Construction d'une Usine de Séparation Isotopique) (Le Plessis-Robinson)	Organization formed by CEA and SRTI (see above) to design and construct CEA's gaseous diffusion plant at Pierrelatte.

FREE RADICAL

An electrically neutral (uncharged) atom, molecule, or molecular fragment having an unpaired electron in an outer electron shell and hence chemically unstable and highly reactive. Free radical formation can be induced in matter by chemical means, by an electrical discharge, by ultraviolet light, and by ionizing radiation. The process of formation is complex and not yet fully understood. It is believed that transient free radical phenomena are involved in many of the chemical and biological effects of ionizing radiation.

FUEL CELLS

Battery-type devices for the direct conversion of chemical energy to electrical energy by electrochemical techniques. This topic, while peripheral to atomic energy development, warrants mention because fuel cells represent a means of power generation that is potentially competitive with thermal power generating techniques (both conventional and nuclear). Also, as will be noted, there is some interest in the use of ionizing radiation as a means of regenerating the fuel consumed in chemical fuel cells.

The simplest example of a fuel cell is the so-called "hydrox" cell in which hydrogen and oxygen are reacted to produce water and a low-voltage direct current. In one such system, porous carbon electrodes connected into an electrical circuit (i.e., tied in with an external load) are immersed in an electrolyte solution, such as potassium hydroxide. Hydrogen is continuously fed to the anode and oxygen (or air) is continuously fed to the cathode. Electrons are released at the anode by the following reaction.

$$H_2 + 2OH \longrightarrow 2H_2O + 2e$$

The electrons flow to the cathode where the following reaction takes place:

$$O_2 + 2H_2O + 4e \longrightarrow 4OH$$

The over-all reaction can then be written as follows:

$$2H_2 + O_2 \longrightarrow 2H_2O$$

As a rough approximation, the amount of useful energy obtained by reacting chemicals in a fuel cell is within 10% (plus or minus) of that which would be obtained by burning the same materials in a conventional combustion chamber. The advantage of the electrochemical process, relative to a conventional combustion process, is that it is not subject to Carnot-type thermodynamic losses. In theory, fuel cells can achieve chemical-to-electrical energy conversion efficiencies approaching 100%. An efficiency of 98% has been demonstrated under special laboratory conditions, and efficiencies above 60 or 65% are attainable under practical conditions. Fuel cells thus offer the possibility of achieving low fuel costs even without provision for fuel regeneration.

The types of fuel cell currently under development can be broadly categorized as follows:

1. Cells fueled with hydrogen and oxygen of air: These are primarily of interest for military applications requiring power outputs in the range, 500 watts to 5 kilowatts for a sustained period of time.* The basic feasibility of such cells is well established; some have operated continuously for two years or longer. The principal problem is the weight and cost of the equipment. (A 1-kilowatt hydrox cell weighs 100-150 pounds and consumes about 1 pound of fuel per hour). Designs fall into two general categories—low-pressure, low-temperature cells (1-50 psi, 100-300°F); and high-pressure, medium-temperature cells (400-1000 psi, 400-600°F).

* Cells with outputs of 1000–15,000 kilowatts have been supplied for specialized military applications.

2. Cells fueled with hydrocarbons and oxygen or air: These are of interest for large-scale power applications, such as supplying low-voltage d.c. current for industrial electrochemical manufacturing operations and, ultimately, central electrical power generation. The principal effort is being devoted to high-temperature low-pressure cells (700-1500°F) employing a fused salt electrolyte. Systems being studied include the use of oxygen or air as oxidant and methane, carbon monoxide, propane, kerosene, or other hydrocarbons as fuel in combination with a catalytic agent. Such systems are at an early stage of development and are subject to various difficulties (coking of the electrode, excessive corrosion of equipment surfaces, etc.), especially in long runs at high-power outputs.

3. Cells fueled with methanol and oxygen: These are of long-range interest for commercial applications such as providing motive power for automobiles. They are also at an early stage of development.

4. Other: Various other fuel cell systems are being studied with particular emphasis on space vehicle applications. One of the more promising systems, because of its compactness, is a cell fueled with a sodium amalgam and oxygen.

Companies engaged in the fuel cell field include Allis-Chalmers Manufacturing Company; California Research Corporation; Curtiss-Wright Corporation; Electric Storage Battery Company; General Electric Company; Lockheed Aircraft Corporation; Monsanto Chemical Co.; M. W. Kellogg Company; Patterson Moos Division of Leesona Corporation (formerly Universal Winding) in liaison with United Aircraft Corporation; Pittsburgh Consolidation Coal Company; Standard Oil Company of New Jersey; Thompson, Ramo and Woolridge, Inc.; Union Carbide Corporation; and Westinghouse Electric Corporation.

Mention was made earlier of fuel regeneration. In principle, the reactants used in a fuel cell can be regenerated by breaking up the reaction product. This can be done in some cases by the application of heat (pyrolysis) and in other cases by means of ionizing radiation (radiolysis). An example of a radiolytic regeneration system is the use of gamma radiation to dissociate ferrous sulfate and sulfuric acid into ferric sulfate and hydrogen ions. This system is used in connection with a 5-watt fuel cell being developed for specialized military applications.

FUEL CYCLE

(1) The basic fuel system used in a nuclear reactor as defined by the fissionable and fertile nuclides contained in the fuel and the fissionable nuclide formed during irradiation. (2) The sequence of operations involved in supplying fuel for nuclear power generation.

With reference to the first definition, there are two fuel systems which are true cycles:

1. The U^{233}-Th^{232}-U^{233} cycle in which uranium-233 is used as the fissionable material and thorium as the fertile material, and uranium-233 is produced during irradiation. This is the optimum cycle for **thermal breeder reactors.**

2. The Pu^{239}-U^{238}-Pu^{239} cycle in which plutonium-239 is used as the fissionable material and uranium-238 as the fertile material, and plutonium-239 is produced during irradiation. This is the optimum cycle for **fast breeder reactors.**

There are additionally two fuel "chains," loosely referred to as cycles, which involve the substitution of uranium-235 for uranium-233 or plutonium-239 as the starting fissionable material. These are the U^{235}-TH^{232}-U^{233} and the U^{235}-U^{238}-Pu^{239} chains. The latter is the most commonly used fuel system by reason of the natural occurrence of U^{235} in combination with U^{238}. There are also combination chains, such as U^{235}-U^{238}/Th^{232}-Pu^{239}/U^{233}, and Pu^{239}/U^{235}-U^{238}-Pu^{239}. The former is used in certain power reactors; * the latter is the basis

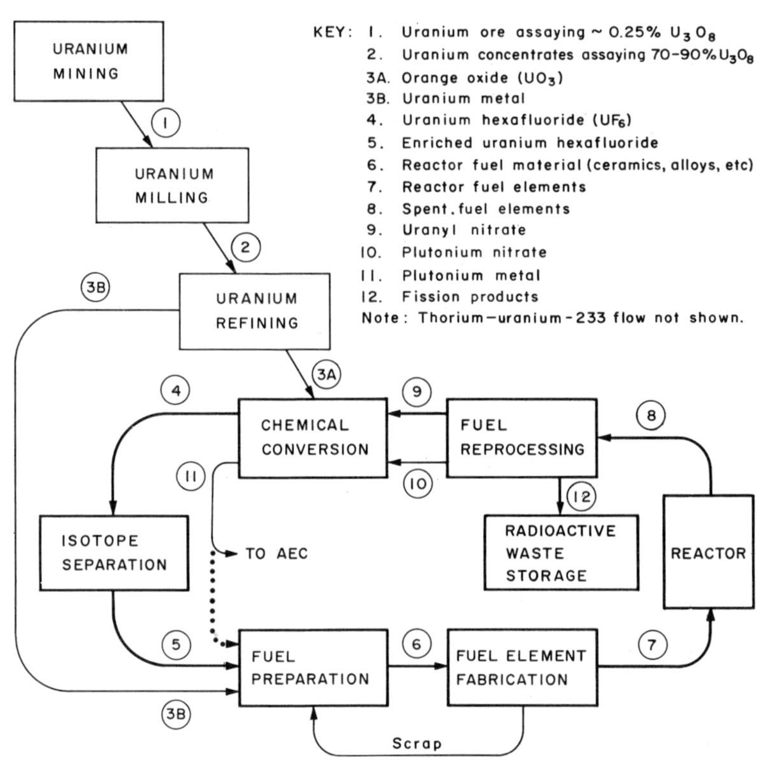

Fig. 65. Operations involved in supplying fuel for nuclear power generation (heavy line denotes "fuel cycle").

* See **Indian Point Station, Elk River Plant.**

for the U.S. Atomic Energy Commission's Plutonium Recycle Program.*

With reference to the second of the above definitions, Fig. 65 shows the major operations involved in supplying fuel for nuclear power generation. For information on fuel-cycle costs, see **nuclear power economics.**

* See **Plutonium Recycle Test Reactor.**

FUEL ELEMENT

A fabricated piece or subassembly of pieces of nuclear fuel, an array of which constitutes

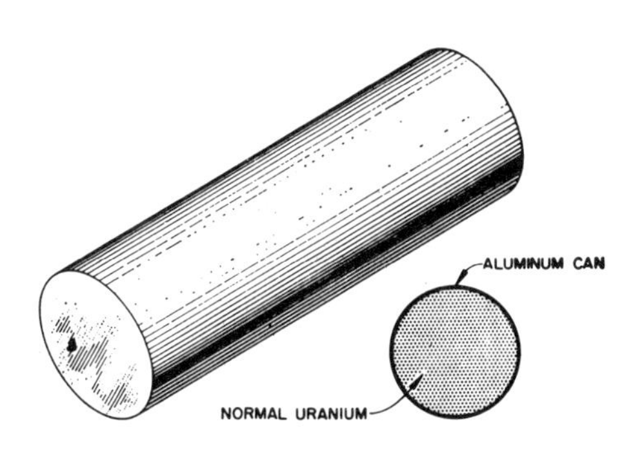

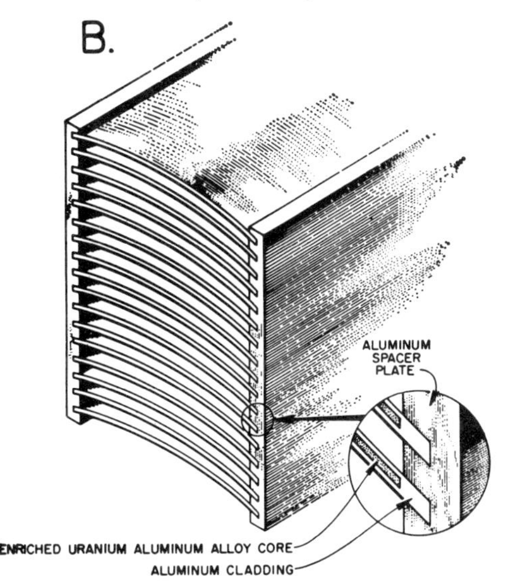

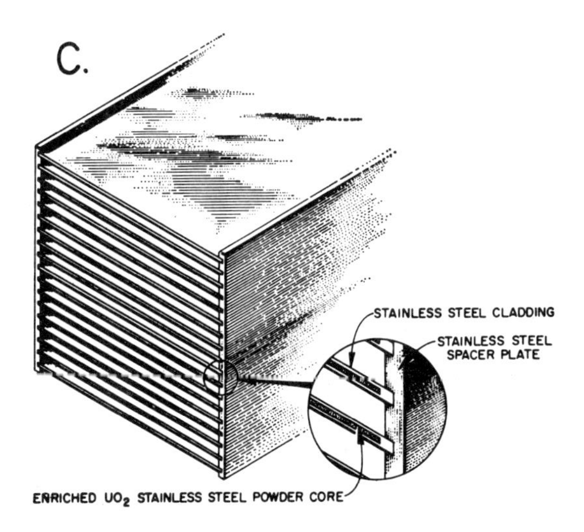

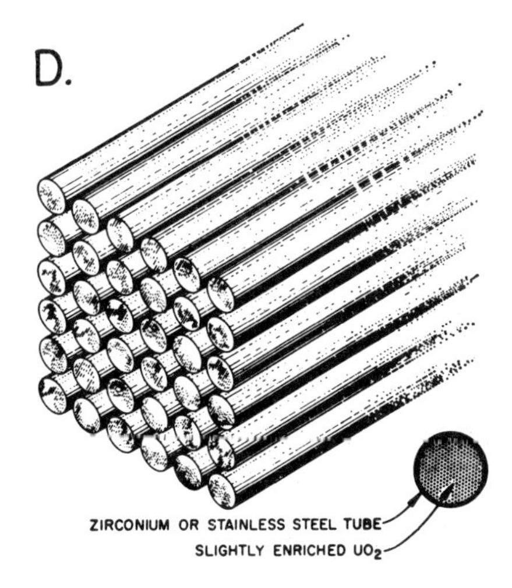

Fig. 66. Representative types of fuel elements. A. Aluminum-clad slug of normal uranium (used in the Oak Ridge Graphite Research Reactor and the Hanford plutonium production reactors). B. Assembly of flat aluminum-clad plates fabricated of enriched uranium-aluminum alloy (the so-called "MTR-type" fuel element used in the Materials Testing Reactor and in many research reactors). C. Assembly of stainless steel-clad plates containing a dispersion of enriched uranium dioxide in a stainless steel matrix (an example of a dispersion-type fuel element used in some power reactors). D. Cluster of zircaloy or stainless steel tubes loaded with slightly enriched uranium dioxide pellets (commonly used in pressurized and boiling water power reactors). (Reprinted from "Management of Nuclear Materials," D. Van Nostrand Co., Inc., 1960)

the core of a nuclear reactor. An integral part of a fuel element is the cladding provided to protect the fuel from corrosion by the reactor coolant and/or to contain the fission products formed during irradiation. Fuel elements range from simple solid cylindrical slugs to complex subassemblies of pellets, tubes, rods, plates or other fabricated shapes. (See **reactor, nuclear; fuel element fabrication)**

FUEL ELEMENT FABRICATION

Discussion of this topic will be mainly devoted to the metallurgical, mechanical, and quality control operations involved in solid fuel element fabrication, with particular reference to the types of fuel elements of interest in civilian nuclear power development, and to notes on the fuel element fabrication industry. For information on the materials used in fuel elements for civilian power reactors, see **reactor materials.** For information on fuel element fabrication costs, see **nuclear power economics.**

Fuel element fabrication encompasses (1) preparation of the fuel material; (2) forming it into the desired shapes; (3) applying a protective cladding; (4) providing for an effective thermal bond between the fuel and cladding; (5) inspection and assembly of fuel elements; (6) nondestructive testing of the completed fuel elements; and (7) recovery of scrap materials. Certain of these steps may be combined in a single operation (see below). Throughout the fabrication sequence, close control of inventories of nuclear material must be maintained (see **accountability for source and special nuclear materials).** Also, care must be taken to control radiation, pyrophoric and criticality hazards. For information relating to the first, see **radioactive waste disposal.**

The simplest fuel elements presently in service are those used in plutonium production reactors. They consist of short cylindrical slugs of unalloyed natural uranium metal encased in and bonded to close-fitting thin-walled aluminum cans. In contrast, the fuel elements used in high-performance military power reactors characteristically consist of precision assemblies of plates, discs, pins or other shapes fabricated to extremely close dimensional tolerances from alloys or dispersions of highly enriched uranium clad with zircaloy, stainless steel or other relatively expensive protective materials. Fuel elements used in civilian power reactors range between the two extremes. The principal types, in order of increasing difficulty of fabrication, can be categorized as follows:

1. Unalloyed metal.
2. Alloys.
3. Oxides or other ceramics.
4. Dispersions.
5. Fuels containing plutonium and hence requiring semiremote fabrication techniques.
6. Fuels requiring remote fabrication techniques.

The fabrication procedures are briefly described in the paragraphs immediately following.

Unalloyed Metal Fuel Elements. The only power reactors that are fueled with unalloyed natural uranium metal are low-temperature (Calder-Hall-type) **gas-cooled reactors** and **heavy water-moderated power reactors.** The former use magnox *-clad fuel rods; the latter use zircaloy-2 clad tubular fuel elements. Fabrication involves casting large ingots or dingots, which are worked to final shape by rolling, forging or extrusion. The cladding is applied by hot rolling, pressure bonding, or extrusion. A coextrusion process for fabricating clad tubular fuel elements has been developed.

Alloy Fuel Elements. Uranium-molybdenum alloys clad with stainless steel are currently used in **organic cooled reactors,** and **sodium-graphite reactors** and **fast breeder reactors.**** The alloy material is usually prepared by vacuum induction melting, skull melting with nonconsumable electrodes, or consumable electrode arc melting. It is then

* Magnesium containing 1% beryllium.

** Other alloy fuels include uranium-zirconium alloys (used in Naval propulsion reactors); uranium-aluminum (used in many research reactors); uranium-thorium alloys; and uranium-niobium alloys; as well as many ternary alloy formulations.

Fig. 67. Examples of equipment used in fabricating metallic fuel elements. Top left, vacuum arc melting furnace for melting fuel alloy. Top right, equipment for making graphite molds used in precision casting of fuel shapes. Center, rolling mill for precision rolling of fuel strips. Bottom, equipment for welding fuel elements in an inert atmosphere. (*Courtesy of M&C Nuclear, Inc., a subsidiary of Texas Instruments, Inc. and National Lead Company* (top right).

Fig. 68. Hermetically sealed facilities for semi-remote fabrication of plutonium fuel elements at Argonne National Laboratory. Top, general view. Bottom left, conveyor line as seen through viewing window. Bottom right, analytical balance. (*Courtesy of Argonne National Laboratory*)

Fig. 69. Steps in fabricating oxide fuel elements. Top left, uranium dioxide (UO_2) powder is mixed with an inert binder preparatory to being compacted into pellets. Center left, compacted pellets are placed in heat-resistant boxes and sintered at high temperatures. The pellets are then inspected and loaded into tubes. Bottom left, tube subassemblies are tested in a battery of autoclaves before final assembly. Above, final fuel element being lowered into storage drum; 462 of these fuel elements make up a core loading for the 180-megawatt (electrical) Dresden Nuclear Power Station. (*Courtesy of General Electric Co.*)

cast and worked into final shape by rolling, forging or extrusion. In some cases fuel rods are loaded into stainless steel tubes with sodium added for thermal bonding. In other cases the cladding is applied by hot-rolling, pressure bonding or extrusion. The clad shapes are then assembled into a fuel element. With some exceptions, alloy-fuel fabrication techniques are not as well developed as those for unalloyed uranium. A common problem is maintaining uniform distribution of the component metals during the casting process.

Ceramic Fuel Elements. Uranium dioxide (UO_2) fuel pellets are commonly used in **boiling** and **pressurized water reactors** and are one of the fuel forms used in high-temperature **gas-cooled reactors.** Mixtures of uranium and thorium dioxide are also used.* The fuel pellets are loaded into stainless steel or zircaloy-2 tubes; helium is added to provide a **thermal bond,** and caps are welded onto the ends of each tube. A bundle of fuel tubes constitutes a fuel element. The pellets, which measure ~ 3/16 inch in diameter by ~ 3/4 inch in length, are fabricated by powder metallurgical techniques. Finely divided oxide powder is cold-pressed into pellet form and sintered at high temperature (~ 1400°C). The pellets are then inspected and where necessary are machined to final size. Rejects are pulverized and repelletized. By use of high compacting pressures (60,000 psi), densities up to 95% of the theoretical density of UO_2 have been achieved. While the results have been satisfactory from a quality standpoint, the costs are high and difficulties are encountered due to variations in powder characteristics. Alternative fuel shapes and new fabrication methods, such as vibratory compacting, swaging or wet extrusion, are being studied in an effort to reduce manufacturing costs.

Uranium monocarbide (UC) is a fuel material of considerable interest, especially for high-temperature power reactors. It is prepared by reacting carbon with uranium metal, uranium dioxide, or other uranium compounds, all of which reactions are difficult to control from a stoichiometric standpoint. Massive uranium carbide is extremely difficult to fabricate. Arc melting and casting techniques are under development but are not yet suited for large-scale production. Uranium monocarbide in powder form is highly pyrophoric but can be fabricated by powder metallurgical techniques under careful atmosphere control.

Dispersion-Type Fuel Elements. Dispersions of fissionable material in a metal or graphite matrix are also of interest for high-temperature reactor applications. An example is the fuel element being developed for the High Temperature Gas-Cooled Reactor (HTGR), which consists of a graphite can containing a dispersion of fully enriched uranium carbide and thorium carbide in a graphite matrix (see **gas-cooled reactors).** Fuel dispersions are prepared by powder metallurgical techniques (see above). Techniques for the fabrication of this type of fuel element are under intensive development.

Plutonium Fuel Elements. The use of plutonium as a reactor fuel is being studied under the U.S. Atomic Energy Commission's Plutonium Recycle Program.** Of particular interest is the possibility of using plutonium in combination with natural or depleted uranium as a substitute for isotopically enriched uranium, i.e., as a means of "synthetic" fuel enrichment. Both alloy and ceramic plutonium fuels are being developed. Plutonium-aluminum alloys have been prepared by adding metallic plutonium to molten aluminum in pot furnaces; and by heating plutonium oxide (PuO_2) and aluminum in the presence of a flux (sodium aluminum fluoride). The resulting alloy casting is extruded into fuel rods, which are clad with zircaloy-2 by drawing and swaging techniques and assembled into cluster-type fuel elements. Aluminum-clad rods have been produced by coextrusion. Methods of casting plutonium-aluminum alloy directly into aluminum, stainless steel, or zircaloy-2 sheathing are under development. PuO_2 and PuO_2-UO_2 mixtures have been prepared by powder metallurgical techniques and fabri-

---

* See **Indian Point Station, Elk River Plant.**

** See **Plutonium Recycle Test Reactor.**

cated into rods by cold-swaging and other methods. All these operations are complicated by the extreme toxicity of plutonium, which requires that it be handled by semiremote techniques in glove-boxes or other gas-tight enclosures, and also by criticality hazards.

Remote Fabrication. It is hoped to be able to operate **fast breeder reactors** with a "closed fuel system." * Spent fuel elements would be removed from the reactor to an adjoining facility in which they would be disassembled and the fuel partially decontaminated by **pyrometallurgical reprocessing.** The fuel, still intensely radioactive, would then be upgraded by the addition of fresh fuel material, refabricated, reassembled into fuel elements and returned to service. Success of this scheme depends upon the feasibility of conducting fuel element fabrication operations and doing maintenance work on the fabrication machinery by remote manipulation and control. Techniques for these tasks, including a method of centrifugally casting fuel pins, have been developed and are being piloted. (See **Experimental Breeder Reactor No. II)**

It should be added that the problem of remote refabrication also arises in connection with the thorium-uranium-233 fuel cycle. This is due to the formation of certain heavy isotopes that are not removed by reprocessing and which, by radioactive decay, form intense gamma-emitting daughter products. (See discussion under **fuel reprocessing)**

Quality Control. Fuel element fabrication requires exceedingly close quality control at all stages since malfunction of fuel elements, e.g., cladding failures, can have serious consequences in reactor operation. The cost of quality control is a significant factor in the total cost of fuel element fabrication, and may account for as much as 40 or 50% of the total even in semistandardized production runs. A major aspect of quality control is nondestructive testing of completed fuel shapes and fuel element assemblies. The qualities tested include fuel content and distribution; isotope content and distribution; physical dimensions; quality of the thermal bond; and integrity of the cladding. Various test methods are employed. Examples are radiographic inspection to detect variations in fuel density; ultrasonic tests to detect unbonded areas in metallurgically bonded fuel elements; eddy current tests to detect variations in cladding thickness; and helium leak testing to detect gross cladding defects.

Fuel Element Manufacturers. At one time fuel element fabrication operations were exclusively conducted in government-owned plants and laboratories. Today fuel elements used in plutonium production continue to be manufactured in government-owned plants ** and fuel elements for many experimental reactors continue to be fabricated in government-owned laboratories. However, all other fuel element fabrication activity is conducted by manufacturing concerns on a license or contract basis. Firms holding AEC licenses for fuel element fabrication as of December 31, 1961 are listed in Table 1, p. 190.

FUEL HANDLING MECHANISMS

Remotely operated mechanisms used in power reactor installations for loading and unloading individual fuel elements or complete core assemblies. The fuel handling system employed in the Shippingport Atomic Power Station may be taken as an example.

The head closure of the Shippingport reactor vessel is removed when it is desired to install or replace a complete core assembly. Core replacement is carried out by means of a crane-operated precision grappling tool which engages the core, lifts it out of the reactor vessel, and carries it into an adjoining fuel-handling facility through a water-filled canal. The pit in which the reactor is located and a section of the canal extending over it are flooded to provide a water shield during the removal operation.†

* See discussion under **fuel reprocessing.**

** See **Feed Materials Production Center, Weldon Spring Plant, Hanford Works, Savannah River Plant.**

† The procedure described is known as "wet refueling." The plant is also equipped for "dry refueling," which involves the use of shielded coffins.

TABLE 1. FIRMS LICENSED TO FABRICATE FUEL ELEMENTS OR PROCESS FUEL MATERIALS (DECEMBER 31, 1961)

Firm	*Location*	*Notes* [1]			
		A	*B* [2]	*C*	*D*
Aerojet-General Corp.	San Ramon, Calif.	X			
Babcock & Wilcox Co.	Lynchburg, Va.	X	X		
Battelle Memorial Institute	Columbus, Ohio				X
Carborundum Co.	Niagara Falls, N.Y.				X
Clevite Corp.	Cleveland, Ohio				X
(Combustion Engineering Co.) [3]	Windsor, Conn.	X	X		
Davison Chemical Co.	Erwin, Tenn.			X	
Engelhard Industries, Inc. (D. E. Makepeace Division)	Plainville, Mass.				X
General Atomic (Division of General Dynamics Corp.)	San Diego, Calif.	X			
General Electric Co.	San Jose, Calif.	X	X [4]		
M & C Nuclear Inc. (Division of Texas Instruments, Inc.	Attleboro, Mass.		X		X
The Martin Co.	Middle River, Md.	X			
National Lead Co.	Albany, N.Y.			X	
Nuclear Materials and Equipment Corp. (NUMEC)	Apollo, Pa.			X	X
Nuclear Metals, Inc.	Concord, Mass.				X
Olin Mathieson Chemical Co.	New Haven, Conn.		X		X
Spencer Chemical Co.	Kansas City, Mo.			X	
Sylvania Corning Nuclear Corp.	Hicksville, N.Y.				X
United Nuclear Corp. (Chemicals Division) [5]	Hematite, Mo.			X	
Westinghouse Electric Corp.	Blairsville and Forest Hills, Pa.	X	X		

[1] A—Reactor manufacturer; B—Supplier of cores for Naval propulsion reactors; C—Engaged in the preparation of fuel materials or in nonirradiated scrap recovery; D—Other (research and development organization, independent fuel fabricator, etc.).
[2] Contract, as opposed to licensed, activity.
[3] License application pending.
[4] Operations conducted at Knolls Atomic Power Laboratory, Schenectady, N.Y.
[5] Formerly an operation of Mallinckrodt Chemical Works.

The head closure contains a number of access ports by means of which individual fuel elements can be replaced without removing the closure. This is done by means of a crane-operated precision extraction tool. A diaphragm seal is placed over the reactor pit so that only the overhead canal needs to be flooded during this operation. (Fig. 70)

FUEL MATERIALS, REACTOR. See **reactor materials.**

FUEL REPROCESSING

The chemical or metallurgical treatment of irradiated reactor fuel for the purpose of recovering and decontaminating fissionable and/or fertile materials contained therein.

In the operation of a nuclear reactor it is necessary to replace the fuel when only partially consumed for one or more of the following reasons: (1) to prevent excessive loss in reactivity due to the accumulation of fission product poisons; (2) to avoid excessive radiation damage to solid fuel elements—in particular, rupture of fuel element cladding and release of radioactive fission product contaminants into the coolant stream; (3) to recover bred fissionable material. The degree of allowable irradiation exposure is determined by reactor design. In power reactors fueled with natural or slightly enriched uranium, the fuel **burn-up** presently achieved is of the order 1 to 2% of the total amount of fissionable and fertile material originally contained. In reactors fueled with highly enriched uranium, burn-up may be as high as 40 or 50%.

The principal operations involved in reprocessing solid fuel elements are: (1) decay cooling, (2) decladding and/or dissolution, (3) chemical separation of the fissionable and fertile constituents, (4) decontamination (i.e., removal of fission product contaminants), (5) product recovery, and (6) disposal of radioactive wastes. The latter operation is discussed under separate heading. (See **radioactive waste disposal**)

Due to the intense radioactivity of irradiated fuel, a considerable portion of the main process systems of a reprocessing plant must be installed behind massive shielding and operated essentially by remote control. Features such as these make fuel reprocessing facilities very much more expensive to build than conventional chemical plants of comparable size and process complexity.

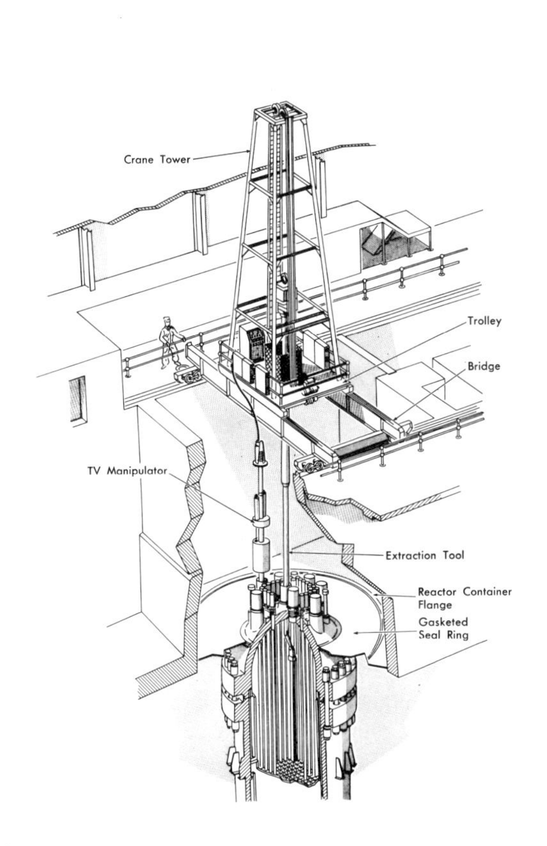

Fig. 70. Left, crane-operated tool used to load and unload fuel elements in the Shippingport Atomic Power Station. (Reprinted from "The Shippingport Pressurized Water Reactor," Addison-Wesley Publishing Co., 1958.) Right, fuel-handling mechanism built for Hallam Nuclear Power Facility seen prior to being dismantled and shipped to the Hallam site. (*Courtesy of Atomics International*)

Existing Facilities. The need for fuel reprocessing first arose in the United States in connection with the operation of plutonium production reactors. During the **Manhattan Project,** a chemical precipitation process was used at Hanford for the separation and decontamination of plutonium (see **bismuth**

phosphate process). The plants built at that time operated on a batch basis and there was no provision for recovering uranium, which was piped to underground waste storage tanks in contaminated form. After the war new plant facilities were installed at Hanford and Savannah River for the continuous separation and decontamination of uranium and plutonium by means of **solvent extraction** (see **Redox process, Purex process).** Also installed at Hanford were temporary facilities for the recovery of the uranium that had accumulated in the underground waste tanks.

The production reprocessing facilities at Hanford and Savannah River are designed to handle fuel elements fabricated of normal uranium metal clad with aluminum. Another important reprocessing facility is the **Idaho Chemical Processing Plant** at the National Reactor Testing Station. This plant uses a modified version of the Purex Process for uranium recovery and decontamination (see **25-TBP process).** It is used to reprocess highly enriched fuel principally of the aluminum-clad, aluminum-uranium alloy type used in many materials testing and research reactors.

An additional reprocessing facility which should be noted is the Metal Recovery Plant at Oak Ridge National Laboratory. This is a relatively small-scale facility originally built to pilot the **Thorex process** for the reprocessing of irradiated thorium by solvent extraction. It currently serves as a reprocessing "job shop" handling normal and enriched uranium fuel elements from various research and developmental reactors.

Technology. In recent years, a number of methods have been studied for reprocessing power reactor fuels, especially those used or planned for use in civilian nuclear power plants. The nature and variety of the fuel and cladding materials used in power reactors and the variety of fuel element designs combine to make the aggregate reprocessing problem exceedingly complex. By way of introduction to this topic, a distinction should be made between "open-cycle" and "closed-cycle" reactor fuel systems. In the former, the unconsumed fuel recovered from spent fuel elements is refabricated by conventional means involving direct contact with the material; hence a high degree of decontamination must be accomplished during reprocessing. In the latter, the fuel is only partially decontaminated during reprocessing and, being still intensely radioactive, must be refabricated by remote techniques. At the present time, closed-cycle operation is principally of interest in connection with **fast breeder reactors.**

The above distinction is important when considering the logistics of providing fuel reprocessing services to the nuclear power industry. Thus, it is generally envisioned that open-cycle reprocessing services will be supplied by a "central station" reprocessing facility serving a number of power reactor installations—this on the expectation that savings in unit costs due to high through-put will more than offset the costs of transporting the intensely radioactive fuels to the central reprocessing plant. In the case of closed-cycle reprocessing, it is expected that reprocessing loops will be built as an integral part of the reactor installations and that only product recovery operations will be conducted at an off-site facility.

Two basic reprocessing methods are applicable to open-cycle operation: (1) solvent extraction and (2) **fluoride volatility.** Both methods can achieve high **decontamination factors** ($\sim 10^7$). For closed-cycle operation, various **pyrometallurgical** reprocessing techniques are being developed which, in general, can only achieve decontamination factors of the order of 10 or 100. These three basic reprocessing methods are discussed below.

Solvent Extraction. The operations involved in the solvent extraction reprocessing of normal or slightly enriched uranium fuel are generally as follows:

1. Decay cooling: On removal from the reactor, the fuel elements are stored, generally under water, for 90-180 days to allow for the decay of uranium-237 and short-lived fission products. The fuel elements are then transported to the reprocessing site in heavily shielded shipping casks equipped with means for heat dissipation.

2. Head-end treatment: Where feasible the fuel element fittings and cladding are wholly or partially removed by mechanical devices. The fuel and any residual cladding is then chemically dissolved, and the resulting aqueous solution is adjusted for proper extraction conditions.

3. Chemical separations: The nitrate solution then enters the first cycle of the solvent extraction system wherein a gross separation is effected between the fission products and the uranium/plutonium mixture. This is accomplished by counterflow with an organic solvent. The fission products remain in the aqueous phase, the uranium/plutonium transferring to the organic phase. In a second cycle of treatment the uranium and plutonium are separated. In a third cycle, the uranium and plutonium streams are separately processed to remove fission products.

4. Product recovery: The decontaminated uranium and plutonium streams are then concentrated by ion exchange or other methods and leave the plant as uranyl and plutonium nitrate solutions. The uranium can be handled in a direct fashion, i.e., without the need for shielding or remote manipulation. The plutonium, while "clean" from the standpoint of fission product contamination, requires special handling, as always, due to its alpha radioactivity and extreme toxicity.

Flexibility can be built into such a processing sequence in two ways: (1) By installing two or more head-end systems to accommodate different fuel element constituents. A number of methods of head-end treatment are being developed, including the **Darex** and **Sulfex** processes (for stainless steel-clad fuel elements) and the **Zirflex** and **Zircex** processes (for zircaloy-clad fuel elements). (2) By designing the system so that subcritical conditions can be safely maintained when fuels of different degrees of enrichment are handled. This is partly a matter of equipment sizing and partly a matter of adjusting stream flow and concentration.

The above described techniques are commonly referred to as "aqueous reprocessing." The technology of the chemical separation and product recovery steps is well established by virtue of applicable experience gained in the solvent-extraction reprocessing of spent fuel from production and research reactors. The technology of the head-end operation is under development and, for some power reactor fuels, is at an early stage of experimentation.

Fluoride Volatility. In this method of reprocessing, advantage is taken of the volatility of uranium hexafluoride (UF_6) relative to that of fission product fluorides. After decay cooling, the fuel elements are dissolved, using hydrogen fluoride (HF) for high-alloy fuels and an interhalogen compound such as bromine trifluoride (BrF_3) for low-alloy fuels. The UF_6 is then distilled off at temperatures of about 100°C. Plutonium recovery by this method presents a difficult and as yet unsolved problem; however, some favorable results have been achieved.

Fluoride volatility techniques have been successfully demonstrated on a limited scale in pilot facilities. The potential advantages of this reprocessing method, relative to aqueous reprocessing, are: (1) Fewer process operations are required; hence there is a good possibility of achieving lower equipment costs. (2) Much smaller (i.e., more concentrated) volumes of high-level radioactive wastes are generated.

Pyrometallurgical Techniques. These are high-temperature methods in which the fuel is processed in a molten state. The techniques that have been studied include **oxide slagging** (also known as oxide drossing), **metal-to-metal extraction, fused salt extraction, electrorefining, vacuum distillation, fractional crystallization,** and **zone melting.** Of these, oxide slagging and fractional crystallization appear the most promising. As was noted earlier, pyro-reprocessing is limited to closed-cycle reactor fuel systems. It should be added that the feasibility of this method of operation is contingent on the practicability of remote fabrication of fuel elements. (See **fuel element fabrication)**

Thorium Reprocessing Complication. Mention should be made of the fact that the open-cycle reprocessing of thorium fuel or blanket elements is complicated by the presence in the irradiated material of alpha-emitting uranium-232 and its daughter product, thorium-228, also an alpha emitter. These isotopes are not removed by reprocessing as are the fission product contaminants. Thus, the separated thorium will contain some unstable thorium-228, whose decay products include bismuth-212 and thallium-208, both of which are intense gamma emitters. Similarly, the separated uranium-233 will contain some uranium-232, which decays to thorium-228, leading in turn to the formation of the gamma emitters just noted. In this fashion, both the reclaimed fertile material (thorium) and the product fissionable material (uranium-233) become sufficiently radioactive *after* fission-product decontamination to create handling problems during subsequent fuel-cycle operations.

Fig. 71. One of the operating corridors in the Idaho Chemical Processing Plant. (*Courtesy Phillips Petroleum Co.*)

Reprocessing Services. With several large-scale civilian nuclear power plants already in operation, and others to follow, the problem of providing reprocessing services to the nuclear power industry has come to the foreground. As early as 1956, the U.S. Atomic Energy Commission sought to interest industry in providing such services on a commercial basis. In July, 1962, an industrial firm announced plans for a commercial reprocessing venture subject to completion of contract negotiations (see **Nuclear Fuel Services, Inc. Project**).

Pending the construction of commercial reprocessing facilities, the AEC has undertaken to provide the necessary services and has established a pricing formula. The formula is keyed to estimates of the cost of operating an hypothetical solvent extraction plant, designated the "Multipurpose Chemical Processing

Plant," having the capacity and flexibility deemed necessary to handle the near-future reprocessing load of the nuclear power industry. The capital investment required was estimated in 1957 at $20.5 million based on the AEC's experience with the Idaho Chemical Processing Plant and other solvent extraction facilities. Annual operating costs, including depreciation and overhead, have been estimated at $4.6 million, leading to a daily charge, based on 300 days of operation per year, of $15,300 (see Table 1). This daily charge is subject to escalation to reflect estimated changes in construction and operating costs.

TABLE 1. ESTIMATED ANNUAL COSTS OF "MULTIPURPOSE CHEMICAL PROCESSING PLANT"

Direct operating personnel and supervision	$ 382,000	
Supplies	170,000	
Maintenance	130,000	
Analytical services	102,000	
Health physics	36,000	
Utility services: Steam, air, electricity, water	122,000	
Operating overhead	467,000	
Total Operating Costs		$1,409,000
Waste storage	527,000	
Depreciation (10%)	2,057,000	
AEC overhead	599,000	
Total Nonoperating Costs		3,183,000
Total Annual Costs		$4,592,000
Standard AEC daily charge (300 days/year)		15,300 [1]

[1] Based on 1957 cost factors and subject to escalation. Adjusted value as of August, 1960 = $16,988.

In pricing its reprocessing services, the AEC estimates the number of days of operation required to handle a given sized batch of a particular fuel, including processing time and "turn-around" time, i.e., the time taken up in readying the plant to receive the next batch. It then computes the reprocessing cost by multiplying the number of "plant days" by the standard daily use charge. Following, for purposes of illustration, is an estimate for a power reactor fueled with uranium dioxide pellets of 2.5% enrichment in stainless steel tube assemblies:

Rate of dissolution	—	1,000 KgU/day
Rate of extraction	—	1,000 KgU/day
Assumed batch size	—	22,000 KgU
Processing time	—	22 days
Turn-around time	—	8 days
Total plant time	—	30 days
Processing charge	—	30 × 16,988 [1] or $510,000
Unit cost	—	~$24/KgU [2]

[1] Standard daily charge with escalation. Reflects cost as of August 1960.
[2] Including allowance for losses.

For information on the importance of fuel reprocessing costs in nuclear power generation, see **nuclear power economics.**

Consistent with its policy to encourage private industry to enter the reprocessing business, the AEC has stated that all reprocessing contracts entered into under this plan will be subject to cancellation within 1 year of the initiation of a commercial enterprise offering comparable services at reasonable prices. While the AEC has not ruled definitely on the point, it has indicated that commercial prices will be considered reasonable if they come within 15% of those set by the AEC formula.

The AEC has stated that it has no intention of constructing the hypothetical "Multipurpose Chemical Processing Plant." Instead, modifications have been planned to permit existing AEC reprocessing facilities to accommodate the anticipated requirements of the nuclear power industry on an *ad hoc* basis. On a provisional basis, it has been indicated that low- and intermediate-enrichment fuels are to be assigned to Savannah River, and high-enrichment fuels to the Idaho Chemical Processing Plant.

FUSED SALT EXTRACTION

The use of molten mixtures of halide salts as an extraction medium in **fuel reprocessing** applications. One application under investigation is the separation of plutonium from irradiated uranium blanket material. It has been found that extraction with a mixture of calcium, lithium and uranium fluorides (CaF_2-LiF_2-UF_4) will achieve as high as 99% recovery of the contained plutonium. A large amount of the fission-product activity accompanies the plutonium in this extraction, so that supplementary processing is required for decontamination purposes. Another application that has been studied is the use of fused chloride salts to bleed gross fission-product poisons from uranium-bismuth fuel solutions (see **Liquid Metal Fuel Reactor Concept**). Fused salt extraction techniques are also of interest in connection with the application of **fluoride volatility processes** to the reprocessing of high-alloy fuels.

FUSED SALTS. See **molten salts.**

FUSION (nuclear)

The general name for the process in which nuclei of lightweight elements combine to form heavier and more tightly bound nuclei with the simultaneous release of significant amounts of energy. "Thermonuclear" fusion reactions are those processes in which the interacting nuclei are traveling at high velocity (in contradistinction to reactions between externally accelerated ions and "static" target nuclei). The enormous energy generated in the sun and other stars is attributed to fusion processes (see below). Thermonuclear fusion reactions are of practical interest in the following contexts:

1. Use in nuclear weapons of the "hydrogen bomb" type. (See **weapons**)
2. Possible use in explosives for civil works and other constructive applications. (See **Plowshare Program**)
3. Possible use in electrical power generation. (See **thermonuclear power**)

The first two of the above fields of application are based on the "uncontrolled" release of energy from fusion reactions; the third is based on the "controlled" release of energy from fusion reactions—a process referred to as "controlled fusion" (see below).

For fusion to occur the interacting nuclei must come sufficiently close together to permit short-range nuclear forces to operate. This means that one or both nuclei must be accelerated to velocities sufficient to overcome the strong electrostatic repulsion that exists between particles having the same electrical charge. The velocities required are equivalent to particle "temperatures" of the order of hundreds of millions of degrees.

Controlled-Fusion Reactions. Various isolated thermonuclear reactions have been observed in laboratory experiments; the ones that appear promising for controlled energy release are reactions between **deuterium** (D) and/or **tritium** (T) (the heavy isotopes of hydrogen), and possibly the reaction between deuterium and the rare isotope, helium-3. The electrostatic repulsion factor is minimized in reactions between these isotopes, since their nuclei have either a single or a double charge. The primary reactions of interest are:

Reaction	*Practical Ignition Temperature*	
	Ion Energy (ev)	*Ion Temperature * (°K)*
Deuterium-tritium reaction		
$D + T \longrightarrow He^4 + n + 17.6$ Mev	6000	70,000,000
Deuterium-deuterium reactions		
$D + D \nearrow He^3 + n + 3.2$ Mev $D + D \searrow T + p + 4.0$ Mev	53,000	600,000,000

* See **stellar temperatures.**

At any given ion energy, the D-T reaction has a substantially higher cross section (probability) than the D-D reactions. This means that the D-T reaction has a substantially lower **ignition temperature** than the D-D reactions. For example, at an ion energy of 100 kilovolts the fusion cross sections are 5 and 0.018 **barns,** respectively. Another advantage of the D-T reaction is the fact that it releases four or five times as much energy as the D-D reactions. An important disadvantage of the D-T reaction lies in the fact that one of the reactants (namely, tritium) is costly to produce.

While the energy released by the fusion of two lightweight atoms is considerably less than the approximately 200 Mev released by the **fission** of a single heavy atom, the energy yield per unit of mass is comparable to (in the case of the D-D reactions) or greater than (in the case of the D-T reaction) that obtained in fission.

In the case of the D-T reaction, if an equal mixture of deuterium and tritium is used as fuel, the kinetic energy of the neutrons emitted accounts for about four-fifths of the energy released, the balance being accounted for by the kinetic energy of the reaction products. In the case of D-D reactions, the energy distribution is roughly reversed, the neutrons accounting for about one-third, and the reaction products, two-thirds of the energy released.

Stellar Fusion. The primary energy-producing thermonuclear reaction in the sun and other stars is believed to involve the formation of a helium nucleus from four protons. Two ways in which such a reaction may occur have been proposed. The carbon cycle, proposed by Bethe and von Weizsäcker, follows the sequence:

$$p + C^{12} \longrightarrow N^{13} + \text{energy}$$

$$N^{13} \longrightarrow C^{13} + e^{+}$$

$$p + C^{13} \longrightarrow N^{14} + \text{energy}$$

$$p + N^{14} \longrightarrow O^{15} + \text{energy}$$

$$O^{15} \longrightarrow N^{15} + e^{+}$$

$$p + N^{15} \longrightarrow C^{12} + He^{4}$$

or in summary

$$4p \longrightarrow He^{4} + 2e^{+} + 26.7 \text{ Mev}$$

The second method, the so-called proton-proton chain, was suggested by Bethe and Critchfield. This chain follows the sequence:

$$p + p \longrightarrow H^{2} + e^{+} + \text{energy}$$

$$p + H^{2} \longrightarrow He^{3} + \text{energy}$$

Two He^3 nuclei produced in identical reactions then react yielding

$$He^{3} + He^{3} \longrightarrow He^{4} + 2p + \text{energy}$$

or in summary

$$4p \longrightarrow He^{4} + 2e^{+} + 26.7 \text{ Mev}$$

In the sun and similar stars having temperatures of about 20,000,000°K, the carbon cycle and the proton-proton chain processes are believed to occur with roughly equal probability. At lower temperatures the proton-proton chain is probably of greater importance, while at higher temperatures the carbon cycle probably predominates.

Catalytic (Low Temperature) Fusion. It has been demonstrated in laboratory experiments that isolated fusion reactions can be achieved at substantially lower temperatures than those indicated above, by means of a catalytic technique. The technique makes use of mu-**mesons,** which temporarily replace the orbital electrons of an atom. Since the mass of the mu-meson is greater than the mass of the replaced electron, the orbit is closer to the nucleus thus decreasing the size of the atom. The smaller size allows the nuclides to approach each other very closely thus increasing the probability of fusion occurring. The mu-meson leaves unchanged and goes on to catalyze further fusion. The technique is not practiced because the mu-meson has a short natural lifetime and decays into an electron and two neutrinos. In this short lifetime, it cannot catalyze enough fusions to release sufficient energy to create another meson; thus the technique of catalytic fusion has been only of academic interest.

G

G-VALUE

In radiation chemistry, a value used to express the amount of product formed (or destroyed) per unit amount of radiation energy absorbed; specifically, the number of molecules of the given product produced (or destroyed) per 100 ev of radiation energy absorbed in the reacting system. Given the absorbed dose in units of kilowatt-hours of energy absorbed per pound of product, G-value can be computed as follows:

$$G = \frac{1.22 \times 10^9}{(\text{absorbed dose})\,(\text{molecular weight})}$$

A G-value can be assigned to each of the reactants or products in the irradiated system, or to the system as a whole.

Typical G-values for the formation of decomposition products of organic molecules range from less than 0.1 (for aromatic compounds, which resist decomposition) to 10-100 (for condensation reactions of unsaturated compounds). In chain reactions such as the chlorination of toluene or benzene, G-values of 50,000 and higher have been reported.

(See **radiation applications in the chemical industry**)

GADOLINIUM

Element No. 64 (symbol, Gd; atomic weight, 156.9), a **rare earth** with a very high thermal neutron absorption cross section (~ 39,000 barns), of interest for use as a neutron-absorbing material in reactor control rods. (See **reactor materials**)

GAGES

One of the major industrial uses of radioisotopes is in gages for the measurement and/or control of thickness, density or liquid level. These are commonly referred to as beta gages or gamma gages, depending on the radiation source employed. The principle involved in most applications is that the amount of radiation absorbed in passing through a material, and hence the intensity of the exiting beam, is an inverse function of the mass traversed. Thus, if the density of the material being

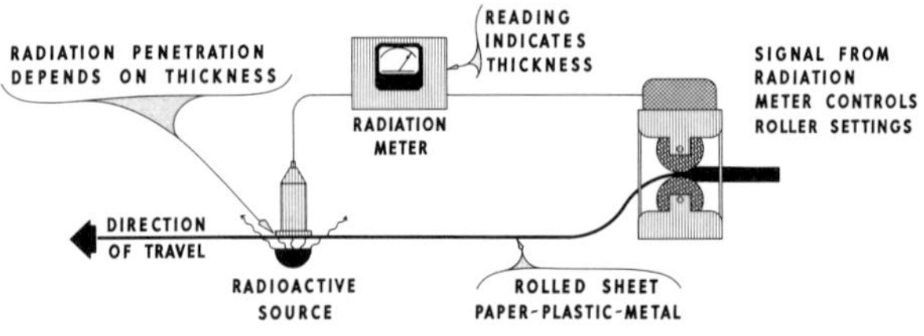

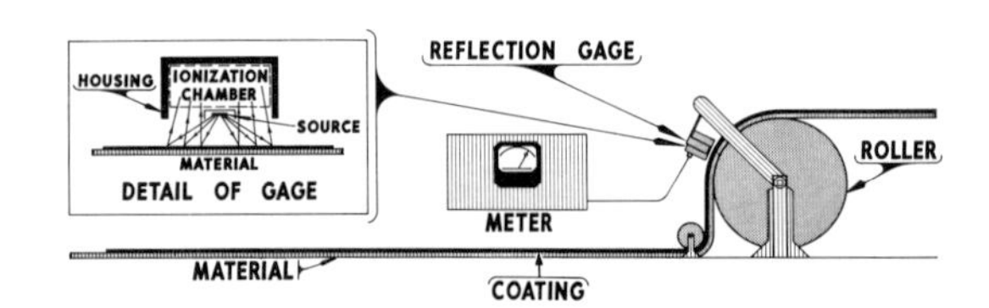

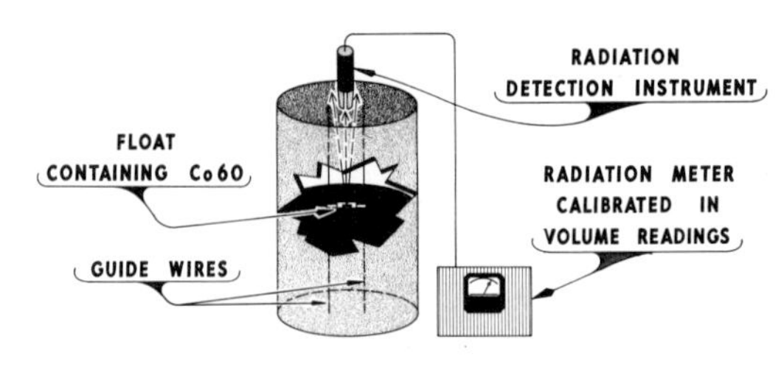

Fig. 72. Gaging techniques. Top, penetration-type thickness gage. Center, back-scattering-type thickness gage. Bottom, liquid-level gage. (*Courtesy of USAEC*)

gaged is held constant, variations in the intensity of the exiting beam denote nonuniformities in thickness. Conversely, if the thickness is held constant, variations denote nonuniformities in density. Most gages therefore consist essentially of a small radiation source placed on one side of the material and a radiation counter on the other side. By calibration, the radiation measurements are converted to thickness or density readings. Also, the measurement outputs can readily be used as inputs to actuate thickness or density control mechanisms. In many applications, thickness or density can be controlled to within 0.1%, and control to within 0.01% or less is possible under ideal conditions.

In the case of liquid-level indicating or control applications, advantage is taken of the difference in density between the liquid and the air or vapor space above the liquid to locate the interface. The radiation source and detector may be slide-mounted on vertical tracks on opposite sides of the tank containing the liquid, or they may be top and bottom mounted in fixed positions.

Some thickness or density gages operate on the principle of backscattering. In this case the radiation source and the radiation counter are mounted on the same side of the material being gaged, and reflected radiation is measured. Backscattering gages are particularly useful in measuring or controlling the thickness or density of a coating applied to a base material.

Fig. 73. Beta gage being used to measure thickness of adhesive coating on cellophane tape. (*Courtesy of Tracerlab, Inc.*)

The selection of a radiation source for a particular gaging application depends primarily on the degree of penetration required. Gamma sources, such as cobalt-60 or cesium-137, are used when a high degree of penetration is required, for example, in gaging the rolling of steel strips or measuring the liquid level in a steel tank. Cobalt-60 emits 1.33 Mev gamma rays, which can penetrate up to about 5 inches of steel. Cesium-137, whose daughter product (barium-137) emits 0.662 Mev gamma rays, can be used in gaging steel up to thicknesses of about 3 inches. Where applicable, cesium-137 has the advantage of having a substantially longer radioactive **half-life** than cobalt-60 (26.6 vs. 5.2 years), therefore requiring less frequent source replacement. X-ray machines are also used as sources of highly penetrating radiation.

Beta sources are used in gaging paper and boxboard sheet, in rubber calendering operations, in coating operations, and in various other applications requiring less penetrating radiation. A considerable range of beta sources is available. A partial listing follows:

Source	*Half-life*	*Beta Energy (Mev, max)*	*Thickness Range* [1]
Carbon-14	~5600 years	0.16	0.5-5
Promethium-147	26 years	0.23	1-10
Thallium-204	4 years	0.77	10–150
Strontium-90/ Yttrium-90	28 years	2.18	50–650
Cerium-144/ Praesodymium-144	290 days	2.98	100–1000
Ruthenium-106/ Rhodium-106	1 year	3.53	130–1200

[1] The approximate range of thickness over which the source can be used, expressed in milligrams of mass per square centimeter of surface area.

Beta and gamma gages are manufactured by a number of firms and are widely used in industry. Shipments of such devices by U.S. manufacturers totalled ~ $6.6 million in 1959, according to Department of Commerce data.* (See **nuclear instruments industry)**

For background information, see **radioisotopes in industry.**

GAMMA GAGES. See **gages.**

GAMMA PINCH

The name given an experimental device built in 1956 at the Livermore Branch of the E. O. Lawrence Radiation Laboratory for research on controlled **fusion.** It is used to study techniques for achieving stabilized pinch-confinement of an ionized gas, or **plasma,** in a straight-tube configuration. (See **Pinch Program)**

* Source: Bureau of Census data as reported in U.S. Atomic Energy Commission's 1960 Annual Report.

GAMMA RAYS (γ)

High-energy, short-wave length **electromagnetic radiation** emitted by the nuclei of many radioactive atoms during radioactive decay. The fact that they are of nuclear origin distinguishes gamma rays from **x-rays,** which have similar properties but derive from the excitation of orbital (extranuclear) electrons.

Gamma rays are given off by many radionuclides undergoing **alpha** or **beta decay.** Also many nuclides become gamma emitters as the result of the so-called neutron-gamma reaction (see **nuclear reactions).** The latter is the basis for the production of cobalt-60 from elemental cobalt (cobalt-59).

Gamma rays are highly penetrating relative to **alpha** or **beta particles** (see **shielding).** They lose energy in passing through matter by three distinct mechanisms known as pair production, Compton effect, and photoelectric effect. In pair production, a gamma ray converts to an **electron** and a **positron** and is absorbed in the process. At high gamma energies (above 1 Mev) and for absorbers of high **atomic number,** pair production is the predominant absorption mechanism. The Compton effect (after A. H. Compton) involves the inelastic scattering of gamma rays by electrons. In the process the electron gains and the gamma ray loses energy. Gamma rays of intermediate energy interacting with materials of low atomic number tend to be absorbed in this fashion. The photoelectric effect involves the complete transfer of energy from a gamma ray to an electron, resulting in the displacement of the latter from the electron lattice of the absorbing material. This is the predominant absorption mechanism when low-energy gamma rays interact with materials of high atomic number.

By extension, the same three mechanisms explain the ability of gamma rays to induce **ionization** as they traverse matter, i.e., they cause the ejection of energetic electrons, which by interaction with surrounding atoms produce additional ion pairs.

GAMMA-RAY SPECTROMETER

An instrument for determining the energy distribution of gamma rays.

GAS CENTRIFUGE PROCESS

A method of isotope separation based on the fact that when a fluid mixture is subjected to a gravitational field (as by spinning in a centrifuge) the heavier components tend to separate from the lighter components just as cream separates from milk in a cream separator. The degree of separation in a single stage of operation depends upon the strength of the gravitational field (i.e., the speed at which the centrifuge rotates) and is directly proportional to the absolute difference in the molecular weights of the heavy and light components. These factors are the key characteristics of the gas centrifuge process and give rise to the following two considerations:

1. They make it natural to consider the gas centrifuge method for uranium isotope separation by reason of the fact that there is a difference of three mass units between uranium-238 and uranium-235. This leads to a larger **separation factor** than in **gaseous diffusion** where the degree of separation in a single stage is a function of the mass ratio rather than the mass difference.

2. The centrifuge process has the interesting theoretical property that the separative work performed varies with the fourth power of the speed, all other factors being equal. This means that doubling the speed would, in theory, increase the separative work performed by a factor of sixteen.

Wartime Development. The original theoretical work on the gas centrifuge method was done at Columbia University's SAM Laboratory, which was a special center set up for the **Manhattan Project.** Development work centered at Standard Oil Development Company's laboratory in Bayway, New Jersey, and at the University of Virginia. Westinghouse Electric

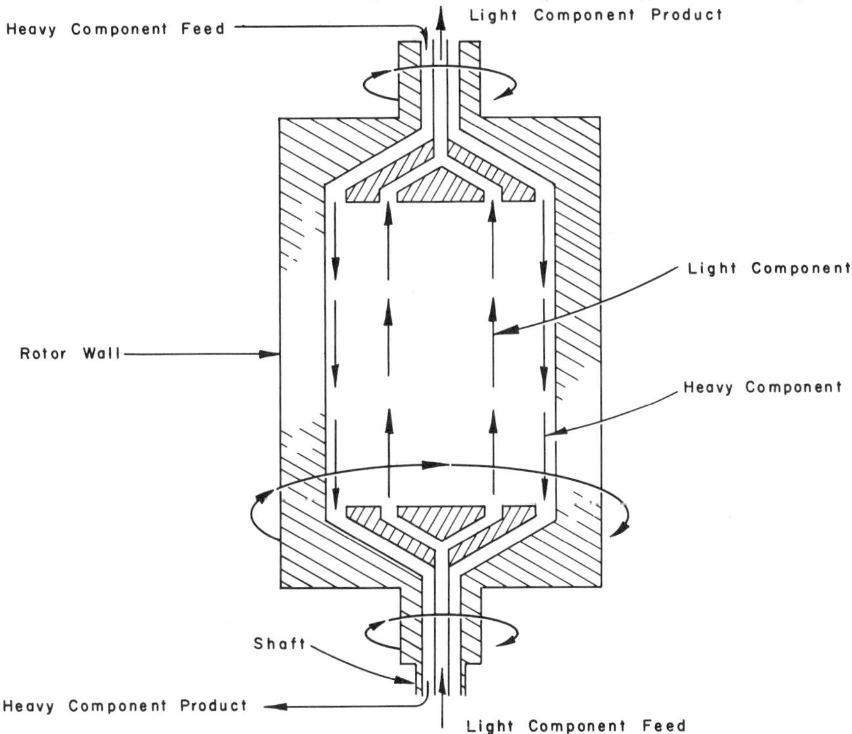

Fig. 74. Schematic diagram of gas centrifuge unit.

Company undertook the task of building the centrifuges required. However, when the time came to decide between the centrifuge and gaseous diffusion methods the latter was selected, largely on the grounds that it involved fewer engineering problems. One factor that weighed against the gas centrifuge method was uncertainty that the materials then available for centrifuge construction would stand up under the stress of sustained high-speed operation.

Details of the centrifuge process developed during the war are not available; however it has been disclosed that the process involved counter-current flow of uranium hexafloride (UF_6) in a series cascade of cylindrical centrifuge units.

Recent Developments. Because of the excellent performance of the gaseous diffusion process, the U.S. Atomic Energy Commission has sponsored relatively little postwar development of the gas centrifuge method. Current AEC-sponsored activity includes: (1) basic research at the University of Virginia, (2) theoretical studies at Yale University, (3) centrifuge experiments by Union Carbide Nuclear Company at Oak Ridge, and (4) a program of development work by the Garrett Corporation's AiResearch Manufacturing Division in Los Angeles. The latter program was initiated in the fall of 1961.

There has been postwar interest in the gas centrifuge method abroad (most notably in West Germany and the Netherlands) as a means for the limited-scale production of slightly enriched uranium for use in nuclear power reactors. The basis for this interest is the belief that the gas centrifuge process can be operated efficiently on a small scale. Also, postwar developments in high-strength materials give the centrifuge designer somewhat greater latitude in materials selection than was the case during World War II. In West Germany, research on centrifuge design and related materials problems has been in progress at Bonn University in collaboration with the industrial firm, Degussa.

Considering the present stage of development of the gas centrifuge process, economic evaluation is difficult.* The technology of the process has been kept on a classified basis on the grounds that it relates to fissionable materials production and does not bear importantly on civil atomic energy development. Access is being provided via **access permits** to U.S. firms interested in undertaking process development on a commercial basis.

GAS-COOLED REACTOR EXPERIMENT (GCRE)

A gas-cooled reactor test facility at the National Reactor Testing Station. The facility

Fig. 75. Reactor vessel for Gas-Cooled Reactor Experiment in final stages of assembly at manufacturer's plant. In operation, the gas coolant enters the upper plenum, flows down the tubes (which contain the fuel elements), and passes out the lower plenum to a gas-turbine. (*Courtesy of Aerojet-General Nucleonics*)

* For example, experience is limited to the operation of individual centrifuge units; hence no data are available on the performance of a cascade system.

was built under the **Army Nuclear Power Program** to obtain engineering data for the design of a prototype mobile power plant for military use (see **ML-1**). It was designed and is operated by Aerojet-General Corporation.

Cooled with nitrogen and moderated with water, the GCRE operates at a power level of 2.0 megawatts (thermal). It is not equipped with electrical generation facilities.* The reactor operated initially with concentric ring-type fuel elements. It went critical in February, 1960, and first reached full power in July, 1960. In September, 1960, a second core, consisting of pin-type fuel elements loaded with UO_2-BeO pellets, was installed and full-power operation was resumed in November, 1960. In 1962 the reactor was shut down for several months for mechanical repairs occasioned by deterioration of pressure tubes in the reactor vessel.

GAS-COOLED REACTORS

Gas-cooled reactors are under development for the following applications: (1) central station power plants; (2) small mobile power plants for use in remote locations or as an emergency power source in devastated areas (see **Army Nuclear Power Program**); (3) ship propulsion (see **Maritime Reactors Program**); and (4) rocket propulsion (see **Rover Project**). (Also see **Aircraft Nuclear Propulsion Program**).

The systems being developed for the latter three applications, discussed under separate headings, are of the direct-cycle type, i.e., the reactor coolant serves also as the working fluid, so that there is a direct connection between the reactor and the power or propulsion mechanism. The systems being developed for central station use, discussed herein, are of the indirect-cycle type.** In this type of system the gas is circulated in a closed loop, referred to as the primary loop, which includes a heat exchanger (steam generator). In passing through the steam generator, the primary coolant transfers heat to water thereby generating steam used to run a steam turbine (see Fig. 76).

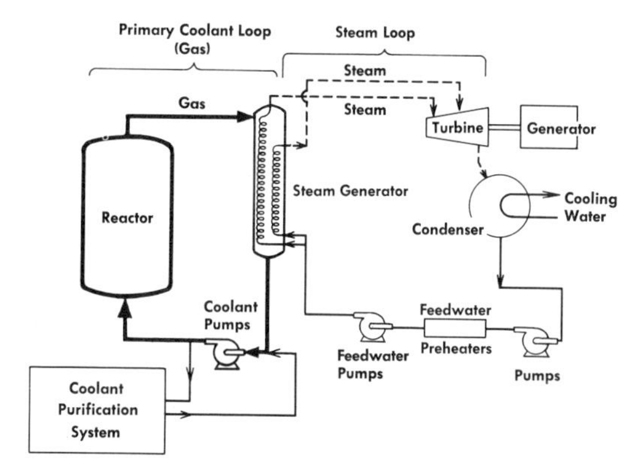

Fig. 76. Simplified flow diagram of indirect cycle gas-cooled reactor plant.

The major advantages and disadvantages inherent in the use of gas cooling in power reactors may be summarized as follows:

Advantages:

1. The operating temperature and pressure are independent variables; thus the only limit to the temperature which can be attained in a gas-cooled reactor is that imposed by the ability of reactor components, in particular the fuel elements, to withstand temperature effects.
2. Corrosion problems are minimized.
3. Any of several high-performance moderators can be used.
4. Largely as a consequence of (3), gas-cooled reactors can be fueled with natural uranium if desired (see discussion below).

Disadvantages:

1. Gas is a poor heat transfer medium relative to water or other reactor coolants.
2. Because of (1), gas-cooled reactors cannot operate at high power densities and therefore have large core structures relative to water-cooled reactors.† Also, finned or other extended-surface fuel element designs are re-

* The generation of electric power by means of a nitrogen gas turbine is being studied separately (see **Gas Turbine Test Facility**).

** This is not an inherent requirement. Ultimately gas turbines may replace steam turbines in large-scale gas-cooled power plants.

† Some designs are subject to a ceiling on power output imposed by the maximum size of reactor pressure vessel that can be economically fabricated.

quired to maximize the heat transfer surface area.

Background. The United Kingdom and France have concentrated on gas-cooled reactors to meet their short-term nuclear power requirements. A desire to avoid dependence on enriched uranium led to the concept of a carbon dioxide-cooled, graphite-moderated reactor, usually referred to as the "Calder Hall" concept (after the name of the U.K.'s first large-scale power reactor installation). The first such reactor was placed in operation in December, 1956. At this writing, eight reactors of this type are operated by the United Kingdom Atomic Energy Authority at Calder Hall and Chapelcross,* ten are being installed at commercial power stations to be operated under the auspices of the Ministry of Power, and other commercial installations are planned (see **United Kingdom**). Similar reactors are being developed in France as a collaborative effort of the Commissariat à l'Energie Atomique and the French national utility, Electricité de France. (See **France**)

While good progress has been made along the Calder Hall line of development, the use of a natural uranium-graphite system has certain basic limitations (see below) which result in high capital costs. In an effort to get around these limitations, the British several years ago began development of an advanced gas-cooled reactor concept involving higher temperature operation and the use of slightly enriched fuel. A prototype installation is under construction at the United Kingdom Atomic Energy Authority's Windscale site (AGR Project).

While various gas-cooled power reactor schemes had been considered from time to time, development of such reactors for civilian power purposes did not begin in the United States until 1957.** It was determined at the outset that the Calder Hall concept had little chance of proving economic in the United States † and accordingly efforts have been focused on higher performance systems. The major emphasis is being placed on high-temperature systems fueled with enriched uranium ceramics and moderated with graphite, which is essentially the same approach the British are following in their advanced gas-cooled program. An experimental reactor facility of this type is under construction at Oak Ridge National Laboratory (see **Experimental Gas-Cooled Reactor**). A privately financed prototype power plant is being built at Peach Bottom, Pennsylvania, as part of the U.S. Atomic Energy Commission's Power Demonstration Reactor Program (see **High Temperature Gas-Cooled Reactor**). A second approach, recently terminated, was based on the use of natural uranium oxide in a heavy-water moderated pressure-tube system. (See **Florida West Coast Reactor Project**)

Of the approximately $476 million spent by the AEC for civilian reactor research and development through mid-1960, $32 million (7%) related specifically to gas-cooled reactor programs. §

Plant Characteristics. The accompanying Table summarizes some of the characteristics of two of the three gas-cooled concepts mentioned above, namely, the natural uranium-graphite (or Calder Hall) concept and the enriched uranium-graphite (or high-temperature) concept. Important features of these concepts are briefly discussed in the paragraphs immediately following.

Limitations of Natural Uranium-Graphite Concept. Reactivity considerations require that natural uranium be in undiluted form,

---

* For plutonium production as well as electrical power generation.

** There were several reasons. For one, the desire to capitalize on the reactor technology developed under the Naval Reactors Program led to an initial concentration on water-cooled reactors. For another, the existence in the U.S. of large-scale uranium isotope separation facilities made it possible to capitalize on the design flexibility afforded by the use of enriched uranium fuel and, by the same token, make it unnecessary to place any special premium on reactor concepts permitting the use of natural uranium.

† Construction costs are higher in the U.S. than in the U.K. Also, investor-owned utility companies in the U.S. bear higher fixed charges on capital investment than are applied to power stations operated by the nationalized utility industry of the U.K. Hence the high capital cost characteristics of the Calder Hall concept would be penalized in the U.S. economy.

§ These figures are exclusive of capital costs. Source: AEC Annual Report for 1960.

i.e., in the form of essentially pure metal, when used in a graphite-moderated system.* This requirement limits the performance of a natural uranium-graphite reactor in two ways: (1) Metallic uranium fuel elements are subject to severe dimensional distortion at temperatures above 1100°F. Since there are pronounced temperature peaks due to nonuniformities in power distribution across the core, the coolant temperature must be kept well below that level to avoid overheating of fuel elements in the hot zones. The British experience indicates that the ceiling for the average coolant outlet temperature is in the range, 700-800°F. (2) While the British estimate that the **reactivity lifetime** of a metallic uranium core is approximately 5500 MWD per metric ton U, the radiation damage characteristics of existing fuel elements presently limit the allowable burn-up to ~ 3000 MWD/ton.

The temperature ceiling limits the thermal efficiency that can be achieved in power generation, which is one of the factors accounting for the high capital cost of natural uranium-graphite power plants. Another factor is the low-power density of natural uranium-graphite systems (see table). This results in core structures of a size requiring field fabrication of the reactor pressure vessel. The largest reactors now under construction in the United Kingdom, which are rated at 250 megawatts (electrical), require pressure vessels 70 feet in diameter and 3½ inches in wall thickness. Difficulties of welding, stress relieving and inspecting such vessels under field conditions have led to interest in the use of reinforced concrete construction for future installations. (See **United Kingdom**)

Problems of the High Temperature Concept. The use of enriched fuel in a graphite-moderated system brings two major benefits: (1) It results in a more compact fuel-moderator lattice and hence in higher power densities and smaller core sizes relative to a natural uranium system. (2) It permits the use of ceramic fuel materials capable of operation at much higher temperatures and burn-ups than metallic fuels.

The latter is the key point since it enables the reactor designer to capitalize on the intrinsic advantages of gas cooling. Two types of fuel element are being developed, one for a heterogeneous core and the other for a homogeneous core. The former, consisting of slightly enriched uranium dioxide clad with stainless steel, will be used in the Experimental Gas-Cooled Reactor (EGCR). The latter, consisting of a graphite can, containing a dispersion of fully enriched uranium carbide and thorium carbide in a graphite matrix, is planned for use in the High-Temperature Gas-Cooled Reactor (HTGR). The EGCR fuel element is being designed to operate at burn-ups in the range 7500-10,000 MWD/metric ton U at a coolant outlet temperature of 1050°F; the design objectives for the HTGR fuel element are 80,000 MWD per metric ton U-Th at 1380°F. The principal difficulty in each case stems from the formation of fission product gases. In the case of the EGCR fuel elements, it is the ability of the steel cladding to withstand the pressure of the confined gases that is expected to determine the allowable burn-up. (Uranium dioxide *per se* is dimensionally stable at burn-ups in excess of 50,000 MWD/metric ton U.) In the case of the HTGR fuel elements, the problem assumes a different form due to the fact that the cladding material (graphite) has some permeability; hence it will not completely contain the fission products. Provision must therefore be made to purge fission product gases from the fuel element channels to avoid radioactive contamination of the coolant stream. The factors likely to prove limiting are thus the rate at which fission product gases diffuse through the graphite cladding at high burn-ups, and the efficiency of the purge system.

Chemical interaction with graphite at elevated temperatures (above 1100°F) rules out the use of carbon dioxide in high-performance gas-cooled reactors. Both ECGR and HTGR

---

* This limitation does not apply to a heavy water-moderated natural uranium system. Heavy water is a more effective moderator than graphite and the presence of a diluent, such as the oxygen in uranium dioxide, can be tolerated.

will use helium, which has comparable heat-transfer properties and is chemically inert. It has the disadvantage of being more expensive; also, little is known about the problems of handling helium in a reactor system. The development of equipment components of proven integrity and of leak detection methods of adequate sensitivity are among the engineering problems that must be solved before the feasibility of high-performance gas-cooled reactors can be demonstrated.

Economics. See **nuclear power economics.**

GASEOUS DIFFUSION

The isotope separation process used for the production of **enriched uranium.**

The process is based on the fact that the molecules of a gas mixture, which are constantly in random motion, have the same average kinetic energy—a function expressed mathematically as the mass times the square of the velocity (mv^2). Thus the heavier molecules in the mixture will, on the average, travel more slowly than the lighter molecules. The difference in speed and hence the "separation factor" is a function of the weight difference, being proportional to the square root of the ratio of molecular weights. The process gas in uranium isotope separation is uranium hexafluoride (UF_6), the only uranium compound that exists as a gas at suitable temperatures. Therefore the gas mixture is $U^{235}F_6$ and $U^{238}F_6$ and the molecular weights are 349 and 352, respectively. The theoretical separation factor is thus $\sqrt{352/349}$ or 1.0043. In actual practice the separation factor is

NOTES ON GAS-COOLED POWER REACTOR CONCEPTS

	Calder Hall Type [1]	*High Temperature Gas-Cooled Reactor (HTGR)*
System parameters:		
Pressure in primary system	200 psi	300 psi
Coolant	carbon dioxide	helium
Coolant outlet temperature	710°F	1382°F
Steam conditions	500 psi, 650°F	1450 psi, 1000°F
Thermal conversion efficiency	24.1%	34.8%
Power density	5.2 tkw/liter	8.5 tkw/liter
Specific power	3.0 tkw/kg U	83.4 tkw/kg U-Th
Fuel:		
Enrichment	none	fully enriched uranium
Form	uranium metal	uranium/thorium carbide
Cladding material	Magnox	graphite
Maximum surface temperature	730°F	2400°F
Average burn-up	3000 MWD/metric ton U	~80,000 MWD/metric ton U-Th
Notes:	Proven concept. Being developed in United Kingdom and France. No U.S. interest.	Small-sized prototypes under construction in the U.S. and U.K.

[1] Data given are taken from an optimized design of a 200-megawatt (electrical) plant prepared under AEC auspices in the fall of 1959, based on British experience. Reference TID-8516, Part II.

GAS TURBINE TEST FACILITY (GTTF)

An experimental closed-cycle gas turbine system being tested at Fort Belvoir, Virginia, under the **Army Nuclear Power Program.** The GTTF uses nitrogen as the working fluid and has a rated output of 0.4 megawatt (electrical). It is oil-fired. It is being used to obtain engineering data for the design of the power conversion portion of mobile power plants (see **ML-1**). The facility was designed and is operated by Aerojet General Corporation.

lower than this due to non-ideal operating conditions and inefficiencies. Inherently, then, hundreds of separation "stages" are required to effect a significant separation of uranium-235 from uranium-238.

To visualize how the process works, it is helpful to think in terms of a microporous

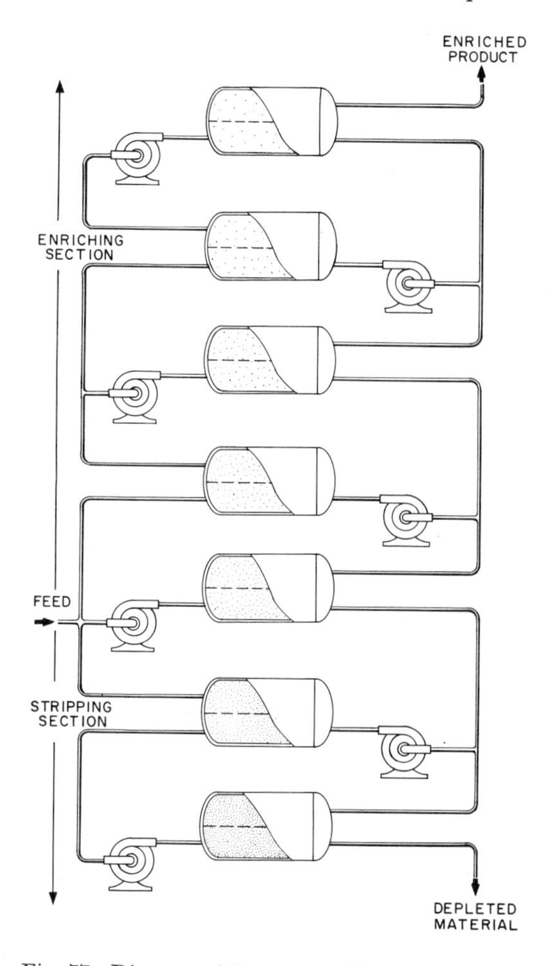

Fig. 77. Diagram of the gaseous diffusion process.

"barrier" dividing a chamber into two zones, one maintained at a somewhat lower pressure than the other and both having outlet ports (see Fig. 77). Assume that as the process gas is pumped through the high-pressure zone half of it diffuses through the barrier into the low-pressure zone. Then the gas leaving the low-pressure zone will be found to be somewhat richer in uranium-235, and the gas leaving the high-pressure zone correspondingly poorer in this isotope. The reason is that the $U^{235}F_6$ molecules, being lighter and faster, are more mobile and thus have a better chance of passing through.

The process may be carried out at lower than atmospheric pressure to lengthen the "mean free path" of the gas molecules, i.e., the distance they travel between collisions. For efficient separation this distance must be large relative to the size of the barrier pores. Otherwise, instead of the desired condition of individual gas molecules diffusing through the barrier, what is known as "mass flow" would occur, i.e., the gas mixture would stream into the barrier openings with little or no separative effect. In practice some mass flow occurs, and this is one of the inefficiencies referred to above.

For information on U.S. gaseous diffusion facilities, operations and costs, see **uranium enrichment.** Also see **isotope separation.**

GAUSS

The metric unit of magnetic field strength (i.e., of magnetic flux density); 1 gauss = 1 line of magnetic force (or maxwell) per square centimeter (see **magnetic pressure**). The earth's magnetic field has an intensity of about 1 gauss; the fields used in experimental devices for controlled **fusion** have strengths up to 100,000 gauss.

GEIGER COUNTER

A radiation detection instrument consisting of a Geiger-Müller tube, together with associated circuitry (including either a battery or an a.c. voltage supply). A Geiger-Müller or G-M tube consists of a metal-lined glass tube filled with a gas and containing an axial wire electrode. The metal lining serves as the cathode and the wire as the anode. Frequently a thin window is provided to allow weak radiation to enter.

The G-M tube is related to other ionization instruments (see **ionization chamber, proportional counter**) but is distinguished from them by its manner of operation. Specifically, the voltage potential across the electrodes is maintained at a high enough level so that when an ionization event occurs the primary ions are accelerated sufficiently to produce an avalanche of secondary electrons, which essentially flood the anode. The pulse of current which results is thus essentially independent of the number of primary ions formed by the ionization event,* being strictly a function of the configuration of the tube and of the ionization characteristics and pressure of the gas it contains. The pulse quenches itself in some G-M tubes due to space charge effects and in others is quenched by external circuitry. A "dead period" thus results between pulses, which acts to limit counting rate that can be achieved by this type of instrument. Within this limit, the frequency of pulses indicates the intensity of the incident radiation.

The pulses are sufficiently strong to register as a series of clicks in a headphone, or to be counted by a **scaler** or a **ratemeter.** There is thus no need for an electronic amplifier in many applications.

Geiger counters are inherently simple and comparatively inexpensive instruments and are widely used as portable survey meters in prospecting for radioactive minerals and in routine monitoring of radioactivity. They can detect and measure beta and gamma radiation alone if so designed. They are seldom designed to detect alpha radiation due to the short range and low penetrating power of alpha particles.

The Geiger counter takes its name from the G-M tube, which was designed by H. Geiger in collaboration with W. Müller in Germany in the late twenties.

GENERAL ADVISORY COMMITTEE (GAC)

A statutory committee, consisting of nine members appointed by the President, whose function is to advise the U.S. Atomic Energy Commission on scientific and technical matters relating to materials, production, and research and development. Membership of the GAC is drawn from civilian life. Each term of appointment is for six years. Meetings are held at least four times each calendar year. The chairman is elected by the membership. Membership listed in Appendix D.

* Which means that it is essentially independent of the energy of the incident radiation.

GENERAL ELECTRIC TEST REACTOR (GETR)

A general-purpose **test reactor** owned and operated by General Electric Company at Pleasanton, California. It is used in support of G.E.'s commercial power reactor development program and also for contract irradiation testing and research. *Type:* Modified tank reactor (tank-in-pool). *Power rating:* 30,000 thermal kilowatts. *Fuel:* MTR-type fuel elements (but with uranium of lower enrichment). *Coolant:* H_2O. *Moderator:* H_2O. *Neutron flux:* Average thermal-neutron flux, $\sim 1.2 \times 10^{14}$ n/cm²sec. Average fast-neutron flux, $\sim 6 \times 10^{14}$ n/cm²sec.

Fig. 78. General Electric Test Reactor (GETR). (*Courtesy of General Electric Co.*)

GENETIC EFFECTS, OF IONIZING RADIATION.

See **biological effects of ionizing radiation.**

GENEVA (ATOMS FOR PEACE) CONFERENCES

Two International Conferences on the Peaceful Uses of Atomic Energy have been held at the Palais des Nations, Geneva, Switzerland, under the auspices of the United Nations.

The first Conference (August, 1955) was attended by 1428 delegates from 73 nations and 8 specialized U.N. agencies, and 1076 scientific papers were submitted to the Conference proceedings. Homi J. Bhaba of India served as Conference President, and Walter Whitman of the United States was Secretary-General. The Conference was the occasion of general declassification of civilian nuclear power technology.

The second Conference (September, 1958) was attended by 2700 delegates from 69 nations and 9 specialized U.N. agencies, and 2135 scientific papers were submitted to the Conference. François Perrin of France served as Conference President and Sigvard Eklund of Sweden was Secretary-General. The Conference was the occasion of general declassification of information on research on controlled fusion. The U.S. Technical Exhibit at this Conference included full-size operating laboratories and experimental devices staffed by U.S. scientists and technicians, as well as technical literature and films. The United States

Fig. 79. Plenary session of the Second U.N. International Conference on the Peaceful Uses of Atomic Energy, Geneva, September, 1958. (*Courtesy of the United Nations*)

also took part in the concurrent industrial exhibit on the peaceful uses of atomic energy.

GEOMETRY

A term commonly used by physical scientists or engineers to indicate the spatial configuration, pattern, arrangement, or relationship of one or several components in an experimental set-up or operating model. For example, in reactor technology the term "geometry" refers to the shape, size, and location of the fuel elements, moderator, and reflector with respect to each other.

GEORGE

The name of a high-speed electronic digital **computer** developed and used at Argonne National Laboratory.

USS *GEORGE WASHINGTON* (SSB(N)598)

First of the Polaris solid fuel surface-to-surface missile class of nuclear-powered submarines. *George Washington* displaces 5600 tons and is powered by an S5W pressurized water plant designed by Bettis Atomic Power Laboratory. The ship, constructed by the Electric Boat Division of General Dynamics Corporation, was launched on June 9, 1959, and commissioned December 30, 1959.

Through mid-1961, 28 additional Polaris submarines had been built or authorized. This and the fast attack class (see USS ***Skipjack***) constitute the two basic types of nuclear-powered submarine now being built. (See **Naval Reactors Program**)

GEORGIA INSTITUTE OF TECHNOLOGY RESEARCH REACTOR (GTRR)

A 1000-kilowatt (thermal) research reactor of the heavy water-moderated tank-type located on the Institute's campus in Atlanta, Georgia. It was designed by General Nuclear Engineering Corporation and is scheduled to begin operation late in 1962. (See **research and training reactors**)

GERMANY, EAST

Agencies. The Scientific Council for the Peaceful Applications of Atomic Energy advises the Council of Ministers on atomic energy matters. The Office for Nuclear Research and Technology, East Berlin, is responsible to the Council of Ministers for implementation of the East German atomic energy program.

International Relationships. East Germany has a technical assistance agreement with the U.S.S.R. and participates in the **Joint Institute for Nuclear Research** at Dubna in the U.S.S.R.

Research Center. The Central Institute for Nuclear Physics, under construction in Rossendorf (a suburb of Dresden) is to be the principal research center. Its experimental facilities will include a 2000-kilowatt (thermal) pool-type research reactor supplied by the U.S.S.R.

Production Activity. Uranium is mined on a substantial scale, principally in the Ore Mountains, the Thuringian Forest and the Harz Mountains. The operations are conducted by the Wismut Company (jointly owned by East Germany and the U.S.S.R.) and essentially the entire output is shipped to the U.S.S.R. for processing.

Nuclear Power Program. A 70-megawatt (electrical) nuclear power plant is being constructed, largely by Soviet engineers, at a site 45 miles north of Berlin. The reactor is heavy water-moderated, gas-cooled, and fueled with natural and enriched uranium. A second and larger plant is scheduled for completion by 1964 at a site in the vicinity of Lake Malchin. A total of some 3000 megawatts of nuclear power capacity is reportedly targeted for 1970.

GERMANY, WEST

Agencies. Bundesministerium für Atomkernenergie und Wasserwirtschaft (Federal Ministry for Atomic Energy and Water Resources), Bad Godesberg, is the official agency responsible for atomic energy matters. Gesellschaft für Kernforschung, Karlsruhe, is a quasi-official organization sponsored jointly by the Federal Government (60%) and the State of Baden-Württemberg (40%) and responsible for future development of German facilities at the Karlsruhe Reactor Center.

International Relationships. Member of **International Atomic Energy Agency,** the European Atomic Energy Community **(Euratom),** the **European Nuclear Energy Agency,** and the European Organization for Nuclear Research **(CERN).** Both the Federal Government and the City of West Berlin have **Agreements for Cooperation** with the United States.

Research Center. The North Rhine-Westphalia Research Center at Stetternich Forest, near Julich, is scheduled for completion in 1962. The experimental facilities include two reactors: One, a pool-type research reactor supplied by AEI-John Thompson Nuclear Energy Company Ltd. (U.K.), is designed to operate at a power level of 5000 kilowatts (thermal). The other, a heavy water-moderated tank-type materials testing reactor supplied by Head Wrightson Processes Ltd. (U.K.), is designed to operate at a power level of 10,000 kilowatts (thermal). Another facility under construction at this site is a prototype power reactor (see AVR Reactor below).

The Karlsruhe Reactor Center, Karlsruhe, originally intended as a national laboratory, is now to operate in part as an **Euratom** laboratory. The experimental facilities include two reactors: FR-2, a heavy water-moderated tank-type research reactor of German design, operates at a power level of 12,000 kilowatts (thermal). SAR-2, an Argonaut-type research and training reactor being supplied by Siemens-Schuckert Werke, is designed to operate at a power level of 10 kilowatts (thermal).

Production Activity. Uranium mining operations started recently in the Rhineland-Palatinate region, and significant ore deposits have been found in Bavaria. Ore processing facilities are in operation at Ettweiler. Pilot facilities for uranium refining are in operation at Wolfgang, and plants with a total capacity of 300 tons per year are planned for construction at Elberfeld and Karlsruhe. The development of an ultracentrifuge process for uranium isotope separation is reported to be at an advanced stage. Heavy water is produced commercially on a limited scale (6 tons per year) and additional production facilities are planned.

Energy Economy. West Germany's electrical power capacity is approximately 23,000 megawatts, three quarters of it coal-fired and the balance hydroelectric. Coal reserves are substantial.

Fig. 80. The RWE Atomic Power Station at Kahl-am-Main. This 16-megawatt (electrical) boiling water reactor plant was supplied by the General Electric Company (U.S.). (*Courtesy of General Electric Co.*)

Nuclear Power Program. Tentative plans call for several hundred megawatts of nuclear power capacity to be in operation by 1965, and 6000 megawatts are targeted for 1975. Following are notes on specific projects (see table for identification of German company names):

RWE Atomic Power Station, Kahl-am-Main: This is a prototype power reactor of the boiling water type, rated at 15 megawatts (electrical) with provision for later operation at twice this power level. The reactor, which was privately financed, was supplied by the International General Electric Company through its licensee, AEG, and is operated by Versuchsatom Kraftwerke Kahl. It began operation in 1961.

AVR Project, Julich. This involves the construction of a prototype high-temperature gas-cooled graphite-moderated power reactor of the "pebble bed" type at the North Rhine-Westphalia Research Center. The reactor will initially operate at 15 megawatts (electrical) but is being designed to permit later operation at 100 megawatts. The reactor is being supplied by Brown, Boveri/Krupp Reaktorbau and will be operated for an interim period by AVR in collaboration with BB/KR. Construction began in 1960.

Fig. 81. Water boiler research reactor at the University of Frankfurt.

KBWP Project, Baden-Württemberg.* This is a project for the construction of either a small (15-megawatt) or a large-scale (150-megawatt) organic cooled reactor, the nuclear components of which are to be supplied by Atomics International through its licensee, INTERATOM, and the non-nuclear components by Brown, Boveri & Company. The reactor is to be operated by KBWP. Design studies of the two plant alternatives are being jointly financed by KBWP and the federal government. A decision on plant construction is scheduled to be reached before the end of 1962.

MZFR Reactor, Karlsruhe. This is a multipurpose reactor installation to be constructed at the Karlsruhe Reactor Center by Siemens-Schuckert Werke under contract to the Federal Ministry. MZFR, from Mehrzweck Forschungs (multipurpose) Reaktor, will be a heavy water-moderated, natural-uranium-fueled system with a rated power output of 200 megawatts (thermal). It will be used to test fuel elements and other reactor materials, to produce radioisotopes, and to supply heat for electric power generation. Facilities for the latter purpose are to be jointly financed by the state of Baden-Württemberg and private utility interests (reportedly KBWP). Completion is scheduled for 1964.

Other projects under consideration include the addition of a small-scale boiling water reactor with integral nuclear superheating to the RWE Atomic Power Station; the construction of a large-scale nuclear power plant of unspecified type in West Berlin (BEWAG Project); and the construction of a large-scale nuclear power plant of an advanced gas-cooled type in northern Germany (SKW Project). Also, RWE is reportedly evaluating proposals for a large-scale project.

A nuclear ship propulsion project is in progress under the sponsorship of GKSS, a syndicate of shipyards and related interests. Under this project, Interatom is designing a 10,000 shaft horsepower organic cooled reactor for installation in a 16,000-ton (deadweight) bulk carrier. Reactor development work is scheduled to be completed by early 1962, at which time construction orders are to be placed.

The Federal Ministry has authorized approximately $375,000 toward a 20,000 shaft horsepower gas-cooled ship propulsion reactor being developed by Deutsche Babcock and Wilcox AG., Oberhausen for Blohm & Voss AG., Hamburg. The designing and preliminary test program will require two years. The reactor is expected to have a high thermodynamic efficiency and low fuel requirement.

GEV

Shorthand expression for 10^9 **electron volts** meaning "giga electron volts;" may be written

* Formerly known as the AKS Project.

Partial Listing of West German Industry
Active in Atomic Energy

Firm or Group	*Notes*
Deutsches Atomforum (Düsseldorf)	Industry association comparable to the U.S. Atomic Industrial Forum.
AEG (Algemeine Elektricitätsgesellschaft) (Frankfurt)	Major electrical equipment manufacturer active in reactor design and manufacture. Licensee of International General Electric Company.
AKS (Stuttgart)	See KBWP.
AVR (Arbeitsgemeinschaft Versuchs-Reaktor) (Düsseldorf)	Syndicate of municipal electric utilities in west central Germany formed to sponsor nuclear power projects.
BB/KR (Brown, Boveri/Krupp Reaktorbau) (Essen)	Joint subsidiary of Brown, Boveri of Mannheim and Friedrich Krupp of Essen, formed for reactor design and manufacture.
BEWAG (Berliner Kraft- und Licht Aktiengesellschaft) (Berlin)	The electric utility serving West Berlin.
Degussa (Deutsche Gold- and Silber Scheideanstalt) (Frankfurt)	Major chemical firm. Operates uranium ore processing facilities and a pilot uranium refinery at Wolfgang, and is planning the construction of large-scale plants for uranium refining and heavy water production. The former, to be located at Karlsruhe, is a joint venture with Metallgesellschaft of Frankfurt. The latter is a joint venture with Friedrich Uhde of Dortmund. Degussa also exports uranium processing equipment and is interested in fuel element fabrication (see NUKEM).
Deutsche Babcock & Wilcox (Oberhausen)	Major heavy equipment manufacturer and licensee of Babcock & Wilcox Company, active in reactor design and in the supply of nuclear and non-nuclear components of reactors.
Farbwerke Hoechst (Frankfurt)	Major chemical company engaged in the commercial production of heavy water and reportedly interested in fuel reprocessing.
GKSS (Gesellschaft für Kernenergieverwertung in Schiffbau und Schiffahrt) (Hamburg)	Syndicate of shipbuilding and related interests formed to handle nuclear ship propulsion projects.
INTERATOM (Internationale Atomreactorbau) (Duisburg)	Joint subsidiary of Demag (Germany) and Atomics International Division of North American Aviation Company (U.S.), active in reactor design and manufacture.
MAN (Maschinenfabrik Augsburg-Nürnberg) (Nürnberg)	Major heavy equipment manufacturer interested in supplying nuclear and non-nuclear components for power reactor installations.
NUKEM	Joint subsidiary of Degussa, Rio Tinto (U.K.) and United Nuclear (U.S.), formed for fuel element manufacture.
Metallgesellschaft (Frankfurt)	See reference under Degussa above.
Pintsch Bamag (Berlin)	Major chemical company planning the construction of heavy water production facilities.
RWE (Rheinisch Westfälisches Electrizitatswerke) (Essen)	The largest electric utility in Germany and an active sponsor of nuclear power programs.
Siemens-Schuckert Werke (SSW) (Erlangen)	Major electrical equipment manufacturer active in reactor design and manufacture. Licensee of Westinghouse Electric Corporation.
SKW (Studiengesellschaft für Kerndraftwerke) (Hannover)	Syndicate of electric utilities in northern Germany formed to sponsor nuclear power projects.

gev, or Gev. Most common in international usage. Synonymous with **Bev.**

GHANA

Joined the **International Atomic Energy Agency** in 1960.

GLOVE BOXES

Gas-tight enclosures used in laboratories for the safe handling of alpha- and some beta-emitting radioactive materials. The laboratory worker handles the materials using rubber gloves connected to ports in the apparatus (see Fig. 82). The boxes are always kept under negative pressure (in the range from 0.25 to 2.0 inches of water) to ensure that any leakage will be inward. Glove boxes cannot be used for most gamma-emitting materials because of the penetrating nature of gamma radiation. (See **shielding**)

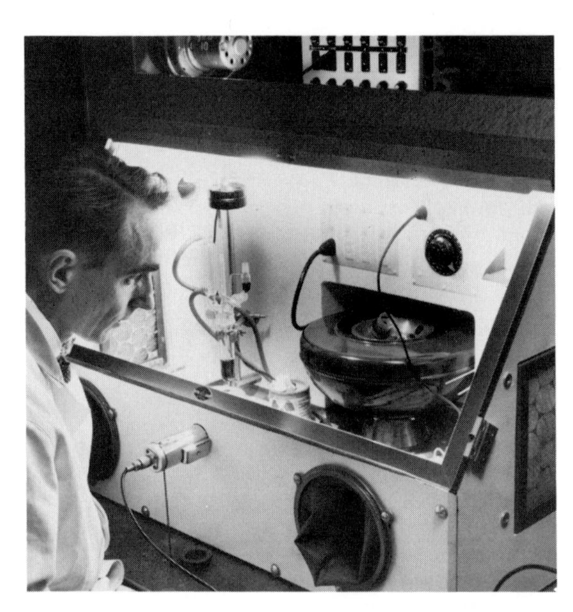

Fig. 82. Glove box. (*Courtesy of Brookhaven National Laboratory*)

GNOME EXPERIMENT

An experiment to study certain phenomena associated with the detonation of a nuclear explosive in a deep underground salt bed; part of the U.S. Atomic Energy Commission's program of research and development on peaceful uses of nuclear explosives. (See **Plowshare Program**)

A small nuclear device with a yield of approximately 5 kilotons was detonated on December 10, 1961, at a depth of about 1200 feet in a thick salt bed deposit in the Salado Salt Basin near Carlsbad, New Mexico. The major purposes of the experiment were: (1) to study the technical feasibility of recovering useful heat from the molten salt mass created by the explosion; (2) to study the feasibility of recovering useful radioisotopes produced by neutron activation at the instant of the detonation; (3) to conduct neutron physics experiments; (4) to study underground cratering and related phenomena. The detonation was highly successful, and at this writing, a large body of experimental data is being collected and evaluated.

The Livermore Branch of the E. O. Lawrence Radiation Laboratory and Los Alamos Scientific Laboratory are the principal participants in the Gnome Experiment. Observers from a number of foreign countries were present at the detonation and attended subsequent technical briefings.

GODIVA

The name of a remotely controlled, uranium-235-fueled **critical experiment** facility at Los Alamos Scientific Laboratory.

GOLD

Element No. 79 (symbol, Au; atomic weight, 197.2). The radioisotope gold-198, a beta and gamma emitter with a radioactive half-life of 2.7 days produced by neutron irradiation of gold-197, is of interest in medical therapy. (See **medical aspects of atomic energy)**

Elemental gold has been studied for use as a protective cladding for equipment surfaces in aqueous homogeneous reactors employing a uranyl phosphate solution. (See **Los Alamos Power Reactor Experiments (LAPRE-1, -2)**

GRAFT POLYMERIZATION

In chemical technology, the grafting of one type of plastic molecule onto another type. The process involves the formation and interconnection of side chains, rather than the transverse connection of base chains as in **cross linking.** (See **radiation applications in the chemical industry)**

GRAND JUNCTION PILOT PLANT

A former U.S. Atomic Energy Commission facility for the development and testing of processes for the recovery of uranium from domestic ores, and related purposes. It was located at Grand Junction, Colorado. The operating contractor from 1954 to 1958 was the National Lead Company. The plant was shut down in the latter part of 1958.

GRAPHITE

A soft form of carbon used as moderator in various thermal reactors, including the Hanford production reactors; research reactors of the type represented by the Brookhaven Research Reactor (BRR); and several types of power reactor. It is also under study for use as a matrix and cladding for fuels such as uranium carbide dispersions (see **gas-cooled reactors).** Graphite is not a particularly effective moderator in terms of neutron slowing-down power; however it combines a very low thermal-neutron absorption cross section with other desirable properties. These include good

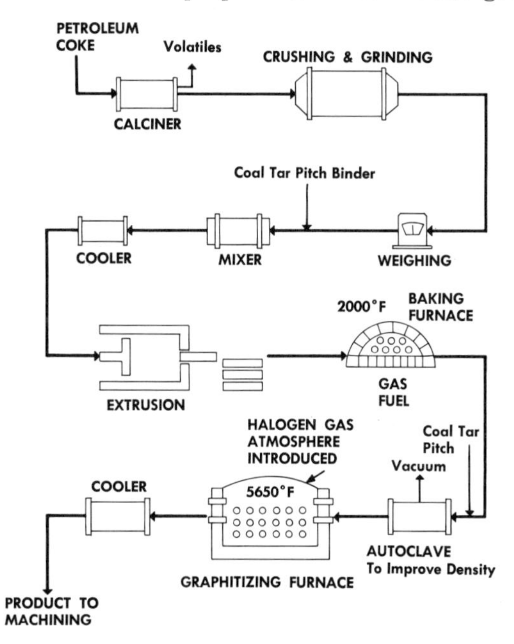

Fig. 83. Production of reactor-grade graphite.

thermal conductivity, a high melting point, excellent mechanical strength at elevated temperatures, excellent resistance to thermal shock and good machinability. In addition to these properties, the low price and availability of graphite make it attractive for reactor uses. (See **reactor materials)**

Graphite is susceptible to radiation damage at low temperatures and to oxidation or corrosion at high temperatures. Radiation damage effects include a tendency toward expansion under long-term irradiation, accompanied by some embrittlement and loss of thermal conductivity. A related problem is that of **stored energy**—effectively a stress-strain build-up due to crystal distortion. In general most of these effects can be allowed for in reactor design or can be corrected by a period of annealing at higher than normal operating temperatures.

Production. Reactor-grade (i.e., high purity) graphite is produced artificially by the "graphitization" of petroleum coke. The feed material is first calcined to drive off volatile compounds. It is then finely ground and mixed at high temperatures with a binder of coal-tar pitch, after which it is extruded to the desired shape and baked at temperatures up to 3,000°F to set the binder. The product at this stage is suitable for industrial purposes, but further purification is necessary for reactor applications. This is done by adding additional binder, followed by heating at very high temperatures (up to 5600°F) in a halogen atmosphere, an operation that serves to drive off residual impurities. The product is then cooled and machined to the user's specifications. The price varies with the degree of purity, but in general fabricated graphite costs about $1 per pound.

GREECE

Agency. The Greek Atomic Energy Commission (GAEC), Athens, is the official government body responsible for atomic energy matters.

International Relationships. Member of the **International Atomic Energy Agency,** the **European Nuclear Energy Agency,** and the European Organization for Nuclear Research **(CERN).** Research-type **Agreement for Cooperation** with the United States.

Research Center. Democritus Nuclear Center, Mt. Hymettus, is the principal research center of the GAEC. The facilities include a pool-type research reactor supplied by AMF Atomics, Inc. which is designed to operate at a power level of 1000 kilowatts (thermal). The United States contributed $350,000 to the cost of this installation under its program of Foreign Research Reactor Grants.

Production Activity. None. Uranium deposits have been reported in eastern Macedonia and western Thrace but not yet proved significant.

Energy Economy. Greek electric power capacity is about 600 megawatts. While two-thirds of it is thermal, recent additions have been hydroelectric and additional hydro capacity is planned.

GREEN SALT

Uranium tetrafluoride (UF_4).

GROUND TEST REACTOR (GTR)

A portable, special-purpose **test reactor** formerly operated by the Corvair Division of General Dynamics Corporation, Fort Worth, Texas, under contract to the U.S. Air Force, and now in stand-by status. It was designed for radiation effects and shielding studies in support of the development of air frames for nuclear-propelled aircraft. (See **Aircraft Nuclear Propulsion Program)** *Type:* Modified pool reactor. The core can be removed from its pool, placed in a portable moderator tank, suspended in air from a gantry crane, and operated 75 feet above ground to study air and ground scattering of radiation. *Power rating:* 3000 thermal kilowatts. *Fuel:* MTR-type fuel elements. *Coolant:* H_2O. *Moderator:* H_2O. *Neutron flux:* Of the order of 10^{13} n/cm^{2}sec (maximum thermal). *Start-up:* 1954. Operation discontinued in 1961.

GUATEMALA

The Comision Nacional de Energia Nuclear, Guatemala City, is the agency responsible for atomic energy matters. Training programs to promote medical and agricultural uses of radioisotopes are conducted on a limited scale. Guatemala is a member of **International Atomic Energy Agency** and **Inter-American Nuclear Energy Commission,** and has a research-type **Agreement for Cooperation** with the United States.

GUN-TYPE WEAPON

One of the possible designs of a nuclear weapon. In a gun-type weapon, a small charge of conventional explosive is used to propel two or more subcritical pieces of fissionable material into contact, thereby assembling a critical mass. (See **weapons)**

H

H-BOMB

A shorthand expression for a nuclear weapon whose explosive energy derives in part from nuclear **fusion.** (See **weapons**)

HAFNIUM

Element No. 72 (symbol, Hf; atomic weight, 178.6), a metal closely resembling zirconium in its chemical and metallurgical properties and invariably associated with that element in ore deposits, but notably different in its nuclear properties. Specifically, zirconium has a very low and hafnium a relatively high thermal neutron absorption cross section (0.18 and 105 barns, respectively). Interest in the use of zirconium for reactor applications led to the development of processes for zirconium-hafnium separation and, as the result, both metals are produced in high purity—zirconium as the main product, and hafnium as a by-product. (See **zirconium**)

Hafnium is used as a control rod material in some power reactors. While it is not as effective an absorber of thermal neutrons as other available materials, notably **cadmium,** its performance across the complete neutron energy spectrum is comparatively good. Also, it has excellent mechanical properties and corrosion resistance, the latter property obviating the need for cladding. Its cost at the present time is ~ $15-30 per pound in nonfabricated form, subject to its availability as a by-product from the production of reactor-grade zirconium. (See **reactor materials**)

HAITI

The Commission Haitienne a'l'Energie Atomique, Port-au-Prince, is the agency responsible for atomic energy matters. Haiti is a member of the **International Atomic Energy Agency** and the **Inter-American Nuclear Energy Commission.**

HALDEN PROJECT

A project sponsored by the **European Nuclear Energy Agency** of the **Organization for Economic Cooperation and Development,** involving the joint operation of the Halden Boiling Heavy Water Reactor (HBWR), located at Halden in southern Norway. The participants are: Austria, Denmark, Norway, Sweden, Switzerland, the United Kingdom, and **Euratom** (representing Belgium, France, West Germany, Italy, Luxembourg and the Netherlands). The international agreement creating the Halden Project was signed on June 11, 1958, and provided for a three-year joint program of experimentation with HBWR, which program was budgeted at about $4 million. The agreement was subsequently extended for an additional three-year period (until mid-1964). The staff includes some 60 scientists and engineers drawn from the sponsoring countries.

The first boiling heavy water reactor, the HBWR was designed by the staff of the Netherlands-Norwegian Joint Establishment for Nuclear Energy Research (JENER) and was built as a project of the Norwegian Institutt for Atomenergi. When fueled with zircaloy-clad uranium dioxide of 1.5% enrichment, it has a rated power output of 20 megawatts (thermal). The reactor operates as a direct cycle system with steam produced in the primary circuit at a temperature of ~ 450°F. The reactor pressure vessel is fabricated of carbon steel with a stainless steel liner. The heavy water inventory is approximately 16 tons. The installation is located underground in a cave blasted out of rock, thereby eliminating the need for a conventional containment vessel.

The Norwegians planned the HBWR as an experimental process heat reactor. The reactor concept is also of interest for possible use in electrical power generation, however, and it is within this context that the present joint project was undertaken. The idea of jointly operating the reactor as an experimental nuclear power facility was first suggested by the Norwegian Government at an OECD conference in May, 1957.

HALF-LIFE, RADIOACTIVE

The time required for one-half of the atoms of a radioactive substance to disintegrate; hence the time it takes for the particular substance to lose half of its radioactive strength (activity). The process of radioactive disintegration (decay) is independent of temperature, pressure or chemical conditions. Each radionuclide (i.e., every species of radioactive atom) decays at a fixed rate and thus has a characteristic half-life. Values range from less than a millionth of a second to millions of years. (See **radioisotopes**)

In atomic energy parlance, the adjectives "short-lived" and "long-lived" usually refer to the radioactive half-life of any substance so described. There are, however, other half-life terms. (See **biological half-life, effective half-life**)

U.S.S. *HALIBUT* (SSG(N)587)

A nuclear-powered submarine designed to operate as a mobile and far-ranging launching base for Regulus air-breathing surface-to-surface missiles. *Halibut* displaces 3555 tons and is powered by an S3W pressurized water reactor plant designed by Bettis Atomic Power Laboratory. The ship, constructed at the Mare Island Naval Shipyard, was launched on January 9, 1959, and commissioned January 4, 1960. (See **Naval Reactors Program**)

HALLAM NUCLEAR POWER FACILITY

A nuclear power plant of the **sodium-graphite** type at Hallam, Nebraska. This project is being carried out under the "first round" of the U.S. Atomic Energy Commission's Power Demonstration Reactor Program. The AEC is financing most of the cost of reactor construction and related research and development. Consumers Public Power District of Nebraska provided the site and the electrical portion of the plant; and operates the plant, making payment to the AEC for the steam used. Consumers Public Power also made a contribution toward the cost of reactor construction. Atomics International, a division of North American Aviation Company, Inc., was the reactor contractor. Bechtel Corporation was the architect-engineer for the reactor installation, and Peter Kiewit Sons, the construction contractor. The **Sodium Reactor Experiment** provided the basic information needed for design of the Hallam Facility, which in effect represents an intermediate step toward the design of a full-scale sodium-graphite power station. The following notes reflect the status of the project as of mid-1962:

Power: 76 megawatts (net electrical). *Fuel:* Slightly enriched uranium (3.6% U^{235}) in the form of a uranium-molybdenum alloy (10 weight % Mo).* *Fuel element design:* A single fuel element consists of a cluster of stainless steel tubes containing stainless steel-clad fuel slugs bonded with sodium. *Fuel inventory:* 27,600 kilograms of slightly enriched uranium. *Coolant:* Sodium inlet temperature, 607°F; outlet temperature, 945°F. *Steam conditions:* Superheated steam at 850 pounds pressure and 833°F. *Thermal conversion efficiency:* 31.6%. *Control materials:* 19 control rods containing gadolinium-samarium oxides. *Containment:* Concrete vaults in a gas-tight building. *Construction cost:* Estimated at $49.6 million, exclusive of research and development. For other project costs, see Table 3 under **nuclear power development.** *Dates:* Consumers Public Power signed the contract for the project with AEC in September, 1957. Construction started in April, 1959. The plant began preliminary operation in January, 1962, and is scheduled for power operation in the fall of 1962.

---

* It is tentatively planned that the second core will contain uranium carbide fuel elements.

Fig. 84. The Hallam Nuclear Power Facility (at left) adjacent to conventional coal-fired power plant. (*Courtesy of Atomic International*)

HAND-AND-FOOT MONITOR

An instrument routinely used to monitor the hands and feet of atomic energy workers as they leave work locations in which radioactive materials are handled. Hand-and-foot monitors consist of a radiation **counter,** together with related circuitry and indicating and alarm devices, and are usually step-on type installations.

HANFORD WORKS (HEW)

A U.S. Atomic Energy Commission plutonium production plant located on the Columbia River at Hanford, Washington. *Operating contractor:* General Electric Company (Hanford Atomic Products Operation, HAPO). *AEC investment in plant and equipment:* \$1.137 billion.* *Employment:* ~ 9000, including ~ 1000 scientists and engineers.

The Hanford Works, originally known as the Hanford Engineer Works, was established during the wartime **Manhattan Project** and has since gone through major expansion programs. Its primary function is the production of **plutonium** by the irradiation of natural uranium and subsequent chemical separation and decontamination of the irradiated material. The irradiation is conducted in large water-cooled, graphite-moderated reactors. Megacurie amounts of **strontium-90** and **cesium-137** are produced as a by-product. Hanford is also an important research and development center.

The principal production facilities of the Hanford Works are as follows:

1. Fuel element fabrication facilities: Hanford receives natural uranium metal in the form of short slugs, which, after inspection, are canned in aluminum and tested.

2. Production reactors: There are eight production reactors, of which three (B-, D- and F-Reactors) were built during the war, and five (C-, DR-, H-, KE- and KW-Reactors) are postwar additions. A ninth unit is being built (see below).

3. Chemical separations plants: Originally there were three chemical separation plants which recovered plutonium by a chemical precipitation method (see **bismuth phosphate process**) and operated in batch fashion. No provision was originally made for the recovery of uranium, which was piped to underground

* Includes facilities authorized or under construction as of June 30, 1960. Not adjusted for depreciation.

storage tanks as radioactive waste. These facilities have been replaced by two postwar processing facilities, one employing the **Redox** solvent extraction process and the other and more recent facility, the **Purex** solvent extraction process. Both plants recover uranium as well as plutonium and both operate on a continuous cycle. (See **fuel reprocessing** for supplementary information)

An important operation which was conducted on an interim basis and is no longer required was the recovery of the uranium which had accumulated in stored radioactive waste solutions during the war and early postwar years. For this purpose one of the bismuth-phosphate plants was stripped of its original equipment and equipped with a solvent-extraction system for uranium decontamination. The modified facility was known as the Metal Recovery Plant. The reclamation project put a thousand tons of uranium back into the AEC's production "pipeline."

A ninth production reactor, known as the New Production Reactor (NPR), is under construction at Hanford. This unit is equipped with a recirculating cooling system and is designed to permit the incorporation of electric power generating facilities, should funds for this purpose be authorized at some future date. (Up to 800 electrical megawatts of electric power could be generated from this facility.) Apart from limited use in building heating, the low-temperature heat produced in the present Hanford reactors is dissipated in the Columbia River.

Research and development activity at Hanford, in addition to producing necessary support to production operations, is addressed to a range of problems of general interest to the AEC program. Examples of research and development activities are (1) studies of radiation damage to reactor materials, including investigation of **"stored energy"** effects in irradiated graphite; (2) research on fuel reprocessing techniques for application to power reactor fuels; (3) development of processes for the selective removal of industrially useful fission products from radioactive waste mixtures; and (4) research on the biological and environmental effects of radiation. Of particular importance to the nuclear power field is a program currently being conducted at Hanford on the possible use of plutonium as a fuel for power reactors. (See **nuclear power development, Plutonium Recycle Test Reactor)**

Prime contractor for the design, construction and operation of the original Hanford installation was E. I. duPont de Nemours & Company. In 1946, having fulfilled its commitment, duPont desired to be relieved of the operation * and, at AEC's request, the General Electric Company became the prime contractor. The postwar modernization and expansion program was conducted under General Electric's direction with the assistance of various architect-engineer and construction contractors. The former have included Burns & Roe, Chas. T. Main, Inc., and Vitro Engineering Company; the latter, the Blaw-Knox Company, Hoffman Construction Company, J. H. Jones Construction Company, Kaiser Engineers, and Morrison Knudson.

HARD-CORE PINCH

A technique for **plasma confinement** developed and under study as part of the **Pinch Program** of research on controlled **fusion** at the Livermore Branch of the E. O. Lawrence Radiation Laboratory. Theory indicates that, when confined by a magnetic field, a plasma should be hydromagnetically stable if the plasma-field interface is everywhere convex toward the plasma (see **plasma stability).** The hard-core pinch system, which differs from conventional stabilized-pinch discharges in that the axial and azimuthal fields are reversed, is designed to achieve such a configuration.

Because of interesting results obtained in preliminary experiments with a linear hard-core discharge, a toroidal hard-core system, called the Levitron, has been constructed.

---

* duPont later re-entered the field as prime contractor for a second plutonium production center. (See **Savannah River Plant)**

HEAD-END

A term applied to the dissolution portion of an aqueous **fuel reprocessing** system, i.e., that part of the reprocessing plant in which irradiated fuel elements are dissolved preparatory to separation and decontamination of the fuel constituents by solvent extraction.

HEALTH AND SAFETY LABORATORY (AEC)

A laboratory established by the U.S. Atomic Energy Commission to provide assistance on health and safety problems to university and small industrial contractors. It is located at 376 Hudson Street, New York City, with the AEC's New York Operations Office. Its staff numbers ~ 50 scientists and engineers and a like number of supporting personnel, and receives technical direction from the AEC's Division of Biology and Medicine.

The laboratory has three divisions, whose functions and activities can be summarized as follows:

1. Environmental Sciences Division: Provides industrial hygiene and radiation control services to AEC contractors. Activities have included the development of equipment and techniques for controlling environmental and atmospheric hazards encountered in the production and processing of uranium, beryllium and other materials; measurement of background radioactivity levels; and criticality studies.
2. Analytical Division: Provides analytical services and directs a world-wide network for monitoring **radioactive fallout** from nuclear weapons tests. A related activity is study of the **strontium-90** content of fallout, food and other materials.
3. Instrumentation Division: Provides instrument services to the other divisions and additionally conducts a basic instrumentation development program.

HEALTH PHYSICS

The science and practice of radiation protection. At the outset of atomic energy development the problems of protecting atomic energy workers and their environment from radiation hazards were solved by a cooperative effort of life scientists, physical scientists and engineers. Today many of the functions involved in radiation protection are handled by the health physicist—a scientist or engineer with specialized training in radiation protection principles and procedures. The responsibilities of the health physicist usually include review of laboratory and plant procedures and practices from the standpoint of conformity with established radiation protection standards and regulations; design and supervision of radiation monitoring procedures, including personnel, area and environmental surveillance; and general cognizance over safety problems stemming from criticality, radioactivity, toxicity, and other special hazards. The health physicist is thus concerned with aspects of all laboratory or plant operations involving the handling or shipping of radioactive, toxic, or otherwise hazardous materials, including the disposal of radioactive wastes. (See **radiation protection, radiation protection standards and regulations**)

HEAT EXCHANGERS

Discussion of this topic will be limited to heat exchangers used in civilian power reactor installations to transfer heat from the reactor coolant to the working fluid used in power generation.

In the case of **pressurized water reactors,** the heat exchangers transfer heat from the reactor coolant to a secondary water stream, converting the latter to steam. In the case of boiling water reactors, steam is generated in the reactor vessel proper; however, in some designs * an external heat exchanger is employed to generate additional steam utilizing condensate from the primary steam system as the heat source. In either case the heat exchangers differ from the steam generators employed in conventional steam-electric power plants in the following respects:

* "Dual-cycle" plants.

1. Leakage specifications are much more stringent due to the radioactivity associated with reactor coolants (see discussion under **radioactive waste disposal**). To minimize leakage, the heat-exchanger tubes are welded to the tube sheets, which is a departure from conventional steam-generator practice. Also, in some reactor systems, provision must be made for detecting leaks in heat-exchanger tubes.

Fig. 85. Half of U-shaped tube bundle for nuclear heat exchanger. (*Courtesy of Combustion Engineering Co.*)

2. Corrosion tolerances are much lower due to the need to keep the coolant stream as free as possible of corrosion products which would act to foul heat transfer surfaces in the reactor core and also, through neutron activation, lead to increased coolant radioactivity. To minimize corrosion, stainless steel or other alloy materials are presently specified for nuclear heat exchangers in place of carbon steel.

3. Nuclear heat exchangers are subject to much greater thermal stress due to the fact that power reactor systems are subject to rapid thermal cycles. (Temperature changes which occur gradually over a period of hours in a conventional power plant take place in a matter of minutes in a nuclear plant.) This complicates the design of nuclear heat exchangers and requires heavier construction.

Partly because of these factors and partly because of generally more conservative design and quality control practice, the cost of primary heat exchangers for water cooled reactor installation is presently of the order of $20-40

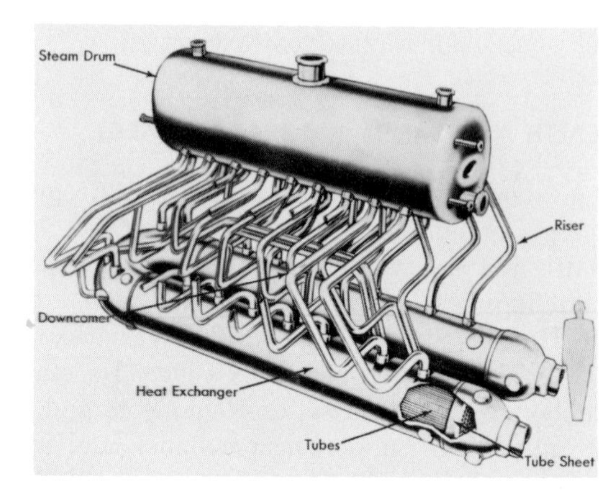

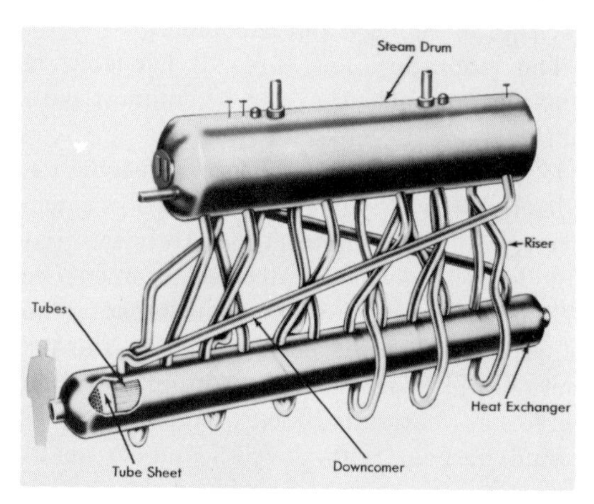

Fig. 86. Heat exchanger configurations used in Shippingport Atomic Power Station. Top, U-shaped tube section. Bottom, straight tube section. Reprinted from "The Shippingport Pressurized Water Reactor," 1958, Addison-Wesley Publishing Co.

per square foot of heat transfer surface, as compared with $5.00-7.00 per square foot for conventional steam generators. Units for large-scale civilian power plants of the pressurized water type cost several hundred thousand dollars each.

In the case of sodium-cooled reactors two additional considerations are involved. One is the fact that sodium becomes intensely radioactive under neutron irradiation due to the formation of sodium-24, a gamma emitter with a radioactive half-life of 15 hours. The other is the potential danger of an exothermic chemical reaction in the event of sodium-water contact in the presence of air (see **metal-water reactions**). To avoid the possibility of radioactive sodium becoming involved in a chemical explosion, and for other reasons, an intermediate sodium-to-sodium heat exchanger has been provided in the sodium-cooled power plants designed to date. To minimize the possibility of an explosive reaction in the secondary (sodium-to-water) heat exchanger, double-wall tube construction has been employed in two plants, resulting in costs of the order of $200 per square foot of heat transfer surface for these installations. In another plant, once-through flow through single-wall tubes is employed, resulting in lower costs ($55 per square foot). (See discussion under **sodium-graphite reactors**)

There are many variations of nuclear heat-exchanger design—vertical and horizontal, straight and U-shaped tube bundles, single and multiple steam separator drums, etc. Figure 85 illustrates the two types used in the Shippingport Atomic Power Station, which are horizontal, single-drum units with U-shaped (Fig. 86A) and straight (Fig. 86B) tube sections.

HEAT REACTORS.

See **process heat applications for reactors.**

HEAT TRANSFER REACTOR EXPERIMENTS.

See **Aircraft Nuclear Propulsion (ANP) Program.**

HEAVY-AGGREGATE CONCRETE

Concrete to which high-density materials have been added to increase its gamma-ray stopping power and thereby reduce the thickness required for radiation shielding applications. The additives commonly used include barite (a barium sulfate mineral), iron ores such as limonite and magnetite, and various forms of steel scrap. Shield thickness is important from a functional standpoint in the case of research reactors or high-energy particle accelerators furnishing beams to experimental equipment located outside the shield, and it factors directly or indirectly in the construction cost of reactors and accelerators in general. Depending on its composition heavy-aggregate concrete may cost from two to ten times as much per cubic yard as ordinary structural concrete, however its higher unit cost is usually compensated for by the fact that considerably less material is required and by indirect savings stemming from reduced space requirements. Following, by way of illustration of heavy-aggregate formulas, is the mix used in constructing the biological shield of the Massachusetts Institute of Technology Reactor (MITR):

Material	*Lb*
1 bag Portland cement	94
Magnetite	298
¼-inch steel punchings	336
¾-inch steel punchings	125

HEAVY HYDROGEN.

See **deuterium.**

HEAVY WATER

Deuterium oxide (D_2O). (See **deuterium**)

HEAVY WATER COMPONENTS TEST REACTOR (HWCTR)

A **test reactor** built to study the performance of fuel elements of interest for use in **heavy water-moderated power reactors.** The HWCTR is located at the Savannah River Plant. The operating contractor is E. I. duPont de Nemours & Company. *Type:* Tank reactor. *Power rating:* 61,000 thermal kilowatts. *Fuel:* Zirconium-clad fuel tubes fabricated by co-extrusion of zirconium and highly enriched uranium-zirconium alloy. *Coolant:* D_2O. *Moderator:* D_2O. *Start-up:* Start of preliminary operation, January, 1962; start of power operation, April, 1962.

HEAVY WATER-MODERATED POWER REACTORS

Table 1 summarizes the several ways in which heavy water (D_2O) is being used or has been studied for use in power reactor systems.

The concepts involving the use of heavy water only as moderator are discussed under separate headings (see **Florida West Coast Reactor Project, Chugach Electric Association Project, spectral shift reactor concept).** The notes which follow thus relate only to systems in which heavy water is used as moderator and coolant.

General Considerations. The basic reason for considering the use of heavy water (D_2O) in lieu of ordinary water (H_2O) in a water-moderated and cooled power reactor is that it permits operation with natural uranium fuel.* The reason is that since D_2O absorbs fewer neutrons than H_2O, a D_2O system can tolerate a less reactive fuel. (The thermal neutron capture cross section of deuterium is 0.0005 barn as compared with 0.330 for hydrogen). The possibility of using natural uranium fuel is of obvious importance to countries that do not have enriched uranium resources and do not wish to be dependent on external supplies of this material. Where there is a free choice between natural and enriched fuel, the decision for or against heavy water is essentially a matter of weighing the savings in fuel cycle cost which accrue from the use of cheaper fuel against the direct and "indirect" costs of using heavy water.

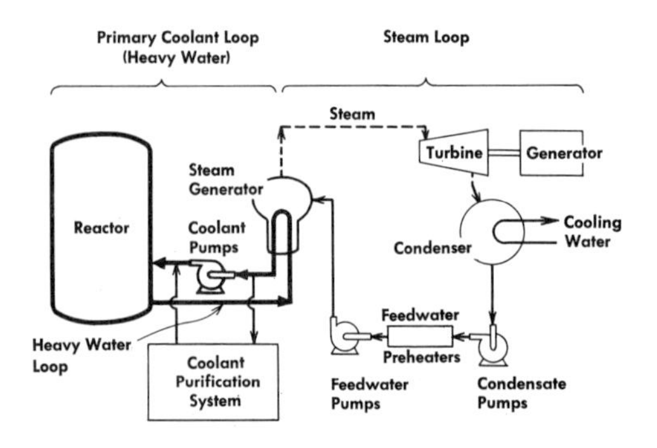

Fig. 87. Simplified flow diagram of heavy-water moderated and cooled reactor plant.

The direct heavy water costs are readily defined; they include the initial cost of the D_2O inventory; the annual cost of replacing D_2O losses; and annual carrying charges associated with the D_2O inventory. By the "indirect" costs is meant added capital costs attributable to the use of heavy water. These stem mainly from the fact that D_2O is a less effective neutron moderating medium than H_2O, so that an appreciably larger core volume and hence a considerably larger reactor vessel is required than in an H_2O system.

The latter factor imposes practical limitations on the operating pressure and hence the temperature that can be achieved in a pressurized heavy water reactor of the massive pressure vessel type (see Fig. 87). This is reflected in the following comparison of plant characteristics: **

	Pressurized H_2O System	*Pressurized D_2O System*
Rated plant output	200 MWe	200 MWe
Reactor vessel		
Inside diameter	11.75 ft [1]	14.7 ft
Height	31 ft	34 ft
Wall thickness	7 in.	4.5 in.
Material	SS-clad carbon steel	SS-clad carbon steel
Operating pressure	2200 psi	750 psi
Coolant outlet temperature	574°F	480°F
Thermal conversion efficiency	24.8%	23.2%

[1] About the largest diameter that can be achieved with 7-inch thick clad steel in existing pressure vessel manufacturing facilities.

In a pressurized heavy water reactor of the pressure-tube type, there are two D_2O zones—a high-pressure zone within the tubes, and a low-pressure zone surrounding the tubes. A relatively thin-walled reactor vessel can thus

* The only other power reactor concepts currently under development that permit the use of natural uranium are the gas-cooled graphite-moderated, or "Calder Hall" concept (see **gas-cooled reactors**), and the organic-cooled heavy water-moderated concept (see **Canada**). In principle, natural uranium could also be used in the **sodium-graphite** concept (q.v.).

** The data given are taken from optimized designs prepared under AEC auspices in late 1959.

be used. This method of pressure containment lifts the temperature ceiling considerably, and largely for this reason appears more promising than the massive pressure-vessel method. Difficulties associated with the use of pressure tubes include the fact that they introduce a significant mass of neutron-absorbing structural material into the reactor core, which is undesirable from the tsandpoint of neutron economy. Also, they complicate the mechanical design of the reactor vessel.

In considering heavy water for use in a boiling water reactor system, it is again the effect on core size that must be reckoned with. See discussion of core size problem associated with conventional (i.e., H_2O) **boiling water reactors.**

U.S. Program. Development work on heavy water power reactors began in the United States in 1957.* U.S. heavy water power reactor projects, summarized in Table 1, are discussed in individual entries. Various design studies and collateral research investigations are also in progress. Of the approximately $476 million spent by the U.S. Atomic Energy Commission for civilian reactor research and development through mid-1960, $36 million (8%) related specifically to heavy water reactor projects; however, it should be added that these projects have been able to draw extensively on the technology of "conventional" pressurized and boiling water reactors, and also on the technology of the heavy water-moderated production reactors at Savannah River.

* The reasons for not starting earlier are essentially those noted in similar context under **gas-cooled reactors.**

TABLE 1. HEAVY WATER POWER REACTOR CONCEPTS

Concept	*U.S. Reactor Projects*	*Notes*
1. *D_2O used as moderator and coolant:*		
a. In pressurized heavy water systems		
(1) Pressure-vessel type	**Heavy Water Components Test Reactor**	Began operation in 1962.
(2) Pressure-tube type	**Carolinas-Virginia Tube Reactor**	Start-up scheduled for late 1962. Began operation in 1960.
	Plutonium Recycle Test Reactor [1]	Small-scale (NPD-2) and large-scale (CANDU) demonstration plants under construction in **Canada.**
b. In boiling heavy water systems	none to date [2]	See **Halden Project** (Norway).
2. *D_2O used as moderator only:*		
a. In a gas-cooled system	**Florida West Coast Reactor Project**	Project cancelled in 1961.
b. In a sodium-cooled system	**Chugach Electric Association Project**	Project cancelled in 1959.
c. In a H_2O-cooled system	none to date	See **spectral shift reactor concept.**
d. In an organic-cooled system	none to date	Reactor experiment (OCDRE) planned in **Canada.**

[1] The primary purpose of this reactor is to study the characteristics of recycled plutonium as a reactor fuel; however, it will also contribute information on the performance of a pressure-tube D_2O system.

[2] Argonne National Laboratory's Experimental Boiling Water Reactor (EBWR), which operates with H_2O, is so designed that D_2O could be used.

Plant Characteristics. See Table 2.
Economics. See **nuclear power economics.**

HELIUM

Element No. 2 (symbol He; atomic weight, 4.003), a gas that is chemically inert and has a negligible thermal neutron absorption cross section (~ 0.007 barn). Helium is of interest as the primary coolant in certain high-temperature gas-cooled power reactors (see **gas-cooled reactors, reactor materials**). It is also used as a thermal bond in oxide fuel-element assemblies, and as an inert medium for various metallurgical operations requiring a nonoxidizing atmosphere.

Helium ions, i.e., nuclei of the helium atom, are known as **alpha particles.**

HELIUM LEAK TEST

A rapid and sensitive nondestructive technique for locating leaks in equipment such as valves, piping and tanks. The object under test is continuously evacuated while a probe of helium gas is played on the exterior surfaces. Traces of helium appearing in the exhaust gases provide an instantaneous indication of a leak. A mass spectrometer is used as the helium-sensing device.

HETEROGENEOUS REACTOR

A nuclear reactor in which the fuel and moderator are arranged as discrete bodies (usually in a regular pattern) of such dimensions as to present a nonhomogeneous medium to neutrons; as distinct from a **homogeneous reactor.**

HEX

Shorthand for **uranium hexafluoride** (UF_6).

HEXONE

Methyl isobutyl ketone, the organic solvent used in the **Redox process.**

HIGH ALTITUDE BURST

The detonation of a nuclear weapon at an altitude above 100,000 feet.

HIGH BOILER RESIDUES

A term for the high molecular weight substances formed by radiolytic degradation of the

TABLE 2. SOME CHARACTERISTICS OF HEAVY WATER POWER REACTOR DESIGNS

	Recent Design[1] *(Pressurized system pressure-vessel type)*	*Projection*[2] *(Boiling system direct-cycle type)*
System parameters:		
Pressure in primary loop	750 psi	800 psi
Primary coolant outlet temperature	480°F	
Steam conditions	150 psi, 366°F	750 psi, 510°F
Thermal conversion efficiency	23.2%	26%
Power density	18.0 tkw/liter	35 tkw/liter
Specific power	31.6 tkw/kg U	
Fuel:		
Enrichment	natural uranium	
Form	uranium metal	
Cladding material	Zircaloy-2	
Maximum surface temperature	575°F	
Average burn-up	3960 MWD/metric ton U	7000 MWD/metric ton U

[1] Based on an optimized design of a 200-megawatt (electrical) plant prepared under AEC auspices in the fall of 1959. Source: TID-8516, Part I.
[2] Projected for a 300-megawatt (electrical) plant placed in operation in 1967–1968, assuming success of development work now in progress. Source: TID-8516, Part II.

organic mixtures used in **organic cooled reactors.** It has been found that the rate of degradation of the organic mixtures decreases as the high-boiler ("HB") concentration increases, however, the concentration is usually kept below 30% to avoid excessive fouling of heat transfer surfaces. Effect on the viscosity and heat-transfer characteristics of the organic liquid are other limiting factors.

HIGH-ENERGY ION INJECTION. See **Molecular Ion Ignition Program.**

HIGH-FLUX ISOTOPE REACTOR (HFIR)

A high-flux research reactor under construction at Oak Ridge National Laboratory. It is to be used primarily to produce isotopes of heavy (transplutonium) elements and special isotopes of lighter elements for research purposes. The basic nuclear design of the HFIR was developed by the ORNL staff. *Type:* Flux-trap tank reactor. *Power rating:* 100,000 thermal kilowatts. *Fuel:* Aluminum-clad involute fuel plates fabricated of highly enriched uranium-aluminum alloy. *Coolant:* H_2O. *Moderator:* H_2O. *Reflector:* Beryllium. *Neutron flux:* Maximum (unperturbed) thermal-neutron flux in flux trap, $\sim 6 \times 10^{15}$ n/cm²sec. Maximum fast-neutron flux in fuel region, $\sim 6 \times 10^{15}$ n/cm²sec. *Start-up:* Scheduled for 1963.

HIGH-TEMPERATURE GAS-COOLED REACTOR (HTGR)

A prototype **gas-cooled** nuclear power plant under construction on the Susquehanna River at Peach Bottom, Pennsylvania. The project is being carried out under the "third round" of the U.S. Atomic Energy Commission's Power Demonstration Reactor Program by the Philadelphia Electric Company, who will operate the plant, in cooperation with High Temperature Reactor Development Associates.* The AEC is contributing up to a maximum of $14.5 million for research and development assistance, and will waive its normal use charge for nuclear fuel material during the preconstruction period and for the first five years of operation (corresponding to a finan-

Fig. 88. High-temperature gas-cooled reactor. Half-scale mockup of prototype HTGR reactor vessel at General Atomic's Laboratory near San Diego, Calif. This equipment is used to obtain coolant flow data for design of the 40-megawatt (electrical) high-temperature gas-cooled reactor plant being built at Peach Bottom, Pa. (*Courtesy of General Atomic*)

cial contribution of $2.5 million). Bechtel Corporation is the prime contractor for the plant; General Atomics, a Division of General Dynamics Corporation, is the reactor contractor.

The following notes reflect the status of the project as of mid-1962:

Power: 40 megawatts (net electrical). *Fuel:* Fully enriched uranium and thorium in the form of a dispersion of uranium carbide and thorium in a graphite matrix. *Fuel element design:* A single fuel

---

* An organization representing 52 investor-owned electric utility companies.

element consists of a rod of fuel encased in a graphite sleeve. *Fuel inventory:* 173 kilograms of fully enriched uranium and ~ 2000 kilograms of thorium. *Coolant:* Helium at 350 pounds pressure; inlet temperature, 622°F; outlet temperature, 1382°F. *Steam conditions:* Superheated steam at 1450 pounds pressure and 1000°F. *Thermal conversion efficiency:* 34.8%. *Construction cost:* Estimated at $29.2 million, exclusive of research and development. For other project costs, see Table 3 under **nuclear power development.** *Dates:* Project announced in August, 1959. Construction started in February, 1962. Start of operation targeted for late 1964.

HILAC

Acronym for heavy-ion **linear accelerator.**

HIROSHIMA

Target of the first of the two nuclear weapons used by the United States against Japan in the final phase of World War II. The attack on Hiroshima, an important seaport and military base on the southwestern coast of Honshu, was made by a single U.S. Airforce plane and came at 8:15 A.M. on August 6, 1945. The bomb had a **yield** of about 20 kilotons (TNT equivalent) and was detonated at an altitude of approximately 1850 feet. The fissionable material used was uranium-235.

The effects of the attack have been reported as follows:

Total population	~ 255,000
Square miles destroyed	4.7
Killed and missing	~ 70,000
Injured	~ 70,000

Hiroshima was characterized by flat terrain, predominately wood-frame construction, and high population density. The population was completely unprepared for the attack. An alert had been sounded, but when only one plane was spotted the "all clear" was given on the assumption that there would be no attack. Thus the bomb fell at a time shortly after most of the residents had left shelter.

HISTORICAL ADVISORY COMMITTEE

An *ad hoc* (nonstatutory) committee established by the U.S. Atomic Energy Commission in 1958, to advise on matters relating to the preparation of a history of the AEC. Membership listed in Appendix D.

HOMOGENEOUS REACTOR

A nuclear reactor in which the fuel and moderator are mixed intimately enough to constitute a homogeneous medium—as distinct from a **heterogeneous reactor.** This condition may be achieved either by a solution of fuel in moderator or by an admixture of discrete particles having dimensions small in comparison with the average distance traveled by neutrons between collisions.

HOMOGENEOUS REACTOR EXPERIMENTS (HRE-I, -II)

Two experimental power reactors built to study the feasibility and operating characteristics of **aqueous homogeneous reactor** systems (see table). Both were designed and

HOMOGENEOUS REACTOR EXPERIMENTS

	HRE-I	*HRE-II*
Rated heat output (kilowatts-thermal)	1000	5000
Rated power output (kilowatts-electrical)	140	negligible
Fuel	40 grams of fully enriched uranium as uranyl sulfate solution (light water)	10 grams of fully enriched uranium as uranyl sulfate solution (heavy water)
Operating conditions	1000 psi; 482°F	2000 psi; 572°F
Steam conditions	200 psi; 382°F	250 psi; 406°F
Core vessel	Stainless steel	Zircaloy-2
Reflector	Heavy water	Heavy water
Capital investment	$1.1 million	$3.3 million
Start-up	April, 1952	December, 1957
Terminated	March, 1954	April, 1961

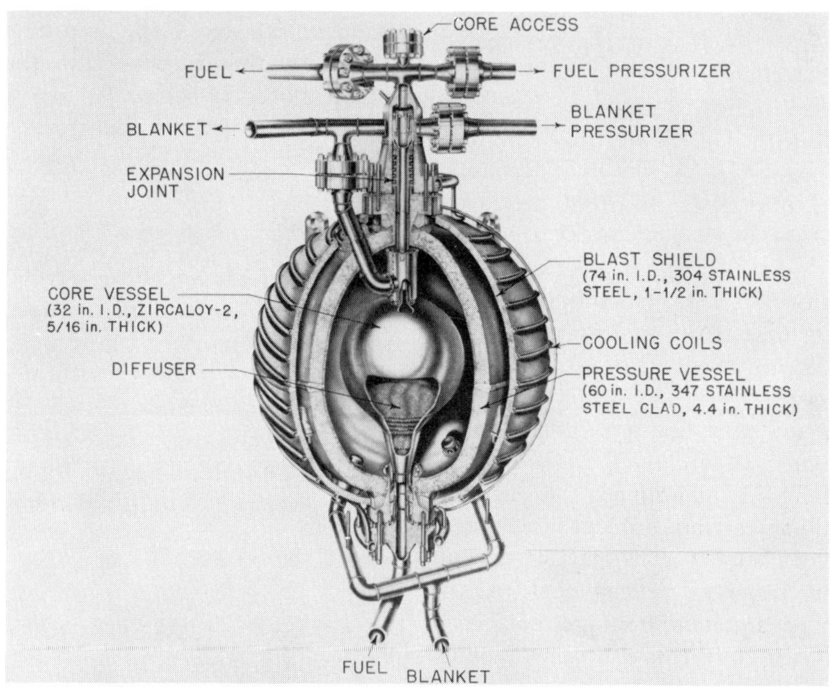

Fig. 89. Homogeneous Reactor Experiment No. 11 (HRE-11). Above, cutaway view of installation with core seen in center foreground. Below, cutaway of core. (*Courtesy of Oak Ridge National Laboratory*)

operated by Oak Ridge National Laboratory, which has been the main center of AEC research and development on this reactor concept.

HRE-I was operated over a two-year period before being dismantled to make room for HRE-II. It logged a total of nearly 2000 hours of criticality, operating about one-third of the time at power levels greater than 100 kilowatts (thermal). The maximum power level attained was 1600 kilowatts (thermal). The experiment demonstrated the nuclear stability and afforded a short-term test of the chemical integrity of a circulating-fuel system at moderately high power densities.

HRE-II * began operation in December, 1957. It attained a maximum power level of 6300 kilowatts (thermal) in April, 1958; however, after a brief period of operation at that level, a hole developed in the zircaloy-2 core tank (due to excessive corrosion), permitting the fuel solution to leak into the reactor blanket zone.** The reactor was operated intermittently at reduced power levels with fuel in both core and blanket zones from May, 1958, until January, 1960, by which time there was evidence of a second failure in the core tank. The reactor was then shut down to patch the holes in the core tank and to make additional general repairs. This work was carried out by remote techniques over an eight-month period. Analysis indicated that the fuel stability and associated corrosion problems encountered stemmed from the hydrodynamic design of the core vessel, and that improved hydrodynamics (higher flow rates) could be achieved by the simple expedient of reversing the flow through the core. Operation was resumed in November, 1960, with reversed flow, and marked improvement in system performance was observed.

Confirming and extending many of the positive results achieved with HRE-I, the experience with HRE-II underlined the difficult materials and engineering problems associated with the aqueous homogeneous reactor concept in its present stage of development. As is discussed under **aqueous homogeneous reactors,** consideration of this and other factors led to the decision to discontinue this line of development and operation of HRE-II was terminated in April, 1961.

---

* Also known as the Homogeneous Reactor Test (HRT).

** The reactor was designed to operate as a two-region system with an aqueous slurry of thorium oxide in the blanket zone; however, that mode of operation has not been attempted to date.

HOMOPOLAR SERIES

The name of a series of experimental devices of the "magnetic mirror" type built at the Berkeley Branch of the E. O. Lawrence Radiation Laboratory for research on controlled **fusion** (see **magnetic mirror systems).** These experiments involved superimposing a radial electric field on the transverse magnetic field used for **plasma** confinement, thereby causing the plasma to turn on its axis, i.e., to rotate (see **rotating plasma).** The principle is that the resulting centrifugal force acts to help keep the plasma in its "magnetic bottle" and thereby enhances the stability of magnetic mirror confinement. The results to date have been encouraging and research is continuing on this technique. The concept of a rotating plasma has also been applied in the experimental fusion known as **Ixion,** used at Los Alamos Scientific Laboratory, and in the **ion magnetron** at the Berkeley Brench of the E. O. Lawrence Radiation Laboratory.

HONDURAS

The Honduras Atomic Energy Commission, Tegucigalpa, is the agency responsible for atomic energy matters. Interest at present centers in medical and agricultural applications of radioisotopes, and related training programs. Honduras is a member of the **International Atomic Energy Agency** and the **Inter-American Nuclear Energy Commission.**

HORACE HARDY LESTER REACTOR FOR MATERIALS RESEARCH

A 1000-kilowatt (thermal) pool-type research reactor at Watertown Arsenal, Watertown, Massachusetts. It is owned by the U.S. Army and used for research on materials of interest to the Army Ordnance Corps. The reactor was supplied by Curtiss-Wright Corporation and began operation in 1961. (See **research and training reactors)**

HOT CELL

A shielded cubicle in which laboratory operations on multicurie quantities of high-intensity gamma-emitting radioactive materials can safely be conducted by means of **manipulators** and observed by means of **shield windows** or indirect viewing devices (periscopes, etc.); also referred to as a hot cave. Hot cells may be designed for general-purpose work or for specialized chemical, metallurgical or other operations. Another design factor is the amount and nature of the radioactive material to be handled. A **hot laboratory** normally contains one or more hot cells.

HOT LABORATORY

A laboratory designed and equipped for the safe handling of highly radioactive materials. Following are typical design features:

1. To facilitate the control of radiation

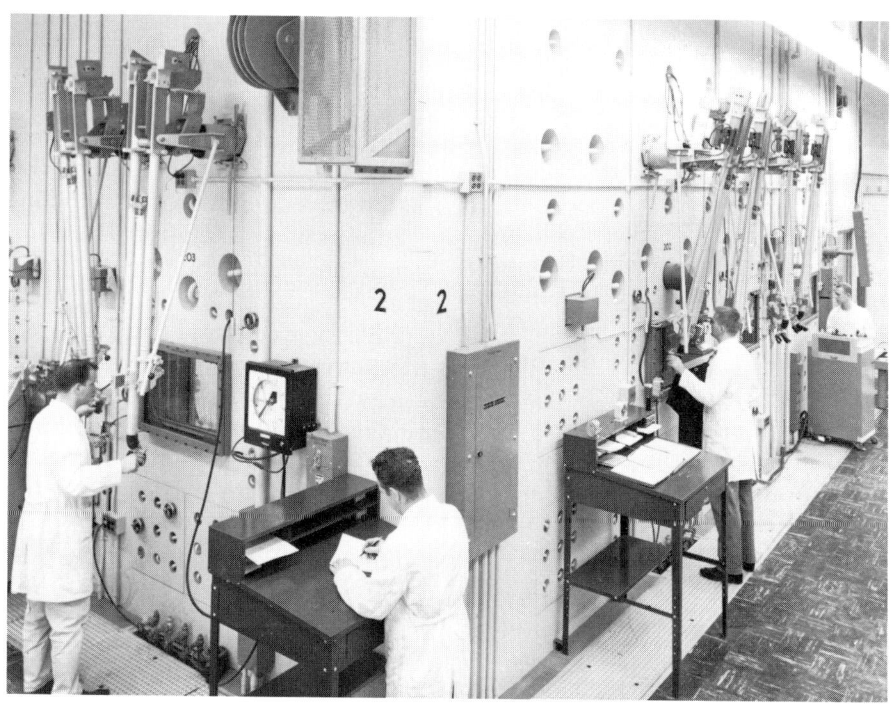

Fig. 90. Hot cells. Below, installation at General Electric Company's Vallecitos Atomic Laboratory in Pleasanton, Calif. Above, technicians preparing apparatus for experiment in hot cell at Brookhaven National Laboratory. (*Courtesy of General Electric Co. and Brookhaven National Laboratory*)

levels and simplify ventilation problems, a hot laboratory is arranged to segregate high-level, low-level and "cold" areas with intermediate radiation monitoring stations and personnel change rooms.

2. The ventilation system is designed to minimize airborne contamination. The static pressure in areas in which radioactive materials are handled is kept somewhat below atmospheric pressure. Exhaust air from hoods, hot cells, or other enclosures is filtered and scrubbed and then vented through a high stack before being discharged to the atmosphere.

3. Shielding in operating areas is designed to maintain exposure levels well below established tolerance limits.

4. Extensive **radiation monitoring** facilities are provided.

5. All laboratory surfaces likely to become contaminated are designed to facilitate decontamination. In areas where the possibility of contamination is high, walls, floors and equipment are usually coated with strippable paint.

For information on special equipment used in hot laboratories see **hot cells, shield windows, manipulators, glove boxes,** etc.

HUMBOLDT BAY POWER PLANT

A nuclear power plant of the direct-cycle **boiling water** type at Humboldt Bay near Eureka, California. The project is being financed by the Pacific Gas and Electric Company, who will operate the plant. Bechtel Corporation is the prime contractor. General Electric Company is the reactor designer and supplied the principal nuclear components. A new type of **containment** system, known as vapor-suppression containment, is used. The following notes are based on 1962 information:

Power: 48.5 megawatts (net electrical). *Fuel:* Slightly enriched uranium (2.6% U^{235}) in the form of uranium dioxide (UO_2) pellets. *Fuel element design:* A single fuel element consists of an assembly of thin stainless steel tubes loaded with fuel pellets. *Fuel inventory:* 17.3 metric tons of uranium dioxide. *Steam conditions:* Steam leaves the reactor at 1025 pounds pressure and 547°F. *Thermal conversion efficiency:* 30%. *Control materials:* 32 boron-steel rods. *Containment:* Vapor suppression system. *Cost:* Capital investment estimated at $20.6 million based on fixed-price contract. *Dates:* Construction started in November, 1960. Operation scheduled for the latter part of 1962.

HUNGARY

Agency. An 11-man Atomic Energy Committee in Budapest, coordinates Hungarian atomic energy activity, with primary emphasis being placed on training.

International Relationships. Member of the **International Atomic Energy Agency.** Technical assistance agreement with the U.S.S.R. Participant in the **Joint Institute for Nuclear Research** at Dubna in the U.S.S.R.

Research Centers. The Central Institute of Physical Research, Csielleberg (near Budapest), is the principal nuclear research laboratory. Its facilities include a 2000-kilowatt (thermal) pool-type research reactor supplied by the U.S.S.R. The Institute of Nuclear Research, Debrecen (Eastern Hungary) was established in part to develop methods of recovering uranium from Hungarian ores. A low power research reactor is to be installed in the near future. A radioisotope laboratory, reportedly the largest in Central Europe, has been established on Csepel Island in Budapest.

Production Activity. Uranium is being mined on a moderate scale from low-grade ores.

Energy Economy. Hungary's present electric power capacity is about 1500 megawatts, nearly all of it thermal. Coal and lignite production is adequate for present requirements but supplementary energy sources are believed to be required to permit the desired rate of industrial expansion.

Nuclear Power. A 200-megawatt (electrical) nuclear power station of Soviet design is reportedly scheduled for completion in 1963, however no details on this project are available.

HYDRIDES

Metal hydrides, i.e., solutions of hydrogen in metals, and metal-hydrogen compounds, are of interest for use as high-temperature reactor materials, especially in applications where weight and space need to be conserved. The interest derives from hydrogen's effectiveness as a neutron slowing-down medium, combined with the fact that metal hydrides have superior thermal stability and mechanical strength relative to other hydrogenous materials. Hydrides of metals of low thermal neutron absorption cross section (e.g., beryllium) are being studied for use as moderator or reflector materials. Hydrides of metals of high thermal neutron absorption cross section are being studied for use as radiation shielding materials. There is also interest in the use of uranium alloy hydrides as combined fuel-moderator in solid homogeneous reactor systems. (See **reactor materials**)

Fabrication of hydrides requires specialized techniques since in general these materials are quite brittle and in some cases pyrophoric. Much is to be learned regarding hydrided alloy systems to attain improved mechanical and physical properties. Cladding techniques are also of considerable importance.

Metal hydrides also have application in the production of small amounts of high-purity hydrogen; in the powder metallurgy field as chemical reagents; and as fluxes for welding and brazing.

HYDROGEN

Element No. 1 (symbol, H; atomic weight, 1.008). As it occurs in nature, hydrogen is a mixture of two stable isotopes—H^1 (99.985%) and H^2 (0.015%). The latter, sometimes referred to as "heavy hydrogen," has been given the name, **deuterium** (symbol, D). The only other isotope of hydrogen is the artificially produced radioisotope, H^3—a 12.26-year beta emitter, formed from lithium-6 by the neutron-alpha reaction. H^3, sometimes referred to as "heavy heavy hydrogen," has been given the name, **tritium** (symbol, T).

Because its mass (1.0081) is approximately the same as that of the neutron (1.0089), hydrogen is the most effective of all materials in slowing down neutrons by elastic collisions. Deuterium is the next most effective material and, having a significantly lower thermal neutron absorption cross section than hydrogen, is over-all a better moderator for reactor use. In practice both hydrogen and deuterium are used in reactors—hydrogen, in the form of ordinary water or in organic form, as coolant or coolant-moderator; and deuterium, in the form of heavy water, as moderator or moderator-coolant. Hydrogen-metal compounds (i.e., **hydrides**) are currently being considered for reactor use, primarily as solid moderators for high-temperature reactor applications. Hydrogenous materials are usually incorporated in radiation shields.

Hydrogen ions, i.e., the nuclei of hydrogen atoms, are known as **protons.**

HYDROGEN BOMB

A term for a nuclear weapon whose energy derives from nuclear **fusion** as well as from nuclear **fission.** The term derives from the fact that the isotopes of hydrogen, namely, tritium and deuterium, may be used in such a device. A more accurate term, used in the technical literature, is "thermonuclear weapon." (See **weapons**)

HYPERONS

A class of **elementary particles** with masses greater than the mass of a **nucleon** and which yield a nucleon as a decay product. For example, the neutrally charged lambda (Λ^0) particle, with a rest mass of 2181 electron masses, is an unstable particle which decays with a mean life of about 2.8×10^{-10} second into a proton and a negative pi-meson. There are also Σ^+ (sigma plus), Σ^- (sigma minus), and Ξ^- (xi minus) particles with somewhat greater masses, very short half-lives, and analogous decay modes. The hyperons are included among the "strange particles," because their roles in the scheme of elementary particles are not yet understood.

I

ICELAND

The Iceland Nuclear Science Commission, Reykjavik, is the agency responsible for atomic energy matters. Iceland's principal interests in atomic energy lie in the medical, agricultural and industrial applications of radioisotopes and in the possibility of using geothermal steam sources as a starting point for the production of heavy water. Hydroelectric resources are considered adequate for the country's power needs for the foreseeable future. No research, power or propulsion reactor projects have been announced. Iceland is a member of the **International Atomic Energy Agency** and the **European Nuclear Energy Agency.**

IDAHO CHEMICAL PROCESSING PLANT (CPP)

A U.S. Atomic Energy Commission **fuel reprocessing** facility located at the National Reactor Testing Station, near Idaho Falls, Idaho. *Operating contractor:* Phillips Petroleum Company. *AEC investment in plant and equipment:* ~ $66 million.*

The CPP is used to reprocess enriched-uranium fuel elements from a variety of research, testing and developmental power reactors. It employs a solvent extraction process and is designed for **direct maintenance.** The main process steps are: (1) Fuel dissolution: The spent fuel elements are dissolved in an appropriate acid. To accommodate process variations, the plant is equipped with several "head-end" (dissolver) facilities. (2) Feed preparation: The uranium concentration and other conditions are adjusted to provide satisfactory feed for the solvent extraction process. (3) Solvent extraction: The adjusted fuel solution passes through a continuous 3-cycle solvent extraction system for uranium decontamination. The solvent used is **hexone.** (4) Product handling: The decontaminated uranium solution is concentrated, analyzed and packaged for shipment in "safe-critical" containers. (5) Waste handling: Off-gases are discharged to the atmosphere after filtration and dilution. Liquid wastes are partially concentrated by evaporation and then stored in underground waste tanks (see **radioactive waste disposal).** There are, in addition, solvent recovery and other process auxiliaries.

The plant is situated on a 77-acre plot surrounded by an exclusion fence. The principal facilities are as follows:

1. Fuel Storage Building: This consists principally of water-filled storage and transfer basins in which incoming spent fuel elements are held pending processing. The spent fuel is received in lead shipping casks, unloaded under water, and stored in stainless steel buckets suspended from overhead tracks. A minimum of 15 feet of water cover is maintained at all times to satisfy radiation shielding requirements.

2. Main Process Building: This is a large rectangular structure, built largely below ground level, which houses the main process system. It contains approximately 1 million square feet of work space. The main process system is installed in massive concrete cells, divided into two rows with operating, service, and access corridors running between. The cells are lined with stainless steel to facilitate

* Includes facilities authorized or under construction as of June 30, 1960. Not adjusted for depreciation.

decontamination and the floors are so pitched that, in the event of a major spill, subcritical conditions are assured. Chemical make-up equipment and other "cold" auxiliary process units are located above cell level in unshielded galleries. Laboratory and office facilities are located in an adjoining structure.

3. Waste Disposal Building: This contains waste storage tanks, evaporator facilities for preliminary concentration of liquid water, and facilities for disposing of gaseous wastes.

4. Waste Calcination Building: This contains an experimental calcination system for treating liquid radioactive wastes.

Fig. 91. The Idaho Chemical Processing Plant. (*Courtesy of Phillips Petroleum Co.*)

5. Waste Tank Farm: This consists of a series of stainless steel storage tanks enclosed in concrete vaults under a 10-foot earth shield.

Two aspects of the design of the CPP should be noted. One is that it is designed to handle uranium of various degrees of enrichment, including "fully" enriched material. The means used to maintain safe critical conditions include: (1) controlling the concentration of uranium in the process solutions; (2) limiting the mass of uranium that can accumulate in any one process vessel; and (3) "safe-critical" equipment geometry. An example of the latter is the use of spacer attachments to product containers to prevent them from being placed too close to each other. The other noteworthy aspect of the CPP is the fact that it is designed for direct maintenance. In the event of equipment failure, the process cell requiring maintenance is shut down and decontaminated; maintenance workers subsequently enter and perform necessary repairs in a more or less conventional manner.

The CPP began operation in 1953. The basic process used was developed at Oak Ridge National Laboratory.

IGNITION TEMPERATURE

In controlled **fusion,** the temperature (see below) at which the energy generated in a fuel **plasma** by fusion reactions just equals the energy lost from the system by **bremsstrahlung** radiation is the "ideal ignition temperature," or "critical temperature." In theory, it represents the threshold temperature for achieving a "self-sustaining" fission system, i.e., one that stays hot enough to keep the reaction going. In practice, additional energy losses occur, so that temperatures above the ideal ignition point must be achieved and maintained in a practical fusion device. These are known as "practical ignition temperatures."

The term, temperature, as used here relates to the kinetic energy of the charged particles (ions and electrons) comprising the plasma (see **stellar temperatures**). Since it is the ions of the plasma that undergo fusion (and not the electrons), it is the energy of the ions which must be raised to a level corresponding to the ignition temperature of the plasma. Most plasma heating techniques are such that the energy (and hence the temperature) of the ions in the plasma is considerably higher than that of the electrons.

The ideal and practical ignition temperatures for the two basic fusion reactions of interest in connection with research on **thermonuclear power** are given in Table 1.

IMPLOSION-TYPE WEAPON

One of the possible designs of a nuclear weapon. In an implosion-type weapon, a peripheral charge of conventional explosive is used to compress (implode) a subcritical spherical assembly of fissionable material into a critical mass. (See **weapons**)

TABLE 1. IGNITION TEMPERATURES FOR BASIC FUSION REACTIONS

	Ideal Ignition Temperature		*Practical Ignition Temperature*	
	Ion Energy (electron volts)	*Ion Temperature (°K)*	*Ion Energy (electron volts)*	*Ion Temperature (°K)*
Deuterium-tritium (The so-called D-T reaction) $D + T \rightarrow He^4 + n + 17.6$ Mev	4,000	46,000,000	6,000	70,000,000
Deuterium-deuterium (The so-called D-D reactions) $D + D \nearrow He^3 + n + 3.2$ Mev; $\searrow T + p + 4.0$ Mev	36,000	410,000,000	53,000	600,000,000

IMPROVED CYCLE BOILING WATER REACTOR. See **boiling water reactors** (table).

IN-PILE

A general descriptive term used in reference to apparatus that is placed in a nuclear reactor for experimental or test purposes, e.g., in-pile loops used to study the behavior of materials in a reactor environment.

IN-PILE TESTS

Insertion of materials or equipment into a nuclear reactor for the purpose of studying radiation effects such as dimensional changes, altered physical properties or the like.

INCIDENT PARTICLE

In a nuclear reaction, the particle inducing the reaction, i.e., striking the "target" nucleus.

INDEMNIFICATION. See **insurance and indemnification against atomic energy risks.**

INDIA

Agency. The Indian Atomic Energy Commission, Bombay, is the official agency responsible for atomic energy matters.

International Relationships. Members of the **International Atomic Energy Agency.** See reference to CIR Reactor below.

Research Center. The Indian Atomic Energy Establishment at Trombay, near Bombay, is developing into a major research center. The experimental facilities completed to date include three reactors: "Apsara," a pool-type research reactor designed by the Trombay staff except for the fuel elements (supplied by the United Kingdom), operates at a power level of 1000 kilowatts (thermal). The Canada-India Reactor (CIR), a high-flux materials testing unit patterned after Canada's NRX Reactor, operates at a power level of 40,000 kilowatts (thermal). This reactor was built under Canadian technical direction and Canada made a major contribution toward the cost of the installation pursuant to an agreement reached with India within the framework of the Colombo Plan for Asian economic development. The third reactor, a zero-power facility, was designed and built by the Trombay staff. Facilities under construction include an extensive "hot" laboratory designed by Vitro International, a division of Vitro Corporation of America.

Production Activity. India has extensive deposits of thorium, with known reserves of 250,000 tons and assumed additional reserves of 250,000 tons. Uranium deposits in the Province of Rajasthan are currently being worked. Facilities for processing monazite are located at Alwaye. Facilities for producing thorium nitrate and uranium metal are located at Trombay.

Facilities for producing 10-20 tons per year of heavy water are located at Nangal near the site of the giant Bhakra hydroelectric project. The heavy water is produced on a by-product basis by a low-temperature hydrogen distillation process of French design. The process operates on electrolytic hydrogen used for ammonia synthesis in the manufacture of fer-

Fig. 92. The Canada-India Reactor (CIR) at Trombay, as it looked in the final stages of construction. (*Courtesy of Atomic Energy of Canada, Ltd.*)

tilizer. Vitro Corporation of America provided technical and management services for the over-all fertilizer-heavy water installation.

Energy Economy. India's electric power capacity is about 4500 megawatts, most of it coal-fired and the balance hydroelectric. There are substantial reserves of coal, however many deposits are remote from load centers. Much of India's capacity is operated at low plant factors.

Nuclear Power Plans. The Indian Government has placed considerable emphasis on nuclear power development in connection with its industrialization objectives. In 1960, the Indian AEC called for bids for a 300-megawatt (electrical) nuclear power station to be located at Tarapur, near Bombay.

Tentative plans have been announced for the design and construction, by Indian engineers, of a small-scale (~ 20 megawatts electrical) natural uranium-fueled, heavy water-moderated and organic cooled power reactor at the Trombay site.

INDIAN POINT STATION

A large-scale nuclear power plant of the **pressurized water** type, located on the Hudson River at Indian Point, New York. The plant, built for development and demonstration purposes, is owned and has been wholly financed by Consolidated Edison Company of New York. Babcock & Wilcox Company designed the reactor and supplied the principal nuclear components. Vitro Engineering Company furnished consulting and architect-engineering services.

A mixture of thorium and fully enriched uranium dioxides is used in the initial fuel loading; however, it has been announced that the second and third cores are to be fabricated of slightly enriched uranium dioxide.

The plant employs two conventional oil-fired superheaters to raise the temperature of the steam before feeding it to the turbine-generator, thereby improving the thermal conversion efficiency of the system. The reactor containment vessel is encased in a concrete radiation shield. The reason for this feature is that Consolidated Edison contemplates locating additional power generating facilities on the Indian Point site at some time in the future. The containment shield is so designed that, even in the event of major radioactive contamination of the interior of the containment vessel, safe radiation levels would be maintained in the immediate plant vicinity.

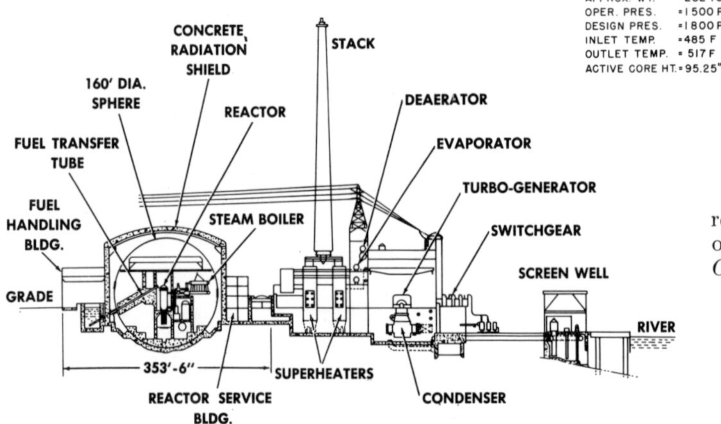

Fig. 93. Indian Point Station. Above, reactor arrangement. Left, plant layout. (*Courtesy of Consolidated Edison Co. of New York*)

The following notes reflect the status of the project as of mid-1962 and relates to the initial core loading:

Power: 255 megawatts (net electrical) of which 104 megawatts derive from energy supplied by two oil-fired superheaters. *Fuel:* A mixture of fully enriched uranium dioxide (UO_2) and thorium dioxide (ThO_2). *Fuel element design:* A single fuel element consists of a zircolay-2-clad assembly of thin stainless steel tubes loaded with fuel pellets. *Core arrangements:* The core is arranged in three radial zones with the U^{235} concentration in the fuel mixture lowest in the inner zone and highest in the outer zone. *Fuel inventory:* ~ 18,400 kilograms of fuel mixture averaging 6 weight % U^{235}. *Coolant:* Ordinary water at 1500 pounds pressure; outlet temperature, 517°F. *Steam conditions:* From the steam generator; saturated steam at 405 pounds pressure and 449°F; from the superheaters, superheated steam at 370 pounds pressure and 1000°F. *Thermal conversion efficiency:* 32.5%. *Control materials:* 21 hafnium control rods; boron incorporated in fuel-element cladding as a burnable poison. *Containment:* Steel sphere, 160 feet in diameter, encased in a concrete radiation shielding structure. *Construction cost:* Estimated at ~ $110 million, exclusive of research and development. For other project costs, see Table 3 under **nuclear power development.** *Dates:* Provisional construction permit issued in May, 1956. Major construction work started in January, 1958. Start of operation scheduled for July, 1962.

INDIRECT CYCLE

A term applied to a power reactor system in which a secondary or tertiary fluid, rather

Fig. 94. Indian Point Station, Indian Point, N.Y. (*Courtesy of Consolidated Edison Co.*)

than the primary reactor coolant, is used to operate the power or propulsion machinery. An example is an indirect-cycle boiling water reactor in which the steam-water mixture leaving the reactor is passed through a heat exchanger wherein it transfers heat to a secondary water supply, thereby generating the steam used to run the steam-turbine. (See **direct cycle**)

INDIUM

Element No. 49 (symbol, In; atomic weight, 114.76) of interest in the nuclear energy field when alloyed with **cadmium** and **silver** for use in reactor control rod applications. (See **reactor materials**)

INDONESIA

The Institute for Atomic Energy, Djakarta, is the agency responsible for atomic energy development. Limited research activity is in progress at the University of Indonesia's Institute of Technology, which has received a commitment from the United States for a Foreign Research Reactor Grant to help finance the purchase of a Triga Mark II research and training reactor from General Atomic. A radioisotope laboratory is being established at Gadiah Mada University with the aid of a U.S. grant. A radioisotope receiving, distribution and training center has been established at Pasar Minggu, near Djakarta. In 1961, Indonesia announced an agreement with the U.S.S.R. providing for the installation of a research reactor at Djakarta University and a critical experiment facility at Gadiah Mada University.

Indonesia's present electric power capacity is about 300 megawatts and there are substantial undeveloped hydro resources as well as abundant supplies of coal and oil. There is no apparent need for early nuclear power development, however the U.S.S.R. has reportedly offered to construct a nuclear power plant in a remote area of the country.

Indonesia is a member of the **International Atomic Energy Agency** and has a research-type **Agreement for Cooperation** with the United States.

INDUCED RADIOACTIVITY

Radioactivity resulting from bombardment of a stable nuclide with subatomic particles. While some **natural radioactivity** is of the induced variety, the term usually connotes artificial radioactivity, i.e., radioactivity induced by subatomic particles that have been artificially produced or accelerated. Of the types of radiation associated with nuclear reactors, only neutrons can induce radioactivity —a process referred to as neutron activation. Radioactivity can also be induced by high-energy charged particles (deuterons, alpha particles, heavy ions, etc.) produced by **particle accelerators.**

INDUSTRIAL REACTOR LABORATORIES, INC. RESEARCH REACTOR

A 5000-kilowatt (thermal) pool-type research reactor located at Plainsboro, New Jersey. It is operated by Columbia University on behalf of Industrial Reactor Laboratories, Inc., an organization formed by the following ten companies: American Machine & Foundry Company, American Tobacco Company, Atlas Powder Company, Continental Can Company, Corning Glass Works, National Distillers and Chemical Corporation, National Lead Company, Radio Corporation of America, Socony Mobil Oil Company, Inc., and United States Rubber Company. The participating companies maintain laboratories at the reactor site. The IRL reactor was supplied by AMF Atomics, Inc. and began operation in 1959. (See **research and training reactors)**

Fig. 95. Building housing Industrial Reactor Laboratories, Inc. Reactor (*Courtesy of AMF Atomics*)

INELASTIC SCATTERING

A type of nuclear reaction in which an incident particle is deflected by a nucleus and the total kinetic energy of the system is reduced. The reduction in kinetic energy is the result of the process in which some of the energy of the incident particle is absorbed by the target nucleus, which in turn goes to a higher energy state. (See **scattering)**

INFORMATION SERVICES, AEC. See **Atomic Energy Commission—Information Services.**

INFORMATION SOURCES, ATOMIC ENERGY SUBJECTS. See **Appendix B;** also, **Atomic Energy Commission—Information Services.**

INSURANCE AND INDEMNIFICATION AGAINST ATOMIC ENERGY RISKS

Statutory Provisions. Pursuant to Section 170 * of the Atomic Energy Act of 1954, as amended, and with the exceptions noted below, the U.S. Atomic Energy Commission requires, as a condition for a license or construction permit for a **production** or **utilization facility,** proof of financial protection against public liability claims arising out of a nuclear incident. Financial protection is the ability to respond in damages for public liability, including the costs of investigating and defending claims and settling suits. Financial protection may be furnished in the form of a nuclear

* This section was added to the federal atomic energy statute by the Price-Anderson Act (Public Law 85-256), enacted in 1957. Certain clauses were added by later amendments. (See **legislation, federal)**

energy liability insurance policy, self-insurance, or such other form as the AEC may approve. In the case of reactors having a rated capacity of 100 megawatts or more of electrical power, the maximum amount of financial protection (see below) is required.

Section 170c provides that the AEC shall enter into an agreement with the licensee which indemnifies him, or any other person who may be legally liable, against public liability claims in excess of the amount of financial protection that has been required of the licensee. The maximum federal indemnity for a single nuclear incident is set at $500 million. In the case of reactor facilities, the fee for indemnification is set at $30 per year per megawatt of thermal capacity. For other types of licenses, the fee is determined by the AEC. The minimum annual fee in any case is $100.

Section 170d provides for the indemnification of AEC contractors engaged in activities under the risk of public liability for a substantial nuclear incident.

Section 170e limits the maximum public liability arising from a single nuclear incident to $500 million plus the amount of financial protection required of the licensee.

Section 170k exempts nonprofit educational institutions from the requirement for financial protection and provides for the indemnification of such institutions from public liability in excess of $250,000. As a matter of policy, the Commission also has exempted other Federal agencies from its financial protection.

AEC Regulations. AEC regulations relating to financial protection and indemnification are contained in Part 140, Title 10 of the Code of Federal Regulations (10 CFR 140). The amount of financial protection required of reactor licensees required to furnish proof thereof is set at: (a) $1 million for reactors authorized to operate at a thermal power level not exceeding ten kilowatts; (b) $1.5 million above 10 kilowatts but not exceeding 1 megawatt; and (c) $2.5 million above 1 megawatt but not exceeding 10 megawatts, except for power and testing reactors. For other reactors the amount of financial protection is determined by the formula prescribed by 10 CFR 140 except that for power and testing reactors the amount may not be less than $3.5 million nor more than $60 million.

Private Insurance. Early in 1955, the AEC requested the private insurance industry to study the problems involved in providing insurance against atomic energy risks. These problems had been brought to the forefront by the passage of the 1954 Act, which removed the statutory prohibition against private ownership of reactors and other facilities utilizing or capable of producing significant amounts of **special nuclear material,** thereby spurring private initiative. In 1957, four private insurance pools were formed:

1. Nuclear Energy Liability Insurance Association **(NELIA),** a syndicate of capital stock insurance companies, and Mutual Atomic Energy Liability Underwriters **(MAELU),** a counterpart syndicate of mutual insurance companies.

2. Nuclear Energy Property Insurance Association **(NEPIA),** a syndicate of stock companies, and Mutual Atomic Energy Reinsurance Pool **(MAERP),** a counterpart syndicate of mutual companies.

The first two pools (NELIA and MAELU) provide liability insurance in amounts up to $46.5 and $13.5 million, respectively. They write joint policies which have been accepted by the AEC as satisfying its requirements for proof of financial protection against public liability claims in connection with licensees of production and utilization facilities. These policies cover third party liability but do not cover damage to the on-site property of the insured. The latter two pools (NEPIA and MAERP) provide insurance against damage to the property of the insured through joint policies in which NEPIA assumes approximately 85% of the risk and MAERP approximately 15%.

Insurance rates depend upon the nature of the risk. In the case of reactor facilities, the factors taken into account include the reactor type, its use, its rated thermal output, the degree of containment, the location of the facility, and the population density of the environs. NELIA and MAELU have established a system of base premiums for broad risk categories and a rate structure keyed to the amount of coverage as follows:

Coverage	*% of Base Premium*
$ 0–1 million	100
$ 1–5 million	50
$ 5–10 million	20
$10–20 million	10
$20–40 million	5
$40–50 million	2

NEPIA and MAERP have organized a rating agency, the **Nuclear Insurance Rating Bureau** (NIRB), to set rates within a broad rate structure taking into account the highly specific factors that enter into property risk evaluation.

International Aspects. The AEC has taken an active role in encouraging international organizations and foreign governments to enact legislation which, among other purposes, would limit the potential liability of U.S. exporters of atomic energy equipment, materials and services.

The Organization for Economic Cooperation and Development (OECD), of which the United States is a member, has developed a liability convention containing the following principal provisions:

1. The maximum liability for a single nuclear incident relating to a land-based reactor is limited to $15 million (with individual signatories retaining the right to raise or lower this ceiling, but not below $5 million).

2. The reactor operator is required to have insurance or other proof of financial responsibility adequate to cover the liability ceiling.

3. The reactor operator's recourse against a supplier is limited to (a) any individual who intentionally causes a nuclear incident, or (b) instances in which recourse is specifically provided by contract.

This convention has been signed by the following countries: Austria, Belgium, Denmark, France, Germany, Greece, Italy, Luxembourg, the Netherlands, Norway, Portugal, Spain, Sweden, Switzerland, Turkey, and the United Kingdom. No ratifications have been accomplished to date, and five are required to bring the convention into effect.

The European Atomic Energy Community **(Euratom)** has drafted but not yet adopted a convention which presupposes the simultaneous or previous coming into effect of the OECD convention and additionally provides for payment from public funds for damage up to a limit of $120 million.

The **International Atomic Energy Agency** has under consideration a liability convention that is similar in many respects to the OECD convention. Certain provisions, including the amount of the liability limit have yet to be worked out by intergovernmental negotiations.

Foreign governments that have enacted national liability legislation include Japan, Sweden, Switzerland, the United Kingdom and West Germany. National legislation is before the Philippine Congress and is in various stages of preparation in Austria, Denmark, France, Israel, Italy, the Netherlands, Norway, Spain and Venezuela.

An international convention applicable to maritime reactors (nuclear ships) was drafted at a diplomatic conference in Brussels in April, 1961, at which some 50 countries were represented. The provisions of this draft convention generally conform to the views of the United States. The liability of the nuclear ship operator is limited to $100 million for any one nuclear incident.

INTER-AMERICAN INSTITUTE OF AGRICULTURAL SCIENCES

An agency of the Organization of American States (OAS) serving the development of agricultural science in the member countries; located at Turrialba, Costa Rica. Under a contract with the U.S. Atomic Energy Commission, the Institute is using radioisotopes and gamma irradiation in research on problems in tropical agriculture, and is providing training in these techniques.

INTER-AMERICAN NUCLEAR ENERGY COMMISSION (IANEC)

An agency of the **Organization of American States** (OAS), established on April 22, 1959, to foster Inter-American cooperation in the atomic energy field; headquarters in the Pan American Union, Washington, D.C. Functions include assistance in the coordination of research, training and information dissemination programs; planning of conferences, such as the series of Inter-American Symposia on the Peaceful Applications of Atomic Energy; technical studies and surveys; and advice and assistance on health and safety standards.

Member nations are as follows: Argentina, Bolivia, Brazil, Chile, Colombia, Costa Rica, Cuba, the Dominican Republic, Ecuador, Guatemala, Haiti, Honduras, Mexico, Nicaragua, Panama, Paraguay, Peru, Salvador, the United States, Uraguay and Venezuela.

INTERCHANGE INSTABILITY

With reference to experimental controlled-**fusion** devices of the twisted-torus stellarator type, a form of instability in the **plasma confinement** system in which the plasma and surrounding magnetic fields tend to exchange places, resulting in plasma dispersion; also referred to as flute type instability. Efforts to overcome this plasma instability have led to the development of particular preventive measures such as **rotational transform.** (See **Stellarator Program)**

INTERMEDIATE NEUTRONS

Neutrons having energies above **thermal-neutron** values but below **fast-neutron** values. The intermediate range is usually taken to be 0.5 to 100,000 ev. The terms epithermal neutron and intermediate neutron are used more or less synonymously; strictly speaking, however, epithermal neutrons are neutrons having energies in the low portion of the intermediate neutron energy spectrum.

INTERMEDIATE REACTOR

A nuclear reactor in which the fission chain reaction is sustained mainly by neutrons of intermediate energy, i.e., faster than **thermal neutrons** but slower than **fast neutrons.** The intermediate energy range is usually considered to be between 0.5 and 100,000 ev. An intermediate reactor contains a moderator, but not enough to reduce the average neutron energies to thermal values. The terms epithermal reactor and intermediate are used more or less synonymously. (See **intermediate neutrons)**

INTERNATIONAL ATOMIC ENERGY AGENCY (IAEA)

An organization established under the aegis of the United Nations in October, 1957, to promote internatioanl cooperation in the peaceful uses of atomic energy. The agency's headquarters are in Vienna, Austria. See accompanying table for a list of member nations. See **international control of atomic energy** for background information.

Functions. The major functions of the IAEA are as follows:

1. To encourage and assist peaceful atomic energy research, development, and application.
2. To make provision for needed materials, services, equipment and facilities.
3. To foster the exchange of scientific and technical information.
4. To encourage the exchange and training of scientists.
5. To establish and administer safeguards to insure that special nuclear materials supplied by the Agency to member nations are not used to further any military purposes.
6. To establish or adopt standards of safety for the protection of health and minimization of danger to life and property.

The IAEA's charter requires it to "conduct its activities in accordance with the purpose and principles of the United Nations to promote peace and international cooperation." Agreements have been entered into between the IAEA and the United Nations and its specialized agencies providing for close working relations in areas of mutual interest. (See **United Nations)**

Organization. A General Conference, at which each member country is represented and has one vote, is held annually to approve the program and budget for the forthcoming year, act on applications for membership, consider proposals to amend the charter of the organization, and the like. A 23-member Board of Governors, comprising representatives designated by the General Conference for 2-year terms, is responsible to the General Conference for management of the Agency. A Director General, appointed for a four-year term and responsible to the Board of Governors, is the chief administrative officer. The first Director General, W. Sterling Cole of the United States, served from 1957 to 1961. He was succeeded by Sigvard Eklund of Sweden.

The permanent staff of the Agency is divided into five departments: Training and Technical Information; Technical Operations; Research and Isotopes; Safeguards and Inspection; and Administration, Liaison and Secretariat.

Funding. The Agency's activities are funded in several ways: (1) by assessments levied on all member nations; (2) by voluntary contributions by member nations; (3) by funds received through participation in the United Nations Expanded Program of Technical Assistance (EPTA); and (4) by revenues received for services, materials or equipment furnished by the Agency to member nations. Following is a breakdown of the funding to date:

IAEA OPERATING FUNDS

Year	*Assessed Contributions*	*Voluntary Contributions*	*EPTA*	*Miscellaneous Income*	*Total*
		(in thousands)			
1958	4,089	129	—	—	4,218
1959	5,225	1,183	304	735 [1]	7,447
1960	5,843	996	639	227	7,705
1961	6,168	1,181 [2]	815	200 [3]	8,364
Total	21,325	3,489	1,758	1,162	27,734

[1] Includes special contribution of $600,000 by the United States for construction of an Agency laboratory.
[2] As of June 30, 1961.
[3] Estimated.

The three largest contributors to the Agency are the United States, the Soviet Union and the United Kingdom. They have accounted for the following percentages of Agency funds:

PERCENTAGE OF FUNDS CONTRIBUTED BY THE THREE LARGEST CONTRIBUTORS

Year	*Assessed Contributions* U.S.A.	*Assessed Contributions* U.S.S.R.	*Assessed Contributions* U.K.	*Voluntary Contributions* U.S.A.	*Voluntary Contributions* U.S.S.R.	*Voluntary Contributions* U.K.
1958	33.3	15.0	7.2	50.0	—	19.0
1959	32.5	14.7	7.3	50.0	10.6	10.6
1960	32.5	14.7	7.3	50.0	—	12.6
1961	32.4	14.7	7.2	50.0	—	11.9

Facilities. Some laboratory facilities are located at the Agency's Vienna headquarters. In addition, a research and analytical laboratory has been constructed at Siebersdorf, near Vienna. The Siebersdorf laboratory is used for IAEA research projects and to conduct analyses and measurements in support of the IAEA's role in the control of special nuclear materials supplies (see below). The United States contributed $600,000 toward the cost of building and equipping this facility, which represents a total investment of approximately $1 million.

Program. Major areas of IAEA program activity include:

Technical Assistance. Technical missions have been sent to nearly half of the member nations in connection with surveys of resources and opportunities for atomic energy development. In addition several hundred man-months of expert consultative assistance are furnished each year in connection with specific projects being undertaken in particular countries.

Training. Several hundred student fellowships are awarded each year by the IAEA. The Agency also sponsors a program of visiting professorships. Aided by 2 mobile laboratory units donated by the United States, the Agency provides courses in radioisotope technique; and is considering the establishment of regional centers in order to provide training in this field.

Fig. 96. The International Atomic Energy Agency. Above, the annual general conference in session. Below, Mobile Isotope Laboratory donated by the United States for the IAEA's use. (*Courtesy of tho IAEA*)

Research. The Agency has been conducting limited research in its Vienna headquarters, using equipment donated by several member countries. In the main, however, its research program has to date taken the form of contract awards to existing institutions in various member countries. Between October, 1959, and October, 1960, the Agency appropriated approximately $0.5 million for such contracts, which were awarded as follows:

IAEA RESEARCH CONTRACTS—FY 1960

Field	*No. of Contracts*	*% of Total Appropriation*
Radiobiology	20	32
Radiation protection	11	26
Radioactive waste disposal	13	21
Medicine and agriculture	9	12
Safeguards	3	7
Small and medium power reactors	1	2
Total	57	100

Studies. The IAEA is keeping abreast of the technical and economic status of power reactor development in member countries, and on request, is undertaking studies of the opportunities for nuclear power applications in particular countries. Studies have also been undertaken in the field of radioisotope applications, especially in medicine and agriculture.

Materials Supply. The United States, the United Kingdom and the Soviet Union have signed agreements with the IAEA providing a basis for transfer of nuclear materials to the Agency's account for use in meeting requests from member countries. The U.S.-IAEA agreement formalized an offer made by the United States in 1956, to supply 5000 kilograms of uranium-235 and to match such quantities of this material as might be offered by other member countries over the period July, 1957, through June, 1960. The first nuclear fuel transaction handled by the Agency was completed in 1959, when 3 tons of natural uranium (donated by Canada) were sold to Japan under interim safeguards provisions.

Safeguards. Safeguards, principles and procedures have been developed and approved by the IAEA's Board of Governors covering (1) the design and operation of power and test reactors having a thermal power output of less than 100 megawatts, (2) the control of source and special nuclear materials used or produced in such reactors, and (3) small atomic energy research and development facilities. These safeguard measures have been applied in two instances and negotiations are in progress which, if successfully concluded, will in certain instances result in transfer to the IAEA of cognizance for the administration of safeguards procedures now covered by bilateral agreements between member nations. (For background information, see **international control of atomic energy)**

Legal and Regulatory. In the area of health and safety, basic safety standards have been developed and circulated for comment to member nations with the view to eventual worldwide adoption. Draft regulations for the safe transport of radioactive materials have been prepared and it is hoped they will be used by member nations as a basis for national regulations. Codes of practice governing the safe handling of radioisotopes, and the use of film badges for personnel monitoring have been prepared. Work is proceeding on a study of the organizational, administrative and legal measures which might be taken at an international level with respect to the control of radioactive waste disposal.

In the area of insurance and indemnification, a draft Convention on Minimum International Standards Regarding Civil Liability for Nuclear Damage has been prepared for consideration by an international *ad hoc* diplomatic conference planned to be convened in 1962. A draft convention on the Liability of Operators of Nuclear Ships is in process of ratification. (See **insurance and indemnification against atomic energy risks)**

Information. The IAEA publishes the proceedings of its scientific conferences and symposia; prepares and publishes special reports and compendia; and furnishes bibliographic and reference services. Publications issued to date include the proceedings of conferences on radiation applications and radioactive waste disposal; directories of nuclear reactors and radioisotopes; and bibliographies of literature in such diverse fields as safety and atomic energy law. A manual on the safe handling of radioisotopes has been issued and one on the safe critical assemblies and research reactors is in preparation.

MEMBERSHIP OF IAEA

(October, 1961)

Afghanistan	France	Pakistan
Albania	West Germany	Paraguay
Argentina	Ghana	Peru
Australia	Greece	Philippines
Austria	Guatemala	Poland
Belgium	Haiti	Portugal
Brazil	Holy See	Romania
Bulgaria	Honduras	Senegal
Burma	Hungary	Soviet Union
Byelorussian SSR	Iceland	Spain
Cambodia	India	Sudan
Canada	Indonesia	Sweden
Ceylon	Iran	Switzerland
Chile	Iraq	Thailand
China	Israel	Tunisia
Colombia	Italy	Turkey
Congo, Republic of	Japan	Ukrainian SSR
Cuba	Korea	Union of South Africa
Czechoslovakia	Lebanon	United Arab Republic
Denmark	Luxembourg	United Kingdom
Dominican Republic	Mali	United States of America
Ecuador	Mexico	Venezuela
El Salvador	Monaco	Vietnam
Ethiopia	Morocco	Yugoslavia
Finland	Netherlands	
	New Zealand	
	Nicaragua	
	Norway	

INTERNATIONAL BANK FOR RECONSTRUCTION AND DEVELOPMENT (WORLD BANK)

An international organization whose establishment was recommended by the United Nations Monetary and Financial Conference at Bretton Woods in 1944, and which come into being in December, 1945, with headquarters in Washington, D.C. The function of the World Bank is to facilitate economic development projects in member nations by guaranteeing private loans or, where adequate sources of private capital are not available, by granting loans from its own resources. The Bank has played a major role in one of Italy's first nuclear power projects, namely, the ENSI Project (Energia Nucleare Sud Italia) of SENN

(Societa Elettronucleare Nazionale) involving the construction of a large-scale plant at Punta Fiume. This project was undertaken largely at the Bank's initiative, and the Bank is financing the initial cost of the fuel plus 30% of the cost of plant construction. (See **Italy, U.S.-Euratom Joint Program)**

INTERNATIONAL COMMISSION ON RADIOLOGICAL PROTECTION (ICRP)

A committee established by the International Congress of Radiology whose function is to recommend international standards for radiation protection. The ICRP has 12 members, all scientists active in the field of radiation protection, and has 5 subcommittees whose areas of interest are as follows:

1. Dose limits for external radiation.
2. Dose limits for internal radiation.
3. Protection against x-rays and gamma radiation below 3 Mev.
4. Protection against x-rays above 3 Mev, and against heavy-particle radiation.
5. Radioactive waste handling and disposal.

The ICRP was formed in 1928. Since 1956, it has acted in an advisory capacity to the **World Health Organization.** (See **radiation protection standards and regulations** for background information)

INTERNATIONAL COMMISSION ON RADIOLOGICAL UNITS AND MEASUREMENTS (ICRU)

An international committee principally concerned with measurement techniques and standards for radiation dosimetry and radiation treatment. The ICRU has four subcommittees whose areas of interest are as follows:

1. Standards and measurement of radioactivity for radiological use.
2. Standards and measurement of radiological exposure.
3. Measurement of absorbed dose and clinical dosimetry.
4. Standard methods of measurement of characteristics of radiological equipment and materials.

The ICRU coordinates its work with the **International Commission on Radiological Protection.**

INTERNATIONAL CONTROL OF ATOMIC ENERGY

The subject is treated here in broad outline to provide general historical orientation. An effort is made to highlight important stages in the evolution of control negotiation but in no sense does the discussion purport to be a complete or authoritative review of events in this complex field.

Background. The United States has sought since the close of World War II to achieve effective international control of atomic energy. In November, 1945, President Truman and Prime Ministers Attlee and King of the United Kingdom and Canada jointly urged the formation of an *ad hoc* United Nations Atomic Energy Commission to make proposals "for control of atomic energy to the extent necessary to ensure its use only for peaceful purposes," and "for effective safeguards by way of inspection and other means to protect complying states against the hazards of violation and evasion." Such a Commission was established in January, 1946, by resolution of the United Nations General Assembly and began its formal deliberations in June, 1946.

At the opening session of the Commission (June 14, 1946), the United States outlined a plan for the control of atomic energy. The U.S. plan was largely based on a report prepared under State Department auspices by Dean Acheson and David Lilienthal with the assistance of a team of technical experts. As presented by Bernard Baruch ("We are here to make a choice between the quick and the dead"), the plan called for the establishment of a supranational authority to manage all "dangerous" atomic activities and to make international inspections to guard against clandestine activities. The plan outlined successive stages for the achievement of control and contained the statement: "As the successive stages of international control are reached, the United States will be prepared to yield, to the extent required by each stage, national control of activities in this field to the (proposed) Authority."

A majority of the Commission members were in favor of the U.S. control plan but action thereon was blocked by the Soviet Union's refusal to agree to what the West considered to be essential control and inspection measures. Also, the Soviet Union took the position that certain features of the U.S. plan were designed to protect, rather than end, the U.S. monopoly in the field of atomic weapons. By 1948, the Commission had reached a total impasse. In August, 1949, the Soviet Union successfully detonated an atomic bomb, thereby ending the U.S. monopoly. Since that time the military aspects of international control of atomic energy have been closely linked with general disarmament matters, such as limitations on conventional armaments.

Atoms for Peace. On December 8, 1953, President Eisenhower made his historic "atoms for peace" proposal in an address before the United Nations General Assembly. That proposal was designed to "provide a way to bring the benefits of peaceful uses of atomic energy to all the people of the world despite the deadlock with the Soviet Union over the question of disarmament." It called for the establishment of an International Atomic Energy Agency to foster the development of peaceful uses of atomic energy and to exercise control over stocks of fissionable materials supplied

Fig. 97. President Eisenhower making his historic "atoms for peace" proposal before the United Nations General Assembly on December 8, 1953. (*Courtesy of Associated Press*)

for such purposes to protect against their diversion to military purposes. In March of 1954, the United States described in a memorandum to the Soviet Union the kind of safeguards it believed to be required for control purposes:

"...the Agency would have the continuing authority to prescribe certain design and operating conditions, require accountability and operating records, specify disposition of byproduct fissionable materials and wastes, retain the right of monitoring and require progress reports. The agency would also have authority to verify status of allocated material inventories and to verify compliance with the terms of issuance."

Behind the U.S. interest in establishing an International Atomic Energy Agency with effective safeguards authority and procedures was (1) the desire to promote peaceful applications of atomic energy in an environment of control, and (2) the hope that the successful establishment of effective international control in the area of peaceful atomic energy development might improve the atmosphere for negotiation of international control over military atomic energy activities.

For a while the Soviet Union blocked action on the U.S. proposal, taking the position that prohibition of atomic weapons had to come first (see below). During this period the United States took the following initiatives:

1. The Congress made basic modifications to the U.S. atomic energy statute to permit broader cooperation with other countries in the development of peaceful uses of atomic energy. (See **legislation, federal**)

2. The U.S. Atomic Energy Commission then initiated a series of bilateral agreements with other countries for such cooperation. These agreements contained safeguard provisions designed to apply until such time as an effective international control system became available. (See **Agreements for Cooperation**)

In July, 1955, the Soviet Union indicated its willingness to take part in negotiations for the establishment of the proposed international agency. These negotiations led to the establishment of the present **International Atomic Energy Agency** (IAEA) in Vienna on October 1, 1957.

Article XII of the statute of the IAEA contains general safeguards provisions designed to "ensure, so far as (the Agency) is able, that assistance provided by it or at its request is not used in such a way as to further any military request." Under this Article, the IAEA has the right and responsibility:

1. "To examine the design of specialized equipment and facilities, including nuclear reactors, and to approve it only from the viewpoint of assuring that it will not further any military purpose, that it complies with applicable health and safety standards, and that it will permit effective application of the safeguards provided for in this article;
2. "To require the maintenance and production of operating records to assist in ensuring accountability for source and special fissionable materials used or produced in the project or arrangement;
3. "To call for and receive progress reports;
4. "To approve the means to be used for the chemical processing of irradiated materials solely to ensure that this chemical processing will not lend itself to diversion of materials for military purposes and will comply with applicable health and safety standards; to require that special fissionable materials recovered or produced as a byproduct be used for peaceful purposes under continuing Agency safeguards for research or in reactors, existing or under construction, specified by the member or members concerned; and to require deposit with the Agency of any excess of any special fissionable materials recovered or produced as a byproduct over what is needed for the above-stated uses in order to prevent stockpiling of these materials;
5. "To send into the territory of the recipient State or States inspectors, designated by the Agency after consultation with the State or States concerned, who shall have access at all times to all places and data and to any person who by reason of his occupation deals with materials, equipment, or facilities which are required by this Statute to be safeguarded, as necessary to account for source and special fissionable materials supplied and fissionable products to determine whether there is compliance with the undertaking against use in furtherance of any military purpose."

Procedures to implement these general provisions were drafted by the IAEA and were provisionally endorsed by the fourth annual General Conference of the Agency which convened in Vienna in the fall of 1960. During that Conference the United States offered to place four U.S. reactors * under IAEA safeguards procedures for trial purposes and to demonstrate that these procedures could be implemented without infringement on national sovereignty.

Certain regional international organizations have also taken steps to provide safeguards over atomic energy activities. The **Organization for Economic Cooperation and Development** (OECD), which bars military atomic energy activities, has adopted control provisions patterned after the IAEA Statute. They apply to joint undertakings of member nations or to national undertakings which employ fissionable materials obtained from joint projects, but not to independent national undertakings. They are administered by the **European Nuclear Energy Agency.** The European Atomic Energy Community **(Euratom),** which does not bar military atomic energy activities, has adopted control provisions designed to ensure that designated fissionable materials are used for their given purpose.

In its bilateral dealings with foreign countries and in its associations with regional international groups, the United States has maintained as a central objective the ultimate establishment of the IAEA as the agency with primary responsibility for the administration of safeguards.

Control of Atomic Weapons. As was brought out above, by 1949, negotiations for the international control of military aspects of atomic energy had reached an impasse, and since that time such negotiations have been inextricably linked with general disarmament questions. Discussion of these negotiations is beyond the scope of this book. Suffice it to note that the U.S. Atomic Energy Commission has served in a liaison and technical consulting capacity with the responsible agencies, namely, the Department of State and, more recently, the Disarmament Agency. Mention should also be made of the fact that since 1957 efforts have been made to negotiate, separately from disarmament *per se,* a cessation of atomic weapons testing. (See reference to test moratorium under **weapons testing;** also see **weapons test detection)** These negotiations have been unsuccessful to date, the principal areas of disagreement being inspection provisions and the right of veto over inspection.

* Brookhaven Medical Research Reactor, Brookhaven Graphite Research Reactor, Piqua Organic Moderated Reactor, and Experimental Boiling Water Reactor.

INTERNATIONAL COOPERATION IN ATOMIC ENERGY DEVELOPMENT **

The United States has sought in various ways to promote international cooperation in the development of peaceful uses of atomic energy. Major forms of U.S. initiative in this area are discussed under separate headings, which may be briefly referenced as follows:

1. For information on the U.S. role in the establishment of the **International Atomic Energy Agency** see **international control of atomic energy.**

2. For a summary of bilateral agreements providing for U.S. assistance to foreign countries and international organizations in research and/or nuclear power development see **Agreements for Cooperation.**

3. For information on U.S. provisions for the training of foreign students see **education and training programs, AEC.**

4. For information on libraries of U.S. atomic energy literature maintained overseas see **Atomic Energy Commission—Information Services.**

Certain other forms of U.S. initiative in international cooperation are discussed in the paragraphs which follow.

Research Reactor Grants. In May, 1956, the United States initiated a program providing for financial grants toward the construction of foreign research reactors. The grants have been in the sum of $350,000 and all have

** Discussion limited to U.S. role in international cooperation.

been made to countries having Agreements for Cooperation with the United States. Through 1960, 22 such grants had been made or committed by the U.S. Atomic Energy Commission (see Table 1). A special grant of $50,000 has additionally been made for a research reactor in the Republic of the Philippines.

the International Cooperation Administration (ICA).

Materials and Fuel Assistance. Since 1955, the United States has made various atomic energy materials available to foreign countries on a sale or lease basis. For example, through 1960, a total of 630 kilograms of (contained) uranium-235 and 468 tons of heavy water had been sent overseas for use in research and training programs. The United States also furnishes certain services in this connection, such as reprocessing heavy water that has become degraded in the course of research operations.

TABLE 1. U.S. GRANTS FOR FOREIGN RESEARCH REACTORS
(Through December, 1961)

Country	*Type of Reactor* *	*Location*	*Reactor Manufacturer*
Austria	5 MW Pool	Siebersdorf	American Machine and Foundry
Belgium	25 MW Tank	Mol	Centre d'Etudes de l'Energie Nucleaire, Nuclear Development Associates
Brazil	5 MW Pool	Sao Paulo	Babcock & Wilcox
China	1 MW Pool	Hsinchu	International General Electric
Denmark	5 MW Tank	Riso	Foster-Wheeler
Greece	1 MW Pool	Mt. Hymettus	American Machine and Foundry
Indonesia	100 KW Tank	Bandung	General Atomic
Israel	1 MW Pool	Nebi-Rubin	American Machine and Foundry
Italy	5 MW Tank	Ispra	American Car and Foundry
Japan	10 MW Tank	Tokai-Mura	American Machine and Foundry
Korea	100 KW Tank	Seoul	General Atomic
Netherlands	20 MW Tank	Petten	American Car and Foundry
Norway	10 KW Pool	Kjeller	Noratom
Pakistan	1 MW Pool	Taxila	American Machine and Foundry
Portugal	1 MW Pool	Lisbon	American Machine and Foundry
Spain	3 MW Pool	Moncloa	International General Electric
Sweden	30 MW Tank	Studsvik	American Car and Foundry
Thailand	1 MW Pool	Bangkok	Curtiss-Wright
Turkey	1 MW Pool	Istanbul	American Machine and Foundry
Venezuela	3 MW Pool	Caracas	International General Electric
Vietnam	100 KW Tank	Dalat	General Atomic
West Germany	1 MW Pool	Munich	American Machine and Foundry
Yugoslavia	100 KW Tank	Ljubljana	General Atomic

* The indicated power ratings refer to thermal power output. In some cases the reactors are convertible to higher ratings.

Equipment Grants. In 1958, the United States initiated a program providing for financial grants for equipment for training or research. In most instances the grants have covered a self-sufficient unit of laboratory equipment such as a general radioisotope training laboratory, a medical radioisotope research and training laboratory, a nuclear engineering laboratory, a cobalt-60 teletherapy laboratory, or a cobalt-60 agricultural irradiation facility. Through 1960, a total of 21 such grants had been made by the AEC to 18 countries. Additional equipment grants have been made by

INTERNATIONAL INSTITUTE OF NUCLEAR SCIENCE AND TECHNOLOGY

An institute at Argonne National Laboratory that provides advanced training in several major areas of nuclear science and technology, including reactor design, nuclear engineering, physical sciences research, life sciences research, and nuclear facilities engineering, administration and operation. Minimum entrance requirements are a Masters degree or the equivalent, and some appointments require Doctoral or Post Doctoral training. The Institute is open to U.S. students as well as foreign nationals.

Fig. 98. Student receiving training in reactor operation at the International School of Reactor Engineering (now the International Institute of Nuclear Engineering) at Argonne National Laboratory. (*Courtesy of Argonne National Laboratory*)

The Institute is an outgrowth of the International School of Nuclear Science and Engineering, which from 1955, through 1959, provided basic training in the nuclear field to more than 400 students from 45 countries. For several years the School curriculum included preparatory courses at North Carolina State College and Pennsylvania State College. The increasing availability of equivalent instruction in colleges and universities in the United States and abroad led to the decision to reorient the curriculum toward more advanced work and to upgrade the entrance requirements; hence the present Institute, the first session of which began in February, 1960.

INTERNATIONAL LABOR OFFICE (ILO)

A specialized agency of the United Nations which, through its Occupational Safety and Health Division, maintains an interest in international standards for radiation protection.

INTERNATIONAL STANDARDS ORGANIZATION (ISO)

A nonofficial but generally recognized international authority on standard nomenclature, measures, etc., in various fields of science and technology. ISO's Technical Committee ISO/TC 85 (Nuclear Energy) has four subcommittees whose interests are terms, signs, and symbols; radiation protection; reactors; and radiation instruments. In these and other areas ISO coordinates the work of national standards organizations, such as the American Standards Association, and works closely with specialized international groups such as the **International Commission on Radiological Protection.**

IODINE-131

A radioactive isotope of iodine, routinely used in medical diagnosis and therapy (see **medical aspects of atomic energy**), and also used extensively in agricultural research. A beta emitter with a radioactive half-life of 8 days, iodine-131 is a product of uranium-235 fission and is produced by irradiation of uranium capsules. Because of its short half-life, rapid processing is required to separate the iodine-131 from the other fission debris present in the capsule. Processing is usually accomplished by dissolving the material in acid and separating the volatile radioiodine by a sparging technique.

The volatility of iodine-131, while advantageous in the above context, is a disadvantage in the handling of irradiated fuel discharged from reactors, being one of the factors that determines the length of the cooling period required before fuel reprocessing operations can be started (see **decay cooling**). It also contributes to the need for exhaust gas filtration or scrubbing facilities in reactor installations where there is a possibility of fission product escape in the event of fuel element rupture. Relatedly, in the siting of nuclear power plants, the calculated rate of escape of iodine-131 from the reactor **containment** vessel in the event of a major accident is an important factor in determining allowable reactor locations.

ION

An electrically charged atom or molecule. (See **ionization**)

ION CHAMBER. See **ionization chamber.**

ION CYCLOTRON WAVES

With reference to controlled-**fusion** research, natural oscillations that occur within the body of ions of a fuel **plasma** when the plasma is subjected to an external electric field of a critical frequency. These oscillations of ions occur in moderately dense plasmas (greater than 10^{12} or 10^{13} particles per cubic centimeter) at frequencies slightly lower than the ion (single-particle) **cyclotron frequency** in the given magnetic field. Ion cyclotron waves are a complicating factor in plasma heating by cyclotron resonance. (See **cyclotron resonance heating**)

ION EXCHANGE

A method of recovering products or removing impurities from solutions based on adsorption-desorption phenomena involving an exchange of ions between the solution and an insoluble resin. Ion exchange techniques lend themselves particularly well to the recovery or removal of small amounts of solutes from large solution volumes. In the atomic energy field, ion exchange processes are used:

1. In **uranium milling,** as a means of recovering uranium from acid leach liquors.
2. In **fuel reprocessing,** as a means of final product decontamination and/or concentration.
3. To recover certain industrially useful fission products contained in the high-level radioactive wastes from fuel reprocessing operations.
4. To decontaminate low-level radioactive waste solutions. (See **radioactive waste disposal**)
5. To purify and/or decontaminate water used as a reactor coolant.

The mechanism of ion exchange is not completely understood but can be accounted for by a process of reversible ion transfer. The resins used are high molecular weight organic polymers. Anion-exchange resins contain immobile amine groups and associated mobile anions such as chloride or hydroxyl ions. Cation-exchange resins contains immobile phenolic, sulfonic, carboxylic, or phosphoric acid groups and associated mobile cations such as sodium or hydrogen ions. The resins are virtually insoluble but are porous and contain about 50% water so that the mobile ions can diffuse through the resin.

Ion exchange processes vary considerably in flowsheet detail but have in common three basic operations, namely: sorption, flushing and elution. During the first operation, the process stream is passed through a bed of ion exchange resins, which absorb the desired solute ions or, as the case may be, the undesired impurities. This operation is continued until the resins have become saturated. In the second operation, the process solution remaining in the resin bed is flushed, or displaced, by water into another unsaturated resin bed for adsorption. In the third operation a wash solution, or elutriant, is introduced to strip the adsorbed material away from the resin surfaces. In this washing, the resin bed is reactivated for reuse. The solutions which have been stripped into the elutriant stream are recovered or sent to waste depending on their value. Continuous operation of an ion exchange system is usually achieved through the use of multiple equipment units with staggered operating cycles.

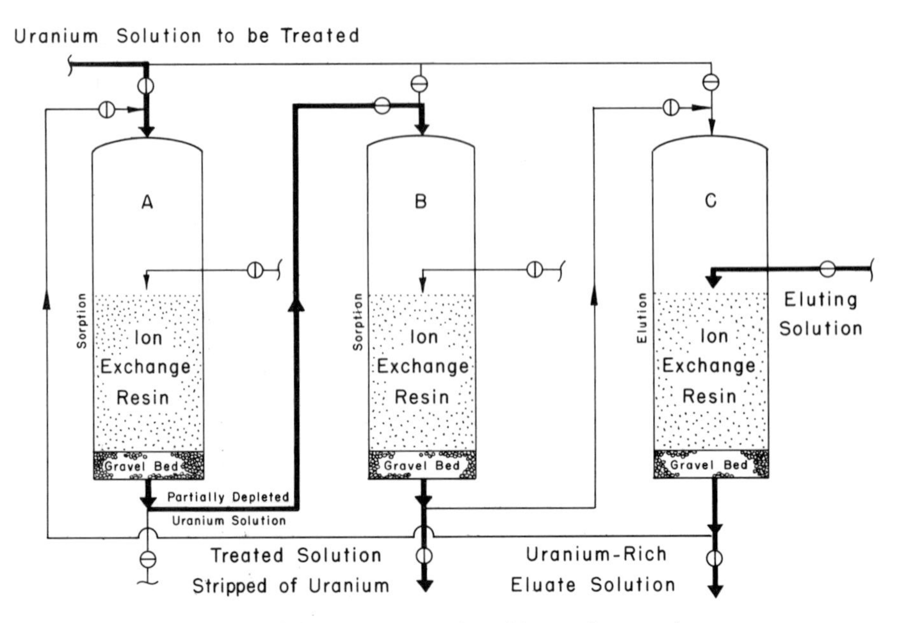

Fig. 99. Simplified diagram—operation of ion exchange columns.

In conventional ion exchange systems the ion beds are held in a fixed position in **packed columns**; however, other arrangements are possible. For example, in the **resin-in-pulp process** used in some uranium mills, the resins are moved back and forth by means of oscillating baskets.

ION MAGNETRON

The name of an experimental device of the "magnetic mirror" type built at the Berkeley Branch of the E. O. Lawrence Radiation Laboratory for research on controlled **fusion** (see **magnetic mirror systems**). Its purpose is to study plasma rotation as a means of improving magnetic-mirror confinement. As distinct from the Homopolar and Ixion **rotating plasma** systems, the ion magnetron operates under continuous, instead of pulsed, conditions.

ION PROPULSION. See **rocket propulsion (nuclear)**.

IONIZATION

A process by which an atom (electrically neutral under normal conditions) becomes electrically charged due to losing or gaining one or more orbital (extranuclear) electrons. An atom which has lost one or more orbital electrons is a positive ion, and one which has gained one or more extranuclear electrons is a negative ion.

IONIZATION CHAMBER

An instrument that detects and measures **ionizing radiation** by metering the ionization events produced in a gas volume; * also called an ion chamber.

One class of ionization chamber consists either of an insulated metal chamber containing parallel plate electrodes, or a tube with a metal lining, which serves as the cathode, and an inner wire anode. The chamber (or tube) is filled with air, carbon dioxide, argon or other suitable gas. The ions produced in the gas by a radiation-induced ionization event are converted into a measurable electrical impulse (or current) by means of a voltage ap-

* Proportional counters and Geiger counters also answer this description but differ in their method of operation. See text.

plied across the electrodes. The voltage, often supplied by a storage battery, is just sufficient to drive the primary ions to the electrodes; i.e., they are accelerated enough to prevent ion recombination but not enough to induce secondary ionization. There is thus no internal amplification of the ionization signal—a fact which distinguishes ionization chambers from **proportional counters** and **Geiger counters.**

Instruments of the above described class can be designed to register each ionization event individually and thereby measure the rate of ionization (pulse devices), or to deliver a continuous current which is a direct measure of the total amount of ionization (integrating devices). The latter devices employ a sensitive electrometer connected in parallel with an electrical resistance for direct reading of the current values.

Pulse devices employ a vacuum tube to provide linear amplification of the ionization signals, and either a **scaler** or a **ratemeter** to count the amplified signals. Such an instrument system can be used to measure any form of ionizing radiation but is particularly suited to counting alpha particles and neutrons, which have a high **specific ionization** and hence generate relatively strong ionization signals. When it is desired to discriminate alpha radiation in the presence of beta and/or gamma radiation, a **pulse height analyzer** ("kicksorter") is used to screen out the relatively weak signals induced by the latter so that only the alpha signals are counted. In similar manner, a differentiation can be made between alpha signals of different strength, thereby making it possible to identify specific alpha-emitting radionuclides in a radioactive mixture. In the case of neutron measurements, a gas medium is used in the ionization chamber that has a high cross section for the neutron-alpha reaction, i.e., the capture of a neutron, followed by ejection of an alpha particle. It is thus the alpha particles which are actually counted. Pulse-type ionization chambers containing boron trifluoride gas are commonly used as neutron sensing devices in **reactor control** systems.

A different class of ionization chamber—and an example of an integrating device—operates on the principle of an electroscope, i.e., instead of fixed electrodes, there is movement of one electrode relative to another. One design employs a fine metal-coated quartz fiber positioned in parallel with and connected at one end to a rigid wire. The fiber-wire coupling is mounted inside but insulated from a cylindrical metal case. When a charge is applied to the coupling (by briefly connecting the device to a battery), the fiber swings into a position perpendicular to the wire, due to electrical repulsion. When the device is in use, ionization events act to reduce the charge and the fiber moves toward its original position. The rate of movement, is a function of the rate of ionization; the total change of position is a function of the total amount of ionization. Miniaturized devices of this type are commonly used as pocket **dosimeters** for measuring radiation exposure of atomic energy workers.

IONIZING RADIATION

Radiation that causes **ionization,** either directly or through secondary effects. Types of ionizing radiation of nuclear origin include **gamma rays, alpha particles, beta particles, neutrons,** and fission fragments.

Ionization occurs due to excitation phenomena. In the case of gamma rays, which are a form of **electromagnetic radiation,** there are several ionization mechanisms, including pair production, the Compton effect, and the photoelectric effect (discussed under **gamma rays).** In the case of charged particles, such as alpha and beta particles, ionization is caused by direct collision with the nucleus of the target atom, or by interaction between the electrical field of the incident particle and that of the outer electron structure of the target atom. In the case of neutrons, ionization occurs as a secondary effect, being induced by ionizing radiation resulting from capture or scattering reactions between the incident neutron and the target atom.

IOWA ORDNANCE PLANT. See **Atomic Energy Commission—Facilities** (Table).

IRAN

An Atomic Energy Committee, made up of representatives of the various government ministries, coordinates and advises on Iranian atomic energy activity. A Center for Nuclear Studies has been established at Tehran University and will be equipped with a 5000-kilowatt (thermal) pool-type research reactor to be supplied by AMF Atomics. Iran has applied to the United States for a Foreign Research Reactor Grant for this installation. Also located at the university is the Central Treaty Organization (CENTO) Institute of Nuclear Science, which at present operates a regional training center for middle-eastern members of the CENTO Pact. A program of uranium exploration has been initiated.

Iran is a member of the **International Atomic Energy Agency** and has a research-type **Agreement for Cooperation** with the United States.

IRAQ

The Iraqi Atomic Energy Commission, Baghdad, is the agency responsible for atomic energy matters. Activity to date has been limited to training; however, efforts in this area have been intensive. A research center (the Tuwaitha Atomic Center) is being established around a nucleus of laboratory facilities built with Western funds when Iraq was a member of the Baghdad Pact. Under a recent agreement with the U.S.S.R., a 2000-kilowatt (thermal) pool-type research reactor is to be installed at this center. Also, Russia will install and operate a laboratory at the center for the processing of radioisotopes.

Iraq is a member of the **International Atomic Energy Agency.** A research-type **Agreement for Cooperation** with the United States was signed in 1960, subject to ratification procedure.

IRELAND

The Department of Education is responsible for atomic energy matters pending parliamentary action on a recommendation to establish an Atomic Energy Board. There is no national plan for atomic energy development at present; however, research and training programs are being carried out in universities, notably the Irish University Colleges at Cork and Dublin, and Trinity College in Dublin. All three institutions are equipped with radioisotope laboratories installed with the aid of a U.S. grant.

No need for nuclear power is foreseen for at least the next ten years. Ireland is a member of the **European Nuclear Energy Agency,** and has a research-type **Agreement for Cooperation** with the United States.

IRIDIUM-192

A radioisotope of iridium, produced by irradiating the natural element in a nuclear reactor. Iridium-192 is formed from the iridium-191 isotope by the neutron-gamma reaction.

$$_{77}Ir^{191} + {}_0n^1 \longrightarrow {}_{77}Ir^{192} + \gamma$$

Iridium-192 emits gamma rays of 0.31 and 0.47-Mev and has a radioactive half-life of approximately 74 days, transforming by **beta decay** into platinum-192. It is used as a source of gamma radiation for industrial **radiography,** and is applicable to the radiographic inspection of steel specimens ranging in thickness from $\frac{1}{4}$-$2\frac{1}{2}$ inches. It is commercially available at **specific activities** up to $\sim$ 200 curies per gram at costs (without encapsulation) of $5.00 per curie or less, depending on the specific activity and quantity ordered.

IRON-59

A radioisotope of iron commonly used in biological and medical research. A beta and gamma emitter with a radioactive half-life of 45 days, iron-59 is produced in reactors (usually) by neutron absorption in the natural iron element.

IRRADIATION

Exposure to radiation, whether in the form of electromagnetic rays, charged particles or neutrons.

ISOBAR

In nuclear physics, one of several nuclides having the same number of particles in their nuclei and hence having approximately the same atomic mass. For example, $_6C^{14}$, $_7N^{14}$, and $_8O^{14}$ are isobars.

ISOTOPE

A variant form of a given chemical element. Chemical elements are identified (and distinguished one from another) by their atomic number (indicated by symbol Z), which is the number of protons contained in their nucleus. Isotopes of a given chemical element by definition have the same atomic number but they have different mass numbers (symbol A) due to the differences in the number of neutrons contained in their nuclei. For example, $_6C^{12}$, $_6C^{13}$, and $_6C^{14}$ are isotopes of the element, carbon, the subscript denoting the atomic number Z and the superscript the mass number A.

ISOTOPE SEPARATION

Any process designed to change the relative abundance of the isotopes of a given chemical element and hence to produce a form of the element enriched in any particular isotope. In some applications the degree of the enrichment required results in almost complete separation of a particular isotope, e.g., in heavy water production, the relative abundance of deuterium is increased from 0.015 to $\sim$ 99.75%. In other applications only slight enrichment may be required, e.g., in producing slightly enriched uranium for use as fuel in certain types of power reactor, the relative abundance of uranium-235 may only be doubled or quadrupled (from 0.71 to $\sim$ 1.5-3.0%).

Since the isotopes of an element belong to the same chemical species, they cannot be separated by ordinary chemical means. The methods used are based on such things as mass differences and mass-dependent properties. The processes and applications of principal interest in atomic energy development are summarized in the table on p. 258. (See individual entries for additional information.)

ISRAEL

Agency. The Israeli Atomic Energy Commission, Tel Aviv, is the agency responsible for atomic energy matters.

International Relationships. Member of the **International Atomic Energy Agency.** Research-type **Agreement for Cooperation** with the United States.

Research Centers. A 1000-kilowatt (thermal) pool-type research reactor supplied by AMF Atomics, Inc., and constructed with the aid of a $350,000 Foreign Research Reactor Grant from the United States was placed in operation in 1960, at Nebi-Rubin, 30 miles west of Jerusalem. This site is being developed as the Israeli Nuclear Center.

An Institute of Nuclear Science has been established as part of Weizmann Institute at Rehovoth. The program emphasizes research in nuclear physics but includes other atomic energy sciences. The facilities include a 3-Mev Van de Graaff accelerator.

A 24,000-kilowatt (thermal) reactor is under construction in the Negev desert south of Beersheba. The Israeli Government has stated that this reactor will be used for research and as an experimental facility for future nuclear power reactor development. The reactor is reportedly a natural uranium-fueled, heavy water-moderated, gas-cooled unit of Israeli design. Private French industrial interests are participating in the project.

Production Activity. Low-grade deposits of uranium have been found in phosphate beds in the Negev desert and elsewhere. Under certain conditions, recovery as a by-product in fertilizer production might prove feasible. Pilot heavy water production facilities have been in operation since 1954; however, no plans for commercial production have been announced to date.

ITALY

Agencies. CNEN (Comitato Nazionale Energia Nucleare), a commission recently established within the Ministry of Industry and Trade, is the agency now responsible for

ISOTOPE SEPARATION PROCESSES

Process	*Characteristics*	*Applications*	*Notes*
Dual-temperature chemical exchange	Based on the superimposition of temperature differentials on classical chemical exchange between liquid and gaseous media.	Production of heavy water (analogous process used in the production of boron in boron-10).	The base process in postwar U.S. heavy water production facilities.
Electrolysis	Based on relative rate of dissociation in an electrolyte solution.	Production of heavy water (also applicable to the separation of lithium isotopes).	Used in U.S. for final stages of deuterium concentration and in Norway for all stages.
Electromagnetic separation	Based on principle of **mass spectograph,** i.e., on relative degree of curvature of the path of charged gas ions in a magnetic field.	Production of enriched uranium; separation of various stable isotopes for use in research.	Used during the Manhattan Project for uranium-235 production and subsequently abandoned in favor of gaseous diffusion process. Units of original plant now used to separate stable isotopes for use in research.
Gas Centrifuge process	Unit separation factor is a function of mass difference between isotopes.	Potentially useful for the production of enriched uranium.	Studied by U.S. during Manhattan Project. Promising recent developments reported in West Germany. No known production application to date.
Gaseous diffusion	Unit separation factor is a function of the square root of the ratio of masses of the gas molecules.	Production of enriched uranium.	Large-scale production application in the U.S., the U.S.S.R., the U.K. Production plant under construction in France.
Liquid-hydrogen distillation	Based on relative rate of distillation in an electrolyte solution.	Production of heavy water.	Studied but not used in the U.S. Present or planned applications in France and India.
Thermal diffusion process	Based on the use of temperature differentials to achieve concentration gradients in counter flowing liquid streams.	Production of enriched uranium.	Used on an interim basis during the Manhattan Project.
Water distillation	A fractionation process based on differences in boiling point.	Production of heavy water.	Used in the U.S. for intermediate stages of deuterium concentration.

Italy's nuclear program. Formerly, the program came under an independent commission known as CNRN (Comitato Nazionale per le Richerche Nucleari).

CISE (Centro Informazioni Studi ed Experienze), Milan, is a research and development organization sponsored 50% by public interests (ENI, IRI and others) and 50% by private interests.

ENI (Ente Nazionale Idocarburi), Rome, is a government-owned holding company responsible for the exploration and exploitation of natural energy resources. ENI's interests in the atomic energy field are channeled through a subsidiary company, AGIP Nucleare. AGIP Nucleare, in turn, has established SOMIREN (Societa Minerali Radioattivi Energia Nucleare) as a subsidiary responsible for raw materials operations, and owns 75% of SIMEA (see below).

IRI (Instituto per la Reconstruzione Industriale), Rome, is a government-owned holding company whose subsidiary, FINELLETTRICA, manages the public sector of Italy's electric power industry. FINELLETTRICA owns 75% of SENN (see below) and 25% of SIMEA (see below).

International Relationships. Member of the **International Atomic Energy Agency,** the European Atomic Energy Community **(Euratom),** the **European Nuclear Energy Agency,** and the European Organization for Nuclear Research **(CERN).** Comprehensive **Agreement for Cooperation** with the United States.

Research Centers. The Center for Nuclear Studies at Ispra, on Lake Maggiore, was originally intended as a national laboratory but is now operating as a **Euratom** laboratory. The agreement with Euratom provides, on the one hand, that the Italian Government will continue its existing programs at Ispra; and, on the other, that Euratom will share the existing facilities and contribute $40 million toward the construction of new facilities, including a nuclear training school and a computer laboratory. Italian programs at Ispra are conducted by NUCLIT (Nucleare Italiana), a government-owned corporation established for this purpose by CNRN (now CNEN). Ispra is a diversified applied research center whose present facilities include Ispra-1, a heavy water-moderated tank-type research reactor supplied by ACF Industries, which operates at a power level of 5000 kilowatts (thermal). The United States contributed $350,000 toward the construction of the reactor under its program of Foreign Research Reactor Grants.

The Frascati National Laboratory, at Frascati, 12 miles south of Rome, is a center for fundamental research in nuclear physics. It is operated by the National Institute for Nuclear Physics (INFN) under contract to CNEN. Its facilities include a 1 Bev electric synchrotron.

The Casaccia Center for Nuclear Studies, at Casaccia, 23 miles north of Rome, is Italy's principal reactor development laboratory and is also engaged in process development, studies of radiation applications, and research on controlled fusion. It is operated under CNEN. Its facilities include a Triga Mark II research and training reactor, supplied by General Atomic, which operates at a power level in the range 10-30 kilowatts (thermal).

CISE (see above) operates extensive laboratory facilities near Milan. Its program includes development work on processes for uranium refining and heavy water production, and research on an advanced power reactor concept.

The Enrico Fermi Center of Nuclear Studies, Milan, is a physical research center operated as part of the University of Milan Technical Institute. Its facilities include an L-54 water-boiler research reactor, supplied by Atomics International, which operates at a power level of 50 kilowatts (thermal).

CAMEN (Centro Autonomo Militaire Energia Nucleare), at San Piero, between Pisa and Livorno, is a center for research on military applications of atomic energy, notably naval nuclear propulsion. It is operated jointly by the University of Pisa and the Naval Academy at Livorno. Its facilities include a pool-type research reactor, supplied by Babcock & Wilcox Company, which operates at a power level in the range of 3000-5000 kilowatts (thermal).

Production Activity. The principal deposits of uranium are near Prazzo in western Italy and near Troni and Bergamo in northeast Italy. Production to supply pilot processing operations has been undertaken at these sites. Production is expected to reach about 170 tons of uranium metal during 1962. Pilot ore processing facilities are being constructed by SOMIREN (see below) at San Donato, near Milan. Pilot refining facilities, owned by the government, are in operation near Milan.

Energy Economy. Italy's electric power capacity is about 17,500 megawatts, four-fifths of it hydroelectric. By 1965, virtually all of the economic hydro potential is expected to be in use. Coal resources are negligible. Fairly substantial deposits of oil have been found in Sicily, but current production satisfies only 15% of Italy's annual requirements.

Nuclear Power Program. Italy looks to nuclear power to stabilize her energy economy and reduce dependence on fuel imports. A goal of 1000 megawatts (electrical) of installed nuclear power capacity has been set for 1970. Information on specific projects follows.

Project SIMEA: This is a project of AGIP Nucleare, involving the construction at Latina, 60 miles south of Rome, of a 200-megawatt (electrical) power station of the Calder Hall type, i.e., natural uranium, gas-cooled, graph-

Fig. 100. Top, the CNRN's heavy water-moderated research reactor installation at Ispra. Bottom, the pool reactor installation of the Societa Ricerche Impranti Nucleari (SORIN) in Turin.

ite-moderated. The contractor is the Nuclear Power Plant Company (U.K.). The plant will be operated by SIMEA. Start-up is scheduled for 1962.

Project ENSI (Energia Nucleare Sud Italia), also known as the SENN Project: This is an undertaking of SENN (see below), involving the construction at Punta Fiume, 35 miles south of Rome, of a dual-cycle boiling water plant similar to the Dresden Station in the United States. The plant will initially be rated at 150 megawatts (electrical), but provision is being made in the design to accommodate later operation at 230 megawatts. The contractor is International General Electric Company, through its European subsidiary, IGEOSA. Start-up is scheduled for 1963. The **International Bank for Reconstruction and Development** has participated in the planning and financing of this project, which is being carried out under the terms of the **U.S.-Euratom Joint Program.**

Project Enrico Fermi: This is an undertaking of SELNI (see below), involving the construction at Trina, on the Po River between Turin and Milan, of a pressurized water plant similar to the Yankee Atomic Power Station in the United States. The plant will initially be rated at 165 megawatts (electrical) but provision is being made for the later addition of a superheater which will raise the power to 225 megawatts. The contractor is Westinghouse International. Start-up is scheduled for 1964. The **Export-Import Bank** is helping finance the project.

Project PRO: This project, sponsored by CNEN, involves the design and construction of a 30-megawatt (thermal) prototype organic-moderated power reactor. The location has not been announced. The reactor is to be built by SORIN (see below) with AGIP Nucleare providing architect-engineer services.

AGIP Nucleare is considering the construction of a 150-megawatt pressurized water plant in northern Italy. Vitro Corporation of America (through Vitro Italiana) was retained to conduct a design study but no definite plans have been announced.

CNEN has contracted with Allis-Chalmers Manufacturing Company (U.S.) for design, construction and operation of a pilot thorium-oxide fuel reprocessing facility, scheduled to be completed by mid-1963 at a site to be selected in southern Italy. This facility will be

Fig. 101. Project SENN planto. Construction view of the containment sphere of the 150-megawatt (electrical) Garigliano Nuclear Power Station at Punta Fiume. This is a dual-cycle boiling water reactor plant supplied by the General Electric Company (U.S.). (*Courtesy of General Electric Co.*)

used to study the technical feasibility and economic characteristics of the thorium-232—uranium-233 fuel cycle for nuclear power generation. The fuel elements initially processed in this facility will be those from the U.S. **Elk River Plant,** which was designed by Allis-Chalmers under contract to the U.S. Atomic Energy Commission.

There is also considerable Italian interest in nuclear ship propulsion, and in 1961, CNEN contracted with an Italian syndicate for a 2-year joint research project to determine the feasibility of building a nuclear-powered supertanker. The syndicate includes Fiat and Ansaldo (see table).

Industry Notes. See table.

PARTIAL LISTING OF ITALIAN INDUSTRY ACTIVE IN ATOMIC ENERGY

Firm or Group	*Notes*
Forum Italiano dell'Energia Nucleare (FIEN) (Milan)	Industry association similar to the U.S. Atomic Industrial Forum.
AGIP Nucleare (Rome)	Subsidiary of ENI (see Agencies) for atomic energy matters. It has research facilities at San Donato, near Milan; is sponsoring several nuclear power projects; and, through SOMIREN, is active in raw materials development.
Societa Ansaldo San Giorgio (Genoa)	Major heavy equipment manufacturer interested in supplying power and propulsion reactor equipment. Licensee of International General Electric Co.
CRDA (Cantieri Riuniti dell'Adriatico) (near Trieste)	Association of shipyards interested in nuclear ship propulsion.
Societa Edisonvolta (Milan)	Italy's largest privately owned electric utility company, actively engaged in nuclear power activity through SELNI.
Societa Fiat (Turin)	Major equipment manufacturer interested in supplying power and propulsion reactor equipment and, through SORIN, engaged in a variety of research and development activity. Licensee of Westinghouse Electric Corp.
FINELLETTRICA (Rome)	Subsidiary of IRI (see Agencies). Manages the public sector of Italy's electric utility industry. Owns 75% of SENN, 25% of SIMEA, and 15% of SELNI.
Italatom (Milan)	Joint subsidiary of Montecatini (Italy), the Mallinckrodt Chemical Works (U.S.) and the Anglo-American Corporation (South Africa), established recently to supply nuclear fuel materials to European markets. Montecatini owns 50% of this new enterprise and is generally responsible for its management.
Societa Montecatini (Milan)	Italy's largest chemical manufacturer, actively engaged in the atomic energy field through SORIN and Italatom.
SELNI (Societa Elettronucleare Italiana) (Rome)	Corporation owned 85% by private interests (principally Edisonvolta) and 15% by FINELLETTRICA, actively engaged in nuclear power activity (SELNI Project).
SENN (Societa Elettronucleare Nazionale) (Rome)	Corporation owned 75% by FINELLETTRICA and 25% by private electric utility interests, actively engaged in nuclear power activity (ENSI Project).
SIMEA (Societa Italiana Meridionale Energia Atomica) (Rome)	Joint subsidiary of AGIP Nucleare (75%) and FINELLETTRICA (25%) will operate the nuclear power station at Latina (SIMEA Project).
SOMIREN (Societa Minerali Radioattive Energia Nucleare) (Milan)	Subsidiary of AGIP Nucleare for uranium exploration and ore processing.

SORIN (Societa Ricerche Impianti Nucleari) (Milan)	Joint subsidiary of Fiat (50%) and Montecatini (50%) interested in supplying reactor systems and components and, reportedly, in providing fuel reprocessing services. SORIN has an applied research laboratory at Saluggia, 25 miles east of Turin. Its facilities include a pool-type research reactor supplied by AMF Atomics, which is designed to permit operation at power levels up to 5000 kiloawtts (thermal).

IXION

The name of an experimental device of the "magnetic mirror" type placed into operation in 1958, at Los Alamos Scientific Laboratory for research on controlled **fusion** (see **magnetic mirror systems**). Its purpose is the study of plasma rotation in a magnetic mirror confinement system, using crossed electric and magnetic fields. Of particular interest is the possible use of the rotational kinetic energy as a means of heating the plasma as well as contributing to its stability.

J

JANUS

A 200-kilowatt (maximum thermal) tank-type **test reactor** at Argonne National Laboratory. JANUS was designed by the ANL staff and is used for test irradiations in support of biological research programs. Its name derives from the fact that it has two faces (one for low and the other for high-flux neutron irradiation).

JAPAN

Agencies. The Japan Atomic Energy Commission, Tokyo, advises the Prime Minister on atomic energy matters and has jurisdictional authority over the national program. The Atomic Energy Bureau of the Science and Technics Agency, Tokyo, is the administrative agency responsible for research and development relating to peaceful atomic energy applications.

The Japan Atomic Fuel Corporation, Tokyo, is a government company responsible for research and development relating to nuclear fuels. The National Institute of Radiological Sciences, Chiba, is a government institution responsible for research relating to medical applications and radiation protection. The Japan Radioisotope Association is a government organization responsible for the importation and distribution of radioisotopes. The Japan Nuclear-Powered Ship Research Institute, Tokyo, is a government-sponsored institute for research and development relating to nuclear ship propulsion.

International Relationships. Member of the **International Atomic Energy Agency.** Comprehensive **Agreement for Cooperation** with the United States.

Research Center. The Japan Atomic Energy Research Institute (JAERI) at Tokai-mura, 50 miles northwest of Tokyo, is the principal national laboratory. Its facilities include 3 reactors: JRR-1, a water-boiler research reactor supplied by Atomics International, operates at a power level of 50 kilowatts (thermal). JRR-2, a high-flux heavy water-moderated tank-type research and testing reactor supplied by AMF Atomics, is designed to operate at a power level of 10,000 kilowatts (thermal) but has not been operated above 1000 kilowatts to date. The United States contributed $350,000 toward the construction of this unit under its program of Foreign Research Reactor Grants. JRR-3, a research reactor of the NRX type (see **Canada)** designed to operate at a power level of 10,000 kilowatts. It was constructed by a Japanese industrial combine under JAERI supervision.

The Japan Atomic Fuel Corporation operates laboratory and process development facilities at Tokai-mura adjacent to JAERI.

Production Activity. Deposits of uranium have been discovered, notably in the Ningyo Toge area, but mining operations have not yet started. Processes for extracting and refining uranium are being piloted at Tokai-mura. Heavy water and graphite production have been studied but not yet planned.

Energy Economy. Japan's electric power capacity is about 20,000 megawatts, nearly 60% of it hydroelectric and the balance coal-fired. Very little economic hydro potential remains to be developed. Reserves of bituminous coal are substantial, however the average quality is poor and the rate of production cannot be increased significantly without incurring higher mining costs. 90% of Japan's petroleum requirements are met by imports.

Nuclear Power Program. Japan has targeted the installation of 1000 megawatts of nuclear power capacity by 1970, and 7000-

8500 megawatts by 1980. Information on specific projects follows.

JPDR (Japan Power Demonstration Reactor): This project involves the construction of a prototype boiling water power reactor with a net output of 12 megawatts (electrical) at Tokai-mura near the site of JAERI. The reactor is being supplied by General Electric Company through its affiliate General Electric Japan, Ltd. Non-nuclear components are being supplied under subcontract by members of the Nippon Atomic Industries Group. Completion is scheduled for 1963.

A 159-megawatt (electrical) power station of the Calder Hall type, i.e., natural uranium, graphite-moderated, gas-cooled, is under construction at Tokai-mura under the sponsorship of the Japan Atomic Power Company. The contractor is the British General Electric Company (U.K.), aided by FAPIG (Japan). Completion is scheduled for 1964.

Industry Notes. The Japan Atomic Industrial Forum, Tokyo, is an industry association similar to the U.S. Atomic Industrial Forum.

First Atomic Power Industry Group (FAPIG), Tokyo, is a consortium of 16 companies, including Fuji Electric, taking part in the construction of the 159-megawatt power station at Tokai-mura under subcontract to the British General Electric Company.

The Japan Atomic Power Company, Tokyo, is a quasi-governmental enterprise established to finance the Tokai-mura station. The company comes under the Ministry of Trade and Industry, which owns 18% of the shares. Other holdings are distributed between 9 private electric utilities (42%), 5 manufacturing interests (20%), and the Electric Power Development Company (20%).

Fig. 102. Artist's sketch of the Japan Power Demonstration Reactor (JPDR), under construction at Tokai-Mura. JPDR is a boiling water reactor plant designed to operate at 12.5 megawatts (electrical). The reactor is being supplied by the General Electric Company (U.S.). The nonnuclear components of the plant are being supplied by the Nippon Atomic Industries Group. (*Courtesy of General Electric Co.*)

General atomic energy enterprises organized by Japanese industrial interests include Mitsubishi Atomic Power Company, Tokyo (mainly Mitsubishi interests), which has license agreements with Westinghouse Electric Corporation; Nippon Atomic Power Industries Group, Tokyo (Toshiba, Mitsui and others), which has license agreements with General Electric Company; Sumitomo Atomic Energy Industries, Ltd., Osaka (mainly Sumitomo interests); and Tokyo Atomic Industrial Consortium (Hitachi and others), which is also a General Electric licensee.

JEZEBEL

The name of a plutonium-fueled **critical experiment** facility at Los Alamos Scientific Laboratory.

JOINT COMMITTEE ON ATOMIC ENERGY (JCAE)

A joint committee of the U.S. Congress, originally established by the Atomic Energy Act of 1946, and continued by the Atomic Energy Act of 1954, whose purpose is "to make continuing studies of the activities of the U.S. Atomic Energy Commission and of problems relating to the development, use, and control of atomic energy."

The JCAE has equal representation (9 members each) from the Senate and the House of Representatives, and maintains a staff having competence in legal and scientific aspects of atomic energy. The chairmanship now alternates between the Senate and the House with each Congress. Membership of the JCAE and its several subcommittees, as of 1961 (87th Congress, 1st Session), is given in Table 1.

The Chairmen and Vice Chairmen of the JCAE since 1946 are listed in Table 2.

The JCAE is one of the few joint committees of the U.S. Congress established by statute, rather than by rule of each house, and is the only such committee authorized to receive and recommend to the Congress proposed legislation. The principal functions of the JCAE are as follows:

1. Legislative: All bills, resolutions and other matters in the Senate or House of Representatives relating primarily to atomic energy are referred to the JCAE for its consideration.

2. "Watchdog": The JCAE closely monitors the operation of the AEC.

3. Policy review: The JCAE, or individual members thereof, may propose policy changes or innovations in the national atomic energy program.

4. Informational: The JCAE holds annual hearings on the state of the U.S. atomic industry (see **"202" hearings**) and on AEC appropriations requests. In addition, the JCAE from time to time holds special hearings on particular topics. During 1960, for example, special hearings were held on such topics as "Frontiers in Atomic Energy Research," "Indemnity and Reactor Safety," "National Food Irradiation Research Program," "Radiation Protection Criteria and Standards; Their Basis and Use," and "Technical Aspects of Detection and Inspection Controls of a Nuclear Weapons Test Ban." Also during 1960, JCAE sponsored a comprehensive study entitled "Review of International Atomic Policies and Programs of the United States" (see **McKinney Reports**). Public transcripts of the JCAE's routine and special hearings may be purchased from the Superintendent of Public Documents, U.S. Government Printing Office, and constitute a valuable source of detailed information on U.S. atomic energy matters.

5. International: All proposed international atomic energy agreements of the United States must be submitted to the JCAE before they become effective. (See **Agreements for Cooperation**)

JOINT INSTITUTE FOR NUCLEAR RESEARCH (JINR)

A major research center located on the Volga River at Dubna, some 60 miles from Moscow in the U.S.S.R. JINR was established by an agreement signed on March 26, 1956, by representatives of the U.S.S.R. and ten Soviet Bloc nations. Membership now includes Albania, Bulgaria, Communist China, Czechoslovakia, East Germany, Hungary, Mongolia, North Korea, North Vietnam, Poland, and Rumania.

TABLE 1. MEMBERSHIP OF JOINT COMMITTEE ON ATOMIC ENERGY

87th Congress, 1st Session

Member	*Subcommittee(s)* [1]							*Record of Service as Member of Committee*
	1	*2*	*3*	*4*	*5*	*6*	*7*	
Rep. Chet Holifield (Calif.), Chairman	x		x	x	x	x		1946, to present
Sen. John O. Pastore (R.I.), Vice Chairman			x*	x		x	x	1952, 1953, to present
Sen. George D. Aiken (Vt.)		x		x		x		1959, to present
Sen. Clinton P. Anderson (N.M.)	x			x	x		x*	1951, to present
Rep. Wayne N. Aspinall (Colo.)			x		x*			Mar., 1958, to present
Rep. William H. Bates (Mass.)			x				x	1959, to present
Sen. Wallace F. Bennett (Utah)	x				x		x	1959, to present
Sen. Henry Dworshak (Idaho)			x		x			1957, to present
Sen. Albert Gore (Tenn.)	x*	x	x			x		1953, to present
Sen. Bourke B. Hickenlooper (Iowa)	x		x		x	x		1946, to present
Rep. Craig Hosmer (Calif.)				x		x		Jan., 1958, to present
Sen. Henry M. Jackson (Wash.)		x	x	x*		x	x	1949–1952; 1955, to present
Rep. Thomas G. Morris (N.M.)		x*			x			—
Rep. Melvin Price (Ill.)	x					x*		1946, to present
Sen. Richard B. Russell (Ga.)								1946, to present
Rep. Albert Thomas (Tex.)		x					x	1959, to present
Rep. James E. Van Zandt (Pa.)	x		x	x		x		1947, to present
Rep. Jack Westland (Wash.)		x			x		x	1959, to present
James T. Ramey, Exec. Dir.				—				—
John T. Conway, Ass't Dir.				—				—

[1] 1. Subcommittee on Agreements for Cooperation.
2. Subcommittee on Communities.
3. Subcommittee on Legislation.
4. Subcommittee on Military Applications.
5. Subcommittee on Raw Materials.
6. Subcommittee on Research, Development and Radiation.
7. Subcommittee on Security.
* Denotes chairman of subcommittee.

TABLE 2. CHAIRMEN AND VICE CHAIRMEN OF JOINT COMMITTEE ON ATOMIC ENERGY

Congress	*Term*	*Chairman*	*Vice Chairman*
87th	1961– —	Rep. Chet Holifield (Calif.)	Sen. John Pastore (R.I.)
86th	1959–1960	Sen. Clinton P. Anderson (N.M.)	Rep. Carl T. Durham (N.C.)
85th	1957–1958	Rep. Carl T. Durham (N.C.)	Sen. Clinton P. Anderson (N.M.)
84th	1955–1956	Sen. Clinton P. Anderson N.M.)	Rep. Carl T. Durham (N.C.)
83rd	1953–1954	Rep. W. Sterling Cole (N.Y.)	Sen. Bourke B. Hickenlooper (Iowa)
82nd	1951–1952	Sen. Brien McMahon (Conn.)	Rep. Carl T. Durham (N.C.)
81st	1949–1950	Sen. Brien McMahon (Conn.)	Rep. Carl T. Durham (N.C.)
80th	1947–1948	Sen. Bourke B. Hickenlooper (Iowa)	Rep. W. Sterling Cole (N.Y.)
79th	1946	Sen. Brien McMahon (Conn.)	Rep. Ewing Thomason (Tex.)

JINR is a center for research and training with particular emphasis on high energy physics. The experimental facilities include two large particle accelerators—a **680-Mev** proton synchrocyclotron and a 10-Bev proton synchrotron.

JUGGERNAUT

A 250-kilowatt (thermal) research reactor of the graphite/water type at Argonne National Laboratory. (See **research and training reactors**)

K

K-MESONS

Elementary particles with masses of about 1000 electron masses. There are several varieties, characterized by their modes of decay: τ-mesons decay into three charged pi-mesons; ρ^{0}-mesons decay into two charged pi-mesons; a ρ^{+}-meson decays into one charged and one neutral pi-meson. In addition to these types of K-mesons, several other decay schemes have been observed, which probably represent alternate decay modes of the above particles. The K-mesons are included among the **"strange particles."**

K-25 PLANT

The original gaseous diffusion plant, built at Oak Ridge, Tennessee during the **Manhattan Project** for the separation of uranium isotopes, and still in operation. (See **Oak Ridge Gaseous Diffusion Plant)**

KANSAS CITY PLANT. See **Atomic Energy Commission—Facilities.**

KEV

Shorthand expression for thousand **electron volts**; may be written kev, or Kev.

KICKSORTER

Synonym for **pulse height analyzer.**

KILOTON (TNT EQUIVALENT)

A unit used to express the **yield** of nuclear weapons. Thus, a 1-kiloton weapon is one which will produce an amount of energy corresponding to that produced by one thousand tons of TNT ($\sim 1 \times 10^{12}$ calories).

KILOWATT

A unit of electrical power, more specifically a rate of electrical energy generation. One kilowatt is equivalent to the following:

1000	watts
1.341	horsepower
3413	Btu per hour
1×10^{10}	ergs per second

Reactor engineers often use the term in context with the heat generated in a reactor and, in so doing, speak of thermal kilowatts as distinct from electrical kilowatts. The equivalence between thermal and electrical kilowatts depends upon the efficiency with which the heat energy is converted to electrical energy. At 25% thermal efficiency, 4 kilowatts of heat generation could produce 1 kilowatt of electricity output.

KILOWATT-HOUR

A unit of electrical energy, more specifically the electrical work accomplished by the expenditure of 1 **kilowatt** of power over 1 hour.

KINETIC EXPERIMENT ON WATER BOILERS (KEWB)

A small **test reactor** operated for the U.S. Atomic Energy Commission by Atomics International at a site in the Santa Susanna Mountains near Los Angeles, California. It is used to study the safety characteristics of **aqueous homogeneous reactor** systems during power excursions. Such reactors are inherently self-regulating in that a sudden increase in power level is accompanied by increased radiolytic decomposition of the aqueous fuel solution. The gases formed (H_2 and O_2) force some of the fuel solution out of the core into an overflow region, thereby shutting down the reactor by depriving the core of a critical mass.

The KEWB test series, initiated in 1956, has demonstrated that large amounts of excess reactivity can be introduced into such reactor systems without structural damage. The facility is designed to operate at a power level of 50 thermal kilowatts on a steady-state basis. During power excursions, the power level has exceeded 500,000 kilowatts for periods of time of the order of microseconds.

KINETIC PRESSURE

In controlled **fusion,** the pressure exerted by a group of particles as a result of their kinetic energy. Since energy per unit volume is equivalent to pressure, the kinetic pressure of a plasma is simply the number of ions and electrons per unit volume times their average energy. (See **beta factor)**

KIWI SERIES

A series of land-based reactor experiments being conducted by Los Alamos Scientific Laboratory at the U.S. Atomic Energy Commission's Nevada Test Site in connection with the development of direct-cycle nuclear rocket engines for the propulsion of space vehicles. The Kiwi-A series was conducted in 1959, and 1960, and consisted of Kiwi-A (June, 1959), Kiwi-A Prime (July, 1960) and Kiwi-A3 (October, 1960). A second series, designated Kiwi-B, began in December, 1961. (See **Rover Project)**

KNOLLS ATOMIC POWER LABORATORY (KAPL)

A U.S. Atomic Energy Commission power reactor development center, principally for Naval reactor programs, at Schenectady, N.Y. *Operating contractor:* General Electric Company. *General Manager:* Bascom H. Caldwell, Jr. *AEC investment in plant and equipment:* ~ $110 million, including $69 million in reactor prototype facilities.* *Staff:* ~ 670 scientists and engineers, plus ~ 1500 supporting personnel.

The laboratory proper is in a suburb of Schenectady. A facility for operating reactor prototypes is located at West Milton, New York, 20 miles northwest of Schenectady.

KAPL was established in the fall of 1946, and initially concentrated its efforts on research on an intermediate breeder reactor concept for central station power generation. In 1950, the program was redirected and the emphasis placed on Naval reactor development. The projects assigned to KAPL to date are: (1) SIG Project: Development of the sodium-cooled intermediate reactor system originally installed in the submarine, *Seawolf.* (2) S3G Project: Development of the twin-unit pressurized water reactor system used in the submarine, *Triton.* (3) DIG Project: Development of the twin-unit pressurized water reactor system used in the destroyer, *Bainbridge.* (4) S5G Project: Development of a natural-circulation pressurized water reactor system for submarine applications. For background information, see **Naval Reactors Program.**

KAPL has also done extensive research in support of the operation of AEC plutonium production facilities at Hanford and Savannah River and continues to provide technical assistance to these facilities. Through its early breeder reactor research and subsequent work on the SIG project, KAPL laid the foundations of the liquid metals technology underlying the development of **sodium-graphite** and **fast breeder reactors** for civilian power applications.

KOREA

The Office of Atomic Energy, Seoul, is the agency responsible for atomic energy matters.

---

* Includes facilities authorized or under construction as of June 30, 1960. Not adjusted for depreciation.

The Atomic Energy Research Institute, near Seoul is a government research center located adjacent to the College of Engineering of Seoul National Laboratory. The facilities include a radioisotope laboratory and a Triga Mark II research reactor, supplied by General Atomic, which operates at a power level of 100 kilowatts (thermal). The United States contributed $350,000 toward the cost of this reactor under its program of foreign Research Reactor Grants.

Low-grade deposits of uranium and thorium have been found but appear to have little commercial value. Korea's present electric power capacity is 500 megawatts, two-thirds of it thermal. Some coal and oil used in power generation is imported. There is interest in nuclear power to meet increasing power requirements, however no projects have been planned.

Korea is a member of the **International Atomic Energy Agency** and has a research-type **Agreement for Cooperation** with the United States.

KRYPTON

Element No. 36 (symbol, Kr; atomic weight, 83.80), an inert gas, several isotopes of which are formed as fission products. Of these, the only one of note is krypton-85, a 10.6-year beta emitter, which is of interest in two ways: (1) It is one of several radioactive gases given off during the fuel dissolution step in aqueous **fuel reprocessing** operations, others being xenon-133, xenon-135 and iodine-131. The radioiodine can be removed by chemical means. Radiokrypton and radio-xenon, being chemically inert, must either be removed by physical means (such as condensation or absorption) or reduced in concentration (by air dilution) for release through a stack exhaust system. (2) The other aspect of interest in krypton-85 is that it represents a potential source of long-lived beta radiation for industrial use. One application that shows promise is the activation of luminescent phosphorus, as in railroad signal lamps or aircraft emergency exit signs.

L

LABELED COMPOUND

A chemical compound containing one or more labeled atoms; also commonly referred to as a tagged compound. (See **labeling**)

LABELING

In an exact sense, labeling refers to the substitution, for purposes of using a **tracer technique,** of a radioisotope or a rare stable isotope for the naturally occurring isotope of a particular element in a chemical molecule. In a more general sense, any instance in which a distinguishable isotope is introduced into a material as a tracer may be referred to as labeling, whether or not isotopic substitution is involved. In either sense the terms labeling and tagging are commonly used interchangeably.

LABORATORY REACTORS (L SERIES)

Trade name of a line of small nuclear reactors manufactured by Atomics International, a division of North American Aviation, Inc., at Canoga Park, California. Through 1960, 11 Laboratory Reactors had been supplied or were scheduled for delivery to laboratories in the United States or abroad, for limited re-

Fig. 103. Model L-77 Laboratory Reactor. Control panel at left. (*Courtesy of Atomics International*)

search and/or student training programs. *Type:* Water boilers (also known as solution reactors). *Power ratings:* L-54 series, 50 thermal kilowatts. L-77 series, 10 watts. *Fuel:* H_2O. *Moderator:* H_2O. *Reflector:* Lead. *Neutron flux:* Of the order of 10^{12}n/cm^{2}sec (thermal) at a power level of 50 thermal kilowatts.

For a listing of laboratory reactor installations and general background information, see **research and training reactors.**

LA CROSSE BOILING WATER REACTOR

A nuclear power plant of the **boiling water** type near Genoa, Wisconsin, being built under the terms of the "second round" of the U.S. Atomic Energy Commission's Power Demonstration Reactor Program. The AEC is financing the construction of the reactor, which will incorporate forced circulation and internal steam separation and have a power rating of 50 megawatts (net electrical). The reactor is to be supplied by Allis-Chalmers Manufacturing Company under a fixed-price contract in the amount of approximately $11.0 million, including fabrication of the first core, operator training, and preacceptance testing of the reactor installation. The land and the electrical portion of the plant are being furnished by the Dairyland Power Cooperative of La Crosse, Wisconsin, who will operate the plant, making payment to the AEC for the steam used. The plant is tentatively scheduled to begin operation in late 1964, or early 1965.

The La Crosse project is the outgrowth of the AEC's plan to sponsor an "Improved Cycle Boiling Water Reactor (ICBWR)," i.e., a boiling water reactor with an improved steam cycle. Originally the cities of Los Angeles and Pasadena, California, were to have participated with the AEC in constructing and operating such a plant but they withdrew from the project in February, 1961, because of an increase in the estimated cost of power from the plant.

The following notes are based on 1962 information:

Power: 50 megawatts (net electrical). *Fuel:* Slightly enriched uranium (3.2% U^{235}) in the form of uranium dioxide (UO_2) pellets. *Fuel element design:* A single fuel element consists of an assembly of thin stainless steel tubes loaded with fuel pellets. *Steam conditions:* Steam leaves the reactor at 1250 pounds pressure and 574°F. *Cost:* Capital investment estimated at $20.8 million. *Dates:* Contracts signed in June, 1962. Operation scheduled to start in late 1964, or early 1965.

LAMINATED SHIELD

A radiation shield consisting of alternate layers of materials with different shielding characteristics, e.g., of water (for neutron **attenuation)** and steel (for gamma ray attenuation). (See **shielding)**

LARC (LIVERMORE ADVANCED RESEARCH COMPUTER)

One of the largest and fastest solid-state electronic digital computers in existence, the LARC was designed and built by Remington Rand Univac, a division of the Sperry Rand Corporation for the E. O. Lawrence Radiation Laboratory.

The computer contains nearly 80,000 transistors and 600 vacuum tubes, and has a high-speed magnetic core memory capable of storing 97,500 eleven-digit numbers. The bulk of the LARC's usage is on nuclear weapons projects and on fundamental studies of problems in nuclear physics of direct or potential application to the United States' weapons program.

LAW, ATOMIC ENERGY. See **legislation, federal.**

LAWRENCE MEMORIAL AWARD

An award, honoring the late E. O. Lawrence, established in 1959, by the U.S. Atomic Energy Commission, pursuant to Section 157b of the 1954 Atomic Energy Act, for recent, meritorious contributions to the development, use, or control of atomic energy. The award is made on the recommendation of AEC's General Advisory Committee with the approval of the President. It consists of a medal, a citation, and up to $25,000 to be shared by not more than five recipients in any one year. It is restricted to U.S. citizens not more than 45 years of age. It may or may not be awarded annually.

Recipients of the award are as follows:

1960 Award

Harvey Brooks, Harvard University
John S. Foster, Jr., E. O. Lawrence Radiation Laboratory
Isadore Perlman, E. O. Lawrence Radiation Laboratory
Norman F. Ramsey, Jr., Harvard University
Alvin M. Weinberg, Oak Ridge National Laboratory

1961 Award

Leo Brewer, E. O. Lawrence Radiation Laboratory
Henry Hurwitz, Jr., General Electric Company Research Laboratory
Conrad L. Longmire, Los Alamos Scientific Laboratory
Wolfgang K. H. Panofsky, Stanford University
Kenneth E. Wilzbach, Argonne National Laboratory

1962 Award

Andrew A. Benson, University of California
Richard P. Feynman, California Institute of Technology
Herbert Goldstein, Columbia University
Anthony Turkevich, University of Chicago
Herbert F. York, University of California

See **Fermi Award, Atoms for Peace Award.**

LAWRENCE RADIATION LABORATORY. See E. O. Lawrence Radiation Laboratory.

LAWRENCIUM

Proposed name for element no. 103 (proposed symbol, Lw), first identified in 1961, by A. Ghiorso, T. Sikkeland, A. E. Larsh, and R. M. Latimer in experiments conducted at the E. O. Lawrence Radiation Laboratory. The experiments involved bombarding a **californium** target with boron ions accelerated in the Laboratory's heavy-ion **linear accelerator** ("hilac"). Identification of the new element was based on analysis of the radioactivity associated with it, marking the first time a new chemical element has been discovered by purely nuclear techniques, i.e., without reliance on chemical analytical methods.

Lawrencium is the eleventh **transuranium element** discovered in the past two decades. The name was proposed in honor of the late Ernest Orlando Lawrence, Nobel laureate and founder of the Laboratory.

LEACH LIQUOR

In **uranium milling,** a sludge-like solution or "pulp" of uranium obtained by treating (leaching) uranium ore with an acid or an alkaline reagent.

LEAD

Element No. 82 (symbol, Pb; atomic weight, 207.21), commonly used as a radiation shield because of its high density and relatively low cost. Forms in which it is used include lead bricks for use in experimental setups, lead containers for shipping radioisotopes, and lead casks for storing radioactive materials. It is also used as a component in reactor shielding, especially where space is at a premium, as, for example, in shipboard installations. (See radiation **shielding**)

Lead alloyed with bismuth has received some consideration as a possible reactor coolant for high-temperature systems. A eutectic mixture of these metals melts at 102°F and, while highly corrosive, has excellent thermal conductivity and neutron-absorption characteristics.

LEAD TELLURIDE

A semiconductive binary metallic compound (formula, PbTe) used as a thermocouple material in thermoelectric systems for converting heat to electricity. Lead telluride melts at

922°C and its maximum operating temperature is in the range of 600-700°C. (See **thermoelectric conversion, SNAP Program)**

LEAKAGE

(1) Loss of neutrons by diffusion from the core of a nuclear reactor. Leakage can be reduced by surrounding the core with a **reflector**; the term then refers to the net loss, i.e., the neutrons that diffuse through the reflector. (2) Escape of neutrons through the radiation shielding surrounding a nuclear reactor.

LEGISLATION, FEDERAL

The basic federal statute governing atomic energy matters in the United States is Public Law 703, "Atomic Energy Act of 1954," as enacted by the second session of the 83rd Congress and subsequently amended. This Act became effective on August 30, 1954, superseding the Atomic Energy Act of 1946. Highlights of major federal atomic energy legislative actions are noted in the paragraphs which follow.

1946 Act (Public Law 79-585 *): The original U.S. atomic energy statute was the Atomic Energy Act of 1946, sometimes referred to as the McMahon Act since the bill on which it was based was introduced by the late Senator Brien McMahon of Connecticut, then Chairman of the Senate Special Committee on Atomic Energy. The 1946 Act established the civilian U.S. Atomic Energy Commission (AEC) as the agency responsible for the national atomic energy program. Transfer of responsibility from the wartime Manhattan Engineer District, War Department (see **Manhattan Project)** to the AEC was accomplished by Executive Order 9816 and became effective as of midnight, December 31, 1946.

At the time of enactment of the 1946 Act, the United States was the only country capable of producing fissionable materials and manufacturing atomic weapons. The Act contained provisions designed to ensure, to the extent possible by legislative action, the retention of this position pending establishment of effective **international control of atomic energy.** To this end, the government (AEC) was assigned title to **source materials** and **special nuclear materials,** and private ownership of facilities capable of producing the latter was prohibited. The exchange of information on industrial or military applications with other nations was prohibited.** Tight government control over atomic energy information and patents relating to industrial or military applications was established. In short, the government (AEC) was given a virtual monopoly in the atomic energy field. At the same time, the AEC was charged with "assisting and fostering private research and development to encourage maximum scientific progress" and, within the restraints imposed by security considerations, with "(disseminating) scientific and technical information to encourage scientific progress."

The 1946 Act contained a number of provisions that have been retained in subsequent legislation. For example, it established the **Joint Committee on Atomic Energy** of the U.S. Congress to monitor U.S. atomic energy developments, the **General Advisory Committee** to advise the AEC on scientific and technical matters, and the **Military Liaison Committee** to provide for the participation of the Department of Defense in military aspects of AEC activity.

The 1946 Act was passed after extensive public hearings and congressional debate on the merits of civilian *versus* military administration of atomic energy.

1954 Act (Public Law 83-703): By 1954, circumstances had changed to an extent that fundamental changes in the law were considered necessary. Most notably, the U.S. no longer held a monopoly in the atomic weapons field (see nuclear **weapons).** Also, sufficient progress had been made in research on civilian applications of atomic energy, notably power, to make it apparent that the time had come to open the way for private enterprise and international cooperation in the development of such applications.

* I.e., Public Law 585 enacted by the 79th Congress.

** A 1951 amendment to the 1946 Act made provision for the limited exchange of classified information with other nations (see **Agreements for Cooperation**).

The bill which formed the basis for the Atomic Energy Act of 1954 was introduced by Representative Sterling Cole of New York, then Chairman of the Joint Committee on Atomic Energy. The law as enacted provided, in part, for the following:

1. Private ownership of atomic energy facilities, such as research and power reactors, subject to compliance with AEC license requirements. (See **licenses**)

2. Private leasing of special nuclear materials under license and use-charge arrangements. (Again see **licenses**)

3. Private access to certain categories of classified information, including restricted data, subject to compliance with AEC procedures. (See **Access Permits**)

4. A more liberal patent policy. (See **patents**)

5. Broadened international cooperation in the development of peaceful uses of atomic energy. (See **Agreements for Cooperation**)

6. Exchange with other nations of classified information on certain aspects of military applications of atomic energy. (Again see **Agreements for Cooperation**)

As was noted earlier, the 1954 Act and subsequent amendments thereto constitute the basic atomic energy law of the United States. Certain of the amendments are noted in the paragraphs immediately following.

IAEA Participation Act (Public Law 85-177): This amendment to the 1954 Act provided for U.S. participation in the **International Atomic Energy Agency** and authorized the AEC to distribute to the Agency, subject to enrichment limitations and other statutory provisions, 5000 kilograms of contained uranium-235, plus an additional amount of special nuclear material matching the total quantity of such material made available by other members of the Agency up to July 1, 1960.

Indemnification Act (Public Law 85-256): This amendment to the 1954 Act provided for a program of government indemnification and limitation of liability in the event of a **nuclear incident** in a licensed facility (see **insurance and indemnification against atomic energy risks**). It also established a statutory requirement for an **Advisory Committee on Reactor Safeguards.** It is commonly referred to as the Price-Anderson Act, having been sponsored by Representative Melvin Price of Illinois and Senator Clinton Anderson of New Mexico.

Cooperation With States (Public Law 86-373): This amendment added a new section to the 1954 Act (Section 274) to clarify the respective responsibilities of the federal government and the states with regard to regulatory functions, and to establish a basis for effective cooperation in the control of radiation hazards and in the coordination of radiation protection standards. (See **state activities in the atomic energy field**)

Atomic Energy Community Act of 1955 (Public Law 84-221): This statute was enacted to facilitate the establishment of local self-government in the communities of **Oak Ridge, Tennessee,** and **Richland, Washington,** and to provide for the disposal of federally owned properties in these communities.

Euratom Cooperation Act (Public Law 85-846): This statute was enacted to provide for cooperation with the Euratom Atomic Energy Community (see **Euratom**) and is the charter for the **U.S.-Euratom Joint Program** of nuclear power development.

Nuclear-Powered Merchant Ship Authorization (Public Law 85-107): This amended title VII of the Merchant Marine Act of 1936 to authorize the construction of a nuclear-powered merchant ship for operation in foreign commerce of the United States, and for other purposes (see NS ***Savannah***).

Other: Other federal atomic energy legislation enacted to date can be categorized as follows:

1. Annual appropriations bills.

2. Omnibus bills making miscellaneous amendments to the 1954 Act.

3. Special statutes for specific purposes, e.g., Public Law 85-31, which provided for the construction of the AEC's present headquarters building at Germantown, Maryland.

LEGISLATION, STATE. See **State activities in the atomic energy field.**

LETHAL DOSE (LD)

In a literal sense, a dose of ionizing radiation sufficient to cause death.

In technical usage, lethal dose is usually defined in terms of the dose required to kill a given percentage of the individuals in a statistical group of animals or organisms within a specified period of time. Thus, the notation, LD30/30, for a given species means the dose required to kill 30% of a sample population within 30 days. See **median lethal dose** for the level of exposure fatal to man.

LICENSES, AEC

The Atomic Energy Act of 1954, as amended, provides the legal basis for the U.S. Atomic Energy Commission's regulation of civilian atomic energy activity. The policy of Congress in enacting this legislation and the purposes of this legislation are set forth in sections 1, 2, and 3 of the statute.

The following types of authorizations are required under the Act:

Special Nuclear Material. License to receive, possess, use, and transfer special nuclear material, as provided in sections 53 and 57a (1)-(2); for its use in the conduct of research and development activities under section 31; for its use in research and development activity or in medical therapy under noncommercial licenses pursuant to section 104; for its use under commercial licenses pursuant to section 103; and for other appropriate uses.

Source Material. License to transfer, deliver, receive, possess, import, or export source material after removal from the place of deposit in nature, as provided in sections 62 and 63; for its use in the conduct of research and development activities under section 31; for its use in research and development activities or in medical therapy under noncommercial licenses pursuant to section 104; for its use under commercial licenses pursuant to section 103; or for "any other use approved by the Commission as an aid to science or industry."

By-Product Material. License to transfer, receive, manufacture, produce, acquire, own, possess, import, or export by-product material, as provided in sections 81 and 82; and for its use in research and development, medical therapy, industry, agriculture, and "such other useful applications as may be developed."

Utilization or Production Facility. Construction permit for construction prior to licensing, or alteration after licensing, of a facility licensed under sections 103 and 104, as provided in section 185; license for a commercial facility as provided in sections 101, 102, and 103; license for a noncommercial facility as provided in sections 101 and 104 for medical therapy and research and development activities; license to individuals as provided in section 107 as operators of various classes of facilities under the Act.

More detailed information on the requirements for a license in any particular case may be found in Title 10 of the Code of Federal Regulations. (See **Atomic Energy Commission—Rules and Regulations** for references, for licensing procedure see **Atomic Energy Commission—Licensing and Regulatory Procedure)**

LIGHT WATER

Ordinary water (H_2O) as distinct from "heavy water" (D_2O). (See **reactor materials)**

LINAC. Acronym for **linear accelerator.**

LINEAR ACCELERATORS

A class of **particle accelerators** in which radiofrequency power is employed to accelerate charged particles along a straight-line path of travel; often referred to as linac machines. Standard models of electron linacs with beam energies in the range 3-24 Mev are supplied commercially for use in research and in industrial radiation applications. Electron linacs with beam energies up to about 1 Bev, and heavy-ion linacs ("hilacs") with beam energies

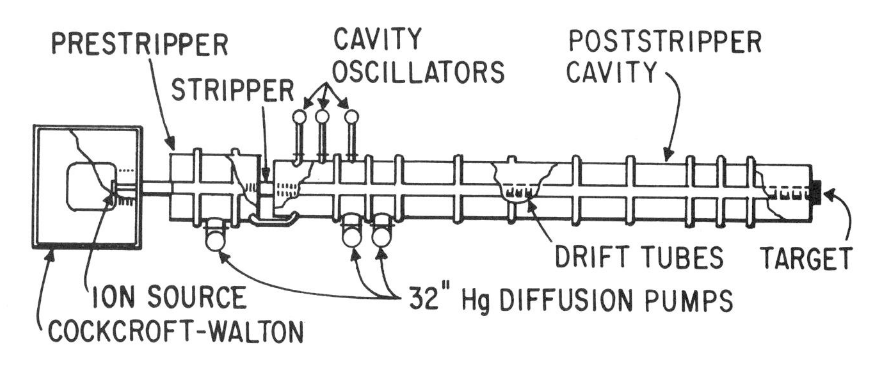

Fig. 104. Heavy-ion linear accelerator ("Hilac"). Top, diagram of machine. Bottom, view inside post-stripper cavity. (*Courtesy of E. O. Lawrence Radiation Laboratory*)

up to about 10 Mev are used for high-energy and particle physics research.

Electron Linacs. The principal components of an electron linac are as follows:

1. A radiofrequency power source consisting essentially of a power supply and one or more klystron tubes.
2. An electron source, consisting of a cathode and an electron gun.
3. An evacuated tube (wave guide) and related vacuum apparatus.

In operation, traveling waves of high-frequency power are directed down the evacuated tube. Pulses of electrons fed into the tube become trapped in the electromagnetic fields associated with the waves and are thereby accelerated.

The concept of a traveling-wave electron linac was developed in 1946. The most powerful machine ($\sim$ 1 Bev) built to date is at Stanford University, and construction of a giant machine (10-20 Bev) with a 2-mile long tube is planned at that institution (see **Stanford Linear Electron Accelerator Project**). Small (3-24 Mev) electron linacs are supplied commercially by several companies, including

High Voltage Engineering Company * and Varian Associates.

Positive-Ion Linacs. Heavy-ion linacs (called hilacs) are in operation at the E. O. Lawrence Radiation Laboratory and Yale University. These machines accelerate ions of elements as heavy as neon to energies of ~ 10 Mev.**

The principal components of a hilac are illustrated in Fig. 102. An ion injector, comprising an arc-type ion source and a **Cockcroft-Walton machine,** feeds pulses of ions into an evacuated linear assembly consisting essentially of two accelerator sections (cavities) divided by a stripper. Power is supplied to the accelerator sections by high-frequency oscillators. Each section contains a series of cylinders (drift tubes) of progressively increasing length separated by gaps and so wired that, at any instant, adjacent tubes carry opposite electrical signs. Energy is imparted to the ions as they cross the gaps; they are insulated as they pass through the drift tubes, during which time the voltage changes phase. Thus, the ions are accelerated by a series of "kicks," being kept in proper phase with the alternating voltage by reason of the progressively lengthening path of travel through the drift tubes. The total energy gained is approximately equal to the potential multiplied by the number of gaps. In the stripper separating the two accelerator sections (see Fig. 104), a transverse jet of mercury improves the charge-to-mass ratio of the ion stream by accomplishing additional ionization, i.e., electrons are stripped away from residual neutral atoms in the particle stream. To provide radial stability of the very rapidly moving particles "downstream" of the stripper, the post-stripper accelerator section is equipped with strong-focusing magnets. At the end of this section, the fully accelerated ions are directed to any of various targets.

* Recently acquired Applied Radiation Corporation, another supplier of electron linacs.

** Such ions are easier to accelerate in a linear machine than in a cyclic machine, such as a cyclotron, since in the latter extremely strong magnetic forces would be required to maintain the heavy particles in proper orbit.

Linacs have also been built for proton acceleration, as in the preacceleration system of Brookhaven National Laboratory's **Alternating Gradient Synchrotron.**

LINEAR DYNAMIC PINCH EXPERIMENTS

Experimental devices built as part of the **Pinch Program** of research on controlled **fusion.** These devices are used for research on fast, unstabilized pinch-confinement of an ionized gas or **plasma,** in a straight-tube configuration.

LINEAR ENERGY TRANSFER (LET)

A measure of the ability of biological matter to absorb ionizing radiation; specifically, the radiation energy absorbed per centimeter of path through a given biological medium. LET values depend on the type and energy of the radiation and on the chemical composition of the tissue or other biological medium traversed. In general, the higher the LET value is, the greater is the "relative biological effectiveness" (RBE) of the radiation. (See **radiation dose)**

LIQUID FLUIDIZED BED REACTOR (LFBR) CONCEPT

A power reactor concept in an early experimental stage in the laboratories of The Martin Company.† The LFBR concept, attractive for its simplicity, is based on the use of small (pea-sized) fuel pellets immersed in liquid in an upright cylindrical reactor core. The liquid —either water or an organic compound—would serve as moderator and coolant as well as fluidizer, and would be circulated in a closed loop, entering the core through a perforated plate. In steady-state operation, turbulent flow of the liquid through the core would maintain the fuel pellets in a fluidized state, i.e., randomly suspended in the liquid medium. In principle, the power level could be controlled by regulating the liquid flow and hence the

† A similar concept is being developed in Europe. See reference to "Suspop" experiment under the **Netherlands.**

volumetric fuel-to-moderator ratio, obviating the need for control rods. Similarly, the reactor could be shut down by stopping the liquid flow, since the fuel pellets would then sink to the bottom of the core in a noncritical configuration (due to the absence of sufficient moderator within the fuel mass).

The Martin Company began work on the LFBR concept in 1955. In 1958, a preliminary feasibility study was carried out for the U.S. Atomic Energy Commission, and in 1959, the AEC authorized a research and development program, including construction and operation of a critical experiment facility. The critical facility was constructed in 1960, and began operation in 1961.

The feasibility of the LFBR concept hinges on the following:

1. Demonstration of the nuclear and hydrodynamic stability of a fluidized bed system.
2. Development of abrasion-proof, corrosion-resistant fuel pellets.

Also of importance, though not necessarily essential to the feasibility of the concept, is confirmation of the predicted ability to operate a fluidized bed system without control rods.

Both clad and unclad uranium dioxide (UO_2) pellets are being studied for use in a LFBR system. The possibility of adding lubricants to the liquid to reduce pellet abrasion has been explored and appears promising.

LIQUID-HYDROGEN DISTILLATION

A low-temperature method of concentrating **deuterium** (for heavy water production) based on volatility differences between liquid deuterium and liquid hydrogen (see Fig. 105). Hydrogen (see below) is refrigerated to a temperature of approximately −250°C and fed as a liquid to the midpoint of a distillation tower. The deuterium, because of its lower volatility, tends to concentrate in the lower section of the tower. Two streams leave the tower—an "overhead" stream of hydrogen stripped essentially free of deuterium, and a "bottoms" stream enriched in deuterium. The latter enters a second, smaller, tower for final enrichment. In this case three streams are taken off—an overhead stream, which is recycled to the first tower, a bottoms stream of essentially pure deuterium product, and an intermediate stream of deuterium hydride (DH). This last stream is put through a catalytic chemical exchange process to recover its deuterium content.

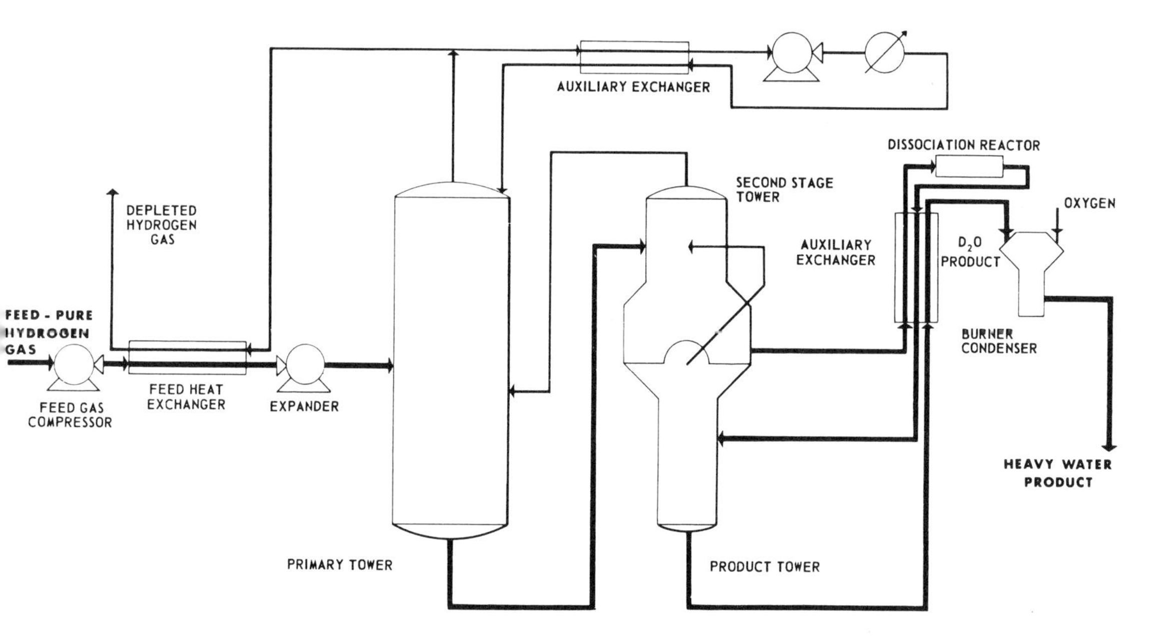

Fig. 105. Production of heavy water by liquid hydrogen distillation. Reprinted from "Atomic Energy Facts."

It is not economic to produce hydrogen solely as a starting point for a deuterium concentration process; therefore hydrogen distillation can only be considered in cases where tonnage quantities of hydrogen are available from other operations, as, for example, where electrolytic hydrogen or synthesis gas (75% H_2, 25% N_2) are being produced for the manufacture of ammonia.

Liquid-hydrogen distillation has not yet been used for heavy water production in the U.S. but is being applied elsewhere (see **France, West Germany** and **India**). Also, it should be noted that this was essentially the experimental method used in the discovery of deuterium by H. C. Urey, G. M. Murphy and F. G. Brickwedde in 1932.

LIQUID-LEVEL GAGES. See gages.

LIQUID METAL FUEL REACTOR (LMFR) CONCEPT

A fluid-fuel power reactor concept studied at Brookhaven National Laboratory for a number of years but no longer under development. The objective of the LMFR program was to achieve a thermal breeder capable of operation at high temperature.

The following notes describe an LMFR system as envisioned by a 1958 design study: *

1. Fuel: Solution of enriched uranium (ultimately uranium-233) in molten bismuth.
2. Blanket: Slurry of thorium bismuthide (an intermetallic compound) in molten bismuth.
3. Moderator: Graphite.
4. Primary coolant: The circulating fuel serves as the primary heat transport medium, entering the critical region (core) at 750°F and leaving it at 1050°F.
5. Intermediate coolant: On leaving the critical region, the fuel stream transfers heat to liquid sodium, which carries the heat to a steam generator. (The reason for an intermediate coolant is to avoid using a radioactive fluid for steam generation.)
6. Construction materials: Alloy steel (2¼% chromium, 1% molybdenum) used as the container material in the primary loop.
7. Fuel reprocessing: **Fluoride volatility process.**

The choice of bismuth as the fuel and blanket medium was prompted by its low thermal neutron capture cross section (0.032 barn) and low vapor pressure, the latter property making it possible to achieve high operating temperatures in a low-pressure system. Disadvantages of bismuth include low uranium solubility, which necessitates the use of high-enrichment fuel; and the formation (under irradiation) of polonium, which represents a potential safety hazard.

The most serious problem encountered in the LMFR development, as has been true of all fluid-fuel reactor concepts, was that of engineering an equipment system capable of containing the fuel and blanket streams with adequate long-term integrity. Factors in this problem included the intense radioactivity of the fuel and blanket stream, requiring that the equipment loops handling these streams be designed for remote maintenance; the highly corrosive and erosive nature of these streams; and the difficulty of maintaining the fissionable and fertile materials properly distributed in the bismuth medium.

Work on the LMFR concept was terminated in 1960, following a decision by the U.S. Atomic Energy Commission to concentrate on other lines of fluid-fuel reactor development. For a discussion of this decision, see **aqueous homogeneous reactors.**

LITHIUM

Element No. 3 (symbol, Li; atomic weight, 6.940). As found in nature, lithium consists of a mixture of two stable isotopes—**lithium-6** (7.5%) and **lithium-7** (92.5%). Lithium-6 has been proposed for radiation shielding and re-

* Conducted by Babcock & Wilcox Company, based on the Brookhaven development work. The two-region system described was one of several alternatives then under consideration.

actor control applications, because it has a high thermal neutron absorption cross section (~ 947 barns) and, with reference to its use in shielding, because it absorbs neutrons without emitting gamma rays and hence does not require a secondary shield. Lithium-7 has been proposed for use as a high-temperature reactor coolant because it combines excellent thermodynamic and heat-transfer characteristics with a very low thermal neutron absorption cross section.

Lithium-6 is also of interest as a possible fuel or source thereof for the generation of power from controlled thermonuclear reactions, assuming this method of power generation is found to be feasible. This interest stems from the fact that reactions between lithium-6 and **deuterium** and between **tritium** (made from lithium-6) and deuterium are considered to be possible mechanisms for controlled fusion. (See **thermonuclear power)**

Experimental amounts of tritium for use in research are currently produced by neutron irradiation of lithium-6:

$$_3Li^6 + _0n^1 \longrightarrow _1T^3 + _2He^4$$

Because of the possible future importance of lithium in context with thermonuclear power, some information on lithium occurrences and reserves should be given. Lithium constitutes approximately 0.006% of the earth's crust, making it a more abundant element than lead or tin. It occurs principally in igneous rock but occurs also in sedimentary deposits. The principal mineral species are spodumene (a lithium aluminum silicate), amblygonite (a lithium aluminum fluophosphate), lipidolite (a fluosilicate of lithium, potassium and aluminum), and petalite (a quartz-like substance composed of silica, alumina and lithia). Based on studies conducted shortly after World War II, U.S. reserves are roughly estimated as follows:

Principal Mineral	*Grade (Avg. % LiO_2)*	*Estimated Reserves (tons of LiO_2)*	
		Known	*Inferred*
Spodumene	1.2–1.7	54,000	1,244,000
Brine	.015	90,000	—

Preliminary exploration indicates that there are extensive lithium deposits in Canada (of the order of 50 times the inferred U.S. reserves) and southern Africa; and also in areas of Europe, Latin America and Australia. No estimate of total world reserves is known to have been made.

LIVERMORE LABORATORY. See **E. O. Lawrence Radiation Laboratory, Livermore Branch.**

LIVERMORE POOL-TYPE REACTOR (LPTR)

A 2000-kilowatt (thermal) research reactor at the Livermore Branch of the E. O. Lawrence Radiation Laboratory. The core is suspended in a deep concrete-shielded tank, rather than in a large pool as in most pool reactor designs. The LPTR was supplied by Foster-Wheeler Corporation and began operation in 1957. (See **research and training reactors)**

LOAD FACTOR

In electric power generation, the ratio of the average load in kilowatts supplied by a generating unit or station during a designated period to the peak load occurring in that period. The peak load is usually taken to be the maximum load experienced during a 60-minute demand interval. (See **capacity factor)**

U.S.S. *LONG BEACH* (CG(N)9)

First nuclear-powered Naval surface ship. A guided-missile cruiser, *Long Beach* displaces about 15,000 tons and is powered by twin C1W pressurized water reactors. The reactor plant was designed by Bettis Atomic Power Laboratory. The ship was constructed by the Shipbuilding Division of Bethlehem Steel Company, launched on July 14, 1959, and commissioned September 9, 1961. (Fig. 106)

No additional nuclear-powered cruisers had been authorized through mid-1961. (See **Naval Reactors Program)**

Fig. 106. USS *Long Beach*. Official U.S. Navy Photograph.

LOS ALAMOS FAST REACTOR (CLEMENTINE)

An experimental nuclear reactor built at Los Alamos Scientific Laboratory at the close of the Manhattan Project to test the feasibility of operating a reactor in the fast-neutron spectrum. It is of interest as the first fast reactor (average neutron energy, 0.5 Mev); the first reactor to be fueled with plutonium; and the first reactor to employ a liquid-metal coolant. "Clementine," so-named because it was installed "in a cavern in a canyon" and because the wartime code for plutonium-239 was "49," first went critical in 1943. After the initial feasibility demonstration it was used for fast-neutron experiments and reactor studies. The coolant stream became contaminated when the cladding of one of the fuel elements corroded through and the reactor was dismantled in 1953. *Fuel:* Small plutonium rods clad with stainless steel and arrayed in a cylindrical core 6 inches high and 6 inches in diameter. *Power level:* 25 kilowatts (thermal). *Moderator:* None. *Reflector:* Natural uranium. *Coolant:* Mercury.

LOS ALAMOS MOLTEN PLUTONIUM REACTOR EXPERIMENT NO. 1 (LAMPRE-1)

An experimental reactor facility at Los Alamos Scientific Laboratory. The purpose of LAMPRE-1 is to study the feasibility and short-term operating characteristics of a reactor system fueled with molten plutonium. The reactor is cooled with liquid sodium and is designed to operate at a power level of 1000 kilowatts (thermal). The operating temperature is $\sim$ 950°F.

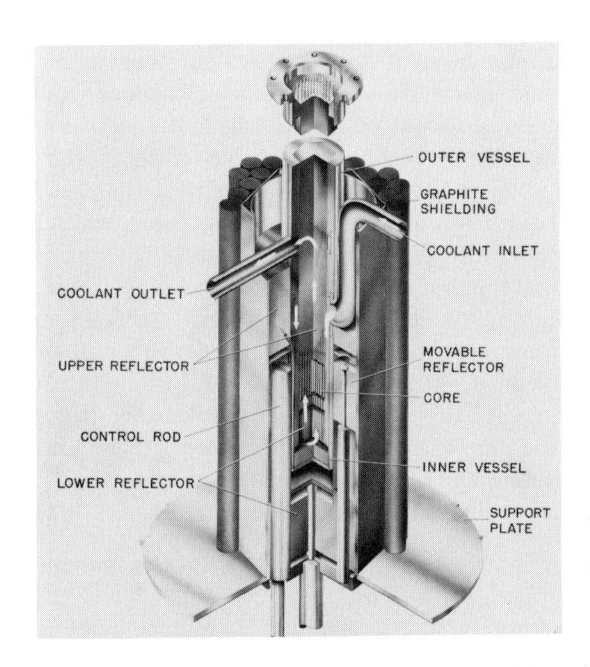

Fig. 107. Cutaway view of Los Alamos Molten Plutonium Reactor Experiment (LAMPRE-I). (*Courtesy of Los Alamos Scientific Laboratory*)

LAMPRE-1 began operation in April, 1961. The initial experiments are being conducted on a plutonium-iron alloy fuel (10 weight % Fe). Other plutonium fuels, including ternary alloys, are to be tested in a general effort to obtain data needed for the design of a higher power reactor facility.

LOS ALAMOS, NEW MEXICO

A community located approximately 30 miles northwest of Santa Fe and the residential center for personnel employed at Los Alamos Scientific Laboratory. The 1960 Census listed the population of Los Alamos as 12,584.

Los Alamos was established by the government in conjunction with the wartime Manhattan Project. Public access to the community was restricted until 1950.

Los Alamos is a county and the citizens control the local government. There is a private housing development on lots developed and sold by the government, but the majority of the buildings in the community are federally owned and all of the land is federally controlled. Under a contract with the U.S. Atomic Energy Commission, the Zia Corporation operates government-owned community facilities and provides other community services.

LOS ALAMOS POWER REACTOR EXPERIMENTS (LAPRE-1, -2)

Two reactor experiments conducted at Los Alamos Scientific Laboratory to study the corrosion properties and other characteristics of uranyl phosphate solutions when used as the fuel medium in an **aqueous homogeneous reactor** system. Following are some of the particulars of the two experiments:

Fig. 108. Gold-plated apparatus which formed the core of Los Alamos Power Reactor Experiment No. II (LAPRE-II). (*Courtesy of Los Alamos Scientific Laboratory*)

LOS ALAMOS SCIENTIFIC LABORATORY

A major U.S. Atomic Energy Commission research center at Los Alamos, New Mexico, 36 miles southwest of Santa Fe. *Operating contractor:* University of California. *Director:* Norris E. Bradbury. *AEC investment in plant and equipment:* ~ $177 million.* *Staff:* ~ 1000 scientists and engineers, and ~ 2300 supporting personnel.

LASL was established in 1942, as the organization responsible for the weapons research, design and testing phases of the war-

* Includes facilities authorized or under construction as of June 30, 1959. Not adjusted for depreciation.

	LAPRE-1	*LAPRE-2*
Rated heat output (kilowatts-thermal)	2000	800–1000
Rated electrical output	none	none
Fuel	Concentrated light water solution of uranyl phosphate	Dilute light water solution of uranyl phosphate
Circulation	Forced circulation	Natural circulation
Fuel temperature	740°F	800°F
Equipment cladding	Gold or platinum	Gold
Start-up	October, 1956	February, 1959
Dismantled	November, 1956 [1]	May, 1959 [2]

[1] Leaks, attributed to excessive corrosion, forced abandonment of the experiment.
[2] Desired results achieved.

time **Manhattan Project.** The Laboratory has continued to carry major responsibility in this field, and additionally has engaged in fundamental and applied research in a number of other areas of science and technology. Some major areas of LASL activity are as follows:

1. Weapons: Development of both nuclear and thermonuclear devices; supporting research in physics, metallurgy and other sciences, including general studies of the phenomenology of explosions.

2. Controlled fusion: LASL is one of the principal centers of the U.S. program of research on controlled **fusion.** The laboratory is active in research on **pinch** and **magnetic-mirror** devices, **plasma diagnostics,** and related studies. Experimental devices built to date include the **Columbus** and **Perhapsatron** series, **Ixion** and **Scylla.**

3. Reactor development: Studies of advanced power and process heat reactor concepts. (See **Los Alamos Power Reactor Experiments, Los Alamos Molten Plutonium Reactor Experiment,** and **Turret Reactor)**

4. Nuclear rocket propulsion: LASL is the prime contractor for the **Rover Project.**

5. Direct energy conversion: Research on thermionic fuel cell concept for direct conversion of reactor heat to electricity. (See **thermionic conversion)**

6. Peaceful uses of nuclear explosives: Participation in the Gnome Experiment and other **Plowshare Program** activities.

7. General research: Areas include theoretical and experimental nuclear physics; mathematics; chemistry, especially of uranium, plutonium, deuterium and tritium; metallurgy, especially of plutonium and of high-temperature refractories; chemical engineering; and biomedical research.

Fig. 109. Section of Los Alamos Scientific Laboratory. (*Courtesy of Los Alamos Scientific Laboratory*)

Over the years LASL has made a number of important contributions to atomic energy development quite apart from its pioneering of weapons systems. The Laboratory built the first plutonium-fueled reactor (see **Clementine),** and was the first to operate aqueous homogeneous reactor systems (see **Los Alamos Water Boilers).** Its contributions to basic research include experimental confirmation of the existence of the neutrino.

LASL facilities occupy some 300 permanent buildings spread over 77 square miles of mountain and canyon country. There are a number of particle accelerators, include Van de Graaffe and Cockcroft-Walton machines, three betatrons and a cyclotron; two research reactors, namely the **Los Alamos Water Boiler** (SUPO) and the **Omega West Reactor;** extensive facilities for critical experiments on weapon systems; a large computer center; and a variety of other special experimental apparatus.

LOS ALAMOS WATER BOILERS (LOPO, HYPO, SUPO)

A series of small nuclear reactors of the aqueous homogeneous, or solution, type, built at Los Alamos Scientific Laboratory (see Table 1). The first of the series (LOPO, from "low power") was operated in 1944, and provided the initial experience with the use of a fluid fuel reactor system. LOPO was dismantled and reconstructed as HYPO, which in turn was dismantled and reconstructed as SUPO. Reactors of this general type are now used in a number of laboratories for limited research and/or student training programs. (See **research and training reactors**)

LOW-INTENSITY TEST REACTOR (LITR)

A reactor facility at Oak Ridge National Laboratory. It was originally used to provide design information for the Materials Test Reactor, serving first as a mechanical mock-up and then as a critical experiment facility for that reactor. Since 1951, it has been used as a general-purpose research reactor. *Type:* Tank reactor. *Power rating:* 3000 thermal kilowatts. *Fuel:* MTR-type fuel elements. *Coolant:* H_2O. *Moderator:* H_2O. *Reflector:* Beryllium. *Neutron flux:* Of the order of 10^{13}n/cm^{2}sec (maximum thermal). *Start-up:* 1950. (See **research and training reactors**)

TABLE 1. LOS ALAMOS WATER BOILERS

	LOPO	*HYPO*	*SUPO*
Type	Water boiler	Water boiler	Water boiler
Fuel	Highly enriched uranyl sulfate solution	Highly enriched uranyl nitrate solution	Highly enriched uranyl nitrate solution
Moderator	H_2O	H_2O	H_2O
Reflector	Beryllium oxide	Beryllium oxide and graphite	Graphite
Coolant	None	H_2O	H_2O
Power	0.05 watts (thermal)	6 kilowatts (thermal)	25 kilowatts (thermal)
Neutron flux	n.a.	$\sim 10^{11}$ n/cm^2 sec (max. thermal flux)	$\sim 10^{12}$ n/cm^{2}sec (max. thermal flux)
Start-up	1944	1944	1951

M

MAELU

Mutual Atomic Energy Liability Underwriters, a syndicate formed by mutual insurance companies to insure privately owned atomic energy facilities against **public liability** claims relating to atomic energy hazards. MAELU is a voluntary, nonprofit, unincorporated association with headquarters in Chicago. Policies are written in conjunction with a counterpart syndicate of capital-stock insurance companies (see **NELIA**). Maximum coverage available from MAELU under a joint MAELU-NELIA policy is $13.5 million. (See **insurance and indemnification against atomic risks**)

MAERP

Mutual Atomic Energy Reinsurance Pool, a syndicate formed by mutual insurance companies to insure privately owned atomic energy facilities against property damage arising from atomic energy hazards. MAERP is a voluntary, nonprofit, unincorporated association with headquarters in Chicago. Policies are written in conjunction with a counterpart syndicate of capital-stock insurance companies (see **NEPIA**), with MAERP assuming approximately 15% of the risk coverage. (See **insurance and indemnification against atomic energy risks**)

MAGNESIUM

Element No. 12 (symbol, Mg; atomic weight, 24.32), of interest in the nuclear field in three unrelated ways: (1) Its extremely low thermal neutron absorption cross section (~ 0.06 barn) and excellent thermal conductivity suggest its use as a cladding or diluent material for reactor fuel elements. Other considerations act to limit its usefulness in this application—principally its low mechanical strength at elevated temperatures (magnesium melts at ~ 1202°F), and its poor corrosion resistance. Accordingly, it is primarily of interest in connection with gas or organic cooled reactors designed to operate at moderate temperature levels. Magnesium cladding has not been used to date in the United States but is used in gas-cooled power reactors in the United Kingdom and in France. Also, uranium-magnesium fuel dispersions in stainless steel tubes are reportedly used in the water cooled power reactors under development in the U.S.S.R. See **reactor materials.** (2) Magnesium is the reduction agent used in converting normal uranium tetrafluoride to massive metal (see **uranium refining and conversion**) and in other metal reduction processes. (3) Liquid magnesium is one of the metal solvents being studied in research on high-temperature metal-to-metal extraction techniques for certain **fuel reprocessing** applications.

MAGNETIC BOTTLE

In context with devices for controlled **fusion,** a magnetic field of such a configuration as to confine an ionized gas, or **plasma,** i.e., to constrict the plasma and/or prevent it from escaping into a surrounding vacuum region. The term is most commonly used in reference to the magnetic field configuration of devices of the magnetic mirror type (see **magnetic mirror systems**), but it also may be applied to other more or less closed magnetic confinement systems. (See **cusped geometry, Stellarator Program, Astron Program**)

MAGNETIC COMPRESSION EXPERIMENTS

A series of experiments at the Naval Research Laboratory on methods for heating an ionized gas, or **plasma**, for application in controlled-**fusion** systems. The central theme of the experiments is the use of a pulsed magnetic field to amplify the energy imparted to plasma by shock waves, a technique variously known as the theta pinch, azimuthal pinch, or orthogonal pinch.

At the outset of the work, the effort was focused on **shock heating** phenomena and the magnetic force was used strictly to accelerate plasma ions that had been shock-heated by a sudden electrical discharge. Techniques for accomplishing this were developed to the point where temperatures of the order of one million degrees were achieved, but since no provision was made to confine the plasma, the energy dissipated itself within a fraction of a microsecond.

The focus of the effort then shifted and, by incorporating a confining magnetic field, a technique was developed which makes use of transient "magnetic mirrors" (see **magnetic mirror systems**). The later technique has achieved comparable ion temperatures and held them (i.e., confined the plasma) for periods of the order of 10 microseconds. (For notes on a similar approach see **Scylla.**)

MAGNETIC MIRROR SYSTEMS

One of several types of system under study in U.S. research on controlled **fusion**; these studies are sometimes referred to as the Pyrotron Program (see **thermonuclear power**). In magnetic mirror devices an ionized fuel, or **plasma**, is confined in a "magnetic bottle" within a straight tube by means of a nonuniform magnetic field. The "magnetic mirrors" are regions of reinforced magnetic field strength at the ends of the tube which serve to reflect escaping plasma particles back into the central region, thereby stoppering the "bottle." Work on this approach to the problem of plasma confinement began in 1952.

Concept. The lines of magnetic force in a magnetic mirror device are axial and, as noted, are more dense at the ends of the cylindrical reaction chamber than at the center. Upon injection of a beam of ionized fuel particles (**deuterium** and/or **tritium**), the charged particles are trapped in the central region of the chamber and move in spiral paths along the axial lines of magnetic force. As they approach the ends of the chamber and encounter the stronger field their forward motion is stopped and some of them are reflected back into the central region. As the plasma particles move about in the chamber they make thousands of such traverses. If the level of magnetic field strength is progressively but slowly raised, the particles will gain energy in the process and the temperature of the plasma can thus be increased. This process is known as adiabatic compression. However, if the particles travel in too flat a spiral orbit, i.e., if they parallel the lines of the force too closely—they will tend to leak past the magnetic mirrors and escape confinement. Since the particles tend to move randomly and collide and interact with each other, it is inevitable that a fraction of the plasma will be lost in this manner.

In this concept it is the function of an ion source to deliver a high-current beam of plasma ions and electrons of moderately high energy (1-5 Kev). It remains for the magnetic mirror system to trap the already dense plasma and heat it to the **ignition temperature.** Before describing the experimental work being done on this concept, it should be noted that this is not the only way in which magnetic mirrors can be used. For example, one approach is to inject a weak beam of high-energy ions and electrons or neutral atoms (see **Alice**) and then use a magnetic-mirror system to build up the density of the plasma to practical values. (See **Molecular Ion Ignition Program**)

Program and Results. Since 1952, about a dozen experimental devices incorporating magnetic mirror confinement have been built in

U.S. laboratories (see summary table). Pending the availability of plasma sources capable of furnishing adequately dense beams in the 1-5 kilovolt range, most of the experimentation has been done in relatively small-scale apparatus with low-energy (tens of electron volts) injectors. In spite of difficulties caused by the presence of neutral particles and impurity ions in the plasma, it has been possible to confirm the theory of trapping and heating plasma in magnetic mirror systems. Ion temperatures above 35 million degrees have been achieved by adiabatic compression techniques, and re-

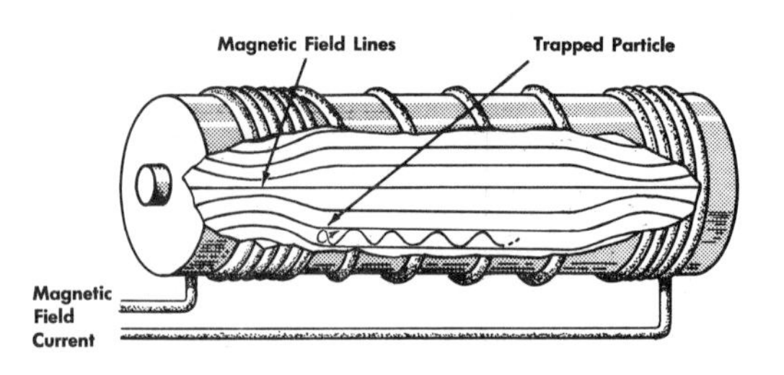

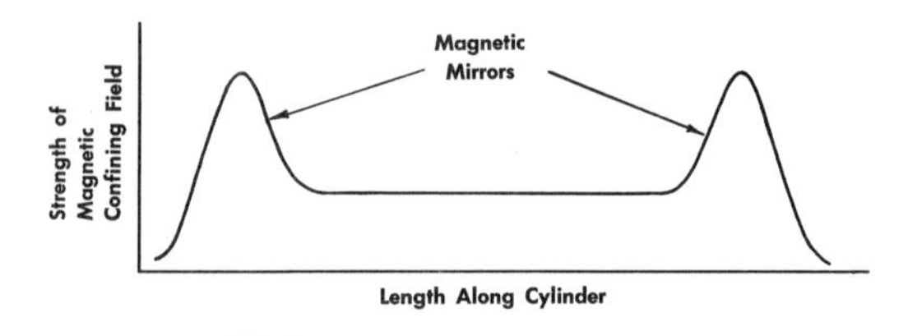

Fig. 110. Principle of magnetic-mirror confinement of plasma.

search has also been done on **shock heating,** i.e., the creation of shock waves prior to or during the period of adiabatic compression.

From the beginning, attention has been focused on developing adequate plasma sources, and plasma ion energies approaching 1 Kev are now becoming available. Steady progress is also being made on the problem of beam neutralization, i.e., delivery of beams in which the ions and electrons are in balance, and also on the problem of reducing the content of impurity ions.

A considerable number of experiments made in a variety of mirror systems have established the fact that, in agreement with theoretical expectations, plasmas can be confined for periods of several milliseconds. In one case, x-ray and electron signals persisted for 30 milliseconds, indicating that particles had been confined for that period of time. Although these confinement times are of interest, they are much less than those which would be required in a thermonuclear reactor.

It is of special significance that, in spite of early fears to the contrary, there has been no definite evidence so far of any gross instability of the plasma confined in a magnetic mirror geometry, such as is of common occurrence in **pinch** and **stellarator** systems. The stability has been ascribed to two circumstances in particular: (1) The magnetic field lines are "tied down" outside the plasma by means of conductors, and (2) no electric currents flow parallel to the field lines. The possibility still exists that plasma instabilities will develop at higher temperatures and plasma densities.

MAGNETIC PRESSURE

All devices conceived to date for achieving controlled-**fusion** reactions rely on the use of magnetic fields to confine an ionized gaseous fuel, or **plasma.** It is convenient to treat confinement force as magnetic pressure, defined as $\frac{B^2}{8\pi}$, where B is the magnetic field strength in **gauss.** As is seen, the magnetic pressure is proportional to the square of the intensity of the magnetic field. The units of magnetic pressure are ergs per cubic centimeter or, alternatively, dynes per square centimeter. (See **kinetic pressure, beta factor)**

MAGNETIC PUMPING

A method of heating the magnetically confined ionized gas, or **plasma,** in experimental controlled-**fusion** devices of the stellarator type. By successively increasing and decreasing the strength of the magnetic field in rapid oscillations in one or more sections of the stellarator tube, the plasma is compressed and expanded. The resulting pumping action preferentially imparts energy to the plasma ions and thereby rapidly raises the temperature of the plasma. (See **Stellarator Program)**

MAGNETIC MIRROR-TYPE EXPERIMENTAL MODELS

Model	*Date*	*Purpose and Description*	*Over-all Length (feet)*	*Discharge Tube Diameter (inches)*	*Peak Central Field (kilo-gauss)*	*Energy Input (joules)*	*Estimated Ion Temperatures (°K)*
Lawrence Radiation Laboratory (Livermore)							
Albedo	1953	To test magnetic mirror concept	10	6	3	—	—
Toy Top	1954	Very high compression ratio	1	1	200	5×10^4	—
Q-cumber	1954	To determine plasma diffusion rate across the mirrors	—	—	—	—	—
Table Top (I, II, and III)	1954	Single-stage compression	4	6	50	10^6	3×10^5–10^6
Toy Top	1954	Multiple compression stages	20	18 to 3	100	5×10^5	3.5×10^7 [1]
Felix	1957	Five to ten kev ion source	9	20	—	10^6	—
Alice	1962	To test high energy neutral atom injection and iron trapping	—	—	—	—	—
Los Alamos Scientific Laboratory							
Scylla	1958	To test shock-heating with magnetic compression	0.3	1	100	3×10^4	2.3×10^7 [2]
Ixion	1958	To test rotating plasma	3	10	10	5×10^3	2×10^5
Naval Research Laboratory							
Shock Mirror Device	1956	Magnetic compression and shock heating	1	1	500	3×10^5	10^6
Lawrence Radiation Laboratory (Berkeley)							
Homopolar	1956	To test production and confinement of rotating plasma	0.2	18	20	5×10^4	—
Ion Magnetron		To test rotating plasma under continuous operating conditions	—	—	8	—	—
Oak Ridge National Laboratory							
DCX-1	1957	To test feasibility of trapping and dissociating a high-energy molec-	6.6	—	10	—	3×10^9
DCX-2	1962	ular ion beam in a magnetic field	13	—	12	—	3×10^9

[1] Thermonuclear plasma believed to have been produced for 90 microseconds.
[2] Thermonuclear plasma believed to have been produced for a few microseconds.

MAGNETOHYDRODYNAMIC (MHD) CONVERSION

A technique for the conversion of heat to direct-current electricity by passing an ionized (and hence electrically conductive) gas through a magnetic field. Research is being conducted under private sponsorship to determine the feasibility of using MHD conversion in central station power generation from fossil fuels. There is interest in the possibility of using MHD conversion in nuclear power systems but such use must await the development of reactors capable of sustained operation at extremely high temperatures (see below).

Principles. Two basic principles are involved in MHD conversion: (1) the fact that high-temperature heat can induce sufficient ionization in a gas to make it electrically conductive; and (2) the fact that an electrical voltage is induced when an electrical conductor moves within a fixed magnetic field (Faraday's law).

In a conventional thermal power system such as a steam-electric power plant, heat energizes a working fluid which, in expanding through an energy conversion apparatus (turbogenerator), causes an armature to spin within a magnetic field, thereby generating electricity. There is thus an initial conversion of thermal to mechanical energy, followed by a conversion of mechanical to electrical energy. In an MHD system, heat energizes and also ionizes a working fluid which, in expanding through a magnetic field, generates electricity directly. No mechanical conversion is involved. While MHD conversion is thus a more direct method than the conventional process, it is not a true "direct energy conversion" process, since it employs a working fluid. (Examples of true direct conversion processes are thermoelectric conversion and thermionic conversion; see **direct energy conversion.**)

Energy losses in MHD systems occur due to internal electrical resistances in the apparatus; heat conduction through the walls; ionization inefficiencies (i.e., electrode losses); and inefficiencies in the magnetic field system (i.e., joule losses). These losses tend to be disproportionally high at low power levels. The indications are that a power output of the order of one megawatt (electrical) probably represents the minimum power level for an operable MHD system, and outputs of 100 megawatts or more appear necessary to achieve optimum conditions. Thus, MHD conversion is inherently best suited for large-scale power applications.

The critical parameter in MHD conversion is the electrical conductivity of the gaseous working fluid. Fortunately adequate conductivity can be achieved by ionizing a small fraction (~ 0.1%) of the gas atoms or molecules; also, gases which do not ionize readily can be "seeded" with small amounts of a readily ionized volatile material, such as cesium. Even so, extremely high operating temperatures are required. Taking into account ionization requirements and other relevant factors (such as practical limits of magnetic field strength), minimum gas inlet temperatures of the order of 2500°K (4000°F) appear to be required. The feasibility of MHD conversion hinges on the development of materials suitable for long-term operation at such temperatures.

The efficiency of energy conversion falls off rapidly with decreasing temperature, so that gas is discharged at temperatures of the order of 1800°K (2700°F). Assuming that provision is made to utilize this waste heat by means of some form of conventional regenerator, overall thermal efficiencies as high as 50 or 60% appear possible of achievement. If the waste heat is dissipated, the thermal efficiency would not be expected to exceed 25 or 30%.

Firms reportedly engaged in research on MHD conversion systems include Avco Manufacturing Corporation, General Electric Company, and Westinghouse Electric Corporation.

Nuclear Application Possibilities. Two schemes for the application of MHD conversion to nuclear power systems have been considered on a speculative basis. One is based on passing the hot coolant gas from an ultra high-temperature gas-cooled reactor through an external MHD converter. On leaving the converter, it would flow through a regenerator and then be pumped back into the reactor in a closed-cycle system. Reactors capable of operating at the requisite temperature levels are under development for use in nuclear rocket propulsion engines (see **Rover Project**); however, it should be added that the service requirements are not truly comparable since rocket engines are only required to operate for brief time intervals (seconds or minutes).

The other scheme that has been considered is entirely speculative, being based on incorporating the MHD converter within a gas-cooled reactor (so-called "cavity reactor" concept).

Until experience has been gained with MHD conversion using conventional fuels, the problems that would be introduced by use of a radioactive working fluid or by subjecting the conversion process to a reactor environment cannot be foreseen.

MAGNETOHYDRODYNAMICS

That branch of the physical sciences which deals with the motion of electrically conducting fluids interacting with a magnetic field; sometimes referred to as hydromagnetics. Magnetohydrodynamic phenomena are of particular importance in research on controlled **fusion,** which involves the behavior of **plasmas** (ionized gases) confined by a magnetic field (see **thermonuclear** power); and also in connection with the so-called "MHD" technique for converting heat to electrical energy. (See **magnetohydrodynamic conversion)**

Magnetohydrodynamics is based upon equations which govern the macroscopic behavior of the conducting fluid without taking into consideration the individual particle motions. The basic magnetohydrodynamics equations contain elements of both classical hydrodynamic theory and electromagnetic theory.

MAINTENANCE. See **direct maintenance, remote maintenance.**

MALI

Joined the **International Atomic Energy Agency** in 1960.

MANHATTAN PROJECT

The World War II atomic bomb project, directed by the Manhattan District, a special administrative unit established for the purpose by the U.S. Army Corps of Engineers.

Administrative Highlights. As has been chronicled in the official report on the project,* the first approach to the U.S. Government to stimulate interest in atomic energy development was made by G. B. Pegram (then Dean of Engineering of Columbia University) in March, 1939, the month following the hypothesis and confirmation of the discovery of nuclear fission (see **fission (nuclear)).** Dean Pegram telephoned the Navy Department to arrange a conference between representatives of the Navy and Enrico Fermi. Subsequently Leo Szilard and E. P. Wigner urged Albert Einstein to write to President Roosevelt and, supported by that letter, Alexander Sachs succeeded in interesting the President in the possibilities. The President appointed an "Advisory Committee on Uranium" under the chairmanship of L. J. Briggs (then Director of the National Bureau of Standards) to look into the problems involved. The first government "appropriation" for atomic energy purposes was made in February, 1940, and took the form of a $6000 transfer of funds from the Army to the Navy for the purchase of research materials.

In June, 1940, the Advisory Committee on Uranium was reconstituted as a subcommittee of the National Defense Research Committee (NDRC) of the Office of Scientific Research and Development (OSRD) headed by Vannevar Bush. A year later (July, 1941) the membership of the subcommittee, still chaired by Dr. Briggs, was broadened and it became known as the Uranium Section of NDRC or S-1 Committee or OSRD. In May, 1942, the committee was superseded by the OSRD S-1 Executive Committee, chaired by J. B. Conant.

On June 18, 1942, Colonel J. C. Marshall of the U.S. Army Corps of Engineers was charged with forming a new engineer district (the Manhattan District) to launch a full-scale development effort. The Manhattan District was officially established on August 13, 1942. The security code, "DSM Project" (Development of Substitute Materials), was adopted to identify its work. On September 17, 1942, Major (then Brigadier) General Leslie R. Groves was placed in charge of the Manhattan District. The Manhattan District immediately took over procurement and engineering responsibilities for the project and on May 1,

* "Atomic Energy for Military Purposes," commonly referred to as the "Smyth Report" after its author, Henry DeWolf Smyth, at the time Chairman, Department of Physics, Princeton University and consultant to the Manhattan District. A more detailed account of the project is to be found in Volume I of the official history of the U.S. Atomic Energy Commission. This volume is entitled "The New World" and was published in 1962 by the Pennsylvania State University Press.

1943, took over the responsibility for research and development. Transfer of the latter responsibility marked the end of the formal connection of OSRD with the project. Total appropriations for the project under the aegis of NDRC and OSRD amounted to **$15.1** million.

General Groves directed the project to a successful conclusion and remained in charge until responsibility was transferred to the civilian U.S. Atomic Energy Commission on January 1, 1947 (see **legislation, federal**). His deputy was Brigadier General T. F. Farrell. Appropriations under the Manhattan District amounted to **$2,218.3** million, bringing the total pre-AEC investment to **$2,233.4** million. (See **Atomic Energy Commission–Financial Data**)

Project Highlights. There were four principal lines of activity: uranium supply; uranium-235 production, plutonium production, and bomb development.

Uranium Supply. The principal supplies of uranium ore came from the Shinkolobwe mine of Union Miniere du Haut Katanga in the Belgian Congo, and from the Canadian Radium and Uranium Company at Port Radium, Canada. Various organizations worked on the problems of processing the ore into acceptably pure metal and other forms required by the project. They included E. I. duPont de Nemours & Company, Harshaw Chemical Company, a group at Iowa State College (now Ames Laboratory), Mallinckrodt Chemical Works, Metal Hydrides Company, the National Bureau of Standards, Union Carbide and Carbon Corporation, and Westinghouse Electric Corporation. The processes ultimately used for metal production were developed by the Ames group and reduced to practice by Mallinckrodt. DuPont and Harshaw produced the uranium feed materials used in the uranium isotope separation plants (see below).

Uranium-235 Production. The isotope separation methods used or seriously considered for use in the production of uranium-235 were **electromagnetic separation, thermal diffusion, gaseous diffusion,** and the **gas centrifuge process.**

Research on the electromagnetic method centered at the Radiation Laboratory of the University of California at Berkeley (now the E. O. Lawrence Radiation Laboratory) under the direction of E. O. Lawrence. Construction of a large-scale production plant (the **Y-12** plant) began at Oak Ridge * in the spring of **1943**, and portions of the plant were placed in operation that winter. The plant was constructed by Stone & Webster, Inc. and operated by Tennessee Eastman Company. The plant operated initially on uranium of normal isotopic concentration, and later on material partially enriched by other methods.

Research on the thermal diffusion method was conducted at the Naval Research Laboratory under the direction of P. H. Abelson. A production facility (the S-50 Plant) was constructed at Oak Ridge by H. K. Ferguson Company and operated by Fercleve Corporation. This plant was built on a crash basis in approximately six months' time to provide an interim means of enriching the feed to Y-12. As the gaseous diffusion plant came into production (see below), S-50 gradually was shut down.

Research on the gaseous diffusion process centered at the "SAM" (Substitute Alloy Material) Laboratory of Columbia University under the direction of Harold C. Urey and John R. Dunning, and in the laboratories of the Kellex Corporation, a special subsidiary of M. W. Kellogg Company established under the direction of P. C. Keith and A. L. Baker to engineer the production facilities. Various other laboratories made important contributions, notably in connection with the development of "barrier material"—the porous membrane used in the diffusion process. Construction of large-scale production (the K-25 Plant) began at Oak Ridge in mid-**1943**, and operations were started early in **1945**. The construction contractor was J. A. Jones Con-

* A 70-mile tract of land on the Clinch River, about 30 miles west of Knoxville, had been selected in July, 1942, for what was known as the "Clinton Engineer Works." The town of Oak Ridge was constructed to provide housing for the permanent employees. Construction labor was housed primarily in temporary trailer camps.

struction Company; the operating contractor, Union Carbide and Carbon Chemicals Corporation. A notable accomplishment of this project was the completion of a 235,000-kilowatt power plant within 10 months of the decision to install such a facility. Also, K-27, a major addition to the main gaseous diffusion plant, was designed, built and placed into operation in six months' time.

Research on the gas centrifuge process centered at the University of Virginia under the direction of J. W. Beams. Pilot centrifuge units were built and operated by Westinghouse Electric Corporation. This method was considered as an alternative to gaseous diffusion and was abandoned late in 1942, when it appeared that the latter method offered greater promise of success.

Plutonium Production. The plutonium program involved the development of nuclear reactors for the production of plutonium by the **transmutation** of uranium-238, and the development of a chemical process for recovering the plutonium from the irradiated uranium. The research centered at the Metallurgical Laboratory,* an organization established for the purpose by the University of Chicago under the direction of A. H. Compton and S. K. Allison. The duPont Company was brought in at an early stage to engineer and operate the ultimate production facilities; their effort was headed by Crawford H. Greenewalt and Roger Williams.

A major breakthrough, not only for the plutonium program but also for atomic energy development generally, was the successful operation on December 2, 1942, of the first nuclear reactor (see **Chicago Pile No. 1).** This unit, built in a squash court underneath Chicago University's Stagg Field under the direction of Enrico Fermi and W. H. Zinn, established the feasibility of achieving and controlling a fission chain reaction.

A pilot plutonium production reactor (see **Oak Ridge Graphite Reactor)** and chemical separations facility were constructed at what was known as the Clinton Laboratory (X-10) at Oak Ridge. This installation was built by duPont and operated by the University of Chicago under the direction of M. D. Whitaker. The reactor began operation in November, 1943, and produced the first significant amounts (milligrams and later grams) of plutonium available up to that time. By the spring of 1944, successful performance of the chemical separations process had been demonstrated.

Large-scale plutonium production facilities were built and operated by duPont at Hanford, Washington (see **Hanford Works).** Construction of the first of three production reactors began in June, 1943, and reactor operation started in September, 1944. Three chemical separation plants were also built. (See **fuel reprocessing)**

Graphite was selected as the moderator material for the Hanford production reactors. Prior to that decision, steps had been taken to ensure a supply of heavy water for use as moderator if required (see **deuterium).** Also, a small heavy water-moderated reactor was built and operated to study the uranium-heavy water lattice. (See **Chicago Pile No. 3)**

Bomb Development. In November, 1942, Los Alamos, New Mexico, was selected as the site for a laboratory for weapons research (Los Alamos Scientific Laboratory). J. R. Oppenheimer, who had been directing theoretical studies of weapon design under the cognizance of the Metallurgical Laboratory, was placed in over-all charge. Laboratory groups were established for theoretical physics (H. Bethe), experimental nuclear physics (R. R. Wilson), chemistry and metallurgy (J. W. Kennedy and C. S. Smith), ordnance problems (Captain W. S. Parsons, U.S. Navy), explosives (G. B. Kistiakowsky), and bomb physics (R. F. Bacher) and advanced development (E. Fermi).

On July 16, 1945, the first atomic bomb was successfully tested in a remote section of Alamogordo Air Base, 120 miles southeast of Albuquerque. The event, which bore the code designation, "Trinity," occurred at 5:30 A.M. The bomb, mounted on a steel tower, was as-

* Predecessor to Argonne National Laboratory.

sembled by R. F. Bacher; K. T. Bainbridge supervised the detonation.

Foreign Contributions. The United States exchanged information throughout the Manhattan Project with the United Kingdom and with a group of British, Canadian and French scientists working at Chalk River in Canada. Belgium and Canada supplied uranium ore. Individuals from overseas, such as J. Chadwick of the United Kingdom and Niels Bohr of Denmark, devoted considerable time to the research at Los Alamos.

Start of National Laboratories. The Manhattan District established the policy, also adopted by the U.S. Atomic Energy Commission, of contracting with university and industrial organizations for research and development as well as for the engineering, construction and operation of plant facilities. As the Manhattan Project drew to a close, the District took steps to ensure continuity of the major research and development organizations that had been created and thereby laid the foundations for the present system of national laboratories. In addition to converting the Metallurgical Laboratory (now Argonne National Laboratory), Clinton Laboratory (now Oak Ridge National Laboratory), the Radiation Laboratory at Berkeley (now the E. O. Lawrence Radiation Laboratory), and Los Alamos Scientific Laboratory from a wartime to a peacetime footing, plans were made for the creation of a new research center, Brookhaven National Laboratory, at Upton, New York.

MANIAC

The name given a series of high-speed electronic computers developed and used at Los Alamos Scientific Laboratory. MANIAC I and II are in operation; MANIAC III is in the design stage. The name derives from *M*athematical *A*nalyzer, *N*umerical *I*ntegrator *a*nd *C*alculator.

MANIPULATORS

Mechanical devices designed to enable an operator behind a biological shield to handle and perform operations with highly radioactive materials.

Some types of manipulators can perform all operations that can be done by hand with precision and dexterity and, in addition, have greater mechanical strength and power and can operate under extreme temperatures or

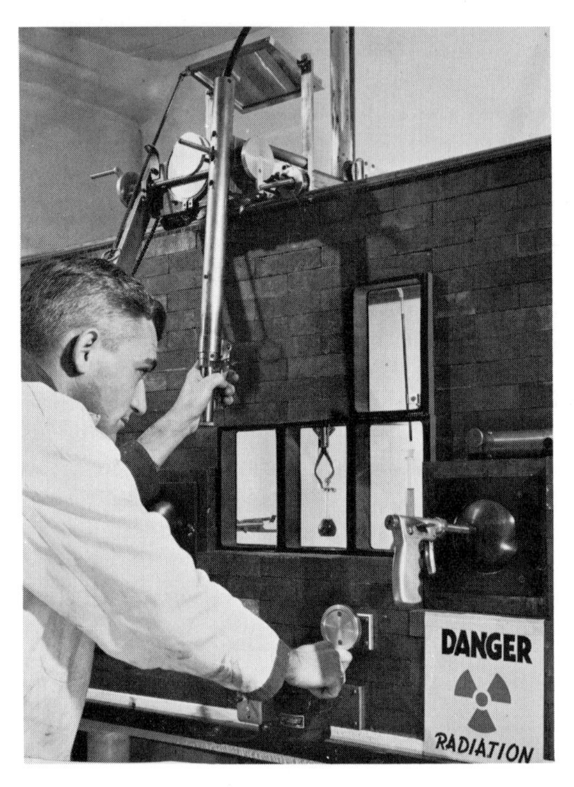

Fig. 111. Manipulator being used to handle radioactive materials behind shielding wall of lead bricks and special lead glass. (*Courtesy of Brookhaven National Laboratory*)

pressure conditions. Three basic types of manipulators are used:

1. Master-slave manipulator: A device with two similar arms, one for performing work within the hot cell and the other for control outside the cell. The normal motions of the hand are reproduced effectively by efficient mechanical linkages, or in more recent equipment, by force-reflecting positional servomechanisms by means of which force reacting on the slave arm is reflected back and "felt" by the master arm. Operation of this type of manipulator is easy to learn and the

operator can quickly achieve considerable dexterity in its use.

2. Rectilinear-electric manipulator: This device is mounted on a bridge on rails with a carriage providing horizontal motion and a vertical boom to provide vertical motion. The lower end of the boom is equipped with a wrist joint giving at least three degrees of freedom and with gripping tongs. The total number of motions may total seven or more, each driven by an electric motor controlled by switches singly or in combination. Units may be designed to handle loads up to several hundred pounds. Since this type of manipulator does not have a feedback circuit, it must be carefully controlled to avoid damaging the apparatus being handled.

3. Ball-joint manipulator: This device passes through a wall-mounted shielding ball and is usually in the form of a shaft with tongs on one end and a handle on the other. The shaft, which passes through the ball, is free to slide along its own axis. Although it may be equipped with articulated wrist joints, the manipulator is limited in dexterity, size, and range of action.

MARITIME GAS-COOLED REACTOR (MGCR) PROJECT

A program of research and development on an advanced gas-cooled reactor and closed-cycle gas turbine for maritime nuclear propulsion applications. The project, jointly sponsored by the U.S. Atomic Energy Commission and the U.S. Maritime Administration, is being conducted by General Atomic, a division of General Dynamics Corporation. The concept, which shows promise for central station power applications as well as maritime applications, is based on the use of metal-clad ceramic fuel elements in a helium-cooled, beryllium-oxide-moderated system.

The MGCR was initiated in 1958. A facility for critical experiments, located at General Atomic's laboratory near San Diego, California was completed and placed in operation in August, 1960. An experimental reactor, known as the Experimental Beryllium Oxide Reactor (EBOR) and located at the National Reactor Testing Station, is scheduled to be in operation in 1963. This facility will have a rated power output of approximately 10 megawatts (thermal). It will be used to test BeO-moderated cores and other reactor components at elevated temperatures and pressures and thereby provide data needed for the design of a prototype propulsion plant. (See **Maritime Reactors Program**)

MARITIME REACTORS PROGRAM

A program, jointly sponsored by the U.S. Atomic Energy Commission and the U.S. Maritime Administration, aimed at demonstrating the safety and reliability of the use of nuclear propulsion systems in merchant ships and at reducing the capital and operating costs of such systems to encourage commercial application. The program was initiated in 1956, and has included the following major lines of activity: (1) Construction of a government-owned demonstration ship powered by a pressurized water reactor plant (see NS ***Savannah***). (2) Development of an advanced gas-cooled reactor for use in a closed-cycle gas turbine marine propulsion system (see **Maritime Gas-Cooled Reactor Project**). (3) Design studies of propulsion systems for nuclear tankers based on proven reactor concepts—namely, direct and indirect-cycle boiling water and pressurized water. (4) Economic studies of various marine propulsion applications.

Through mid-1960, AEC's cumulative research and development expenditures under this program totalled approximately $15 million, exclusive of capital costs (also ~ $15 million). The principal contractors have been the Babcock & Wilcox Company, supplier of the propulsion system for the NS *Savannah*; New York Shipbuilding Corporation, constructor of the NS *Savannah*; and General Atomic Division of General Dynamics Corporation, contractor for the MGCR Project. In addition, Combustion Engineering Company, General Electric Company and Westinghouse Corporation have conducted reactor design studies

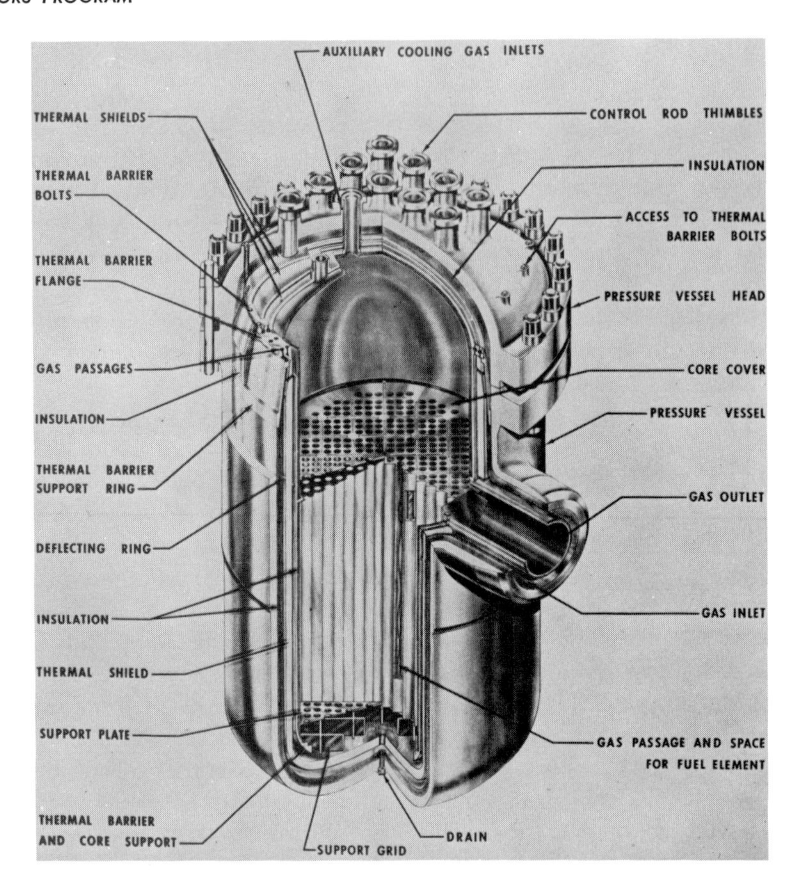

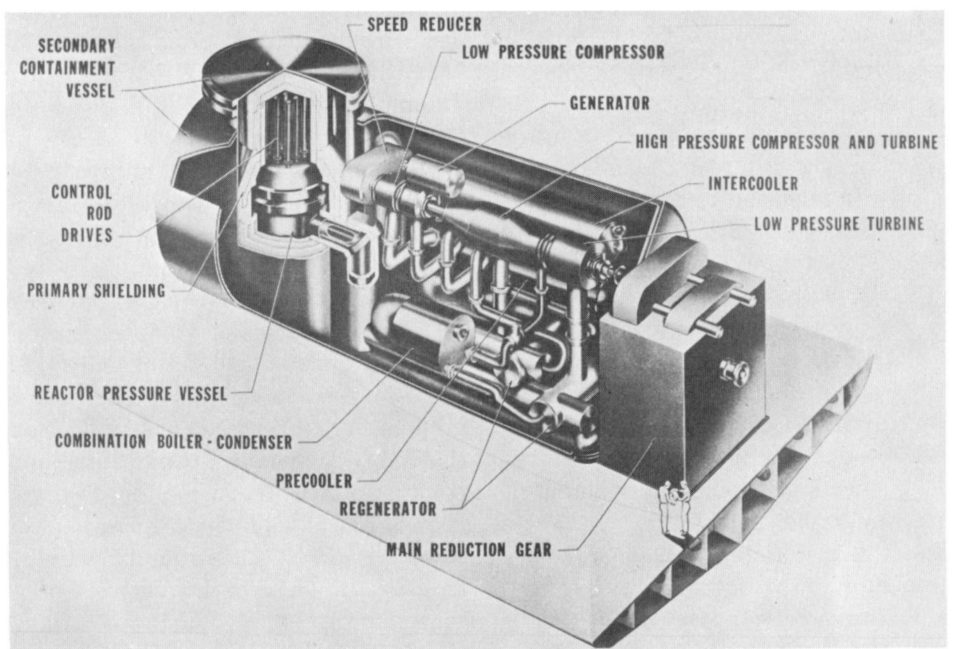

Fig. 112. Maritime Gas-Cooled Reactor project. Above, conceptual drawing of MGCR power plant. Below, conceptual drawing of reactor core. (*Courtesy of General Atomic*)

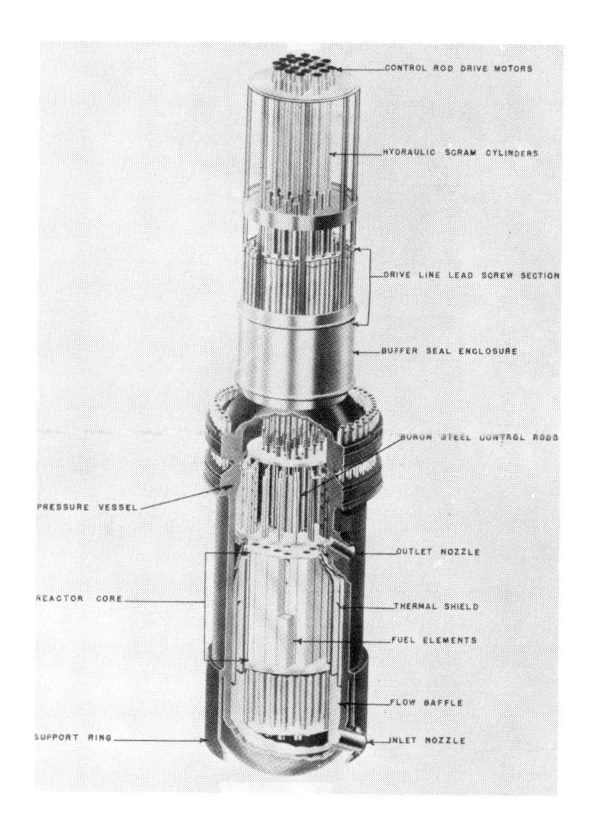

Fig. 113. The NS *Savannah.* Above, the ship shortly after launching. Below, diagram of reactor core. (*Courtesy of Babcock & Wilcox Co.*)

for nuclear tanker applications; and the Atomic Energy Division of American Radiator and Standard Sanitary Corporation has conducted an extensive economic study.

The technical feasibility of nuclear ship propulsion was first demonstrated by the submarine, U.S.S. *Nautilus* in 1955 (see **Naval Reactors Program**). The first nonmilitary ship to go to sea under nuclear power was the Russian icebreaker, *Lenin*, which began sea trials in the fall of 1959 (see **Soviet Union**). The second was the United States cargo-passenger vessel, NS *Savannah*, which began sea trials in March, 1962.

Commercial use of nuclear ship propulsion is expected to develop as soon as competitive costs can be achieved and reliability and safety have been demonstrated. In the latter connection, the performance of nuclear-powered Naval vessels has provided convincing evidence of reliability and safety. However, the commercial use of nuclear ship propulsion introduces considerations not involved in military operations, e.g., the need for international insurance and liability agreements and for an agreed policy on the entry of nuclear ships into commercial harbors. Also, Naval reactors would not be economical in commercial applications, hence the experience with these reactors is not entirely applicable.

The economic attraction of marine nuclear propulsion stems primarily from the compactness of nuclear fuel, which conserves cargo space, and from the ability of nuclear ships to operate at high power for long periods without refueling, which is a potentially important operational advantage. The economic status of marine nuclear propulsion is similar to that of central station nuclear power generation, i.e., noncompetitive at present, primarily because of high capital costs. It follows that the applications most likely to provide early commercial opportunities are those in which the most favorable distribution of fixed charges can be realized. Here the important considerations are (1) large ships (to take advantage of economies of scale, especially in reactor construction); (2) fast ships and long voyages (to maximize the "load factor"); and (3) bulk cargoes (to minimize in-port operations). On this basis, the most promising applications (in descending order) appear to be (1) bulk-cargo vessels (tankers and ore carriers); (2) high-speed passenger liners, and (3) passenger-cargo ships.

MASS-ENERGY EQUIVALENCE

The equivalence of a quantity of mass m and a quantity of energy E, the quantities being related by the mass-energy relation, $E = mc^2$. The relation is a consequence of Einstein's special (or restricted) theory of relativity, and has been verified experimentally by measurements of mass and energy in nuclear reactions. The factor c^2, the square of the speed of light in vacuum, may be regarded as the conversion factor relating units of mass and energy. The units used most often are:

$$1 \text{ atomic mass unit} = 1.66 \times 10^{-24} \text{ gm} = 931.16 \text{ Mev}$$

MASS NUMBER (A)

The number of protons and neutrons contained within the nucleus of an atom; it is the nearest whole number to the atomic weight of that atom.

MASS SPECTROGRAPH

An instrument for the determination of atomic masses. The design has the following essential features: The material to be analyzed is ionized in an ion source. The ions are deflected into curved paths by means of a magnetic of electrostatic field. Each path has a radius of curvature which depends on ratio of the ionic charge to the mass. If the deflected ions fall on a photographic plate a line is formed corresponding to each value of the charge-to-mass ratio. Comparison of the positions of the lines with those corresponding to ions of known standard substances makes it possible to determine the atomic masses.

MASS SPECTROMETER

A device similar to the **mass spectrograph** except that the ions corresponding to a given value of the charge-to-mass ratio are focused on an electrode and detected. This instrument provides a means of determining isotopic abundances. If the electrode is replaced by a suitable receiver the ions can be collected. A mixture of isotopes can be separated in principle by collecting the ions corresponding to different atomic masses in separate receivers, and this possibility forms the basis of the **electromagnetic separation** process.

MASSACHUSETTS INSTITUTE OF TECHNOLOGY REACTOR (MITR)

A heavy water-moderated research reactor located on the Institute's campus at Cambridge, Massachusetts. The reactor was designed by the MIT staff with ACF Industries as the principal contractor.* The installation includes a medical therapy facility. It is used for contract as well as Institute research.

* ACF's nuclear organization was subsequently acquired by Allis-Chalmers Manufacturing Company.

Type: Tank reactor. *Power rating*: 2000 thermal kilowatts. *Fuel*: MTR-type fuel elements. *Coolant*: D_2O. *Moderator*: D_2O. *Reflector*: Graphite. *Neutron flux*: Of the order of 10^{14}n/cm^{2}sec (maximum thermal). *Start-up*: 1958. (See **research and training reactors**)

MATERIALS TESTING REACTOR (MTR)

A large, general-purpose **test reactor** located at the National Reactor Testing Station and used primarily to study the effects of radiation on fuel, moderator and structural materials of interest to power reactor designers. It is also used for limited radioisotope production and for neutron and reactor physics experiments. The MTR was designed as a joint project of Oak Ridge and Argonne National Laboratories. The architect-engineer was Blaw-Knox Company, and the builder was The Fluor Corporation. The construction cost, including supporting experimental facilities and modifications made through 1958, was

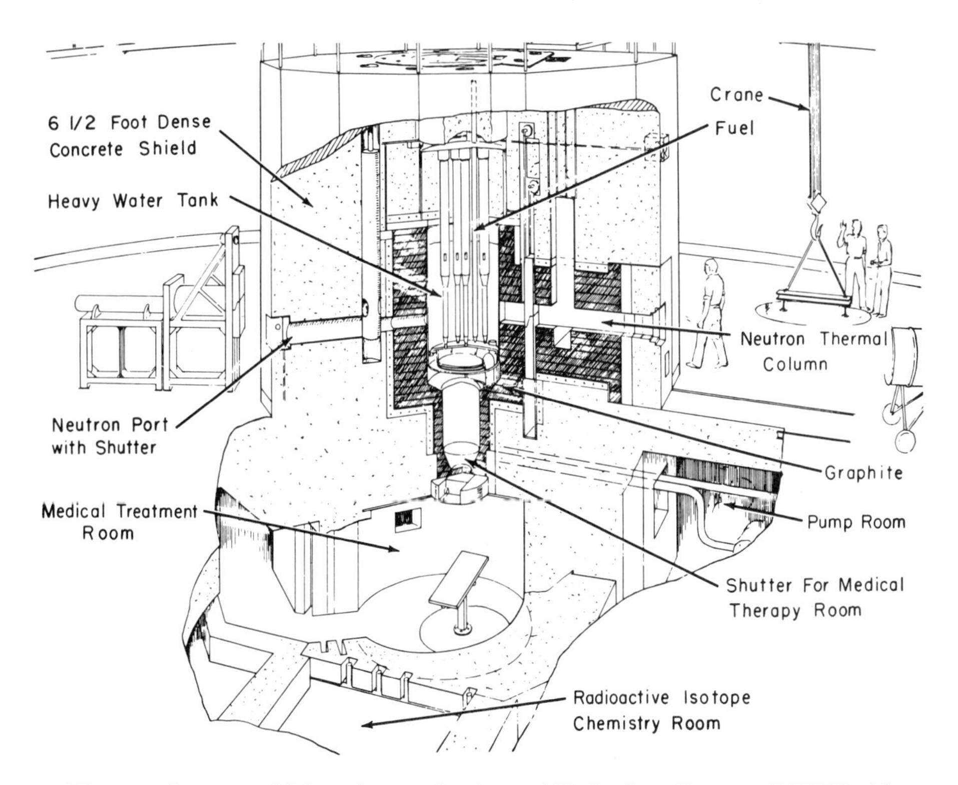

Fig. 114. Cutaway of Massachusetts Institute of Technology Reactor (MITR). (*Courtesy of Allis-Chalmers Manufacturing Co.*)

Fig. 115. General view of the Materials Testing Reactor (MTR). (*Courtesy of Phillips Petroleum Co.*)

~ $20 million. The MTR is operated for the U.S. Atomic Energy Commission by Phillips Petroleum Company. *Type*: Tank reactor. *Power rating*: 40,000 thermal kilowatts. *Fuel*: An individual fuel element consists of an assembly of aluminum-clad fuel plates fabricated of a highly enriched uranium-aluminum alloy. The isotopic enrichment of the uranium in the fuel alloy is 93.4%. The weight percent of aluminum in the fuel alloy is 18.8%. (Fuel elements of this general type have been widely used in research and test reactors and are commonly referred to as MTR-type fuel elements.) *Coolant*: H_2O. *Moderator*: H_2O. *Reflector*: Beryllium. *Neutron flux*: Maximum thermal-neutron flux, $\sim 5 \times 10^{14}$ n/cm^2 sec. Average thermal-neutron flux, $2 - 3 \times 10^{14}$ n/cm^2 sec.

MATTERHORN PROJECT

A term once used to denote the thermonuclear research program at the Forrestal Research Center, Princeton University. When it started in 1951, this project was primarily concerned with theoretical studies relating to hydrogen bomb development, but since 1954, it has been devoted entirely to research on controlled **fusion.** It was renamed the Plasma Physics Laboratory in early 1961. (See **Stellarator Program, thermonuclear power)**

MAXIMUM CREDIBLE INCIDENT

A term used in analyzing the safety characteristics of a nuclear reactor—specifically, an incident representing the upper limit of hazard that can be hypothesized, assuming an adverse combination of operating conditions resulting from equipment malfunction, maloperation, or other foreseeable causes. (See **Atomic Energy Commission—Licensing and Regulatory Procedure**)

MAXIMUM PERMISSIBLE CONCENTRATION (MPC)

The maximum concentration of radioactive material in air, water and food stuffs which, in the light of present knowledge, can be allowed without creating undue risks to human health. The criterion applied is that 50 years of inhalation or ingestion by the human system must not result in a **body burden** of radioactivity sufficient to produce a radiation dose in excess of the **maximum permissible dose.** Various factors must be taken into account in applying this criterion, including the rate of body uptake of the particular radionuclide, its **biological half-life,** the characteristics of the radiation emitted, and the **radiosensitivity** of the organ affected.

The MPC values recommended by the **National Committee on Radiation Protection and Measurements** (NCRP) are published in National Bureau of Standards Handbook No. 69, entitled "Maximum Permissible Body Burdens and Concentrations of Radionuclides in Air and Water for Occupational Exposure." The recently established **Federal Radiation Council** has proposed the term "Radioactivity Concentration Guide (RCG)" to take the place of "maximum permissible concentration" but has not yet developed a detailed RCG standard. (See discussion under **radiation protection standards and regulations**)

MAXIMUM PERMISSIBLE DOSE (MPD)

The maximum dose of ionizing radiation which, in the light of present knowledge, can be absorbed within a specified period of time without undue risk to human health. The MPD values recommended by the **National Committee on Radiation Protection and Measurements** (NCRP) are published in National Bureau of Standards Handbook No. 59, entitled "Permissible Dose from External Sources of Ionizing Radiation." The recently established **Federal Radiation Council** has essentially adopted the NCRP values but has introduced the term, "Radiation Protection Guide" to take the place of "maximum permissible dose." (See discussion under **radiation protection standards and regulations,** where will also be found a tabulation of RPG values.)

McKINNEY REPORTS

Two comprehensive survey reports prepared on behalf of the **Joint Committee on Atomic Energy** of the U.S. Congress under the direction of Robert McKinney, in private life editor and publisher of the Santa Fe *New Mexican.* The first was a two-volume report of the "Panel on the Impact of the Peaceful Uses of Atomic Energy," January, 1956. The second was a five-volume report, entitled, "Review of the International Atomic Policies and Programs of the United States," October, 1960.

MECHANICALLY SEALED MAIN COOLANT PUMPS.

See **pumps.**

MEDIAN LETHAL DOSE (MLD)

The dose of ionizing radiation required to kill, within a specified period of time following the event, 50% of the individuals in a statistical group of animals or organisms; also referred to as LD/50 (lethal dose 50%). When written MLD/30 or LD/50/30, the additional numeral defines the number of days in the specified period.

The median lethal dose for man is usually given as 400 $\pm$ 100 roentgens.

MEDIAN LETHAL TIME

The time required, following administration of a given lethal dose of ionizing radiation, for death of 50% of the individuals in a statistical group of animals or organisms.

MEDICAL ASPECTS OF ATOMIC ENERGY

This subject is discussed in three parts. The first part deals with the U.S. Atomic Energy Commission's biomedical research program, which is primarily concerned with protecting the health and safety of atomic energy workers and the general public against potential radiation hazards associated with civil and military uses of atomic energy. The second part deals with the uses of radioisotopes and radiation machines in medical diagnosis. The third deals with the use of radioisotopes and radiation machines in medical therapy.

AEC Biomedical Research Program. The AEC budget for life sciences research has trended gradually upward from just under $20 million in FY 1950 to $54 million in FY 1961.* The following notes illustrate the diversity of this activity:

Medical Research. Study of the long-term effects of cesium-137 and other biologically significant constituents of **radioactive fallout**; genetic and other studies relating to the delayed effects of chronic external radiation exposure (see **biological effects of ionizing radiation**); research on means of combatting radiation injury (notably the use of transplanted bone marrow and complex prophylactic agents as body preconditioners, and of chelating agents to remove radioactive substances once they have entered the body); toxicological research on new reactor materials; research on the radiobiological hazards associated with space travel; etc.

Biological Research. Basic research on the genetic effects of radiation at the cellular level; studies of the metabolism of particular radionuclides in mammalian biological systems; research on the possible hazards of radioactive contamination arising from reactor operations with particular reference to contamination of the human food chain; etc.

Environmental Sciences Research. Long-range studies of the total environment, including background radioactivity, at AEC installations; programs in which advantage is taken of radioactive fallout as a tool in studying ecological phenomena; sampling and analysis of radioactive weapon debris in residence in the stratosphere; meteorological and oceanographic research; etc.

* These figures include research relating to **agricultural applications of atomic energy.**

Medical Diagnosis. Medical diagnostic technique based on the use of radioisotopes and radiation machines include the following:

Dilution Method of Analysis. In this method a known quantity of a radioactive tracer is added to a biological system. After allowing time for the tracer to become evenly distributed, a sample is taken and the concentration of the tracer in the sample (determined by radioactivity count) affords a measure of the volume of the system. An example is the determination of blood volume in a patient by the injection of human serum albumin labeled with iodine-131 or chromium-51. **Deuterium** ("heavy hydrogen") and, more recently **tritium** ("heavy heavy hydrogen"), are used in an analogous fashion to determine body water volume.

Flow or Diffusion Measurement. By using sensitive radioactivity scanning instruments in combination with a radioactive tracer it is possible to determine rates of circulation or diffusion within the human system. An example is the use of human serum albumin labeled with iodine-131 to measure cardiac output. Another is the use of sodium-22 to measure the rate of circulation in the peripheral blood system (vascular flow).

Biochemical Placement. Certain substances are selectively absorbed by particular body organs. Iodine, for example, tends to concentrate in the thyroid. By injecting iodine-131 and measuring uptake in the thyroid (done by radioactivity count, usually after 6, 8 and 24 hours), it is possible to detect hyperthyroidism and other malfunctioning of the thyroid gland. Another example of the biochemical concentration technique is the use of vitamin B-12 labeled with cobalt-60 in the diagnosis of pernicious anemia.

Neutron Activation Analysis. This technique (see separate entry) is used in medical diagnosis as a means of estimating the concentration of particular elements in the body, especially **trace elements,** more accurately than is possible with conventional microchemical methods. It is applied by taking samples, e.g., of blood, and irradiating them in a nuclear reactor or by means of an external neutron source. It has been used to determine the presence and/or concentration of gold in the blood; sodium and potassium in the muscle; and cobalt, iron and zinc in other human tissues.

Radiography. Several radionuclides have been used as radiation sources for radiographic purposes in lieu of conventional x-ray machines. (See discussion under teletherapy below).

General. An indication of the scale on which clinical use is made of radioisotopes in diagnosis, and of the principal radioisotopes employed, is given in Table 1.

TABLE 1. NUMBER OF U.S. MEDICAL INSTITUTIONS LICENSED TO USE PARTICULAR RADIOIOSOTOPES [1] (1958 data)

Radioisotope	*Use*	*Number of Licensed Institutions*
Iodine-131	diagnosis	1313
Iodine-131	therapy	1112
Phosphorus-32	therapy	992
Cobalt-60	diagnosis	590
Gold-198	therapy	557
Chromium-51	diagnosis	425
Iron-59	diagnosis	154

[1] Adapted from "Radioisotopes in Medicine," Stanford Research Institute, December, 1959.

Medical Therapy. Medical therapeutic techniques based on the use of radioisotopes and radiation machines (other than conventional x-ray units) include the following:

Biochemical Placement. An extension of the biochemical placement diagnostic technique noted above is the use of the same selective absorption phenomenon as a means of applying local radiotherapy. Examples are the use of iodine-131 in treating hyperthyroidism, and in reducing thyroid activity (thereby easing body metabolic needs) in treating congestive heart failure. Contrary to popular belief, radioiodine therapy is not generally applicable to the treatment of thyroid tumor metastases—i.e., cancers originating in the thyroid but growing elsewhere in the body—which growths, in the majority of cases, are treated by surgery or external radiation (see teletherapy below).

Differential Turnover. Although an element may not concentrate strongly enough in an organ to permit the application of the biochemical placement technique, its rate of accumulation in or turnover by that organ may be sufficiently greater than in other organs or tissues to provide a basis for radiotherapy. An example of the so-called differential turnover technique is the use of phosphorus-32 in treating polycythemia vera, a disease of the bone marrow. (This disease is accompanied by greatly increased activity of the red blood-cell forming tissues, which in turn exhibit an abnormally high phosphorus turnover rate; hence the possibility of using phosphorus-32 as an effective radiotherapy tool.) Radiophosphorus has been used in an analogous manner in the treatment of chronic leukemia.

Physical Placement (Brachytherapy). The insertion into the body of radium "needles" or radon "seeds" has long been used as a means of applying local radiotherapy. Certain radionuclides permit the use of smaller sources for a given radiation dose and are in general safer to handle, and hence have replaced radium in some applications. Because of their small size, radionuclide needles or seeds are especially useful in interstitial (as differentiated from intracavity) implants. An example is the use of yttrium-90 pellets in destroying the pituitary gland as a palliative measure in cancer therapy. Radionuclides are also used to a limited degree in intracavity implants; for example, cancer of the bladder, which cannot be treated by surgery, has been treated by insertion of a small "balloon" containing a solution or suspension of sodium-24, bromine-82, cobalt-60, or other gamma-emitting radionuclides.

Colloid Treatment. The injection of colloidal suspensions of radionuclides has been used as a palliative measure in cancer ther-

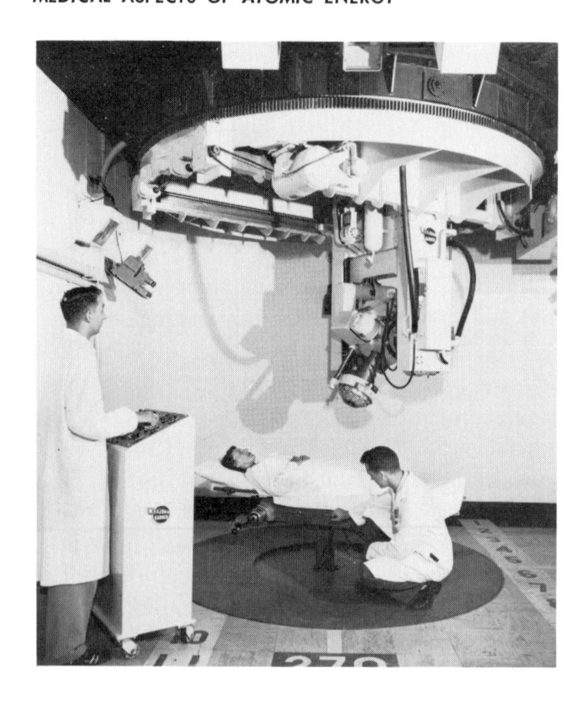

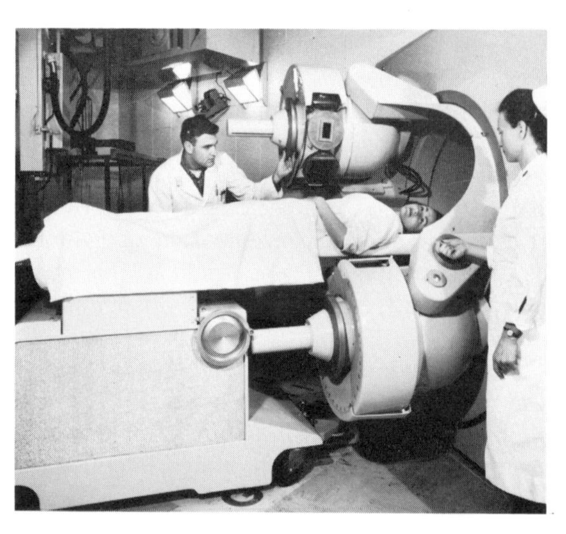

Fig. 116. Radionuclide teletherapy units. Top, rotational unit employing two cobalt-60 sources. Left, rotational unit employing cesium-137 source. (*Courtesy of Oak Ridge Institute of Nuclear Studies, Medical Division*)

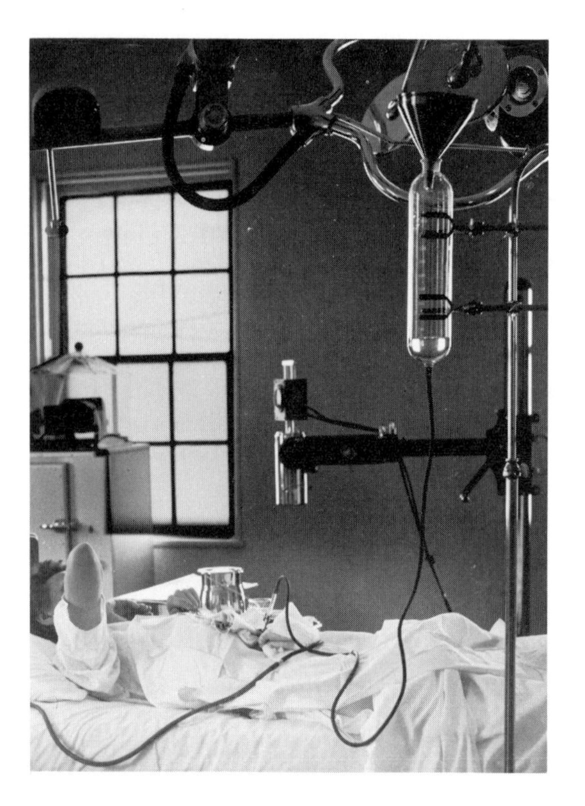

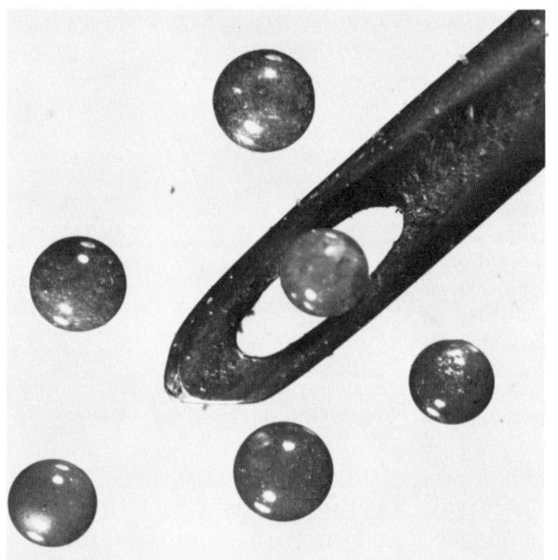

Fig. 117. Cancer therapy. Left, a solution of the short-lived radioisotope, chlorine-38, is being administered to a patient 15 minutes after removal of the isotope from a nuclear reactor. After six hours the material will have lost virtually all of its radioactivity. Above, tiny clay beads impregnated with radioactive yttrium are used for beta irradiation of deep-seated tumors by implant techniques. (The eye of a needle is shown for size comparison.) (*Courtesy of Brookhaven National Laboratory*)

apy. An example is the intracavity injection of gold-198 in colloidal form for the control of malignant liquid effusions.

Teletherapy. A major medical development is the use of radionuclides as an external radiation source in radiotherapy. The principal radionuclide so used is cobalt-60; however cesium-137 and thulium-170 have also been used. The first cobalt-60 teletherapy unit was designed in 1950. Since then some 200 units have been placed into service in U.S. hospitals, clinics, and medical offices.

Cobalt-60 emits 1.17 Mev and 1.33 Mev gamma rays and hence a cobalt-60 teletherapy unit is comparable to a "million volt" x-ray machine. The principal advantages of a cobalt-60 unit, relative to conventional x-ray apparatus, are (1) lack of dependence on a power supply; (2) dose penetration characteristics such that undesirable skin effects are materially reduced; and (3) dose absorption characteristics such that there is little bone and cartilage involvement. The principal disadvantages are (1) higher room shielding costs and (2) the need to replenish the cobalt-60 periodically to compensate for radioactive decay. (The radioactive **half-life** of cobalt-60 is 5.2 years, which corresponds to a loss in source intensity of about 1.1% per month.) Cobalt-60 teletherapy units are especially suited to the treatment of deep-seated tumors or tumors adjacent to bone or cartilage.

Cobalt-60 teletherapy units have been built with sources ranging in size from 30-3000 curies; the average, which has been trending upward, is a little under 1500 curies. They are available from a number of commercial suppliers. Following is a rough indication of the cost factors associated with a unit of average size (i.e., ~ 1500 curies):

Capital Costs:	
Cost of unit	$65,000
Cost of auxiliary equipment	7,500
Cost of installation	15,000
	$80–90,000

Operating Costs:	
Heavy use	$2–3 per treatment
Light use	~$10 per treatment

Use of Nuclear Reactors. The principal medical interest in nuclear reactors (apart from their service in producing radioisotopes for medical purposes) is in connection with the treatment of certain brain cancers (see **neutron capture therapy**). The first reactor tailored expressly for medical use is the recently completed **Brookhaven Medical Research Reactor,** which is designed to facilitate neutron capture therapy and to supply short-lived isotopes for biomedical research needs; however, other reactors, such as the **Massachusetts Institute of Technology Reactor,** are equipped with auxiliary biomedical research facilities.

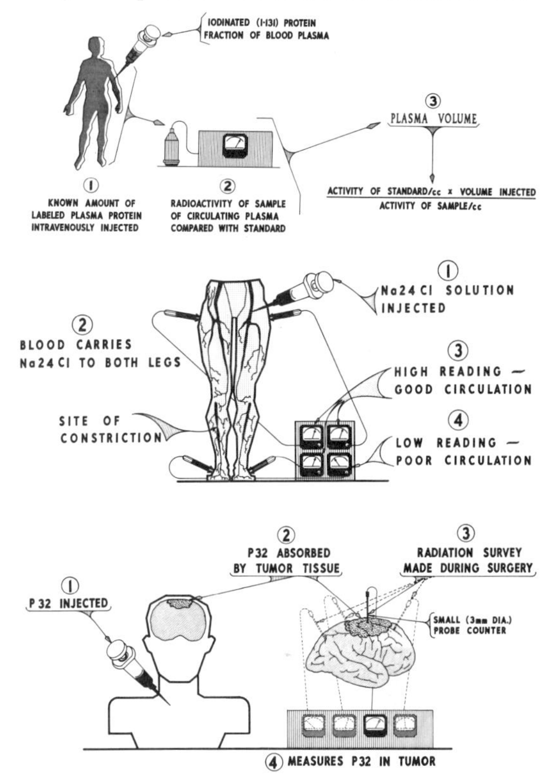

Fig. 118. Examples of the use of radioisotopes in medical diagnosis. Top, injection of radioiodine to determine blood plasma volume: Center, injection of radiosodium to determine quality of blood circulation. Bottom, injection of radiophosphorus to determine extent of brain tumor. (*Courtesy of USAEC*)

Use of Accelerators. **Particle accelerators** (cyclotrons, synchrotrons, linear accelerators, etc.) provide a flexible source of radiation for

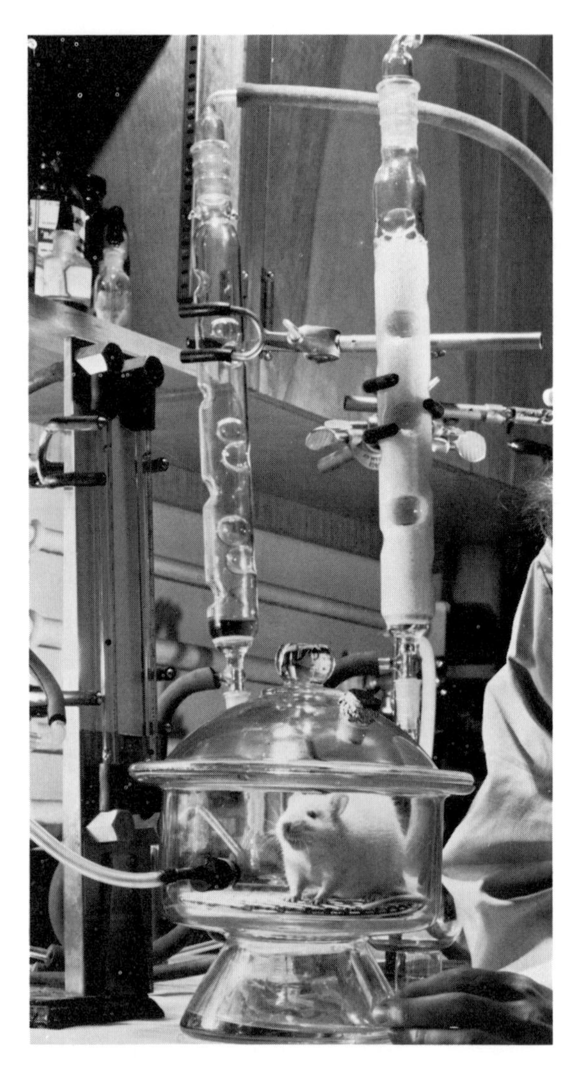

Fig. 119. Basic research in biochemistry. Here a white rat is being fed by stomach tube a fatty substance labeled with carbon-14. The concentration of carbon-14 in the carbon dioxide exhaled by the animal affords a measure of the rate of body metabolism of lipides (fats) from recently digested food relative to that from lipide deposits accumulated in body tissue. (*Courtesy of Brookhaven National Laboratory*)

medical purposes in that the particle energies can be adjusted to provide the desired depth of penetration. Also, the beams can be narrowly collimated and directed at very small target areas or, by scanning techniques, they can be made to provide uniform irradiation of relatively large areas. For these reasons accelerators are widely used in biomedical research, and are beginning to be used in medical therapy. An example of therapeutic use is the palliative treatment of patients with advanced metastatic cancer of the breast.

MEGATON (TNT EQUIVALENT)

A unit used to express the **yield** of large nuclear weapons. Thus, a 1-megaton weapon is one which will produce an amount of energy corresponding to that produced by 1 million tons of TNT ($\sim 1 \times 10^{15}$ calories).

MEGAWATT

1,000,000 watts, or 1000 kilowatts.

MEGAWATT-DAY

24,000 kilowatt-hours. When used in context with fuel **burn-up** in a nuclear reactor, megawatt-day refers to heat generated rather than electricity produced. (See **megawatt-days per ton**)

MEGAWATT-DAYS PER TON

A unit used to express fuel **burn-up** in a nuclear reactor—specifically, the number of **megawatt-days** of heat generated per metric ton of fuel over its lifetime in the reactor.

Some confusion in the use of the term arises from the fact that it is sometimes based on short tons (2000 pounds). The base is usually indicated; if not, a metric-ton base should be assumed. The abbreviation is MWD/tonne, which is usually written MWD/ton.

MENDELEVIUM

Element No. 101 (symbol, Mv), first identified in 1955, by A. Ghiorso, B. G. Harvey, G. R. Choppin, S. G. Thompson and G. T. Seaborg at the E. O. Lawrence Radiation Laboratory. The discovery followed particle accelerator experiments in which minute quantities of einsteinium-253 were bombarded with high-energy alpha particles. It was a notable feat of detection in that, at most, only a few atoms of the new element were formed. Named in honor of the Russian chemist and father of the periodic table of elements, Dmitri Mendeleyev, mendelevium is one of the eleven **transuranium elements** discovered in the past two decades.

MERCURY

Element No. 80 (symbol, Hg; atomic weight, 200.61), of some interest as a possible control material in thermal reactor systems and as a possible coolant for fast reactors (see **mercury cooled fast reactor concept**). Interest in the former application stems from the fact that mercury has a relatively high thermal neutron absorption cross section (380 barns). Interest in the latter is due principally to mercury's low melting point (it is liquid at room temperature) and its inertness to water. Mercury is of some historical interest in the reactor field, having served as the coolant in the first liquid metal-cooled reactor, namely, the fast reactor experiment known as "Clementine" conducted at Los Alamos Scientific Laboratory shortly after the close of World War II. (See **Los Alamos Fast Reactor**)

Two radioactive isotopes of mercury (Hg^{197} and Hg^{203}) have found medical usefulness, primarily in tracer work and chemotherapeutic studies.

MERCURY COOLED FAST REACTOR CONCEPT

An advanced power reactor concept being studied by the Atomic Energy Division of American Radiator and Standard Sanitary Corporation under an Atomic Energy Commission contract awarded in 1960. The advantages of mercury, relative to other liquid metal reactor coolants, are its low melting point (minus 40°F) and the fact that it is chemically inert to air and water. Its principal disadvantages are toxicity and high density (heavy pumping load). Also, it can only be considered for use in a fast reactor system due to its extremely high thermal neutron capture cross section (390 barns).

It is of interest to note in this connection that the first fast reactor ever operated was mercury cooled. (See **Los Alamos Fast Reactor**)

MESON

A general term for **elementary particles** with masses between that of the electron and that of the proton or neutron. There are several varieties: positive and negative mu-mesons, with rest mass equal to 206.8 electron masses; positive and negative pi-mesons with rest masses of 273.2 electron masses, and a neutral pi-meson with a rest mass of 264.4 electron masses; and K-mesons, positive, negative, and neutral with masses of about 1000 electron masses. Pi-mesons are thought to be associated with nuclear forces, while the role of mu-mesons and K-mesons is not yet understood, so that these are classified among the **"strange particles."**

All of the mesons are unstable, with very short half-lives, and with different decay schemes. The existence of mesons was postulated in 1935, before their discovery, as particles associated with a nuclear forcefield in a way analogous to that in which photons are associated with the electromagnetic field. The meson theory of nuclear forces has not yet been successful in accounting quantitatively for the properties of atomic nuclei.

Mu-mesons are of interest in connection with a catalytic fusion process. (See **fusion (nuclear)**)

METAL-TO-METAL EXTRACTION

One of several **pyrometallurgical** techniques of interest for possible use in **fuel reprocessing** in closed-cycle reactor fuel systems. Metal-to-metal extraction is based on the fact that uranium is immiscible in some liquid metals—notably magnesium and silver. One process under development involves the use of liquid magnesium to extract plutonium from irradiated uranium blanket material. The plutonium is then recovered from the magnesium phase and simultaneously partly freed of fission product contamination by distillation. Another potential application of magnesium extraction is in the recovery of uranium-233 from irradiated thorium blanket material. In this case the thorium readily enters the magnesium phase, leaving behind the uranium-233. The two phases stratify if held quiescent and can readily be separated. Supplementary processing is required to retrieve the thorium from the magnesium phase and to decontaminate the recovered materials. Other process studies are directed toward the use of silver extraction in the reprocessing of irradiated core materials.

Experimental studies of metal-to-metal extraction have been conducted at Argonne National Laboratory, Ames Laboratory, and Atomic International Division of North American Aviation Company.

METAL-WATER REACTIONS

In reactor technology, explosive chemical reactions which may occur in the event of a core meltdown in a water-cooled reactor. When one or more fuel elements become so overheated as to melt, reactions between the fuel cladding and water, or between liberated hydrogen and oxygen, are theoretically possible. Metal-water reaction phenomena are not well understood. When reactions have occurred the energy release has generally been less than would have been expected from theoretical calculations. Pending better understanding, allowance is made in the design of reactor safeguard features for the maximum possible release of chemical as well as nuclear energy.

In a different category is the familiar reaction associated with sodium-water systems which can occur at any temperature. Inleakage of air into such systems can result in a violent explosion arising from the following reactions:

$$2Na + H_2O \longrightarrow NaOH + H_2$$
$$2H_2 + O_2 \longrightarrow 2H_2O$$

It is the latter reaction which accounts for the explosive energy release, not the reaction between sodium and water *per se*; hence in the absence of air, sodium and water do not present a problem. The H_2-O_2 reaction represents a potential hazard in nuclear power plants in which sodium (or a sodium-potassium mixture) is used as the heat-exchange medium. (See **sodium-graphite reactors, fast breeder reactors.**) Where this is the case, two precautions are currently taken in the design of the steam generation portion of the plant:

1. An intermediate coolant loop is placed between the primary (i.e., reactor) loop and the steam generator, thereby avoiding the presence of radioactive sodium in the steam generator and the complications radioactivity would introduce in the event of an explosion.
2. Either double-walled tube construction or "once through" flow of the sodium is used in the steam generator to minimize the possibility of sodium-water contact.

In the latter connection, it should be added that the solid reaction products from the sodium-water reaction are effective in plugging leaks and hence act to forestall air inleakage.

METEOROLOGY

Meteorological studies are conducted in the atomic energy field to provide information needed for the safe release, by dilution and dispersion, of radioactive gases from certain atomic energy operations (see **radioactive waste disposal**), and also in connection with the problem of **radioactive fallout** from weapons tests. The U.S. Weather Bureau and other federal agencies cooperate with the U.S. Atomic Energy Commission in these studies.

Applications made to the AEC for a license to construct a nuclear power facility must be accompanied by sufficient meteorological and other environmental data to permit an evaluation of the suitability of the proposed site. (See **Atomic Energy Commission—Licensing and Regulatory Procedure**; also see discussion of site requirements under **nuclear power economics**) (Fig. 120)

MEV

Shorthand expression for million **electron volts**; may be written mev, or Mev.

Fig. 120. Meteorological measurements. Here smoke released from three different levels of Brookhaven meteorological tower provides visual indication of wind currents. Periodic "smoke runs" are made to check atmospheric conditions bearing on operation of the air-cooled Brookhaven Graphite Research Reactor. (*Courtesy of Brookhaven National Laboratory*)

MEXICO

The Comision Nacional de Energia Nuclear, Mexico City, is the agency responsible for atomic matters. Mexico conducts limited uranium mining operations to provide material for an experimental ore processing plant. A program of uranium exploration is in progress. Other atomic energy activity has principally been in radioisotope training and research, and in nuclear physics. Plans for the immediate future include the initiation of a program of research on food irradiation at the University of Veracruz, and the construction of a subcritical reactor assembly for training purposes at the National University of Mexico. Mexico is a member of the **International Atomic Energy Agency** and the **Inter-American Nuclear Energy Commission.**

MIDWESTERN UNIVERSITIES REASEARCH ASSOCIATION (MURA)

A cooperative association established by 15 midwestern universities for research in high-energy accelerators and, under AEC sponsorship, currently conducting theoretical and experimental studies to determine the feasibility of constructing a **fixed-field alternating gradient synchrotron.** Headquarters of MURA are at Madison, Wisconsin. The participating institutions are: the Universities of Chicago, Illinois, Wisconsin; Iowa State College; and Michigan State, Northwestern, Notre Dame, Ohio State, Purdue and Washington (St. Louis, Missouri) Universities.

MILITARY APPLICATIONS OF ATOMIC ENERGY

The development of military applications of atomic energy is a joint activity of the U.S. Atomic Energy Commission and the Department of Defense (DOD). Military requirements, both in terms of the type and number of weapon systems needed, originate with the respective Armed Services. The AEC is responsible for producing the necessary amounts and kinds of special nuclear materials, and for developing and proof-testing nuclear portions of the specified weapon systems, e.g., the warhead for a rocket, and obtains its own funds for these purposes via congressional appropriations. The non-nuclear portions, e.g., the rocket proper, are developed and manufactured under direct DOD control and with DOD funds.

Nuclear Weapons. The AEC is required by law to maintain a separate division, known as the Division of Military Application (DMA), to handle all nuclear weapons activity. A Military Liaison Committee, also required by law, represents the Department of Defense in the coordination of nuclear weapons activity.

The Military Liaison Committee is comprised of a chairman appointed by the President and representatives of the Departments of Army, Navy and Air Force appointed by the secretaries of these departments.

Information on or relating to nuclear weapons is covered in this book under the following principal headings: **weapons; weapons phenomenology; weapons effects; weapons testing; weapons test detection**; and **radioactive fallout.**

Military Reactor Programs. Other AEC activity relating to military requirements comes under the Aircraft, Army and Naval Reactors Branches of the Division of Reactor Development. These branches act in a dual capacity; they act on behalf of AEC in matters relating to the development of the nuclear portions of military reactor systems, and on behalf of DOD in matters relating to the non-nuclear portions. They thus handle integrated system development programs which are funded in part by the AEC and in part by DOD. For information on current military reactor activities, see **Army Nuclear Power Program, Naval Reactors Program,** and **Pluto Project** (ram-jet propulsion). Also see **Aircraft Nuclear Propulsion Program.**

Certain activities initiated by the Aircraft Reactors Branch are no longer administered as military programs. They include the **Rover Project** (rocket propulsion) and the **SNAP Program** (auxiliary power systems for specialized applications).

MILITARY COMPACT REACTOR (MCR) PROJECT

A project to develop the prototype for an "MM" (Mobile Medium Powerplant) class of power reactors for a variety of military applications; part of the **Army Nuclear Power Program.**

In 1960-1961, under a prime contract with the U.S. Atomic Energy Commission, United Nuclear Corporation * developed a preliminary design for a mobile, light-weight nuclear power plant with an output of 2-3 megawatts (electrical). The design was based on the concept of a liquid metal-cooled reactor coupled, by the primary coolant loop, to an open-cycle power conversion system. The Allison Division of General Motors Corporation designed the power conversion equipment under subcontract to United Nuclear Corporation.

In June, 1962, the AEC entered negotiations with the two companies for the actual development of the MCR, based on the preliminary design concepts and keyed to a power output of 3 megawatts (electrical). This work will be jointly sponsored by the AEC and the U.S. Army Corps of Engineers.

* Then known as Nuclear Development Associates (NDA).

MILITARY LIAISON COMMITTEE (MLC)

A statutory committee through which the U.S. Atomic Energy Commission maintains liaison with the Department of Defense on all matters relating to nuclear weapons or other military applications of atomic energy.

The membership includes a chairman appointed by the President, by and with the advice of the Senate, and equal representation (two members at present) from the Departments of Army, Navy, and Air Force. Matters of major interest to the Department of Defense include the development, manufacture, use, and storage of nuclear weapons; the allocation of **special nuclear material** for military research; and the control of information relating to the manufacture or utilization of nuclear weapons. Membership listed in Appendix D.

MILLING. See **uranium milling.**

MINING. See **uranium mining.**

MIXER-SETTLER

One of three principal types of liquid-liquid contact equipment used in **solvent extraction** systems, the others being **pulse columns** and **packed columns.** An advantage cited for mixer-settlers, relative to pulse or packed columns, is that they permit a more compact plant layout and thereby reduce construction costs.

The so-called "pump-mix" mixer-settler developed for use in fuel reprocessing applications is a rectangular box-shaped device divided into two chambers—a mixing chamber and a settling chamber. The mixing chamber contains a rotating impeller and a baffle plate. The aqueous and organic process streams enter this chamber through separate ports, are thoroughly mixed, and flow by gravity into the settling chamber. Here the two phases separate and leave through top and bottom outlets. A number of such devices connected as a cascade serve each cycle of a solvent extraction system.

Mixer settlers are used in the **Purex** facilities at Savannah River, and in the recovery of uranium from ore leaching liquors in uranium mills (**Amex** and **Dapex** processes).

ML-1 (ARMY NUCLEAR POWER PLANT)

Mobile Low-Powerplant-1, a small gas-cooled nuclear power plant at the National Reactor Testing Station. ML-1 was developed under the **Army Nuclear Power Program** as a prototype for mobile power plants in the 0.3-0.5 megawatt range for field use. It consists of a nitrogen-cooled water-moderated reactor linked with a closed direct-cycle gas turbine system. The ML-1 reactor achieved initial criticality in March, 1961.

ML-1 was engineered by Aerojet-General Corporation based on data obtained from the **Gas Cooled Reactor Experiment** and **Gas Turbine Test Facility.** The plant consists of two skid-mounted equipment packages—the reactor and the power conversion system—each weighing 15 tons, plus a control cab and auxiliaries. The total weight is less than 40 tons. The plant can be transported by military semitrailer, railroad flatcar, barge, cargo aircraft or arctic sled. It can be placed in operation within 12 hours after arrival on site, and can be moved within 24 hours after shutdown. Particulars follow:

Power: 0.4 megawatt (electrical). No provision for space heating. *Fuel:* Highly enriched uranium in the form of uranium dioxide (UO_2). *Fuel element design:* "Hastelloy"-x tubes loaded with UO_2 and UO_2-BeO pellets. *Core life:* 3.3 thermal megawatt-years. *Coolant:* Nitrogen at 300 psi; outlet temperature, 1200°F. *Dates:* Initial criticality, March 1961.

ML-1A (ARMY NUCLEAR POWER PLANT)

Mobile Low-Powerplant-1A, a small, trailer-mounted nuclear power plant to be procured by the Department of Defense for use in support of Army field operations. Award of a contract for this unit is scheduled for 1962. ML-1A will be a gas-cooled unit similar to **ML-1,** and will have a capacity of 0.3-0.5 megawatt of electricity.

MODERATOR

In a nuclear reactor, a material used to slow down neutrons to speeds at which they have a higher probability of inducing fission. As released in fission, neutrons have energies of about 2 Mev; they are **fast neutrons.** Reactors that employ highly enriched fuels can maintain a fission chain reaction with fast neutrons and hence require no moderator; they are called **fast reactors.** Reactors that employ natural or slightly enriched fuel cannot maintain a fission chain reaction unless the neutrons are slowed down to energies at which they are essentially at equilibrium with the atoms constituting the reactor **core.** Such reactors require a moderator; they are called **thermal reactors** when they operate with neutrons mostly of thermal energy (*ca.* 0.025 ev) or **intermediate reactors** when they operate with neutrons of intermediate energy (0.5-100,000 ev).

A moderator slows down neutrons primarily by a collision process known as **elastic scattering** in which the neutron gives up part of its kinetic energy to the nucleus with which it collides. Nuclei whose mass is close to that of the neutron are the most effective slowing-down agents, hence low atomic weight is one criterion for a good moderator. Since neutrons lose their energy by coming into contact with moderator nuclei, there is the danger that they will be absorbed and thereby removed from the chain-reacting system. Hence a second criterion for a good moderator is that it must not absorb too many neutrons, i.e., it must have a low **cross section** for neutron **capture.** Other criteria include low cost, reasonable density, and acceptable stability under irradiation. Materials that have been used as moderator include light and heavy water, graphite, beryllium and certain organic compounds. See **reactor materials.**

Reactors in which the fuel and moderator are separate bodies are referred to as **heterogeneous reactors;** those in which the fuel is in solution or intimately mixed with the moderator are referred to as **homogeneous reactors.**

Where the moderator in a heterogeneous system is a fluid, it often also serves as the reactor coolant; where it is a solid it constitutes a lattice in which solid fuel elements are arrayed or through which a fluid fuel is channeled.

MODERATOR MATERIALS. See reactor materials.

MOLECULAR ION IGNITION PROGRAM

One of several lines of U.S. research on controlled **fusion;** also referred to as the High Energy Injection Program (see **thermonuclear power**). The approach being followed is to use a closed magnetic field to trap a low-current beam of ionized particles of deuterium and/or tritium that have been accelerated to very high energies. The particles enter the **"magnetic bottle"** at energies great enough to sustain fusion reactions, so that if a sufficient density and random motion can be built up before the **plasma** escapes confinement, fusion can be achieved. This is just the opposite to what is being attempted in most other controlled-fusion programs, which start with a dense plasma of "lukewarm" ions and seek by various means to raise the temperature of the system to the level necessary to achieve operating conditions.

Concept. The idea behind the high-energy injection concept is that it is far easier to raise the energy of individual particles by accelerating them than it is to raise the temperature of a plasma held in a confined space. Thus, given a means of trapping a beam of high-energy particles in a confining magnetic field, the difficult problem of plasma heating could be circumvented. The key words in this postulate are "trapping" and "confining." With regard to the former, it is an axiom of physics that a particle entering a steady magnetic field will not be trapped unless its orbit can somehow be changed while it is in the field. A possible way of doing this was independently suggested in 1955, by J. S. Luce of Oak Ridge National Laboratory and H. F. York of the E. O. Lawrence Radiation Laboratory. The suggestion was to inject a beam of *molecular* ions (e.g., D_2+) and arrange for them to be dissociated into *atomic* ions (e.g., D+) while in the magnetic field; the atomic ions, being of lighter mass, would travel in smaller orbits and hence could be trapped. The means for accomplishing this became available early in 1956, when a new type of carbon arc was devised and was found to be highly effective in dissociating molecular ions into atomic ions. With this development the conceptual basis for molecular ion ignition was seen as follows: * A high-energy beam of molecular ions would be injected into a closed magnetic field (see below). In passing through a carbon arc established within the field, atomic ions would be formed

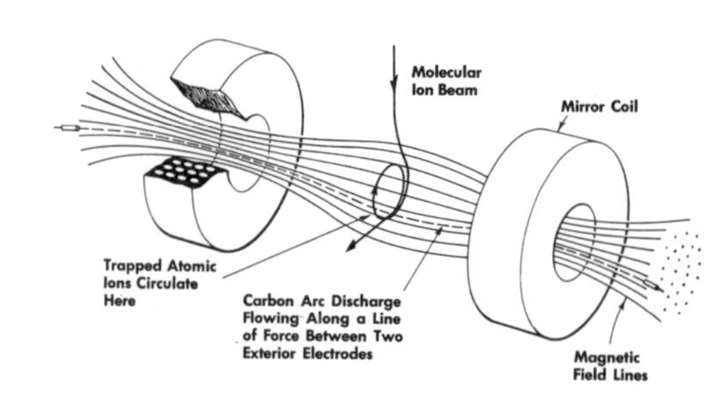

Fig. 121. High energy ion injection concept.

* An alternate method of molecular ion dissociation, utilized in the Russian device OGRA, is achieved by collisions in the background gas and subsequently in the trapped plasma itself.

which would be trapped in the field. As the trapped ions accumulated and built up a dense plasma their motion, at first highly ordered, would tend to become randomized. Once a critical density had been reached the randomized plasma would ignite.

The second key consideration noted above relates to the problem of plasma confinement. Clearly, if the density of the plasma is to be built up, the rate at which injected ions are trapped must exceed that at which trapped ions leak out of the "magnetic bottle" or are otherwise lost to the system. The rate of trapping is a function of the intensity of the injected beam and the dissociation efficiency of the carbon arc. The rate of escape of trapped ions is a function of the strength and stability of the magnetic field configuration. While these are all important parameters, the most critical problem arises in connection with the loss of trapped ions by the process known as **charge exchange,** which involves collisions between plasma ions and neutral atoms present in the system.

One way to minimize this problem is to achieve more perfect vacuum conditions before injecting the high-energy beam. However, a point is reached where the techniques involved become excessively expensive. Fortunately it does not appear necessary to resort to extreme vacuum techniques, due to a phenomenon known as **burn-out.** Theoretically, if the rate of ion injection is made high enough and the initial "background" of neutral atoms kept within reasonable limits, the dynamics of the system will be such that the concentration of

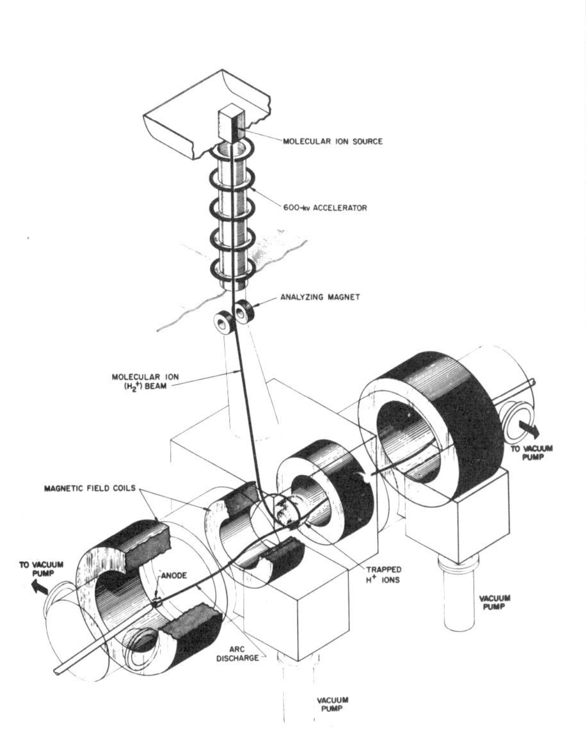

Fig. 122. The DCX-1 experiment at Oak Ridge National Laboratory. Left, schematic diagram. Right, general view of apparatus. (*Courtesy of Oak Ridge National Laboratory*)

neutral atoms will drop off rapidly enough to prevent serious interference with the molecular-ion ignition process.

Program. To date the only experimental devices built to test the high-energy molecular injection concept are the **DCX Experiment,** which was placed in operation at Oak Ridge in 1957, and a Russian apparatus known as OGRA. In the DCX device, a "magnetic mirror" configuration is used to trap and confine the plasma (see **magnetic mirror systems).** The vacuum obtained in the reaction chamber has been of the order of 10^{-8} millimeter of mercury.

Most of the experimentation has been done with injection of 600-kilovolt H_2^+ ions. The results have been encouraging. Fast proton densities of 2×10^9 per cubic centimeter have been trapped and held in the magnetic field for periods of a few milliseconds. Burn-out has not yet been demonstrated but an extrapolation of the DCX results from the configuration of a single passage of the H_2^+ ions through the carbon arc (with a dissociation efficiency of about 5%) to an arrangement that permits multiple passes (expected dissociation efficiency, 100%) suggests that a device of the latter type might produce trapped ion densities much higher than 2×10^9. A second experiment, called DCX-2, began operation early in 1962.

For information on a related program, see **Alice.**

MOLTEN SALT REACTOR EXPERIMENT (MSRE)

An experimental facility under construction at Oak Ridge National Laboratory to study the suitability of **molten salt reactors** for use in civilian power applications. The MSRE will be fueled with a molten mixture of uranium, thorium, beryllium, lithium and zirconium fluorides and moderated with graphite. The fuel will be circulated in a closed primary loop. On passing through the primary heat exchanger the fuel stream will transfer heat to a secondary molten salt stream similar to the fuel mixture but containing no uranium. The heat carried by the latter stream will be dissipated to the atmosphere (i.e., there will be no steam generation) since the experiment is concerned only with the performance of the primary reactor loop. The rated heat output will be 10 megawatts.

The basic design of MSRE was developed by the laboratory staff. The facility is being installed in a building previously used for molten salt reactor studies in connection with the **Aircraft Nuclear Propulsion Program.** Operation is tentatively scheduled for January, 1964. The estimated construction cost, exclusive of supporting research and development, is $6.5 million.

MOLTEN SALT REACTORS

A type of fluid fuel power reactor first studied in connection with the development of an indirect-cycle aircraft nuclear propulsion system (see **Aircraft Nuclear Propulsion Program)** and now also being studied for possible use in civilian power applications. The fuel consists of a "fused salt" solution of enriched uranium and, if desired, thorium. Binary or ternary mixtures of beryllium, zirconium, lithium, potassium, or sodium fluoride have received the most study as the solvent medium. Such mixtures have good solubility for uranium and thorium tetrafluoride (UF_4, ThF_4), forming eutectics which melt in the general range, 850-950°F. The resulting fuel solutions have good stability under irradiation and appear to have acceptable handling characteristics.

General Considerations of Fluid-Fuel Systems. Molten salt reactors have the usual advantages and disadvantages associated with a fluid fuel system, which may be briefly stated as follows:

Advantages:

1. The promise of lower fuel cycle costs than in solid fuel systems, due to such factors as elimination of the expense of fuel element fabrication; elimination of radiation damage as a limiting factor in fuel burn-up; and simplification of spent fuel reprocessing.

2. Advantages in neutron economy due to the possibility of continuously removing fission product poisons from the circulating fuel stream; and, in some designs, to the absence of a need for neutron-absorbing structural materials in the reactor core.

3. Excellent control characteristics, due to a strong negative temperature coefficient of reactivity. Relatedly, the possibility of adding additional fuel as needed makes it unnecessary to build excess reactivity into the sytsem, thereby minimizing if not eliminating altogether the need for control rods.

Disadvantages:

1. The problem of engineering an equipment system capable of handling the intensely radioactive fuel stream with long-term integrity. These are two principal factors: First, the system must be designed to withstand corrosion and erosion by the circulating fuel stream. Second, the entire primary loop must be massively shielded and all maintenance tasks carried out by remote techniques.

2. The problem of maintaining the fissionable and fertile components properly distributed in the fuel stream.

Special Considerations of Molten Salt Concept. A unique feature of the molten salt concept is the solubility of thorium in the fused salt medium. (All other fluid fuel systems require the use of thorium slurries.) This gives the concept considerable flexibility in that several molten salt schemes can be considered: (1) heterogeneous converter systems, e.g., the use of a uranium solution in a graphite moderated reactor; (2) homogeneous converter systems, e.g., the use of a uranium solution containing a sufficient concentration of beryllium to satisfy moderator requirements; (3) heterogeneous thermal breeder systems, e.g., the use of a uranium-thorium solution in a graphite moderator; and (4) homogeneous thermal breeder systems—e.g., the use of a uranium-thorium solution containing a sufficient concentration of beryllium to satisfy moderator requirements. The last is perhaps the most promising scheme in that it combines low-cost fuel-cycle operation with the possibility of breeding.

Relative to the **aqueous homogeneous reactor** concept, the molten salt concept has the following strong and weak points:

Strong Points:

1. The capability of high temperature operation in a low-pressure system, due to the low vapor pressure of molten salt mixtures. This is advantageous in two respects: First; it eases the problem of containing the fuel stream. Second, it results in high thermal conversion efficiencies in power generation with attendant capital cost benefits.

2. Less severe corrosion and erosion problems.*

3. Avoidance of the problem of radiolytic dissociation of water.

4. The solubility of thorium in the fuel medium.

Weak Points:

1. The high melting point of molten salt mixtures, which requires that means be provided to preheat the primary loop equipment and is a complicating factor in plant operation.

2. Molten salts are less effective neutron moderators than heavy water, resulting in larger critical mass requirements and core structures.

3. There is greater parasitic neutron capture in molten salt systems than in a heavy water system, and as a result molten salt reactors cannot achieve as high breeding gains as can be achieved in an aqueous homogeneous reactor.

Status. The basic feasibility of a circulating molten salt reactor system was first demonstrated by the successful operation of the Aircraft Reactor Experiment (ARE) at Oak Ridge National Laboratory in 1954.

In 1959, following a review of its over-all civilian power reactor development program, the U.S. Atomic Energy Commission concluded that none of the fluid-fuel concepts then

---

* Nickel-base alloys appear promising as container materials for molten salt fuels.

being studied* showed promise of meeting short-term objectives. This finding led to a decision to concentrate on the concept that appeared to offer the best long-range promise as a thermal breeder. As is discussed under **aqueous homogeneous reactors,** an evaluation was undertaken which resulted in the selection of the molten salt concept as the basis for continued fluid fuel development. As a first step under the new program, an experimental molten salt reactor is to be constructed at Oak Ridge National Laboratory. (See **Molten Salt Reactor Experiment)**

Plant and Economic Characteristics. The molten salt concept is at too early a stage of development in relation to civilian power applications to permit defining plant characteristics or evaluating capital and operating costs.

MOLTEN SALTS

Molten mixtures of salts (usually halides), of interest as a working fluid for high temperature reactor systems and as a fuel reprocessing medium; also referred to as fused salts. For information on reactor applications, see **Aircraft Nuclear Propulsion Program, molten salt reactors.** For information on fuel reprocessing applications, see **fused salt extraction, fluoride volatility processes.**

MOLYBDENUM

Element No. 42 (symbol, Mo; atomic weight, 95.95), a refractory metal with a fairly low thermal neutron absorption cross section (~ 2.4 barns), sometimes used as an alloying material to improve the mechanical properties and radiation stability of uranium fuels. Molybdenum's excellent mechanical properties at high temperatures (it melts at ~ 4760°F) would suggest its use as a structural material for reactor systems but this application is outruled by its poor corrosion resistance. In addition, the oxide of molybdenum is volatile. (See **reactor materials)**

Molybdenum is one of the important **trace elements.** Mo^{99} is one of the radioisotopes used in biomedical and agricultural research.

MONAZITE

A cerium-lanthanum phosphate mineral, usually containing thorium and uranium, as well as varying amounts of other rare earth elements; the principal source of thorium and of many rare earth metals. Monazite generally occurs as a minor constituent of igneous rocks, such as granite, gneiss, and pegmatite. The natural process of erosion tends to concentrate monazite in beaches and stream beds. Large deposits of monazite sands occur in India and Brazil, and in the Carolinas, Florida, and Idaho in the United States. (See **thorium deposits and reserves)**

MONITORING. See **radiation monitoring, air monitors, radioactive fallout.**

MOUND LABORATORY

A U.S. Atomic Energy Commission research laboratory, principally for classified programs relating to weapons, located at Miamisburg, Ohio. *Operating contractor:* Monsanto Research Corporation, a wholly owned subsidiary of Monsanto Chemical Company. *General Manager:* H. K. Nason. *AEC investment in plant and equipment:* ~ $34 million.**

During the **Manhattan Project,** Monsanto Chemical Company's Central Research Department conducted studies of the chemical, physical and physiological properties of materials of importance to the atomic energy program. Mound Laboratory, permanent facilities for which were completed in **1948,** is an outgrowth of that activity. While the Labora-

* Fluid-fuel concepts under development at the time of the review included, in addition to the molten salt concept, the **aqueous homogeneous** concept, the molten plutonium concept (see **Los Alamos Molten Plutonium Experiment No. 1**), and the **Liquid Metal Fuel Reactor Concept.**

** Includes facilities authorized or under construction as of June 30, 1959. Not adjusted for depreciation.

tory has been primarily active in classified research relating to weapons, it has also made a number of contributions to the civilian atomic energy field. These include: (1) development of sensitive quartz-fiber balances for attaining microgram accuracy in weight measurements; (2) research on techniques for handling radioactive wastes, including the development of an incinerator for the safe disposal of combustible waste matter; (3) research on the toxicity of polonium and other alpha-emitting materials; (4) research on nuclear batteries and other applications for radioactive materials, and (5) development of neutron sources, such as polonium-beryllium.

MU MESON (μ-meson)

An **elementary particle** whose existence was predicted in 1935, and was subsequently discovered in 1937, in **cloud-chamber** studies of cosmic rays; also known as muon.

A mu meson can be either positively or electrically charged, has a mass 207 times as great as that of the electron, and has an average lifetime before spontaneous decay of 2.15×10^{-6} seconds. It decays into an electron and two **neutrinos.**

Mu mesons are of academic interest in connection with a catalytic fusion process. (See **fusion (nuclear),** also see **mesons, strange particles)**

MULTICHANNEL ANALYZER

A type of **pulse height analyzer.**

MULTICURIE FISSION PRODUCTS PILOT PLANT

A pilot facility for the recovery and encapsulation of kilocurie quantities of certain long-lived fission products, located at Oak Ridge National Laboratory; also known as the Fission Products Development Laboratory.

The facility was completed in 1958, at a cost of $2.2 million. It consists of a two-story structure containing 18 massively shielded "hot" cells in which the operations are conducted. Feed to the facility consists of concentrated aqueous radioactive waste resulting from **fuel reprocessing** operations at U.S. Atomic Energy Commission sites. Five principal fission products of interest for industrial radiation applications are individually recovered: **cesium-137, promethium-147, cerium-144, strontium-90,** and **technetium-99.**

MULTIPLICATION FACTOR

In nuclear reactor theory, the ratio of the number of neutrons in a given neutron generation to the number in the previous generation; sometimes called the multiplication constant or **criticality factor** and usually denoted by the symbol, k. When k is equal to unity, the fission chain reaction sustains itself and the reactor is "critical." If k is less than unity, the chain reaction dies out and the reactor is said to be "subcritical"; if it is greater than unity, the reaction is said to be "supercritical" or "divergent."

The infinite multiplication factor, k_∞, relates to a reactor from which there is no leakage, i.e., from a reactor of infinite size. The effective multiplication factor, k_{eff}, relates to the actual reactor of finite size from which leakage does occur.

MUTUAL ATOMIC ENERGY LIABILITY UNDERWRITERS (MAELU). See **insurance and indemnification against atomic energy risks.**

MUTUAL ATOMIC ENERGY REINSURANCE POOL (MAERP). See **insurance and indemnification against atomic energy risks.**

N

NAGASAKI

Target of the second of the two nuclear weapons used by the United States against Japan in the final phase of World War II. The attack on Nagasaki, an industrial center on the western coast of Kyushu, came at 11:02 A.M. on August 9, 1945, three days after the bombing of **Hiroshima.** The bomb had a **yield** of about 20 kilotons (TNT equivalent) and was detonated at an altitude of approximately 1850 feet. The fissionable material used was plutonium.

The effects of the attack have been reported as follows:

Total population	155,000
Square miles destroyed	1.8
Killed and missing	36,000
Injured	40,000

Nagasaki was characterized by hilly terrain, a mixture of industrial structures and wood-frame houses, and uneven population density. As in the case of Hiroshima, the population was unprepared for the attack. The fact that both the area of destruction and the number of casualties were only about half as large as at Hiroshima is attributable principally to the difference in terrain.

NAME-PLATE RATING

In electric power generation, the equipment capacity guaranteed by the manufacturer under specified operating conditions.

NASA TEST REACTOR. See **Plum Brook Reactor Facility.**

NATIONAL BUREAU OF STANDARDS, HANDBOOKS. See **National Committee on Radiation Protection and Measurements.**

NATIONAL COMMITTEE ON RADIATION PROTECTION AND MEASUREMENTS (NCRP)

An independent (i.e., nongovernmental) U.S. scientific committee long active in the development of **radiation protection standards.**

The NCRP is an outgrowth of the Advisory Committee on X-ray and Radium Protection whose original membership was made up of representatives from medical societies, x-ray equipment manufacturers, and the National Bureau of Standards. In 1946 the NCRP was reorganized and its membership broadened to include representatives of other organizations having a scientific interest in radiation protection. The NCRP is represented on the **International Commission on Radiological Protection** and works closely with that body. The Chairman of NCRP is a consultant to the recently established **Federal Radiation Council.**

While not officially connected with the National Bureau of Standards, the NCRP maintains offices in that agency and publishes its recommendations in the form of NBS Handbooks. A series of such handbooks has been issued (see Table), covering recommended radiation exposure limits for external and internal sources (Handbook Nos. 59 and 69, respectively); recommended procedures for handling radioactive materials; and various specialized aspects of radiation.

The present Chairman of NCRP is Dr. Lauriston S. Taylor, Chief, Atomic Radiation Physics Division, Bureau of Standards.

National Bureau of Standards Handbooks
Relating to Radiation Standards

Number	*Title*	*Price* [1]
42	Safe Handling of Radioactive Isotopes	$ .20
48	Control and Removal of Radioactive Contamination in Laboratories	.15
49	Recommendations for Waste Disposal of Phosphorus-32 and Iodine-131 for Medical Users	.15
50	X-ray Protection Design	.20
51	Radiological Monitoring Methods and Instruments	.20
53	Recommendations for the Disposal of Carbon-14 Wastes	.15
54	Protection Against Radiations from Radium, Cobalt-60, and Cesium-137	.25
55	Protection Against Betatron-Synchrotron Radiations up to 100 Million Electron Volts	.25
57	Photographic Dosimetry of X and Gamma Rays	.15
58	Radioactive-Waste Disposal in the Ocean	.20
59	Permissible Dose from External Sources of Ionizing Radiation	.30
60	X-ray Protection	.20
61	Regulation of Radiation Exposure by Legislative Means	.25
62	Report of the International Commission on Radiological Units and Measurements (ICRU) 1956	.40
63	Protection Against Neutron Radiation up to 30 Million Electron Volts	.40
64	Design of Free-Air Ionization Chambers	.20
65	Safe Handling of Bodies Containing Radioactive Isotopes	.15
66	Safe Design and Use of Industrial Beta Ray Sources	.20
69	Maximum Permissible Body Burdens and Maximum Permissible Concentrations of Radionuclides in Air and Water for Occupational Exposure	.35
72	Measurement of Neutron Flux and Spectra for Physical and Biological Applications	.35
73	Protection Against Radiations from Sealed Gamma Sources	.30

[1] Sold by the Superintendent of Documents, U.S. Government Printing Office, Washington 25, D.C.

NATIONAL NUCLEAR ROCKET DEVELOPMENT CENTER. See **Rover Project.**

NATIONAL REACTOR TESTING STATION (NRTS)

A large U.S. Atomic Energy Commission experimental station, principally for reactor experiments and prototype testing, located on a 572,000-acre tract of land 25 miles west of Idaho Falls, Idaho. Phillips Petroleum Company operates certain permanent technical and technical support facilities serving the station as a whole. Other facilities are operated by contractors charged with particular development projects. (See Table for a summary of the major NRTS facilities and operating contractors.) Total AEC investment in NRTS facilities, including construction projects authorized as of June 30, 1960, was approximately $327 million.* Employment is in the neighborhood of 4000, exclusive of construction workers.

NATURAL RADIOACTIVITY

Radioactivity due to naturally occurring materials and phenomena, as oposed to artificially induced ("man-made") radioactivity. Following are the principal categories of natural radionuclides:

1. Primary radionuclides having half-lives of hundreds of millions of years or more and hence presumed to have existed since the time of nucleogenesis. They include:

Nuclide	*Type of Radiation*	*Half-life (order of magnitude)*
Indium-115	beta	10^{14} yr
Lanthanum-138	beta	10^{11} yr
Lutecium-176	beta	10^{10} yr
Potassium-40	beta	10^{9} yr
Rhenium-187	beta	10^{10} yr
Rubidium-87	beta	10^{10} yr
Samarium-147	alpha	10^{11} yr
Thorium-232	alpha	10^{10} yr
Uranium-235	alpha	10^{8} yr
Uranium-238	alpha	10^{9} yr

* Not adjusted for depreciation.

MAJOR FACILITIES AT THE NATIONAL REACTOR TESTING STATION
(Mid-1961)

Facility	*Status*	*Operating Contractor*
GENERAL-PURPOSE TEST REACTORS:		
Materials Testing Reactor (MTR)	Operational	Phillips Petroleum Co.
Engineering Test Reactor (ETR)	Operational	Phillips Petroleum Co.
Advanced Engineering Test Reactor (ETR-II)	Planned	Phillips Petroleum Co.
POWER REACTOR EXPERIMENTS (Civilian):		
Boiling Reactor Experiments (BORAX-1,2,3,4)	Dismantled	Argonne National Laboratory
Experimental Breeder Reactor No. 1 (EBR-1)	Operational	Argonne National Laboratory
Organic Moderated Reactor Experiment (OMRE)	Operational	Atomics International
Experimental Breeder Reactor No. 2 (EBR-2)	1961 Start-up	Argonne National Laboratory
Boiling Reactor Experiment No. 5 (BORAX-5)	1961 Start-up	Argonne National Laboratory
Experimental Organic Cooled Reactor (EOCR)	1962 Start-up	Atomics International
Experimental Beryllium Oxide Reactor (EBOR) [1]	1963 Start-up	General Atomic
SPECIALIZED TEST REACTORS (Civilian):		
Special Power Excursion Reactor Test (SPERT-1,2,3)	Operational	Phillips Petroleum Co.
Transient Test Reactor Experiment (TREAT)	Operational	Argonne National Laboratory
Argonne Fast Source Reactor (AFSR)	Operational	Argonne National Laboratory
Special Power Excursion Reactor Test (SPERT-4)	1961 Start-up	Phillips Petroleum Co.
ARMY NUCLEAR POWER PROGRAM FACILITIES:		
Stationary Low Power Plant No. 1 (**SL-1**) [2]	Being dismantled	Combustion Engineering Co.
Gas Cooled Reactor Experiment (GCRE-1)	Operational	Aerojet-General Nucleonics
Mobile Low Power Plant No. 1 (**ML-1**)	Operational	Aerojet-General Nucleonics
Military Compact Reactor Pilot Plant (MCRPP)	Planned	United Nuclear Corp. (NDA)
NAVAL REACTOR PROGRAM FACILITIES:		
S1W Reactor Facility	Operational	Bettis Atomic Power Laboratory
Large Ship Reactor Prototype (A1W)	Operational	Bettis Atomic Power Laboratory
Expended Core Facility	Operational	Bettis Atomic Power Laboratory
Natural Circulation Reactor (S5G)	1963 Start-up	Knolls-Atomic Power Laboratory
AIRCRAFT NUCLEAR PROPULSION PROGRAM FACILITIES:		
Heat Transfer Reactor Experiment (HTRE-1)	Dismantled	General Electric Co. (ANPD)
Heat Transfer Reactor Experiment (HTRE-2,3)	Operational [3]	General Electric Co. (ANPD)
Advanced Core Test (ACT)	Planned [3]	General Electric Co. (ANPD)
Shield Test Pool Facility (SUSIE)	Operational [3]	General Electric Co. (ANPD)
Experimental Reactor (PWAC-IIC)	Under construction [3]	Pratt and Whitney Aircraft (CANEL)
OTHER FACILITIES:		
Idaho Chemical Processing Plant (CPP)	Operational	Phillips Petroleum Co.
Central Facilities Area (central warehouses, shops, technical library, etc.)	Operational	Phillips Petroleum Co.

[1] Formerly designated BORE. See **Maritime Gas-Cooled Reactor Project.**
[2] Formerly known as the Argonne Low Power Reactor (ALPR).
[3] Status of these facilities uncertain at this writing, due to cancellation of ANP program.

2. Decay products of the above comprising various radionuclides having geologically short half-lives and ranging in atomic number from 81 (thallium) to 92 (uranium). Radium-225 and its daughter radon are notable examples.

3. Induced radionuclides, resulting from reactions between natural radiation (cosmic rays, free neutrons, etc.) and elements in the earth's atmosphere or crust. An example is carbon-14, which is formed by neutron interaction with nitrogen-14.

Natural radioactivity is an important contributor to **background radiation.**

For a listing of naturally occurring radioisotopes, see Appendix F.

NATURAL URANIUM. See **normal uranium.**

U.S.S. *NAUTILUS* (SSN-571)

The first nuclear-powered ship. An attack-class submarine with a displacement of 3,180 tons, *Nautilus* is powered with an S2W pressurized water reactor plant designed by Bettis Atomic Power Laboratory. The ship was constructed by the Electric Boat Division of General Dynamics Corporation, launched on January 21, 1954 and commissioned September 30, 1954.

Nautilus was refueled in 1957, after traveling 62,562 miles, and in 1959, after an additional 153,886 miles. (See **Naval Reactors Program**)

NAVAL REACTORS PROGRAM

A program of nuclear power reactor development for Naval propulsion applications. The program is a joint effort of the U.S. Atomic Energy Commission and the Department of Defense (DOD), and is directed by a joint AEC-Navy group. The head of the group functions in a dual capacity serving AEC as Manager, Naval Reactors, Division of Reactor Development; and the Navy as Assistant Chief of the Bureau of Ships for Nuclear Propulsion.

Major emphasis has been placed on nuclear reactor propulsion for submarines, with 22 submarines having been commissioned thus far and 39 additional submarines either authorized by Congress or under construction. Two nuclear reactor-powered surface ships have joined the Navy thus far, the aircraft carrier ***Enterprise*** and the guided-missile cruiser ***Long Beach;*** one has been launched but not commissioned, the guided-missile destroyer leader (frigate) ***Bainbridge;*** and an additional guided-missile destroyer leader has been authorized. A tabulation of these ships

Fig. 123. USS *Nautilus*. Official U.S. Navy photograph.

Fig. 124. Left, USS *Skipjack,* lead ship of fast-attack class of nuclear-powered submarines. Below, USS *George Washington,* lead ship of polaris-missile class. (*Courtesy of Electric Boat Division of General Dynamics Corp.*)

is given at the end of this entry. Further information on the surface ships and the lead ships of each submarine type may be found in individual entries. (See ***George Washington, Skipjack*** and ***Skate)*** There are also entries on the two prototype submarines, ***Nautilus*** and ***Seawolf,*** and the three special-purpose submbarines, ***Halibut, Triton*** and ***Tullibee.***

Interest in nuclear propulsion for Naval applications in general and submarines in particular was originally sparked by four intrinsic properties of nuclear reactors: (1) the compactness of nuclear fuel; (2) elimination of oxygen supply as a requirement in power generation; (3) longer operation before refueling is required and (4) the ability to operate at full power for long periods of time. The revolutionary impact which nuclear propulsion has had on Naval strategy and tactics derives from the fact that it has proved possible to engineer rugged and dependable reactor power plants that capitalize on these properties to a remarkable degree.

A non-related development that has heightened the strategic significance of Naval nuclear propulsion is the advent of solid-fuel missiles armed with nuclear warheads—notably, the Polaris. The compactness and simplicity of the Polaris greatly facilitate the use of submarines as missile carriers and launchers, and led to the present Polaris missile class of nuclear-powered submarines.

Nuclear-powered submarines characteristically operate submerged 85% or more of the time. They can travel at full power for sustained periods (days or even weeks) * and travel faster underwater than on surface (due to their hull design). The speed they can attain is classified, the only published statement being "faster than 20 knots." Their range is remarkable; for example, *Nautilus* steamed 62,562 miles ** on her first core and 153,886 miles on her second core.

Conventional diesel-powered submarines operate submerged on the average of 15% or less of the total time they are on sea duty. Their maximum speed on the surface is about 18 knots, which they can only sustain for about half an hour. Their performance when submerged is even more sharply limited. (World War-II submarines could not make better than about 8 knots for longer than an hour before having to surface to recharge their batteries.) The cruising range of conventional submarines is also limited.

Active development of Naval nuclear propulsion systems began in the late forties, with development of two basically different types of systems:

1. A pressurized light water-cooled and moderated thermal reactor fueled with highly enriched uranium; and
2. A liquid sodium-cooled, beryllium-moderated intermediate reactor fueled with highly enriched uranium.

Both types were developed simultaneously because the need at that time to develop a nuclear-powered submarine was great and it was not known then that either type would work. The sodium system then appeared to offer several advantages over water as a coolant including the promise of reducing weight and improving plant efficiency; however, leaks in the steam-generating system of the *Seawolf* led to the replacement of this reactor type by a pressurized water reactor in the *Seawolf* and discontinuance of development of this system in favor of the pressurized water reactor system. The sodium technology that was developed has, however, proved extremely useful in civilian power reactor development (see **sodium-graphite reactors; fast breeder reactors**). The basic technology of pressurized water reactor systems has been adopted as the basis for a major avenue of civilian power reactor development (see **pressurized water reactors**) and is the system of the first large-scale civilian nuclear power plant. (See **Shippingport Atomic Power Station**)

The major organizations engaged in the development of Naval pressurized water systems are: (1) Bettis Atomic Power Laboratory at Pittsburgh, Pennsylvania, and related test facilities † at the National Reactor Testing Station, operated under contract for the Atomic Energy Commission by Westinghouse Electric Corporation; (2) Knolls Atomic Power Laboratory at Schenectady, New York, and nearby test facilities, operated under contract for the Atomic Energy Commission by General Electric Company; and (3) combustion Engineering Company's Windsor Laboratory in Windsor, Connecticut. Supporting development work is conducted by the manufacturers who supply individual reactor components and by other specialist organizations.

* In 1956, SLW (the land-based prototype of the *Nautilus* reactor plant) operated continuously at full power for 66 days and nights. This was enough time to have carried a ship twice around the world without refueling and contrasts with the 4-hour full power run which is required for acceptance of new naval ships.

** A conventional submarine would have consumed 2 million gallons of diesel oil in traveling this distance. It would require a train of tank cars over a mile and a half long to carry this amount of fuel.

† These include a recently completed Expended Core Facility used for postmortem studies of expended Naval reactor cores.

Following are data on AEC-funded research and development expenditures under the Naval Reactors Program:

	R & D Costs ($ millions)		*Capital Costs ($ millions)*
	Fiscal Year Ending 6/30/60	*Cumulative Through 6/30/60*	*Cumulative Through 6/30/60*
Submarine reactors	31.1	327.1	129.3
Surface ship reactors	43.3	171.8	56.9
General	14.4	57.9	7.6
TOTAL	88.8	556.8	193.8

A list of land-based prototypes for reactors installed in Naval ships is given in Table 1. A key to the symbols used in designating reactors, the type of each reactor and the ship for which each reactor is designed is given in Table 2. Table 3 lists all nuclear-powered Naval vessels built or authorized as of December 1961. They represent a total capital investment of over $6 billion. Supplementary information on the various classes of submarines and surface ships will be found in separate entries mentioned earlier. Table 4 lists some of the feats of nuclear-powered submarines.

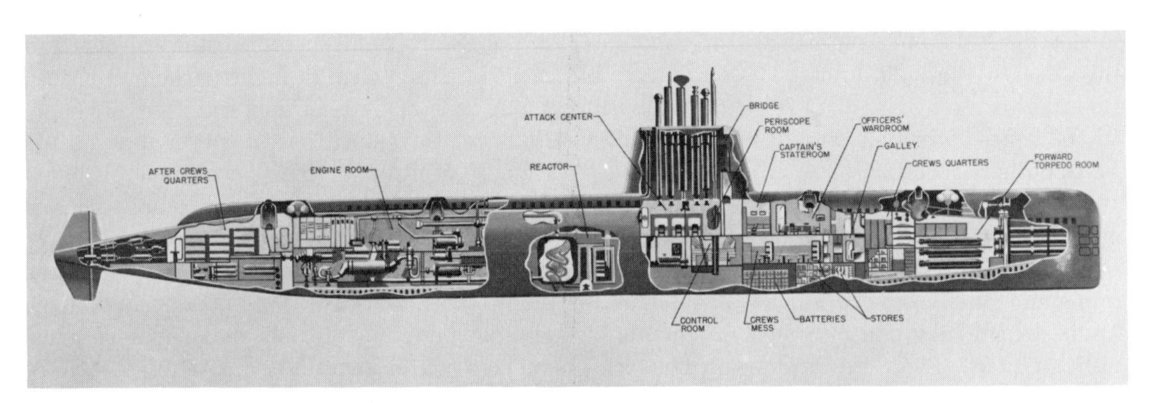

Fig. 125. Cutaway view of USS *Nautilus*. (*Courtesy of U.S. Navy*)

Fig. 126. Largest Naval vessel—the USS *Enterprise,* nuclear-powered aircraft carrier, seen here after launching at Newport News, Va. Official U.S. Naval photograph.

Table 1. Naval Reactors Program

Land-Based Prototypes[1]

Designation	*Name*	*Location*	*Contractor*	*Start-up*	*Notes*
S1W	S1W Reactor Facility[2]	National Reactor Testing Station	Westinghouse (Bettis)	1953	Originally operated as prototype for the reactor plant installed in the attack submarine, *Nautilus*. Now operated as a flexible test facility in support of advanced reactor development.
S1G	S1G Reactor Facility[3]	West Milton, N.Y.	General Electric (KAPL)	1955	Operated as prototype for the sodium-cooled reactor plant originally installed in the attack submarine *Seawolf*. Shut down in 1957.
S3G	Submarine Advanced Reactor	West Milton, N.Y.	General Electric (KAPL)	1958	Originally operated as prototype for the reactor plant installed in the submarine *Triton*. Now operated in support of advanced reactor development.
A1W	Large Ship Reactor	National Reactor Testing Station	Westinghouse (Bettis)	1958	A 2-reactor installation being run as a test facility and in support of the operation of the reactor plants in the aircraft carrier, *Enterprise*, and the guided-missile cruiser, *Long Beach*.
S1C	Small Submarine Reactor	Windsor, Conn.	Combustion Engineering	1959	Being run as a test facility in support of the operation of the reactor plant in the submarine, *Tullibee*.
D1G	Destroyer (Frigate) Reactor	West Milton, N.Y.	General Electric (KAPL)	1962	Prototype for the reactor plant installed in the destroyer, *Bainbridge*.
S5G	Natural Circulation Reactor	National Reactor Testing Station	General Electric (KAPL)	(1963)	To test a natural-circulation pressurized water reactor system for submarine application.

[1] All pressurized water reactors except for S1G.
[2] Formerly known as a Submarine Thermal Reactor (STR), Mark I.
[3] Formerly known as Submarine Intermediate Reactor (SIR), Mark A.

Table 2. Symbols Used in Designating Naval Reactors

Symbol	*Ship*	*Type Reactor*
A1W	Aircraft Carrier Prototype	Large Ship Reactor
A2W	*Enterprise* (CVA(N)65)	Large Ship Reactor
A3W	To be designated	Advanced Large Ship Reactor
C1W	*Long Beach* (CG(N)9)	Guided Missile Cruiser Reactor
D1G	Frigate Prototype	Frigate Reactor
D2G	*Bainbridge* (DLG(N)25)	Frigate Reactor
	DLG(N)	Frigate Reactor
D1W	To be designated	Single Reactor Destroyer
S1C	*Tullibee* (Prototype)	Submarine Reactor Small
S2C	*Tullibee* (SSN597)	Submarine Reactor Small
S1G	*Seawolf* (Prototype)	Submarine Intermediate Reactor
S2G	*Seawolf* (SSN575) (First Reactor)	Submarine Intermediate Reactor
S3G	*Triton* (Prototype)	Submarine Advanced Reactor
S4G	*Triton* (SSN586)	Submarine Advanced Reactor
S5G	To be designated	Natural Circulation Reactor
S1W	*Nautilus* (Prototype)	Submarine Thermal Reactor
S2W	*Nautilus* (SSN571)	Submarine Thermal Reactor
S2Wa	*Seawolf* (SSN575) (Second Reactor)	Submarine Thermal Reactor
S3W	*Skate* (SSN578) *Sargo* (SSN583) *Halibut* (SSG(N)587)	Submarine Fleet Reactor
S4W	*Swordfish* (SSN579) *Seadragon* (SSN584)	Submarine Fleet Reactor
S5W	Fast attack type (*Skipjack* was the first) Fleet Ballistic Missile (Polaris) (*George Washington* was the first)	High Speed Submarine Reactor

Table 3. Nuclear-Powered Naval Ships
(December 1961)

Class	*Number*	*Name*	*Reactor Plant*
SUBMARINES:			
Attack	SSN-571	***Nautilus***	S2W
"	SSN-575	***Seawolf***	S2W-A [1]
Small attack	SSN-578	***Skate***	S3W
Three additional submarines of this class are in operation: *Swordfish, Sargo* and *Seadragon.*			
Fast attack	SSN-585	***Skipjack***	S5W
Six additional submarines of this class are in operation: *Scamp, Scorpion, Sculpin, Shark, Snook* and *Thresher.* Three additional submarines have been launched: *Permit, Plunger* and *Tinosa.* Ten additional submarines are presently under construction but not launched: *Barb, Pollack, Haddo, Jack, Dace, Guardfish, Flasher, Greenling, Gato* and *Haddock.* Three additional submarines have been authorized but construction has not yet started. All submarines of this class are powered by the S5W reactor plant.			
Polaris missile	SSB(N)598	***George Washington***	S5W
Seven additional submarines of this class are in operation: *Patrick Henry, Theo. Roosevelt, Robert E. Lee, Abraham Lincoln, Ethan Allen, Sam Houston* and *Thomas Edison.* One additional submarine has been launched but is not yet in operation: *John Marshall.* Ten additional submarines are under construction: *Lafayette, Alexander Hamilton, Thomas Jefferson, Andrew Jackson, John Adams, James Monroe, Nathan Hale, Woodrow Wilson, Henry Clay* and *Daniel Webster.* Ten additional submarines have been authorized. All submarines of this class are powered by the S5W reactor plant.			
Attack	SSN-586	***Triton***	S4G (2 reactors)
Regulus missile	SSG(N)587	***Halibut***	S3W
Hunter-killer	SSN-597	***Tullibee***	S2C
SURFACE SHIPS:			
Guided missile cruiser	CG(N)9	***Long Beach***	C1W (2 reactors)
Aircraft carrier	CVA(N)65	***Enterprise***	A2W (8 reactors)
Guided missile destroyer	DLG(N)25	***Bainbridge***	D2G (2 reactors)
One additional missile destroyer has been authorized.			

[1] Originally fitted with an S2G sodium-cooled reactor plant.

The symbols consist of three characters. The first character designates the ship type: A—Aircraft Carrier, C—Cruiser, D—Destroyer-type, S—Submarine. The second denotes the sequence number of the plant by the prime contractor for each ship type; and the third character designates the name of the contractor responsible for the design of the reactor plant: C—Combustion Engineering, Inc., G—General Electric Company, W—Westinghouse Electric Corporation.

Ship designations are: CVA(N)—Aircraft Carrier, Attack (Nuclear); CG(N)—Cruiser, Guided-missile (Nuclear); DLG(N)—Destroyer Leader, Guided-missile (Nuclear); SSN—Submarine, Nuclear; SSG(N)—Submarine, Guided-missile (Nuclear).

Table 4. Feats of Nuclear-Powered Submarines

1957	In May, *Nautilus* steamed submerged from Panama to San Diego (3049 miles) at average speed of 19 knots.
	In September, *Nautilus* traveled under Arctic ice to latitude of 87°N. Steamed submerged under ice for 5½ days (100 miles). Then steamed submerged through open water 5007 miles at average speed of 15 knots.
1958	On March 28, *Skate* completed submerged transatlantic crossing—from Portland, England to New London, Connecticut in 7 days, 5 hours.
	On August 3, *Nautilus* crossed North Pole in the course of a submerged passage from Hawaii to Iceland.
	On August 11, *Skate* crossed North Pole in the course of submerged passage under polar ice cap.
	On August 18, *Nautilus* completed submerged transatlantic crossing (6 days, 11 hours, 55 minutes).
	On October 6, *Seawolf* surfaced after 60 days of submerged maneuvers in Atlantic waters.
1959	In March, *Skate* made first extensive trip in winter under polar ice cap. Steamed 11,495 miles, of which 11,220 were traveled submerged and 3090 were traveled under ice. Punched through ice to surface on ten occasions.
	From January through March, *Sargo* steamed 19,000 miles, being fully submerged for all but 120 miles.
1960	On March 10, *Triton* completed submerged circumnavigation of world, traveling 36,014 nautical miles in 83 days, 10 hours on a route paralleling that taken by Ferdinand Magellan's expedition in 1519–1522.

NEGATIVE TEMPERATURE COEFFICIENT

A characteristic of a nuclear reactor whose **reactivity** decreases as the temperature rises. (See **reactor control**)

NELIA

Nuclear Energy Liability Insurance Association, a syndicate formed by capital-stock insurance companies to insure privately owned atomic energy facilities against **public liability** claims relating to atomic energy hazards. NELIA is a voluntary, nonprofit, unincorporated association with headquarters in New York City. Policies are written in conjunction with a counterpart syndicate of mutual insurance companies (see **MAELU**). Maximum coverage available from NELIA under a joint NELIA-MAELU policy is $46.5 million. (See **insurance and indemnification against atomic energy risks**)

NEPIA

Nuclear Energy Property Insurance Association, a syndicate formed by capital-stock insurance companies to insure privately owned atomic energy facilities against property damage arising from atomic energy hazards. NEPIA is organized as a voluntary, nonprofit, unincorporated association. The Factory Insurance Association of Hartford, Connecticut, handles the day-to-day administration of NEPIA affairs. Policies are written in conjunction with a counterpart syndicate of mutual insurance companies(see **MAERP**), with NEPIA assuming approximately 85% of the risk coverage. (See **insurance and indemnification against atomic energy risks**)

NEPTUNIUM

Element No. 93 (symbol, Np), of interest as short-lived intermediate product in the transmutation of fertile uranium-238 into fissionable plutonium-239. Neptunium was first identified in 1940 by E. M. McMillan and P. H. Abelson at the University of California. They prepared 2.3-day neptunium-239 by exposing uranium-238 to a beam of thermal neutrons. It is this isotope which decays, by beta emission, to plutonium-239. Other neptunium isotopes were quickly identified. Neptunium was named by McMillan after the planet Neptune, which lies beyond Uranus in the solar system. Ten other **transuranium elements** have since been discovered.

NERVA. See **Rover Project.**

NETHERLANDS

Agencies. A ministerial Nuclear Energy Commission (Commisie Voor Atoom Energie) has recently been established as the executive atomic energy agency.

RCN (Reactor Centrum Nederland), the Hague, is a quasi-official organization responsible for implementation of the national atomic energy research and development program, including operation of national laboratories. Four interests have equal representation in RCN, namely, the government, private industry, the scientific community (through FOM), and the publicly owned utility industry (through SEP).

FOM (Fundamental Onderzoek der Materie), Utrecht, is a scientific organization, supported primarily by the government, whose function is the coordination of basic research in the nuclear field.

SEP (Samenwerkende Electriciteits-Productiebedrijwen), Arnheim, is an association of 9 municipal or provincial electric utilities which, as spokesman for the Dutch utilities industry, is active in the planning and implementation of nuclear power development.

International Relationships. Member of the **International Atomic Energy Agency,** the European Atomic Energy Community **(Euratom),** the **European Nuclear Energy Agency,** and the European Organization for Nuclear Research **(CERN).** Partner with Norway in the Joint Establishment for Nuclear Energy Research (JENER). Comprehensive **Agreement for Cooperation** with the United States.

Research Centers. The National Reactor Center, located near Petten, was originally conceived as a national laboratory, but, by recent agreement, it is now partly operated as a **Euratom** laboratory. The experimental facilities include a low-power research and training reactor of the **Argonaut** type, and a high-flux materials testing reactor. The latter, known as HFR, is a light water-moderated tank-type unit supplied by ACF Industries. It was completed in 1961 and operates at a power level of 20,000 kilowatts (thermal). The United States contributed $350,000 toward the cost of HFR under its program of Foreign Research Reactor Grants.

Fig. 127. The high-flux materials testing reactor (HFR), near Pelten, as it looked in the final stages of construction. (*Courtesy of Allis Chalmers Manufacturing Co.*)

KEMA Laboratories, Arnheim, is a research center serving the Dutch utilities industry and operated by the utility cooperative, SEP. Development work on the SUSPOP power reactor concept (see below) is in progress at this facility under a contract with RCN.

An Institute for the Application of Atomic Energy in Agriculture is planned at Wageningen.

Energy Economy. The present electric power capacity of the Netherlands is about 5000 megawatts, virtually all of it steam-electric. A substantial fraction of the fuel used for power generation is imported.

Nuclear Power Program. The Netherlands looks to nuclear power as a means of stabilizing her energy economy and reducing her dependence on conventional fuel imports. Present targets for the installation of nuclear power capacity call for several hundred megawatts by 1965, 1200 megawatts by 1970, and 3000 megawatts, by 1975 (by which time nuclear power would account for 50% of Dutch electricity generation). Information on specific projects follows.

SUSPOP: A small-scale experiment is in progress at KEMA Laboratories to test the technical feasibility of a reactor system fueled with enriched uranium in the form of pellets in a water suspension. If the results are favorable, a 10-30 megawatt (electrical) demonstration reactor will be built as the next step in the development of this concept.

SEP Project: Construction of a 150-megawatt (electrical) nuclear power station in North Brabant Province under the **U.S.-Euratom Joint Program** was contemplated by SEP, but it was decided in 1960 that the 1965 completion deadline specified in that program could not be met. In 1961, SEP entered into cooperative arrangements with the General Electric Company to develop plans for a nuclear power project based on the boiling water concept.

There is also active interest in marine (tanker) propulsion.

Industry Notes. Netherlands Atom Forum is a recently established association analogous to the U.S. Atomic Industrial Forum.

NERATOOM, Amsterdam, is a consortium of 6 industrial firms (including Philips Eindhoven) interested in supplying nuclear and non-nuclear components for nuclear power stations.

SKK (Stichting Kernvoortstuwing Koopvaardijschepen), the Hague, is an association of shipyards established to coordinate research and studies in the field of marine nuclear propulsion. RCN, TNO, and the University of Delft participate in the work of SKK. Installation of a pressurized water-reactor propulsion system in a tanker is planned.

TNO, the Hague, is a nonprofit government-sponsored research organization collaborating with RCN in the field of marine nuclear propulsion and with FOM in controlled fusion research.

NEUTRINO

A neutral **elementary particle** with a rest mass less than a thousandth that of the electron, and possibly zero. The existence of the neutrino was originally postulated by W. Pauli in 1930 to conserve energy and angular momentum in beta decay. A neutrino (or antineutrino) is thought to be emitted in every beta-decay process as well as in some meson-decay processes. The properties required of the neutrino for its role in these processes are such as to make it extremely difficult to detect. Convincing evidence for the existence of the neutrino has, however, been obtained in absorption experiments conducted by Los Alamos Scientific Laboratory (C. L. Cowan *et al.*) with radiation from one of the large production reactors at the U.S. Atomic Energy Commission's Savannah River Plant.

NEUTRON

A neutral (uncharged) elementary particle with a mass approximately the same as the **proton,** and associated with protons in the nuclei of all atoms with a **mass number** above 1 (i.e., heavier than the hydrogen atom). Two or more **nuclides** containing the same number of protons but a variant number of neutrons are called isotopes.

Neutrons are not given off in any radioactive decay process but are ejected from nuclei as the result of some nuclear reactions. The most notable neutron-producing reactions are nuclear **fission** and nuclear **fusion,** both of which reactions are also induced by neutrons. Another neutron-producing reaction is the so-called alpha-neutron reaction (see **alpha particle, neutron sources.** Neutrons ejected from atomic nuclei, commonly referred to as "free neutrons," are unstable; they have a radioactive half-life of approximately 13 minutes and disintegrate into a proton, a **beta particle** and a neutrino. It is postulated that neutron disintegration also takes place within certain atomic nuclei, accounting for the process known as **beta decay.**

Free neutrons, being electrically neutral, are not affected by the negative electrical field which surrounds an atomic nucleus or by the strong positive electric charge associated with the nucleus. For this reason neutrons can readily enter into nuclear reactions. At the same time such reactions can only occur as a result of a direct hit on an atomic nucleus. For the latter reason and bearing in mind that the nucleus of an atom takes up an infinitesimal amount of space in atomic structure, neutrons pass through matter with ease until they collide with a nucleus. They are, in other words, a highly penetrating form of radiation. (See radiation **shielding)** Free neutrons enter into three types of nuclear reaction:

1. Elastic scattering: In this reaction the neutron is deflected, transferring some of its kinetic energy to the target nucleus; there is

no net loss of kinetic energy. The amount of kinetic energy transferred is a function of the mass of the target nucleus, being greater for nuclei of low mass number. Elastic scattering is the mechanism by which moderators slow down neutrons in a nuclear reactor.

2. Inelastic scattering: In this reaction the incident neutron displaces a neutron from the target nucleus. The latter is ejected with a lower kinetic energy than that of the incident neutron and there is a net loss of kinetic energy, leaving the target nucleus in an excited state.

3. Capture: In neutron capture, the incident neutron is absorbed by the target nucleus, which is thereby made unstable. In **radiative capture,** the only prompt emission is gamma radiation. (This is also called the neutron-gamma reaction.) If the target nucleus is a **fissionable material,** fission may occur. Other possibilities include the emission of a proton or a **deuteron.** In a nuclear reactor, any neutron capture event not resulting in fission or in the production of new fissionable material (by radiative capture in a **fertile material** and subsequent beta decay) is referred to as parasitic capture.

In reactor technology, free neutrons are classified by energy. Those with energies above 100,000 electron volts (ev) are called fast neutrons. Those with energies below 1 ev are called slow neutrons. Those with intermediate energies are called intermediate neutrons. (The energy break points are somewhat arbitrary.) Slow neutrons are commonly also referred to as thermal neutrons, although the term is sometimes (and more accurately) restricted to neutrons in thermal equilibrium with their environment, which at "room temperature" means an energy of about 0.025 ev. Another term often used is epithermal neutrons, which is usually taken to mean neutrons in low intermediate range, i. e., from 1 ev up to $\sim$ 100 ev.

The existence of the neutron was first postulated by James Chadwick of England in 1932.

NEUTRON ACTIVATION ANALYSIS. See **activation analysis, neutron sources.**

NEUTRON CAPTURE

A **capture** process in which an atomic nucleus absorbs a neutron. The probability of a given material absorbing neutrons is referred to as the neutron capture cross section and is a function of the energy of the neutrons. (See **cross section,** also **resonance absorption)**

NEUTRON CAPTURE THERAPY

A technique being studied for the treatment of certain types of brain cancer (notably glioblastoma multiforma) based on the use of a beam of thermal neutrons from a nuclear reactor. In this technique, a boron-10 compound is injected into the patient's bloodstream. The boron compound tends to localize for a brief period in the tumorous tissue in the

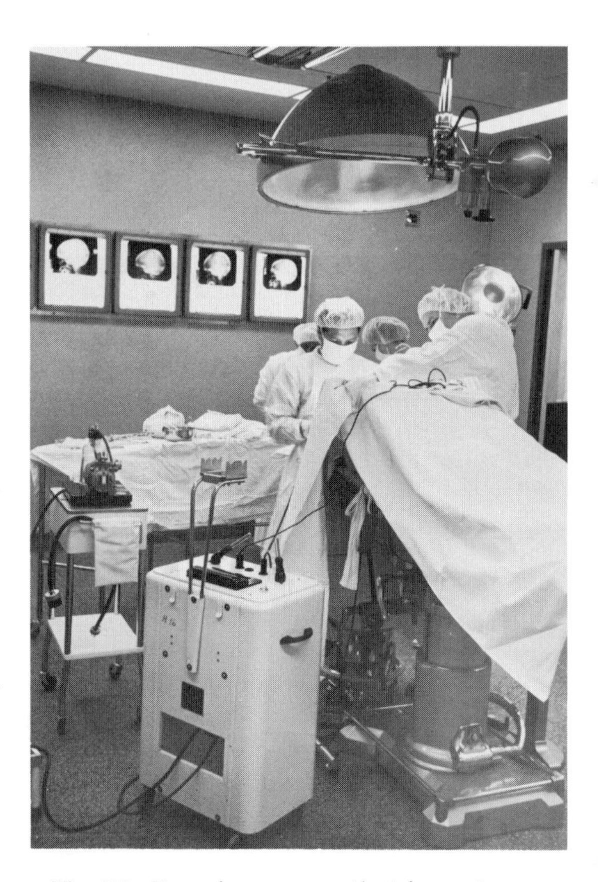

Fig. 128. Preparing cancer patient for neutron capture therapy. (*Courtesy of Brookhaven National Laboratory*)

brain. At the proper time the area under treatment is exposed to a collimated thermal neutron beam. The neutrons are preferentially captured by the boron-10 isotope, resulting in the prompt emission of an energetic alpha particle. The alpha particles are absorbed within a millimeter or two of their point of origin, and so afford an extremely localized means of applying radiation therapy to the tumor.

Research on neutron capture therapy has been conducted at Brookhaven National Laboratory for a number of years, and a reactor (the **Brookhaven Medical Research Reactor**) has been recently completed with this research as one of its major purposes. Treatment, so far restricted to terminal cancer patients, has shown some encouraging results, however the method is still in an early stage of development. Massachusetts General Hospital in Boston has initiated research on neutron capture therapy using special facilities of the **Massachusetts Institute of Technology Reactor.**

NEUTRON CHOPPER

An instrument for obtaining periodic pulses of neutrons by the mechanical interruption of a continuous beam of neutrons from a reactor. Depending on the design of the instrument the neutrons may be slow or fast and the instrument is called a "slow chopper" or a "fast chopper," respectively. The energies of the neutrons in the pulses are determined by means of multichannel time-of-flight analyzers.

NEUTRON DENSITY

The number of neutrons per unit volume in the core of a nuclear reactor. Neutron density

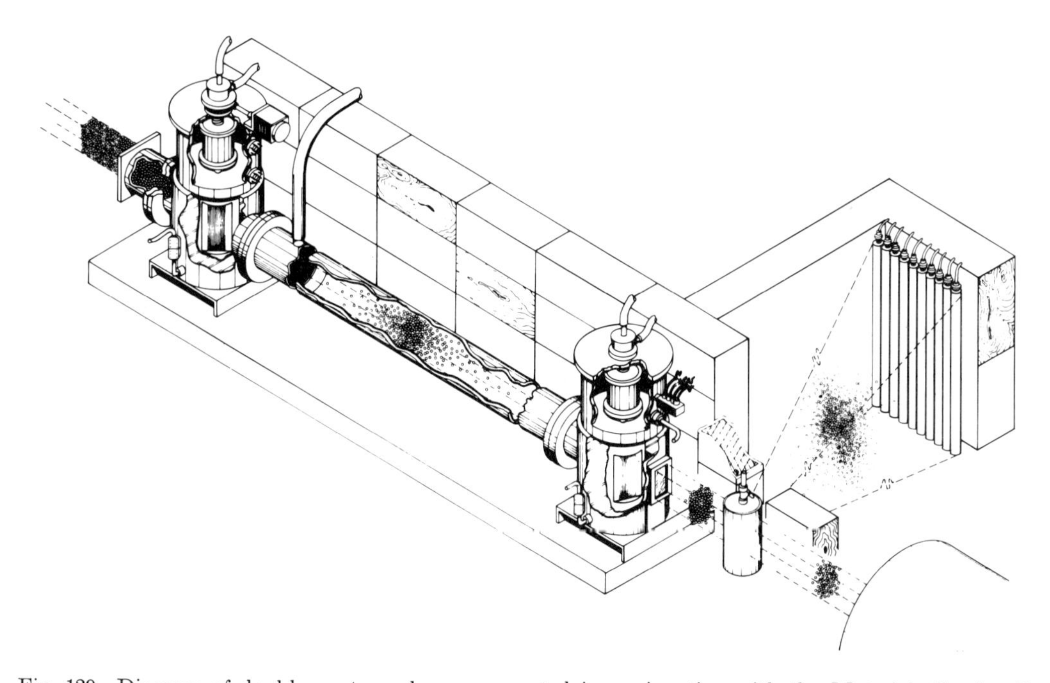

Fig. 129. Diagram of double neutron chopper operated in conjunction with the Materials Testing Reactor. A beam of neutrons from one of the beam ports in the MTR enters the first chopper (at left). The emerging burst undergoes time-of-flight separation so that the second chopper acts as a velocity selector, "releasing" successive bursts of essentially monoenergetic neutrons. These strike a sample in the target chamber. Neutrons scattered by the sample are detected by an array of counters in a scattering chamber (at upper right). Signals from these counters feed into a multi-channel analyzer (not shown), the readings from which provide information on the energy and angular distribution of the scattered neutrons. The unscattered neutrons are absorbed in a beam catcher tank (lower right). (*Courtesy of Phillips Petroleum Co.*)

may be expressed in terms of the total neutron population, or values may be given for segments of the total population defined by energy or other criteria. (See **neutron flux)**

NEUTRON ECONOMY

The management of neutrons in a nuclear reactor: more specifically, the balance between the productive and nonproductive use of the neutrons produced in the reactor. Productive uses include the propagation of the chain reaction; the conversion of **fertile** to **fissionable materials;** and, in research or test reactors, the use of neutrons for radioisotope production or experimental purposes. Nonproductive uses include the parasitic capture of neutrons in fissionable materials (as in the formation of uranium-236 and other nonfissionable isotopes of uranium); the absorption of neutrons in moderator, coolant, control or structural materials; the absorption of neutrons in fission-product **poisons** or in other impurities present in the system; and the loss of neutrons by leakage through the **reflector.**

Neutron economy is an important consideration in reactor design since it has a direct bearing on the efficiency of fuel utilization and hence on fuel costs, and also affects the capital investment required to achieve a given level of reactor performance. The parameters that enter into neutron economy are different for different reactor systems. For example, because neutron absorption **cross sections** are lower at high neutron energies, the nonproductive absorption of neutrons in structural materials is less important in the design of **fast reactors** than it is in the design of **thermal reactors;** therefore the designer of a fast reactor system has greater latitude in the selection of structural materials than does the designer of a thermal system.

NEUTRON FLUX

The intensity of neutron radiation, i.e., the number of neutrons passing through a unit area in a unit time (Symbol: ϕ). Neutron flux is equal to the product of **neutron density** and the average velocity, and has the unit of neutrons per square centimeter per second. Values are usually given for neutrons of a particular energy range, as for example, for **thermal neutrons.** The rate of a neutron-induced **nuclear reaction** is the product of the neutron flux and the **cross section** for the particular reaction.

Nuclear reactors used to produce neutrons for experimental or test purposes are often rated by their neutron flux and are generally considered to be "high-flux" units when the maximum thermal-neutron flux exceeds 5×10^{14} neutrons per square centimeter per second. (See **research and training reactors, test reactors)**

NEUTRON SOURCES

Discussion of this topic will be limited to neutron sources other than nuclear reactors, which are discussed separately (see **research and training reactors).** These fall into two basic categories: radionuclide sources and particle accelerators. Neither can deliver the high-neutron fluxes of which reactors are capable; however they have a variety of uses, including:

1. Supplying neutrons for laboratory-scale experiments in basic neutron physics and biomedical research.
2. Irradiation of target materials for purposes of neutron **activation analysis.**
3. Irradiation of target materials to produce short-lived radioisotopes for research purposes.
4. Pulsing of neutron-multiplying lattices, as in **exponential experiments.**
5. **Oil-well logging.**
6. Simulation of neutron phenomena associated with nuclear weapons. (This use requires an accelerator-type source).

Oil-well logging is an example of a purely industrial application. There is also industrial interest in the use of compact neutron sources for activation analysis, both as a research and a quality control tool.

Radionuclide Sources. The principal type of radionuclide source for neutron supply consists of a mixture of an alpha-emitting radionuclide and a target material which yields neutrons by the alpha-neutron reaction (see **nuclear reactions**). Commonly used mixtures include:

Alpha Emitter	*Target Material*	*Yield* [1] *(neutrons per second per curie of alpha-active material)*
Polonium^{210}	Beryllium	2.3×10^6
Radium [2]	Beryllium	1.7×10^7
Plutonium^{239}	Beryllium	1.5×10^6

[1] Not to be confused with **neutron flux.**
[2] Naturally radioactive substance.

The neutrons emitted by such sources have a broad energy spectrum, ranging from 1 to 10 Mev or higher. They can readily be moderated to the thermal energy range by means of a sheet of paraffin or other hydrogen-containing material.

A second type of radionuclide source consists of a mixture of a gamma-emitting radionuclide and a target material which yields neutrons by the mechanism of photodisintegration. An example is the use of sodium-24 (produced in a nuclear reactor) in combination with beryllium, yielding essentially monoenergetic $\sim$ 1 Mev neutrons.

Particle Accelerators. Neutrons of various energy characteristics can be obtained by bombarding a suitable target material with high-energy charged particles. Reactions commonly used include:

The types of particle accelerator used include:

1. Electrostatic generators, such as the **Van de Graaff generator.**
2. Cascade-type accelerator, such as **Cockroft-Walton machines** and **resonant transformers.**
3. **Linear accelerators.**
4. Small accelerator tubes.

The latter type includes a number of compact devices that have been developed for use as portable neutron sources for field applications, such as oil-well logging.

The neutron yield * from accelerators depends on the particular system used but falls in the general range of 10^{10}-10^{14} neutrons/second for laboratory machines, and 10^{7}-10^{10} neutrons/second for portable devices.

NEVADA TEST SITE (NTS)

A U.S. Atomic Energy Commission experimentation station located at Mercury, Nevada, approximately 65 miles northwest of Las Vegas; formerly known as the Nevada Proving Ground. The site encompasses an area of about 600 square miles of desert land adjacent to a U.S. Air Force Gunnery Range.

The NTS is used in part for testing of small nuclear weapons and related devices, and for study of weapons effects for military and Civil Defense purposes. When in progress, weapon test operations are conducted under the scientific direction of the sponsoring laboratory (either Los Alamos Scientific Laboratory, the Livermore branch of the E. O. Lawrence Radi-

* Not to be confused with **neutron flux.**

Charged Particle	*Target Material*	*Neutron Energy*	
		Range	*Distribution*
Protons	Lithium	30–500 Kev	Monoenergetic
Deuterons (>1 Mev)	Beryllium	500–60 Kev	Monoenergetic
Deuterons	Lithium	2–6 Mev	Monoenergetic
Deuterons (<1 Mev)	Tritium	10–16 Mev	Monoenergetic
Electrons (>1.7 Mev)	Beryllium	1–2 Mev [1]	Continuous spectrum
Electrons (>2.2 Mev)	Deuterium	1–2 Mev [1]	Continuous spectrum
Electrons (>9 Mev)	Uranium	1–2 Mev [1]	Continuous spectrum

[1] Peak energy range within broad energy spectrum.

ation Laboratory, or the Sandia Laboratory). Weapons test facilities at the site, representing an AEC investment of ~ $72 million,* are maintained by an AEC contractor (Reynolds Electrical and Engineering Company), who also furnishes technical support to test operations. (See **weapons testing**)

The NTS is also used as a proving grounds for systems being developed for nuclear rocket and ramjet propulsion. It is the site of the Kiwi rocket-propulsion reactor experiments being conducted by Los Alamos Scientific Laboratory (see **Rover Project**); and also of the Tory series of ramjet-propulsion reactor experiments being conducted by the Livermore branch of the E. O. Lawrence Radiation Laboratory (see **Pluto Project**). The Kiwi and Tory experiments are conducted in the Jackass Flats area of the NTS.

NEW BRUNSWICK LABORATORY

A U.S. Atomic Energy Commission chemistry laboratory at New Brunswick, New Jersey, whose primary purpose is to develop analytical techniques and standards for uranium compounds and other materials of interest to the U.S. atomic energy program. Additional activities have included research on uranium production processes and assistance to AEC contractors in connection with uranium assay and quality control procedures. Established in 1949, the Laboratory is staffed with AEC personnel and administered by the AEC's Oak Ridge Operations Office. The Director is C. J. Rodden. The investment in plant and equipment is ~ $2 million.

NEW PRODUCTION REACTOR (NPR). See **Hanford Works.**

NEW ZEALAND

Atomic energy matters come under the Department of Scientific and Industrial Research (DSIR), Wellington, which is advised by an Atomic Energy Committee. DSIR has a division of nuclear sciences actively engaged in isotope research, and is constructing an Institute of Nuclear Science at Gracefield, near Wellington. Facilities of the Institute will include a 3-Mev Van de Graaff accelerator being supplied by High Voltage Engineering Corporation, and a research reactor is planned for installation in 1962 or 1963.

Approximately 95% of New Zealand's electric power plant is hydroelectric, and there are abundant undeveloped hydro resources; hence there is no interest in nuclear power at the present time in this primarily agricultural country. New Zealand is a member of the **International Atomic Energy Agency.**

* Includes facilities authorized or under construction as of June 30, 1960. Not adjusted for depreciation.

NICARAGUA

The Comision Nacional de Energia has responsibility for atomic energy matters. Nicaragua is a member of the **International Atomic Energy Agency** and the **Inter-American Nuclear Energy Commission,** and has a research-type **Agreement for Cooperation** with the United States.

NICKEL

Element No. 28 (symbol, Ni; atomic weight 58.69), of interest in the nuclear field in two unrelated ways: (1) It is used in a binary alloy with chromium to provide a fuel element cladding material of exceptional corrosion resistance and high-temperature properties in air. It is also alloyed with steel and other metals for the same purpose. The thermal neutron absorption cross section of nickel is appreciable (4.6 barns), so that it must be used sparingly in materials for thermal reactor systems. This limitation does not apply in the case of fast reactors. (See **reactor materials**) (2) As "sintered nickel," it is used as a material of construction of the diffusion membrane (barrier) used in the **gaseous diffusion** process for the separation of uranium isotopes.

NIOBIUM. See **columbium.**

NOBELIUM

Element No. 102. A team of scientists from the U.S., the United Kingdom and Sweden announced its discovery in 1957 as the result of a chain of experiments culminating at the Nobel Institute in Stockholm. Scientists at other laboratories have as yet been unable to duplicate the specific results reported, but it seems probable that the Element No. 102 has been produced and that it is formed by heavy-ion bombardment of **curium.** (See **transuranium elements)**

NOMINAL YIELD WEAPON

A nuclear weapon having about the same **yield** as those used at Hiroshima and Nagasaki, i.e., about 20 kilotons (TNT equivalent).

NONAUTOCATALYTIC

A term applied to a power reactor whose reactivity decreases as the power level increases; for example, a reactor with a **negative temperature coefficient.** This is a desirable characteristic from a safety standpoint.

NONTHERMONUCLEAR NEUTRONS

In the operation of experimental controlled-**fusion** devices, a distinction is made between neutrons released by "true" thermonuclear reactions and neutrons produced by any of various other mechanisms; the latter are known as nonthermonuclear or "false" neutrons. True thermonuclear conditions exist only when fusion occurs in a uniformly hot **plasma** (i.e., ionized gas) as the result of interaction between ions in random thermal motion. False conditions exist—to cite one example—when some plasma ions become preferentially accelerated and cause fusion by striking relatively "cold" ions present in the plasma or absorbed on the surfaces of the apparatus. An important aspect of current work in the field of **plasma diagnostics** is the analysis of neutron emission patterns to distinguish false neutrons from neutrons of true thermonuclear origin.

NORMAL URANIUM

Uranium containing the natural abundance (0.7115 weight %) of the uranium-235 isotope. The terms "normal uranium" and "natural uranium" are used interchangeably.

NORTH CAROLINA STATE COLLEGE REACTORS (NCSR-1, -2, -3)

NCSR-1, the first privately owned nuclear reactor licensed by the U.S. Atomic Energy Commission, was a 10-kilowatt (thermal) water boiler-type research reactor designed by the College staff. It began operation in 1953, and in 1955 was dismantled because of corrosion damage. It was known as the Raleigh Research Reactor.

For information on NCSR-2 and -3, see **research and training reactors** (Tables 3 and 2, respectively).

NORTHERN STATES POWER PROJECT. See **Pathfinder Plant.**

NORWAY

Agency. The Institutt for Atomenergi (IFA), Kjeller, is the organization for atomic energy matters.

International Relationships. Member of the **International Atomic Energy Agency,** the **European Nuclear Energy Agency,** and the European Organization for Nuclear Research **(CERN).** Partner with the Netherlands in the operation of JENER (see below). Comprehensive **Agreement for Cooperation** with the United States. Bilateral agreement with the United Arab Republic.

Research Centers. The principal nuclear research center is the Netherlands-Norwegian Joint Establishment for Nuclear Energy Research (JENER) at Kjeller, near Lillestrom.

This center is jointly operated by Norway's IFA and the Netherlands' RCN (Reactor Centrum Nederland). Specialized facilities include "hot" laboratories, a fuel reprocessing semi-works, and two reactors, JEEP-1 and NORA. One is a heavy water-moderated research reactor designed to operate at power levels up to 10 kilowatts (thermal). It was supplied by NORATOM (see below). The United States contributed $350,000 toward the cost of the new installation under its program of Foreign Research Reactor Grants. The other is a zero-power reactor facility, recently completed as a joint project of the Norwegian government and the International Atomic Energy Agency. Along with its research activity, JENER produces, processes, and distributes radioisotopes, and conducts the Netherlands-Norwegian Reactor School.

The world's first boiling heavy-water reactor, designed by the JENER staff and now operated as a joint project of the **European Nuclear Energy Agency** of the Organization for Economic Cooperation and Development (OECD), is located at Halden, 60 miles south of Oslo. (See **Halden Project** for details) This facility, known as the Halden Boiling Water Reactor (HBWR), serves as a center for boiling heavy-water reactor development.

Production Activity. Low-grade uranium deposits have been found in southern Norway but are not of commercial interest. Heavy water is produced commercially by Norsk Hydro. The process employed is electrolysis. The plant, which has been in operation for many years, can produce up to 15 tons of heavy water per year.

Energy Economy. Norway's present electric power capacity is approximately 5000 megawatts, virtually all of it hydroelectric.

Nuclear Power Program. Oslo Lyswerk, a private utility serving the Norwegian capital, is reportedly considering the construction of a 25-50 megawatt (electrical) boiling heavy water nuclear power station to replace an obsolete facility. In general, however, Norway's interests in reactor development lie in process heat and marine propulsion applications, rather than in electric power generation.

Industry Notes. NORATOM, Oslo, is an association of some 45 leading industrial, shipping and financial firms, formed to provide consulting and engineering services in the reactor field. REDERIATOM (Nuclear Research Group of Norwegian Shipowners) is an association of 19 shipping firms which, by contract with IFA, is supporting a design study to determine the economic feasibility of constructing and operating a nuclear-powered tanker.

NUCLEAR BATTERIES

(1) Devices for producing small amounts of electric power (watts) using the heat of radioactive decay of radionuclides as the energy source. (2) Devices for supplying a small electrical current (microamperes) or a small electrical discharge (microwatts) by direct amplification or collection of beta radiation from a small radionuclide source.

Devices of the former type are being developed for use as an auxiliary or remote power supply for various military applications (see **SNAP Program**) and also for certain civilian applications (see **radioisotopes in industry**). Devices of the latter type, useful for certain specialized instrument applications, are available commercially.

NUCLEAR BOMB EFFECTS COMPUTER

A pocket calculator designed to provide quick estimates of nuclear weapon effects (see Fig. 130).

NUCLEAR CROSS SECTIONS ADVISORY GROUP

An *ad hoc* (nonstatutory) advisory body to the U.S. Atomic Energy Commission charged with making a continuing review of the AEC's program of nuclear **cross-section** measurements to obtain critically needed data and to prevent needless duplication. The membership is reconstituted annually, each member serving a one-year term corresponding to AEC's fiscal year (i.e., July 1–June 30). Membership listed in Appendix D.

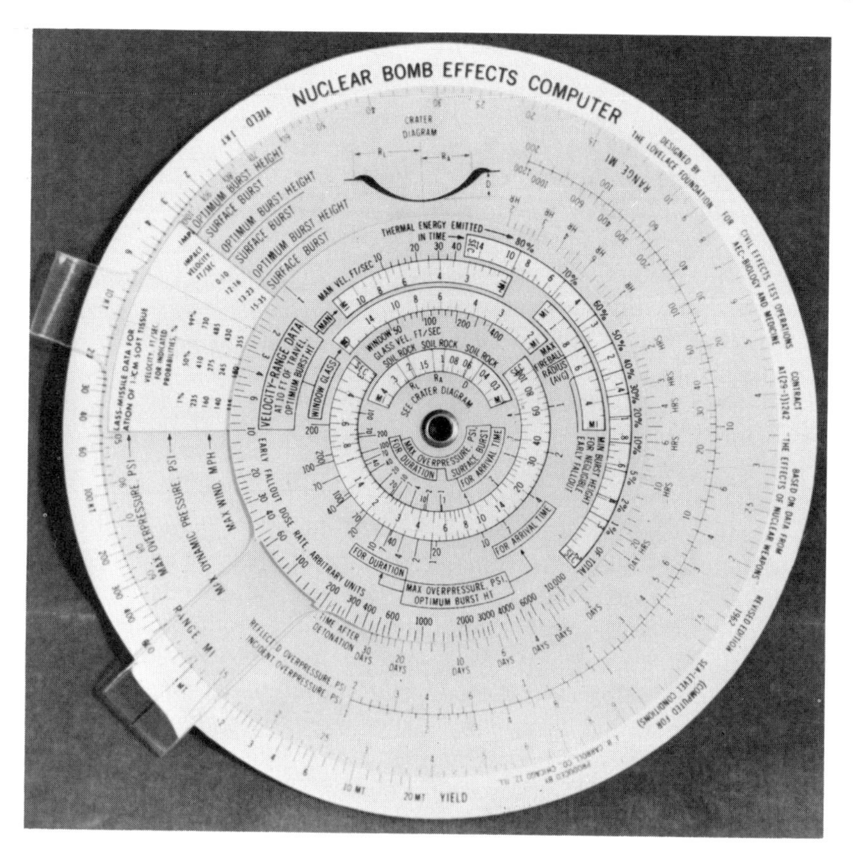

Fig. 130. Nuclear Bomb Effects Computer. (*Courtesy of Lovelace Foundation for Medical Education and Research*)

NUCLEAR ENERGY. Synonymous with **atomic energy.**

NUCLEAR ENERGY LIABILITY INSURANCE ASSOCIATION (NELIA). See **insurance and indemnification against atomic energy risks.**

NUCLEAR ENERGY PROPERTY INSURANCE ASSOCIATION (NEPIA). See **insurance and indemnification against atomic energy risks.**

NUCLEAR EXPLOSIVES, PEACEFUL USES OF. See **Plowshare Program.**

NUCLEAR FUEL SERVICES, INC. PROJECT

A project to furnish **fuel reprocessing** services on a commercial basis to the nuclear power industry. The project, not yet finalized as of this writing (mid-1962), is based on the following plans: (1) Construction, in New York State, of a privately owned fuel reprocessing plant on land leased from the recently established New York State Atomic Research and Development Authority. (2) Operation, under a lease arrangement, of adjoining spent fuel and radioactive waste storage facilities to be owned by the Authority. The reprocessing and related storage facilities are to be located on a 3500-acre tract of land in Cattaraugus County, about 30 miles southeast of Buffalo. The plant is to be designed to handle a variety of fuel elements, will have a capacity of 1 ton per day when treating slightly enriched fuel, and will cost an estimated $22 million to build. Nuclear Fuel Services, Inc., a subsidiary of W. R. Grace Company, will own the reprocessing plant proper and will operate the over-all facility.

Plans for the project were announced in

July, 1962, with the notice that NFS had purchased an option from the Authority for the proposed operations. The option allowed a period of aproximately 3 months (with extension privileges) for the obtaining of a license from the U.S. Atomic Energy Commission for construction of the plant and for completion of negotiation of reprocessing contracts, with utility customers and with the AEC.

The project is an outgrowth of studies conducted by Davison Chemical Company (also a unit of W. R. Grace) in collaboration with several utility companies that have sponsored nuclear power projects, namely, Consolidated Edison Company of New York, Inc. **(Indian Point Station)**, Commonwealth Edison Company **(Dresden Nuclear Power Station)**, Northern States Power Company **(Pathfinder Plant)**, and Yankee Atomic Electric Company **(Yankee Atomic Electric Plant)**.

Empire State Atomic Development Associates, a membership corporation formed by seven investor-owned utilities serving New York State, will contribute $2 million for research and development in support of the project once the plans are finalized.

NUCLEAR INCIDENT

In context with government indemnification agreements (see **insurance and indemnification against atomic energy risks**), a nuclear incident is legally defined to mean "any occurrence within the United States causing bodily injury, sickness, disease, or death, or loss of or damage to property, or for loss of use of property, arising out of or resulting from the radioactive, toxic, explosive, or other hazardous properties of **source, special nuclear,** or **by-product material.**" The restrictive phrase "within the United States" does not apply in the case of the nuclear-powered merchant vessel, NS *Savannah*.

NUCLEAR INDUSTRY, U.S.

In its present stage of evolution, the U.S. nuclear industry involves five broadly defined spheres of activity:

Spheres of Activity	*1960 Order of Rank (1 = largest)*		
	Capital Investment	*Annual Volume*	*Employment*
Defense materials industry	1	1	2
Research and development	2	2	1
Operation of nuclear power plants	3	5	5
Reactor industry	4	3	3
Radiation industry	5	4	4

The following paragraphs provide general orientation on these activities.

Defense Materials Industry. Reference here is to the production of fissionable and special materials and the fabrication of these materials into weapon components. Table 1 summarizes this activity. As is indicated, only the raw materials production activities (mining and ore processing) and a portion of the uranium refining are conducted in privately owned facilities. The other activities are conducted in AEC facilities operated under contract by industrial firms. The total plant investment is approximately $5.7 billion; annual operation and procurement costs amount to approximately $1.5 billion, exclusive of procurement of ore and concentrates from foreign sources; and total employment is approximately 55,000. While weapons are the principal product, this industry also supplies enriched and natural uranium, heavy water and other materials for use in reactors and for research programs.

Research and Development. This sphere of activity is arbitrarily taken to encompass all research and development sponsored by the U.S. Atomic Energy Commission, together with all privately sponsored research and development of a related nature. Table 2 summarizes the AEC-sponsored activity. Comparable data are not available on privately sponsored activity, however on the basis of partial information the following figures for AEC plus privately sponsored research and

TABLE 1. PRODUCTION OF DEFENSE MATERIALS
(1960 data)

Category	*Investment in Facilities ($ millions)*		*Volume of Business— FY 1960 ($ millions)*		*Employment (thousands of persons)*		*Notes*[4]
	AEC[1]	*Private*	*Cost of AEC Opn's*	*AEC Procurement*	*AEC prime Contractors*	*Other*	
Uranium mining	10	unknown[5]	—	298[2]	0	4.1	Several hundred private mining enterprises. They sell to uranium mills but may receive production bonuses from AEC. See **uranium mining.**
Ore processing		144	—		3.4	0	26 privately owned uranium mills. They produce uranium concentrates under negotiated price contracts with AEC. See **uranium milling.**
Feed materials production	256	11		—[3]	11.7	0	Mallinckrodt Chemical Works and National Lead Co. of Ohio operate AEC-owned production plants. Allied Chemical & Dye Corp. produces UF_6 in own plant under AEC contract. See **uranium refining and conversion.**
Uranium-235 production	2,343	0	731	0		0	Union Carbide Nuclear Co. and Goodyear Atomic Corp. operate large AEC-owned plants. See **uranium enrichment.**
Plutonium production	1,657	0		0	35.6	0	duPont and General Electric Co. operate large AEC-owned plants. See **plutonium.**
Heavy water production	163	0		0		0	duPont operates AEC-owned plant. See **deuterium.**
Special materials production	278	0		0		0	ACF Industries, Bendix Aviation Co., Dow Chemical Co., General Electric Co., Mason and Hanger, Monsanto Chemical Co., Union Carbide Nuclear Co., and others operate AEC-owned plants.
Weapon fabrication and storage	821	0	505	0		0	
Totals:	$5,528	$155[5]	$1,236	$298	50.7	4.1	

[1] Nondepreciated investment as of June 30, 1960. Authorized but expended construction funds not included.
[2] Domestic concentrate procurement and bonus payments to miners. Foreign procurement excluded.
[3] Procurement of UF_6 from Allied Chemical & Dye included in cost of AEC operations.
[4] For specific information on AEC-owned plants see **Atomic Energy Commission—Facilities.**
[5] Total investment in uranium mining enterprises is believed to be of the same general order of magnitude as that in ore processing plants but no specific figures have been compiled.

TABLE 2. AEC-SPONSORED RESEARCH AND DEVELOPMENT
(1960 data)

Category [1]	*AEC INVESTMENT in R&D Facilities ($ millions)* [2]	*AEC R&D Expenditures—FY 1960 ($ millions)* [3]	*Employment (thousands of persons)* [4]
AEC-owned laboratories	~$1,412		42.2
Universities and non-profit research institutions	~70	$591	5.3
Industrial laboratories	~40		
TOTALS	~$1,522	$591	47.5

[1] For information on specific laboratories and facilities, see **Atomic Energy Commission—Facilities.**
[2] Nondepreciated investment as of June 30, 1960. Authorized but unexpended construction funds not included. Includes experimental, military and civilian reactors but excludes reactors built under the Power Demonstration Reactor Program.
[3] Exclusive of weapons research.
[4] Approximately one-third are scientists or engineers.

development are believed to be roughly representative: investment in specialized R&D facilities, $1.6-1.7 billion; annual R&D expenditures, $700-750 million; and R&D employment, 60-70,000.*

Of the roughly estimated $700-750 million in annual R&D expenditures, reactor development programs and related research account for at least 60%. Research on radiation applications accounts for less than 5%. The balance is accounted for by a broad spectrum of basic and applied research in the physical and life sciences. Two major areas of this activity are high-energy physics (see **particle accelerators**) and controlled fusion (see **thermonuclear power**). An area just beginning to be explored is that of peaceful uses of nuclear explosives (see **Plowshare Program**). (Also see **agricultural applications** and **medical aspects of atomic energy**)

Nuclear Power Generation. Reference here is to the operation of civilian nuclear power demonstration facilities built either as cooperative projects under the AEC's Power Demonstration Reactor Program or as independent industry projects. At present these facilities are operated primarily for developmental purposes and power generation is of secondary importance. Projects undertaken as of mid-1962 represented a total capital commitment of $712 million with 65% financed by investor-owned utilities, 30% by the AEC and 5% by public power agencies or cooperatives.**

Reactor Industry. This sphere of activity includes:

1. Reactor design. (See **Army Nuclear Power Program, Maritime Reactors Program, Naval Reactors Program, SNAP Program,** and **nuclear power development**)
2. Manufacture of specialized equipment components, and factory-packaged reactor assemblies.† (See **Pressure vessels, fuel-handling mechanisms, control rod drives, pumps, valves,** and **heat exchangers**)
3. Production of special materials used in reactor systems. (See **beryllium, graphite,** and **zirconium**)
4. Plant engineering and construction services.
5. Fuel-cycle services, i.e., the preparation of fuel materials, the fabrication of fuel elements, and the reprocessing of spent fuel. (See **fuel element fabrication, fuel reprocessing**)

* Equivalent full-time personnel; one-third scientists or engineers.

** These totals do not include experimental (as opposed to demonstration) civilian power reactor facilities, which were covered under Research and Development. For a complete breakdown of civilian power reactor facilities, see **nuclear power development**

† Small reactors for training and research, and portable Army power reactors.

Fig. 131. Examples of private investment in atomic energy research facilities. Top, the John Jay Hopkins Laboratory for Pure and Applied Science, San Diego, the headquarters of General Atomic, a division of General Dynamics Corp. Bottom, reactor facilities at General Electric Company's Vallecitos Atomic Laboratory near Pleasanton, Calif.; VBWR at left and GETR at right. (*Courtesy of General Atomic and General Electric Co.*)

Based on incomplete information, order-of-magnitude estimates of the dimensions of this industry are as follows: investment in specialized manufacturing facilities, $100-200 million; annual sales, > $220 million; employment, exclusive of construction labor, ~ 25,000. These estimates do not include reactor development activity, which was covered above under Research and Development.

Radiation Industry. This sphere of activity includes:

1. Production, processing, and the distribution of radioisotopes. (See **radioisotopes**)
2. Manufacture of radioisotopes-containing devices for industrial measurement and control applications. (See **radioisotopes in industry**)
3. Manufacture of radionuclide sources for use in **teletherapy** and **radiography,** and in industrial radiation applications.
4. Manufacture of radiation machines, e.g., **linear accelerators** and **Van de Graaff** generators, used in research and in industrial radiation applications.
5. Design and production of radionuclide-type auxiliary power units. (See **SNAP Program**)
6. Manufacture of radiation detection and measurement instruments. (See **nuclear instruments industry**)
7. Manufacture of equipment used in handling radioactive materials—manipulators, shield windows, shipping containers, etc.
8. Irradiation services.
9. Radioactive waste disposal services.
10. Health physics and radioactive waste disposal services.
11. Consulting services.

Based on incomplete information, order-of-magnitude estimates of the dimensions of this industry are as follows: investment in production and manufacturing facilities, $50-100 million; annual sales, < $100 million; employment, ~ 5,000. These estimates do not include research on radiation applications, which was covered above under Research and Development.

Total Industry. Adding the above estimates yields the following totals for the U.S. nuclear industry as of 1960:

1. Investment in specialized production, manufacturing or research and development facilities: somewhat under $8 billion.
2. Annual volume of specialized products and services and research and development activity: ~ $2.5 billion.
3. Employment: ~ 150,000.

It is stressed that these estimates are based in part on extrapolations from incomplete data.

NUCLEAR INSTRUMENTS INDUSTRY

Approximately 160 U.S. firms are reportedly engaged in the manufacture of radiation detection and measurement instruments and related devices and accessories. The accompanying table shows a roughly categorized breakdown of shipments during 1959, the total value of which is estimated at approximately $48 million.

Many of the companies in this field are small and technically specialized. The larger, more broadly based companies include Baird-Atomic, Inc., Nuclear-Chicago Corporation, Radiation Counter Laboratories, Tracerlab, Inc., and The Victoreen Instrument Company. (See **Geiger counter, ionization chamber, proportional counter, scintillation counter, ratemeter, scaler, air samplers and monitors, gages,** etc.)

NUCLEAR INSURANCE RATING BUREAU (NIRB)

A special rating bureau established by the property insurance syndicates, **NEPIA** and **MAERP.** NIRB handles, on a national basis, the rating functions associated with the issuance of policies insuring atomic energy facilities against property damage arising from

TABLE 1. SHIPMENTS OF RADIATION INSTRUMENTS AND ACCESSORIES
U.S. Manufacturers—1959[1]

Category	*Approximate No. of Units Shipped*	*Estimated Value of $ Millions*
Instrument Components		
Detection heads sold separately		
Geiger-Müller tubes	113,100	1.6
Ionization chambers	2,000	1.2
Scintillation-type	2,100	1.1
Proportional-type	3,300	.7
Scalers	4,300	2.9
Ratemeters	5,500	1.6
Pulse height analyzers	1,700	3.5
Amplifiers	5,400	3.2
Power supplies	32,200	6.3
Sample changers	1,100	.9
Miscellaneous	—	.3
Radiation Monitoring Devices		
Portable survey meters	41,300	6.4
Fixed area and personnel monitoring devices[2]	2,200	1.0
Air monitors (for particulate radioactivity)	200	1.0
Gas and liquid monitors	1,700	3.5
Dosimeters and accessories[3]	105,600	3.9
Industrial Measurement and Inspection Devices		
Gages	1,300	6.6
Radiography units	n.a.	.3
Radiation sources	13,900[4]	1.6

[1] Source: Preliminary Department of Commerce data. Numbers have been rounded.
[2] Excludes hand-and-foot monitors, which are included above under miscellaneous.
[3] Excludes chemical dosimeters.
[4] Containing a total of some 316,000 curies of radioactivity.

atomic energy hazards. Headquarters are in New York City. Policy is set by a nine-member Executive Committee made up of six representatives of NEPIA and three of MAERP. (See **insurance and indemnification against atomic energy risks**)

NUCLEAR MATERIALS MANAGEMENT

A term encompassing the various aspects of the control and management of **SS materials.** It includes **accountability for source and special nuclear materials**; budgeting and allocating of materials to achieve efficient utilization of available inventories; and efficient inventory management to avoid charges for use, losses, or reprocessing. Within the U.S. Atomic Energy Commission, these functions are performed by a Division of Nuclear Materials Management.

NUCLEAR POWER DEVELOPMENT, FOREIGN

See **Belgium, Brazil, Canada, Czechoslovakia, France,** West **Germany,** East **Germany, Hungary, Italy, Japan,** the **Netherlands, Poland, Soviet Union, Spain, Switzerland,** and **United Kingdom.** Also see **Agreements for Cooperation, Euratom, U.S.-Euratom Joint Program.**

NUCLEAR POWER DEVELOPMENT, U.S.

Reference here is to the development of nuclear reactors for civilian electric power generation,* which is perhaps the most important nonmilitary application of atomic energy. For information on a related but longer-range approach to civilian electric power generation see **thermonuclear power.**

General facts on the U.S. program of civilian nuclear power development are summarized in the accompanying exhibits, which are discussed in the paragraphs immediately following. This presentation closes with a

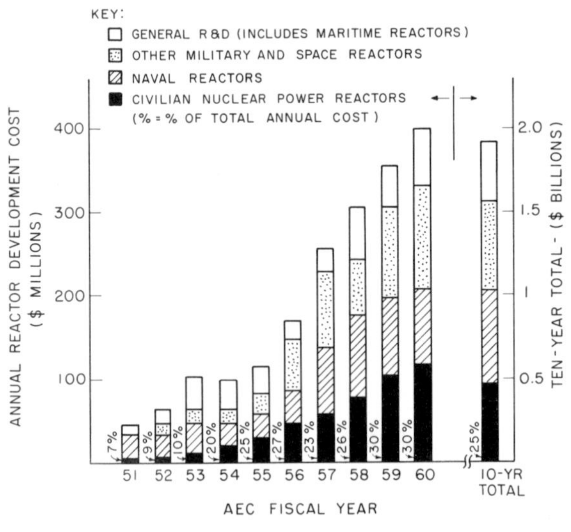

Fig. 132. Trend in reactor development cost—U.S. Atomic Energy Commission (exclusive of capital costs). Source: Data taken from AEC's 1960 financial report.

brief review of the background of the U.S. program. For related information, see **nuclear power economics; nuclear industry, U.S.**

Summary. Figure 132 shows the trend in expenditures by the U.S. Atomic Energy Commission for military and civilian power reactor development from 1950-1960, exclusive of capital costs. Approximately 25% of the total related specifically to civilian power reactor development. Also, the civilian program has received considerable benefit from the somewhat larger Naval reactor effort, which laid the groundwork of pressurized water reactor technology and additionally made important contributions to sodium reactor technology (see **Naval Reactors Program).** The civilian program has also benefited from other military reactor effort, notably the **Aircraft Nuclear Propulsion Program,** and from the research and development that has been conducted in general support of the AEC's over-all reactor program.

In addition to AEC expenditures are those of private industry. Information presented later (Table 3) indicates that electric utilities are supporting at least $60 million of research and development in connection with existing nuclear power plant projects. Allowing for expenditures by reactor and component manufacturers, it is likely that private research and development outlays or commitments through 1961 totaled at least $100 million, exclusive of capital investment.

Reactor Types. Table 1 lists the major types of power reactor that have been studied under the civilian nuclear power program. Each reactor type listed is discussed in some detail in individual entries. The following characterization serves primarily to bring out some of the reasons for a multi-concept approach to nuclear power development:

Pressurized water reactors are cooled and moderated by ordinary water that is pressurized to prevent bulk boiling. Steam is generated in an external heat exchanger. Pressurized water reactors have the best developed technology due to the emphasis they have received in the Naval Reactors Program, and are known to be reliable in operation. Their major disadvantage is that they have a ceiling operating temperature of about 600°F. Their inherently high operating pressure is a disadvantage from a capital-cost standpoint as in the need to employ corrosion-resistant materials to withstand hot-water corrosion. The use of a separate steam-cooled reactor as a superheater offers a way to improve the quality of the steam produced. The achievement of higher power densities offers a way of reducing unit capital costs.

Boiling water reactors are also cooled and moderated by ordinary water but in this case

* For information on other electric power applications of reactors see **Army Nuclear Power Program, SNAP Program.** For information on propulsion applications, see **Aircraft Nuclear Propulsion Program, Maritime Reactors Program, Naval Reactors Program, Pluto Project** (ramjet) and **Rover Project** (rocket).

TABLE 1. FEATURES OF MAJOR POWER REACTOR TYPES
(for central station power applications)

Reactor Type	Fuel[1]	Coolant	Moderator	Operating Characteristics[2]	
				Pressure (psi)	Reactor Outlet Temperature (°F)
Solid-fuel:					
Pressurized water	Slightly enriched uranium dioxide clad in stainless steel or zircaloy	H_2O (pressurized)	H_2O	2000	534
Organic cooled	Slightly enriched uranium-molybdenum alloy clad in aluminum or stainless steel	Terphenyl mixture	Terphenyl mixture	120	575
Boiling water	Slightly enriched uranium dioxide clad in stainless steel or zircaloy	H_2O (boiling)	H_2O	1025	547[3]
Sodium-graphite	Slightly enriched uranium-molybdenum clad in stainless steel	Liquid sodium	Graphite	negligible	945
Fast breeder	Enriched uranium-molybdenum alloy clad in stainless steel	Liquid sodium	None	negligible	800
Heavy-water moderated	Natural uranium metal clad in zircaloy	D_2O (pressurized)	D_2O	(750)	(480)
Gas-cooled (high-temperature type)	Dispersion of fully enriched uranium and thorium in graphite matrix clad in graphite[4]	Helium	Graphite	300	1382
Fluid-fuel:					
Aqueous homogeneous	Aqueous solution of fully enriched uranyl nitrate	Fuel solution	H_2O or D_2O	(2000)	(572)
Molten salt	Fused-salt solution of fully enriched uranium and thorium	Fuel solution	Graphite	(negligible)	(~1000)

[1] Based on current technology. New fuel materials are under development in most cases.
[2] Data reflect the most advanced conditions achieved by plants in operation or under construction. The data given in parentheses are based on reactor experiments rather than on actual power plant design.
[3] This is for a conventional boiling water reactor. A boiling water reactor employing integral nuclear superheating is expected to achieve a reactor outlet temperature of 825°F (see **Pathfinder Plant**).
[4] This is the fuel planned for use in the **High-Temperature Gas-Cooled Reactor** (HTGR) at Peachbottom, Pa. The AEC's Experimental Gas-Cooled Reactor (EGCR) at Oak Ridge will use slightly enriched uranium dioxide clad in stainless steel.

bulk boiling is allowed. This is advantageous from a capital-cost standpoint, since it permits lower operating pressures and also eliminates the need (in some designs) for an external heat exchanger (since steam is produced in the reactor core). Boiling water reactors utilize much of the technology that has been developed for pressurized water reactors and also depend on superheating to achieve operating temperatures significantly higher than 600°F. In this case, however, provisions for superheating can be built into the reactor (integral nuclear superheating), obviating the need for a separate superheater. Boiling water reactors inherently operate at lower point densities than pressurized water reactors, which is a capital-cost disadvantage (since it requires a larger core for a given power output).

Organic cooled reactors are conceptually similar to pressurized water reactors except that in place of water a mixture of organic compounds (terphenyls) is used. The organic coolant has a lower vapor pressure than water, permitting substantially lower operating pressures; and is essentially noncorrosive, permitting the use of cheaper materials of construction. As a consequence, organic cooled reactors have relatively low unit capital costs. Their principal disadvantage derives from the poor heat-transfer properties of the organic coolant, which creates problems in fuel element design. Also organic mixtures are subject to deterioration under neutron irradiation.

Sodium-graphite reactors are cooled by liquid sodium which has a very high boiling point and thus permits the attainment of high operating temperatures in an essentially unpressurized system. The moderator is graphite. While a good deal of experience in the use of sodium as a reactor coolant was inherited from the Naval Reactors Program and considerable effort has been expended since under the civilian nuclear power program, sodium technology is not nearly as well developed as water technology. Partly for this reason and partly because of other factors sodium-graphite reactors are presently characterized by high unit capital costs. Also further research is needed to achieve fuel element materials and designs. In the main these are developmental, rather than conceptual problems.

Fast breeder reactors are cooled by liquid sodium and employ highly enriched fuel in an unmoderated system. They hold considerable long-range promise of low fuel cost and high fuel utilization efficiency. They can achieve high power densities. Also, the use of a fast-neutron system gives the designer greater latitude in the selection and use of construction materials than is the case in a thermal neutron system. The principal problem of fast breeders is that they are at an early stage of development, especially in the area of fuel element technology.

There are several **heavy water-moderated power reactor** concepts. In the one receiving greatest emphasis in the United States, heavy water (D_2O) serves as coolant as well as moderator. The advantage of heavy water relative to ordinary water is that it absorbs considerably fewer neutrons due to the fact that deuterium has an appreciably lower thermal neutron capture **cross section** than hydrogen. The difference in neutron economy is such that a D_2O-moderated reactor can be fueled with natural uranium, whereas an H_2O-moderated reactor requires the use of enriched fuel. This holds out the possibility of achieving low fuel costs, which is the potential advantage of all heavy water-moderated concepts. There are offsetting considerations, the most obvious being the cost of the heavy water inventory and operating losses. Another is the fact that D_2O is not as effective as H_2O in slowing down neutrons, which necessitates larger core dimensions. Work on heavy water-moderated reactors for civilian power requirements began relatively recently in the United States and, while experience gained in the design of heavy water-moderated plutonium production reactors for the AEC's Savannah Power Plant has been of benefit, this type of reactor is at a relatively early stage of development.

Gas-cooled reactors offer an obvious route to high-temperature operation since the operating pressure can be set independently of the temperature, and since the use of an "inert" gas minimizes corrosion problems. Another conceptual advantage is that any of several high-performance moderators can be used. The major disadvantages are the poor heat-transfer properties of gases and the consequent inability to operate at high power densities. Development of high-temperature gas-cooled reactors started relatively recently in the United States and is presently at an early stage.

In **fluid fuel reactors,** a fuel solution or suspension is circulated through a piping loop containing a region of critical geometry (the core) and a heat exchanger (steam generator). The conceptual advantage of such systems is that they eliminate the use of solid fuel elements, thereby avoiding problems of structural damage to fuel during irradiation and saving the cost of fuel element fabrication. Also, such systems offer promise as **thermal breeders** since the absence of any need for structural material in the core permits the achievement of excellent neutron economy. Offsetting these advantages are various practical difficulties arising from the corrosive and/or erosive nature of the fuel stream; the problem of maintaining proper distribution of the fissionable components in the stream; and the fact that the entire primary loop of the system, being intensely radioactive, must be remotely maintained. In the **aqueous homogeneous reactor** concept, the fuel consists of an aqueous (H_2O or D_2O) solution of highly enriched uranium. While the operation of such a system has been demonstrated in short-term experiments, operating difficulties were encountered (notably excessive corrosion) which indicated that a sizeable effort would be required to develop materials of requisite integrity and reliability. Partly for this reason, and partly because of inherent operating temperature limitations, the decision was made in 1960 to base fluid fuel development on a different concept.

The concept provisionally selected was that of **molten salt reactors.** In this case the fuel consists of a solution of highly enriched uranium and thorium in a mixture of molten salts (fluorides of beryllium, zirconium, lithium, potassium, etc.). Such solutions have high boiling points, permitting the achievement of high operating temperatures in an essentially unpressurized system; and appear to be manageable from a corrosion standpoint. In other respects they have both advantages and disadvantages relative to aqueous solutions. A short-term molten salt reactor experiment was successfully conducted in 1954 under the **Aircraft Nuclear Propulsion Program.** An experiment to explore its suitability for civilian applications is in the planning stage.

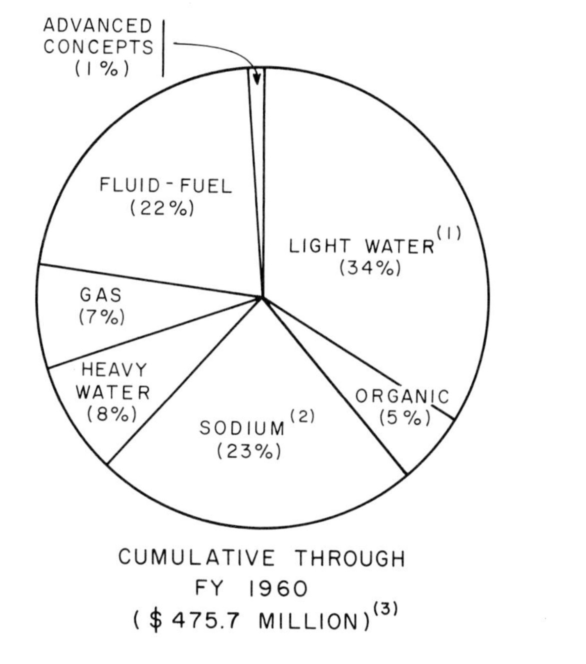

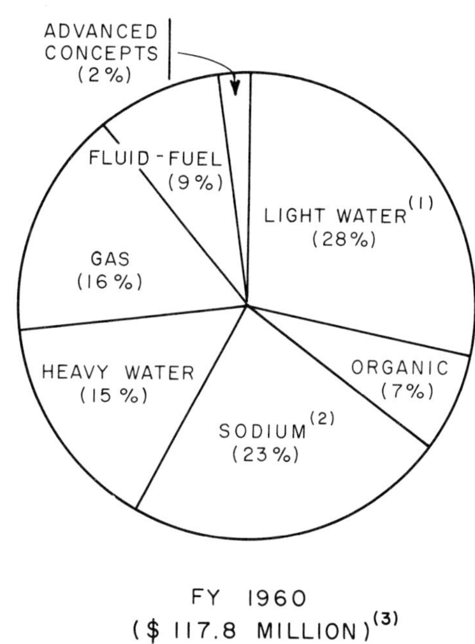

Fig. 133. Distribution of civilian power reactor development costs by reactor type—U.S. Atomic Energy Commission.

Notes: (1) Includes pressurized and boiling water reactors. (2) Includes sodium-graphite and fast breeder reactors. (3) Excludes capital costs. Also excludes general R&D. Source: Data taken from AEC's 1960 financial report.

In addition to these major reactor types, various other reactor concepts have been or are being studied. (See **Advanced Epithermal Thorium Reactor Concept; Liquid Fluidized Bed Reactor Concept; Liquid Metal Fuel Reactor Concept; Los Alamos Molten Plutonium Reactor Experiment No. 1; Mercury Cooled Fast Reactor Concept; Pebble Bed Gas-Cooled Reactor Concept; Spectral Shift Reactor Concept; Variable Moderator Reactor Concept)**

Figure 133 shows the distribution of the AEC's civilian power reactor devleopment effort, both in terms of cumulative research and development expenditures during 1960. As is seen, water-cooled reactors (pressurized and boiling water) and sodium-cooled reactors (sodium-graphite and fast breeders) have received the greatest emphasis. Also, comparison of the two pie charts shows the deemphasis that has recently taken place in fluid fuel reactor development.

Table 2 logs the stages of each development program, i.e., the date of the first reactor experiment, the date of the first demonstration power installation, and the date of the first large-scale power plant. It also lists the organizations that have designed the installations built to date or now under construction.

Projects. Table 3 lists all U.S. civilian power reactor experiments or projects involving the actual production of electricity. As is seen, projects completed, under construction, or definitely scheduled for construction as of mid-1962 account in the aggregate for appoximately 1400 megawatts of electric generating capacity. The total capital investment represented by these projects is $712 million, nearly

TABLE 2. HISTORY OF MAJOR POWER REACTOR TYPES
(Dates refer to start of operation)

	First Reactor Experiment	*First Demonstration Nuclear Power Plant*	*First Large-Scale (100 MWe) Nuclear Power Plant*	*Designers* [1]
Solid Fuel:				
Pressurized water	— [2]	1957—Shippingport	1960—Yankee	Bettis Atomic Power Lab. (AEC) Westinghouse (p)
Organic cooled	1957—OMRE	1962—Piqua		Atomics International (AEC)
Boiling water	1953—BORAX-I	1956—EBWR	1959—Dresden	Argonne Nat'l Lab. (AEC) General Electric (p) Allis-Chalmers (AEC, p) General Nuclear Eng. Corp. (AEC)
Sodium-graphite	1957—SRE	1962—Hallam		Atomics International (AEC)
Fast breeder	1951—EBR-I	1962—EBR-II	(1962, -3)—Enrico Fermi	Argonne Nat'l Lab. (AEC) Atomic Power Development Assoc. (p)
Heavy-water moderated	(1962)—HWCTR	(1962)—CVTR	—	duPont (AEC) Westinghouse (p)
Gas-cooled (high-temperature type)	(1964)—EGCR	(1964)—HTGR	—	Kaiser Eng.-Allis-Chalmers (AEC) General Atomic (p)
Fluid Fuel:				
Aqueous homogeneous	1952—HRE-I	—	—	Oak Ridge Nat'l Lab.
Molten salt	(1964)—MSRE [3]	—	—	Oak Ridge Nat'l Lab.

[1] List restricted to organizations that have designed one or more civilian power installations or related experiments. (AEC) denotes AEC contract. (p) denotes private contract. See entries on each reactor type for complete list of installations.
[2] Feasibility was established in 1953 by operation of the Submarine Thermal Reactor (STR, now designated S1W) under the Naval Reactors Program.
[3] Basic technical feasibility was established in 1954 by operation of the Aircraft Reactor Experiment (ARE) under the Aircraft Nuclear Propulsion Program.

Table 3. Summary of U.S. Civilian Nuclear Power Projects
(Mid-1962)

Name of Project [1] (in chronological order)	Reactor Type	Power Output (megawatts electrical-net)		Project Costs—$ Millions						Reported R&D Costs of Utilities	Notes [2]
				Estimated Construction Cost			AEC Assistance under Power Demonstration Reactor Program (PDRP)				
		Project	Cumulative Total —U.S.	AEC	Public Utility or Coop	Private	R&D; Preliminary Operation	Waiver of Use Charge	Fuel Fabrication		
Plants operating prior to 1959:											
Experimental Boiling Water Reactor (EBWR)	Boiling water	4.5		7.0							
Sodium Reactor Experiment (SRE)	Sodium-graphite	5.0		11.0		2.3					
Vallecitos Boiling Water Reactor (VBWR)	Boiling water	5.0				3.1					
Shippingport Atomic Power Station	Pressurized water	60.0	74.5	49.9		24.1 [2]					
1959 additions:											
Dresden Nuclear Power Station	Boiling water	184.0	258.5			36.0 [3]				15.0	
1960 additions:											
Yankee Atomic Power Electric Plant	Pressurized water	140.0	398.5			40.4	5.0	3.7		0.2	1st Round, PDRP
Scheduled 1962 additions:											
Experimental Breeder Reactor No. 2 (EBR-II)	Fast breeder	16.5		33.8							
Saxton Experimental Nuclear Reactor	Pressurized water	3.0				6.3 [4]					
Piqua Organic Moderated Reactor	Organic cooled	11.4		8.3	3.9		3.5		1.2		2nd Round, PDRP
Hallam Nuclear Power Facility	Sodium-graphite	76.0		28.9	20.6		16.0		2.9		1st Round, PDRP
Indian Point Station	Pressurized water	151.0 [5]				110.4				12.0	
Humboldt Bay Power Plant	Boiling water	48.5				20.6					
Carolinas-Virginia Tube Reactor (CVTR)	Heavy-water moderated	15.5 [5]				17.7	13.9	1.2		2.9	3rd Round, PDRP
Consumers Power Company Project (Big Rock Point)	Boiling water	48.0				27.6	4.2	1.7			3rd Round, PDRP
Elk River Plant	Boiling water	15.0 [5]		9.3	1.6				0.5		2nd Round, PDRP

←— actual chronology

TABLE 3. SUMMARY OF U.S. CIVILIAN NUCLEAR POWER PROJECTS (*Continued*)
(Mid-1962)

Name of Project [1] *(in chronological order)*	*Reactor Type*	*Power Output (megawatts electrical-net)*		*Project Costs—$ Millions*						*Reported R&D Costs of Utilities*	*Notes* [2]
				Estimated Construction Cost			*AEC Assistance under Power Demonstration Reactor Program (PDRP)*				
		Project	*Cumulative Total —U.S.*	*AEC*	*Public Utility or Coop*	*Private*	*R&D; Preliminary Operation*	*Waiver of Use Charge*	*Fuel Fabrication*		
Enrico Fermi Atomic Power Station	Fast breeder	60.0	843.4			57.5	3.6	3.7		23.2	1st Round, PDRP
Scheduled 1963 additions:											
Pathfinder Plant	Boiling water (with nuclear superheat)	62.0				22.4	8.3	1.8		0.2	3rd Round, PDRP
Shippingport modification (new core)	—	40.0 [6]		9.0							
Boiling Reactor Nuclear Superheat Project (Bonus)	Boiling water (with nuclear superheat)	16.3	961.7	9.3	3.5		1.4		0.8	0.3	2nd Round, PDRP
Scheduled 1964 additions:											
Experimental Gas-Cooled Reactor	Gas-cooled	22.0		36.5							
High-Temperature Gas-Cooled Reactor (HTGR)	Gas-cooled	40.0	1024.1			29.2	14.5	2.5		5.6	3rd Round, PDRP
Scheduled 1965 additions:											
La Crosse Boiling Water Reactor	Boiling water	50.0		13.0	7.8		n.a.		n.a.		2nd Round, PDRP
Bodega Bay Atomic Park	Boiling water	313.0	1387.1			61.0					
	Totals:		1387.1	216.0	37.4	458.6					

Planned but not scheduled:		
AEC projects		
New Production Reactor [7]	—	800.0
Private projects reported under negotiation:		
Southern California Edison Co.	Pressurized water	360.0

Notes: [1] See individual project entries for details.
[2] Cost of land and electrical portion of plant plus $5.5 million contributed to cost of nuclear construction.
[3] Excludes $15 million written off as R&D expense. Based on fixed-price quotation of manufacturer. Actual costs not known.
[4] Reactor connected to existing turbogenerator.
[5] Exclusive of capacity contributed by conventional superheaters.
[6] New core will increase reactor capacity by 90 MWe but turbogenerator can only accommodate additional 40 MWe. 1963 date tentative; may be 1964.
[7] This project involves the proposed installation of power generation facilities to utilize the byproduct heat to be generated in a new plutonium production reactor at the AEC's Hanford Works. As of mid-1962 no funds had been appropriated for construction.

(*Note:* Cost data are largely based on AEC Annual Report for 1961.)

two-thirds of which is being financed by investor-owned utilities.

Additional capacity is listed as planned or under negotiation but not definitely scheduled as of mid-1962. (For a projection of U.S. nuclear power plant construction, see **nuclear power economics**).

Background. The AEC's Division of Reactor Development (DRD) was established in 1948. While studies of power reactor applications and some research on reactor systems had been conducted prior to that date, it can be taken as marking the formal beginning of the U.S. power reactor development program. The early emphasis of the program was placed on military applications and on building a groundwork of reactor technology for future civilian applications. Major projects undertaken in the first several years included:

1. Establishment of the National Reactor Testing Station (NRTS) as a power reactor proving grounds.
2. Construction at NRTS of a high-flux reactor for testing materials. (See **Materials Testing Reactor**)
3. Construction at NRTS of a prototype pressurized-water reactor for submarine propulsion. (See **Naval Reactors Program**)
4. Construction of experimental reactor facilities to study the characteristics of aqueous homogeneous, boiling water, and fast breeder reactor systems (see Table 2).

The program was strictly a government effort conducted in government-owned facilities by national laboratory and industrial contractor organizations. The law then in effect (the Atomic Energy Act of 1946) prohibited private ownership of reactors or other facilities using or capable of producing significant quantities of fissionable materials.

In 1951, the AEC invited private industry, at its own expense, to study the technical and economic feasibility of "duel-purpose" reactors, i.e., reactors that would produce plutonium for defense stockpiles and use the byproduct heat for electric power production. A number of industrial study groups were formed and given access to classified reactor data for this purpose. In 1953 AEC interest shifted from dual-purpose to straight power reactors, and the following year actions were taken which placed civilian power reactor development on an entirely new footing:

1. It was decided to accelerate the development of civilian nuclear power reactors to ensure continued U.S. leadership in atomic energy applications.
2. Construction of a large-scale demonstration nuclear power plant was undertaken as a joint AEC-private utility project. (See **Shippingport Atomic Power Station**)
3. Construction of prototype boiling water and fast breeder and an experimental sodium-graphite reactor was undertaken (see Table 2).
4. New atomic energy legislation (the Atomic Energy Act of 1954) was enacted providing for private ownership of nuclear power facilities and containing other provisions designed to encourage private initiative nuclear power development. The new law also provided for broadened international cooperation in nuclear power development and other civilian applications of atomic energy. (See **legislation, federal**)

Power of Demonstration Reactor Program. Early in 1955 the AEC launched the first of a series of programs designed to encourage private investment in nuclear power development program facilities.

The "first round" of the AEC's Power Demonstration Reactor Program aimed primarily at encouraging private utilities to finance the construction of large-scale nuclear power plants based on well developed reactor concepts such as pressurized and boiling water. The AEC offered to help defray the research and development costs associated with such projects, and to waive its use charge for leased fuel for the initial years of plant operation. Two projects were undertaken on this basis and a third * was undertaken on a modified basis (see right-hand column of Table 3). In addition two utilities elected to build large-scale plants without AEC assistance (see In-

* The Hallam Nuclear Power Facility. In this case the utility is publicly owned and the AEC is funding the construction of the reactor portion of the plant.

dian Point Station and Dresden Nuclear Power Station in Table 3).

Later in 1955, the AEC announced a "second round" of its Power Reactor Demonstration Program, aimed primarily at encouraging public power agencies or cooperatives to finance the construction of small-scale nuclear power plants, preferably incorporating advanced reactor technology. A number of proposals were received but difficulties which arose in contract negotiation led ultimately to a revision of program conditions. On the revised basis, the AEC owns the reactor, bears related research and development costs, and bears the cost of fabricating the first core. The utility owns the electrical portion of the plant and operates the complete facility. Three projects have been undertaken on this basis (see Table 3).*

In 1957 the AEC announced a "third round" of its Power Demonstration Reactor Program, aimed primarily at encouraging private utilities to finance the construction of nuclear power plants incorporating advanced reactor technology. The terms of AEC assistance are the same as for the "first round." Four projects in the 15-60 megawatt range have been undertaken under the program (see Table 3).

AEC Ten-Year Program. Early in 1960, after making a detailed evaluation of the status of civilian power reactor technology, the AEC published a report ** outlining a long-range program of research and development designed to meet the following principal objectives:

1. Achievement of nuclear power generating costs of approximately 7.5 mills per kilowatt-hour in the United States by 1968. This level of performance would make nuclear power competitive in areas in which the cost of fossil fuels exceeds 35 cents per million Btu. (See **nuclear power economics**)

2. Contribute to the achievement of nuclear power costs of approximately 6.5 mills/KWH by the mid-seventies.

3. Advance the development of fast and thermal breeder reactors with reasonable **doubling times.**

4. Advance the development of reactors capable of operation without dependence on supplies of enriched uranium, i.e., reactors fueled with natural uranium and reactors fueled with uranium-plutonium mixtures.†

The plan called for expenditures by the AEC or by industry in cooperative projects with the AEC, of approximately $1.2 billion for research and development plus a like amount in capital costs, distributed roughly as follows:

TENTATIVE PLAN OF EXPENDITURES
CIVILIAN NUCLEAR POWER PROGRAM—1960–1970

	R&D (*$1.2 billion*)	*Construction* (*$1.2 billion*)
Water-cooled reactors	18% [1]	22%
Organic cooled reactors	6%	8%
Sodium-graphite reactors	7%	13%
Gas-cooled reactors	9%	10%
Fast and thermal breeders	18%	23%
Heavy water reactors	7%	16%
Plutonium recycle program	6%	2%
General	29%	6%
	100%	100%

[1] Includes major experimental program at the Shippingport Atomic Power Station.

The ten-year program is subject to change as developments unfold and the above breakdown is thus tentative both as to level and distribution of effort.

Program Review. In March, 1962, President Kennedy called for a comprehensive review of the U.S. program of civilian power reactor development, which review is in progress at this writing.

NUCLEAR POWER ECONOMICS

This topic is discussed in four parts as follows: U.S. Electric Power Trends; Economic Status of Nuclear Power; Nuclear Power Cost

* For information on two projects that were proposed and subsequently cancelled, see **Chugach Electric Association Project,** and **Wolverine Electric Project.**

** "Civilian Power Reactor Program, Parts I-IV" (TID-8516).

† See **Plutonium Recycle Test Reactor.**

Factors; and Projected Nuclear Power Plant Construction. For information on fossil and nuclear fuel reserves, see **energy statistics, U.S.**

U.S. Electric Power Trends. To provide a frame of reference for discussion of nuclear power, some general information is first presented on over-all U.S. electric power requirements and on the cost of generating electric power from conventional fuels (coal, oil and gas). Discussion is limited to power generated and distributed by electric utilities; that produced and consumed by industrial establishments, amounting to about one-tenth of total U.S. power production, is not covered.

Growth in Requirements. Table 1 gives actual and projected figures for total U.S. electric utility power generation and installed generating plant capacity. As is shown, requirements for electric power are expected nearly to double during the present decade. Another point of interest is the importance of thermal (i.e., steam-electric) power generation; in 1959, steam-electric plants accounted for approximately 79% of the total installed capacity, and in 1975, they are expected to account for approximately 82%.

TABLE 1. U.S. ELECTRIC UTILITY STATISTICS [1]

	Actual	*Projected*			
	1959	*1965*	*1970*	*1975*	*1980*
Power generation (billions of kilowatt-hours)	716	1075	1379	1716	2083
Plant capacity (thousands of megawatts)					
Hydroelectric	31.0	47.0	56.0	62.0	68.0
Steam-electric	123.0	175.7	230.2	293.6	364.0
Internal combustion	2.7	3.3	3.8	4.4	5.0
Total	156.7	226.0	290.0	360.0	437.0

[1] Adapted from Federal Power Commission's Release No. 10,076, 1960. Alaska and Hawaii not included. Others have projected greater growth. For example, the Edison Electric Institute places the 1980 steam-electric capacity at 492.6 thousand megawatts.

Of the existing steam-electric capacity, approximately 86% is owned by private (investor-owned) utility companies; 13% is owned by municipal, state or federal power authorities; and 1% is owned by cooperatives.

Current Costs of Power Generation. The cost of power generation in conventional steam-electric plants depends on a number of factors, notably:

1. The cost of fuel which ranges roughly from 20-40¢ per million Btu (delivered price).

2. The efficiency of fuel utilization, which, in terms of "heat rate," ranges from about 8500 to 11,000 or 12,000 Btu per kilowatt-hour of electrical output, depending on the design and size of the plant.

3. The unit capital cost of the plant, which ranges roughly from $100-250 per kilowatt of power generating capacity, depending on the size of the installation, the type of construction (whether an open refinery-type structure as may be used in a warm climate, or an enclosed structure as is required in a cold climate), and on local construction cost factors.

4. The **capacity factor** at which the plant is operated, which ranges from about 80% (in the case of "base load" operation) to about 30% (in the case of "peak load" operation).

5. The fixed charges applied to the capital investment, which range from about 5% per annum (in the case of an REA-financed cooperative) to about 14% (in the case of an investor-owned utility). Where the plant has been operated for a long enough period of time for the original investment to have been written off, the fixed charges are lower than these figures.

Because of these and other factors, the cost of conventional steam-electric power generation varies widely. Some U.S. plants report costs below 4 mills per kilowatt-hour; others report costs higher than 12 mills.*

The following figures are representative of

* These and other power generating costs cited here refer to the cost of power at the point of transmission from the generating plant, commonly called the "cost at the bus bar." Transmission and distribution costs are in addition.

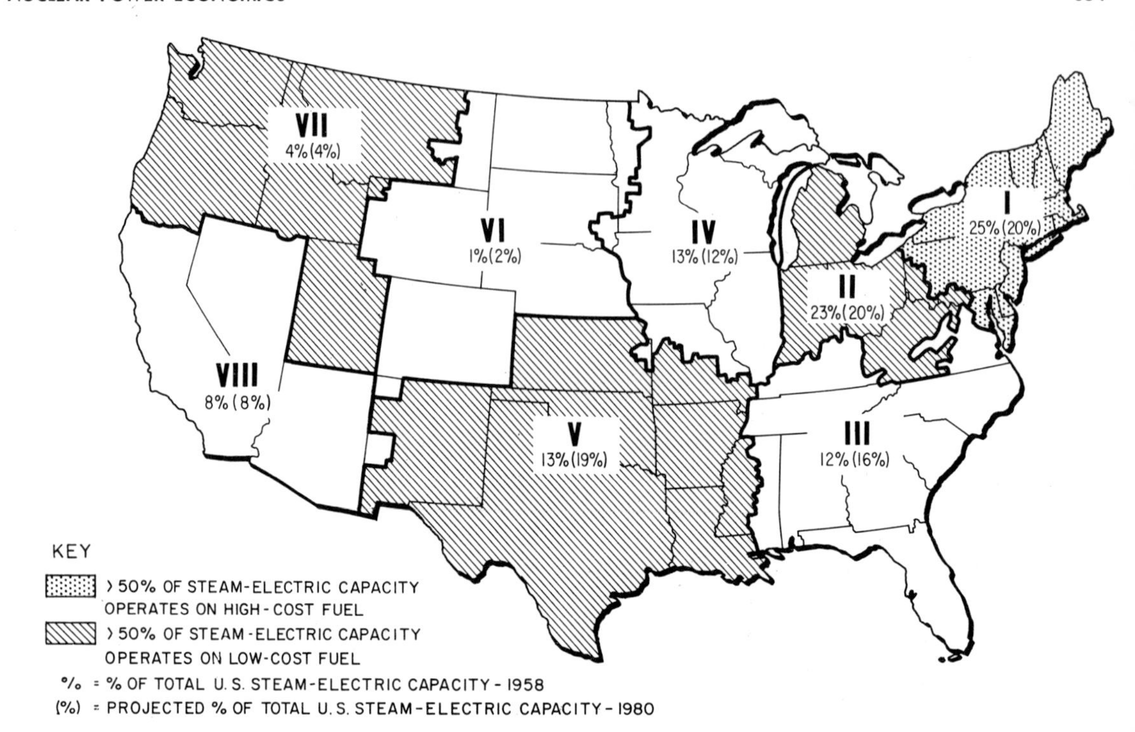

Fig. 134. U.S. Electric power regions as designated by the Federal Power Commission.

the performance in 1960 of a cross section of recently built or expanded power generating facilities: *

% of Capacity	*Level of Cost Performance (mills/KWH)*
87	Below 8
55	Below 7
33	Below 6
Average	6.9

It should be stressed that these data reflect a spectrum of plant sizes, capacity factors, etc., and therefore they do not afford a meaningful measure of the proportion of the new-plant construction market which nuclear power might capture at the indicated cost levels. (See later discussion.)

* Based on data reported by *Electrical World* ("Twelfth Steam Station Cost Survey," October 2, 1961) for a sampling of relatively modern power stations. The stations covered by the survey had an aggregate capacity of about 20,000 megawatts.

Breakdown of Plant Capacity. Table 2 shows the distribution of conventional steam-electric plant capacity by region and by level of fuel cost. As is seen, only about 16% op-

TABLE 2. DISTRIBUTION OF POWER PLANT CAPACITY [1] (1959 data)

FPC Region [2]	*Low-cost Fuel* [3] (%)	*Medium-cost Fuel* [4] (%)	*High-cost Fuel* [5] (%)	*Total* (%)
I	1.4	7.0	13.3	21.7
II	14.3	9.7	.4	24.4
III	8.0	8.4	.5	16.9
IV	4.5	8.9	.6	14.0
V	12.5	.7	—	13.2
VI	.6	.5	.1	1.2
VII	.4	.1	neg.	.5
VIII	—	7.1	1.0	8.1
Total	41.7	42.4	15.9	100.0

[1] Based on AEC Report, "Costs of Nuclear Power," January, 1961 (TID-8531).
[2] See Fig. 1 for map of Federal Power Commission regions.
[3] Below 25 cents per million Btu.
[4] 25 to 35 cents per million Btu.
[5] Above 35 cents per million Btu.

erates on high-cost fuel, most of which is located in Region I (the New England States, New York, New Jersey, Maryland, Delaware and part of Pennsylvania).

Table 3 shows the distribution of steam-electric installations by size. As is seen, nearly two-thirds of the existing capacity is concentrated in large stations, many of which contain more than one generating unit. Also, large units (> 300 megawatts) account for nearly one-third of the total capacity presently scheduled for addition to the U.S. grid. In the latter connection, the *average* size of new units put in service in the United States tripled (from 40 to 120 megawatts) between 1950 and 1957. By 1970, it is expected that units 300 megawatts and larger in size will account for most new construction.

TABLE 3. SIZE DISTRIBUTION OF POWER PLANTS [1] (1959 data)

Rated Plant Output (Megawatts electrical)	*% of Total Installed Capacity* [2] *(approx.)*	*% of Scheduled Additional Capacity* [3] *(approx.)*
Below 100	8%	8%
100–199	13%	33%
200–299	17%	29%
Above 300	62%	30%
	100%	100%

[1] Estimated from data in AEC Report, "Costs of Nuclear Power," January, 1961 (TID-8531).
[2] These data are for power stations many of which contain two or more individual power generating units.
[3] These data are for individual power generating units.

The trend toward larger unit sizes, which is motivated by economies of scale in power plant construction, promises to be accelerated by the utility industry's mounting interest in "power pooling," i.e., the interconnection of utility company transmission systems to permit interchange of power and thereby reduce individual system requirements for reserve generating capacity. Power pooling is expected to result in the construction of many very large units—750, 1000 and ultimately even 2000 megawatts in size. The feasibility of constructing such units will shortly be demonstrated in the metropolitan New York area, where Consolidated Edison Company of N.Y., Inc. has announced plans for a 1000-megawatt unit to be completed in the mid-sixties.

Trends in Fuel Cost. One of the major factors in the economics of thermal power generation is the cost of fuel, which typically accounts for between one-third (in low-cost fuel areas) and one-half (in high-cost fuel areas) of the total power generating cost in conventional steam-electric facilities. Figure 135 shows the actual trend in fuel costs (national average) over the period 1939-1960. Several points should be noted:

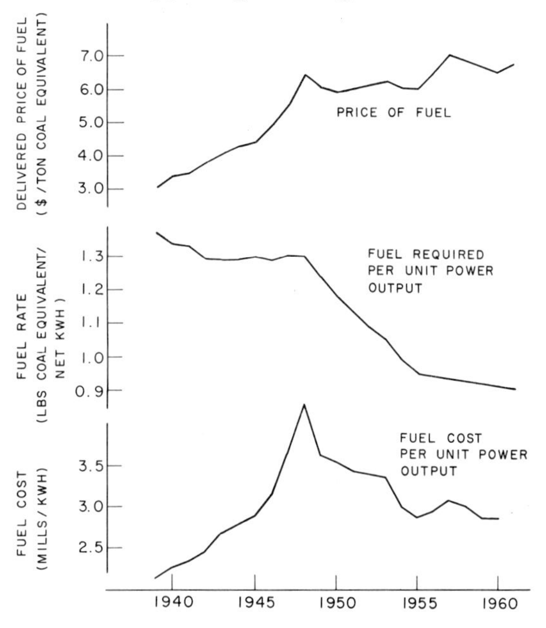

Fig. 135. Fuel trends—conventional U.S. steam plants.

1. Fuel price: As is indicated by the upper curve in Fig. 135, the average price paid for fuel (as delivered), expressed as dollars per ton of coal or an equivalent quantity of oil or natural gas, more than doubled between 1939 and 1960.

2. Fuel utilization: The middle curve shows the average improvement in fuel utilization, expressed as pounds of coal or equivalent consumed per net kilowatt-hour of power output. The improved fuel utilization is due to several factors, notably the achievement of higher

efficiencies in converting heat to electricity through the use of higher steam pressures and temperatures. As is indicated, unit fuel consumption decreased on the average by one-third between 1939 and 1960, with the principal decrease occurring between 1948 and 1955 (reflecting the impact of postwar construction of large amounts of modern steam-electric capacity).

3. Net effect: The net effect of rising fuel prices and improving utilization efficiency is indicated by the lower curve, which shows the national trend in fuel cost in power generation (mills per kilowatt-hour). As is indicated, the average rose from 2.15 mills in 1939 to 4.25 mills in 1948, then fell back to 2.8 mills in 1955, with no significant net change from 1955 to 1960. Thus, in the aggregate, the electric utilities industry succeeded in holding the net fuel cost increase to one-third in the face of a doubling in delivered fuel price.

An expanded view of the trend in fuel utilization, projected to 1980, is given in Fig. 136. Here the measure used is the heat rate, which is defined as the number of Btu of fuel energy consumed per kilowatt-hour of net power output. The smooth curve that has been drawn discounts somewhat the previously mentioned sharp rate of improvement in fuel utilization during the period, 1948 to 1955, and, as indicated, shows a steady but gradually flattening rate of improvement to 1980. This trend, coupled with a projected 34% increase in the average delivered price of fuel between 1954 and 1980,* suggests that the *average* cost of fuel in conventional thermal power generation may remain at approximately the present 2.8-mill/KWH level until 1980. The pattern in a particular region may, of course, be quite different. Indeed in some regions, such as New England, fuel costs have recently trended downward.

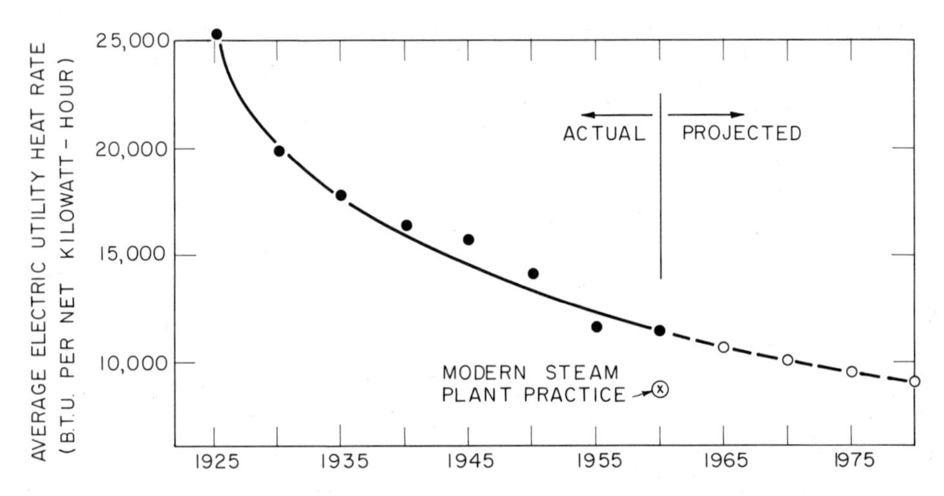

Fig. 136. Trend in fuel utilization—U.S. electric utilities.

Trend in Net Power Generation Cost. The electric utilities industry has been faced with steadily rising costs of labor and materials, which have inflated plant construction cost factors; however, the impact on power generating costs has been offset by the aforementioned trend toward larger-sized power generating installations (with consequent economies of scale) and by technological improvements. In fact, over the past few years during which fuel prices were on the whole stable, the average cost of power generation in the more modern plants was steadily reduced—from 7.1 mills per kilowatt-hour in 1958, to 7.0 mills in 1959, to 6.9 mills in 1960.**

Summary. The following points stand out as having an important bearing on market oppor-

* Source: National Planning Association.

** Figures based on *Electrical World's* "Twelfth Steam Station Cost Survey."

tunities for nuclear power over the next 20 years:

1. To meet fast-growing U.S. requirements for electric power, twice as much steam-electric capacity must be constructed in the next two decades as existed in the United States in 1959. If one assumes an average capital investment of $175 per kilowatt of plant capacity, this will require capital expenditures averaging approximately $2 billion per year for steam-electric plants, exclusive of transmission and distribution facilities. This can be compared with a current (1961) expenditure rate of $1.5 billion per year.

2. As will be brought out, the construction of large plant units in high-cost fuel areas represents the most promising near-future market for nuclear power. Analysis of projection details not covered herein indicates that in the neighborhood of 20% of the projected investment in new generating facilities, or ~ $400 million per year, will be made in areas of preponderantly high fuel costs; and that approximately half of the latter investment, or ~ $200 million per year, will go into large plant units (⋝ 300 megawatts).

3. The threshold for economic nuclear power is set by the capabilities of the most modern fossil-fueled plants, rather than by the average capabilities of the country's existing steam-electric grid. While a substantial fraction (perhaps one quarter) of the country's steam-electric power is generated at costs above 9 mills per kilowatt-hour,* the predicted generating cost of plants now being built in high-cost fuel areas (⋝ 35 cents per million Btu) is today about 7 mills for units of 300 megawatts capacity, and as low as 6 mills for units of 500 megawatts capacity.** Only by escalating fossil-fuel prices due to local factors and thereby arriving at "plant lifetime" forecasts of generating cost higher than the initial cost can the threshold for competitive nuclear performance be put higher than the 6-7 mill range. Nor does this range necessarily represent a fixed target. Despite the substantial technological advances that have been made in conventional power generation over the past several decades, further improvement appears likely, albeit at a diminishing rate of return. In the opinion of some power experts, there is a good possibility that continued technological progress in conventional power generation may more than offset rising construction costs and gradual increases in fossil-fuel prices for another decade or two.

* Taking old as well as new facilities into account.
** Source: Recent estimates reported by utilities and consulting engineering firms.

Economic Status of Nuclear Power. After about a decade of evolution, the status of nuclear power technology at this writing (mid-1962) is as follows (see **nuclear power development** for background):

1. The development of **pressurized water** and **boiling water reactors** is the most advanced. Operating experience has been gained with several demonstration plants of roughly 150-megawatt size, and one plant of roughly 300-megawatt size is about to start construction.

2. Several reactor types are at a stage where small-to-medium sized (15-75 megawatt) prototypes have recently been placed in operation or are now under construction. They include the **sodium-graphite, organic cooled,** and **fast breeder** types, the pressure-tube type of **heavy water-moderated reactor,** and the high-temperature type of **gas-cooled reactor.** Boiling water reactors with nuclear superheating are also at this stage.

3. Still other reactor types are at earlier stages of development, for example, the **molten salt reactor** type, of interest as a possible thermal breeder, is approaching the reactor experiment stage.

It is thus too early to take an actuarial approach in analyzing the available nuclear power cost experience, and some data needed for a definitive analysis of this experience are as yet lacking altogether. Also, it usually takes between 4 and 5 years to design and construct a nuclear power plant; and since the field is rapidly changing, the costs associated with plants now or soon to be in operation do not of themselves fairly represent the current state of the art. For these reasons, the approach followed here is to assess the economic status of nuclear power largely on the basis of quotations for water-cooled plants made in the first half of 1962, by leading reactor manufacturers.

A generalized analysis on the above basis is shown in Fig. 137. The indicated nuclear power cost trend is shown as a dotted line because it is based on progressively larger plant sizes and hence does not reflect a continuum of technological improvement. The following notes serve to amplify the picture given by this chart:

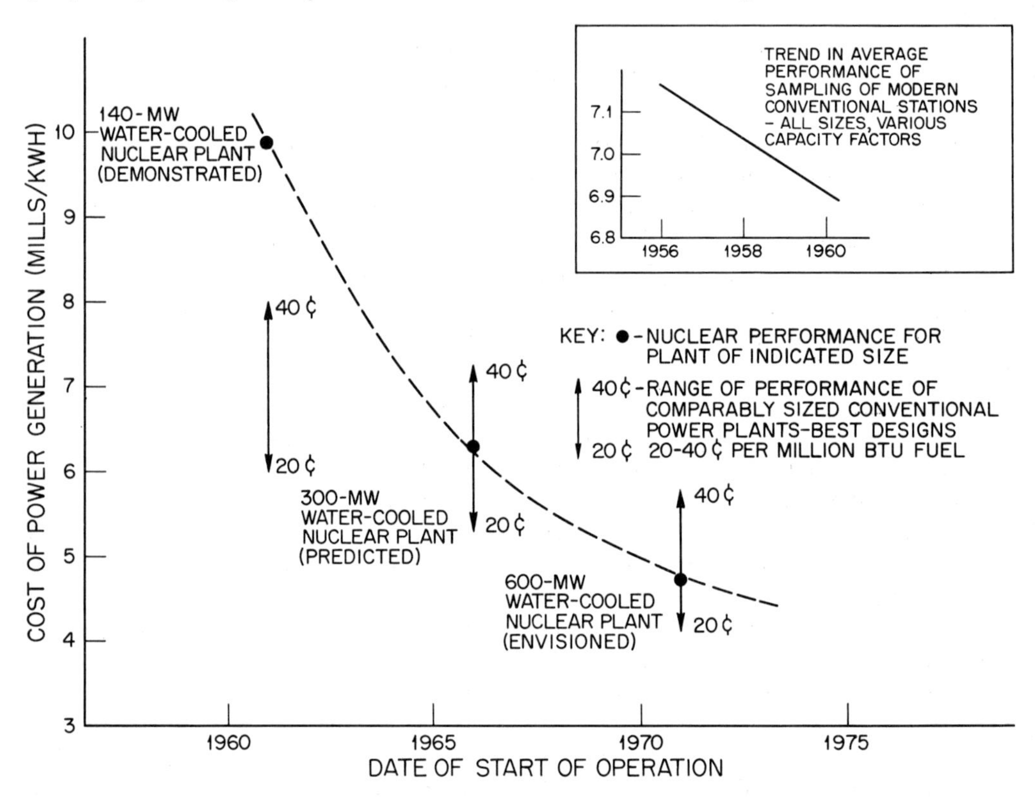

Fig. 137. Projected nuclear *vs.* conventional power cost trend based on 80% plant factor and fixed charges of approx. 14%. Not adjusted for any differences in transmission costs.

1. The figure of just under 10 mills/KWH indicated for 1961 performance of a 140-megawatt water-cooled plant is, by definition, historical and is therefore based on actual experience, being representative of the first core performance of the Yankee Atomic Electric Plant. The corresponding figure for a 140-megawatt water-cooled plant of 1962 design, based on recent quotations, would be about 8 mills. The gain in performance is partially due to a reduction in the price of uranium (see later discussion), but mainly reflects technological progress. As can be inferred from the indicated cost range for comparably sized conventional steam-electric plants, 8-mill nuclear performance would be marginally competitive in very high-cost fuel areas of the United States.

2. The figure of just over 6 mills/KWH indicated for 1966 performance of a 300-megawatt water-cooled plant is consistent with the predicted performance of Bodega Bay Atomic Park.* As can be inferred from the indicated cost range for comparably sized modern conventional steam-electric plants, 6-mill nuclear performance would be generally competitive in high-cost fuel areas of the United States.

3. The figure of just under 5 mills/KHW indicated for 1971 performance of a 600-mega-

* The exact prediction for Bodega Bay at 313 megawatts net output and 80% capacity factor is 6.0 mills based on fixed charges of 13.2%.

watt water-cooled plant must be regarded as highly tentative pending actual commitments for plants of this size. As can be inferred, 5-mill nuclear performance would begin to be competitive in medium-cost fuel areas of the United States.

To summarize the above, the available evidence suggests that, insofar as the general state of the art is concerned, nuclear power plants employing proven reactor types and built in sizes of 300 megawatts and larger can be ordered today on a competitive basis for service in high-cost fuel areas of the United States. There are, however, at least two considerations which can be expected to dampen the rate at which orders for such plants are actually placed:

1. Operation of nuclear plants of this size remains to be demonstrated and their predicted performance is thus not yet confirmed.
2. Local factors may exist which tip the economic balance in favor of a conventional steam-electric installation. As an example, to meet AEC reactor siting criteria (see below), a nuclear plant may have to be located at a distance from the intended load center, thereby incurring a "penalty" in transmission cost relative to a conventional plant. As another example, a utility may have a choice between adding a conventional power generating unit to an existing station and installing a nuclear plant on an undeveloped site. Such a situation would impose a capital-cost "penalty" on the nuclear alternative.

The above remarks relate to the immediate future. Looking ahead a few years, gains in nuclear performance may well be realized via one or more of the presently less developed reactor types which will sharply accelerate the use of nuclear power. In this connection, there is no meaningful basis at present for rating the long-range economic potential of the various types of power reactor presently under development. One point which should be made, however, is that for efficient utilization of nuclear fuel resources (see **energy statistics, U.S.**) **breeder reactors** will be essential, and hence fast and/or thermal breeder reactor types can be expected to figure importantly in the large-scale nuclear power industry of the future.

Nuclear Power Cost Factors. Figure 138 shows the distribution of nuclear power cost as between fixed charges on capital investment, fuel cost, and cost of operation and maintenance—all as a function of plant size. As is indicated, this chart is representative of 1962 designs of water-cooled plants at 80% capacity factor. The fuel cost shown is the pre-

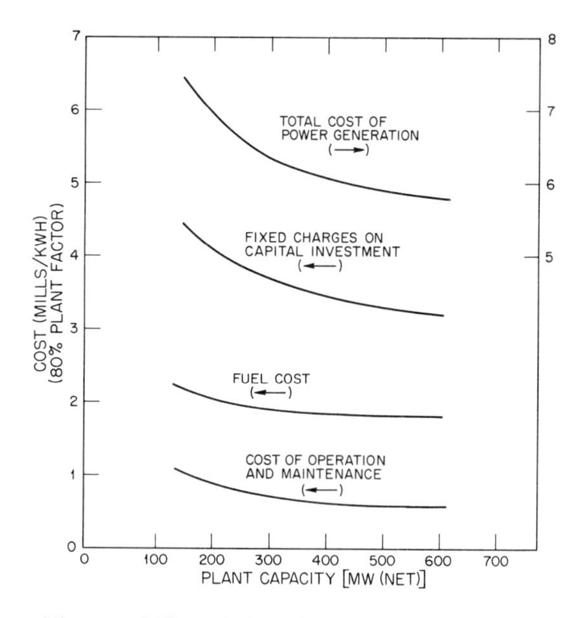

Fig. 138. Effect of plant size on nuclear power costs (water-cooled plants; 1962 designs, i.e., start of operation about 1966; 80% capacity factor; 14% fixed charges; equilibrium fuel cost).

dicted performance at equilibrium, i.e., the average or "levelized" cost predicted over several core loadings.

It is of interest to compare the distribution of power generating costs as between a water-cooled nuclear plant and a conventional steam-electric plant. This is done in Table 4, which shows estimates for a 300-megawatt installation at 60% and 80% capacity factors. This comparison serves to illustrate several points which should be brought out:

1. Nuclear power plants are presently characterized by high capital costs relative to conventional steam-electric plants.
2. Nuclear fuel costs are substantially

lower than can be achieved with high-price fossil fuels.

3. The cost of operating and maintaining nuclear plants is presently substantially higher than for conventional steam-electric plants.

4. Because of (1) and (3), the competitive position of nuclear power weakens as the capacity factor is reduced.

TABLE 4. COMPARISON OF POWER GENERATING COST (300 megawatt installations; 1962 designs)

	Boiling Water Nuclear Plant		*Oil-fired Conventional Plant (40¢/million Btu fuel)*	
	Mills/ KWH	(%) [1]	*Mills/ KWH*	(%) [1]
80% Capacity Factor				
Fixed cost	3.6	58	2.7	44
Fuel cost	1.9	31	3.2	52
Cost of operation maintenance	.7	11	.3	5
Total	6.2		6.2	
60% Capacity Factor				
Fixed cost	4.8	63	3.6	50
Fuel cost	1.9	25	3.2	45
Cost of operation maintenance	.9		.4	6
Total	7.6	12	7.2	

[1] Percentages do not necessarily total 100 because of rounding.

The paragraphs immediately following present more detailed information on nuclear power cost factors.

Capital Cost Factors. The distribution of the capital costs of a nuclear power plant is subject to considerable variance, being affected by the type and size of reactor, its location and site characteristics, and also by the design philosophy of the owner utility. Figure 139 shows an illustrative breakdown for a 300-megawatt boiling water plant of 1962 design. The individual cost categories taken in clockwise order, are discussed under the subheadings immediately following:

Land and land rights: The location of a nuclear power plant is governed by AEC site criteria which take into account the population density and character (residential, farming, etc.) of the environs; the physical characteristics of the site, including seismology, meteorology, geology and hydrology; the characteristics of the reactor, especially its maximum power level and safety characteristics, and the engineering design of the plant.

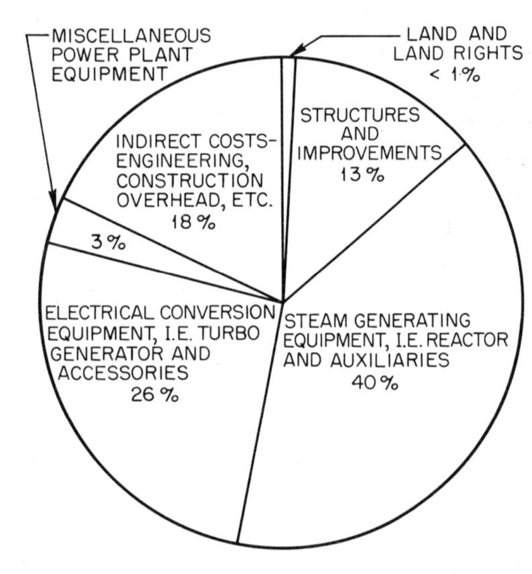

Fig. 139. Breakdown of capital costs 300-mw boiling water plant. (1962 design—capital cost ~ \$190/kw)

In the analysis of a proposed site, three distances are computed:

1. An "exclusion distance," which is the radius of the plant exclusion area, i.e., property in full control of the reactor operator.

2. A "low population zone distance," which is the radial distance (from the reactor) within which the population density is sufficiently low to permit evacuation or other protective measures in the event of a serious accident.

3. A "population center distance," which is the distance (from the reactor) to the nearest boundary of a densely populated center containing more than ~ 25,000 residents.

Table 5 shows distances that have been proposed as a rough guide in reactor site selections. As a first approximation, a 300-megawatt plant would nominally require an exclusion area of about 2000 acres and be surrounded by some 600 square miles of sparsely populated land. In this connection, it should be stressed that reactor site criteria may have a significant effect on the transmission costs of nuclear power plants serving densely populated areas. This would be the case if the distribution of population in a given area were such that compliance with the "population center distance" criterion required locating the plant at a site remote from the intended load center. Since transmission costs are an important element in the cost of power to the consumer, reactor siting may in some instances have an important bearing on the competitive position of a nuclear plant *vis-a-vis* a conventional power plant.

TABLE 5. REACTOR SITE SELECTION GUIDE [1]

Reactor Power Level		*Nominal Distances (miles)*		
Megawatts Thermal	*Equivalent Megawatts Electrical (approx.)*	*Exclusion*	*Low Population Zones*	*Population Center*
1500	420	.88	13.3	17.7
1200	335	.77	11.5	15.3
800	225	.58	8.6	11.5
500	140	.43	6.5	8.7
100	30	.25	2.2	2.9
50	15	.21	1.4	1.9

[1] Source: AEC's TID-14844, March 23, 1962. The distances given are based on calculations for water-cooled reactors and do not necessarily apply to other power reactor types.

Structures and improvements: This category of construction cost includes site preparation; housing for the steam and electrical generating equipment; service buildings and miscellaneous yard facilities. In the case used as the basis for the comparison in Table 4, the structures and improvements item for the nuclear plant was approximately 50% higher than that for the conventional plant. The principal factors in the higher nuclear cost are the need for radiation shielding, vapor **containment,** and related radiation control provisions (special ventilation, air locks, etc.). It is expected that as experience is accumulated in the operation of nuclear power plants, it will prove possible to relax some of the extremely conservative standards currently governing the design of reactor structures and contributing to their high cost.

Steam generating equipment: This category includes all reactor components and auxiliary equipment except for the fuel elements. In a boiling water reactor, for example, the major items include the reactor **pressure vessel** and internal core structures; fuel loading and unloading mechanisms; control rods and **control rod drive** mechanisms; reactor instrumentation; main coolant **pumps** and **valves**; steam generators (i.e., **heat exchangers**); piping; coolant purification and other auxiliary process systems. In the case used as the basis for the comparison in Table 4, the steam generating equipment cost for the nuclear plant was nearly 40% higher than that for the conventional plant. Increasing the size and/or **power density** of nuclear plants will reduce the unit equipment cost appreciably. Another line of attack being followed is to improve the thermal conversion efficiency (and hence the size of reactor required for a given electrical output) by increasing the reactor operating temperature and/or by nuclear superheating. (See **nuclear power development, U.S.**)

Electrical generating equipment: This category includes the turbogenerator and related electrical equipment, exclusive of substation and transmission facilities. In the case used as the basis for the comparison in Table 4, the electrical generating equipment cost for the nuclear plant was approximately 10% higher than that for the conventional plant. In some instances, excess turbogenerator capacity has been provided in anticipation of future increases in reactor power level; however, the higher nuclear cost is primarily due to the inferior quality of the steam produced by the reactor, which ties in with the above statement on thermal conversion efficiency. Modern conventional steam boilers deliver superheated steam at pressures of 1250-3500 psi and temperatures of 950-1050°F. The large-scale water-cooled reactors built to date produce saturated steam at 400-600 psi and 450-485°F.

Annual Fixed Charges. Table 6 gives representative percentage figures for annual fixed charges applied to the capital cost of a nuclear power plant. Where these percentages differ from those applying to a conventional plant the latter are indicated in parentheses.

TABLE 6. REPRESENTATIVE ANNUAL FIXED CHARGES [1]
(% of plant investment)

	Investor-owned Utility	*Public Power Authority*	*Cooperative Financed by REA*
Cost of money [2]	6.75	3.74	2.00
Depreciation [3]	1.11 (0.77)	1.86 (1.43)	2.46 (2.0)
Interim replacements [4]	0.35	0.35	0.35
Insurance [5]	0.4 (0.25)	0.4 (0.25)	0.4 (0.25)
Federal income taxes	3.40	—	—
Other taxes [6]	2.45	1.4	0.8
	14.46 (13.97)	7.75 (7.17)	6.01 (5.4)

[1] Source: "Guide to Nuclear Power Cost Evaluation," vol. 5, March, 1962.
[2] For private financing a 50-15-35 split is assumed between bonds (@ 5% return), preferred stock (@ 5.5% return), and common stock (@ 9.79% return).
[3] A 30-year plant life is assumed (vs. 35 years for a conventional steam plant).
[4] This item covers the cost of replacing equipment having a shorter period of useful service than the plant as a whole.
[5] See **insurance and indemnification against atomic energy risks.**
[6] State and local taxes, including state income tax, property or ad valorem taxes, license fees, unemployment tax, etc.

Fuel cost factors: Under federal law (see **legislation, federal**), the U.S. Atomic Energy Commission has title to all **special nuclear material** * under U.S. jurisdiction. Thus the fuel used in nuclear power generation must be leased from the AEC. The direct fuel costs in nuclear power generation are the cost of fuel element fabrication; the net fuel burn-up cost, which is the reimbursement due the AEC for fuel consumed or lost less a credit received for new fissionable material produced; the cost of transporting the irradiated fuel to a reprocessing site; the cost of fuel reprocessing; and a use charge paid to the AEC for leased fuel. These direct costs are collectively referred to as the **fuel-cycle** costs. There is, in addition, an item of indirect fuel costs, which is the cost of working capital tied up in fuel element fabrication.

* Defined as plutonium, uranium-233, and uranium enriched in the uranium-235 isotope.

Before taking up the subject of cost distribution and discussing the individual cost items, some background should be provided on pricing as a cost factor. The price or fees that are charged for materials supplied or services rendered in the fuel cycle are partly government-determined and partly industry-determined. The division is presently as follows:

Item of fuel-cycle cost	*Price or fee determined by*
Fuel element fabrication	Industry
Net fuel burn-up	AEC
Transportation of irradiated fuel	Industry
Fuel reprocessing	AEC
Use charge	AEC

Items for which unit prices or fees are presently determined by the government account for something like 60% of total fuel-cycle costs; hence it is clear that AEC pricing and fee policy is an important factor in nuclear power economics. Some AEC prices are based on actual production costs; some are necessarily based on hypothetical cost analyses or value judgments; and some are discretionary. The later paragraphs dealing with the individual categories of fuel-cycle cost include a discussion of the bases of AEC pricing.

Distribution of Fuel-Cycle Costs. Figure 140 shows an illustrative breakdown of fuel-cycle costs for a 300-megawatt boiling water plant of 1962 design, based on an average fuel *burn-up* of 15,000 megawatt days per ton. It should be stressed that both the level and the distribution of fuel-cycle costs depend on the burn-up that is achieved. For a given reactor, the higher the fuel burn-up, the lower is the unit fuel-cycle cost. As Fig. 140 shows, the major elements of fuel-cycle cost are the cost of fuel element fabrication and the net fuel burn-up cost. The importance of these cost elements, expressed in terms of their percentage contribution to the total fuel-cycle cost, respectively decrease and increase with improved fuel burn-up. Their combined contribution, again on a percentage basis, remains fairly constant.

Fuel element fabrication cost: This category of fuel-cycle cost includes all steps in the manufacture of fuel elements. The starting ma-

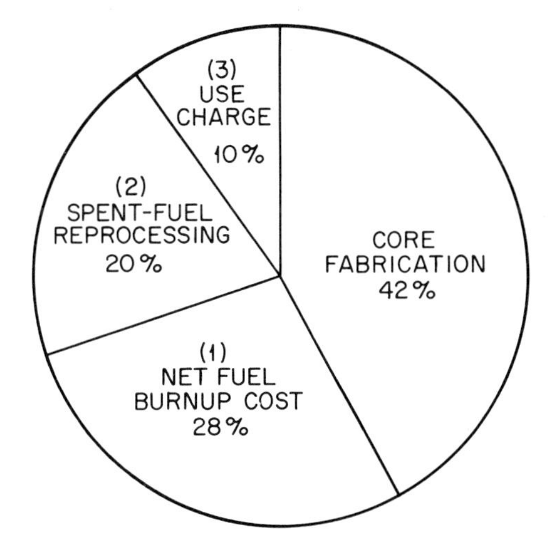

(1) Depletion cost less plutonium credit at \$9.50/gram.
(2) Includes transportation of spent fuel, reprocessing and reconversion.
(3) Use charge at 4.75% per annum.

Fig. 140. Breakdown of fuel costs at equilibrium for 300-MW boiling water plant 1962 design: fuel cost ~ 1.9 mills/KWH based on 15,000 MWD/ton burn up.

terial, in the case of enriched uranium fuel elements, is enriched uranium hexafluoride (UF_6) from one of the AEC's uranium enrichment plants. The manufacturing steps thus include the chemical conversion of the hexafluoride to uranium dioxide or uranium metal (see **uranium refining and conversion**); the metallurgical and mechanical operations involved in forming and cladding fuel elements (see **fuel element fabrication**); the inspection and testing of completed fuel elements; and the recovering of scrap materials. The cost is the value added during these steps, including the cost of cladding material and of any alloying or diluent materials added to the fuel.

The unit cost of fuel element fabrication (usually expressed as dollars per kilogram of fuel contained in the final fuel elements) * depends on the particular fuel-element configuration; the cladding material; the dimensional tolerances and other specifications; and the number of fuel elements fabricated. Another factor is the level of enrichment of the fuel; for example, the criticality hazard (and hence the handling cost) increases with higher enrichment.

Unit fuel element fabrication costs are subject to considerable variance, however, the following figures are indicative of current cost levels for the types of fuel elements now used in water-cooled reactors.

1. Stainless steel-clad oxide fuel elements fabricated of uranium assaying $\leqq$ 3% U^{235}: \$100/kg.

2. Zirconium-clad oxide fuel elements as above: \$140/kg.

3. For U^{235} assays between 3 and 5%, add \$8/kg for each percentage point above 3%.

The cost of fabricating fuel elements to meet current performance standards is expected to come down substantially with improvements in technology and volume increases. Changes in fuel element materials and designs to achieve higher burn-up (for longer fuel life) and higher operating temperatures (for improved thermal conversion efficiency) may result in initially higher fabrication costs per kilogram for fuel used in high-performance reactors, but the net effect would be a reduction in the cost on a mills per kilowatt-hour basis.

Net Fuel Burn-up Cost: The gross fuel burn-up cost is the difference between the value of the uranium in fresh fuel and the value of that in spent (i.e., irradiated) fuel. The *net* fuel burn-up cost is the gross cost less a credit received for new fissionable material (i.e., plutonium or uranium-233) contained in the spent fuel. The price factors involved are determined by AEC price schedules.

* Published figures sometimes include an allowance for the cost of fabricating spare fuel elements as a reserve against defective performance.

On July 1, 1961, and again on July 1, 1962, the AEC reduced its enriched uranium prices (see Table 7). The prices are based on full recovery of actual AEC production costs, the recent price reductions being due to lowered uranium procurement cost (1961) and lowered cost of the enrichment process (1962). It appears extremely unlikely that private industry will enter the uranium enrichment field in the foreseeable future, so that AEC costs can be expected to continue to determine the prices paid for enriched uranium for some years to come. Since the AEC does not earn a profit or pay income taxes, its prices are lower than those an industrial concern would charge given the same operating costs. The AEC's cost accounting procedures are, however, patterned on industrial practice and include depreciation.

TABLE 7. OLD AND NEW AEC PRICE SCHEDULE FOR ENRICHED URANIUM

Enrichment (*weight %* U^{235})	*Price for Enriched Uranium as Uranium Hexafluoride* (*\$/gram of contained* U^{235})		
	Old Schedule (prior to July 1, 1961)	*New Schedule (July 1, 1962)*	*Price Reduction (%)*
1.5	9.70	6.35	35
2.0	11.00	7.33	33
3.0	12.52	8.48	32
5.0	13.96	9.59	31
10.0	15.29	10.62	31
20.0	16.12	11.26	30
90.0	17.07	12.01	30

The plutonium credit (or "buy back price") for material delivered to the AEC by U.S. reactor licenses through June 30, 1962, ranged between $45-30 per gram of metal, depending on the concentration of the plutonium-240 isotope.* The credit for material delivered from July 1, 1962 through June 30, 1963, is $30 per gram irrespective of plutonium-240 content. These are premium prices (see below).

The AEC currently allows a credit of $12 per gram to foreign reactor operators using U.S.-supplied fuel under Agreements for Cooperation. This price is based on a preliminary estimate of the thermal value ** of plutonium relative to that of uranium-235, keyed to the uranium-235 price schedule that was in existence prior to July 1, 1961.

The AEC has indicated that the domestic plutonium credit after June 30, 1963, will be based on its fuel value, which is currently a subject of intensive study. There have been informal indications that the credit, on this basis, may be set in the neighborhood of $9.5 per gram of plutonium metal, or $8 per gram of plutonium in the form of a plutonium nitrate solution; but, as of mid-1962, no actual pricing policy had been announced.

The credit for uranium-233 delivered to the AEC through June 30, 1963, is $15 per gram of uranium-233 in the form of uranyl nitrate. That credit is based on the thermal value of uranium-235 relative to uranium-235, keyed to the uranium-235 price schedule in effect prior to July 1, 1961.

Transportation Cost. The estimates in Table 8 serve to illustrate the factors in the cost of transporting irradiated fuel elements to a reprocessing site.

Fuel Reprocessing Cost. This category of fuel-cycle cost includes the basic chemical separation and decontamination of uranium and plutonium contained in irradiated fuel elements, and the chemical conversion of the resulting purified nitrate solutions to uranium hexafluoride and plutonium metal, respectively.

Pending the availability of commercial fuel reprocessing services,† the AEC has established a price schedule for reprocessing based on a conceptual design of a flexible process facility. The prices are arrived at by comput-

* A long-lived isotope with a high absorption cross section for thermal neutrons and generally an undesirable constituent. The concentration of plutonium-240 increases with increased irradiation. (See **plutonium**)

** I.e., the amount of heat released per unit amount of fuel consumed.

† See **Nuclear Fuel Services, Inc. Project.**

ing the number of days required to process a given batch of irradiated fuel through the hypothetical plant (including make-ready, shutdown, and clean-up operations), and then multiplying the number of days by the estimated daily cost of plant operation. (See **fuel reprocessing** for details.) The AEC has stated its intent to withdraw its price schedule as soon as reprocessing services are available commercially at "reasonable" cost. The AEC has indicated that prices no more than 15% higher than its own schedule would be considered reasonable.

TABLE 8. COST FACTORS IN THE TRANSPORTATION OF IRRADIATED FUEL ELEMENTS

	Estimated Transportation Cost [1] *($/kg of uranium)*	
	30-Ton Cask (containing 910 kg U)	*70-Ton Cask (containing 3450 kg U)*
Freight charge for shipment	$2.40	$1.50
Return of empty casks	2.30	1.40
Cask rental	2.90	2.00
Property insurance	1.50–6.00	1.50–6.00
Total	$9.10–13.60/kg U	$6.40–10.90/kg U

[1] Source: "Costs of Nuclear Power," TID-8531 (Rev.), January, 1961. Assumptions: $\gtrsim$ 120 days decay cooling prior to shipment; 3000-mile shipment; property insurance @ 0.5–2.0% of fuel value, taken at $300/kg U.

Current AEC charges for chemical conversion following reprocessing are: For converting uranyl nitrate to uranium hexafluoride, $5.60 per kilogram of uranium assaying $\leq$ 5% U^{235} and $32 per kilogram of uranium assaying > 5% U^{235}. For converting plutonium nitrate to metal, $1.50 per gram of metal.

The cost of fuel reprocessing and conversion is illustrated by Table 9 which shows an estimate for slightly enriched, stainless steel-clad, uranium dioxide fuel elements of the type used in many water cooled reactors.

Use Charge for Leased Fuel. The AEC use charge applies to the total fuel inventory of a nuclear power plant, including material in storage at the reactor site (i.e., replacement fuel elements and spares); material in the reactor; irradiated material undergoing decay cooling; and irradiated material in transit to or undergoing reprocessing.* For large-scale plants, a representative figure for the value of fuel held in inventory is 150% of the average value of a single core loading. By "average" is meant the average of the value before and after irradiation.

Since the value of fuel under irradiation changes with time, the use charge is usually based on an average-value computation at six-month intervals. The amount and value of fuel held in inventory mainly depend on the type

TABLE 9. ESTIMATE OF THE COST OF REPROCESSING AND CONVERSION

	Estimated Cost ($/kg U) [1]
Reprocessing	24.50
Uranium conversion	5.60
Plutonium conversion	7.40
Uranium losses [2]	4.20
Plutonium losses [2]	1.20
Total	$42.50/kg U

[1] Source: "Costs of Nuclear Power," TID-8531 (Rev.), January, 1961.
[2] In the application of AEC reprocessing and conversion price schedules, process losses are assumed to occur amounting to 1.3% of the value of the uranium and 2.0% of the value of plutonium based on an assay of the irradiated fuel as received.

and size of reactor, the **specific power,** and the degree of enrichment of the initial fuel. For a given reactor type, the inventory value increases with plant size and initial fuel enrichment level and decreases with specific power.

On July 1, 1961, the AEC increased its use charge for leased fuel from 4.0 to 4.75% per annum. In a number of cooperative projects being conducted under the AEC's Power Demonstration Reactor Program, the AEC has waived the use charge for an initial operating period.

If fuel supplies were on a purchase, rather than a lease basis, the charges applied to the

* The use charge for material being fabricated into fuel elements is normally treated as part of the fuel-element fabricator's cost of manufacture.

fuel inventory would increase from the present 4.75% to somewhere between 6 and 11%, depending upon the financing and accounting arrangements. The pros and cons of changing from a lease to an ownership basis have been studied both by government and industry. Amendment to existing legislation would be required and, as of mid-1962, no action appeared likely before 1963, at the earliest. The indications are that if such a change is made there will be a provision giving nuclear power plant owners the option of leasing fuel during a transition period.

Operation and Maintenance Costs. This category of nuclear power generating costs includes the salaries of plant operating and maintenance personnel; payroll burden; the cost of training replacement operating and maintenance personnel, and the cost of expendable materials and supplies other than fuel. It will be several more years before sufficient operating experience has been accumulated to provide meaningful data on these costs. For the interim, they are usually estimated at about twice the costs of operating and maintaining conventional plants (see Table 4). In the case of reactors which employ a high-value coolant or moderator, such as heavy water or an organic compound, an incremental allowance needs to be made for process losses of such material.

Projected Nuclear Power Plant Construction. Any projection made today of the trend of nuclear power plant construction in the coming years is subject to so many uncertainties and imponderables as to be of doubtful value beyond affording an order-of-magnitude indication of future possibilities. The projection made in Table 10 is thus designed purely for general orientation purposes. As is indicated, it involves a series of assumptions as to the percentage of new steam-elec-

TABLE 10. ORDER-OF-MAGNITUDE PROJECTION OF U.S. NUCLEAR POWER PLANT CONSTRUCTION

	1960	*1965*	*1970*	*1975*	*1980*	*Total*
Projected capacity of U.S. thermal power plants (thousands of megawatts) [1]	131.4	175.7	230.2	293.6	364.0	
A. Incremental addition (thousands of megawatts)	—	44.3	54.5	63.4	70.4	225.6
B. Est. % of (A) accounted for by units built in high-cost fuel areas [2]	—	← 20% → (1965–1980)				
C. Est. % of (A) accounted for by units built in medium-cost fuel areas [2]	—	← 40% → (1965–1980)				
D. Est. % of (A) accounted for by units built in low-cost fuel areas [2]	—	← 40% → (1965–1980)				
Assumed market capture by nuclear power on economic grounds						
% of (B) (A)	—	—	15%	40%	75%	
% of (C) (A)	—	—	<5%	10%	30%	
% of (D) (A)	—	—	—	<5%	15%	
Nuclear power capacity added during period based on foregoing (thousands of megawatts)	—	—	2.2	8.6	23.3	
Additional nuclear power capacity in the form of demonstration projects, experiments, etc. (thousands of megawatts)	0.4	0.8	1.0	0.8	0.4	
Cumulative total of installed nuclear power capacity (thousands of megawatts)	0.4	1.2	4.4	13.8	37.5	

[1] Federal Power Commission projection (1960).
[2] Rough estimates inferred from FPC data.

tric capacity that will be captured by nuclear plants.

The projection is shown graphically in Fig. 141, the lower part of which shows successive five-year increments of construction and the upper part of which shows the cumulative

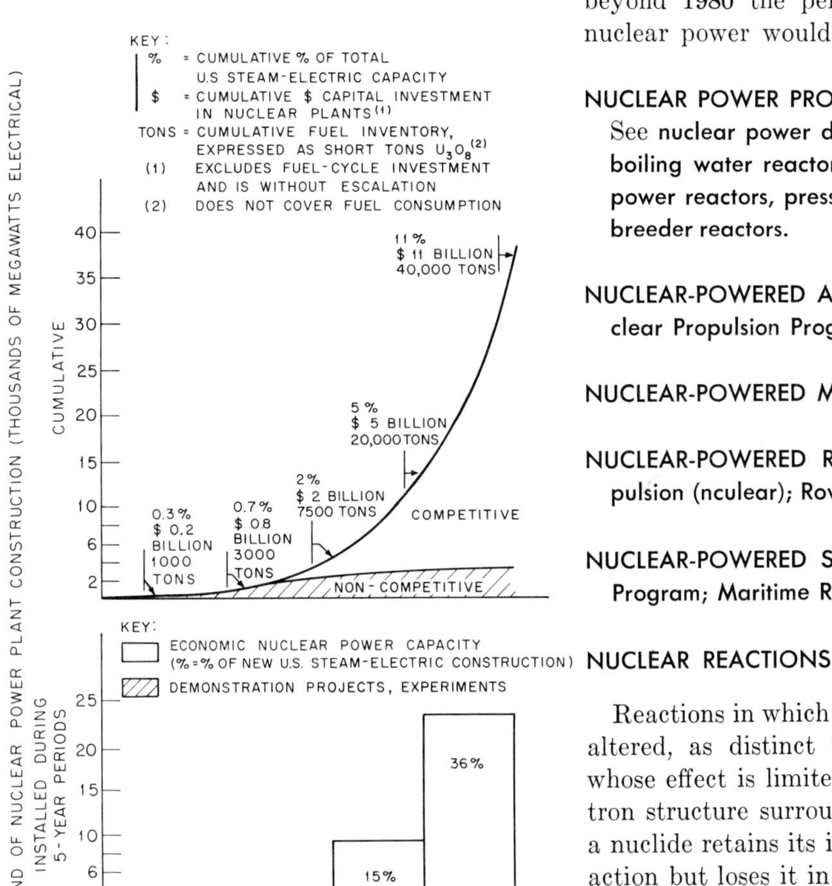

Fig. 141. Order of magnitude projection of U.S. Nuclear power plant construction (based on Table 10).

trend. Included on the cumulative chart are rough estimates which afford additional orientation in terms of (1) the cumulative percentage of total U.S. steam-electric capacity represented by the projected amount of nuclear power capacity; (2) the cumulative total capital investment represented by the nuclear projection; and (3) the cumulative fuel inventory represented by the nuclear projection, expressed as tons of equivalent U_3O_8.

As is seen, the projection indicates that by 1980, nuclear power may account for something like 11% of total U.S. steam-electric capacity.* The trend is such, however, that beyond 1980 the percentage contribution of nuclear power would increase rapidly.

NUCLEAR POWER PROJECTS, TABULATIONS OF. See **nuclear power development, U.S.** Also see **boiling water reactors, heavy water-moderated power reactors, pressurized water reactors, fast breeder reactors.**

NUCLEAR-POWERED AIRCRAFT. See **Aircraft Nuclear Propulsion Program.**

NUCLEAR-POWERED MISSILES. See **Pluto Project.**

NUCLEAR-POWERED ROCKETS. See **rocket propulsion (nculear); Rover Project; SNAP Program.**

NUCLEAR-POWERED SHIPS. See **Naval Reactors Program; Maritime Reactors Program.**

NUCLEAR REACTIONS

Reactions in which the nucleus of an atom is altered, as distinct from chemical reactions whose effect is limited to changes in the electron structure surrounding the nucleus. Thus, a nuclide retains its identity in a chemical reaction but loses it in a nuclear reaction, from which it emerges either as a different isotope of the same element or as a different element. Nuclear reactions occur between an atomic nucleus and an elementary particle (neutron, proton, deuteron, alpha particle or other); between atomic nuclei (as in heavy ion reactions); or may be induced in an atomic nucleus by electro-magnetic radiation (gamma rays or x-rays).

A nuclear reaction may be written in an analogous fashion to that in which a chemical

---

* The amount of nuclear power capacity projected for construction by 1980, corresponds to about one-fourth the amount of steam-electric capacity in service in the United States in 1960.

reaction is written. Take, for example, the reaction between nitrogen-14 and a neutron to form the carbon isotope, carbon-14, accompanied by the release of a proton, which may be expressed as follows:

$$_{7}N^{14} + _{0}n^{1} \longrightarrow _{6}C^{14} + _{1}p^{1}$$

Here the superscripts identify the atomic weights **(mass number)** and the subscripts identify the number of protons contained in the nuclei **(atom number).** A shorthand expression for the same reaction is: N^{14} (n, p) C^{14}. By extension the reaction is referred to as a neutron-proton reaction, or (n, p) reaction. Other examples of nuclear reactions include:

1. The neutron-gamma reaction, as in the production of cobalt-60: Co^{59} (n, γ) Co^{60}.
2. The neutron-alpha reaction, as in the production of tritium: Li^{6} (n, α) H^{3}.
3. The alpha-neutron reaction, as in the use of beryllium as a neutron source: Be^{9} (α, n) C^{12}.

Where a nuclide is bombarded by a particle or exposed to electromagnetic radiation to induce a nuclear reaction, it is usually referred to as the target nucleus. In most nuclear reactions the first step in the reaction process is the formation of a **compound nucleus,** which then breaks down into the products of the reaction. In the first example given above the compound nucleus would be $_{7}N^{15}$.

Nuclear reactions that result in the formation of a different isotope of the target nucleus, accompanied by the release of gamma rays (as in neutron-gamma or proton-gamma reactions) are referred to as **radiative capture** reactions. Nuclear reactions involving the transformation of a nuclide into a different chemical element are generally referred to as **transmutation** processes. There are two special types of reaction to which this general term is usually not applied since they involve fragmentation phenomena. They are nuclear fission and spallation. In the former, the target nucleus splits into two approximately equal parts; in the latter, the target nucleus splinters into a number of parts.

Nuclear reactions are not subject to process variables, such as temperature and pressure, that affect chemical reactions. The primary variable in nuclear reactions is the energy of the particle or intensity of the radiation inducing the reaction. Also, nuclear reactions follow statistical behavior patterns. Thus, given a particular nucleus and a bombarding particle of a given energy value (or radiation of a given intensity), a certain probability exists that a particular reaction will occur. The term used to describe this probability is **cross section.** In many nuclear reactions the probability, or cross section, is highest at a particular range or ranges of energy. This phenomenon is known as **resonance.**

A distinction should be made between nuclear reactions and radioactive **decay** processes. In the former, as has been seen, there is interaction between a nuclide and an energetic particle or radiant energy. In the latter, an unstable nuclide undergoes spontaneous nuclear disintegration. Radioactive nuclides occur naturally, e.g., radium, or can be produced artificially by a nuclear reaction. Many products of nuclear reactions undergo subsequent radioactive decay. e.g., carbon-14.

NUCLEAR REACTOR. See **reactor (nuclear).**

NUCLEAR SAFETY. See **Atomic Energy Commission—Information Services.**

NUCLEAR SCIENCE ABSTRACTS. See **Atomic Energy Commission—Information Services.**

NUCLEAR SUPERHEATING

Superheating steam in a nuclear reactor, as distinct from the use of a coal or oil-fired superheater. Nuclear superheating is of interest in connection with the problem of improving the quality of the steam generated by power reactors and thereby improving the thermal conversion efficiency of nuclear power plants. (See **nuclear power development, U.S.)**

In the case of a **boiling water reactor** nuclear superheating may be done within the reactor in which the steam is generated—a technique known as integral nuclear superheating. Otherwise it is done in a separate steam-cooled reactor and is known as separate nuclear superheating.

NUCLEAR WEAPONS. See **weapons.**

NUCLEON

A constituent particle of the atomic nucleus, i.e., either a proton or a neutron.

NUCLEONICS

A term used in general reference to the science and technology of atomic energy and its applications and thus encompassing a range of disciplines. Also, the name of a leading U.S. trade publication serving the atomic energy field.

NUCLEUS

The dense, positively charged core of an atom. The nucleus of an atom is considered to consist of Z protons and A-Z neutrons, where Z is the **atomic number** and A is the **mass number.** The nucleus is held together by extremely strong forces the nature of which is not completely understood. Study of these forces is one of the major preoccupations of contemporary nuclear physics.

The mass of an atomic nucleus is generally slightly less than the sum of the masses of the constituent particles. The energy equivalent of this mass difference is known as the nuclear **binding energy** and represents the energy that would be required to separate the nucleus into its constituent particles. This energy equivalence is computed by Einstein's formula, $E = mc^2$, where $m =$ the mass difference and $c =$ the velocity of light.

NUCLIDE

A particular species of atom, identified by the characteristics of its **nucleus,** i.e., by its **atomic number** and **mass number.** The isotopes of a given chemical element are different nuclides, so that there are as many nuclides as there are chemical elements and isotopes thereof.

O

OAK RIDGE GASEOUS DIFFUSION PLANT

A U.S. Atomic Energy Commission uranium-235 production facility, located 13 miles west of Oak Ridge, Tennessee. *Operating contractor*: Union Carbide Nuclear Company, a subsidiary of Union Carbide Corporation. *AEC investment in plant and equipment*: ~ $847 million.* *Employment*: ~ 6000.

The U.S. uranium-235 production network consists of the Oak Ridge Plant plus similar facilities at Paducah, Kentucky and Portsmouth, Ohio. See **uranium enrichment** for notes on the operations that take place within this network. See **gaseous diffusion** for supplementary notes on the isotope separation process employed.

The main units of the Oak Ridge plant are the K-25, K-27, K-29, K-31 and K-33 diffusion cascades. The first two were constructed during the wartime **Manhattan Project**; the latter three were constructed during AEC's postwar expansion program. K-25, the original cascade, consists of a windowless, four-story, U-shaped structure (actually composed of 54 contiguous buildings) which extends about half a mile along each leg of the "U" and encompasses an area of some 60 acres. The main process equipment, consisting of several thousand diffusion stages, is at ground level. Piping runs are carried at the second level, and the third level is the operating floor. Auxiliary process equipment is located below ground level.

Basically a diffusion stage consists of a unit of equipment known as a "converter," in which incremental separation of the uranium isotopes takes place, together with centrifugal pumps for circulating the process gas (uranium hexafluoride), heat exchangers to remove the heat of compression, piping interconnections, and control instrumentation. The stages are arranged in series and so connected that the depleted gas fraction leaving a given stage is directed "down" the cascade and the enriched gas fraction leaving the stage is directed "up" the cascade. Feed enters the cascade below the midpoint; enriched product is drawn off at any of various points up the cascade, depending upon the degree of enrichment desired, and depleted "tails" are drawn off at the bottom of the cascade.

The main process system is operated below atmospheric pressure and hence the equipment, which if laid end to end would extend about 20 miles, is required to be virtually leak-free. In the event of a major leak, the piping is arranged to permit bypassing multiples of stages, ranging from a "cell" of six stages to a "section" containing many cells. The cascade is equipped with instruments called "line recorders" which continuously monitor the process stream and detect inleaking air by a mass spectrometric technique. Signals from these and other control instruments are received in a central control room from which point many of the operations of the plant are observed and directed.

Uranium hexafluoride is a solid at room temperature and atmospheric pressure but sublimates to a gas when heated. Product and "tails" fractions are removed from the process system by solidification in refrigerated "cold traps" and leave the plant in the liquid state in pressurized shipping cylinders.

Extremely large amounts of electric power are consumed in operating the gaseous diffusion process, most of it going into driving the

* Includes facilities authorized or under construction as of June 30, 1959. Not adjusted for depreciation.

gas circulating pumps. The Oak Ridge Plant uses about as much power as the State of Texas (about 17 billion kilowatt-hours per year). This is supplied by a 235,000-kilowatt coal-fired, power station located on the plant site, supplemented by power supplied by the Tennessee Valley Authority from hydroelectric and steam-plant sources.

The original portions of the Oak Ridge Plant were designed and engineered during World War II by The Kellex Corporation, then a subsidiary of M. W. Kellegg Company and later acquired by Vitro Corporation of America. The construction contractor for the original installation was J. A. Jones Construction Company. The postwar additions (K-29, K-31 and K-33) were constructed by Maxon Construction Company with architect-engineer services provided by the firms of Giffels and Vallet, Inc.; Sargent and Lundy; and Smith, Hinchman and Grylls, Inc.

OAK RIDGE GRAPHITE REACTOR (X-10)

A large graphite-moderated, air-cooled research reactor at Oak Ridge National Laboratory. It was built during the **Manhattan Project** and originally served as a pilot plutonium production facility. Since the war it has been used to supply radioisotopes (it is the principal U.S. radioisotope production facility) and for general experimentation. *Type*: Graphite reactor. *Power rating*: 3800 thermal kilowatts. *Coolant:* Air. *Moderator:* Graphite. *Neutron flux*: Of the order of $10^{12} n/cm^2$ sec (maximum thermal). *Start-up:* 1943. (See **research and training reactors**)

OAK RIDGE INSTITUTE OF NUCLEAR STUDIES (ORINS)

A nonprofit association of 38 southern colleges and universities established in 1946 to strengthen graduate education and research by drawing on the special facilities at Oak Ridge National Laboratory, and to perform training and research activities on the U.S. Atomic Energy Commission's behalf. Activities of ORINS include arranging for university facility participation in research at AEC laboratories; administering specialized fellowships in nuclear science and engineering, radiological physics, and industral hygiene; providing training in the use of radioisotopes; conducting research in the application of nuclear energy in the treatment of cancer and related diseases; and operating the AEC's Domestic Exhibits Program, including the American Museum of Atomic Energy.

ORINS is located at Oak Ridge, Tennessee. Its facilities are owned by the AEC and ORINS and represent an investment of approximately $4 million. The participating institutions are:

Agricultural and Mechanical College of Texas
Alabama Polytechnic Institute
Catholic University of America
Clemson Agricultural College
Duke University
Emory University
Fisk University
Florida State University
Georgia Institute of Technology
Louisiana State University
Meharry Medical College
Mississippi State College
North Carolina State College
North Texas State College
Rice Institute
Southern Methodist University
Tulane University of Louisiana
Tuskegee Institute
Texas Woman's University
University of Alabama
University of Arkansas
University of Florida
University of Georgia
University of Kentucky
University of Louisville
University of Maryland
University of Miami
University of Mississippi
University of North Carolina
University of Oklahoma
University of Puerto Rico
University of South Carolina
University of Tennessee
University of Texas
University of Virginia
Vanderbilt University
Virginia Polytechnic Institute
West Virginia University

OAK RIDGE NATIONAL LABORATORY (ORNL)

A major U.S. Atomic Energy Commission research center located at Oak Ridge, Tennessee. *Operating contractor*: Union Carbide Nuclear Company, a subsidiary of Union Carbide Corporation. *Director*: A. M. Weinberg. *AEC investment in plant and equipment*: ~ $206 million.* *Staff:* ~ 1600 scientists and engineers, and ~ 280 supporting personnel.

ORNL is an outgrowth of the "X-10" plutonium production pilot plant built by E. I. duPont de Nemours & Company during the wartime **Manhattan Project** under subcontract to the University of Chicago. For a brief period after the war the Laboratory was operated by Monsanto Chemical Company under the name, Clinton Laboratories. Union Carbide Nuclear Company took over the operation early in 1948, at which time it became known as Oak Ridge National Laboratory.

Fields of activity with which ORNL is most closely identified include:

1. Chemical technology: Development of processes for such applications as uranium milling, uranium refining, fuel reprocessing, and hafnium-free zirconium production. In the field of fuel reprocessing, for example, ORNL developed the **Redox** and **Purex processes** for uranium-plutonium separation (the former jointly with Argonne National Laboratory); the **Thorex process** for uranium-thorium separation; the **Darex** and **Zircex processes** for the dissolution of stainless steel and zirconium-bearing fuel elements; and is currently engaged in research on **fluoride volatility** and other nonaqueous separation techniques.

2. Reactor development: The laboratory has done extensive research on thermal breeder reactor systems for civilian nuclear power applications (see **aqueous homogeneous reactors** and **molten salt reactors)** and is responsible for the AEC program of development of high-temperature gas-cooled reactors for civilian power applications (see **Experimental Gas-Cooled Reactor).** It developed the conceptual design of the first plant built under the Army Nuclear Power Program (see **SM-1).** It investigated the use of molten salt reactor systems for aircraft applications and made other major contributions to the Aircraft Nuclear Propulsion Program, notably in the area of radiation shield design. The forerunner of pool-type research reactors was built by ORNL (see **Bulk Shielding Reactor),** and the Laboratory made important contributions to the development and design of the first high-flux test reactor. (See **Materials Testing Reactor)**

3. Controlled fusion: ORNL is one of the major U.S. centers of research on **thermonuclear power.** Its effort in this field is concentrated on the high-energy injection approach to achieving controlled fusion reactions. (See **Molecular Ion Ignition Program)**

4. Radioisotopes: ORNL is the country's largest supplier of isotopes, chiefly in the **Oak Ridge Graphite Reactor;** the production of stable isotopes by electromagnetic separation in apparatus inherited from the wartime **Y-12 Plant;** and the separation and encapsulation of kilocurie amounts of certain long-lived fission-product nuclides in the **Multicurie Fission Products Pilot Plant.**

5. Basic research: ORNL conducts a broad program of basic research in chemistry, physics, metallurgy and biology. For example, the Laboratory's Biology Division is studying radiation effects in plant cytology and genetics, and in mammalian genetics, pathology and physiology; and is additionally conducting research in various areas of biochemistry, including photosynthesis, enzymatic mechanisms in biosynthesis, and nucleic acid structure.

ORNL is also active in educational and training programs, working in this field in close collaboration with the **Oak Ridge Institute of Nuclear Studies** (ORINS). The Laboratory conducted the Oak Ridge School of Reactor Technology (ORSORT) from 1950 to 1959, by which time comparable training had become established in accredited edu-

* Includes facilities authorized or under construction as of June 30, 1960. Not adjusted for depreciation.

cational institutions. In 1959, in collaboration with North Carolina State College, it conducted a special reactor engineering course for faculty members of engineering schools under the joint sponsorship of AEC and the American Society for Engineering Education.

Specialized ORNL research and experimental facilities include: *Reactors*: the **Oak Ridge Graphite Reactor** (X-10); the **Oak Ridge Research Reactor** (ORR); the **Bulk Shielding Reactor** (BSR-1, -2); the **Low Intensity Test Reactor** (LITR); and **Homogeneous Reactor Experiment No. 2** (HRE-2). A new research reactor **(High-Flux Isotope Reactor)** and a new experimental power reactor (the Experimental Gas-Cooled Reactor) are under construction. *Accelerators:* A cyclotron and several van de Graaff generators. *Other*: Facilities for research on controlled fusion (see **DCX Experiment;** a flexible fuel reprocessing facility known as the Metal Recovery Plant; high-speed electronic computer facilities; high-level radiation laboratories; and animal research laboratories.

OAK RIDGE RESEARCH REACTOR (ORR)

A light water-moderated research reactor at Oak Ridge National Laboratory that combines features of tank and pool designs. The core is contained in a closed tank, which is installed in a pool; thus, the reactor can operate at higher power and flux levels than pool reactors but retains much of their operational flexibility. The ORR was designed by the ORNL staff. *Type*: Modified tank reactor. *Power rating*: 20,000 thermal kilowatts. *Fuel*: MTR-type fuel elements. *Coolant*: H_2O. *Moderator*: H_2O. *Reflector*: Beryllium. *Neutron flux*: Of the order of 10^{14}n/cm^{2}sec (maximum thermal). *Start-up*: 1958. (See **research and training reactors)**

OAK RIDGE SCHOOL OF REACTOR TECHNOLOGY (ORSORT)

A school formerly operated at Oak Ridge National Laboratory to provide graduate instruction in the reactor field. ORSORT started in 1946 and was discontinued in 1959, by which time equivalent training had become available at a number of educational institutions.

OAK RIDGE, TENNESSEE

A community approximately 20 miles west of Knoxville and the principal residential center for personnel employed at the U.S. Atomic Energy Commission's plants and laboratories in the area. The 1960 Census listed the population of Oak Ridge as 27,009.

Oak Ridge was established by the government in 1942 in conjunction with the wartime **Manhattan Project,** and was a restricted area until 1949, when it became an open community. In 1955 legislation was enacted (Public Law 84-221) authorizing the sale of government-owned houses, apartment, commercial properties and land at Oak Ridge and **Richland, Washington.** By late 1960 all residences and almost all commercial properties and vacant lots listed for sale at Oak Ridge had been sold with the proceeds totaling $26.5 million.

OCEANOGRAPHY

An understanding of ocean currents and in particular of the circulation of water at great depth is of major concern in the disposal (burial) of radioactive wastes at sea (See **radioactive waste disposal.)** For this reason AEC has supported oceanographic research by other federal agencies and private institutes. The U.S. program is coordinated by the Committee on Oceanography of the National Academy of Sciences-National Research Council.

OFFICE OF TECHNICAL SERVICES

The Office of Technical Services (OTS) acts as a sales agency for unclassified and declassified technical publications of the U.S. Atomic Energy Commission and its contractors (see **Atomic Energy Commission—Information Services).** Lists of publications available may be obtained by writing the Office of Technical

Services, U.S. Department of Commerce, Washington 25, D.C.

OHMIC HEATING

A method of heating the ionized gaseous fuel, or **plasma,** in certain experimental controlled-**fusion** devices (see **Stellarator Program**); sometimes called Joule heating. In this technique a pulsed voltage is applied parallel to the magnetic field in which the plasma is confined, causing a current pulse to flow through the plasma and thereby preferentially accelerating (i.e., heating) the plasma electrons. These in turn heat the plasma ions by colliding with them.

It was predicted as early as 1953 that ohmic heating would be ineffective above plasma temperatures of one milion degrees, or thereabouts, due to two factors: (1) the probability of collisions between electrons and ions tends to drop off as the particle energies increase; (2) there is a problem of "runaway electrons." This prediction, subsequently confirmed in experiments, gave impetus to the development of other methods of heating plasma. (See **magnetic pumping, cyclotron resonance heating**)

OIL-WELL LOGGING

Three techniques involving radioactivity have found application in oil- and gas-well drilling and production operations, namely, gamma logging, neutron logging, and tracer techniques.

Gamma logging involves the lowering of compact radiation measurement devices (usually **Geiger** or **scintillation counters**) into bore holes to obtain a profile of natural radioactivity at various depths. Shale formations tend to contain more natural radioactivity than sands or limestones, so that this technique provides useful information on rock strata and on the depth and thickness of shale formations. The gamma activity measured stems from naturally occurring radioisotopes and their daughter products.

Neutron logging involves lowering a tandem assembly of a small neutron source and a compact radiation counter into bore holes. The counter measures gamma radiation (or thermal neutrons) resulting from neutron capture reactions induced by fast neutrons emanating from the source. Where there is a high hydrogen content in the underground formation and hence an effective neutron-moderating environment, the neutrons tend to be captured close to the source. Conversely, where there is a low hydrogen content, gamma activity is induced at some distance from the source. The radiation counter is so positioned relative to the source as to show high readings in the latter case and low readings in the former, thus affording an inverse measure of hydrogen content in the formation. These readings are indicative of differences in the lithology and porosity of the underground strata at various levels, and, by calibration, permit oil and water to be distinguished from natural gas. The types of neutron source used in neutron logging include radionuclide sources such as radium-beryllium, polonium-beryllium, and plutonium-beryllium mixtures; and miniature accelerator tubes which produce neutrons by the deuterium-tritium reactions. (See **neutron sources**)

Various tracer techniques have been used in well logging and operation. For example iodine-131 has been used as a tracer to determine rates and patterns of flow between input wells and production wells in secondary oil recovery operations. Tritium has been similarly used in connection with the repressuring of gas wells. Also various soluble or particulate radioisotopes have been added to drilling muds or to water pumped into bore holes as an aid in making permeability profiles of underground strata.

OILSAND PROJECT

A privately supported research project whose aim is to test the feasibility of using heat from a nuclear explosion to aid in the recovery of petroleum from extensive but deeply buried oil-sands in the Athabaska area of Alberta, Canada. The project has been supported by the Richfield Oil Corporation and its associates, Cities Service Company and Imperial Oil, Ltd.

While Project Oilsand is not part of the U.S. Atomic Energy Commission's **Plowshare Program,** the sponsors have worked closely with scientists at the Livermore Branch of the E. O. Lawrence Radiation Laboratory and with experts from the U.S. Bureau of Mines. The Canadian government has also established a technical study group to investigate the proposed program.

Tentative plans call for the trial detonation of a 9-kiloton nuclear device at a depth of about 1300 feet under the oil-sand bed. The explosive force and heat of the detonation are expected to force the oil-sand upward and momentarily create a slag-lined sphere about 230 feet in diameter. After cooling a few minutes, this sphere would collapse and a large amount of oil-sand would fall into the cavity. The heat would lower the viscosity of the oil so that it could be extracted by pumping or by other conventional recovery methods. Calculations indicate that no radioactivity would vent into the atmosphere.

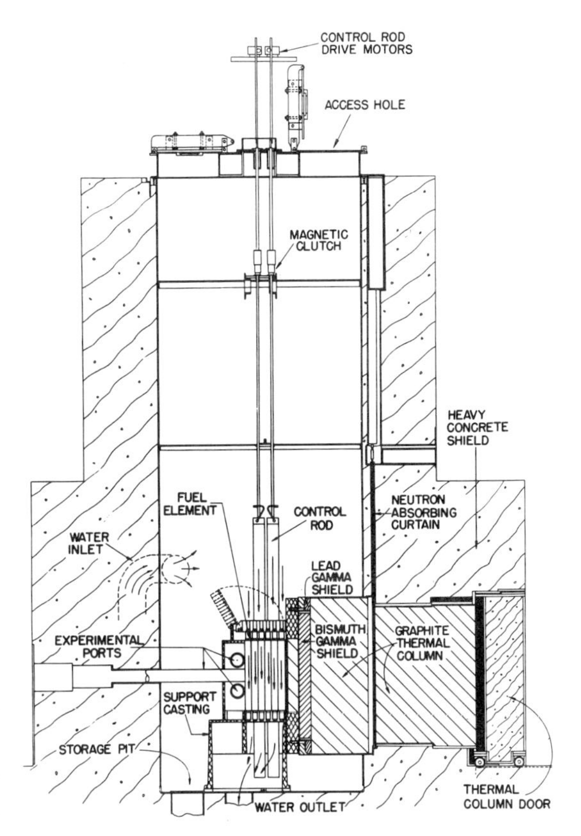

Fig. 142. Diagram of Omega West Reactor (OWR). (*Courtesy of Los Alamos Scientific Laboratory*)

OMEGA WEST REACTOR (OWR)

A 5000-kilowatt (thermal) tank-type research reactor at Los Alamos Scientific Laboratory. It was designed by the LASL staff and began operation in 1956. (See **research and training reactors**)

OPERATORS' LICENSE, AEC. See **licenses; Atomic Energy Commission—Licensing and Regulatory Procedure.**

ORACLE

The name of a high-speed electronic digital computer developed and used at Oak Ridge National Laboratory. The name derives from *O*ak *R*idge *A*utomatic *C*omputer and *L*ogical *E*ngine.

ORALLOY

Code designation for fully enriched uranium metal.

ORANGE OXIDE

Uranium trioxide (UO_3)

ORGANIC COOLED REACTORS

Power reactors that are cooled with an organic fluid (see below), which usually also serves as moderator. They are similar in schematic concept to **pressurized water reactors** but operate at much lower pressures and employ more conventional mechanical equipment. The coolant is circulated in a closed loop, referred to as the primary loop. The primary loop includes a heat exchanger in which the coolant transfers heat to water, thereby generating steam for power production (see Fig. 143).

The organic cooled concept was conceived during the wartime **Manhattan Project** but was not investigated until 1953. Most of the development work has been done by Atomics International, a division of North American Aviation, Inc., under contract to the U.S. Atomic Energy Commission. The feasibility of the concept was first demonstrated by the successful operation of the **Organic Moderated Reactor Experiment** (OMRE) in September, 1957. A second more flexible experiment facility (the **Experimental Organic Cooled Reactor**) was recently placed in service. A small prototype power plant (the **Piqua Organic Moderated Reactor**) began operation in 1962.

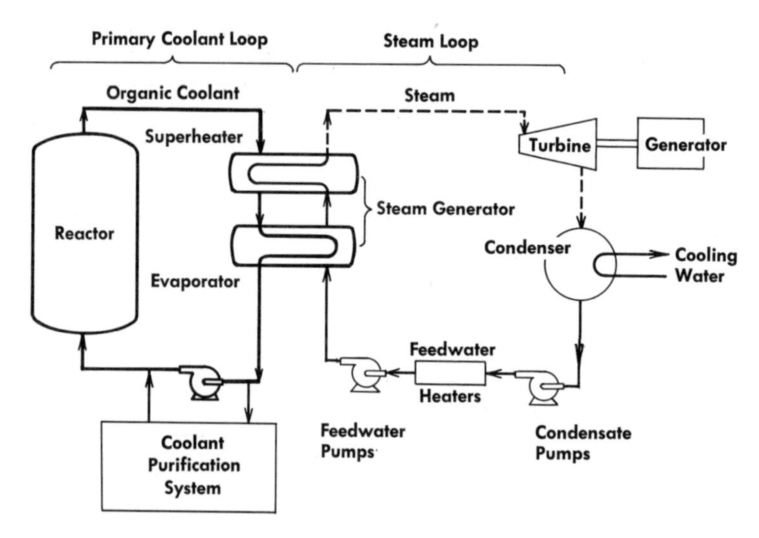

Fig. 143. Simplified flow diagram of organic-cooled reactor.

As yet no large-scale organic cooled reactor project has been undertaken in the United States, although at least one such project is being undertaken in Europe (see reference to KBWP Project under West **Germany**). For information on other foreign activities involving organic cooled reactors, see **Canada** and **Euratom.**

Of a total of $476 million spent by the AEC for civilian reactor research and development through mid-1960, approximately $24 million (5%) was applied to organic cooled reactor development.*

General Considerations. The strong points usually cited for organic cooled reactors are:

1. They operate at low pressure relative to water-cooled reactors (100-300 pounds *vs.* 1000-2000 pounds), due to the fact that organic coolants have a low vapor pressure.

2. They have the potential of operation at higher temperatures than water cooled reactors. The latter have little prospect of operation with exit coolant temperatures above 600-650°F, due in the final analysis to pressure vessel limitations.** Pressure considerations are not limiting in the case of organic cooled reactors, so that the ceiling temperature is determined by the ability of fuel elements and of the coolant itself to withstand temperature effects. The coolants now in use are subject to pyrolytic decomposition at bulk temperatures above 800°F, which may prove to be the ultimate ceiling for terphenyls. The limiting factor at present, however, is the mechanical strength of the fuel cladding (see below).

3. Organics are essentially noncorrosive, so that ordinary materials of construction, such as carbon steel and aluminum, and conventional equipment can be used.

The low operating pressure and the use of conventional construction materials permit substantial savings in equipment fabrication costs. The higher operating temperature per-

* These figures are exclusive of construction costs. Source: AEC Annual Report for 1960.

** This statement does not hold true for **boiling water reactors** of the type employing integral nuclear superheating.

mits higher thermal conversion efficiency in power generation. These features make it appear likely that organic cooled plants can be built at lower capital cost than other types of nuclear power plant now under development.

The major limitations or problems associated with organic cooled reactors at present are as follows:

1. They are at an early stage of development.

2. Organics have poor heat-transfer properties (low thermal conductivity). This tends to limit the power density that can be achieved in organic cooled reactors and complicates the problem of fuel element design (see below).

3. The organic compounds presently available slowly decompose under irradiation, resulting in the formation of decomposition products which, if allowed to accumulate in excessive concentrations, impair heat transfer and fluid flow properties of the coolant. The coolant stream must therefore be continuously purified (by distillation) and fresh organic added to offset losses. It has been estimated that the cost of coolant replacement represents a factor of 0.5-1 mill per kilowatt-hour in the cost of electric power generation.

4. The neutron economy of organic cooled and moderated reactors * is such that they cannot operate on natural (nonenriched) uranium and cannot serve as breeders. This limitation stems from the fact that organic compounds are rich in hydrogen, which has an appreciable cross section for thermal neutron capture. (Water-cooled reactors, of course, have the same limitation.)

Plant Characteristics. See Table.

Materials. Screening of various organic materials has led to the selection of polyphenyls —benzene derivatives—as the most promising for use in organic cooled reactors. The cost of these materials is in the neighborhood of 15¢ per pound. The particular compound currently favored is a mixture of terphenyls marketed commercially under the trade name, "Santowax OMP." The radiolytic (radiation-induced) and pyrolytic (heat-induced) decomposition products of polyphenyls are tarlike compounds with high molecular weights and high boiling points, referred to as "high boiler residue," or "HB residue." It has been found that the rate of decomposition decreases as the HB residue increases, so that organic cooled reactors are operated with as high an HB residue concentration in the coolant as heat transfer and fluid flow considerations will permit—usually ~ 30 weight %. The concentration is controlled by a coolant purification system, which involves continuous distillation of a small side stream diverted from the main coolant flow.

Uranium-molybdenum alloys have been studied extensively in an effort to develop a fuel material that combines good thermal conductivity with good dimensional stability under irradiation. Alloys containing 3.5 weight % molybdenum are believed capable of achieving average burn-ups of ~ 4500 and peak burn-ups in the range 5-7000 MWD/ton. There is some evidence that alloys containing 10 weight % molybdenum may be able to achieve average burn-ups up to 15,000 and peak burn-ups as high as 22,000 MWD/ton; however, at some sacrifice in thermal conductivity. To obtain burn-ups higher than 20-22,000 MWD/ton, it will probably be necessary to use a ceramic fuel material. Uranium dioxide shows excellent promise from a burn-up standpoint, but has the disadvantage of low thermal conductivity.

The trend toward higher fuel burn-up at the expense of thermal conductivity, coupled with the fact that the coolant itself has poor heat transfer characteristics, places a premium on developing a fuel-cladding material that is a good heat conductor, and obliges the use of finned or other extended-surface fuel element designs as a means of obtaining the maximum amount of heat transfer surface area. The cladding material must also have a low cross section for thermal neutron capture and have good mechanical strength at the desired operating temperatures (800°F or higher). Stainless steel, which is the cladding material used

* This limitation does not apply to reactors cooled with organics but moderated with heavy water. (See **heavy water-moderated power reactors**)

SOME CHARACTERISTICS OF ORGANIC-COOLED POWER PLANTS

System Parameters	*1960 Design* [1]	*Projection* [2]
Pressure in primary loop	120 psi	~ 100 psi
Coolant outlet temperature	635°F	725°F
Steam conditions	825 psi, 600°F	1000 psi, 700°F
Thermal conversion efficiency	30.3%	34%
Power density	32.2 tkw/liter	44 tkw/liter
Specific power	15.3 tkw/kg U	25 tkw/kg U
Fuel		
Enrichment	2.5% U^{235}	2.1% U^{235}
Form	uranium-molybdenum alloy (10 wt. % Mo)	uranium dioxide
Cladding material	aluminum	aluminum cement
Maximum surface temperature	750°F	900°F
Average burn-up	8000 MWD/metric ton U	20,000 MWD/metric ton U

[1] Based on an optimized design of a 44-megawatt (net electrical) plant. Source: Atomic International.
[2] Projection for a 300-megawatt (electrical) plant placed in operation in 1967-1968, assuming success of development work now in progress. Source: TID-8516, Part II, supplemented by data from Atomic International.

in the Organic Moderated Reactor Experiment, has too high a neutron capture cross section and too low a thermal conductivity for effective use as a finned cladding. Zirconium alloys cannot be used in organic cooled reactors due to hydriding effects. Metal alloys of aluminum under development appear incapable of operation at surface temperatures above 800°F. The most promising materials appear to be sintered compounds of aluminum and aluminum oxide (6-13 weight % Al_2O_3), known as APM (aluminum powder metallurgy) or SAP (sintered aluminum powder) alloys. These materials, classed as "cermets", have good thermal conductivity, can be extruded into complex shapes, and show promise of being able to operate at temperatures several hundred degrees higher than metallic aluminum alloys.

The principal structural material used in organic cooled reactors is ordinary carbon steel. To prevent rusting of equipment surfaces, the system must be kept essentially free of water or air.

Economics. See **nuclear power economics.**

ORGANIC MODERATED REACTOR EXPERIMENT (OMRE)

A small government-owned experimental power reactor of the **organic cooled** type, located at the National Reactor Testing Station in Idaho. OMRE was designed and is operated by Atomics International, a division of North American Aviation, Inc. It was built to study the feasibility and operating characteristics of the organic cooled reactor concept. In its approximately three years of operation, OMRE has established the feasibility of this reactor concept and has provided a wealth of experimental data on operating variables, such as the effect of irradiation on the performance of the organic coolant. Recently, it has been used to test fuel elements and to obtain other developmental information in support of the design of the **Piqua Organic Moderated Reactor.** Following is a summary of plant particulars:

Power: OMRE operates at power levels up to 12 megawatts (thermal). It is not equipped with a turbine-generator. *Fuel:* Fully enriched uranium in the form of uranium dioxide (UO_2) particles dispersed in a stainless steel matrix. *Fuel element design:* A single fuel element consists of an assembly of stainless steel-clad fuel plates. *Fuel inventory:* ~ 25 kilograms of fully enriched uranium. *Coolant:* a mixture of diphenyl and terphenyl isomers at 300 pounds pressure; inlet temperature, 500-700°F; outlet temperature, 530-710°F. *Control materials:* 12 boron-steel control rods. *Containment:* None. *Cost:* Cost of original installation reported at $1.9 million of which $750,000 was contributed by Atomics International. *Dates:* Reactor first critical in September, 1957. Full power operates first reached in February, 1958.

Fig. 144. The Organic Moderated Reactor Experiment (OMRE). The reactor is housed in the small cylindrical structure at the left. The installation at the right is an air blast heat exchanger used to dissipate the heat generated. (*Courtesy of Atomics International*)

ORGANIZATION FOR ECONOMIC COOPERATION AND DEVELOPMENT (OECD)

An organization originally formed in 1948 as the Organization for European Economic Cooperation (OEEC) to promote the economic growth of Western Europe through cooperative action. The name was changed in September, 1961, to mark a broadening of the scope of this organization and the inclusion of the United States and Canada as full members. Headquarters are in the Château de la Muette, Paris.

It was through this organization that United States economic aid under the Marshall Plan was channeled to Western Europe and coordinated with European efforts.

The OECD is active in promoting joint undertakings in the peaceful uses of atomic energy and has created a specialized agency, the **European Nuclear Energy Agency** (ENEA), for this purpose. Policy for the ENEA is set by a permanent OECD Steering Committee on Nuclear Energy.

While the OECD as now constituted is oriented toward economic and technical assistance to less developed countries, the focus of the ENEA continues to be on Europe.

ORGANIZATION OF AMERICAN STATES (OAS)

An organization for the collective security of Latin America; formed under the Rio Treaty, signed by 20 Latin American countries and the United States in Rio de Janeiro in September, 1947. The members are: Argentina, Bolivia, Brazil, Chile, Colombia, Costa Rica, Cuba, Dominican Republic, Ecuador, El Salvador, Guatemala, Haiti, Honduras, Mexico, Nicaragua, Panama, Paraguay, Peru, United States, Uruguay and Venezuela. OAS policies in the atomic energy field are implemented by the **Inter-American Nuclear Energy Commission.** (See also the **Inter-American Institute of Agricultural Sciences)**

OXIDE SLAGGING

An experimental pyrometallurgical **fuel reprocessing** technique based on selective oxidation and volatility phenomena. Also known as oxide drossing.

If irradiated uranium fuel is melted in a refractory crucible under controlled oxidizing conditions, many fission products (and particularly the rare earth elements, cerium and strontium) are preferentially oxidized and collect as a slag on the surface of the melt, or as a scum on the walls of the crucible. Other fission products, such as cesium, distill off at the temperatures employed in the process (about 1200°C).

Uranium, plutonium and certain residual fission products remain in the molten state and can be withdrawn through an outlet in the bottom of the crucible. The principal residual fission products are zirconium (which, if desired, can be removed from the melt by precipitation with carbon), niobium, molybdenum and ruthenium. In limited concentrations, these elements do not interfere metallurgically with the reconstitution of the metal as fuel elements and, indeed, there is some evidence that they improve its performance under irradiation in certain reactor systems. Periodically, however, an auxiliary processing operation would be needed to avoid excessive build-up of these materials during successive irradiation cycles.

A limitation of oxide slagging, common to all known pyrometallurgical techniques, is that it removes only a portion of the fission product contaminants and thus can only be applied in systems in which the fuel can be reconstituted into fuel elements or solutions without direct contact, i.e., by remote control. Another limitation is that it cannot be used to separate uranium from plutonium, due to the fact that the oxidation characteristics of these elements are too similar. Its conceptual advantages, relative to conventional (solvent extraction) fuel reprocessing methods, are the possibility of reduced fuel inventory requirements and reduced radioactive waste volumes.

Of the various pyrometallurgical reprocessing methods investigated to date, oxide slagging, **metal-to-metal extraction** and **fused salt extraction** have received the greatest research emphasis. Work on oxide slagging has been in progress for several years, notably at Argonne National Laboratory and Atomics International Division of North American Aviation Company. The research has been most closely associated with the **fast breeder** and **sodium-graphite** power reactor concepts. The Experimental Breeder Reactor No. II (EBR-II), at the National Reactor Testing Station incorporates pilot-scale oxide slagging facilities. Atomic Power Development Associates, designers of the Enrico Fermi Atomic Power Station, have conducted engineering studies of full-scale oxide slagging facilities for possible incorporation in that project.

P

PACKED COLUMN

One of several types of fluid contacting equipment used in process systems in the atomic energy field. A packed column consists essentially of a vertical pipe containing a bed of coarse solids through which one or more process fluids are passed. In some applications the solids are inert and merely provide a large surface area for intimate contact between two countercurrent process streams. For example, some **solvent extraction** facilities used in **uranium refining** and **fuel reprocessing** employ packed columns for contacting countercurrent aqueous and organic streams.

In other applications, the solids serve an active function (adsorption) as well as providing a surface for contact. Examples are packed columns containing ion exchange resins, which are used in **uranium milling** (see **column ion exchange process**) and in decontaminating low-level radioactive waste liquids (see **radioactive waste disposal**): and packed columns containing activated charcoal or silica gel, which are used to scrub radioactive noble gases from gaseous effluents from fuel reprocessing plants and some reactor installations.

For information on other types of fluid contacting equipment, see **pulse column, mixer-settler.**

PADUCAH GASEOUS DIFFUSION PLANT

A U.S. Atomic Energy Commission uranium-235 production facility located 16 miles west of Paducah, Kentucky. *Operating contractor:* Union Carbide Nuclear Company, a subsidiary of Union Carbide Corporation. *AEC investment in plant and equipment:* ~ $785 million.* *Employment:* ~ 1800.

The U.S. uranium-235 network consists of the Paducah Plant plus similar facilities at Oak Ridge, Tennessee and Portsmouth, Ohio. See **uranium enrichment** for notes on the operations that take place within this network. See **gaseous diffusion** for supplementary notes on the isotope separation process employed, and **Oak Ridge Gaseous Diffusion Plant** for supplementary notes on plant features.

The Paducah Plant was built in the early fifties as part of AEC's postwar expansion program. The general contractor for construction of the plant was F. H. McGraw and Company. Architect-engineer services were furnished by the Firms of Giffels and Valet, Inc.; Sargent and Lundy; Singmaster and Breyer; and Smith, Hinchman and Grylls, Inc.

Electrical power required to operate the Paducah Plant is supplied by the Tennessee Valley Authority from hydroelectric sources (1,205,000 kilowatts), and by Electric Energy, Inc. from coal-fired power facilities (735,000 kilowatts). The latter is a syndicate organized for this purpose by five private utilities: Central Illinois Public Service Company, Illinois Power Company, Kentucky Utilities Company, Middle South Utilities Company and Union Electric Company.

---

* Includes facilities authorized or under construction as of June 30, 1960. Also includes on-site facilities for converting orange oxide (UO_3) or green salt (UF_4) to uranium hexafluoride (UF_6), the process gas used in the gaseous diffusion process. Not adjusted for depreciation.

PAIR PRODUCTION

A process, first observed in **cloud chamber** experiments, in which a high energy gamma ray, passing through the intense electric field outside an atomic nucleus, is instantaneously transformed into an electron-positron pair. This transformation of energy to mass can occur only when the energy of the gamma ray is greater than 1.02 Mev.

PAKISTAN

The Pakistani Atomic Energy Commission, Karachi, is the agency responsible for atomic energy matters.

An Institute of Nuclear Science is planned for construction in the new capital city of Islamabad, which is near Rawalpindi. Burns & Roe (U.S.) are the architect-engineers for this research center, which will be equipped with a 5000-kilowatt (thermal) pool-type research reactor to be supplied by AMF Atomics (U.S.) The United States has made a commitment to provide $350,000 toward the cost of the reactor under its program of Foreign Research Reactor Grants.

In addition, isotope research and training laboratories are being established at the Universities of Lahore (West Pakistan) and Dacca (East Pakistan), and the establishment of specialized isotope laboratories for medical and agricultural research is planned during 1961.

Low-grade uranium deposits have been found in the northwest and along the Indus River but are not of commercial significance. There is interest in nuclear power and in 1961 two U.S. firms (Gibbs & Hill and Internuclear Corporation) were retained to conduct a study of the economic feasibility of constructing one or more nuclear power plants in the near future.

Pakistan is a member of the **International Atomic Energy Agency.**

PANAMA

Member of the **Inter-American Nuclear Energy Commission.** A research-type **Agreement for Cooperation** with the United States was signed in 1960.

PANTEX PLANT. See **Atomic Energy Commission—Facilities.**

PARAGUAY

The Comision Nacional de Energia Atomica, Asuncion, is the agency responsible for atomic energy matters. Interest at present is limited to the organization of training programs. Paraguay is a member of the **International Atomic Energy Agency** and the **Inter-American Nuclear Energy Commission.**

PARTICLE ACCELERATORS

Particle accelerator is a general term for any device designed to impart kinetic energy to charged particles and thereby produce a beam of high-energy radiation for experimental or other purposes. The basic principle underlying their design is that charged particles (electrons, protons, deuterons, alpha particles, or heavy ions) can be accelerated by the application of an electrical field, which acts to attract particles of unlike charge or to repel particles of like charge. The gain in energy is proportional to the potential difference (voltage) used to create the field. Depending upon the particular design, a magnetic field may or may not be used to control the path of the particles while they are being accelerated (see below).

The major uses for particle accelerators are given below:

1. They are basic tools for research in nuclear and particle physics and nuclear chemistry, being the principal means for inducing nuclear reactions under controlled conditions. Such research customarily involves interaction between the accelerated particles and nuclei in a "target" material. Interpretation of results is aided by **cloud chambers, bubble chambers,** particle counting systems, and other auxiliary apparatus, and may also involve microradiochemical analysis.

2. Prior to the advent of the nuclear reactor, accelerators were the principal means for the

production of radioisotopes for general research use. Their role in this field is now relatively limited. However, they continue to be a principal source of certain radionuclides, notably those formed by alpha or proton bombardment.

3. Linear electron accelerators are sometimes used in lieu of conventional x-ray machines in radiotherapy and radiography.

4. Several types of accelerator (principally **Van de Graaff generators, resonant transformers,** and **linear accelerators)** are of interest as radiation sources for industrial radiation applications. (See **cold sterilization of pharmaceuticals, food preservation, radiation applications in chemical industry)**

The accompanying table summarizes the major types of particle accelerators, which are described in more detail under their respective headings. As is reflected in the table, Mev (million electron volts) and Bev (billion electron volts) are the units commonly used to designate the energy of charged particles. The unit Gev (giga electron volts) is internationally used in place of Bev. Machines delivering beams of particles of energies higher than several hundred Mev are generally referred to as "high-energy" machines.

MAJOR TYPES OF PARTICLE ACCELERATORS

Type	*Principle of Operation*	*Particles Accelerated*	*Maximum Energy (machines operating or under construction)*	*Notes*
ONCE-THROUGH ACCELERATION:				
Cockcroft-Walton machine	Direct high-voltage potential generated by a cascade rectifier system	various	~4 Mev (electrons)	Available commercially
Van de Graaff generator	Direct high-voltage potential generated by a moving-belt electrostatic system	various	~3 Mev (electrons) ~14 Mev (protons-tandem operation)	Available commercially
Resonant transformer	Direct high-voltage potential generated by a transformer whose secondary circuit is tuned to resonance	electrons	~4 Mev	Available commercially
Linear accelerator (positive ion)	Successive application of radio frequency voltages at points along particle path	heavy ions	~10 Mev	Heavy ion linear accelerators ("Hilacs") are at Lawrence Radiation Laboratory and Yale University.
Linear accelerator (electron)	Pulsed radio-frequency wave	electrons	~1 Bev [1]	Installation at Stanford University, originally operated at 730 Mev, now modified for 1.0 Bev. Smaller machines commercially available.

[1] Plans have been developed for the construction of a 10–20 Bev machine at Stanford University (see **Stanford Linear Electron Accelerator**). The machine will be two miles long and will take about six years to build.

(*Table continued on p. 384*)

Major Types of Particle Accelerators (*continued*)

Type	*Principle of Operation*	*Particles Accelerated*	*Maximum Energy (machines operating or under construction)*	*Notes*
CYCLIC ACCELERATION:				
Cyclotron	Constant radio-frequency voltage applied to particles orbiting in fixed magnetic field (no compensation for relativistic mass gain)	mainly protons, deuterons, and alpha particles	~10 Mev (protons)	Numerous installations
Snychrocyclotron	Variable radio-frequency voltage applied to particles orbiting in fixed magnetic field (voltage frequency is decreased as particles accelerate to compensate for relativistic mass gain)	same as cyclotron	~750 Mev (protons)	Also known as frequency-modulated cyclotron; example is 184-inch unit at Lawrence Radiation Laboratory
Electron Synchrotron	Constant radio-frequency voltage applied to particles orbiting in variable magnetic field (magnetic field is increased as particles gain energy to compensate for relativistic mass gain)	electrons	~6 Bev	Major installations are at California Institute of Technology (1.4 Bev) and Cornell University (1.5 Bev). A 6.0 Bev unit is being built as a joint project of Harvard University and Massachusetts Institute of Technology; known as the Cambridge Electron Accelerator.
Proton Synchrotron	Synchronized radio-frequency voltage applied to particles orbiting in variable magnetic field (magnetic field is increased as particles accelerate to compensate for relativistic mass gain)	protons	~12 Bev	Notable examples are the 6.2 Bev "Bevatron" at Lawrence Radiation Laboratory and the 3.0 Bev "Cosmotron" at Brookhaven National Laboratory. Others under construction include the 3.0 Bev Princeton-Pennsylvania Proton Accelerator (PPA), and the 12.5 Bev Zero-Gradient Synchrotron (ZGS) at Argonne National Laboratory.
Alternating-gradient synchrotron (AGS)	Same as synchrotron except in this case successive segments of magnetic field have opposite polarity (for "strong focusing")	protons (can also be applied to electrons)	~30 Bev	Two machines have been built to date, one at Brookhaven National Laboratory, the other at **CERN.**

MAJOR TYPES OF PARTICLE ACCELERATORS (*continued*)

Type	*Principle of Operation*	*Particles Accelerated*	*Maximum Energy (machines operating or under construction)*	*Notes*
Fixed-field alternating gradient synchrotron (FFAG)	Differs from AGS machine in the use of a fixed magnetic field (magnet poles are shaped to provide gradient from inside to outside of particle path)	(protons)	—	Both **Midwestern Universities Research Association (MURA)** and Oak Ridge National Laboratory (ORNL) are studying feasibility of building a 15 Bev "clashing beam" machine.
Betatron	Magnetic induction (electrons are accelerated in an evacuated tube which constitutes the secondary of a transformer and is held between the poles of an electromagnet)	electrons	~300 Mev	The largest machine built to date is at the University of Illinois.

PASTEURIZATION, FOOD. See **food preservation.**

PATENT ADVISORY PANEL

An *ad hoc* (nonstatutory) advisory body to the U.S. Atomic Energy Commission for consultation on questions on policy and procedure relating to patents and inventions. Membership listed in Appendix D.

PATENT COMPENSATION BOARD

A statutory board, advisory to the U.S. Atomic Energy Commission, which reviews applications for patent compensation, awards, or royalty fees in patent proceedings that come under Section 157 of the Atomic Energy Act of 1954. The members of the Patent Compensation Board are appointed by the AEC. Membership listed in Appendix D.

PATENTS

Statutory Provisions. The **Atomic Energy Act of 1954** (Sections 151 to 160 incl.) establishes the statutory framework for U.S. patent policy with regard to inventions and discoveries in the atomic energy field. Key provisions may be summarized in general terms as follows:

1. Re atomic weapons inventions (Section 151): Patents previously issued were revoked to the extent that the invention or discovery was useful in an atomic weapon. No future patent will be granted on any invention or discovery "useful solely" in a nuclear weapon, nor will future patents granted for other purposes grant rights useful in an atomic weapon.

2. Re nonweapon purposes (Section 153): The U.S. Atomic Energy Commission is empowered, after due process, to declare any patent applied for prior to September 1, 1964 * to be "affected with the public interest" if the discovery or invention covered by the patent is (a) "of primary importance in the production or utilization of **special nuclear material** or atomic energy" and (b) the licensing is of

* The 1954 Act as originally enacted limited the applicability of Section 153 to patents applied for before September 1, 1959. The extension of this date to September 1, 1964 was affected by statutory amendment (Public Law 86-50).

primary importance to carry out the policies and purposes of the Act.

Upon such a determination, the AEC has the right to use the patent and, after due process, to issue a nonexclusive license for its use to applicants who have demonstrated that the use of the discovery or invention is "of primary importance to the conduct of an activity by such person authorized" under the 1954 Act.

The AEC is also empowered, after due process, to grant a license to a particular applicant, authorized or licensed to conduct certain specified activities, whom the Commission, after hearing, and in addition to findings (2a) and (2b), finds that the specified activities are "of primary importance to the conduct of the activities of the applicant" and that the applicant cannot otherwise obtain a patent license from the owner on reasonable terms.

3. Re inventions conceived during AEC contracts (Section 152): The AEC is vested with all rights, unless it elects to waive them, to "any invention or discovery, useful in the production or utilization of special nuclear material or atomic energy, made or conceived in the course of or under any contract, subcontract, or arrangement entered into with or for the benefit of the (AEC), regardless of whether the contract, subcontract, or arrangement involved the expenditure of funds by the (AEC)."

4. Re disclosures (Section 151): Any person who makes an invention or discovery useful in the production or utilization of special nuclear material or atomic energy is required to file a disclosure with the U.S. Atomic Energy Commission or, as the case may be, a patent application with the U.S. Commissioner of Patents. The filing must take place within 180 days of the date on which relevancy to the above atomic energy uses first become apparent to the inventor.

5. Re prior art (Section 155): This section states that an invention or discovery described in a patent application cannot be patented if there was prior knowledge or use of same "even though such prior knowledge or use was under secrecy within the atomic energy program of the United States."

6. Re just compensation (Sections 157, 151, 153): The AEC is authorized to give a reasonable royalty, just compensation, or an award to inventors who are deprived of patent rights under Section 151 or whose patents have been subjected to compulsory licensing under Section 153, or who comply with reporting provisions and merit compensation. A **Patent Compensation Board** is established to advise the AEC in this connection.

These and other provisions depart from previous government patent practice in an attempt to (1) protect the U.S. Government's position in the field of military applications of atomic energy, (2) assure the Commission complete freedom of action uninhibited by patent restrictions in the development and growth of peaceful uses of atomic energy; and (3) avoid creation of preferential rights for discoveries or inventions developed using public funds or information generated with public funds.

It should be noted in this connection that the original atomic energy statute (the Atomic Energy Act of 1946) was more restrictive in regard to patent rights. For example, the 1946 Act prohibited the granting of patents for inventions and discoveries solely useful in the production of special nuclear material as well as for those solely useful in connection with atomic weapons.

AEC Policy and Practices. In implementing the 1954 Act the AEC has followed a conservative policy with respect to patent matters, especially in its interpretation of the provisions of Section 152 dealing with inventions made or conceived during AEC contracts or arrangements. It has, for example, continued its pre-1954 practice of writing into all contracts a patent clause along one or another of the following lines:

1. Type "A" clause: In contracts primarily for research and development or for the operation of a facility, the patent clause states that the AEC shall determine the rights in or to any inventions.

2. Type "B" clause: Where the work under contract pertains indirectly to basic research and development and relates to a general field

of activity of the contractor, the patent clause provides for the retention by the contractor of a nonexclusive license for his use of any inventions in fields other than the production or utilization of special nuclear materials or atomic energy.

3. Type "C" clause: Where the work under contract pertains only incidentally to research and development in which the AEC is interested and relates to a field in which the contractor has an established industrial and patent position, the patent clause allows the contractor to retain a sole license and exclusive sub-licensing privileges for the use of inventions in fields other than the production or utilization of special nuclear materials or atomic energy.

All three types of patent clause contain requirements with respect to the prompt disclosure of inventions or discoveries.

Under the above contract procedure, the AEC has acquired many inventions and obtained many patents. Through December 1961 it had made available for licensing more than 2734 patents and it had granted some 850 royalty-free licenses under these patents.

To date the AEC has found no need to exercise its compulsory licensing powers granted by Section 153 of the 1954 Act, and cases involving the determination of "just compensation" or "awards" under Section 157, 151 and 153 have been relatively few in number. Here it should be borne in mind that largely all applied atomic energy research and development conducted prior to 1954, and much of it conducted since that time, has been carried out under contract or agreement with the AEC; and as was seen above, the AEC has maintained patent control over the atomic energy applications of inventions and discoveries made by its contractors.

The AEC is advised on general patent matters by an *ad hoc* **Patent Advisory Panel.**

Foreign Patents. In January, 1961, the AEC adopted revised policies re foreign patents obtained for inventions and discoveries resulting from work performed under AEC contract in privately owned and operated facilities.* Under the new policy, contractors who obtain U.S. and foreign patents will retain (1) a nonexclusive license for all purposes described in the U.S. patent application and (2) the title and rights to the foreign patent. At the same time the U.S. Government retains a nonexclusive license for governmental purposes, along with the right to grant licenses to foreign governments; and the contractor is obligated to grant nonexclusive royalty-free licenses to U.S. citizens and U.S. corporations upon request. Also, if within five years the contractor has not made practical application of the foreign patent, the AEC may require him to grant licenses to others at reasonable royalties.

Also under the new policy, the AEC will charge royalties in connection with the foreign use of AEC-owned foreign patents in those countries whose government exacts royalties from the U.S. Government or U.S. citizens for the use of patents.

PATHFINDER PLANT

A nuclear power plant of the direct-cycle **boiling water** type with integral nuclear superheating located on the Big Sioux River near Sioux Falls, South Dakota. The project is being carried out under the "third round" of the U.S. Atomic Energy Commission's Power Demonstration Reactor Program. Northern States Power, who will own and operate the plant, is financing the cost of construction. A group of private utilities, known as Central Utilities Atomic Power Associates,** is contributing $3.65 million for research and development. The AEC is contributing approxi-

* The new policies are not applicable in cases where the work was performed "in government or Commission contractor operated facilities, or . . . (where) a major part of the equipment employed in the research and development is government or Commission furnished."

** Central Electric & Gas Company, Interstate Power Company, Iowa Power and Light Company, Iowa Southern Utilities Company, Madison Gas and Electric Company, Northern States Power Company, Northwestern Public Service Company, Otter-Tail Power Company, St. Joseph Light & Power Company, and Wisconsin Public Service Company.

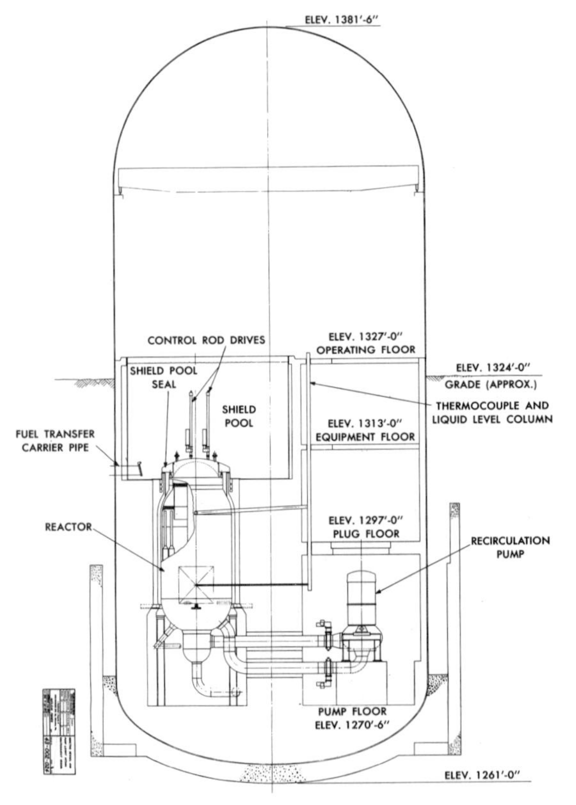

Fig. 145. The Pathfinder Plant. Above, construction view. Left, diagram showing general arrangement of equipment within the containment vessel. (*Courtesy of Allis-Chalmers Manufacturing Co.*)

mately $8 million for research and development and has waived its normal use charge for nuclear fuel material for the first 5 years of operation (corresponding to a financial contribution of $1.8 million). Allis-Chalmers Manufacturing Company has over-all responsibility for the design of the plant and supplied the principal plant components. Pioneer Service and Engineering Company is the architect-engineer-consultant. Fegles Construction Company is the general contractor for the plant.

The following notes are based on **1962** information:

Net Power: 62 megawatts (net electrical). *Fuel:* The boiler section of the core will be fueled with slightly enriched uranium (2.2% U^{235}) in the form of uranium dioxide (UO_2) pellets. The superheater section will be fueled with fully enriched uranium in the form of UO_2 particles dispersed in a stainless steel matrix. *Fuel element design:* A boiler fuel element consists of an assembly or zircaloy tubes loaded with UO_2 pellets. A superheater fuel element consists of two concentric stainless steel-clad UO_2-SS cermet fuel tubes, assembled with a central burnable-poison pin. *Core loading:* Boiler—7.6 metric tons of slightly enriched uranium dioxide, Superheater—47 kilograms of fully enriched uranium dioxide. *Steam conditions:* Steam leaves the superheater section of the reactor at 535 pounds pressure and 825°F. *Thermal conversion efficiency:* 30.5%. *Control materials:* 20 boron-steel control rods; boron carbide is used as the burnable poison in the superheater elements. *Containment:* Steel vessel with hemispherically shaped top. *Construction Cost:* Estimated at $22.4 million, exclusive of research and development. For other project costs, see Table 3 under **nuclear power development.** *Dates:* Proposal submitted to the AEC in May, 1957. Construction started in June, 1959. Preliminary operation scheduled for early 1963.

PEBBLE-BED GAS-COOLED REACTOR CONCEPT

A high-temperature reactor concept based on flowing a gas coolant (helium) through a stationary bed of spherical fuel-moderator pellets (graphite impregnated with enriched uranium). The U.S. Atomic Energy Commission has sponsored work on the pebble-bed concept by Oak Ridge National Laboratory and Sanderson and Porter, Inc. preparatory to a reactor experiment.*

One of the key problems of the pebble-bed concept has been the development of fuel-moderator pellets capable of retaining fission product gases to the degree necessary to avoid excessive radioactive contamination of the gas coolant. The problem arises from the permeability of graphite. A possible solution lies in a technique recently developed at Battelle Memorial Institute for coating grain-sized particles of uranium dioxide with alumina or other impervious refractory materials. The coated particles can readily be dispersed in a graphite matrix and the desired spherical pebbles easily fabricated. Pebbles produced in this manner appear to have good corrosion resistance as well as excellent gas-retention properties, and appear promising for use in a high-temperature gas-cooled reactor environment.

PENNSYLVANIA ADVANCED REACTOR PROJECT

In 1955 Pennsylvania Power and Light Company and Westinghouse Electric Corporation jointly initiated a program of development work and design studies aimed at determining the technical and economic feasibility of constructing a large-scale (150 megawatts-electrical) nuclear power plant of the single-region **aqueous homogeneous** type. The proposed fuel was a suspension, or slurry, of fully enriched uranium oxide and thorium oxide particles in heavy water. At the end of **1957**, by which time the companies had expended $5.5 million, they approached the U.S. Atomic Energy Commission for financial assistance for an estimated two years of additional research and development deemed necessary to provide a firm basis for a decision on plant construction. An understanding was reached that the AEC would contribute $7 million for research during **1958-1959** keyed to a commitment on the companies' part to proceed with construction on a **1963** completion schedule if the proj-

* An experimental pebble bed reactor is under construction in Europe. See reference to AVR Project under West **Germany.**

ect was found to be feasible. Contract negotiations were still in progress in December 1958, when the companies decided to terminate the project. Accordingly, the companies paid for the 1958 work, bringing their total expenditure to ~ $9 million.*

The reason given for stopping the work was that it did not appear technically feasible to proceed with a large-scale plant without first building and operating a small-scale prototype. The major technical problems cited were: (1) The problem of radiolytic gas recombination. An external recombination system appeared too complex; and an internal recombination system could not be designed until a suitable catalyst had been developed. (2) Lack of sufficient information on the effects of irradiation on the properties of the fuel slurry. (3) Lack of sufficient information on hydraulic problems affecting the design of the reactor vessel. (4) Discouraging results from experiments conducted on the corrosion and erosion of exposed surfaces by the fuel slurry. (5) Possible stress-corrosion problems. (6) Uncertainty with regard to the stability of the system during start-up periods, especially following emergency shut-down. (7) Plant design complexities introduced by the need to conduct remote maintenance on the primary reactor system.

This marked the second time an aqueous homogeneous power reactor project had been cancelled. The first was the **Wolverine Electric Cooperative Reactor Project.**

PENNSYLVANIA STATE UNIVERSITY REACTORS

A 4000-kilowatt (thermal) pool-type research reactor is operated by the University at Quehenna, Pennsylvania. This facility was donated to the University by the Curtiss-Wright Corporation, who designed and formerly operated it. The transfer of title became effective in December, 1960.

The University also operates a 200-kilowatt pool reactor, which was designed by the University staff and is located at University Park, Pennsylvania. (See **research and training reactors)**

* Baltimore Gas & Electric Company was a participant during the latter phase and bore part of the cost.

PERHAPSATRON

The name given to toroidal pinch experimental devices built at Los Alamos Scientific Laboratory for research on controlled **fusion.** The original device, built in 1952, was used for the first U.S. experiments on the **pinch effect,** which served to confirm theoretical predictions with regard to the inherent instability of pinch confinement of an ionized gas, or **plasma.** A second device, built in 1956 and modified several times over the next several years, has been used to study techniques for achieving a stabilized pinch in a toroidal (ring-shaped) tube. (See **Pinch Program)**

PERMISSIBLE DOSE, OF IONIZING RADIATION.

See **radiation standards and regulations.**

PERSONNEL SECURITY REVIEW BOARD

An *ad hoc* (nonstatutory) advisory body to the U.S. Atomic Energy Commission established in 1949 primarily to review specific personnel security cases which arise under the AEC's administrative review procedures. The Board also advises the AEC on general questions relating to personnel security, e.g., criteria and procedures for determining eligibility for security clearance or access authorizations. Membership listed in Appendix D.

PERU

The Junta de Control de Energia Atomica, Lima, is the agency responsible for atomic energy matters. Training in basic nuclear engineering, radioisotope technique and related subjects is provided by the Instituto Superior de Energia Nuclear, which is supported by the Junta. Cobalt teletherapy equipment and radioisotope diagnostic and therapeutic techniques are in use. Uranium exploration has been in progress for several years with technical assistance from the United States. Peru's plans for the immediate future include increased use of radioisotopes, and the installation of a subcritical reactor facility for training purposes. Peru is a member of the **International Atomic Energy Agency** and the **Inter-American Nuclear Energy Commission.**

PHILIPPINES

The National Science Development Board, Manila, establishes national scientific policy. The Philippine Atomic Energy Commission, Manila, is responsible for implementation of the Board's policies in the atomic energy field. A Nuclear Research Center is being established by the Philippine AEC at Quezon City (the new capital). The facilities will include isotope and other laboratories, and a pool-type research reactor being supplied by General Electric Company. By a special grant, the United States is contributing $500,000 toward the cost of this reactor, which will operate at a power level of 1000 kilowatts (thermal) and was scheduled to be completed in 1962.

The installed electric power capacity in the Philippines is about 400 megawatts, nearly half of it hydroelectric. Most of the coal and diesel oil used for power production is imported. There is some interest in nuclear power, however there are few load centers requiring large power stations and the economics of nuclear power generation do not appear favorable at the present time. The Philippines are a member of the **International Atomic Energy Agency** and have a research-type **Agreement for Cooperation** with the United States.

PHOENIX MEMORIAL PROJECT

A privately supported program of research in the field of atomic energy, established at the University of Michigan, Ann Arbor.

PHOSPHORUS-32

A 14.3-day beta-emitting radioisotope of phosphorus, used extensively in agricultural and biomedical research and in medical therapy (see **agricultural applications of atomic energy, medical aspects of atomic energy).** Phosphorus-32 is produced by reactor irradiation, either of elemental sulfur:

$$_{16}S^{32} + {}_0n^1 \longrightarrow {}_{15}P^{32} + {}_1p^1$$

or of phosphorus-31:

$$_{15}P^{31} + {}_0n^1 \longrightarrow {}_{15}P^{32} + \gamma$$

It is available in the form of phosphoric acid (99% P^{32}) through U.S. Atomic Energy Commission radioisotope distribution channels, and in the form of **labeled compounds** from commercial pharmaceutical houses.

PHOTOELECTRIC EFFECT

The total absorption of high-frequency **electromagnetic radiation** by an atomic system resulting in the emission of bound electrons from that system. This phenomenon, first diagnosed by Albert Einstein, is of interest in the atomic energy field in several ways. It is one of the mechanisms by which **gamma rays** are absorbed in matter and, at the same time, one of the ways in which such rays produce ionization. Also, it is the mechanism by which photomultiplier tubes convert light flashes to measurable electrical impulses in **scintillation counters.**

PHOTON

A unit quantity of **electromagnetic radiation** (light, gamma rays, or x-rays).

PICKET FENCE

The name given a cusp-shaped magnetic-field configuration studied at Los Alamos Scientific Laboratory in the early stages of U.S. research on controlled **fusion.** As originally conceived, the purpose of the picket fence geometry was to reduce the power required for magnetic confinement of fuel **plasma** by localizing the magnetic field in the vicinity of the walls of the container. It is now recognized that the principal advantage of picket fence and other cusp-shaped geometries is in enhancing the stability of plasma confinement. (See **cusped geometry)**

PILE

Nuclear reactors were originally called "atomic piles," an expression which had its origin in the fact that the first reactor (see **Chicago Pile No. 1**) was built by "piling" up blocks of uranium and graphite. The term, pile, has fallen into disfavor but continues to receive some use, as in the expression **in-pile tests.**

PINCH EFFECT

When a strong electric current flows in an ionized gas, or **plasma,** contained in a tube, it

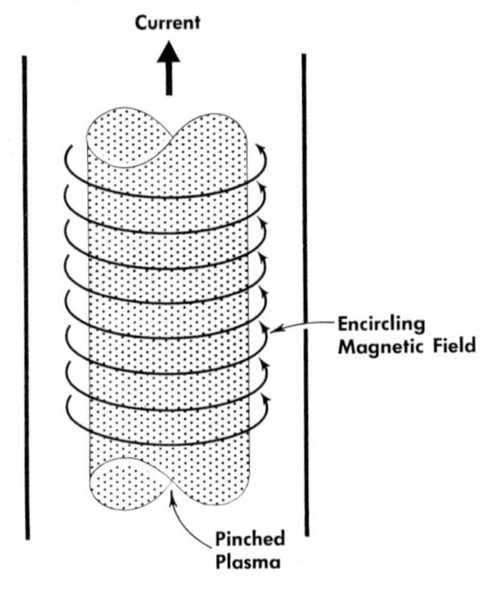

Fig. 146. Principle of pinch effect.

produces an encircling magnetic field which acts to constrict and compress the plasma, thereby heating it and causing it to be confined as a dense, hot "filament" at the center of the tube. This "self-focussing" phenomenon in gaseous conductors was first predicted in 1934 and later became known as the pinch effect. It is of importance in connection with research on controlled **fusion.** (See **Pinch Program**)

PINCH PROGRAM

One of several lines of U.S. research on controlled **fusion** (see **thermonuclear power).** In pinch devices an ionized fuel, or **plasma,** is confined by an internally generated magnetic field (see **pinch effect),** rather than by an externally applied field as in other controlled-fusion concepts. Research in the United States on the pinch concept started in 1951 at Los Alamos Scientific Laboratory and in 1954 at the Berkeley and Livermore Branches of the E. O. Lawrence Radiation Laboratory. The central problem has been the inherent instability of the pinch confinement.

Concept. Early in the Pinch Program it was predicted on theoretical grounds that pinch confinement would be subject to violent instabilities. For example, any small kink or other defect that might develop at some point in the pinched "filament" of plasma would create a local imbalance in the magnetic confinement pressure which, in turn, would so rapidly magnify and distort the defect as to break the filament and disperse the plasma in a matter of microseconds. Other plasma column distortions (bulges) were also foreseen. These predictions were confirmed in early pinch experiments.

Much of the nature of pinch formations became understood in mid-1954, when M. N. Rosenbluth, then of Los Alamos, developed the so-called "M-theory" of pinch formation. This theory is based on the assumption that plasma has a very high electrical conductivity. On this basis, the sudden application of an axial electric voltage to a plasma contained in a tube can be expected to produce a thin sheath of electric current at the outer surface of the plasma. As the current builds up, an encircling magnetic "wall" is formed which rapidly contracts toward the center of the tube, driving the plasma ions and electrons ahead of it and thereby compressing them into a dense, hot filament. The inward velocity of the magnetic wall is directly proportional to the square root of the voltage gradient applied, so that by increasing the voltage the speed of the pinch can be increased. Since energy is imparted to the plasma particles as they rebound inwards from the contracting magnetic wall, and since the energy gain is greater the faster the wall moves, an extremely fast pinch offers a means of **shock heating** the plasma. In principle, a "super fast" pinch might set up thermonuclear conditions in the plasma before instabilities could take effect. This is one of the lines of attack that has been followed in the Pinch Program.

A second line of attack has been to attempt to stabilize the pinch. Here the basic concept has been to set up an axial magnetic field in the plasma to lend "backbone" to the pinched filament and thereby combat short-wave kink instabilities and, at the same time, to sheathe the tube with a conductive layer to combat long-wave kink instabilities.

Program. Since the inception of the Pinch Program various experimental devices have been built in U.S. laboratories (see summary table). The work has followed a complex evolution that is difficult to summarize, however two key turning points can be noted: (1) The first occurred in 1954 when the M-theory pointed the way to shock heating and fast-pinch techniques. Experimental work along this line quickly yielded plasma temperatures of the order of one million degrees and intense neutron bursts were found to be emitted from the plasma. By late 1955, however, it was evident that the neutrons being emitted were non-thermonuclear (i.e., false) neutrons, and it was beginning to be clear that to achieve controlled fusion by the shock-heating route in unstabilized pinch devices would ultimately entail equipment of impractical size. (2) The second turning point came late in 1955 when calculations showed the stabilizing concept described above to be theoretically sound. Again the experimental results were at first encouraging; experiments with both straight and toroidal tubes gave evidence of stability for brief periods at plasma temperatures estimated as high as 5 million degrees. But, as in the fast-pinch approach, difficulties were soon encountered. For one, the presence of the axial stabilizing field inhibited shock-heating. For another, interdiffusion between the externally imposed axial field and the internally generated circumferential field, led to instabilities of a new kind and introduced other complications.

EXPERIMENTAL PINCH-TYPE FUSION MODELS

Model	*Operation Date*	*Shape and Description*	*Tube Diameter (cms)*	*Axial Length (cms)*	*Voltage Gradient (volts/cm)*	*Total Power Input (joules/sec)*	*Peak Pinch Current (amp)*	*Estimated Ion Temperature (°K)*
Los Alamos Scientific Laboratory:								
Perhapsatron	1952	Toroid, slow pinch, unstable	7	70	150	1.6×10^4	5×10^4	—
Columbus I	1954	Linear, fast pinch, unstable	7	30	1,000	5×10^3	10^5	—
Columbus II	1956	Linear, fast pinch, unstable	10	30	2,000	10^5	2×10^6	—
Columbus (S-1 to S-4)	1956	Stabilized linear pinch	13	62	150	10^4	3×10^5	5×10^6
Perhapsatron (S-1 to S-5)	1956	Stabilized toroidal pinch	variable	70	200	9×10^4	4×10^5	6×10^6
Lawrence Radiation Laboratory (Berkeley):								
Linear Dynamic Pinch	1955	Linear, fast pinch, unstable	10	100	10,000	2×10^4	2×10^5	—
Stabilized Linear Pinch	1956	Linear, stable	8	50	500	10^4	2×10^5	—
Triaxial Pinch	1957	Linear, quasi-stable, dynamic pinch	10	50	200	5×10^4	2×10^6	—
Lawrence Radiation Laboratory (Livermore)								
Gamma	1956	Stabilized linear pinch	8	45	200	2×10^4	2×10^5	5×10^5
Stabilized Toroidal Pinch	1956	Toroid, stable	10	60	100	10^5	4×10^5	—
Screw Dynamic Pinch	1956	Quasi-stable dynamic pinch	10	20	2,500	10^4	2×10^6	—
Levitron (Hard-core Pinch)	1960	Toroid, stable	30	—	—	—	—	—

In the past several years the program has broadened to include research on hybrid concepts combining features of the fast pinch and the stabilized pinch. Considerable light has been shed not only on the central problem of pinch instability, but also on the broad phenomenology on pinch systems. Some results from these concepts have been encouraging.

PINELLAS PLANT. See **Atomic Energy Commission—Facilities.**

PIQUA ORGANIC MODERATED REACTOR

A small nuclear power plant of the **organic cooled** type located on the Great Miami River near Piqua, Ohio. The project is being carried out under the "second round" of the U.S. Atomic Energy Commission's Power Demonstration Reactor Program. The AEC is financing the cost of reactor construction and related research and development. The City of Piqua provided the site and the electrical portion of the plant, and will operate the plant and distribute the power produced, making payment to the AEC for the steam used. Atomics International, a Division of North American Aviation, Inc., was the prime contractor for the reactor. The project represents the first use of the organic cooled reactor concept in electric power generation. The following notes reflect the status of the project as of mid-1962:

Power: 11.4 megawatts (net electrical). *Fuel:* slightly enriched uranium (1.94% U^{235}) in the form of an uranium-molybdenum-aluminum alloy (3.5 weight % Mo, 0.1 weight % A). *Fuel element configuration:* Finned concentric-tube construction; aluminum cladding. *Fuel inventory:* 6870 kilograms of slightly enriched uranium. *Coolant:* Mixture of terphenyl isomers ("Santowax OMP") at 100 pounds pressure; inlet temperature, 525°F; outlet temperature, 575°F. *Steam conditions:* 450 pounds pressure and 550°F. *Thermal conversion efficiency:* 25.1%. *Control materials:* 13 boron-steel control rods. *Containment:* originally no containment was to have been provided; however, on the recommendation of AEC's Advisory Committee on Reactor Safeguards, the reactor will be enclosed in a steel containment vessel. *Construction cost:* Estimated at $12.2 million, exclusive of research and development. For other project costs, see Table 3 under **nuclear power development.** *Dates:* Construction started in July, 1959. Preliminary operation began in March 1962, and power operation began in June, 1962.

Fig. 147. Artist's sketch of Piqua Plant. (*Courtesy of Atomics International*)

PITCHBLENDE

A massive form of the primary uranium mineral, **uraninite.** There are some pitchblende occurrences in the United States. Major deposits are in Canada and Czechoslovakia.

PL-3 (ARMY NUCLEAR POWER PLANT)

Portable Low-Powerplant-3, a small nuclear power plant to be installed in an ice tunnel at Byrd Station, a remote base 800 miles inland from McMurdo Sound in Antarctica. The plant, to be prepackaged for air shipment, is scheduled to be delivered to the site late in 1963. It will employ a **pressurized water reactor** and will supply 1.0 megawatt of electricity and 0.44 megawatt of heat for base operations.

The U.S. Atomic Energy Commission awarded a contract for PL-3 to Alco Products, Inc., in October, 1961, but in June, 1962, the contract was reassigned to Allis-Chalmers Manufacturing Company. This change was occasioned by a decision by Alco to discontinue its activities in the atomic energy field.

After a period of test operations by the contractor, the installation will be operated by the Navy. Byrd Station is one of several inland bases operated by the Navy in support of U.S. scientific studies in the Antarctic region.

PLANT AVAILABILITY FACTOR

In electric power generation, the ratio of the number of hours that a generating unit is available for service in a given period of time, to the total number of hours in that same period.

PLANT FACTOR

Synonymous with **capacity factor.**

PLASMA

A partially or completely ionized gas in which positively and negatively charged particles (ions and electrons) move about freely but are in balance so that the medium is electrically neutral. In systems being developed to demonstrate and harness controlled **fusion,** the fuel is in the form of a high-temperature plasma. (See **thermonuclear power)**

PLASMA CONFINEMENT

In controlled-**fusion** experiments, the use of a magnetic field to confine a fuel **plasma** (ionized gas) in the central region of an otherwise evacuated reactor chamber and to hold it in place for a sufficient interval of time to permit its temperature and/or density to be brought up to critical values. Plasma confinement is the key problem in achieving controlled-fusion reactions. (See **plasma stability, thermonuclear power)**

PLASMA DIAGNOSTICS

A general term for the methods and equipment used in diagnosing the performance and behavior of the confined **plasma** in experimental devices for controlled **fusion.** The development of diagnostic techniques has been and will continue to be an important aspect of research on **thermonuclear power.**

In order to analyze what takes place in a controlled-fusion experiment it is necessary to measure various physical characteristics of the ionized gas, or plasma. The characteristics of interest include ion and electron temperature, plasma density, confinement time, and impurity content. It is also important to know the strength of the magnetic field at various points in the reaction chamber and, of course, it is desired to know as much as possible about neutron emission and other reaction phenomena, such as **bremsstrahlung** production.

At plasma temperatures up to several million degrees, high-speed photographic and spectroscopic techniques may be used to obtain information on plasma composition and electron and ion temperatures. At higher temperatures high-purity plasmas become completely ionized and emit little visible light, so that other methods must be used. One such method is to probe the plasma with a microwave beam.

By measuring the phase shift, absorption and scattering of the microwave radiation it is possible to learn a good deal about the electron density of the plasma; and, by measuring the microwave "noise" emitted from the plasma, it is possible to deduce electron temperatures.

Magnetic probes, consisting of tiny coils of wire embedded in small quartz tubes, have proved useful in determining the local field strength at various points within the reaction chamber; however, such probes may introduce impurities into the plasma and create significant local disturbances and distortions which limit their usefulness in some situations.

As thermonuclear conditions are approached in controlled-fusion experiments, measurement of bremsstrahlung radiation and neutron emission becomes increasingly important. Various techniques may be used, including the observation of recoil tracks in photographic emulsions and the use of scintillation counters. The principal problem in this regard is that of distinguishing between **nonthermonuclear** (i.e., false) **neutrons** and neutrons of true thermonuclear origin.

PLASMA DIODE. See **thermionic conversion.**

PLASMA GUN

A device for producing and accelerating into an evacuated apparatus bursts of **plasma** (i.e., ionized gas) at speeds in excess of 10^7 cm/sec; used in research on controlled **fusion.**

PLASMA ROCKET. See **rocket propulsion (nuclear).**

PLASMA STABILITY

All methods conceived to date for the achievement of controlled **fusion** depend on the use of magnetic fields to "confine" an ionized gas, or **plasma,** i.e., to constrict or trap the plasma and hold it away from the walls of the reactor chamber. The interval of confinement must be long enough to allow time for the desired reactions to take place. The time required is inversely proportional to the plasma density. (Plasma temperature is a third critical process variable.) The natural tendency of plasma is to writhe convulsively out of its magnetic confinement, and any of various perturbations can cause plasma instabilities to develop in a matter of microseconds. In contrast, considerably greater confinement times are believed to be required to achieve a practical fusion system. (See **thermonuclear power)**

In the above context, the term, plasma stability, refers to the positional stability of the plasma within the magnetic field that is used to confine it. A plasma is said to be stable if it will return to its equilibrium position after a disturbance; it is said to be unstable if a disturbance causes the plasma to move rapidly away from its equilibrium position, thereby escaping confinement.

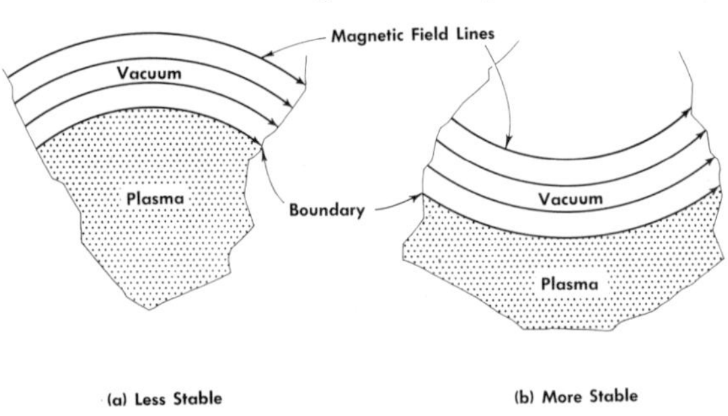

Fig. 148. Principle of plasma stability. Left, less stable configuration; right, more stable configuration.

A simplified illustration of the concept of stability and instability is shown in the accompanying illustration. The configuration suggested by (a) has inherently unstable tendencies due to the fact that the restoring force (i.e., magnetic pressure) decreases with distance from the plasma's most stable position; conversely, that suggested by (b) should inherently be more stable. In actual practice, plasma stability is a much more complex matter than this illustration might indicate, and involves not only configuration stability, but other factors (e.g., internal vibration stability).

The various parts of the U.S. program of research on controlled fusion essentially represent different approaches to the problem of achieving stable plasma confinement (see **Astron Program, cusped geometry, magnetic mirror systems, Pinch Program,** and **Stellarator Program).** The problem of instability takes different forms in these different experimental concepts and hence does not lend itself to generalization.

PLOWSHARE ADVISORY COMMITTEE

An *ad hoc* (nonstatutory) advisory committee to the U.S. Atomic Energy Commission formed in 1959 for consultation on the **Plowshare Program,** including the selection and execution of specific projects as well as matters of general project orientation and policy. Membership listed in Appendix D.

PLOWSHARE PROGRAM

A research and development program established by the U.S. Atomic Energy Commission to investigate peaceful uses of nuclear explosives. The applications of potential interest include:

1. Excavation in connection with the construction of harbors, canals or other civil works.
2. Aiding the recovery of underground mineral resources such as oil contained in oil or tar sands.
3. Establishing underground heat reservoirs for use in supplying steam for industrial use or for the generation of electric power.
4. Quantity production of chemicals or radioisotopes using the earth as a retort.
5. Scientific research.

U.S. interest in such applications was stimulated by the development of thermonuclear devices with a small fission component (and hence a correspondingly low yield of radioactive fission products). Further impetus was provided by the results of underground weapons tests, which shed light on cratering and other characteristics of underground nuclear detonations and established that the radioactivity generated in such explosions can be highly localized and, if the detonation occurs at sufficient depth, essentially confined below ground. The first deep underground test was the Ranier shot, which was part of the Plumbbob series conducted at the Nevada Test Site in 1957. Additional underground tests were conducted at the same site during the Phase II Hardtack series the following year. While all of these tests were primarily for military purposes they shed light on many phenomena of interest in connection with peaceful applications.

On October 31, 1958, the United States joined with the U.S.S.R. and the United Kingdom in a 1-year moratorium on nuclear weapon tests (see **weapons testing),** and until recently continued voluntarily to observe the moratorium. Up until December, 1961, the Plowshare Program was confined to interpretation of 1957-1958 data on military tests, small-scale experiments with conventional chemical explosives, studies of application possibilities, and preparations for nuclear experiments. The first nuclear experiment under the Plowshare Program, the Gnome Experiment, was conducted on December 10, 1961.

As part of a recent change in AEC organization, a new Division of Peaceful Nuclear Explosives was created to administer the Plowshare Program. The major centers of research activity are the Livermore Branch of the E. O. Lawrence Radiation Laboratory, the Los Alamos Scientific Laboratory, and the Sandia Corporation. The scale of the effort has been modest to date. Research and development expenditures through mid-1962 totaled approximately $25 million.

Background. The reader is referred to the entry on **weapons phenomenology** for background information on the events involved in a nuclear detonation. Of particular interest for peaceful applications are the amount of earth displaced and the amount and quality (temperature) of heat generated, the former being the principal factor in civil works applications and the latter being the principal in applications of an industrial nature. (The neutron flux made available is also an important factor.)

Table 1 summarizes estimates of cratering effects (i.e., earth displacement) in desert alluvium at depths calculated to result in maximum crater dimensions. These estimates are based on an extrapolation of limited data from low-yield ($\lesssim$ 1.2 kiloton) underground weapon tests, plus limited data obtained from tests with conventional explosives (up to 20 tons). Included in Table 1 are order-of-magnitude estimates of the unit cost of earth displacement. These are based on rough cost information made available by the AEC in September 1958 to provide a guide for preliminary studies of the economic feasibility of Plowshare applications. As is indicated, they range from a few cents per cubic yard of earth for a megaton nuclear explosion * to $6.50 per cubic yard for a kiloton explosion. By way of comparison, costs of earth displacements by conventional methods are commonly about $2 per cubic yard.

TABLE 1. CRATER DIMENSIONS AND COSTS FOR NUCLEAR EXPLOSIONS OF VARIOUS YIELDS

Yield (kilotons)	*Diameter (feet)*	*Depth (feet)*	*Volume (cubic yards)*	*AEC Charges ($)*	*Construction and Operation*	*Cost ($ per cubic yard)*
1	400	100	230,000	500,000	1,000,000	6.50
10	790	195	1,200,000	750,000	1,500,000	1.90
100	1,550	385	13,000,000	1,000,000	2,000,000	.23
1,000	3,000	760	95,000,000	1,000,000	2,500,000	.04

Source: (1 megaton) Testimony of Gerald W. Johnson, E. O. Lawrence Radiation, before the Subcommittee on Research and Development, Joint Committee on Atomic Energy, March 22, 1960.

Turning to heat generation, a megaton nuclear explosion underground generates of the order of one thousand trillion (10^{15}) calories of heat, which is roughly equivalent to the heat content of 150,000 tons of coal. The heat is released at extremely high temperatures. It has been estimated, for example, that an underground detonation of a 10-kiloton device would for a brief interval of time (milliseconds) raise the temperature of some 2000 tons of earth material to $\sim$ 14,000°F. At this temperature all chemical compounds are unstable and even the most refractory substances are vaporized.

* I.e., a nuclear detonation releasing the same amount of energy as 1 million tons of TNT.

Applications. The following paragraphs briefly expand on the potential applications noted earlier.

Civil Works. Analyses have been made of a number of possible excavation applications, including harbor, canal, and river damming projects at various specific locations. These studies have indicated that the use of nuclear explosives is practical and economically attractive, however experimental programs are required before a definitive evaluation can be made. The lines of research and development that need to be pursued include (1) further work with conventional chemical explosives to extend existing knowledge of basic cratering phenomena; (2) a program of experimental nuclear detonations to establish a correlation between nuclear and conventional cratering phenomena, and to study cratering effects and radioactivity distribution under different soil conditions; and (3) a program of research and testing to develop low-cost nuclear devices tailored for civil applications.

Until very recently, U.S. cratering experience with underground nuclear detonations was limited to energy yields of 1.2 kilotons or less. On July 6, 1962, a thermonuclear device with a design yield in the 100-kiloton range was detonated in a cratering experiment at the Nevada Test Site (Project Sedan). Another cratering experiment (Project Wagon) is planned, and an Alaskan Harbor construction project involving the detonation of four 20-kiloton devices and one 200-kiloton is being evaluated. (See **Project Chariot)**

A vital question in civil works and other applications is control of radioactivity. Experience with small nuclear detonations indicates that under controlled conditions craters can be excavated with 99% or more of the total radioactivity trapped deep underground and the balance deposited locally on the ground surface. The amount of radioactivity reaching ground surface can be reduced by use of devices with minimum fission yield. Another way of minimizing ground contamination is to surround the nuclear explosives with a material, such as boron, having a high cross section for neutron capture, thereby reducing the amount of radioactivity induced in ground materials.

The required minimum depth of detonation in desert alluvium to achieve "99+%" containment is estimated by the following formula:

$$D = 450\sqrt[3]{W}$$

where D = the required minimum depth in feet, and W = the energy yield expressed in equivalent kilotons of TNT. Thus, the minimum required depth in desert alluvium is estimated to range from ~ 450 feet for a kiloton explosion to ~ 4500 feet for a megaton explosion.

Recovery of Mineral Resources. Various schemes have been considered for using nuclear explosives to aid the recovery of mineral resources. One approach is based on fragmenting and/or fluidizing underground mineral deposits, thereby facilitating the recovery of the mineral values. For example, an ore bed might be fragmented to the point where the metal content could be leached out *in situ* instead of having to bring the ore above ground to process it. Another example is the possibility of fluidizing oil contained in oil sands, i.e., increasing its viscosity (by underground retorting) to the point where it could be pumped to the surface. The latter possibility has been under study by private oil interests in connection with deep underground oil sands located in the Athebaska area of Alberta, Canada. (See Project **Oilsand**)

Another approach is based strictly on the cratering effect of nuclear detonations as, for example, in removing the overburden from deeply buried mineral deposits so that they can be economically mined. This approach also has been considered as a way of creating underground water reservoirs. The latter application, while potentially of great interest, must await the development of proven techniques for radioactivity control.

Power Generation. At least two methods have been considered for using nuclear explosives to supply heat for industrial use (process steam) or for electrical power generation. One is based on the observed result that an appreciable fraction of the energy released in underground explosions is "stored" in molten rock at high temperatures. By circulating a working fluid such as water, through the molten mass it is possible, at least in principle, to recover much of this heat for useful purposes. Theoretical calculations indicate that by multiple firings in the same location as much as 50% of the total energy release should be recoverable. Analyses of various possible earth environments has led to the conclusion that salt beds offer the most promise for this application. A test nuclear detonation in a deep underground salt bed was conducted on December 10, 1961. (See **Gnome Experiment**)

A more elegant but also more difficult method would be to excavate a large underground cavern, fill it with water, and then detonate a nuclear device, thereby directly producing high-temperature, high-pressure steam.

Pending further study and experimental results, it is impossible to make a meaningful assessment of the technical or economic feasibility of either scheme. The indications are, however, that low-cost steam generation by such methods is a definite possibility.

Chemical and Isotope Production. The high-temperature heat and high-neutron fluxes made available by underground nuclear detonations are being studied as a means for the large-scale production of chemicals and/or isotopes. As a purely hypothetical example, a nuclear detonation in a limestone bed would produce large quantities of quicklime. Similarly, a detonation in certain clays would produce large quantities of carbon monoxide, hydrogen and silicon carbide which, if practically recoverable, could be used for gasoline synthesis (by reacting CO and H_2 in the presence of a catalyst) and methane production (by reacting the hot SiC with water).

The Gnome Experiment, referred to above, incorporated isotope-production experiments.

Scientific Research. Underground nuclear detonations promise to be very useful for at least two altogether separate lines of scientific inquiry. On the one hand, the high neutron fluxes will make possible various experiments in nuclear and particle physics that cannot be conducted with conventional neutron sources. It has been estimated, for example, that neutron irradiations can be achieved with the flux made available by relatively small nuclear detonations that would take hundreds of years to accomplish in the most powerful nuclear reactors. The experimental possibilities include the production of new isotopes of light and heavy elements, high-resolution neutron spectroscopy, and various types of neutron cross-section measurement. An experiment to study some of these possibilities (Project Coach) is under consideration at this writing.

On the other hand, underground nuclear detonations will contribute new information on the earth's structure. For example tracking of seismic signals of known time and place of origin produced by past underground nuclear tests has contributed to better understanding of natural seismic disturbances.

PLUM BROOK REACTOR FACILITY (NASA-TR)

A large, general-purpose **test reactor** at the Plum Brook facilities of the National Aeronautics and Space Administration near Sandusky, Ohio. The reactor is used in support of the development of nuclear rocket propulsion systems and other NASA interests. The construction cost of the facility was $10.8 million. *Type*: Tank reactor. *Power rating*: 60,000 thermal kilowatts. *Fuel*: Modified MTR fuel elements. *Coolant*: H_2O. *Moderator*: H_2O. *Neutron flux*: Of the order of 10^{15} n/cm^2 sec (maximum thermal). *Start-up*: 1961.

PLUTO PROJECT

A program of research and development in the field of nuclear ramjet propulsion being sponsored jointly by the U.S. Atomic Energy Commission and the U.S. Air Force. The objective is to demonstrate the feasibility of a nuclear ramjet engine—i.e., an air-breathing jet engine powered by a nuclear reactor—for missile propulsion.

Conventional chemical propulsion systems for high-speed missiles require large quantities of fuel, especially when operating at low altitudes, which limits their effective range. Because of the compactness of nuclear fuel, it is believed possible to design a nuclear ramjet engine capable of propelling an unmanned aerodynamic missile at speeds about three times the speed of sound for several hours, thus assuring "unlimited" target range. Such a propulsion system appears particularly promising for Supersonic Low Altitude Missile (SLAM) applications.

Project Pluto was initiated in 1955. Early in 1957, the responsibility for demonstration of the technical feasibility of a nuclear ramjet system was assigned to the Livermore branch of the E. O. Lawrence Radiation Laboratory. Supporting materials research was conducted until mid-1961 by Atomics International, a division of North American Aviation, Inc. Under Air Force contracts, the Marquardt Corporation is engaged in ramjet engine studies and Chance-Vought Aircraft, Inc. is conducting supporting aerodynamic research.

The central effort of the project is a series of ground-based reactor experiments (the Tory II series) being coducted at the AEC's Nevada Test Site (NTS). The first facility constructed, known as "hot Box," was completed in 1958 and is used for elevated-temperature critical experiments to obtain data needed for reactor design. The first experimental reactors, TORY II-A-1 and II-A-2 are direct-cycle, air cooled units fueled with a homogeneous mixture of enriched uranium dioxide (UO_2) and beryllium oxide (BeO). TORY II-A-1 achieved initial criticality in December, 1960 and first operated at appreciable power ($\sim$ 40 thermal megawatts) in May, 1961. In its initial power run, it was operated for about 45 seconds at temperatures in excess of 2000°F. The full design power of this system, to be reached in progressive stages, is 150 thermal megawatts. At this writing, a reactor of more advanced design, which will incorporate some features of a flight unit, is planned for construction. It will be known as TORY II-C.

The TORY II series reactors are mounted on a railroad flat-car and coupled to a concrete field test building for power testing. The tests are conducted by remote control from a distance of about two miles. No significant release of radioactivity is anticipated, however as a precautionary measure, tests are only conducted under favorable meteorological conditions.

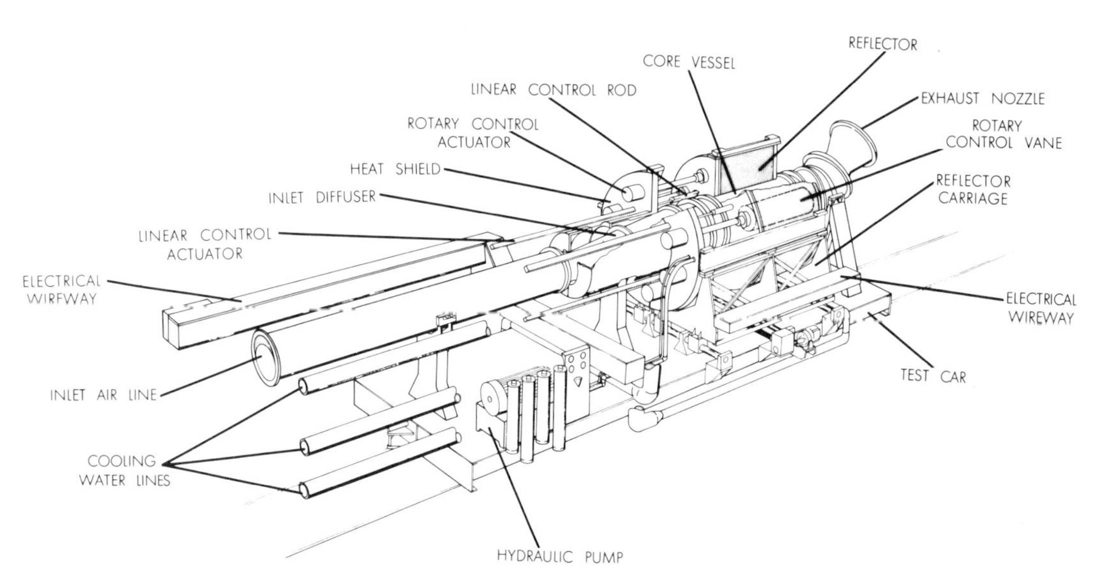

Fig. 149. Pluto Project. Top, Tory II A-1 at its test stand at the Nevada Test Site. Bottom, diagram of this ground-based experimental nuclear ramjet device. (*Courtesy of E. O. Lawrence Radiation Laboratory (Livermore Branch)*)

Through June 30, 1961, cumulative AEC and Air Force expenditures on Project Pluto totaled just under $100 million, distributed as follows:

PROJECT PLUTO FUNDING FY-57 THROUGH FY-61
($ millions)

	Operations	*Facilities*	*Total*
AEC	58.4	15.2	73.6
Air Force	22.6	1.3	23.8
	$81.0	$16.5	$97.4

PLUTONIUM

A heavy, radioactive, highly toxic, metallic element (atomic no. 94), the principal isotope of which (plutonium-239) is one of the three primary fissionable materials. Although traces of plutonium occur naturally, it is to all practical purposes a man-made element and indeed was first identified in controlled transmutation experiments conducted by Seaborg, McMillan and Wahl at the University of California in 1940. The fissionable isotope, plutonium-239, was isolated a year later by Seaborg, Segré, Kennedy and Lawrence.

Plutonium-239 is produced on a large scale in reactors at Hanford and Savannah River by the irradiation of normal uranium. Following is the reaction and decay sequence:

$$(1)\ {}_{92}U^{238} + {}_0n^1 \longrightarrow {}_{92}U^{239} + \gamma$$

$$(2)\ {}_{92}U^{239} \xrightarrow{23.5\ \text{min}} {}_{93}Np^{239} + {}_{-1}e^{o}$$

$$(3)\ {}_{93}Np^{239} \xrightarrow{2.3\ \text{days}} {}_{94}Pu^{239} + {}_{-1}e^{o}$$

The product material is recovered from the irradiated fuel by solvent extraction techniques.

Plutonium-239 is an alpha emitter with a half-life of 2.44×10^4 years. Of the three primary fissionable materials, it has the highest neutron yield in fast fission and hence offers great promise in fast breeding systems.

Various other isotopes of plutonium have been identified. Of these the most significant is plutonium-240, formed by parasitic neutron-capture cross section. The latter factor limits the permissible concentration of plutonium-240 in plutonium intended for weapons use or for use as a reactor fuel. The rate of plutonium-240 "build-up" thus controls the length of time that fuel can be permitted to remain under irradiation in a reactor whose primary purpose is plutonium production.

Plutonium metal is highly reactive and must be stored at low temperatures in dry air to avoid corrosion. It forms compounds with various elements, including uranium, aluminum and magnesium. The chemistry of plutonium, while in many respects similar to that of uranium, is on the whole more complex. There are five valence states: +2, +3, +4, +5, and +6.

Plutonium is an extremely hazardous material because of its radioactivity and the fact that on entering the human system it deposits in bone and is excreted very slowly. Semiremote handling techniques are therefore used and extreme precautions taken to avoid the release of dusts to the atmosphere.

There is considerable interest in the use of plutonium as a reactor fuel for nuclear power applications. One reason is that of the breeding and subsequent fissioning of plutonium represents the only known means by which the energy potential of uranium can be fully utilized. Another is the possibility of using plutonium-enriched fuels in place of fuels enriched with uranium-235, thereby avoiding dependence on uranium isotope separation facilities. Plutonium was first used as a reactor fuel in the Los Alamos Fast Reactor ("Clementine"), an experimental device built at Los Alamos Scientific Laboratory in 1946. The use of molten plutonium as a reactor fuel is being tested in the Los Alamos Molten Plutonium Reactor Experiment (LAMPRE). The Experimental Breeder Reactor No. II (EBR-II) at the National Reactor Testing Station will be fueled with a plutonium-uranium alloy in its second core loading. The Plutonium Recycle Test Reactor (PRTR) at Hanford is used to test various plutonium-based alloys. Supporting research on techniques for the handling and fabrication of plutonium and its alloys and compounds is in progress,

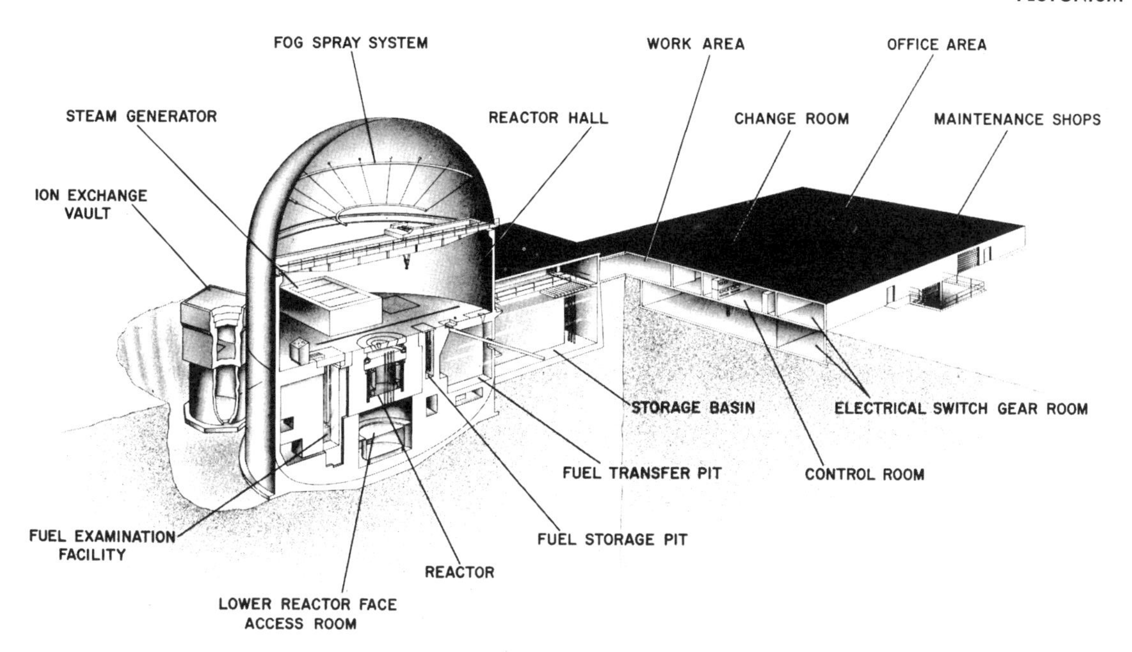

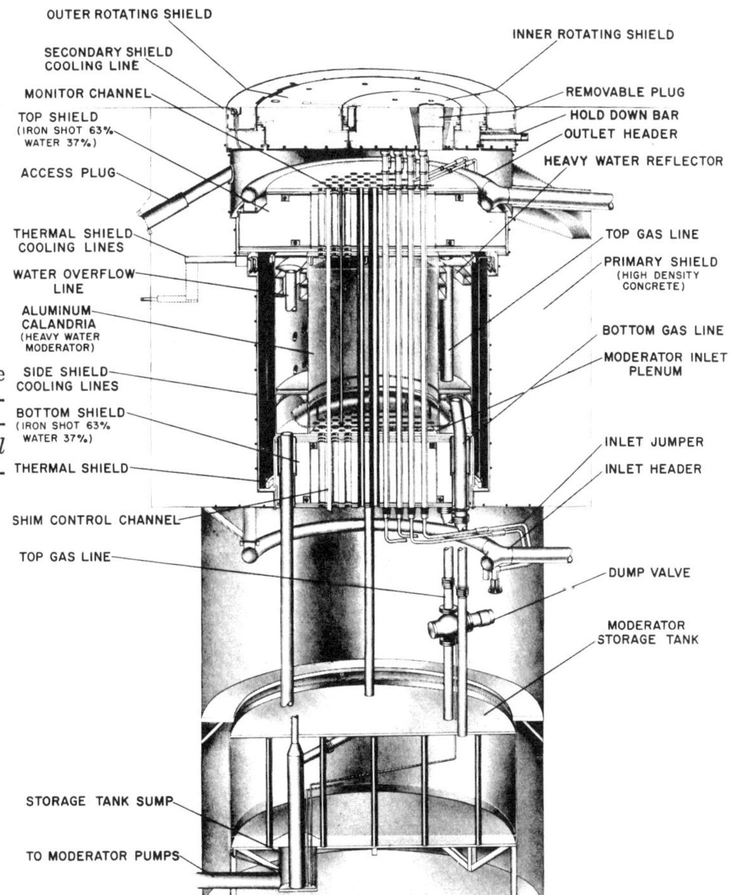

Fig. 150. The Plutonium Recycle Test Reactor (PRTR). Above, general plant layout. Right, core arrangement. (*Courtesy of General Electric Co., Hanford Atomic Products Operation*)

notably at Hanford and at Argonne National Laboratory.

The prices paid by the U.S. Atomic Energy Commission for by-product plutonium from U.S. power and research reactors formerly ranged from $30–45 per gram of plutonium metal depending on the grade (Pu-240 content). From June 30, 1962 to June 30, 1963, a single price of $30 per gram will be in effect. The plutonium credit specified in **Agreements for Cooperation** currently in effect between the United States and foreign countries using U.S. supplied reactor fuel is $12 per gram. This credit was determined on the basis of a preliminary estimate of the value of plutonium as a reactor fuel relative to that of uranium-235, and is keyed to the price of uranium-235 prior to July 1, 1961.

The AEC has indicated that the domestic plutonium credit after June 30, 1963 will be based on its fuel value, which is currently a subject of intensive study. There have been informal indications that the credit, on this basis, may be set in the neighborhood of $9.50 per gram of plutonium metal, or $8.00 per gram of plutonium in the form of a plutonium nitrate solution; but, as of mid-1962, no actual pricing policy had been announced.

Small amounts of plutonium are available from the AEC for research and development use under license agreements. Here there is a use charge of 4% per annum keyed to a base price of $12 per gram.

PLUTONIUM BUYBACK PRICE.

See **nuclear power economics.**

PLUTONIUM RECYCLE TEST REACTOR (PRTR)

A test reactor located at the U.S. Atomic Energy Commission's Hanford Works and used to study the performance of plutonium-bearing fuel elements. The PRTR and an auxiliary Plutonium Fabrication Pilot Plant are the major experimental facilities of the AEC's Plutonium Recycle Program, which aims to demonstrate the feasibility of using plutonium as an alternative, or supplement, to uranium-235 as the fissionable ingredient in low-enrichment fuels for civilian power reactors.

The PRTR is a heavy water-moderated and cooled reactor of the pressure-tube type (see **heavy water-moderated power reactors).** Its rated power output is 70 megawatts (thermal). It is not equipped for electrical power generation, however it operates at power reactor conditions (coolant temperature level of ~ 540°F). It was designed and is operated by the General Electric Company (Hanford Atomic Products Operation). It first went critical in November, 1960, and attained full-power operation in July, 1961.

About one-third of the initial core loading of PRTR consists of plutonium-aluminum alloy fuel elements of 1.8% "enrichment" (i.e., 1.8 weight % Pu). The balance of the core contains natural uranium in the form of uranium dioxide rods clad with zircaloy. Fuel elements containing a mixture of plutonium and natural uranium oxides (PuO_2-UO_2) are to be tested in the second core loading.

PM-1 (ARMY NUCLEAR POWER PLANT)

Portable Medium-Powerplant-1, a small nuclear power plant of the **pressurized water** type located at Sundance Air Force Station, Wyoming. PM-1, formerly known as Army Package Power Reactor No. 2 (APPR-2), was developed under the Army Nuclear Power Program as a prototype for transportable power plants in the 1-2 megawatt (electrical) range for use in remote locations with a minimum operating force (about 15 men). A high degree of factory preassembly permits plants of the PM-1 design to be field erected in 60-90 days time. The parts, totaling 225 tons in weight, can be transported by air in 16 planeloads.

The Martin Company was prime contractor for PM-1, which was funded in part by the Air Force. Particulars follow:

Power: 1.0 megawatt (electrical) + 2.0 megawatts (thermal) for space heating. *Fuel:* Highly enriched uranium in the form of a dispersion of uranium dioxide (UO_2) in a stainless steel matrix. *Fuel element design:* Tubular configuration, clad with stain-

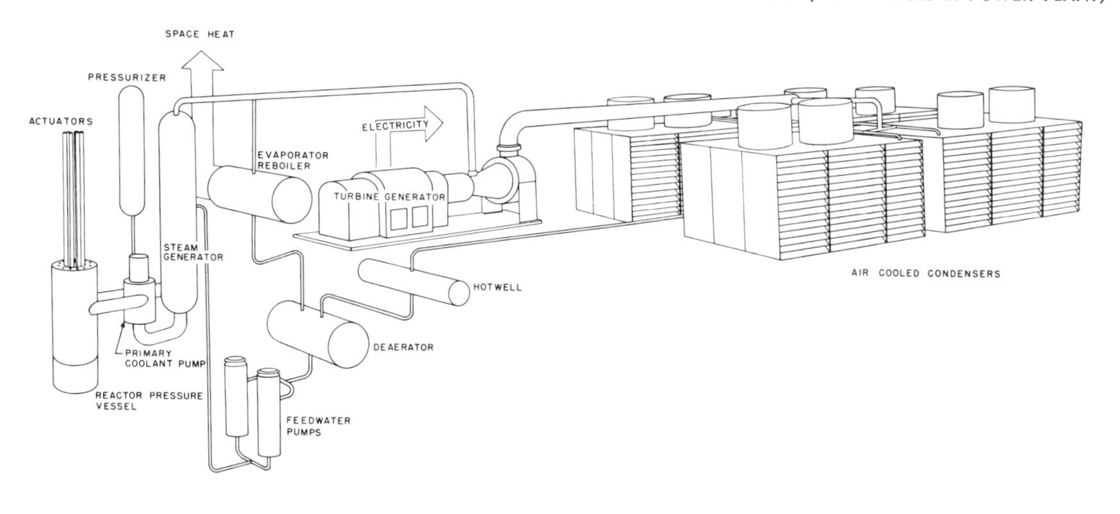

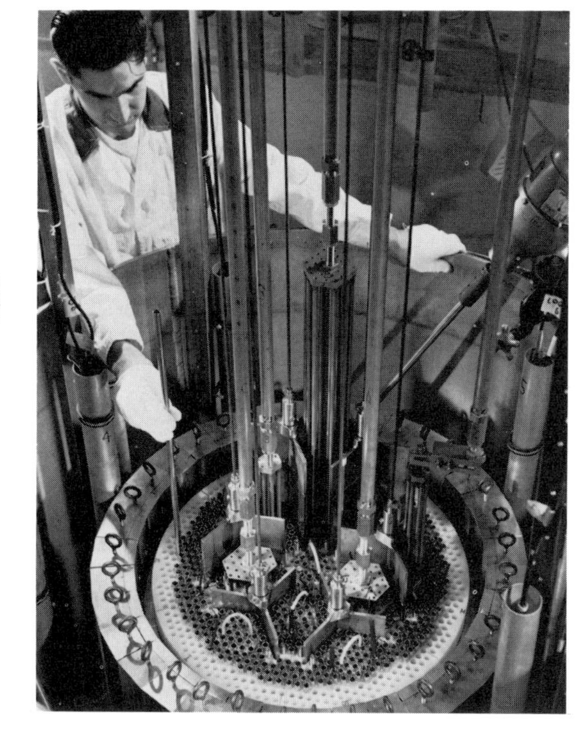

Fig. 151. PM-1 Army Nuclear Power Plant. Above, diagram of principal components. Right, facility used for zero power tests on the PM-1 core. (*Courtesy of the Martin Co.*)

less steel. *Core loading:* 28.8 kg U^{235}. *Core life:* 18.7 thermal megawatt-years. *Coolant:* Ordinary water at 1300 psi; outlet temperature, 479°F. *Dates:* Trial operation began in February, 1962.

PM-2A (ARMY NUCLEAR POWER PLANT)

Portable Medium-Powerplant-2A, a small nuclear power plant of the **pressurized water** type located at Camp Century, about 150 miles east of Thule in northern Greenland. The installation is in snow tunnels. PM-2A incorporates the technology developed for the stationary plant SM-1.

The prime contractor for PM-2A was Alco Products, Inc. under contract to the Army Engineers' Eastern Ocean District. The reactor was mechanically tested at Alco's plant early in 1960 prior to being shipped to its Greenland site. Assembly and nuclear testing at Greenland took 3½ months. Full-power operation was reached in November, 1960, making this the first reactor to supply power and heat to a remote military base. Particulars follow:

Power: 1.5 megawatts (electrical) + 0.293 megawatt (thermal) for space heating. *Fuel:* Highly enriched uranium (> 90% U^{235}) in the form of a dispersion of uranium dioxide in a stainless steel matrix. *Fuel element design:* Flat fuel plates clad with stainless steel. *Core loading:* 19.5 kg U^{235}. *Core life:* 8 thermal megawatt-years. *Coolant:* Ordinary water at 1750 psi; outlet temperature, 518°F. *Dates:* Full-power operation, November, 1960; government acceptance, March, 1961.

PM-3A (ARMY NUCLEAR POWER PLANT)

Portable Medium-Powerplant-3A, a plant similar to **PM-1,** shipped to McMurdo Sound, Antarctica, in November, 1961, and placed in operation in March, 1962. PM-3A has a rated electrical output of 1.5 megawatts and was supplied by The Martin Company.

POISON

In a nuclear reactor, any nonfissionable, nonfertile substance with a high neutron capture **cross section,** i.e., a material that acts as a parasitic neutron absorber and thereby decreases the **reactivity** of the system. It should be noted that some poisons are classified as undesirable while others are deliberately introduced into the system. **Fission product** poisons fall under the former classification because they accumulate during reactor operation and cannot in most cases be removed from the system while it is operating. The major fission product poisons are **xenon-135** and **samarium-149** (see also **xenon poisoning).** Poisons deliberately introduced into reactors include **control rod** materials, which can be moved in and out of the system, and **burnable poisons,** which gradually "burn-off" and thereby compensate for the decline in reactivity attending fuel consumption and fission-product build-up. (Also see **solution poisons)** It should also be noted that structural materials and reactor coolants have a poisoning effect on a reactor, since they absorb some neutrons nonproductively, but they are not classed as poisons because of their relatively low neutron capture cross section.

POLAND

Agencies. The Federal Commission for Nuclear Energy Affairs, Warsaw, has administrative responsibility for atomic energy matters. The Commission receives policy guidance from the Polish Academy of Sciences, which has over-all cognizance over Polish scientific activity. The Academy, in turn, has an atomic energy advisory committee, the State Council on the Peaceful Uses of Atomic Energy.

International Relationships. Member of the **International Atomic Energy Agency.** Technical assistance agreement with the U.S.S.R. Participant in the **Joint Institute for Nuclear Research** at Dubna in the U.S.S.R.

Research Centers. The Institute of Nuclear Research, Warsaw-Żerań, directs Poland's atomic energy research and development program, which is conducted at three research centers.

The Swierk Nuclear Research Center at Swierk, 14 miles south of Warsaw, engages in a diversified program, including reactor studies. Its facilities include a large linear accelerator and a 2000-kilowatt (thermal) pool-type research reactor supplied by the U.S.S.R.

The Żerań Nuclear Research Center at Żerań, 5 miles north of Warsaw, is an applied research laboratory and radioisotope distribution center. Its facilities include an ore processing semi-works, pilot equipment for the production of reactor-grade graphite, and a plutonium laboratory.

The Cracow Nuclear Research Center at Bronowice (near Cracow) is a laboratory for fundamental research in nuclear physics. It is equipped with several particle accelerators, including a large cyclotron supplied by the U.S.S.R.

Production Activity. Limited low-grade uranium deposits have been found and mined at several locations, notably in the regions of Walbrzych and Kladżko in the southwest. It is believed that no one is presently being shipped to the U.S.S.R. for processing and that Poland is developing a processing program to meet her own nuclear fuel requirements.

Energy Economy. Poland's present electrical power capacity is about 5000 megawatts, more than 80% of it coal-fired. Coal is abundant, Polish fields accounting for three-quarters of the total coal reserves of Eastern Europe.

Nuclear Power Program. Poland has geared her nuclear power planning to long-term energy requirements. Plans at present call for the construction of a 200 megawatt (electrical) nuclear power station by 1965. This is expected to be a natural-uranium graphite-moderated gas-cooled unit designed for operation as a dual-purpose facility, i.e., for plutonium as well as power production. 800 megawatts of nuclear power capacity are tentatively targeted for 1970, and 1800 megawatts for 1975.

Poland is also actively interested in marine propulsion applications and is studying an organic-moderated reactor system for use in a merchant ship. This work is being conducted under the direction of the Institution of Nuclear Research in collaboration with the Polish Maritime Institute and the Central Bureau of Ship Construction.

POLONIUM

Element No. 84 (symbol, Po; atomic weight, 210), a radioactive metal of extreme toxicity, most of the isotopes of which are alpha emitters and all of which are unstable. Polonium is commonly used in combination with beryllium as a neutron source for laboratory experiments and for oil-well logging, the alpha radiation from the polonium displacing neutrons from the beryllium nuclei as follows:

$$_4Be^9 + {}_2He^4 \longrightarrow ({}_6C^{13}) \longrightarrow {}_6C^{12} + {}_0n^1$$

Polonium-210, a 138-day alpha emitter, is formed by neutron capture in **bismuth** and represents a potential health hazard that needs to be considered in evaluating the merit of bismuth as a reactor coolant.

Polonium-210 is one of several radionuclides of interest as energy sources for small auxiliary power units (see **SNAP Program**). Polonium-210 has been also used in extremely small quantities as a static eliminator for which purpose it is carefully encapsulated in thin metal foil.

POOL REACTOR

A type of research reactor in which the core is suspended in a large pool of water, which serves as moderator, reflector, coolant and radiation shield; popularly known as a swimming pool reactor. (See **research and training reactors**)

PORTABLE MEDIUM-POWERPLANTS. See PM-1, PM-2A, PM-3A.

PORTSMOUTH GASEOUS DIFFUSION PLANT

A U.S. Atomic Energy Commission uranium-235 production facility located in Pike County, about 20 miles northeast of Portsmouth, Ohio. *Operating contractor*: Goodyear Atomic Corporation, a subsidiary of Goodyear Tire and Rubber Company. *AEC investment in plant and equipment*: ~ $766 million.* *Employment*: ~ 2600.

The U.S. uranium-235 network consists of the Portsmouth Plant plus similar facilities at Oak Ridge, Tennessee and Paducah, Kentucky. See **uranium enrichment** for notes on the operations that take place within this network. See **gaseous diffusion** for supplementary notes on the isotope separation process employed, and **Oak Ridge Gaseous Diffusion Plant** for supplementary notes on plant features.

The Portsmouth Plant was completed in 1955. The principal construction contractor was Peter Kiewit Sons. The process design was handled by Union Carbide Nuclear Company. Architect-engineer services were furnished by a number of firms, including Giffels and Vallet, Inc.; Sargent and Lundy; Singmaster and Breyer; and Smith, Hinchman and Grylls, Inc.

* Includes facilities authorized or under construction as of June 30, 1959. Also includes on-site facilities for converting orange oxide (UO_3) or green salt (UF_4) to uranium hexafluoride (UF_6), the process gas used in the gaseous diffusion process. Not adjusted for depreciation.

Electrical power required to operate the Portsmouth Plant (2,000,000 kilowatts) is supplied by the Ohio Valley Electric Corporation (OVEC), an organization representing fifteen private utilities: Appalachian Electric Power Company, Cincinnati Gas and Electric Company, Columbus and Southern Ohio Electric Company, Dayton Power and Light Company, Indiana and Michigan Electric Company, Kentucky Utilities Company, Louisville Gas and Electric Company, Monongahela Power Company, Ohio Power Company, Pennsylvania Power Company, Potomac Edison Company, Southern Indiana Gas and Electric Company, Toledo Edison Company and West Penn Power Company.

PORTUGAL

Agency. The Junta de Energia Nuclear, Lisbon, is the agency responsible for atomic energy matters.

International Relationships. Member of the **International Atomic Energy Agency** and the **European Nuclear Energy Agency.** Research-type **Agreement for Cooperation** with the United States.

Research Center. The Portuguese Nuclear Research Center, recently established at Sacavem, just north of Lisbon, is the principal research laboratory of the Junta. Its facilities include two particle accelerators, a pilot plant for production of uranium metal, and a 1000 kilowatt (thermal) pool-type research reactor supplied by AMF Atomics. The United States contributed $350,000 toward the cost of the latter under its program of Foreign Research Reactor Grants.

Production Activity. Portugal has deposits of uranium in the area of Guarda. Mining and ore processing operations have been in progress for several years, yielding a 20% uranium concentrate which has largely been sold to the United States. Companhia Portuguesa de Radium, operator of the present or concentration facilities, is now constructing pilot uranium refining and metal production facilities with a capacity of 15 tons of uranium per year. A full-scale plant with a capacity of 200 tons per year is planned for construction near Guarda. Plans are being drawn for facilities to produce heavy water as a by-product of commercial ammonia production.

Energy Economy. Portugal's present electric power generating capacity is about 1000 megawatts, 90% of it hydroelectric.

Nuclear Power Program. The Junta is considering the installation, by 1965 or thereabouts, of a 100-megawatt (electrical) nuclear power station. Companhia Portuguesa de Industrias Nucleares, an association of leading Portuguese industrial concerns interested in promoting industrial atomic energy development, is considering a small-scale nuclear power project.

POSITIVE TEMPERATURE COEFFICIENT

A characteristic of a nuclear reactor whose reactivity increases as the temperature rises. (See **reactor control**)

POSITRON

An **elementary particle** having the same mass as an electron and with an electric charge equal in magnitude but opposite in sign to that of the electron. Positrons were first observed in the cosmic radiation by C. D. Anderson in 1932. They are emitted in the beta-decay of many radionuclides, and can be formed together with an electron in the process of **pair production.** As well, when a positron collides with an electron, mutual annihilation occurs, with the emission of energy.

POTASSIUM-40

A naturally occurring radioisotope of potassium whose presence in the body contributes significantly to the **background radiation** of man's environment. Potassium-40 is a beta and gamma emitter with a radioactive half-life of the order of 10^9 years. Its natural abundance in the potassium element is 0.0119%.

POTASSIUM-42

A radioisotope of potassium used extensively in biological tracer experiments and in medical research and diagnosis. A beta and gamma emitter with a radioactive half-life of 12.4 hours, potassium-42 is produced in reactors by neutron absorption in the natural potassium element.

POWER COSTS. See **nuclear power economics.**

POWER DEMONSTRATION REACTOR PROGRAM. See **nuclear power development, U.S.**

POWER DENSITY

In a nuclear reactor, the rate of heat generation per unit volume of the reactor core, usually expressed in kilowatts per liter or watts per cubic centimeter. Power density is one of the factors that determine the size of a reactor core, a consideration that is especially important in the design of power reactors. The trend of development of these reactors is in the direction of higher power density and hence smaller cores. Limiting factors are the mechanical strength and thermal conductivity of available fuel, cladding and reactor structural materials at elevated temperatures; the problem of providing adequate heat-transfer surface in compact core designs, and the efficiency of available reactor coolants. (See **specific power**)

POWER EXCURSION

In the operation of a nuclear reactor, a sudden increase in the power level of the system caused by a sudden increase in **reactivity.**

POWER REACTOR

A nuclear reactor used as the energy source for electric power generation or for propulsion. Generally, heat produced in the reactor is carried by a coolant to an external heat exchanger (steam generator), wherein steam is raised to operate a steam-turbine; however, in power reactors of the boiling water type steam is generated in the reactor proper. Working fluids other than steam may be used; for example, a gas-cooled reactor may be connected to a gas turbine.

For information on U.S. power reactor development programs see **nuclear power development, U.S.; Aircraft Nuclear Propulsion Program; Army Nuclear Power Program; Maritime Reactors Program; Naval Reactors Program; Pluto Project** (ramjet propulsion); **Rover Project** (rocket propulsion), and **SNAP Program** (space applications). Information on specific power reactors is given in individual entries under the official reactor designation.

PRESSURE TUBES. See **heavy water-moderated power reactors.**

PRESSURE VESSELS

Discussion of this topic will be limited to reactor vessels used in civilian nuclear power plants. The types of power reactor which require pressure vessels for reactor housing include **pressurized** and **boiling water reactors, heavy water-moderated power reactors, gas-cooled reactors** and **organic-cooled reactors. Sodium-graphite** and **fast breeder reactors** operate at nominal pressure and are housed in relatively thin-walled steel tanks.

The most massive reactor vessels are those for pressurized-water reactors, which characteristically operate at pressures of 2000 psi. The reactor vessel used in the Shippingport Atomic Power Station may be cited as an example. It is designed to withstand operating pressures as high as 2500 psi and a hydrostatic test pressure of 3750 psi. Other design conditions, imposed to limit failure due to thermal stress, include an allowable heat-up rate of 70°F per hour, an allowable cool-down rate of 50°F per hour, and allowable thermal transients of 30-50°F in 45 seconds. As is shown in Fig. 152, the Shippingport reactor vessel is essentially a right cylinder with hemispherical top and bottom heads. The top head is removable for core replacement and contains ports through which individual fuel elements may be replaced. It is approximately 31 feet high, has an internal diameter of $\sim$ 9 feet and a wall thickness of 8¾ inches. It was fabricated of carbon steel forgings and plate clad with stainless steel. Its weight, including

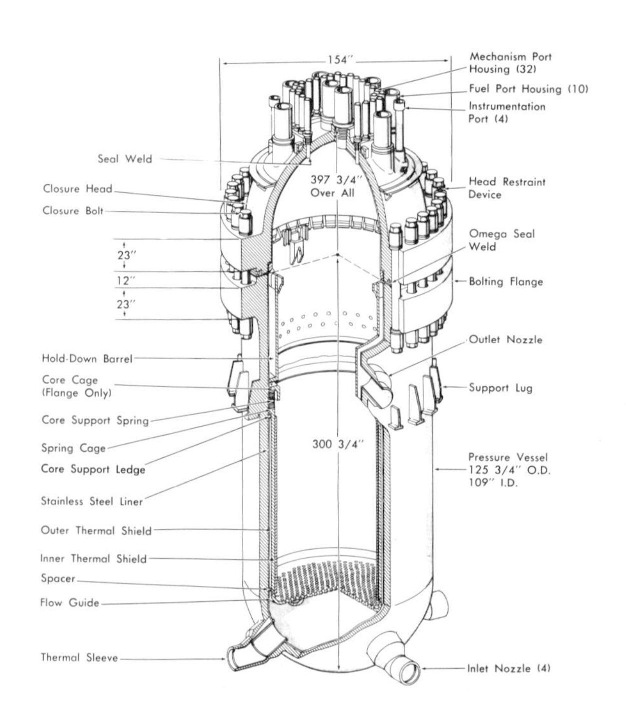

Fig. 152. Reactor vessel of the Shippingport Atomic Power Station. Left, cutaway view. Right, 264-ton unit being lowered into position during plant construction. Diagram reprinted from "The Shippingport Pressurized Water Reactor," Addison-Wesley Publishing Co., 1958. (*Courtesy of Westinghouse Electric Corp.*)

Fig. 153. Reactor vessel and related components of the Hallam Nuclear Power Facility nearing end of journey from Philadelphia, Pennsylvania, to Hallam, Nebraska. The components, from left to right, are: 80-ton reactor vessel, 65-ton containment tank, 13-ton upper cavity liner and 4½-ton upper thermal shock ring. (*Courtesy of Atomics International*)

built-in thermal shields, is approximately 264 tons.

Reactor vessels for boiling water reactors have somewhat thinner wall thicknesses (~ 6 inches) since they operate at lower pressures (~ 1000 psi), but have larger dimensions for a given power output due to the fact that boiling water reactors operate at lower power densities and hence have a larger core than pressurized water reactors. The reactor vessel of the Dresden Nuclear Power Station, which has a rated power output of 180 megawatts (electrical), is approximately 40 feet high and 12 feet in inside diameter. Here it should be noted that the problem of transporting reactor vessels for large-scale boiling water plants may act to limit the maximum size of reactor that can be built. (See **boiling water reactors**)

Reactor vessels for organic-cooled reactors, which operate at pressure of ~ 100 psi, have wall thicknesses of ~ 3.5 inches. Here the noncorrosive nature of the coolant permits the use of carbon steel construction.

Reactor vessels for gas-cooled reactors of the low-temperature (Calder Hall) type, which operate at pressures of 200 psi, are fabricated of carbon steel, have wall thicknesses of 3½ inches. Due to the very low power density at which Calder Hall-type reactors operate, these vessels have very large dimensions. The large (250 megawatt) civil power stations built in the United Kingdom have spherical reactor vessels ~ 70 feet in diameter. Vessels of this size must be fabricated in the field and the practical difficulties of welding, stress relieving and inspecting them under field conditions are considerable. A promising alternative is the use of reinforced concrete construction. (See **United Kingdom**)

High-temperature gas-cooled reactors are being designed to operate at somewhat higher pressures (~ 300 psi) but also at appreciably higher power densities than the Calder Hall-type reactors.

PRESSURIZED WATER REACTORS

A type of power reactor that employs ordinary water (H_2O) as coolant and moderator and is pressurized to keep the exit coolant stream from boiling.* The latter feature distinguishes pressurized water reactors from **boiling water reactors.**

As is shown in Fig. 154, the reactor coolant is circulated in a closed primary loop, which includes a heat exchanger (steam generator). In passing through the heat exchanger, the primary coolant transfers heat to

* Work is being done on the use of pressurized heavy-water (D_2O) as moderator-coolant (see **heavy water-moderated power reactors**); and on the use of variable concentrations of D_2O in H_2O for control purposes in an otherwise conventional pressurized water system (see **spectral shift reactor concept**). Also, consideration has been given to the use of pressurized light water as coolant in combination with graphite moderation. However, the term "pressurized water reactor" usually connotes an H_2O cooled and moderated system and is so treated herein.

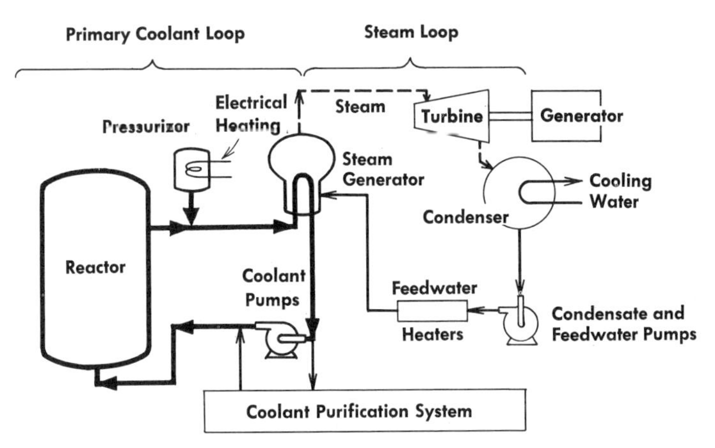

Fig. 154. Simplified flow diagram of pressurized water reactor plant.

water flowing through a secondary loop, thereby generating steam which is fed to a steam-turbine.

Pressurized water reactors were originally developed for Naval ship propulsion, and their feasibility was first demonstrated by the successful operation of the prototype system for the submarine Nautilus in March, 1953 (see **Naval Reactors Program**). The progress made in the Naval program led to the selection of pressurized water as the basis for the first large-scale civilian nuclear power project undertaken in the United States, namely, the **Shippingport Atomic Power Station,** which began operation in December, 1957. A "second generation" plant, the **Yankee Atomic Electric Plant,** was placed into operation 3 years later. Pressurized water was also selected for the first U.S. maritime propulsion project, the N.S. ***Savannah.*** Civilian pressurized water reactor projects are listed in the accompanying Table 1. For information on military pressurized water reactors, see **Naval Reactors Program, Army Nuclear Power Program.**

Pressurized water reactors have received more emphasis in the U.S. power reactor development program than any other type. Most of the approximately $550 million * spent by the U.S. Atomic Energy Commission on Naval reactor research and development through mid-1960 was applied to pressurized water systems. Of the approximately $476 million * spent by the AEC on civilian reactor research and development through mid-1960, $125 million (26%) was applied to pressurized water systems.

TABLE 1. CIVILIAN NUCLEAR POWER PROJECTS—PRESSURIZED WATER REACTORS [1]

Name of Plant or Project	*Location*	*Reactor Designer*	*Rated Power Output (megawatts electrical)*	*Start-up*
U.S. Locations:				
Shippingport Atomic Power Station	Shippingport, Pa.	Bettis Lab.[2]	60	1957
Yankee Atomic Electric Plant	Rowe, Mass.	Westinghouse	110	1960
Consolidated Edison Thorium Reactor	Indian Point, N.Y.	Babcock & Wilcox	255 [3]	(1962)
Saxton Experimental Nuclear Reactor	Saxton, Pa.	Westinghouse	3	1962
Southern California Edison Co. Project [4]	Under Review	Westinghouse	360	(1965–6)
Foreign Locations:				
BR-3 Reactor	**Belgium**	Westinghouse	11.5	1959
Enrico Fermi Project (SELNI)	**Italy**	Westinghouse	165	(1963)
Maritime Propulsion:				
N. S. *Savannah*	—	Babcock & Wilcox	22	1962

[1] For information on military pressurized-water reactors, see **Naval Reactors Program, Army Nuclear Power Program.**
[2] The Shippingport reactor was designed by Bettis Laboratory, operated by Westinghouse on behalf of AEC. The other Westinghouse projects listed in this table were handled by the company's Commercial Atomic Power Department.
[3] Including power from conventional superheater.
[4] A private project in the negotiation stage.
Note: For cost information on U.S. reactors listed, see Table 3 under **nuclear power development.**

General Considerations. The strong points usually cited for pressurized water reactors are:

1. The technology of water-cooled reactors is at an advanced stage of development relative to that of other U.S. power reactor concepts.

2. Pressurized water reactors are stable in operation, have good safety characteristics,

* Exclusive of capital costs. Source: AEC Annual Financial Report for 1960.

and under certain conditions are inherently responsive to load changes in a power system.

3. They can achieve high power densities and hence high power output.

4. Ordinary water has good heat transfer properties, is an effective neutron moderator, and can be maintained at high purity (impurity content less than one part per million) at comparatively low cost. Also, there is a long background of experience in the use of water as a heat exchange medium.

The major limitations of pressurized water reactors are:

1. Their neutron economy is such that they cannot operate on normal (nonenriched) uranium, and cannot serve as breeders. These limitations stem from the fact that ordinary water (hydrogen) is an appreciable absorber of neutrons.

2. Their ceiling operating temperature is probably about 600°F (see below), which limits the thermal conversion efficiency attainable in a power plant without superheating.

3. They tend to have high equipment costs due to the fact that the components of the primary loop must be built to contain high pressure and resist water corrosion.

4. The physical size of the core is limited by the size of reactor pressure vessel that can be fabricated. Wall thicknesses of 7 inches or more are required to contain the operating pressures involved, and existing shop facilities cannot fabricate clad-steel of such thicknesses into vessels much larger than 11 or 12 feet in diameter. Fortunately, because of the high power densities attainable, this limitation does not unduly restrict the power output that can be achieved in a pressurized water plant; indeed, single-reactor installations with power ratings as high as 500 megawatts (electrical) have been proposed. It does, however, impose restraints on the mechanical design of the reactor core structure.

Plant Characteristics. See Table 2.

Design Trends. One factor that limits the operating temperature of pressurized water reactors is the allowable surface temperature of the fuel elements. The fuel elements used at the present time employ rigid ("free standing") cladding which must withstand the high pressure of the system and hence is required to have considerable mechanical strength. Efforts are being made to develop new cladding materials with improved mechanical strength at elevated temperatures. This work is concentrated on new alloys of zirconium. Efforts are also being made to develop "collapsible" cladding, i.e., nonrigid cladding which depends on the fuel material for structural support. This is seen as a way of getting around the mechanical strength problem, and also as a way of achieving thinner cladding and thereby reducing the amount of neutron absorbing material introduced into the reactor core.

TABLE 2. SOME CHARACTERISTICS OF PRESSURIZED WATER POWER PLANTS

System Parameters	*Recent Design* [1]	*Projected Design* [2]
Pressure in primary loop	2200 psi	
Coolant outlet temperature	574°F	
Steam conditions	555 psi, 480°F	1000 psi, 545°F
Thermal conversion efficiency	25–28%	30%
Power density	55 tkw/liter	80 tkw/liter
Specific power	19.5 tkw/kg U	
Fuel		
Enrichment	3.3% U^{235}	
Form	uranium dioxide	
Cladding material	stainless steel	
Maximum surface temperature	636°F	
Average burn-up	13,000 MWD/metric ton U	19,000 MWD/metric ton U

[1] Based on an optimized design of a 200 megawatt (electrical) plant prepared under AEC auspices in the fall of 1959. Source: TID-8516, Part I.

[2] Projected for a 300 megawatt (electrical) plant placed in operation in 1967–1968, assuming success of development work now in progress. Source: **TID-8516, Part II.**

The pressurized water reactors built to date do not permit local boiling at fuel element surfaces. Due to the fact that the power distribution across a reactor core is inherently nonuniform, this design restraint has resulted in lower average coolant temperatures than could have been attained had local boiling been permitted in the hotter zones. Current designs do permit local boiling and the trend is in the direction of allowing some bulk boiling within the hottest fuel channels. Relatedly, research is in progress on the use of solution poisons as a means of reducing the number of control rods and thereby achieving a more uniform power and temperature distribution across the core.*

The ultimate limitation ** on the operating temperature of pressurized water reactors derives from the high vapor pressure of water and from the conceptual requirement that the bulk temperature of the exit coolant be kept *below* the boiling point. At 2000 psi—the highest operating pressure achieved to date—the boiling point of water is approximately 630°F. It appears feasible (see Table 1) to design pressurized water reactors to operate at 2200 psi, which would raise the boiling "ceiling" to approximately 650°F. Operating pressures above 2200 psi appear unlikely of achievement without major advances in pressure-vessel technology.†

Various efforts are being made to capitalize on the ability of pressurized water reactors to operate at high power densities. At this writing it appears likely that power densities approaching 80 thermal kilowatts per liter will be achieved in the relatively near future.

The uranium dioxide fuel currently used in pressurized water reactors is easily fabricated, resists water corrosion, has good ability to retain fission-product gases, and has been found to be dimensionally stable under irradiation. Reactor manufacturers are now offering warranties on oxide cores at average burn-ups up to about 14,000 MWD/ton. It is believed that average burn-ups approaching 20,000 MWD/ton will be achieved in the relatively near future. This is based on the fact that sample fuel elements have demonstrated burn-ups as high as 27,500 MWD/ton, and UO_2 "platelets" have recently been irradiated up to ~ 60,000 MWD/ton. The only real disadvantage of uranium dioxide is low thermal conductivity, which has prompted development work on uranium carbide and other uranium compounds in an effort to develop a fuel material that will retain the advantages noted and at the same time do a better job of heat transfer.

The trend in mechanical design is in the direction of simplification in an effort to reduce capital costs. One change under consideration is elimination of the external **pressurizer.** Another is the possibility of using more conventional pumps and valves in the primary loop, i.e., replacing the present hermetically sealed units with shaft-sealed **pumps** and controlled-leakage valves.

Economics. See **nuclear power economics.**

* Control rods contribute to the nonuniformity of power distribution bysetting up local neutron flux depressions.

** The other factors noted are limiting at the present time.

† An alternative to enclosing the reactor core in a pressure vessel is to confine the coolant in pressure tubes; however, this adds greatly to the amount of structural material contained in the core, thereby increasing neutron losses. Interest in pressure tubes is largely limited to **heavy water-moderated power reactors.**

PRESSURIZER

A component of **pressurized water reactors** whose function is to regulate the operating pressure in the primary coolant system. A pressurizer consists essentially of a pressure vessel equipped with electric heaters and a spray nozzle and connected by a surge line to the primary coolant system. The pressurizer contains water and steam. To increase the pressure in the coolant systems, the electric heaters are employed to increase the steam volume, thereby displacing water through the surge line. To decrease the pressure, the steam volume is decreased by spray condensation, thereby causing a reverse flow of water through the surge line. Figure 155 shows the pressurizer used in the Shippingport Atomic Power Station.

As a means of reducing the capital costs of pressurized water reactor systems, consideration is being given to eliminating the use of an external pressurizer in future civilian power installations.

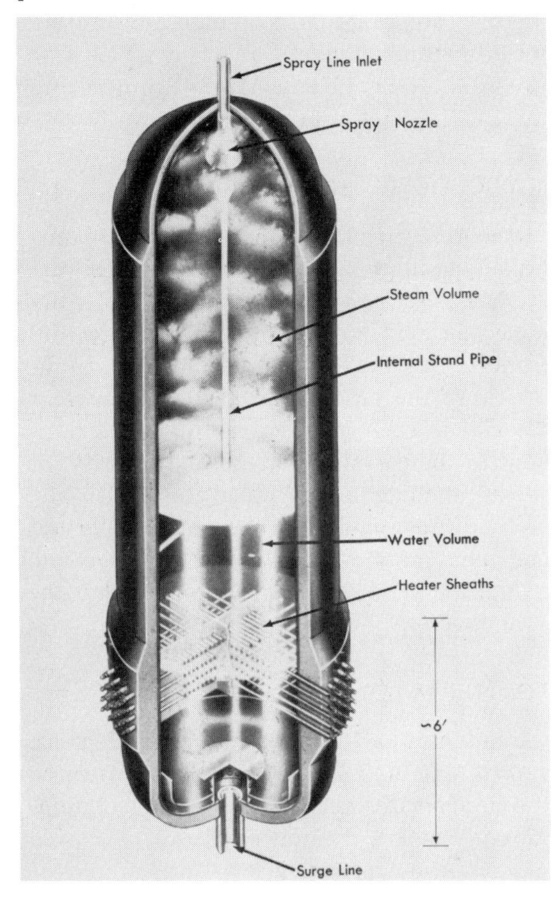

Fig. 155. Configuration of pressurizer used in Shippingport Atomic Power Station. Reprinted from "The Shippingport Pressurized Water Reactor," 1958, Addison-Wesley Publishing Co.

PRICE-ANDERSON ACT. See **insurance and indemnification against atomic energy risk.**

PROCESS DEVELOPMENT PILE (PDP)

A small heavy water-moderated test reactor at the Savannah River Plant, used for physics measurements in support of the Savannah River plutonium production reactors. The PDP operates at power levels up to 1 kilowatt (thermal).

PROCESS HEAT APPLICATIONS FOR REACTORS

Low Temperature. Reactors have been considered as a means of producing low-pressure saturated steam at temperatures up to 400°F for use in various manufacturing industries in such operations as drying, evaporation and distillation. Particular study has been given to the use of process heat reactors in pulp and paper mills, chemical manufacture, and saline water conversion.

Such applications are well within the reach of existing reactor technology; however, unless by-products are involved, at current reactor cost levels the economics appear unfavorable or at best marginal. Following are some of the factors involved:

1. As is discussed under **nuclear power economics,** reactors inherently have higher capital costs than conventional steam boilers and are at a particular disadvantage in this respect when built in small sizes. While many industries, such as pulp and paper, chemicals, textiles, and foods are in the aggregate large consumers of low-quality steam, only a small percentage of the plants serving these industries can absorb the output of a large process heat reactor. The outputs usually required for process heat applications range from 10-50 megawatts (thermal),* as compared with 500-1500 megawatts (thermal) for large central station power applications.

2. Manufacturing industries whose products are subject to a high rate of obsolescence (notably the chemicals industry) require a high rate of return on invested capital. This results in high fixed charges on plant investment which would penalize capital-intensive reactor installations.

3. Some manufacturing industries (notably the textiles and food industries) characteristically operate their facilities at a low average load factor, which again would penalize capital-intensive reactor installations.

* Of the total number of steam boilers installed by U.S. manufacturers in the decade following World War II, less than half had steam capacities greater than 40,000 pounds per hour (~12 Mwt) and only 15% had capacities greater than 100,000 pounds per hour (~33 Mwt).

Pending further reductions in the capital cost of reactors, present indications are that process heat applications are only likely to prove economic in special circumstances, as, for example, where by-product electricity can be utilized, where large installations are involved and/or where the manufacturing operation is located at a site where conventional fuel costs are unusually high. As of mid-1962, no process heat reactor had been built in the United States, but plans for two demonstration projects were being formulated, both involving the generation of by-product electricity and both entailing cooperative AEC-industry managements.

A somewhat related application is the use of reactor-produced steam for space heating. While this application is currently being actively developed in Europe (see **Sweden**), it does not appear promising in the United States due to size considerations and to the low load factors normally associated with space heating installations.

High Temperature. Reactors have also been considered as a means of furnishing heat at temperatures in the range of 1500-3000°F for high-temperature chemical or metallurgical processes, e.g., coal gasification and hydrocarbon synthesis. Temperatures in this range are presently beyond the reach of civilian reactor technology; however, current work on advanced **gas-cooled reactors** for power applications indicates that the lower portion of the range will soon be reached. Pending the availability of high-temperature power reactor technology, and related cost data, no meaningful judgment can be made of the economics of high-temperature process heat reactor applications.

Exploratory research on high-temperature process heat reactor concepts has been in progress as a joint effort of the AEC and the Bureau of Mines. The latter agency has conducted experiments at 2500°F and 250 pounds pressure in a helium-cooled apparatus containing all of the components of a reactor system except for the fuel, which is simulated by an induction-heating coil. This apparatus, known as the Induction Simulated Reactor (ISR) facility, has served to demonstrate the feasibility of operating "reactor-type" equipment at these conditions for sustained periods of time ($\sim$ 1000 hours) albeit in the absence of a radiation environment. The AEC is constructing an experimental high-temperature process heat reactor at Los Alamos Scientific Laboratory. (See **Ultra High-Temperature Reactor Experiment**)

PRODUCTION FACILITY

In context with the Atomic Energy Commission's licensing and regulatory responsibilities (see **licenses**), a production facility is legally defined as "(1) any equipment or device determined by rule of the Commission to be capable of the production of **special nuclear material** in such quantity as to be of significance to the common defense and security, or in such manner as to affect the health and safety of the public; or (2) any important component part especially designed for such equipment or device as determined by the Commission."

PROMETHIUM-147

A radioisotope of the **rare earth element,** promethium. A 2.6-year beta emitter formed as a product of uranium fission, promethium-147 represents a possible source of long-lived beta radiation for use in low-wattage nuclear batteries and as a means of activating phosphors in self-luminous light sources. It is also one of several radionuclides of interest as energy sources for small auxiliary power units. (See **SNAP Program**)

Formerly produced exclusively and on a limited scale by the irradiation of uranium capsules, promethium-147 is now being recovered from fission product wastes and is available in kilocurie quantities and at greatly reduced cost. (See **Multicurie Fission Products Pilot Plant**)

PROMPT-CRITICAL

A term applied to a nuclear reactor when it can sustain a chain reaction solely with

prompt neutrons, i.e., without depending upon the contribution of **delayed neutrons.** It is then not only supercritical but extremely difficult to control since the delayed-neutron effect is not operative.

PROMPT NEUTRONS

Neutrons that are emitted coincident with nuclear **fission** as distinct from **delayed neutrons,** which are emitted at appreciable time intervals after fission has occurred. When fission is induced by neutrons of thermal energy, more than 99% of the neutrons released are prompt neutrons.

PROMPT RADIATION

With reference to nuclear weapons, the nuclear radiation emitted during the first minute following detonation; principally instantaneous gamma rays and neutrons. (See **weapons phenomenology)**

PROPERTY INSURANCE. See **insurance and indemnification against atomic energy risks.**

PROPORTIONAL COUNTER

A radiation measurement instrument related to an **ionization chamber** and a **Geiger counter** but distinguished from them by its manner of operation. All three instruments measure radiation by metering ionization events produced in a gas volume; and (except for the electroscope type of ionization chamber) all utilize a voltage potential applied across two electrodes to convert the ions into a measurable electrical impulse. In the case of ionization chambers, the voltage is proportionate to the number of primary ions. Relative to an ionization chamber, a proportional counter has the advantage of requiring less external amplification. Relative to a Geiger counter, it has the advantage of a shorter operating cycle (less "dead time") and hence is capable of a much faster counting rate.

As is also true of ionization chambers, proportional counters can measure any form of ionizing radiation and are particularly well suited to measuring alpha particles in the presence of beta and gamma radiation. Unlike ionization chambers, they can only operate as pulse devices, i.e., they inherently register each ionization event individually. The signals are amplified by a vacuum tube and are counted by either a **scaler** or a **ratemeter.** A **pulse height analyzer** can be used to sort the amplified signals prior to counting. (See discussion under **ionization chamber)**

PROTECTIVE CLOTHING AND EQUIPMENT

Special clothing and equipment used by workers in laboratory and plant areas in which there is risk of radioactive contamination or of inhalation or ingestion of radioactive particles. Laboratory coats and shoe covers are standard equipment in **radiation areas.** Various types of respiratory equipment are used where there is an inhalation hazard. Full plastic

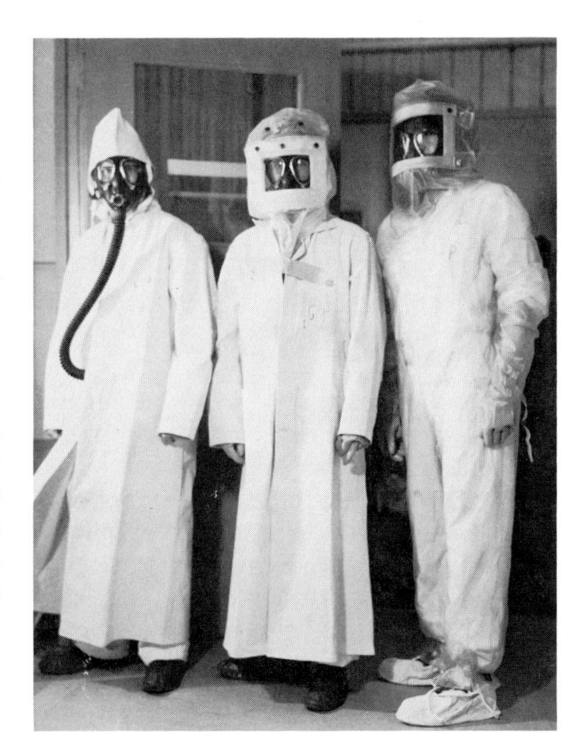

Fig. 156. Examples of protective clothing of the kind used by workers entering an area in which there is a risk of inhalation or ingestion of biologically hazardous materials. (*Courtesy of Nucleonics*)

covering is sometimes required in connection with maintenance or decontamination operations involving biologically hazardous materials such as plutonium (see Fig. 156).

PROTON

An elementary particle carrying one unit of positive electric charge (defined as 4.8025×10^{-10} electrostatic unit) and having a mass at rest of 1.0075 atomic mass units, or approximately 1847 times that of the **electron.** It comprises the nucleus of the hydrogen atom, whose **mass number** is thus defined as 1, and is a constituent of all nuclei of higher mass number. (See discussion under **electron)**

Protons are not a constituent of **radioactivity** since these particles are not emitted spontaneously from atomic nuclei and therefore are not a factor in radioactive decay processes. (See **alpha decay, beta decay, gamma rays)** Protons can, however, be displaced from some nuclei by certain nuclear reactions. An example is the production of phosphorus-32 by neutron bombardment of sulfur-32.

$$_{16}S^{32} + {_0}n^1 \longrightarrow {_{15}}P^{32} + {_1}p^1$$

This type of reaction is known as the neutron-proton reaction.

Certain **particle accelerators** supply high-energy protons for use as subatomic projectiles for research purposes. Protons for this purpose are obtained by ionizing hydrogen.

An elementary particle having the same mass as the proton but an opposite electric charge has been identified. This is known as the anti-proton. (See **anti-particles)**

PROTON SYNCHROTRON

A type of **particle accelerator** for producing beams of very high energy protons (in the Bev range). The basic design concept is as follows:

1. The protons are accelerated by electrical impulses from a radiofrequency oscillator.
2. A magnetic field serves to keep the proton beam traveling in nearly circular orbits of constant radius.
3. To compensate for the relativistic increase in particle mass at high energies * the strength of the magnetic field and the frequency of the oscillator are increased in a synchronized fashion during the acceleration cycle.

In the latter connection, synchronization is obtained by providing for automatic build-up of the magnetic field and then designing the oscillator to match the natural time-change characteristic of the magnetic system. Automatic build up of the magnetic field is accomplished by supplying a pulse of essentially d-c voltage to the magnet coil at the start of the operating cycle. Owing to the self-inductance of the system, the current requires time to build up and the result is a time-rising magnetic field. The oscillator system is designed to increase its frequency at a matching rate. For proper operation the strength of the magnetic field, the frequency of the oscillator, and the energy of the proton beam must be in harmony at every instant during the acceleration cycle, which is of the order of 1 or 2 seconds duration. At the close of the cycle the high-energy beam leaves the machine and the system is restored to its initial condition. It should be added that the protons are usually pre-accelerated to energies of the order of 10 Mev before being injected into the proton synchrotron (see below).

To indicate the general features of a proton synchrotron, there follows a brief description of the 6.2 Bev "Bevatron" at the E. O. Lawrence Radiation Laboratory (see Fig. 157):

1. Magnet: This consists of four magnetized curved quadrants connected by non-magnetized straight sections, an arrangement which permits maintenance workers to gain access to the machine. The magnet iron weighs 10,000 tons—the equivalent of a medium-sized cruiser. The motor generator which energizes the magnet coil has a peak power rating of 100,000 kilowatts and an average power rating of 7000 kilowatts.
2. Electrical field: Acceleration occurs as the protons pass through a rectangular tube in one of the straight sections of the synchrotron. The alternating potential across this tube, sup-

* See discussion under **cyclotron.**

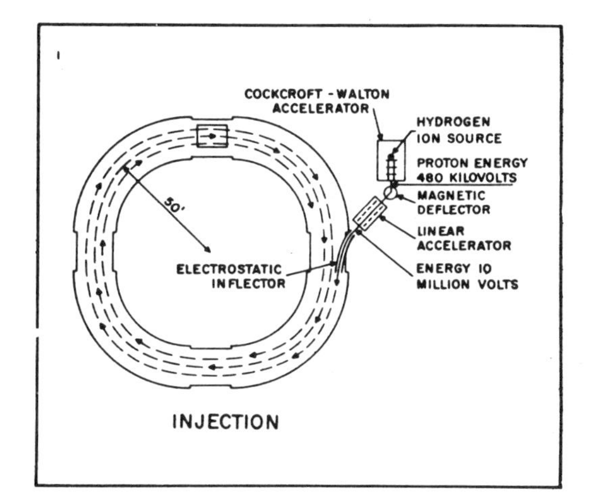

Protons from a hydrogen ion source are accelerated in two stages and inflected into the Bevatron at one of the straight sections.

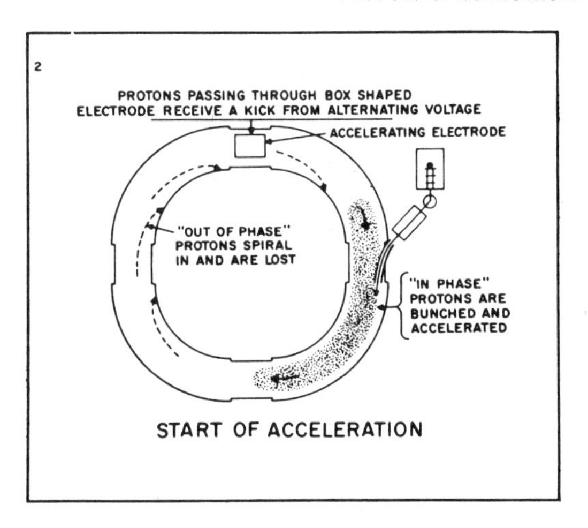

A voltage on an accelerating electrode alternating at the proton revolution frequency gives a kick of one to two kilovolts per revolution to part of the injected beam.

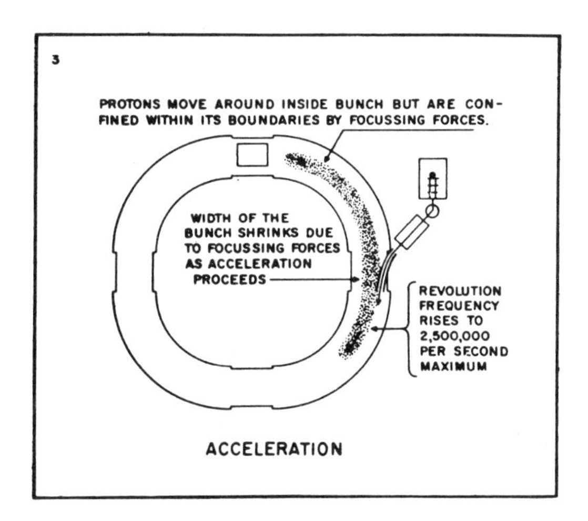

As the magnetic field strength rises, the frequency of the accelerating voltage increases at a rate which keeps the beam centered in the aperture.

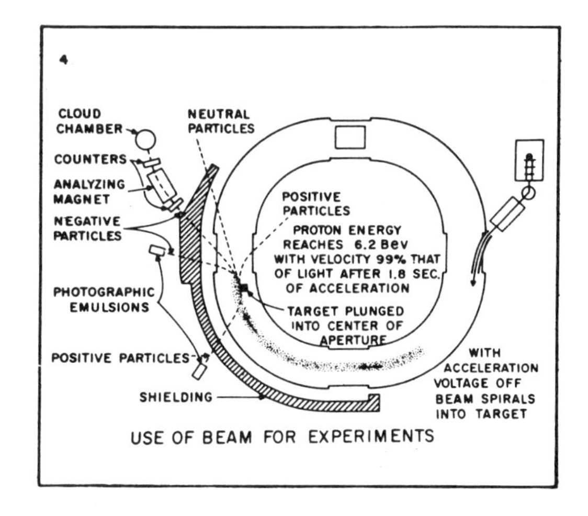

The accelerated beam strikes one of several possible targets producing the nuclear events studied by the physicists and chemists.

Fig. 157. Operating cycle of the 6.2-Bev. Bevatron at Berkeley. (*Courtesy of E. O. Lawrence Radiation Laboratory*)

plied by a bank of ignitron rectifiers, is modulated sinusoidally with time to synchronize with the changing magnetic field strength. This is done by shunting a sample of current from the magnet coil and using it to actuate a control element which determines the frequency of the oscillator system.

3. Injector: Prior to injection into the synchrotron the protons are pre-accelerated to 10 Mev by a tandem arrangement of a **Cockcroft-Walton machine** and a **linear accelerator.** The injection system includes additional equipment which serves essentially to collimate (focus) the proton beam.

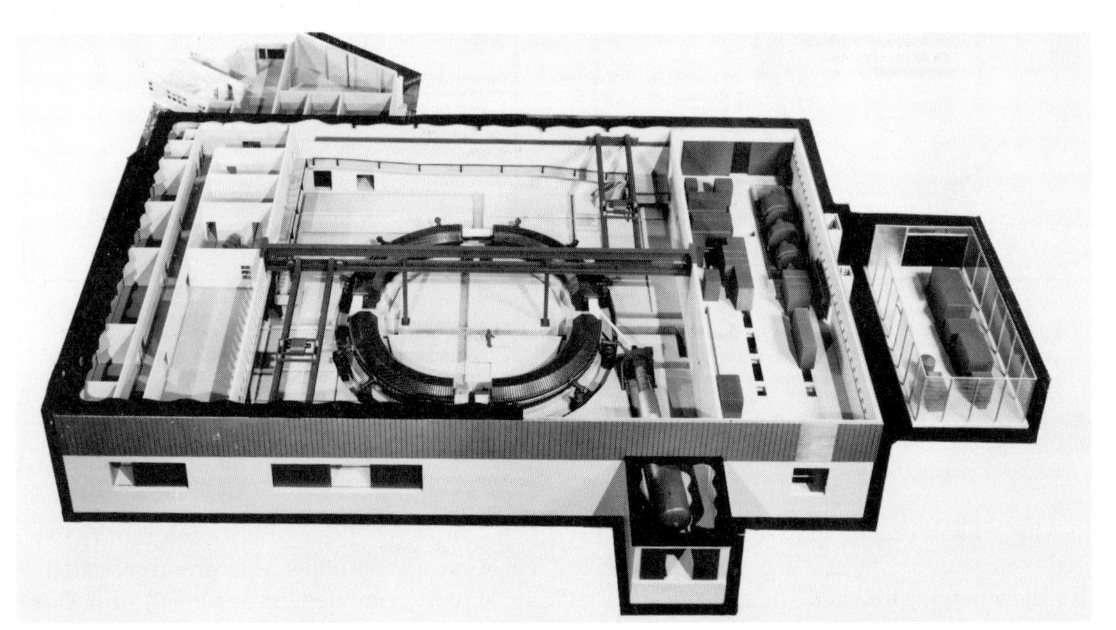

Fig. 158. The Cosmotron, 3-Bev proton synchrotron at Brookhaven National Laboratory. Top, view from control room of 65-foot diameter magnet ring. Bottom, model showing arrangement of equipment. Control room at left, Van de Graaff pre-accelerator and injector in right foreground, power supply and substation at right. Radio frequency amplifier not shown. (*Courtesy of Brookhaven National Laboratory*)

4. Beam delivery: The accelerated proton beam is delivered to the target by turning off the accelerating voltage when maximum energy has been reached. The protons (at this point collimated into a narrow beam) then coast around the circuit without changing their energy but, since the strength of the magnetic field continues to rise, they gradually spiral inward, finally striking a target that has been plunge-inserted through an airlock.

5. Particle path: The path traveled by the protons in a single orbit is 394 feet. (The total distance traversed during the operating cycle is 305,000 miles.) The beam aperture measures 1 foot axially by 4 feet radially.

6. Vacuum system: The operating pressure of the synchrotron is 2×10^{-6} millimeter of mercury (one four-hundred-millionth of an atmosphere). This high vacuum is maintained in an equipment volume of 11,000 cubic feet by a bank of 24 32-inch diffusion pumps.

7. Performance characteristics: The maximum proton energy is 6.2 Bev, equivalent to a velocity 99% that of light. The number of protons per pulse is 10^{11}.

8. Construction cost: $9.6 million.

The major proton synchrotrons now in operation or under construction in the United States, all owned by the U.S. Atomic Energy Commission, are as follows:

1. The 3.0 Bev "Cosmotron" at Brookhaven National Laboratory. This unit began operation in 1952 and was the first accelerator to produce particles with energies in excess of 1 Bev. The original cost of construction was $9.3 million, and subsequent modifications have raised the total investment to approximately $12.8 million.

2. The 6.2-Bev "Bevatron" at the E. O. Lawrence Radiation Laboratory (see description above) which has been in operation since 1953.

3. The 3.0-Bev high-current Princeton-Pennsylvania Proton accelerator (PPA), at Princeton, New Jersey, constructed as a joint project of Princeton University and the University of Pennsylvania and placed in operation in 1961. This unit is similar to the Brookhaven Cosmotron but is designed to achieve proton beam densities one hundred times greater.

4. A 12.5-Bev machine, to be known as the Zero Gradient Synchrotron (ZGS) is under construction at Argonne National Laboratory. This unit is scheduled to be completed in 1962 at an estimated cost of $42 million.

PUBLIC LIABILITY

In context with government indemnification and limitation of liability (see **insurance and indemnification against atomic energy risks**), public liability is legally defined to mean "any legal liability arising out of or resulting from a **nuclear incident**, except claims under State or Federal Workman's Compensation Acts of employees of persons indemnified who are employed at the site of and in connection with the activity where the nuclear incident occurs, and except for claims arising out of an act of war." This definition includes damage to relevant property of persons indemnified, "provided that such property is covered under the terms of the financial protection required." However, property "located at the site of, and used in connection with, the activity where the incident occurs" is not covered.

PUERTO RICO NUCLEAR CENTER

A nuclear research and training center with facilities located at Mayaguez and Rio Piedras, Puerto Rico, operated by the University of Puerto Rico under contract with the U.S. Atomic Energy Commission. The Center was established in late 1957 to provide training and research to Latin Americans in the peaceful uses of atomic energy. The environment is bilingual with instruction largely in Spanish to facilitate the participation of Latin American students.

The facilities at Mayaguez include a 1,000 KW pool-type research reactor (see **Puerto Rico Research Reactor**), a low-power training reactor, a subcritical assembly, a facility for plant research, plus associated laboratories and services. The program at Mayaguez is devoted primarily to training and research in nuclear science and technology, health physics, and agricultural applications.

The Rio Piedras site is a biomedical center equipped for training and research in radiobiology, radiation therapy, and radioisotope techniques, and for clinical work.

PUERTO RICO RESEARCH REACTOR

A 1000-kilowatt (thermal) pool-type research reactor at the Puerto Rico Nuclear Center. It was supplied by AMF Atomics, Inc. and began operation in 1960. (See **research and training reactors**)

PULSE COLUMN

One of three principal types of liquid-liquid contact equipment used in **solvent extraction** systems, the others being **mixer-settlers** and **packed columns.** A pulse column is essentially a vertical pipe containing a series of uniformly spaced, finely perforated, stainless steel plates and equipped with a pulsing mechanism, usually a mechanically operated bellows. The organic and aqueous process streams contact each other within the column in countercurrent fashion. Pulses induced by the bellows travel the column causing the up and down streams to mix intimately as they surge through the perforated plates.

The advantage of pulse columns relative to conventional packed columns is higher mixing efficiency and hence reduced column height and lower construction cost. A recent innovation in pulse column design is the "Zebra column," developed by engineers at the Hanford Works, in which stainless steel plates are alternated with plates fabricated with polyethylene—an arrangement that achieves an incremental gain in mixing efficiency through preferential wetting effects. Pulse columns are used in the **Purex** facility at Hanford, in the Idaho Chemical Processing Plant, and in the Feed Materials Production Center at Fernald, Ohio.

PULSE HEIGHT ANALYZER

An electronic device that sorts pulses from a radiation-sensing instrument, thereby permitting discrimination between photons or particles of incident radiation of different energies; also called "kicksorter." A pulse height analyzer may be used in conjunction with any radiation measurement system having a linear or proportional characteristic, i.e., **ionization chambers, proportional counters,** and **scintillation counters.** Pulse height analyzers designed to make simultaneous measurements across a broad spectrum of energies are called multichannel analyzers.

PUMP OUT

A term relating to a problem of energy loss encountered in experimental devices for controlled **fusion,** especially of the stellarator type. Pump out refers to a not-well-understood phenomenon in which the magnetic confinement rapidly deteriorates and the ionized gas, or **plasma,** moves to the walls of the reaction chamber. (See **plasma stability, Stellarator Program)**

PUMPS

Discussion of this topic will be limited to pumps used to circulate the primary coolant in civilian power reactors; referred to as main coolant pumps. The special considerations involved in the design of such pumps include the following:

1. Little or no leakage is permitted due to the radioactivity of the coolant stream. The problem arises partly from short-lived activity induced in the coolant fluid *per se,* but mainly stems from the presence in the stream of neutron-activated impurities (e.g., corrosion products) and fission products that have been released by defective fuel-element cladding.*

2. Pumps used in reactor systems are required to have a higher order of reliability than their counterparts in conventional power plants since plant shutdown procedures are much more complicated for nuclear than for conventional plants and equipment maintenance is more difficult.

3. Corrosion and erosion of pump surfaces

*For a discussion of coolant radioactivity, see **radioactive waste disposal.**

must be held to a minimum to keep down radioactive contamination of the coolant stream and to avoid fouling of heat transfer surfaces in the reactor core. This requires the use of more costly materials of construction than are normally used in conventional power plant practice.

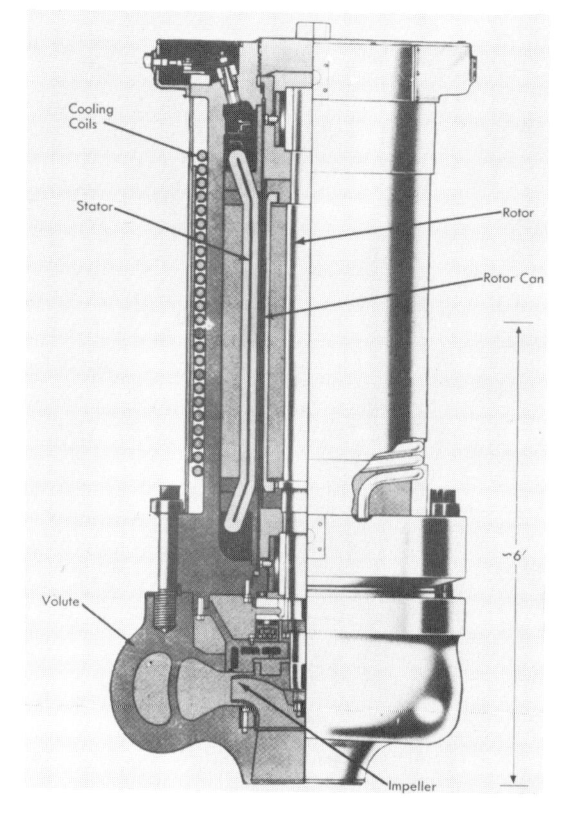

Fig. 159. Diagram of canned pump of the type used in the Shippingport Atomic Power Station. (Reprinted from "The Shippingport Pressurized Water Reactor," Addison-Wesley Publishing Co., 1958.)

4. Pumping requirements tend to be larger for nuclear power plants than for conventional plants so that pump sizes are generally larger.

These and other considerations make main coolant pumps relatively expensive items of equipment. In large-scale nuclear power plants, they account for 8-10% of the cost of the steam generating equipment (i.e., reactor equipment) and thus ~ 3% of the total cost of plant construction.

Water-Cooled Reactors. Main coolant pumps used in water cooled power reactors are motor-driven centrifugal units of two general types: zero-leakage and limited leakage. The former are known as "canned pumps," being hermetically sealed units. As is shown in Fig. 159, the impeller is attached to the rotor shaft of an enclosed induction motor, which is seal-welded to the pump casing. The rotor and stator of the motor are encased in corrosion-resistant cans designed to withstand system pressure. Water of the same purity as the coolant, but maintained at much lower temperature, circulates between the stator and the rotor, lubricating the motor bearings.

Fig. 160. Eight-ton stainless steel volute for 23,700-gpm canned pump for main coolant system of Yankee Atomic Electric Plant. (*Courtesy of Westinghouse Electric Corp.*)

Limited-leakage pumps are more conventional units in which the motor is external to the system and a mechanical seal is employed to minimize leakage around the drive shaft connected to the pump impeller.

Canned pumps were originally developed for use in Naval propulsion reactor systems where zero leakage is essential. They are presently standard equipment for civilian **pressurized water reactor** plants and large-scale civilian **boiling water reactor** plants. Units supplied to date for main coolant and other service range in capacity from 100 to ~ 24,000 gallons per minute; in motor size from 12-1850 horsepower; and in cost from ~ $7000 to ~ $400,000 each. The efficiency of the larger units is in the range, 60-70%. Stainless steel (type 304) is the predominant construction material at the present time. Canned pumps have proven to have excellent reliability.

Mechanically sealed pumps cost appreciably less and have higher efficiency (75-80%) than canned pumps but require more auxiliary equipment and more maintenance and are not as well developed for nuclear applications. Seal design is somewhat simpler for boiling water applications than for pressurized water applications due to the lower operating pressure of boiling water reactors. Mechanical-seal pumps are being used in several small-scale civilian boiling water plants * and are of interest for possible future use in large-scale pressurized as well as boiling water installations. The largest mechanically sealed pump so far built for reactor applications has a capacity of 14,000 gallons per minute. Various types of mechanical seal are under development, including packed stuffing box, labyrinth, face-type and floating-bushing seals.

Sodium-Cooled Reactors. Electromagnetic and mechanical pumps have been developed for sodium-cooled reactor systems. The former, taking advantage of the high electrical conductivity of sodium, use induced electromagnetic force as the motive power and thereby avoid any need for moving parts in the pump proper. They are, however, extremely inefficient; the theoretical maximum efficiency is 44% and actual efficiencies are appreciably lower. Further, when installed directly in the piping system, as is desirable to conserve efficiency, they present a difficult maintenance problem. The line must be broken open to get at the pump, and before this can be done the piping system containing the pump must be shut down for about 10 days to allow for radioactive decay of induced coolant activity (see **sodium-graphite reactors**). To date use of electromagnetic pumps has been restricted to small-scale reactor experiments.

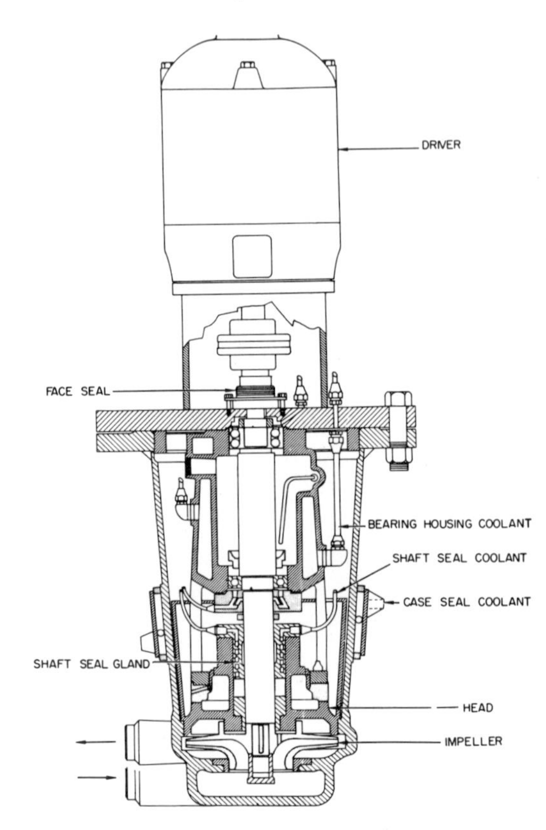

Fig. 161. Diagram of freeze-seal pump used in Sodium Reactor Experiment. (*Courtesy of Atomic International*)

The mechanical pumps are centrifugal units. There are two principal types: "freeze-seal" pumps and "free-surface" pumps. In freeze-seal pumps (see Fig. 161), an auxiliary coolant is employed to freeze sodium around the rotating pump shaft, thereby preventing leakage. In operation, the film of frozen sodium is continuously sheared by the shaft action. To prevent oxidation of the frozen sodium, an inert-gas atmosphere is maintained in the pump casing. This type of pump is used in the Sodium

* They are also being used in other types of water-cooled reactor, e.g., the Heavy Water Components Test Reactor, the Plutonium Recycle Test Reactor, and the New Production Reactor.

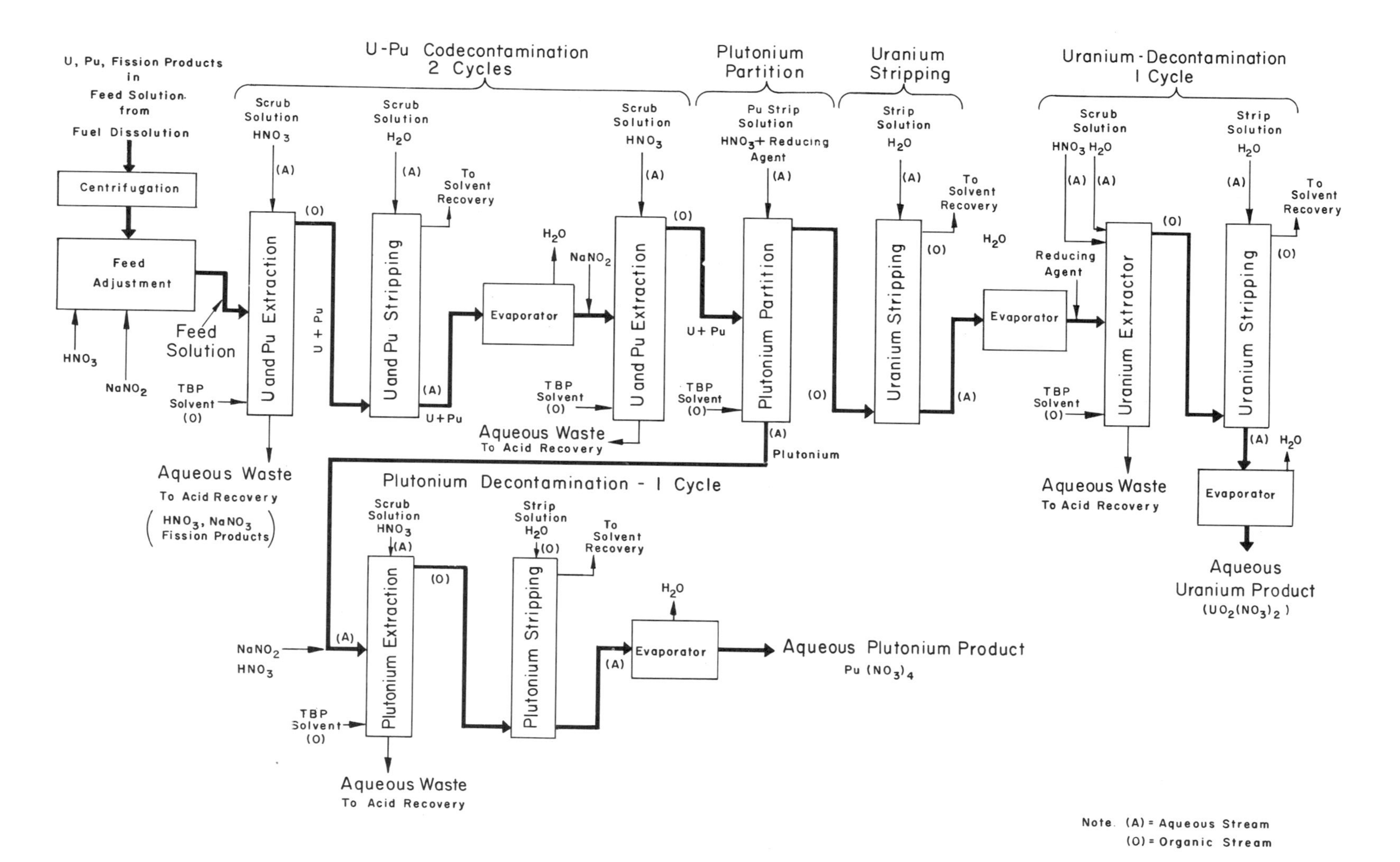

Fig. 162. Simplified flow diagram—Purex Process.

Reactor Experiment and has not proven entirely satisfactory in operation. In free-surface pumps a bearing lubricated by liquid sodium supports the bottom of an overhung impeller at the end of a long drive shaft. This type of pump is used in the Hallam Nuclear Power Facility.

A hybrid device has been developed based on mechanical rotation of a magnetic field. While this device is no more efficient than a straight electromagnetic pump, it has the advantage that the components most likely to require maintenance can be located outside the coolant line and hence made readily accessible for maintenance.

PUREX PROCESS

A **solvent extraction** process used in reprocessing irradiated fuel elements fabricated of normal or slightly enriched uranium. The organic solvent employed is a kerosene solution of tributyl phosphate (TBP). The **salting agent** is nitric acid. As in the **Redox process,** uranium and plutonium are recovered in the form of uranyl and plutonium nitrate solutions essentially free of fission product contamination. The intensely radioactive fission products leave the system in aqueous waste streams, which are concentrated by evaporation and piped to large stainless steel waste tanks located underground for safe storage. The Purex process offers several advantages over the older Redox process: (1) TBP is less toxic, less flammable and therefore more easily handled than **hexone,** the solvent used in the Redox process. (2) The use of nitric acid as the salting agent (instead of aluminum nitrate, as in Redox) reduces the amount of inert solids contained in the process wastes. (3) TBP is a somewhat more efficient solvent than hexone. The Purex process is used in the reprocessing facilities of the Savannah River Plant and in one reprocessing installation at the Hanford Works. (See **fuel reprocessing**) (See Fig. 162)

PURPURA

Livid spots on the skin, due to hemorrhaging in or under the skin or mucous tissues. One of the symptoms of acute radiation exposure. (See **biological effects of ionizing radiation)**

PYROMETALLURGICAL PROCESSES

High-temperature methods under development for **fuel reprocessing** in applications in which a high degree of fission product decontamination is not a requirement. The term pyrometallurgical derives from the fact that the fuel is generally maintained in the molten metallic state during processing. (See **oxide slagging, metal-to-metal extraction, fused salt extraction, electrorefining, vacuum distillation, fractional crystallization,** and **zone melting)**

Q

Q (UNIT OF ENERGY)

A unit of energy used by economists as a convenient way of expressing large-scale energy figures. One Q = 1.0×10^{18} British thermal units (Btu), which is equivalent to the heat contained in 38 billion tons of bituminous coal. (See **energy statistics, U.S.**)

Q-CUMBER

The name of an experimental **fusion** device of the "magnetic mirror" type operated in 1954-1956 at the Livermore Branch of the E. O. Lawrence Radiation Laboratory (see **magnetic mirror systems**). This device provided one of the earliest demonstrations of the use of magnetic mirrors for the confinement of fuel **plasma.**

QUARTERMASTER CORPS, U.S. ARMY. See **food preservation.**

R

RABBIT

A mechanism for rapidly introducing test specimens into a research reactor and rapidly dispatching them to a laboratory in the vicinity of the reactor. Such mechanisms are most commonly used in experiments with short-lived **radioisotopes,** and generally consist of a pneumatic (or hydraulic) circuit not unlike the change-handling system used in many department stores.

RAD

The basic unit of absorbed dose of **ionizing radiation**; 1 rad is equal to an absorption of 100 ergs of radiation energy per gram of matter. A related unit is the **rem.** For background information see **radiation dose.**

RADEX PLOT

A chart showing the observed or predicted distribution of radioactive contamination in the air or on the ground; used in predicting or monitoring **radioactive fallout.** Radex derives from *rad*iation *ex*clusion.

RADIATION

The propagation of energy through space or matter. There are two basic forms of radiation; electromagnetic radiation and corpuscular radiation.

Electromagnetic radiation consists of quanta (photons) of energy traveling in waves at the speed of light. Electromagnetic radiation is classified by wave length; the principal types, ranging from short to long wave lengths, are **gamma rays, x-rays,** ultraviolet light, visible light, infrared light, microwaves, and radio waves (see **electromagnetic radiation).** Gamma rays are the only types of electromagnetic radiation that is of nuclear origin and hence are the only type of such radiation that is involved in **radioactivity.** Types of electromagnetic radiation that have the ability to cause ionization (see **ionizing radiation)** include gamma and x-rays and, in some cases, ultraviolet light having a wave length less than about 1200 ängstroms (i.e., the lower portion of the ultraviolet spectrum).

Corpuscular radiation consists of energetic particles. In the case of the spontaneous decay of radionuclides (see **radioactivity),** corpuscular radiation consists principally of **alpha particles** or **beta particles.** Other forms of corpuscular radiation include neutrons and fission fragments (accompanying nuclear **fission)**; various charged particles such as deutrons or heavy ions (produced in the operation of particle accelerators); and mesons (a component of cosmic rays). All forms of corpuscular radiation have the ability to induce ionization, either directly or as a secondary effect. (See **radiation units)**

RADIATION APPLICATIONS IN THE CHEMICAL INDUSTRY

On interaction with matter, high-intensity **ionizing radiation** creates excited states of atoms or molecules (see **free radicals)** and thereby promotes chemical reactions which would otherwise occur very slowly or not at all. The same excited states can usually be induced by other means, such as heat, chemical catalysts or ultraviolet light, or by the application of an electrical discharge. As a generalization, very few chemical products can be produced using ionizing radiation which cannot be produced by other techniques. Therefore, the decision to use ionizing radiation in a given chemical process almost always hinges on questions of relative cost or convenience.

While most of the potential radiation applications studied to date have been found to be uneconomic because of low product yield and/or presently high radiation costs, some have been found to be promising and a few have been reduced to commercial practice (see below). Here it should be stressed that the field of radiation chemistry is in an early stage of exploration and, also, that substantial reductions in the costs of radiation sources can be expected as commercial markets for such sources develop. Thus, while the use of high-intensity ionizing radiation has as yet had little impact on the chemical industry, beyond proving to be a valuable research tool, there is considerable interest in its long-range potential.

Yield and Cost Considerations. The effectiveness of radiation in inducing a given reaction is generally expressed as the "G-value," which is the number of molecules of product produced (or reactants consumed) per 100 electron volts of radiation energy absorbed. For most reactions this value ranges from substantially zero up to about 5. However, some reactions, once started, proceed with little or no additional energy input. G-values of 50,000 and higher have been reported for such reactions. Since G-values are based on molecular yield, the yield on a weight basis is a function of the molecular weight of the product. The following formula relates the yield on a weight basis to the amount of radiation input, expressed as kilowatt-hours of radiation energy absorbed per pound of product:

$$\text{Lb/KWH} = \frac{(\text{G-value})\ (\text{molecular weight})}{1220}$$

The examples given in Table 1 serve to illustrate the wide range of yields and radiation requirements for radiation-induced reactions.

On a commercial scale, most of the radiation applications considered to date would require radiation sources with outputs in the range of several kilowatts to tens of kilowatts. As is discussed under **radiation sources,** the cost of supplying radiation in these amounts is presently estimated at $1-10 per kilowatt-hour. The lower portion of this range relates to applications requiring tens of kilowatts; the upper portion, to applications requiring two or three kilowatts. In the light of the radiation inputs indicated in Table 1, it is evident that radiation costs of the order of dollars per kilowatt-hour are uneconomic for low G-value applications—unless, of course, the particular product has unique properties and cannot be produced by other means. Present thinking is that radiation costs of the order of cents per kilowatt-hour must be achieved, or yields markedly improved, before many applications for high-intensity radiation techniques will be economically feasible.

Research. A number of companies in the chemical and petroleum fields are conducting research on radiation applications in facilities equipped with electron accelerators and/or radionuclide sources. With some exceptions, this work has been exploratory and largely empirical in character as investigators have attempted to identify reactions that have high product yields or result in unusual product properties. The pattern is changing, however, with increasing emphasis being placed on long-range programs of a more fundamental nature.

The U.S. Atomic Energy Commission is sponsoring an extensive program of basic research in radiation chemistry, along with application studies and development work on improved radiation sources.

Applications. To date relatively few radiation applications have progressed beyond the laboratory stage.

The principal commercial applications at present involve the irradiation of polyethylene to promote **crosslinking.** In the mid-fifties an irradiated polyethylene product with a high melting point was thereby obtained and placed on the market for use as a special electrical insulation. While methods have since been developed which achieve comparable properties by conventional chemical techniques, the irradiated product continues to have a market and is produced by at least two companies.

Quite recently a new irradiated polyethylene product has been introduced and again is being marketed by at least two companies. In this case the novel property is "plastic memory." Material irradiated in a particular shape can be softened with heat and stretched into sheet or tubular form and marketed in that form; on reheating, however, it will return to the shape in which it was irradiated. Such material promises to be a useful packaging medium.

TABLE 1. G-VALUES AND RADIATION REQUIREMENTS FOR SOME RADIATION-INDUCED REACTIONS

Reaction	*G-Value*	*Radiation Input (KWH/lb of product)*
Chlorination of benzene to produce benzene hexachloride [1]	~85,000	0.0005
Oxidation of benzene to produce phenol	50	0.3
Synthesis of ethylene glycol from methanol	3	12.2

[1] Used as an insecticide. Produced commercially using an ultraviolet-light process.

By radiation-induced **graft polymerization** a dyeable form of "Teflon" * has been produced for military uses. Another graft polymerization application is reportedly about to reach the marketing stage. In this case the product, formed by grafting styrene onto polyethylene, is a semipermeable membrane for separating salts from solutions (dialysis). It appears to be a promising material for use in water purification systems, especially for the desalination of sea water.

Several companies reportedly have reached the pilot-plant stage in the development of radiation applications as yet unidentified.

RADIATION AREA

In a laboratory or plant where radioactive materials or other radiation sources are pres-

* Trade name of a fluorinated hydrocarbon polymer with excellent corrosion resistance.

ent, any area in which the radiation dose rate exceeds 5 millirems per hour, or in which a cumulative dose of 150 millirems could be received in a 5-day period. At the entrances of all such areas, the conventional **radiation warning symbol** is required to be displayed, together with such other warning notices as may be relevant.

RADIATION, BIOLOGICAL EFFECTS OF. See **biological effects of ionizing radiation.**

RADIATION COUNTER. See **counter.**

RADIATION DAMAGE

A general term for the adverse effects of radiation on the properties, dimensions or composition of materials. In the case of materials used in nuclear reactors, these effects include the dimensional growth and distortion of **fuel elements,** the embrittlement or weakening of structural materials, and the decomposition of liquids (water, organic compounds or other) used as **moderator** or moderator-coolant. Radiation damage is one of the two principal factors which limit the allowable exposure or **burn-up** of fuel in a reactor (the other principal factor being loss of **reactivity** due to fuel depletion and the accumulation of fission product **poisons).** Excessive exposure can lead to failure of the fuel-element cladding with consequent release of fission products into the coolant stream.

The mechanisms of radiation damage are not completely understood. In the case of solid materials, the effects are attributed to processes involving the displacement of atoms from their normal position in the crystal structure. (In fissionable materials, there is, of course, the additional process of burn-up *per se.*) In the case of liquids, the effects are attributed to ionization and excitation processes.

RADIATION DETECTION. See **radiation instruments.**

RADIATION DOSE

Any biological effect produced by **ionizing radiation** depends on an absorption of energy from the radiation; hence, the most meaningful measure of radiation exposure is the "absorbed dose," which is defined as the energy imparted to matter by ionizing radiation per unit mass of irradiated material at the place of interest. Additional information that must be specified for a definitive dose description includes (1) the type of radiation, (2) the rate at which the dose is delivered, and (3) the portion of the body receiving the dose. (See **biological effects of ionizing radiation)**

Basic Dose Units. Four different radiation dose units are or have been commonly used—the **roentgen,** the **rad,** the **rep,** and the **rem.**

Roentgen (*r*). A measure of the ability of gamma or x-rays to produce ionization in air. Quantitatively, 1 roentgen corresponds to the absorption of about 86 ergs of energy from x- or gamma radiation, per gram of air. The corresponding absorption of energy in tissue may be from one-half to two times as great, depending on the energy of the radiation and the chemical composition of the tissue. For muscle, one roentgen corresponds to about 93 ergs per gram, while for bone the absorption is generally much higher. For this reason the roentgen is more useful as a measure of the amount of gamma or x-rays to which one is exposed than as a measure of the dose of such radiation actually received. However, it is often used in the latter sense.

Rad. A measure (applicable to any form of ionizing radiation) of actual energy absorption, being defined as the amount of energy imparted to matter by ionizing radiation per unit mass of irradiated material at the place of interest. Quantitatively, 1 rad corresponds to the absorption of 100 ergs of energy per gram. It follows from what was stated above that a 1-roentgen exposure to muscle results in an absorbed dose of about 0.93 rad. (In the case of bone the dose might be as high as 1.4 rads.) However, in interpreting standards of radiation protection, it is generally permissible to consider 1-roentgen exposure to gamma or x-rays as roughly equivalent to a dose of 1 rad in soft tissue.

Rep. An obsolete measure of energy absorption, measured on a base of 93 ergs per unit mass of tissue. It has been superseded by the rad and is mentioned here only because it appears in the older literature (pre-1955).

Rem. A dose unit which takes into account the relative biological effectiveness (RBE) of the radiation. The rem (from "*r*oentgen *e*quivalent *m*an") is defined as the dose of a particular type of radiation required to produce the same biological effect as one roentgen of (0.25 Mev) gamma radiation. Numerically, it is equal to the absorbed dose in rads multiplied by an agreed RBE constant. Following are the RBE values currently in use: 1 for gamma and x-rays and beta particles; 10 for alpha particles and for neutrons and protons up to 10 Mev; and 20 for heavy ions. Thus, a 1-rad dose of neutrons is equivalent in its biological effects to 10 rads of gamma radiation, and hence may be expressed as 10 rems. It has been found experimentally that the same number of rems does not always produce the same effects in bone. To adjust for these differences, a numerical factor known as the "relative damage factor" is used.

Dose Terminology. It should be noted that the above dose units are related, directly or indirectly, to the energy absorbed per gram of tissue without reference to the total quantity of tissue exposed. It is therefore essential to specify the portion of the body exposed when describing a radiation dose. Thus doses are usually described as being either "whole body" doses or as doses to particular body areas or organs—hands, feet, eyes, gonads, thyroid, skeleton, etc.

Specialized Dose Expressions. The simple expression "dose" is usually intended to mean "absorbed dose." Other dose expressions, most of them specialized in character, include the following:

1. Air dose: This is a term commonly used by radiologists. It is defined as the number of roentgens of gamma or x-rays delivered at a given point in free air.
2. Cumulative dose: The total absorbed dose received over a given period of time. Usually given in rads or rems.
3. Depth dose: The absorbed dose received at a given depth below the surface of the body, expressed either as a percentage of the surface dose (see below) or as a calibrated percentage of the air dose.
4. Exposure dose: The quantity of incident gamma or x-rays, expressed in roentgens.
5. Exit dose: The absorbed dose at the surface of the body opposite to that facing the radiation source. Usually given in rads or rems.
6. Surface dose: The absorbed dose at the surface of the body at the center of the incident radiation; also referred to as the skin dose. Usually expressed in rads or rems.
7. Threshold dose: The minimum absorbed dose resulting in a detectable clinical effect. Usually expressed in rads or rems. (See qualifying discussion under **biological effects of radiation)**
8. Tissue dose: The absorbed dose received by specific tissue. Usually expressed in rads or rems.

For terms now used in defining allowable doses see **Radiation Protection Guide** and **Radioactivity Concentration Guide**; which have been introduced to replace **maximum permissible dose** and **maximum permissible concentration.** For allowable dose limits see **radiation protection standards and regulations.** Other terms of interest include **median lethal dose, dose rate,** and **dosimeter.**

RADIATION DOSE RATE

The **radiation dose** delivered per unit time. Also the rate at which a radiation dose would be received if exposure occurred. In the latter context, the level of radioactivity in a contaminated area is commonly expressed in terms of dose rate.

RADIATION EFFECTS. See **biological effects of ionizing radiation, radiation damage.**

RADIATION EFFECTS REACTOR (RER)

A special-purpose **test reactor** operated by Lockheed Aircraft Corporation at Dawsonville, Georgia, under contract to the U.S. Air Force. It has been used primarily to test the effects of radiation on materials, equipment components and equipment systems of interest for use in nuclear-propelled aircraft (see **Aircraft Nuclear Propulsion Program).** *Type*: Modified tank reactor. The reactor can be elevated to operate outside its shield and used to irradiate large equipment carried by six remotely-operated railroad flatcars positioned around the facility. *Power rating*: 10,000 thermal kilowatts. *Fuel*: MTR-type fuel elements. *Coolant*: H_2O. *Moderator*: H_2O. *Neutron flux*: Of the order of 10^{13} n/cm² sec (maximum thermal). *Start-up*: 1958.

RADIATION ILLNESS

A general term for a class of effects evidenced in humans who have experienced relatively severe radiation exposure (100-300 roentgens in a short interval of time). See discussion of acute exposure under **biological effects of ionizing radiation.**

RADIATION INSTRUMENTS

Nearly all instruments or devices used for the detection and measurement of **ionizing radiation** depend on one or another of three radiation effects:

1. Direct or indirect ionization.
2. Scintillation of phosphors.
3. Darkening of photographic emulsions.

Table 1 lists the more common types of radiation instruments and indicates their principal fields of application. The first seven instruments listed are described under separate headings (see alphabetical entries). For information on auxiliary instruments used with radiation counters, see **pulse height analyzer, ratemeter, scaler.** For market information, see **nuclear instruments industry.**

TABLE 1. RADIATION INSTRUMENTS

	Method of Detection			*Applications*							
					Radiation Monitoring						
Instrument Type	*Ionization*	*Scintillation*	*Emulsion Darkening*	*Prospecting for Radioactive Minerals*	*Measuring Radiation Intensity*	*Dosimetry*	*Precision Counting or Measuring*	*Neutron Sensing for Reactor Control*	*Misc. Industrial Uses* [1]	*Particle Track Observation*
Ionization chamber	X				X	X [2]	X	X		
Proportional counter	X						X			
Geiger counter	X			X	X		(X)		X	
Scintillation counter		X		X	X		X		X	
Film badge			X			X				
Cloud chamber	X									X
Bubble chamber	X									X
Luminescent chamber [3]		X								X
Emulsion plates			X							X

[1] See **gages, oil-well logging.**
[2] Electroscope-type of ionization chamber.
[3] See **scintillation counter.**

RADIATION MONITORING

The periodic or continuous use of radiation detection and measurement devices to determine the amount of radioactivity or level of radiation in an area or environment, or to detect radioactive contamination of personnel; a routine procedure in any laboratory, plant or locality where there is a potential radiation hazard. Devices used for area and environmental monitoring include portable **survey meters; air samplers and monitors**; and gas and liquid effluent monitors. Devices used for personnel monitoring include **hand-and-foot-monitors** and pocket or badge-type **dosimeters.** Personnel monitoring also involves the maintenance of radiation exposure records for each individual and periodic physical examinations. (See **radiation protection)**

RADIATION PROTECTION

Occupational protection against harm from ionizing radiation involves a number of factors of which the following are of major importance:

1. The establishment of **radiation protection standards and regulations,** including limits for external and internal exposure.
2. Minimization of radiation exposure in places where radioactive materials are handled through radiation **shielding, protective clothing and equipment,** and other physical means; by segregating hazardous operations; by conservative design of plant and equipment; and by conformance to safe operating practices.
3. Control of radiation exposure by the use of **film badges, hand-and-foot monitors,** and other radiation dosimetry or monitoring instruments; by maintaining personnel exposure records; and by making periodic physical examinations.
4. Use of specialists in radiation protection principles, techniques and practices. (See **health physics)**
5. Continuing biomedical research on radiation effects (see **biological effects of ionizing radiation),** and on techniques for protecting against and treating the consequences of radiation exposure (see **medical aspects of atomic energy).**

By careful attention to these and other factors, the U.S. Atomic Energy Commission and its predecessor agency, the Manhattan District, have built up an exemplary safety record as can be seen from the following statistics covering the 15-year period, 1943-1958:

1. Injuries: Total from all causes was 5651. Radiation injuries numbered 35 or 0.6% of total.
2. Lost time: Total from all causes amounted to 0.3% of total man-days worked. Radiation exposure accounted for 3.5% of the lost time (= 0.01% of total man-days worked).
3. Fatalities: Total from all causes was 191, of which 3 were due to radiation exposure. (See **criticality incidents)**

A more definitive record of radiation safety is afforded by actual exposure records of individuals working in laboratories and plants where radioactive materials are handled. The "allowable" limits specified by radiation protection standards for occupational exposure are 12 **rems** during any one year provided the average yearly exposure over a period of years does not exceed 5 rems, i.e., the amount comparable to that received from natural sources of radioactivity (see **background radiation).** Following are actual exposure data compiled by AEC for 65,907 radiation workers for the year 1958:

Accumulated Exposure for the Year (rems)		*Distribution of Exposure Records*	
		Number of Workers	*% of Total*
0–1		59,455	90.21
1–2		4,041	6.13
2–3		1,652	2.51
3–4		407	.62
4–5		171	.26
	Sub-Total:	65,726	99.73
5–12		164	.24
12		17	.03
	Total:	65,907	100.00

Thus only 17 workers, or less than 3 per 10,000, received more than the "allowable" exposure during the year.

RADIATION PROTECTION GUIDE (RPG)

A radiation protection standard issued by the **Federal Radiation Council.** The guide states the Council's recommendations with regard to safe limits for exposure to ionizing radiation (see **radiation protection standards and regulations** for the numerical values). The term "Radiation Protection Guide" was introduced by the Council to replace the expression, **maximum permissible dose.**

RADIATION PROTECTION STANDARDS AND REGULATIONS

Radiation protection standards are essentially guides intended to provide a basis for safe practice with regard to exposure to **ionizing radiation.** Originally they were designed for the protection of persons working with radiation; now, with the use of radiation becoming increasingly widespread, they are designed not only to protect those whose occupation exposes them to radiation, but also the general population. The latest standards are given below.

If there were no compensating factors the safest practice, especially from a genetic standpoint, would be to avoid any radiation exposure above that from natural sources (see **biological effects of ionizing radiation).** Clearly, however, to hold too literally to this practice would seriously handicap, if not deny, the use of radiation in medical diagnosis and therapy as well as the development of nuclear power and other civilian applications of atomic energy. The setting of radiation protection standards thus requires a balancing of negative and positive values and, in the final analysis, involves a degree of calculated risk. At one time, the term "tolerance dose," meaning a threshold value below which no injury results, was commonly used. It was soon recognized, however, that the threshold concept does not apply to radiation-induced gene mutations, and there are now indications that it may not apply to some somatic effects of radiation. Accordingly, the trend has been to become increasingly conservative in setting radiation protection standards. The National Committee on Radiation Protection and Measurement (see below) takes the following position on the current standards for occupational exposure:

"The risk to the individual is not precisely determinable but, however small, it is believed not to be zero. Even if the injury should prove to be proportional to the amount of radiation the individual receives,* to the best of our present knowledge, the new (allowable) levels are thought not to constitute an inacceptable risk. . . ."

The principal groups active in the development of basic radiation standards are as follows:

1. The **International Commission on Radiological Protection** (ICRP), an independent international scientific committee which, since 1928, has published recommendations on radiation exposure and related matters and, since 1956, has acted in advisory capacity to the World Health Organization in the radiation protection field.

2. The **National Committee on Radiation Protection and Measurements** (NCRP), an independent U.S. scientific committee which, as presently constituted, was established in 1946. While having no official connection with the National Bureau of Standards, it uses NBS facilities and its recommendations are published in the form of NBS handbooks. The NCRP is represented on the ICRP and consults with the FRC (see immediately below).

3. The **Federal Radiation Council** (FRC), which is composed of U.S. Government officials and, under a recent amendment to the U.S. Atomic Energy Act is responsible for providing guidance to all federal agencies in the formulation of radiation protection standards. In addition, various groups have been concerned with the development of occupational radiation protection standards for particular industries. The American Standards Association, for example, has been active in the preparation of guides for the uranium mining, milling and fabrication industries. Also, particular laboratories or plants often prepare guides tailored to their individual circumstances. Such guides are usually derived from and consistent with accepted basic guides.

* I.e., linear rather than nonlinear in effect. See discussion under **biological effects of ionizing radiation.**

Current Standards. In its first report, titled "Background Material for the Development of Radiation Protection Standards," and dated May 13, 1960, the FRC uses the terms "Radiation Protection Guide" (RPG) and "Radioactivity Concentration Guide" (RCG) in preference to **maximum permissible dose** and **maximum permissible concentration,** which are the terms used at present by the NCRP and ICRP. It was felt that the word "maximum" implies an exactitude of understanding which is not justified in the light of present knowledge; and that the word "permissible" is misleading in that radiation exposure should always be kept as low as possible regardless of the limits considered safe and, in this sense, permitted.

RADIATION PROTECTION GUIDE

Type of Exposure	*Period of Exposure*	*Maximum "Safe Practice" Dose Limit* [1] *(rems)*
Occupational Worker:		
Whole body, head and trunk, active blood-forming organs, gonads, or lens of eye	Accumulated Dose	5 times number of years beyond age 18
	13 weeks	3
Skin of whole body and thyroid	Year	30
	13 weeks	10
Hands and forearms, feet and ankles	Year	75
	13 weeks	25
Bone	Body Burden	0.1 microgram of radium-226 or its biological equivalent
Other organs	Year	15
	13 weeks	5
General Population:		
Individual	Year	0.5 (whole body)
Average	30 years	5 (gonads)

[1] In light of the limitations of present knowledge of radiation effects, the values given here are inherently approximate; it is recognized that slight variations may be tolerated in particular circumstances.

The values recommended for the Radiation Protection Guide (see table) are, however, in essential agreement with the latest recommendations of the NCRP and/or ICRP. No numerical values are available at this writing * for the Radioactivity Concentration Guide, which is defined qualitatively as that concentration of radioactivity in an environment which results in organ doses equivalent to the values given in the Radiation Concentration Guide.

* To be published by the Federal Radiation Council as "Staff Report No. 2."

The basic exposure recommendations of the NCRP are contained in the following two NBS Handbooks:

No. 59—"Permissible Dose from External Sources of Ionizing Radiation"

No. 69—"Maximum Permissible Body Burdens and Maximum Permissible Concentrations of Radionuclides in Air and Water for Occupational Exposure"

See **National Committee on Radiation Protection and Measurements** for a complete list of the handbooks issued by the NCRP to date.

Regulations. The U.S. Atomic Energy Commission establishes radiation protection regulations which must be observed by its contractors and licensees. The regulation governing contractor operations is Chapter 0524 of the AEC Manual. That governing operations of individuals or organizations holding AEC licenses is entitled "Standards for Protection Against Radiation" and constitutes Part 20 of Title 10 of the "Code of Federal Regulations." Prior to the establishment of the FRC, the AEC used the recommendations of the NCRP as the basis for its regulations. It is now required by law to look to the FRC for guidance; however, as long as the FRC continues to be in essential agreement with the NCRP on what constitutes safe practice, this new arrangement is not likely to result in substantive changes in AEC radiation protection policy.

The states have become increasingly active in radiation protection matters. A number of states have enacted local radiation protection regulations; and the division of the regulatory function, as between the federal and state governments, is currently under general review. (See **state activities in the atomic energy field**)

See **transportation of radioactive materials** for information on protective regulations governing the shipment of radioactive materials.

RADIATION SHIELDING. See **shielding.**

RADIATION SOURCES

Discussion of this topic will be limited to high-intensity radiation sources for industrial applications requiring radiation outputs in the range of several kilowatts to tens of kilowatts. Such applications include **food preservation, cold sterilization of pharmaceuticals,** and chemical manufacture. (See **radiation applications in the chemical industry**)

While there is long-range interest in the possibility of using nuclear reactors as a radiation source, and certain chemical applications require a reactor,* the sources that have received principal consideration are:

1. Radiation machines, such as **linear accelerators, Van de Graaff generators** and **resonant transformers,** which supply high-energy electrons.
2. Radionuclide sources, notably **cobalt-60, cesium-137** and semirefined fission product mixtures (see **zirconium-niobium**), all of which are primarily gamma emitters.

Another radiation source that should be mentioned is irradiated reactor fuel. "Spent" fuel elements are used in a number of laboratories as a source of gamma radiation for experimental purposes; however, they do not appear promising for use in commercial applications.

Machine Sources. Radiation machines have several advantages. Unlike radionuclide sources, they can be turned on and off at will. The electron beams they produce can be focused or bent, facilitating scanning of a target material. They deliver radiation at a constant level. A machine installation is somewhat easier to shield than an installation employing a radionuclide source since a machine source delivers a collimated beam. Maintenance and parts replacement, on the other hand, are more of a problem with machine sources than with radionuclide sources.

It is estimated that machines available commercially today can supply radiation at costs in the range of $1-10 per kilowatt-hour, depending on the size of the machine and the complexity of the installation.

Radionuclide Sources. Extremely large radionuclide sources are required to produce kilowatts of radiation energy. While the requirements depend upon such factors as **specific activity** and source geometry, the following estimates are broadly representative:

Source Output (kilowatts)	*Approximate Amounts of Radionuclide Required (curies)* [1]		
	Cobalt-60	*Cesium-137*	*Zirconium-niobium*
3	250,000	1,200,000	1,000,000
30	2,500,000	12,000,000	10,000,000

[1] These estimates include allowances for self-absorption and for decline in source strength based on practical replenishment intervals.

* Specifically, those based on the use of fission fragment recoil energy. An example is the possibility of forming nitrous oxide (for nitric acid production) by passing nitrogen and oxygen through a reactor.

The capacity to produce radionuclides on a scale sufficient to meet a quantity demand for such sources does not exist at the present time.* While estimates of radionuclide costs for sources of this size are thus inherently speculative, studies indicate that net radiation costs comparable to those from machine

Fig. 163. Gamma irradiation facility at Brookhaven National Laboratory. Here, massive steel cylinder ("pig") containing multi-curie radionuclide source is being lowered into operating position at base of deep water-filled pit. A plug at the top of the cylinder can then be safely removed and small samples inserted for irradiation purposes; alternatively, the radionuclide source can be removed and used to irradiate large samples. (*Courtesy of Brookhaven National Laboratory*)

sources are within the reach of existing technology. It appears certain that the capital costs associated with radionuclide sources would be higher than for machines, but calculations indicate that the difference would tend to be offset by savings in operating costs, especially in applications involving three-shift operation.

* This statement should be somewhat qualified in regard to cesium-137, which is being produced at a rate of 4,000,000 curies per year.

Radionuclide sources provide an inherently dependable supply of radiation. Apart from requiring periodic replenishment to maintain the desired level of radiation output, they present minimal maintenance problems. The quantities of radioactivity involved and the fact that this radioactivity cannot be "turned off" dictate careful operating procedures.

Note on Costs. Radiation costs measured in cents, rather than dollars, per kilowatt-hour are believed to be required to make many radiation applications economically attractive. At this writing there is insufficient experience to indicate whether machines, radionuclides, or reactors will ultimately prove to be the lowest cost source. It is possible that each will be found to have advantages for particular applications.

RADIATION THERAPY. See **radiotherapy.**

RADIATION UNITS

The following units are commonly used in reference to **ionizing radiation:**

1. Energy of radiation: Expressed in **electron volts** (ev). Units commonly used include Kev (thousands of ev); Mev (millions of ev); and Bev or Gev (billions of ev).

2. Intensity of radiation: Defined as the amount of energy (or the number of photons or particles of radiation of given energy) passing through unit area per unit time and usually expressed in units of ergs per square centimeter per second, or watts per square centimeter.

3. Quantity of radiation: Defined as the time integral of intensity and usually expressed in units of ergs per square centimeter or watt-seconds per square centimeter.

4. Dose of radiation: Most meaningfully defined in terms of absorbed dose, i.e., the amount of energy actually imparted to matter per unit mass at the place of interest.** The

** The alternative is to speak of the exposure dose, which is defined by the ability of the incident radiation to cause ionization in air. The unit of exposure dose is the roentgen. It should be added that this unit is only applicable to gamma or x-rays. (See **radiation dose**)

basic unit of absorbed dose is the rad, which equals an absorption of 100 ergs of energy per gram of matter. Another important unit is the rem, which expresses the biological effectiveness of an absorbed radiation dose. For a discussion of this and other dose units and terminology, see **radiation dose.**

Other radiation units which should be noted relate specifically to **radioactivity:**

5. Quantity of radioactivity: Defined as the number of disintegrations occurring in unit time and expressed in curies; 1 curie = 3.7×10^{10} disintegrations per second. Units commonly used include microcuries (millionths of a curie); millicuries (thousandths of a curie); kilocurie (thousands of curies); and megacuries (millions of curies). The same units are commonly used to express quantities of radioactive material, i.e., a curie of a radioactive substance is an amount of that substance having an activity of 1 curie.

6. Intensity of a radioactive source: This is defined by the term **specific activity** and is expressed in units of curies per gram or curies per cubic centimeter. The terms intensity and activity are used interchangeably in this context.

RADIATION WARNING SYMBOL

A standard warning symbol required to be displayed wherever a radiation hazard exists as, for example, in **radiation areas.** The specifications for the symbol, as set forth in Part 20, Chapter 1, Title 10 of the Code of Federal Regulations, are given in the accompanying diagram.

Fig. 164. Radiation warning symbol, a magenta trefoil on a yellow field.

RADIATIVE CAPTURE

A type of **capture** process in which the only prompt emission is electromagnetic radiation, as in neutron-gamma or proton-gamma reactions. (See **nuclear reactions)**

RADIOACTIVE DATING. See carbon-14.

RADIOACTIVE DECAY. See radioactivity.

RADIOACTIVE FALLOUT

(1) The settling to the earth's surface of radioactive debris produced by detonation of a nuclear weapon. (2) Any particulate radioactive contamination of the ground, building exteriors, etc., subsequent to the release of radioactivity to the atmosphere.

The latter definition has been included to cover non-weapon events such as a nuclear reactor accident which, in extreme circumstances, could result in radioactive fallout. However, the text which follows is limited to the first definition, since it is in context with weapons that the phenomenon of radioactive fallout is of greatest import.

Factors Affecting Fallout. The amount, composition and pattern of radioactive fallout produced by detonation of a nuclear weapon depend upon a number of factors, including:

1. The total energy yield of the detonation.
2. The proportion of fission to fusion.
3. The structural components and design of the device.
4. The type of detonation, i.e., whether a high altitude burst, air burst, surface burst, underground burst, or underwater burst.
5. The height or depth of the burst.
6. The nature of the target terrain.
7. Meteorological conditions.

Three sources of radioactivity are involved:

Source	*Type of Radiation*
Fission products	gamma, beta, neutrino
Residual fissionable material	alpha
Induced radioactivity	gamma, beta

These are discussed separately in the paragraphs which follow:

Fission products are by far the most important factor. For every megaton of fission yield, some 110 pounds of these intensely radioactive substances are formed. They constitute a complex mixture of some 200 isotopes of 35 chemical elements. The radioactive decay patterns and other characteristics of certain individual nuclides can be extremely significant (see below); however, the composite decay pattern is of overshadowing importance in relation to events a few hours or days after the detonation. A rough rule-of-thumb is that the gross activity of the mixture decreases by a factor of 10 in the first 7 hours; by another factor of 10 in the next 7×7, or 49 hours; by another factor of 10 in the next $7 \times 7 \times 7$ or 343 hours; etc. Thus, the radiation dose rates that would be received by persons exposed to fission-product contamination various times after the detonation can be compared as follows:

Hours after Detonation	*Relative Dose Rate*
1	100 [1]
2	44
3	27
5	15
7	10
10	6.3
15	3.9
20	2.7
30	1.7
100	.4
1000	.025

[1] Arbitrary index value.

An example of absolute dose rate values is given later on. Suffice it here to indicate the general order of magnitude of the amount of radioactivity involved, which can be gauged from the following:

1. The radioactivity given off by the fission products from a 1-megaton fission yield is comparable, 1 minute after the detonation, to that of tens of millions of tons of radium.

2. In the purely hypothetical event that this amount of fission product activity were deposited uniformly over a region of 1000 square miles, the radiation intensity, 1 hour after the detonation, would exceed 1000 roentgens per hour at a level several feet above the ground.

Residual (i.e., unconsumed) fissionable material is not a significant factor from the standpoint of external exposure since the alpha particles emitted have little penetrating power. (Alpha radiation is completely absorbed in a few inches of air, and is effectively shielded by ordinary clothing.) However, if such material is inhaled or ingested, the internal radiation effects can be serious, particularly if the fissionable species is plutonium-239, which is a bone-seeker with a long **biological half-life** (see later discussion).

Induced radioactivity may or may not be an important factor, depending on the nature and amount of the structural materials used in the weapon, and on where the detonation occurs. Radioactivity induced by neutron capture in the casing or other structural parts of the weapon is a highly variable quantity. Radioactivity induced in the atmosphere consists largely of nitrogen-17 and carbon-14. The former, formed from oxygen, has a radioactive half-life of only a few seconds; it contributes to the "prompt radiation" accompanying a nuclear detonation but is an insignificant factor in the residual radiation. The latter, formed from nitrogen is a long-lived soft-beta emitter; it is not a serious radiation hazard from the standpoint of external exposure but is a potential hazard from the standpoint of inhalation or ingestion. Radioactivity induced in soil elements is a significant factor in the case of a surface or underground burst, principally through the formation of sodium-24 and manganese-56, which are hard-gamma emitters with half-lives of 14.8 hours and 2.6 hours, respectively. Radioactivity induced in water impurities, especially salt, is a significant factor in the case of an underwater burst, principally through the formation of sodium-24 and chlorine-38. The latter is a hard-gamma emitter with a half-life of 37 minutes.

Categories of Fallout. There are two broad categories of radioactive fallout, namely, early and delayed fallout.

Early Fallout. Fallout which occurs within the first 24 hours is known as early fallout. When deposited in the immediate vicinity of the target, it is also referred to as local, or "close-in," fallout. Early fallout consists of the larger particles in the mix of weapon debris; it is heaviest in the case of subsurface or contact burst. Given a relatively high air burst and favorable atmospheric conditions, there may be essentially no early fallout; for example, there was essentially none at Hiroshima or Nagasaki.

Delayed Fallout. Depending on the height attained by the "mushroom cloud," the radioactive dusts may collect in the **troposphere** (i.e., the lower portion of the atmosphere) and be carried by prevailing currents in an easterly direction. While there is some diffusion of the particle cloud, both laterally and vertically, it tends to travel along the same general latitude at which it originated. Delayed fallout from this cloud is referred to as tropospheric, or latitudinal, fallout. It occurs gradually by simple gravitation, but the principal mechanism is precipitation by rain or snow, so that the pattern of deposition is essentially nonuniform and, consequently, significant contamination may occur in widely separated localities. It usually occurs within the first few days following the day of detonation and seldom persists longer than several weeks.

Under some conditions the mushroom cloud may rise up into the **stratosphere** (i.e., the upper atmosphere) where, due to the absence of wind or other weather phenomena, its particles may remain suspended for several years. Delayed fallout of such material is referred to as stratospheric, or world-wide, fallout, and as the latter term implies may result in very general contamination. The mechanisms by which the particles make their way back into the troposphere and thence to earth are not well understood. There is also a good deal of uncertainty with regard to the residence time in the stratosphere and, hence, the amount of radioactivity that may now be stored there as a consequence of nuclear weapon test operations.

Early Fallout. Figure 165 is an illustrative projection of the early fallout from a surface burst with a fission yield in the megaton range. It shows the accumulated **radiation dose** that would be received by exposed persons in the areas and over the time intervals indicated. It will be noted that the exposure areas are defined by dose contours, known as "isodose lines," which are analogous to the elevation contours of a topographical map. The progressive elongation of the exposure

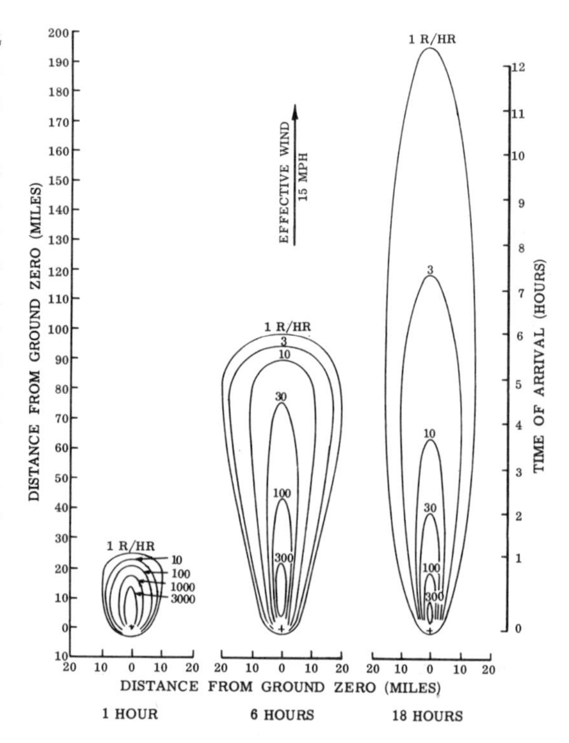

Fig. 165. Dose rate associated with early radioactive fallout from a nuclear weapon in the megaton range, shown as a function of distance from ground zero. A wind velocity of 15 miles per hour is assumed and accounts for the progressive elongation of the dose pattern at the time intervals indicated. Reprinted from revised edition of "The Effects of Nuclear Weapons." (*Courtesy of the USAEC*)

zone reflects the effect of an assumed 15-mph wind current and is characteristic of early fallout patterns. It should be stressed that this hypothetical example is a fairly extreme case.

Delayed Fallout. The health hazards associated with delayed fallout can arise from external or internal exposure. Some of the considerations involved are, briefly, as follows:

1. Heavy contamination of a particular locality (via tropospheric fallout) can result

in radiation injury by either mechanism, i.e., by external exposure or by ingestion or inhalation.

2. A degree of contamination not sufficient to cause detectable somatic effects through the mechanism of external exposure may represent a potential internal exposure hazard because of the presence of particular fission-product nuclides (notably **strontium-90,** which (a) have a long radioactive half-life, (b) are selectively concentrated by plants or animals, and (c) have a long **biological half-life.**

3. Virtually any degree of radioactive contamination is undesirable from the standpoint of possible long-term genetic effects.

Fallout Monitoring. The U.S. Atomic Energy Commission maintains a continuing national and world-wide fallout monitoring program with the cooperation of a number of other government agencies. This activity is the responsibility of AEC's Division of Biology and Medicine. The **Health and Safety Laboratory** plays a key role in the coordination of major segments of the program and in the analysis and reporting of the results. The program involves periodic sampling of the upper and lower atmosphere; the ground; the biosphere (ocean water, tap water, vegetation, foodstuffs, etc.); and man. A partial summary of the program is given in the accompanying table. It should be added that supplementary provisions are made for monitoring fallout during nuclear weapon test operations.

Fallout From Weapon Tests. Due to the precautions taken (see **weapons testing),** local fallout from U.S. weapon test operations has seldom resulted in harmful radiation exposure. This did occur, however, on one occasion.

In the spring of 1954, fallout from a thermonuclear test at the Eniwetok Proving Grounds resulted in radiation injury to 23 crew members aboard the Japanese fishing trawler, Fukuryu Maru ("Fortunate Dragon"), which had inadvertently entered the test exclusion area. All members suffered skin lesions caused by contact with fallout particles, and showed depressed blood counts. One death occurred but this was attributed to hepatitis resulting from blood transfusions given during hospitalization.

An unexpected shift in winds carried the radioactive cloud from the same thermonuclear test over an inhabited area of the Marshall Islands, resulting in sufficiently severe contamination to require evacuation of the population of some of the atolls. Some 300 persons received radiation doses estimated to have ranged from 175 roentgens to 14 roentgens. Some experienced severe skin burns; others showed no detectable effect. All have recovered from the exposure.

Tropospheric and stratospheric fallout from the combined nuclear weapon test operations of the United States, the United Kingdom, the Soviet Union and France, while stimulating widespread concern, has not resulted in any known radiation injury, nor has it created other than scattered and highly local contamination problems. The concern over weapon fallout stems principally from the possibility that continued testing of nuclear weapons under conditions resulting in fallout may have genetic consequences.

Some perspective on one measurable aspect of fallout from the nuclear weapons tests conducted to date may be gained by considering data on the accumulation of strontium-90. Studies have shown that the cumulative deposition of this radionuclide rose steadily in the area of New York City over the period, 1954 through 1958. The 1958 level corresponds to a concentration of strontium-90, in milk, of some 5.9 micro-micro-curies per gram of calcium content. It has been estimated by competent authority that, even had no further weapon tests been conducted, continued stratospheric fallout from the tests conducted prior to the fall of 1961 might ultimately (by 1970) increase this value to something like 11 micro-micro-curies. The same authority estimates that consumption of milk having this degree of strontium-90 contamination would cause a child to develop a skeletal concentration of 5.5 micro-micro-curies of strontium-90 per gram of calcium, and that such a concentration would deliver a radiation dose to bone

U.S. Fallout Monitoring Program
(Partial Description)

Sampling Program	*Year Started*	*Samples Collected By* [1]	*No. of Sampling Stations*	*Frequency of Sampling*	*Radioactivity Analyzed or Measured*
Upper Atmosphere					
"Project Ashcan"	1956	USAF	2	4 per month	strontium-90, strontium-89, zirconium-95, cesium-137, barium-140, cerium-144
Lower Atmosphere					
National Surveillance Network	1956	USPHS	44	daily	gross beta activity
80th Meridian Network	1956	USNRL	21	daily monthly	gross beta activity strontium-90, strontium-89, yttrium-91, cesium-137, cerium-141, cerium-144
AEC Site Network	1953	Contractors	11	daily	gross beta, gamma activity
Carbon dioxide sampling	1958	USWB	5–10	few per year	carbon-14
Ground Deposition					
National Surveillance Network	1956	USPHS	44	daily	gross beta activity
80th Meridian Network	1956	USAF	6	bi-weekly	strontium-90 and other
"Gummed film" network	1951	HASL	197	daily	gross beta activity; estimate of gross gamma & strontium-90
U.S. Soil Program	1955	HASL	17	annual	strontium-90
Foreign Soil Program	1955	USDA	60	biannually	strontium-90
Biosphere					
Ocean sampling	1948	Contractors	10–15	weekly to quarterly	strontium-90 and other
Tap water sampling	1953	HASL	2	monthly	strontium-90
HASL Pasture Program (soil, vegetable, animal bone)	1955	HASL	6	annually	strontium-90
Food Sampling	1957	HASL	variable	Total ~150/yr	strontium-90
HASL Milk Program	1954	HASL	4	monthly	strontium-90
HASL Background Radiation Survey	1957	HASL	400	semiannually	gross gamma activity
Man					
Lamont Human Bone Program	1954	Contractor	30	Total ~1500/yr	strontium-90
Urine sampling	1954	HASL	variable	Total ~30/yr	strontium-90
Whole body counting	1956	Contractor	2	Some	gross gamma activity; cesium-137

[1] USAF—U.S. Air Force.
USPHS—U.S. Public Health Service.
USNRL—U.S. Naval Research Laboratory.
USWB—U.S. Weather Bureau.
HASL—Health & Safety Laboratory (AEC).
USDA—U.S. Department of Agriculture.

marrow of approximately 5.5 milli-rems per year. This is approximately one-twentieth as much as the skeletal dose received from natural sources. (See **natural radioactivity**)

RADIOACTIVE WASTE DISPOSAL

The disposal of waste radioactive substances, or materials and equipment contaminated therewith, in a manner consistent with accepted radiation protection standards governing **maximum permissible concentrations** of radionuclides in air and water.

Problems of radioactive waste disposal arise wherever radioactive materials are produced or used but differ in kind and degree, depending on the amounts and nature of the radioactive materials involved and on the environment in which the materials are handled (characteristics of the site, proximity to population centers, etc.). There are two generic disposal methods: (1) dilution and controlled dispersion to the environment; and (2) concentration and burial * or storage. "High-level" liquid wastes and solid waste matter are invariably stored or buried. In some locations the same applies to "low-level" and "intermediate-level" liquid wastes. In other locations, low and intermediate-level liquid wastes may be safely dispersed. The terms, low, intermediate and high, refer to the concentration of radioactivity, expressed in **curies,** and can be roughly defined as follows:

	Concentration of Radioactivity	
	Curies per cubic centimeter	*Curies per gallon*
Low level	MPC [1] to 0.003 microcurie	MPC [1] to 10 microcuries
Intermediate level	0.003–100 microcurie	10 microcuries–0.4 curie
High level	above 100 microcurie	Above 0.4 curie; may be as high as hundreds or thousands of curies.

[1] MPC = maximum permissible concentration.

Another term that is used is "unrestricted wastes," meaning wastes in which the concentration of radioactivity does not exceed the maximum permissible concentration. There are no restrictions, from a radioactivity standpoint, on the disposal of such wastes.

Despite the extremely large scale on which radioactive materials have been produced over the last two decades and the ever increasing number of plants, laboratories and hospitals using such materials, the health and safety aspects of radioactive waste disposal, while cumbersome, have proven entirely manageable. The principal problem, especially in large-scale operations, is achieving more permanent and lower cost methods of high-level waste storage or burial. Relatedly, efforts are being made to develop uses for refined high-level waste materials (see below).

This presentation outlines the routine radioactive waste disposal problems that arise in the following major categories of activity: (1) the production of uranium and thorium; (2) the operation of nuclear power plants; (3) the reprocessing of irradiated reactor fuel; and (4) the use of radioisotopes and radiation in research laboratories and industrial plants.

Production Operations. These include the mining, milling and refining of uranium and thorium; the production of enriched uranium by isotope separation; and the fabrication of fuel elements. Minor radioactive waste disposal problems are encountered in all of these operations due to the fact that both uranium and thorium are naturally, albeit mildly, radioactive. They decay slowly by alpha-particle emission, which is nonpenetrating, so that the principal health problem is the risk of ingestion.

Mining. Some 23,000 tons of uranium ore containing about 52 tons of uranium are mined daily in the United States. The amount of radioactivity associated with this quantity of

* Underground or in the sea.

uranium is of the order of 100 curies. The principal radiation hazards are radon gas (from the decay of radium associated with uranium in the ore) and radioactive dusts consisting primarily of radon decay products. These hazards are controlled by proper ventilation of the mines. The radon and dust-laden air are vented to the atmosphere. Mine water contains appreciable amounts of radon but can be safely disposed of in the isolated mining areas.

Milling. Uranium mills crush, grind, and chemically process ore to produce uranium concentrates. Ventilation and dust collection are required to control dust concentrations in the air during crushing and grinding operations. Small amounts of uranium and its decay products are contained in large volumes of low-level waste effluents from chemical operations. These waste liquids are diluted and released to streams or to retention ponds from which they gradually seep into the soil. There has been little difficulty in achieving the required degree of dispersion except where supplies of water for dilution are limited.

Refining. Small values of unrestricted or very low-level liquid wastes are generated during chemical operations at uranium refineries. The latter are diluted and dispersed, or concentrated and stored, depending upon their content and on local conditions.

Enrichment. Wastes from uranium enrichment operations (i.e., gaseous diffusion plants) are in the unrestricted category.

Fuel Element Fabrication. The wastes from conventional fuel element fabrication operations consist chiefly of uranium scrap and collected dusts from machining operations; and liquid wastes, usually in the unrestricted category, from cleaning and etching operations. The use of plutonium as a constituent in reactor fuel elements, which is being studied under the U.S. Atomic Energy Commission's Plutonium Recycle Program, will introduce special waste disposal problems; similarly the use of remote or semiremote techniques to fabricate partially decontaminated fuel in closed-cycle reactor systems (see **fast breeder reactors**), also in the experimental stage, will also introduce special waste disposal problems where such techniques are employed.

Nuclear Power Plant Operations. Reactor coolant streams become radioactive in varying degree due to neutron activation of the coolant fluid and additives or impurities in the coolant stream; neutron activation of entrained corrosion products; and contamination by fission products released by defective fuel element cladding. Radioactivity induced in the coolant fluid *per se* is short-lived (see table); therefore

ACTIVATION PRODUCTS IN SEVERAL REACTOR COOLANTS

Coolant	*Activation Product(s)*	*Radioactive Half-life*
Water	Nitrogen-16	7.4 seconds
	Nitrogen-17	4.14 seconds
	Oxygen-19	29 seconds
Air	Argon-41	1.82 hours
Sodium	Sodium-24	15 hours

it is not an important factor in radioactive waste disposal in nuclear power plants.* Activated coolant additives and impurities and fission-product contaminants are the major factors.

Civilian power reactors employ a closed-cycle coolant system. Coolant leakage and draining and flushing of the primary coolant system during shutdown periods result in a considerable volume of low to intermediate-level liquid wastes, which are collected in storage tanks to allow an interval for radioactive

* Mention should be made that a different situation prevails in the case of research reactors of the type cooled by a once-through flow of air, e.g., the Brookhaven Graphite Research Reactor. In this case induced coolant activity (argon-41) is the principal waste disposal problem. As the contaminated air leaves the reactor core it passes through filters, which remove entrained radioactive particles, and is then exhausted through a tall stack. Dilution is accomplished by blending the contaminated air with a fresh air stream before it leaves the stack. When meteorological conditions are unfavorable for proper atmospheric dispersion of the exhaust air, reactor operations are necessarily curtailed. There is no practical alternative since argon is an inert gas and cannot be removed from the air stream by chemical absorbers or other conventional gas cleanup apparatus.

decay prior to treatment and disposal. In water-cooled reactor installations, treatment of these wastes usually involves passing them through a gas stripper (to remove volatile components such as krypton-85) and an evaporator and/or an ion-exchange column (to remove solids). They are then discharged to the river or lake supplying water to the plant.

Another significant source of liquid wastes are the chemical solutions used in equipment decontamination procedures. These are handled in much the same manner as the above waste liquids.

Gaseous wastes consist of volatiles from the gas-stripper, vent gases from the primary coolant system and, in the event of a major accident, gases from the vapor containment vessel enclosing the reactor. Storage tanks are provided for gas collection prior to disposal. Disposal involves passing the gases through a filter and then exhausting them through a tall stack under controlled dilution and dispersion conditions.

Solid wastes include contaminated ion-exchange resins, solids collected in gas filters, contaminated protective clothing, contaminated laboratory apparatus, etc. Usually the solid wastes are divided into combustible and noncombustible categories. The combustibles are usually put through a special incinerator to reduce their volume. The residues, together with the noncombustibles, are encased in concrete in 55-gallon drums, which are shipped off-site for disposal, usually by burial at sea; or, alternatively, are collected in containers and stored in an underground vault.

In the operation of reactors employing metal-clad fuel elements,* nearly all ($>$ 99.9%) of the radioactivity generated normally remains locked in the fuel elements until they undergo off-site fuel reprocessing (see below). The amounts of radioactivity released to the environment or accumulated in storage at the reactor site are remarkably small. Following, by way of example, are maximum design conditions for the Yankee Atomic Electric Station and the Dresden Nuclear Power Station:

	Maximum Design Estimates of Radioactivity[1] *(curies per year)*	
	Yankee	*Dresden*
Radioactivity dispersed to the environment		
Gas	300	300
Liquid	.001	1.6
Solid	40	None initially
Radioactive waste semipermanently stored on site	4000	5000

[1] Source: "Radioactive Waste Handling in the Nuclear Power Industry," Edison Electric Institute, March, 1960.

As a rough approximation, the cost of radioactive waste handling facilities amounts to 3-6% of the total construction cost of large-scale pressurized or boiling water nuclear power plants, and 1-2% of the cost of sodium-cooled plants. (See below for an estimate of the contribution of waste disposal to power generating costs.)

Fuel Reprocessing Operations. In terms of the amounts of radioactivity involved, fission products contained in irradiated fuel elements constitute the dominant radioactive waste disposal problem in the atomic energy industry. For every gram of fuel fissioned in a reactor (or, to put it another way, for every megawatt-day of heat generated) approximately 1 gram of fission-product matter is formed.** Radioactive decay of this material accounts for approximately 6% of the total energy released by the fission process (see **fission**). From the time "spent" fuel is removed from a reactor, the rate of energy emission from fission products is as follows: †

* One type of civilian power reactor under development employs graphite cladding. In this case, greater fission product leakage is expected due to the fact that graphite is slightly permeable. (See **High-Temperature Gas-Cooled Reactor**)

** By way of placing this figure in perspective, a millionth of a gram of a material with a radioactive half-life of about 1 day constitutes a one-curie source; and if contained in 1 gallon of water constitutes a high-level waste solution.

† Computed for exposure of approximately 1 year at a neutron flux of 3×10^{13} n/cm^2 sec.

1. At the time of removal: 38.5 watts of heat per gram of fission products.*

2. The rate reduces by a factor of 10 in 3 hours, i.e., to 3.85 watts per gram.

3. The rate reduces by a factor of 100 in 58 days; by a factor of 1000 in 520 days; and by a factor of 10,000 in 4050 days.

Table 1 ** shows the relative contribution of particular fission-product nuclides which, by reason of their high yield, long radioactive half-lives and/or their potential hazard to man, are of major importance. As is seen, strontium-90 and cesium-137 are the principal factors in long-term waste storage.

* More accurately, per gram of U^{235} fissioned during fuel irradiation.

** Computed for exposure of approximately 1 year at a neutron flux of 3×10^{13} n/cm^2 sec.

Wastes from AEC Reprocessing Operations. As has been noted, it is during **fuel reprocessing** operations that the fission products are freed from the normal confinement of fuel-element cladding. Large-scale fuel reprocessing operations are presently conducted at three

TABLE 1. MAJOR FISSION PRODUCTS [1]

Nuclide (and half-life)	*Principal Emission*	*Approx. % of Total Fission-Product Activity*		
		After 100 days' decay	*After 3 years' decay*	*After 30 years' decay*
Strontium-90 Yttrium-90 (28.0 years)	beta	<2%	15%	~49%
Cesium-137 Barium-137 (26.6 years)	beta, gamma	<2	15	~49
Promethium-147 (2.6 years)	beta	3	15	<1
Krypton-85 (gas) (10.3 years)	beta	<1	1	<1
Cerium-144 Praesodymium-144 (290 days)	beta	45	50	—
Ruthenium-106 Rhodium-106 (1.0 year)	beta, gamma	2	3	—
Zirconium-95 Niobium-95 (63 days)	beta, gamma	33	—	—
Strontium-89 (54 days)	beta	7	—	—
Ruthenium-103 Rhodium-103 (41 days)	beta, gamma	5	—	—
Barium-140 Lanthanum-140 (12.8 days)	beta, gamma	<1	—	—
Iodine-131 (gas) (8.1 days)	beta	<1	—	—
Xenon-133 (gas) (5.27 days)	beta	<1	—	—

[1] Adopted from "Nature of Radioactive Wastes," F. L. Cullen, Jr., 1959, (Testimony before Joint Committee on Atomic Energy).

AEC sites—the Hanford Works and the Savannah River Plant, both of which are plutonium production centers, and the National Reactor Testing Station. At the first two sites, slugs of natural uranium clad in aluminum are processed to separate and recover plutonium and depleted uranium. At the third site (the Idaho Chemical Processing Plant) enriched fuel elements discharged from developmental power reactors, testing reactors, research reactors, etc., are processed to recover residual fuel values. In each case a solvent extraction process is used.

Before being transported to a reprocessing facility, irradiated fuel elements are stored in a water-filled basin for about 3 months to take advantage of the initially high rate of decay of fission-product activity (see **decay cooling**). The first step in reprocessing involves acid dissolution of the fuel and cladding material. During the dissolution operation certain gaseous fission products are given off (see Table 1). These gases are passed through chemical absorbers and filters which serve to remove most of the radioiodine and entrained particulate radioactivity but do not remove chemically inert gases such as radiokrypton and radioxenon. The latter may be held in storage for decay cooling or diluted with air and released to the atmosphere through tall stacks. By controlling the dilution and only releasing the gases when meteorological conditions are favorable, dangerous concentrations in the atmosphere are avoided.

The fuel solution goes from the dissolver system into a solvent extraction system (see **fuel reprocessing** for description). When site conditions and locational factors permit (as is the case at Hanford),* aqueous effluent streams containing small amounts of fission product activity are pumped into seepage ponds (low-level streams) or underground trenches (intermediate-level streams). As these slightly contaminated solutions seep gradually into the ground, the contaminants are absorbed by the soil structure. Routine monitoring of the underlying water table and other environmental surveys serve to ensure that this ground purification process is effective.

* At Savannah River all except very low-level wastes are held in storage tanks.

High-level waste streams from the dissolver and solvent extraction systems are partially concentrated by means of evaporator equipment and then piped to an underground storage farm. These are extremely "hot" aqueous solutions (hundreds to thousands of curies of radioactivity per gallon). A typical storage farm consists of giant (75-foot diameter; 20-40 feet deep; 500,000-1,000,000-gallon capacity) steel tanks surrounded by reinforced concrete and located under a 6-foot ground cover (Fig. 166). The tanks are equipped with facilities to dissipate the decay heat of the solutions (tens to hundreds of Btu per gallon per hour) and with various instrumentation to permit determining tank conditions. Monitoring wells are located at various points in the tank farm to facilitate the detection of leakage. (See below for a discussion of proposed new methods of high-level waste storage.)

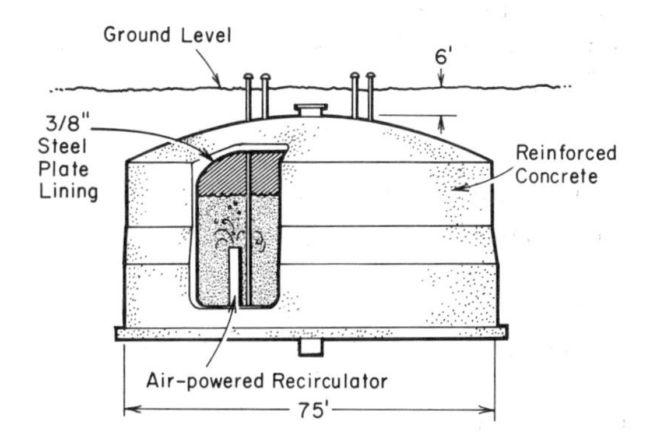

Fig. 166. Typical high-level radioactive waste storage tank. (Source: "Radioactive Waste Management Operations at the Hanford Plant," H. M. Parker, 1959.)

The cost of constructing tank farms for high-level waste storage depends on site conditions and on the chemical nature of the waste solutions. In the case of Hanford and Savannah River, the waste streams are neutralized prior to storage; at the Idaho Chemical Processing Plant, they are stored as acidic solutions. At Hanford, the cost of tankage runs about 40¢ per gallon of storage capacity. At

Savannah River, where site considerations require a different type of tank design, the cost averages $1.15 per gallon. At the ICPP, where the high corrosiveness of the unneutralized solutions requires the use of stainless steel construction, costs are in the range, $2.00 to $3.00 per gallon; however part of this cost is offset by savings realized by the elimination of the neutralization step.

In the mid-fifties, the volume of high and intermediate-level wastes generated in reprocessing operations connected with plutonium production ranged between 1000 and 1500 gallons per ton of uranium processed. Today the most efficient processes generate only about 100 gallons of high-level waste per ton of uranium processed. To illustrate the magnitude of AEC radioactive waste storage operations, as of 1959 approximately 73 million gallons of high-level waste were in storage in a network of 170 tanks with an aggregate capacity of more than 100 million gallons.

Waste from Civilian Power Plants. Requirements for the reprocessing of spent fuel from civilian nuclear power plants are now beginning to develop. Pending the availability of commercial reprocessing services, spent fuel from these plants will be reprocessed (or stored) by the U.S. Atomic Energy Commission (see discussion under **fuel reprocessing**). While alternative methods are being studied, it appears probable that most of the reprocessing will be done initially by solvent extraction. Assuming the use of mechanical decladding of the fuel elements and allowing for the vastly higher fuel **burn-up** achieved in civilian power reactors (relative to plutonium production reactors), it is estimated that between 10 and 20 gallons of high-level radioactive waste will be produced annually per installed electrical megawatt of nuclear power generating capacity.* Elsewhere in this book it is projected that some 37,500 electrical megawatts of civilian nuclear power plant capacity may be in operation in the United States by 1980. On this basis the civilian nuclear power industry would be generating high-level radioactive wastes at a rate of from one-third to two-thirds of a million gallons per year by 1980. The cumulative amount of high-level waste storage required by 1980 would be of the order of several million gallons, and the total amount of radioactivity in storage would be of the order of 10 billion curies. These estimates, while extremely speculative,** indicate that even by 1980 the volume of high-level radioactive wastes from civilian power operations will be small relative to that from plutonium production operations (see above).

* Estimate based on analysis given in Edison Electric Institute report (see previous reference) and applies to water-cooled installations. Assumptions: 150 gallons of high-level waste per ton of fuel processed; 10,000–15,000 MWD/tonne fuel burn-up. The need to dissolve fuel-element cladding chemically would increase this estimate by about a factor of 10.

Note on Costs in Power Generation. Before taking up a different category of radioactive waste disposal operations, it is of interest to examine the impact of radioactive waste disposal on the cost of civilian nuclear power generation. The following analysis is based on water-cooled reactor technology:

	$/Ton of Slightly Enriched Fuel [1]	*Contribution to Cost of Nuclear Power Generation (mills/KWH)* [2]
Mining	$ 1,200	0.02
Milling	1,000	0.01
Refining	100	negl.
Enrichment	100	negl.
Fuel element fabrication	100	negl.
Power station	16,000	0.21
Fuel reprocessing	6,500	0.09
	$25,000	0.33 mill/KWH

[1] Source: Edison Electric Institute report (see previous reference). Ranges given for each estimate have been omitted.
[2] Assumes ∽10,000 MWD/tonne fuel burn-up.

The cost of nuclear power generation in 150-megawatt water-cooled plants is estimated to

** The Edison Electric Institute report, which assumes 35,000 megawatts of nuclear power capacity by 1980, estimates the cumulative 1980 storage volume at between 1–10 million gallons, allowing for a spread of from 10,000–20,000 MWD/tonne in fuel burn-up performance and from 100 to 500 gallons/ton in the volume of waste production. Some estimates place the 1980 volume as high as 30 million gallons.

be in the range, 11-15 mills/KWH, based on 1960 technology (see Table 5, **nuclear power economics**). On this basis, radioactive waste disposal operations are thus estimated to account for between 2 and 3% of total power generating costs at the present time. A point of interest in the above analysis is the indication that the cost of radioactive waste disposal operations conducted at the reactor site is substantially higher than the cost of storing the extremely high-level radioactive wastes handled in off-site fuel reprocessing operations.

Other Waste Disposal Activities. Substantial amounts of radioactive waste, including some high-level liquid wastes, are generated at major atomic energy research centers, and small amounts of radioactive waste are generated at various university and industrial laboratories, hospitals and manufacturing plants.

Atomic Energy Research Centers. Here radioactive waste disposal problems arise in connection with the operation of research or materials testing reactors; high and low-level radiation chemistry laboratories; high-energy particle accelerators; and various specialized experimental facilities. Waste handling practices vary, depending on the particular operations conducted and on locational and site factors. Following, by way of illustration, are notes on procedures used at Brookhaven National Laboratory:

Gaseous Wastes: The handling of contaminated cooling air from the Brookhaven Graphite Research Reactor was discussed earlier in a footnote. Other gaseous wastes, consisting chiefly of vent gases from "hot" laboratory operations, are passed through filters and chemical absorbers and then exhausted through the BGRR stack. Off-gases from the new Brookhaven Medical Research Reactor, which is water-cooled, are exhausted through a separate stack system.

Liquid Wastes: Unrestricted and low-level liquid wastes from sources other than the reactors or the hot laboratory are put into a general sewerage system in which they pass through Imhoff tanks, sand filters and a chlorination bed before being discharged to a nearby river. The wastes are monitored as they leave the Imhoff tanks to ensure that only unrestricted or low-level material enters the filters. A further restraint placed on the system is that the total amount of radioactivity discharged per year be kept below 1.5 curies. Liquid wastes from reactor and hot laboratory operations, together with high-level wastes collected in other laboratory locations, are piped or carried to a battery of holdup tanks with care taken to keep certain categories of waste segregated until their activity level can be measured. Unrestricted and low-level wastes are put into the general sewerage system; high-level wastes are concentrated and stored in a tank farm; and intermediate-level wastes are compounded into concrete and placed in drums for burial at sea.

Solid Wastes: These include materials and apparatus made radioactive in in-pile experiments; left-over radioisotopes; contaminated laboratory apparatus and clothing; and other experimental debris. Material of low activity is accumulated in an isolated dump area; material of high activity is stored in underground concrete-lined pits for decay and possible subsequent disposal; and materials of intermediate activity is compacted, placed in 55-gallon drums and encased in concrete for burial at sea.

Small-scale Disposal. The extensive use of radioisotopes as an aid in research programs, medical diagnosis and therapy, industrial radiography, and measurement and control devices in various industrial production operations, has made radioactive waste disposal a routine procedure in many plants, laboratories and hospitals. While the aggregate amount of radioactivity involved is large (hundreds of thousands of curies), the amount handled at any one location is generally small; moreover, a considerable fraction of the activity is encapsulated,* which facilitates control and disposal. It should be added that supplies of radioisotopes can only be obtained under a license from the U.S. Atomic Energy Commis-

* "Sealed sources," i.e., encapsulated radioisotopes, are used in industrial radiography and gaging applications and in some medical therapy applications.

sion, and their use is subject to federal and/or state radiation protection regulations.

In some applications, the amounts of activity handled are small enough or the wastes are of sufficiently low level to permit disposal *in situ* by the dilution and dispersion method. In applications where sealed sources are used, the "spent" capsule is merely placed intact in a shielded container and shipped to a disposal point. In still other applications, wastes are collected and turned over to a commercial radioactive waste disposal service. Such services usually concentrate or compact the wastes for land or sea burial.

Alternatives to Tank Storage. While tank storage of high-level, liquid wastes is manageable on a short-term basis (tens of years), it is not an attractive permanent solution to the disposal problem in view of the long radioactive half-life of some fission-product nuclides (see Table 1). The critical nuclide in this context is strontium-90, a biologically hazardous substance with a half-life of 28 years for which the maximum permissible concentration in water has been set at approximately 25 billionths of a curie per gallon. The concentration of strontium-90 in freshly stored high-level waste is of the order of curies per gallon so that it would take a period of time of geological magnitude for high-level wastes to decay to an unrestricted activity level. Thus tank storage poses the prospect of perpetual maintenance to prevent leakage and an endless series of transfers of tank contents as tanks successively reach the end of their useful life.

Disposal of high-level wastes by dilution and dispersion is not an attractive solution in view of the large waste volumes involved (see earlier discussion) and the stringent tolerances on strontium-90 concentration in the environment.

These considerations have sparked research on alternative methods. Two basis methods are being studied: (1) immobilization of the wastes by converting them to more easily stored solid form, or by selective fixation of the radioactivity in an inert, nonleachable, and hence buriable solid material; and (2) piping the wastes in liquid form into geological formations where there is little possibility of contamination of groundwater sources.

Research on the former method is being conducted at a number of laboratories and involves studies of various calcination and fixation schemes. An example of one of the schemes is as follows: The waste solution is partly calcined and filtered to remove solid fission-product oxides, which are compacted and packaged for storage. The residual waste solution is passed over a bed of montmorillonite clay which is effective in adsorbing fission-product ions. The clay is then heated to a high temperature, becoming a refractory and essentially non-leachable material which can be buried. This and other schemes have been shown to be technically feasible but require further development to achieve acceptable costs.

The geological formations which have been considered for storage of high-level wastes in liquid form include salt beds, deep underground basins, and excavations in selected shale formations. At present salt beds appear to be the most promising, being dry, impervious to water and hence shut off from groundwater sources.

Fission Product Recovery. Efforts are also being made to develop commercial uses for specific fission products or semirefined fission product mixtures (see **radiation sources; Multicurie Fission Products Pilot Plant).** While success in these efforts would not solve the radioactive waste disposal problem (since the materials used would ultimately require disposal), it could be expected to have a favorable effect on the economics of high-level radioactive waste processing and storage.

RADIOACTIVITY

The spontaneous disintegration of unstable atomic nuclei accompanied by the emission of certain forms of corpuscular or electromagnetic radiation—principally, **alpha particles, beta particles** and **gamma rays.** The process of disintegration is referred to as radioactive decay. The two most common decay mechanisms are **alpha decay** and **beta decay;** other mechanisms include electron capture, isomeric transition, and spontaneous **fission.**

The "daughter" products of many radionuclides are themselves radioactive; however, the ultimate product of any decay "chain" (involving a sequence of daughter products) is a stable nuclide.

Radioactivity is measured by the number of disintegrations taking place within a given time interval; the principal unit is the **curie,** defined as 3.7×10^{10} disintegrations per second. Every species of radioactive atom (i.e., each **radionuclide)** decays at a characteristic rate, which is independent of pressure, temperature or chemical conditions. The time required for a sample of a radionuclide to lose half of its radioactivity, i.e., for one-half of the atoms to disintegrate, is referred to as the radioactive **half-life** of that radionuclide and is independent of the amount of material present.

Some nuclides are naturally radioactive (see **natural radioactivity)**; others are artificially radioactive (see **induced radioactivity).** Radioactivity was discovered by H. Becquerel of France in 1896.

The term activity is used synonymously with radioactivity in atomic energy parlance.

RADIOACTIVITY CONCENTRATION GUIDE (RCG)

A radiation protection term introduced by the **Federal Radiation Council** to replace the expression, **maximum permissible concentration.** Pending preparation of a detailed standard, the Council has defined RCG qualitatively as that concentration of radioactivity in an environment which results in organ doses equivalent to the values given in the Radiation Protection Guide. (See **radiation protection standards and regulations)**

RADIOGRAPHY

The use of penetrating **ionizing radiation** for physical inspection of solid materials, as

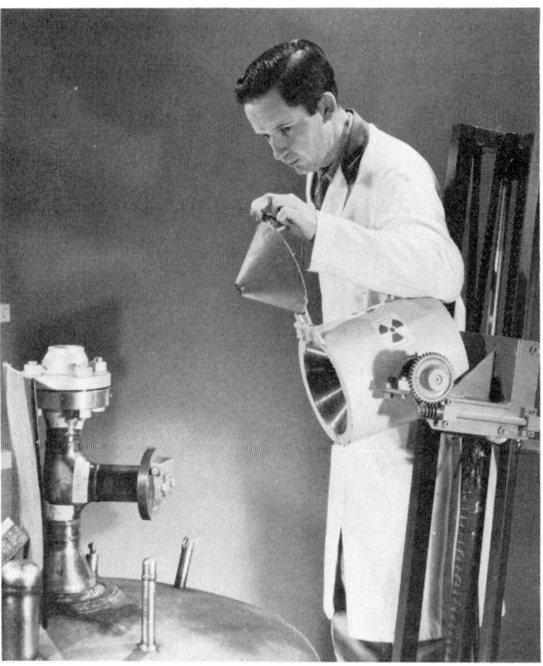

Fig. 167. Gamma radiography. Left, inspection of a circumferential weld in a large pressure vessel using a remotely activated cobalt-60 source. Right, a small cobalt-60 source so designed that it can be operated much as a camera. (*Courtesy of United Kingdom Atomic Energy Authority* (*left*), *Brookhaven National Laboratory, right*)

in testing the integrity of weldments, detecting flaws in castings, etc. Radiation passing through the test specimen develops a shadow image on photographic film, contrasts in which reflect differential absorption of radiation in the material. By careful visual inspection, anomalies in the shadow pattern can be interpreted in terms of gross flaws, presence of imbedded foreign matter, nonuniformities in density, etc.

X-ray radiographic equipment long used in industry has been replaced in many applications by gamma-emitting radionuclide sources. Gamma-ray radiographs in general show less contrast than x-ray radiographs, making interpretation more difficult. Also, the radiation from a radionuclide source cannot be "turned off"; hence, precautions must be taken against improper handling of the source when not in use. In other respects gamma radiography has important advantages relative to x-ray radiography, notably:

1. Cheaper, more compact radiographic equipment which, apart from periodic source replacement, requires essentially no maintenance.
2. Greater ease and flexibility of operation.

The latter characteristic stems in part from the fact that radiation from a radionuclide is omnidirectional, permitting panoramic (360°) exposures. A radionuclide source designed for panoramic exposure can be placed inside a pipe or vessel and accomplish in one operation an inspection that would require multiple x-ray operations; similarly, the source can be placed centrally with respect to a number of test specimens and thus used for simultaneous multiple inspection.

The principal radionuclides used in radiography are **cobalt-60, cesium-137,** and **iridium-192.** Their properties are summarized in the accompanying table.

Radionuclides Used in Radiographic Inspection

	Cobalt-60	*Cesium-137*	*Iridium-192*
Method of quantity production	Irradiation of cobalt	Recovery from fission product wastes	Irradiation of iridium
Representative **specific activity** (curies/gram)	60–100	~30	~200
Half-life	5.2 years	26.6 years	74 days
Maximum gamma energy	1.33 Mev	0.66 Mev [1]	0.47 Mev
Equivalent x-ray machine	2.5 Mev	1.4 Mev	0.7 Mev
Thickness of steel plate that can be inspected	2–5 inches	1.5–3 inches	0.25–2.5 inches

[1] From daughter product, barium-137.

RADIOISOTOPES

Radioactive isotopes of chemical elements. More than 1000 different radioisotopes have been identified, some of them naturally occurring substances (see **natural radioactivity**) but the great majority of them produced artificially (see **induced radioactivity, fission products**). There are of the order of 100 useful varieties; the others are in general either too difficult to produce or have too short a radioactive **half-life** to be of practical interest.

Radioisotopes serve as chemical, biological or physical tracers (see **tracer technique**) and/or as sources of ionizing radiation for medical therapy or industrial applications (see **medical aspects of atomic energy, radioisotopes in industry**). Under existing atomic energy legislation, radioisotopes are classed as **by-product materials** and are distributed and used under license arrangements (see **licenses**). As of September 30, 1961, about 6400 radioisotope licenses were in effect in the United States (see Table 1).

TABLE 1. U.S. RADIOISOTOPE LICENSES
(September 30, 1961)

		No. of Licenses	% of Total
Medical			
Private practitioners	1,384		
Hospitals, etc.	1,365		
Subtotal		2,749	43
Industrial			
Radiography	461		
Other uses	1,474		
Subtotal		1,935	30
Federal and State Laboratories			
Civil defense	1,022		
Other	249		
Subtotal		1,271	20
Colleges and Universities		331	5
Other		116	2
Total		6,402	100%

Production. At one time particle accelerators, such as cyclotrons, afforded the only means of producing artificial radioisotopes. Some radioisotopes continue to be produced in cyclotrons,* however most are now produced in nuclear reactors, which have made them available in greatly increased variety and quantity and at greatly reduced cost. There are four principal production reactions:

1. The neutron-gamma reaction. An example is the production of cobalt-60 by irradiation of the natural cobalt element:

$$_{27}Co^{59} + _0n^1 \longrightarrow _{27}Co^{60} + \gamma$$

Since the product and target nuclides are isotopes of the same chemical element, no chemical separation is involved. Other common radioisotopes produced using this reaction include sodium-24,** potassium-40, iridium-192 and gold-198.

2. The neutron-proton reaction. An example is the production of phosphorus-32 by irradiations of sulfur-32:

$$_{16}S^{32} + _0n^1 \longrightarrow _{15}P^{32} + _1p^1$$

* Notably, those formed by reactions involving the bombardment of a target nucleus with deuterons. An example is cobalt-58, formed from iron-57 by the deuteron-neutron reaction.

** Also produced from aluminum by the neutron-alpha reaction.

Fig. 168. Loading face of the Oak Ridge Graphite Reactor, used extensively for radioisotope production (*Courtesy of Oak Ridge National Laboratory*)

This reaction requires neutrons of higher than thermal energy. The product must be separated from the target material. Other common radioisotopes produced using this reaction include **carbon-14** (from nitrogen) and **sulfur-35** (from chlorine).

duced by irradiating and then processing uranium-235 capsules.

For many applications, radioisotopes of high **specific activity** are desired. The specific activity achieved depends on the irradiation conditions and may also depend on the cleanness of the separation of the product from the target material. In the latter connection, the term "carrier free" is used to describe a radioisotope preparation that is free of any gross diluent material. It should be added that no radioisotope preparation is entirely pure since "foreign" nuclides are inevitably present in trace amounts. Some radioisotopes are used in the form in which they are produced; others are incorporated in chemical compounds (see **labeled compounds**) prior to use. Radioisotopes used as radiation sources are commonly encapsulated in air-tight vials or cylinders to facilitate safe handling. The latter are usually referred to as "sealed sources." Figure 169 shows two typical containers used for shipping radioisotopes.

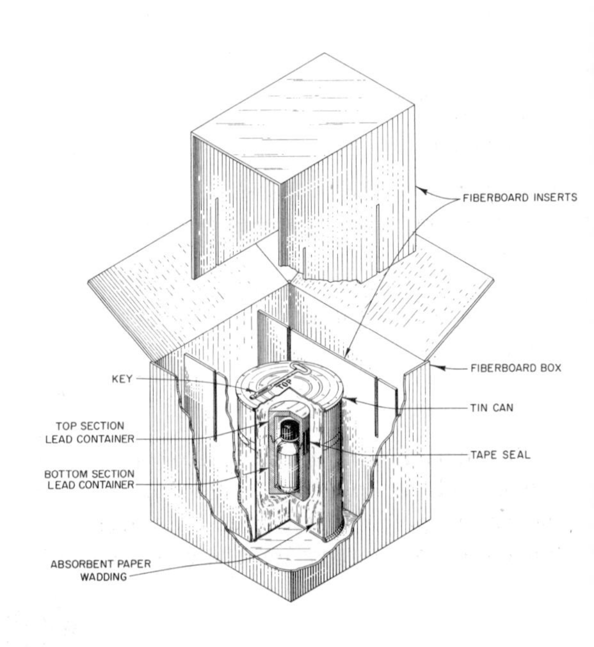

Fig. 169. Left, packaging radioisotopes for shipment. Right, detail of disposable-type shipping container. (*Courtesy of Oak Ridge National Laboratory*)

3. The neutron-alpha reaction. An example is the production of tritium by irradiation of lithium-6:

$$ {}_3\mathrm{Li}^6 + {}_0\mathrm{n}^1 \longrightarrow {}_1\mathrm{T}^3 + {}_2\alpha^4 $$

This reaction requires neutrons of higher than thermal energy. The product must be separated from the target material.

4. Uranium fission, followed by chemical separation. Common radioisotopes produced by this means include **strontium-90**, cesium-137, cerium-144, **promethium-147**, **krypton-85** and iodine-131. The first four mentioned are (or can be) produced on a large scale by recovery from fission product wastes from fuel reprocessing plants (see **Multicurie Fission Products Pilot Plant**). The others are pro-

TABLE 2. SHIPMENTS OF RADIOISOTOPES FROM OAK RIDGE NATIONAL LABORATORY

Radioisotopes	FY 1961		Cumulative Total (1946—Sept. 30, 1961)	
	Curies	Shipments	Curies	Shipments
Cobalt-60	186,101	156	1,057,610	2,313
Cesium-137	21,100	201	157,191	1,690
Tritium	37,217	224	137,718	1,319
Iridium-192	7,007	97	44,517	952
Krypton-85	3,866	150	13,221	544
Iodine-131	297	2,227	7,273	48,057
Promethium-147	1,078	82	4,516	467
Phosphorus-32	151	2,116	1,919	30,172
Strontium-90	17,801	119	99,159	941
Carbon-14	41	377	144	3,735
All others	203	7090	2,544	63,951
Total	274,864	12,839	1,525,812	154,141

The main U.S. center of radioisotope production is Oak Ridge National Laboratory; however, radioisotopes are also produced at various other AEC facilities, such as Argonne National Laboratory, Brookhaven National Laboratory, and in certain private facilities. In the latter connection, in 1960 Abbott Laboratories began production of iodine-131 using rented space in a commercially owned reactor, and General Electric Company and Westinghouse Electric Corporation both announced plans for the commercial production of cobalt-60 in their materials testing reactor facilities (see **General Electric Test Reactor, Westinghouse Testing Reactor**). A large number of private firms purchase radioisotopes in bulk and retail them as labeled compounds or sealed sources.

Distribution from Oak Ridge. The shipment of radioisotopes from Oak Ridge began in August, 1946, under the auspices of the Manhattan District (see **Manhattan Project**). Table 2 summarizes shipments from this center during and through 1960.

As is seen, radioisotopes used as large-scale radiation sources (notably cobalt-60, iridium-92 and cesium-137) account for most of the total activity shipped; whereas, radioisotopes used as tracers or small-scale radiation sources (notably iodine-131 and phosphorus-32) account for the greatest number of shipments. Table 3 summarizes information on the value and allocation of radioisotope shipments.

TABLE 3. VALUE OF RADIOISOTOPES SHIPPED FROM OAK RIDGE NATIONAL LABORATORY [1]

	Value of Shipments ($ thousands)	
	1960	Cumulative Total (1946–1960)
Domestic sales	$1,399	$12,902
Foreign sales	258	1,751
Other [2]	447	6,161
Total	$2,104	$20,814

[1] Source: AEC.
[2] Transfers to AEC sites; medical subsidy program; civil defense supplies, etc.

Table 4 lists specific radioisotopes available from Oak Ridge, arrayed by half-life.

Export-Import. While considerable quantities of radioisotopes are exported from the United States to other countries (see Table 3), many U.S. firms import radioisotopes from foreign suppliers (principally in Belgium, Canada, France, Israel and the United Kingdom). The value of U.S. exports and imports in 1960 has been estimated at $1.3 and $1.4 million respectively.*

* Source: Bureau of Census data. These estimates include the costs of encapsulation, shipping, and insurance and hence are not comparable with the value figures given in Table 3.

TABLE 4. PARTIAL LIST OF RADIOISOTOPES AVAILABLE FROM OAK RIDGE NATIONAL LABORATORY[1]

(Listed by half-life)

Half-Life[2]	*Radioisotope*[3]	*Radiation*
24.2 s	Silver-110	β, γ
30 s	Rhodium-106 (Ru^{106})	β, γ
72 s	Indium-114	$\beta-, \beta+, \gamma$
2.6 m	Barium-137 m (Cs^{137})	γ
17.5 m	Praseodymium-144 (Ce^{144})	β, γ
12.44 h	Potassium-42	β, γ
12.8 h	Copper-64	$\beta-, \beta+, \gamma$
13.6 h	Palladium-109	β, γ
14.3 h	Gallium-72	β, γ
15.06 h	Sodium-24	β, γ
19 h	Iridium-194	β, γ
19.2 h	Praseodymium-142	β, γ
23 h	Mercury-197 m_2	γ
24.1 h	Tungsten-187	β, γ
26.8 h	Arsenic-76	β, γ
35.87 h	Bromine-82	β, γ
38 h	Arsenic-77	β, γ
40 h	Lanthanum-140	β, γ
47 h	Samarium-153	β, γ
53 h	Cadmium-115	β, γ
2.44 d	Ruthenium-97	γ
2.54 d	Yttrium-90	β
2.7 d	Gold-198	β, γ
2.71 d	Mercury-197	γ
2.79 d	Molybdenum-99	β, γ
2.8 d	Antimony-122	β, γ
3.15 d	Gold-199	β, γ
3.87 d	Rhenium-186	β, γ
5.02 d	Bismuth-210	β
7.6 d	Silver-111	β, γ
8.08 d	Iodine-131	β, γ
11.1 d	Neodymium-147	β, γ
11.52 d	Barium-131	γ
12.8 d	Barium-140	β, γ
13.95 d	Praseodymium-143	β
14.3 d	Phosphorus-32	β
16 d	Osmium-191	β, γ
19.5 d	Rubidium-86	β, γ
27.8 d	Chromium-51	γ
32.5 d	Corium-141	β, γ
35 d	Niobium-95	β, γ
39.8 d	Ruthenium-103	β, γ
43 d	Cadmium-115 m	β, γ
45 d	Hafnium-181	β, γ
45 d	Mercury-203	β, γ
45.1 d	Iron-59	β, γ
49 d	Indium-114 m	γ
53 d	Strontium-89	β
59.5 d	Yttrium-91	β, γ
60 d	Antimony-124	β, γ
65 d	Zirconium-95	β, γ
72d	Cobalt-58	$\beta+, \gamma$
73.2 d	Tungsten-185	β
74.37 d	Iridium-192	β, γ
85 d	Scandium-46	β, γ
87.1 d	Sulfur-35	β
112 d	Tin-113	γ
115 d	Tantalum-182	β, γ
120 d	Selenium-75	γ
163 d	Calcium-45	β
250 d	Zinc-65	$\beta+, \gamma$
270 d	Silver-110 m	β, γ
282 d	Cerium-144	β, γ
1.0 y	Ruthenium-106	β
2.3 y	Cesium-134	β, γ
2.6 y	Promethium-147	β
2.7 y	Antimony-125	β, γ
4.0 y	Thallium-204	β
5.27 y	Cobalt-60[4]	β, γ
9.5 y	Barium-133	γ
10.27 y	Krypton-85	β, γ
12.46 y	Hydrogen-3	β
13 y	Europium-152	β, γ
16 y	Europium-154	β, γ
25 y	Strontium-90	β
30 y	Cesium-137	β
85 y	Nickel-63	β
5568 y	Carbon-14	β
2.12×10^5 y	Technetium-99	β
3.08×10^5 y	Chlorine-36	β
1.72×10^7 y	Iodine-129	β, γ

[1] Source: Oak Ridge National Laboratory.
[2] s, second; m, minute; h, hour; d, day; y, year.
[3] The radioisotope in parenthesis is the one under which the listed radioisotope is catalogued.
[4] Supplied when not available from commercial sources. (See **cobalt-60**)

Training Courses. See **education and training programs, AEC.**

RADIOISOTOPES, AGRICULTURAL USES OF. See **agricultural applications of atomic energy.**

RADIOISOTOPES IN INDUSTRY

Radioisotopes are used or of interest for use in industry in a variety of ways, notably:

1. As a substitute for x-ray techniques in the inspection of weldments, castings, etc. (See **radiography**)
2. In the measurement and control of industrial operations. (See **gages**)
3. As a means of supplying small quantities (watts) of electrical power (see below).
4. As a means of sterilizing drugs and medical supplies. (See **cold sterilization of pharmaceuticals**)
5. As a means of extending the shelf life of foodstuffs. (See **food preservation**)
6. As a process tool in chemical manufacture. (See **radiation applications in chemical industry**)
7. In numerous tracer applications. (See **tracer techniques**)
8. In the detection and measurement of trace quantities of chemical elements (in semiconductor materials, petroleum products, etc.) by neutron **activation analysis.** (See **neutron sources**)
9. As a means of activating phosphors in self-luminous signs.

As of November 30, 1960, some 1800 licenses for industrial uses of radioisotopes were in effect in the United States. Savings due to improved quality control, simplified measurement procedures, etc., are estimated to be of the order of tens of millions of dollars annually.*

In 1958, the U.S. Atomic Energy Commission initiated a series of research and development contracts designed to open up new industrial radioisotope applications. This activity is known as the Isotope Development Program. Some of the current objectives are the development of small radionuclide power sources ("nuclear batteries") for the transmission of weather information from remote locations and for telemetering data from underwater seismographic instruments;** the development of tracer techniques for the improved utilization of water resources, and for the control of air and water pollution; the development of new techniques for neutron activation analysis; the development of improved methods for process control based on tracer techniques; and research and development on high-intensity radiation applications using radionuclide sources.

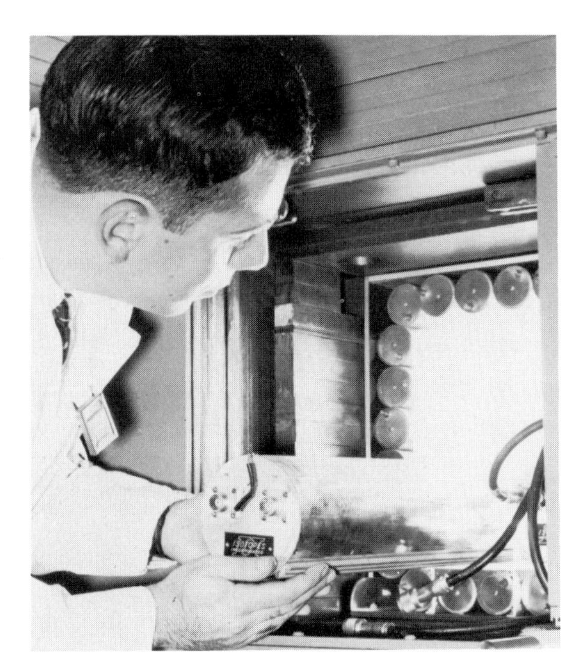

Fig. 170. An example of the use of radioisotopes in industrial research is the addition of trace amounts of a radioactive substance to gasoline samples as a means of studying causes of the formation of engine deposits. Deposits formed in the combustion chamber of a test engine are gasified and collected in a cylinder, here seen being placed in a special radioactivity measurement chamber for analysis.

RADIOISOTOPES, MEDICAL USES OF. See **medical aspects of atomic energy.**

---

* A study made by the National Industrial Conference Board in 1959 credited radioisotopes with effecting tangible savings of some $39 million during a 12-month period in 1957–1958.

** For convenience, these applications are discussed in the entry on the AEC's **SNAP Program,** which covers closely related activities.

RADIOLOGICAL ASSISTANCE PLAN

A plan established by the U.S. Atomic Energy Commission to provide emergency radiological assistance in the event of accidents or incidents involving radioactive materials.

Upon request, assistance is made available to any AEC licensee or contractor, and to federal, state, local, or private organizations or persons reporting an incident suspected to involve misplacement or loss of control of (1) ionizing radiation sources or (2) **source, byproduct,** or **special nuclear material.**

The plan is administered from AEC Headquarters through eight operations offices assigned geographical areas of responsibility for radiological assistance field operations. Regional office areas include Puerto Rico, the Virgin Islands, and the Canal Zone.

Since 1958 the AEC and the Department of Defense have mutually exchanged and coordinated radiological emergency assistance in weapons and nonweapons radiological accidents through a Joint Nuclear Accident Coordinating Center (JNACC) at Albuquerque, New Mexico. Under the provisions of the July 1961 Interagency Radiological Assistance Plan (IRAP) AEC and DOD radiological incident assistance operations will be coordinated with the radiological assistance health and safety activities of several other federal agencies. The AEC is the agency responsible for administration of the IRAP.

Available emergency assistance includes alpha, beta, or gamma monitoring; sampling and radiation monitoring of air, water, or food; radiological decontamination advice and emergency assistance; medical advice on the care and handling of persons exposed to radiation; and radiochemical sample analysis services.

RADIOLOGICAL PHYSICS. See **health physics.**

RADIOLOGY

The science of medical uses of ionizing radiation. (See **medical aspects of atomic energy**)

RADIONUCLIDE

Shorthand for radioactive **nuclide.** Radionuclide and radioisotope are synonymous terms.

RADIOSENSITIVITY

The relative susceptibility of biological matter (cells, tissues, organs, etc.) to injury from ionizing radiation. In the case of the human system, degrees of radiosensitivity can be roughly characterized as follows:

1. Radiosensitive (greatest susceptibility): white blood corpuscles, bone marrow, germ cells.
2. Radioresponsive (intermediate susceptibility): endothelium, epithelium of the skin and gastrointestinal tract, connective tissue, growing bone.
3. Radioresistant (least susceptibility): kidney, liver, thyroid, brain.

Radiosensitivity is only one of the factors that determine the biological effects of a particular radiation dose. Other factors include the importance of the affected organs to the well-being of the body; and, in the case of internal exposure, the ability of particular organs to concentrate the radioactive substance involved. Also, the radiosensitivity of particular organs is known to depend to some degree on the age and general health of the individual, and on the rate at which the dose is delivered. (See **biological effects of ionizing radiation**)

RADIOTHERAPY

Any treatment of disease with ionizing radiation—x-rays, gamma rays, or other. (See **medical aspects of atomic energy**)

RADIUM

Element No. 88 (symbol, Ra; atomic weight, 226.05), a radioactive metal associated in trace amounts with pitchblende and other uranium ores. Radium is extremely costly ($6-9000 per gram). It is one of the few radioactive materials not under the licensing control of the U.S.

Atomic Energy Commission. Prior to the availability of cheaper, artificially produced radioisotopes, radium was the principal source of radiation for medical use. It has also been used fairly commonly in combination with beryllium as a neutron source for laboratory experiments, alpha radiation from the radium displacing neutrons from the beryllium nuclei as follows:

$${}_4Be^9 + {}_2He^4 \longrightarrow {}_6C^{12} + {}_0n^1$$

Radium's daughter element, **radon,** is a potential health hazard in uranium and ore handling operations.

The standard measure of radioactivity, namely the **curie,** is based on radium.

RADIUS OF EFFECT

A term used in predicting nuclear weapons effects; specifically, the distance in yards from ground zero (see **zero point)** at which there is a 50% probability of achieving a specified degree of damage.

RADON

Element No. 86 (symbol, Rn; atomic weight, 222), a heavy radioactive gas formed by **radium** decay. An alpha emitter with a decay half-life of 3.82 days, radon is inherently associated with radium in uranium ores. Radon and its radioactive daughters, radium A and radium C, constitute a potential health hazard in uranium mining and ore handling operations. The latter are particulate and tend to be retained in the lungs. Thorough ventilation is required to prevent dangerous accumulations of radon and its daughters in any confined space.

RAMJET PROPULSION, NUCLEAR. See **Pluto Project.**

RARE EARTH ELEMENTS

A group of metallic elements, ranging in atomic number from 57 (lanthanum) to 71 (lutetium), which have virtually identical chemical properties and are combined together in one position of the periodic table as the "lanthanum" or "lanthanide" series:

Element	*Symbol*	*Atomic No.*
Lanthanum	La	57
Cerium	Ce	58
Praseodymium	Pr	59
Neodymium	Nd	60
Promethium [1]	Pm	61
Samarium	Sm	62
Europium	Eu	63
Gadolinium	Gd	64
Terbium	Tb	65
Dysprosium	Dy	66
Holmium	Ho	67
Erbium	Er	68
Thulium	Tm	69
Ytterbium	Yb	70
Lutetium	Lu	71

[1] Also known as illinium (symbol Il).

The rare earth elements occur naturally in the form of oxides (rare earths) and are found in various minerals, notably **monazite.** They are of interest in the nuclear field in several ways: (1) As constituents of monazite, the principal source of **thorium,** they are a factor in thorium milling and purification processes (see **thorium production technology).** (2) Isotopes of at least six rare earth elements are formed as **fission products** and are therefore a factor in **fuel reprocessing** and **radioactive waste disposal.** (3) Certain rare earth elements have extremely high thermal neutron absorption cross sections and are of interest to reactor designers as possible reactor control materials. Notable examples are **gadolinium, samarium, europium** and **dysprosium.** (4) Thulium-170 is of interest as a source of low energy gamma rays for diagnostic radiography, and promethium-147 is a potentially useful radionuclide for industrial radiation applications.

Prior to the Manhattan Project, rare-earth separation technology was extremely limited and only relatively crude concentrates were available in practical quantities. During the project improved separation techniques based on **ion exchange** were worked out at Ames Laboratory, and these have since been refined and applied on an industrial scale. Today various high-purity rare earths and rare earth metals are available from commercial suppliers.

RATEMETER

An electronic device that measures the average pulse rate of a radiation-sensing instrument and thereby provides a continuous indication of the average intensity of the inci-

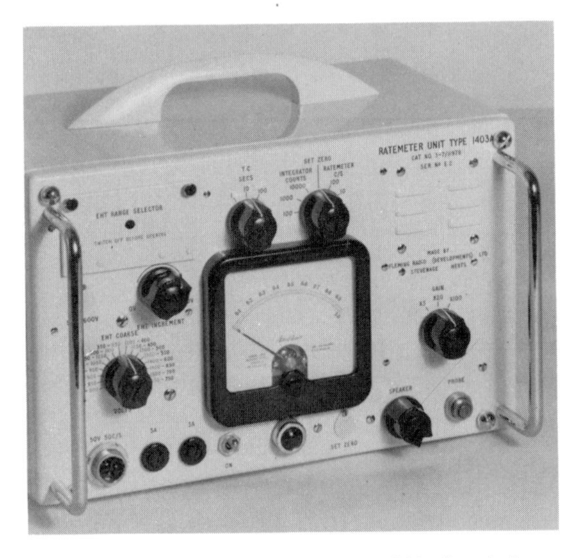

Fig. 171. Ratemeter. (*Courtesy of Nucleonics*)

dent radiation; also called a counting ratemeter. Ratemeters may be used in conjunction with pulse-type **ionization chambers, proportional counters, Geiger counters,** or **scintillation counters.** They can be fitted with both linear and logarithmic scales to permit measuring a wide range of radiation intensity.

Portable survey meters used in uranium prospecting and **radiation monitoring** employ ratemeters in combination with a Geiger or scintillation counter. (See **scaler)**

RAW MATERIALS

Ores and crude concentrates of uranium and thorium. The term is used to differentiate between these materials and "feed materials" (refined uranium and thorium or compounds).

RAW MATERIALS DEVELOPMENT LABORATORY

A small U.S. Atomic Energy Commission laboratory at Winchester, Massachusetts, used for a number of years for research on ore processing problems and shut down in 1961. The operation contractor was National Lead Company of Ohio, a subsidiary of National Lead Company.

The Laboratory was originally established to study methods for the recovery of uranium from domestic ores, especially those of low grade, and later worked on methods for controlling radiological hazards in uranium milling operations.

RBE

Relative biological effectiveness (of ionizing radiation). (See **radiation dose)**

REACTIVITY

A measure of the departure of a nuclear reactor from criticality. A positive value of reactivity means that the reactor is supercritical and the neutron density and power will rise exponentially with time. A negative value means that it is subcritical and the neutron density and power will fall with time.

Reactivity may be expressed as the ratio $\frac{K_{\text{eff}-1}}{K_{\text{eff}}}$, where K_{eff} is the effective **multiplication factor.** (See **reactor control** for further discussion of the reactivity of a reactor system.)

References are frequently made to the reactivity of reactor fuel, and in particular to the loss of reactivity due to fuel **burn-up** and to the accumulation of fission product **poisons.** In the light of the above definition, it should be noted that a critical reactor always contains some "latent" **excess reactivity** (i.e., more fuel than is necessary to achieve criticality), which is balanced by the poisoning effect of the **control rods** used to regulate the system and in some reactors by the presence of **burnable poisons** as well. Such excess reactivity is gradually drawn upon in the course of reactor operation to compensate for fuel burn-up and fission-product poisoning effects. This is done by gradually pulling out the control rods or, where burnable poisons are used, occurs automatically as the burnable poisons are consumed.

REACTOR (nuclear)

An assembly of nuclear fuel capable of sustaining a controlled chain reaction based on nuclear **fission**; sometimes called a "pile." A reactor may be built for one or more of the following purposes:

1. To provide intense beams or fluxes of neutrons for experimental purposes. (See **research and training reactors, test reactors**)
2. To produce **radioisotopes.**
3. To produce fissionable materials for defense stockpiles. (See **production reactors**)
4. To generate heat for space heating or chemical process applications. (See **process heat applications for reactors**)
5. To produce heat for electric power generation. (See **power reactors**)
6. To supply motive power for ship, aircraft, or rocket propulsion. (See **power reactors**)

The operation of a nuclear reactor depends upon two fundamental characteristics of nuclear fission:

(1) the fact that every atom undergoing fission releases on the average between two and three neutrons, which makes a chain reaction possible; and (2) the fact that some of the neutrons are not released until seconds or minutes after fission has occurred (see **delayed neutrons**), which allows time for instruments to function so that the chain reaction can be controlled. Other characteristics of nuclear fission which bear importantly on the operation of a nuclear reactor are (1) the fact that in the neighborhood of 90% of the fission energy released is converted to heat essentially at the point of fission, so that if the reactor is to be operated at an appreciable power level (above a few watts) it must be cooled; and (2) the fact that a chain-reacting fission system is intensely radioactive, so that an installation to be operated at an appreciable power level must be heavily shielded.

Since a fission chain reaction can only be sustained with uranium-235, plutonium-239 or uranium-233, the fuel for a nuclear reactor always contains one of these primary **fissionable materials.** It usually also contains one of the primary **fertile materials,** uranium-238 or thorium-232. The fuel may also contain an inert (i.e., nonfissionable, nonfertile) ingredient used as an alloying agent, solvent, or diluent. Various fuel formulations are thus possible; however, when viewed from a physics standpoint, reactor fuels can be categorized as follows:

1. Normal uranium, i.e., uranium containing uranium-235 and uranium-238 in the same proportion in which they occur naturally. The concentration of the fissionable component in the fissionable-fertile mix is thus 0.71%.
2. Slightly enriched fuels, i.e., fuels in which the concentration of the fissionable component is in the range from 0.72% to several percent.
3. Highly enriched fuels, i.e., fuels in which the concentration of the fissionable component is from 20 or 30% to 92%.
4. Fully enriched fuels, i.e., fuels in which the concentration of the fissionable component is from 92% to 93+%.

The enrichment referred to in (2), (3) and (4) can be achieved in several ways, namely, by the isotopic enrichment of uranium; by blending uranium-235 with thorium, or plutonium-239 with uranium or thorium; or by the use of **spiked or seed cores.** The basic distinctions between the three fuel categories from a physics standpoint can be summarized as follows:

1. Normal or slightly enriched fuels can only sustain a chain reaction when a **moderator** is present to slow down the neutrons (see **thermal, intermediate reactors**). Fully enriched fuels do not require a moderator (see **fast reactors**).
2. The ability of normal uranium to sustain a chain reaction is marginal and imposes

certain limitations on the reactor designer. Reactors fueled with normal uranium must be large in over-all dimensions in order to reduce neutron leakage to a very small value. Another limitation is that ordinary water (H_2O) cannot be used to moderate a reactor fueled with normal uranium (because of excessive neutron absorption).

The first of these limitations applies in part to slightly enriched fuels, but the second does not.

Where a moderator is employed, two basic arrangements are possible. In **heterogeneous reactors,** the fuel and moderator are discrete bodies usually arranged in a regular pattern, e.g., uranium slugs in a graphite lattice. In homogeneous reactors, the fuel and moderator are intimately mixed (as in a solution). Materials used as moderator include light and heavy water, graphite, beryllium, and certain organic compounds.

The physical form of the fuel is another fundamental variable in reactor design. Most of the reactors built to date are fueled with an assembly of fabricated **fuel elements** held in a fixed matrix in the reactor core. In **fluid-fuel reactors** the fuel consists of a solution (aqueous, liquid metal, molten salt or other) that circulates through or is contained within the reactor core. (See also **slurry, pebble bed gas-cooled** and **liquid fluidized bed reactor concept)**

Another important reactor design variable is the coolant employed. Materials used as coolant include light and heavy water, gases, liquid metals, fused salts, and certain organic compounds.

An important consideration in the design of any nuclear reactor is **neutron economy,** i.e., the efficient utilization of the neutrons released by the fission process. This influences and often determines the selection and specification of all materials used in the core of the reactor and affects many design features.

In any reactor containing fertile material, whether this be present as part of the fuel mixture or as a separate component of the system (see below), some new fissionable material will inherently be formed in the course of reactor operation. This is an important factor in the economics of large-scale power reactors and, of course, is the primary factor in the design and operation of production reactors. Where the new material formed is different from that consumed in the operation of the reactor, the system is sometimes known as a "converter." (*Example*: the formation of plutonium in a reactor fueled with normal uranium.) Where the same material is formed as is consumed, the system is known as a breeder. (*Example*: the formation of plutonium in a reactor fueled with a plutonium-uranium mixture.) Here it should be noted that most authorities limit the use of the term, breeder, to reactors that produce more new fissionable material than is consumed in the operation of the system. (See **breeder reactor)**

Major functional components of a nuclear reactor, not all of which are required or used in a given reactor design, include:

1. The fuel (including facilities for loading and unloading or circulating same).
2. The moderator.
3. A reflector, namely, a layer of material placed around the core for the purpose of reflecting escaping neutrons back into the fission zone and hence improving the neutron economy of the system.
4. A blanket, namely, a zone of fertile material located adjacent to the core for the purpose of utilizing escaping neutrons for the production of new fissionable material.
5. Controls to regulate the chain reaction and to shut it off quickly in an emergency.
6. A cooling system (including, in the case of power reactors, facilities for steam generation).
7. Structural materials such as **cladding** for fuel and **core supports** to support and align the fuel.
8. A reactor vessel, which houses the reactor core.
9. Radiation shielding. (See **thermal shield, biological shield)**
10. A radiation monitoring system for personnel protection.
11. A containment mechanism, namely, an

enclosure or other means of preventing the escape of radioactivity in the event of an accident. (Containment is normally only required for reactors operating at high power levels.)

(See **reactor materials, reactor components, reactor control**)

REACTOR APPLICATIONS.

See **reactor (nuclear); power reactor.**

REACTOR COMPONENTS

For information on major mechanical equipment components of civilian power reactors, see **pressure vessels, pressurizer, pumps, valves, heat exchangers, control rod drives, fuel handling mechanisms,** and **containment.** Also see **nuclear power economics** and alphabetical entries on specific reactor types (boiling water reactors, pressurized water reactors, etc.)

REACTOR CONTROL

Control of a nuclear reactor is essentially a matter of controlling the **excess reactivity** that is built into the system and without which it could not operate. A reactor with no excess reactivity, i.e., one loaded with exactly the amount of fuel needed for criticality, would be incapable of maintaining a chain reaction since it would have no means of compensating for reactivity losses due to fuel depletion and the accumulation of fission product **poisons.** A reactor must therefore contain extra fuel upon which it can draw as the operation proceeds. In most reactors this excess reactivity is controlled by introducing a corresponding amount of poisoning agents in such a way that they can be removed (or remove themselves) when no longer needed. One method is to use poison-containing **control rods** which can be moved in and out of the system at will. A supplementary method is to use **burnable poisons,** i.e., poisons incorporated in the fuel or fuel cladding that "burn off" at a rate equal to or faster than that at which fuel is consumed. (Also see **solution poisons**)

Given then a reactor with a predetermined amount of excess reactivity and a corresponding amount of control poisons, say in the form of control rods, the rudiments of reactor control are readily apparent. Before start-up, the control rods would be lodged in the reactor. To start the reactor they would be gradually withdrawn until criticality had been achieved. During operation they would be further withdrawn as needed to sustain power output at a constant level. To shut down the reactor they would be reinserted. The following paragraphs deal with some of the considerations which underlie this simple control principle and provide some additional information on control systems.

Delayed Neutrons. The rate of energy generation (power level) in a reactor is a direct function of the neutron flux, assuming the geometry of the system is fixed. During steady-state operation the flux, and hence the power level, is held constant. When it is desired to make an adjustment in the neutron flux, say to increase the power level, the system must briefly enter a "supercritical" phase, i.e., a phase during which the number of neutrons in successive generations is allowed to increase. This must be done in such a fashion (1) that the rate of change in neutron flux and hence of power level does not create excessive thermal stress in reactor materials or otherwise compromise the integrity of the system, and (2) that the reaction does not get out of control.

If all the neutrons released in fission were emitted promptly (see **prompt neutrons**), a runaway reaction would be extremely difficult to avoid for such neutrons have an extremely short lifetime—of the order of one ten-thousandth of a second between the time they are released by fission of one atom and the time they induce fission in another. This means that a very slight increase in the rate of the reaction can cause an enormous rate of increase in neutron flux and hence in power level. For example, if the neutron flux is increased by only one-tenth of 1% per neutron generation (corresponding to an effective **multiplication factor** of 1.001), with 10,000 neutron generations formed per second the power level of the system would increase 20,000 fold per second.

Fortunately, some (0.7%) of the neutrons released in fission are not emitted until seconds or minutes after the fission event (see **delayed neutrons**), so that the average neutron lifetime for a reactor system is about one-tenth of a second and, given the same rate of increase in flux noted above, the power level would only increase by about 1% per second. That is a small enough rate of increase to allow time for mechanical controls to be actuated and to take effect. Thus, the effect of delayed neutrons is to decrease the sensitivity of the reactor system to *small* changes in reactivity, thereby facilitating reactor control. When large changes of reactivity are involved, the delayed-neutron safety factor no longer applies and the control characteristics of the system are governed by the prompt neutrons. Specifically, this occurs when the effective multiplication factor exceeds 1.007, in which event the system becomes "prompt-critical," i.e., the contribution of delayed neutrons is no longer required to help maintain criticality.

Fig. 172. Main control room of Dresden Nuclear Power Station. (*Courtesy of General Electric Co.*)

Temperature Coefficients of Reactivity. Other factors bear on the control characteristics of a nuclear reactor. For example, changes in temperature affect the reactivity of the system by altering the reaction cross sections and the densities of the various reactor materials. A reactor is said to have a **negative temperature coefficient** when its reactivity decreases with rising temperatures—a desirable characteristic since it makes the system somewhat self-regulating. The converse, namely, a **positive temperature coefficient**, is undesirable since it means that the power level will rise that much further in a given reactor excursion. (Also see **void coefficient**)

Control Components. The functional components of a control system for a **power reactor** typically include the following:

1. Control poisons, introduced by means of

control rods, or by a combination of control rods and burnable poisons. Three types of control rods are generally used: **regulating rods** for fine adjustments, **shim rods** for coarse adjustments, and **safety rods** for reactor shutdown. The use of burnable poisons is a means (a) of increasing the amount of excess reactivity that can safely be loaded into the reactor and thereby extending the core life, and/or (b) of reducing the number of, and hence the cost of, the mechanical controls.

2. **Control rod drive** mechanisms, i.e., electromagnetic, hydraulic or other types of drive mechanism equipped with fail-safe devices for the reliable movement of control rods.

3. Instrumentation, basically consisting of (a) neutron sensing devices to measure neutron flux (see **ionization chamber**), (b) thermocouples to detect "hot spots" in the fuel, (c) instruments to measure the inlet and outlet temperature and flow rate of reactor coolant, and (d) computer-type devices to convert the instrument measurements into control parameters, e.g., conversion of the coolant measurement data into power level readings.

REACTOR HAZARDS REPORTS. See **Atomic Energy Commission—Licensing and Regulatory Procedure.**

REACTOR MATERIALS

Reactor materials can be categorized by function as follows: fuel materials, coolants, moderators, control materials, structural materials, and shielding materials. What follows is a brief summary presentation of the principal materials used or of interest for use in the first five of these categories, with particular reference to civilian power reactors. Supplementary information will be found in individual entries on specific materials (beryllium, graphite, etc.) and in entries on the major power reactor types (pressurized water reactors, boiling water reactors, etc.). For information on shielding materials, see **shielding.**

Fuel Materials. These include fissionable and fertile materials; alloying or diluent materials; and, in the case of solid fuel elements, cladding materials. Usually the term "fuel" refers to the fuel formulation,* e.g., uranium dioxide, exclusive of the cladding material.

Desirable properties for solid fuel elements for use in civilian power reactors include: (1) high burn-up capability, which depends partly on the nuclear characteristics of the fuel and partly on the dimensional stability of the clad fuel elements under thermal cycling and irradiation; (2) good mechanical strength at elevated temperatures; (3) good heat-transfer characteristics, which depend on the thermal conductivity of the fuel and cladding, the quality of the thermal bond between the fuel and cladding, and the surface-to-volume ratio of the fuel element design; (4) low fabrication costs, which depend on the fuel element design, the mechanical characteristics of the fuel and cladding, and the cost of the non-nuclear fuel materials; (5) good chemical and metallurgical compatibility between the fuel and cladding; (6) adequate chemical compatibility between the fuel and the reactor coolant; (7) good chemical compatibility between the cladding and the reactor coolant; and (8) low reprocessing costs, which depend on the chemical characteristics of the fuel and cladding and the ease of mechanically removing all or a part of the latter as a first step in reprocessing. In addition, it is desirable that the cost of the nuclear component of the fuel be as low as possible; and, of course, the governing consideration is the over-all fuel cost in terms of mills per kilowatt-hour of power generated.

Table 1 lists the fuels and cladding materials now used or under development for use in the major types of civilian power reactor. See individual reactor types for further information. (Also see **fuel element fabrication**)

Coolants. The choice of coolant determines many of the basic parameters of power reactor design. In many power reactor systems the coolant serves also as moderator. Coolant properties often directly determine the oper-

* Fuel *burn-up,* however, is computed on the basis of the fissionable and fertile constituents, and sometimes only the fissionable constituent.

TABLE 1. FUEL MATERIALS FOR CIVILIAN POWER REACTORS

Reactor type	*Technology ca. 1959*			*Under Development*
	Fuel	*Cladding*	*Burn-up* [1]	
Pressurized water reactors	Slightly enriched uranium dioxide	Stainless steel or zircaloy	13,000	Oxide fuel elements being developed for burn-ups approaching 20,000
Boiling water reactors	Slightly enriched uranium dioxide	Zircaloy or stainless steel	11,000	
Organic-cooled reactors	Slightly enriched uranium-3.5% molybdenum alloy	Stainless steel or aluminum	4,500	Oxide fuel and aluminum cement cladding
Sodium-graphite reactors	Slightly enriched nium-10% molybdenum alloy	Stainless steel	11,000	Uranium carbide
Fast breeder reactors	Enriched uranium-10% molybdenum alloy	Stainless steel	15,000	Plutonium Oxide dispersion in uranium-molybdenum matrix
Gas-cooled reactors (low-temperature)	Natural Uranium	Magnox	3,000	Slightly enriched uranium dioxide
Gas-cooled reactors (high-temperature)	Enriched uranium dioxide	Stainless steel	10,000	Enriched uranium and thorium carbide dispersion in graphite matrix, clad in graphite
Heavy water-moderated power reactors (D_2O cooled type)	Natural Uranium	Zircaloy	4,000	Objective to obtain 7000 megawatt-days per ton burn-up with same fuel
Molten salt reactors	Enriched uranium and thorium in fused salt solution	None	?	In early stage of development
Aqueous homogeneous reactors	Aqueous solution of enriched uranium	None	?	Not under active development

[1] Megawatt-days of heat per metric ton of uranium. Values based on AEC report, "Civilian Power Reactor Program," February, 1960.

ating pressure and may directly or indirectly limit the operating temperature. The heat-transfer characteristics of the coolant have an important bearing on the allowable power density in the reactor core. The chemical characteristics of the coolant are a major consideration in the selection of other reactor materials (fuel, cladding, structural, etc.).

Desirable coolant properties include: (1) high specific heat, (2) high density, (3) good heat-transfer properties; (4) high boiling point and low vapor pressure (to minimize the operating pressure required at a given operating temperature); (5) low thermal neutron-absorption cross section;* (6) low activation cross section; (7) chemical compatibility with fuel and structural materials; and, in the case of materials that are nonfluid at room temperature, (8) a reasonably low melting point. The cost of the coolant material is also a consideration but is only one of the factors in the economic balance of coolant selection.

Table 2 summarizes some of the properties of the coolants of major interest in the U.S. civilian power reactor development.

*This is not as important a consideration in intermediate or fast reactor systems as it is in thermal reactor systems.

Moderators. Desirable **moderator** properties include (1) low atomic weight; (2) high atomic density; (3) low thermal neutron absorption cross section; (4) high neutron scattering cross section; (5) chemical compatibility with the reactor coolant; (6) good thermal and radiation stability; (7) good heat-transfer characteristics; and, in the case of solid moderator materials, (8) mechanical strength and (9) ease of fabrication. The cost of the moderator material is also a consideration but is only one of a number of factors in the economic balance of moderator selection.

The nuclear performance of moderator materials is measured by their neutron slowing-down power and moderating ratio. These two expressions are defined as follows:

$$\text{Slowing-down power} = N\sigma_s\xi$$

where N = the atomic density (atoms per cubic centimeter); σ_s = the microscopic scattering cross section; and ξ is a function of the

TABLE 2. NOTES ON COOLANTS FOR CIVILIAN POWER REACTORS [1]

Material	*Order of rank (1 = best)*			*Melting Point °F*	*Boiling Point °F*	*Notes*
	Specific Heat	*Heat Transfer Coefficient*	*Thermal Neutron Cross Section*			
Light water (H_2O) Heavy water (D_2O)	1	3	6 2	liquid at room temp.	212	High operating pressures (1500–2000 psi) impose ultimate ceiling on operating temperature (600–700°F). Radiolytic dissociation of water a problem. Corrosion-resistant materials include zircaloys, stainless steel, hafnium, titanium.
Organics (terphenyl)	2	4	4	~150	500	Permits lower operating pressure (~100 psi) and use of carbon steel. Thermal stability of available organic compounds imposes ultimate ceiling on operating temperature (700–800°F). Radiation damage to organics a problem.
Sodium	3	1	3	208	1621	Permits high operating temperatures at nominal pressure. Danger of explosive chemical reactions in the event of air leakage complicates design of steam generator. Induced radioactivity in sodium a problem.
Sodium-potassium	4	2	5	52	1508	Advantage of lower melting point than sodium, however, high thermal neutron absorption cross section precludes use in thermal reactor systems.
Helium	5	5	1	gas at room temp.		Permits high operating temperatures but poor heat-transfer characteristics limit power density. Moderately high operating pressures required (300–500 psi). Noncorrosiveness of helium and fact that moderator can be selected independently of coolant are advantages.

[1] Restricted to coolants of major interest. Others include carbon dioxide, lithium-7, fused salt mixtures, and fluid fuel streams.

atomic weight (and hence a measure of neutron energy loss per collision with a moderator atom).

$$\text{Moderating ratio } (\sigma_s/\sigma_a)\xi$$

where σ_a = the absorption cross section. Slowing-down power expresses a moderator's ability to thermalize neutrons in a given distance, and hence has an important bearing on reactor core dimensions. Moderating ratio expresses a moderator's efficiency in thermalizing neutrons without excessive neutron capture, and hence has an important bearing on the **neutron economy** of the reactor system. A comparison of moderator properties is given in Table 3.

Control Materials. Desirable properties for control rod materials include (1) high neutron absorption cross section; (2) adequate mechanical strength; (3) chemical compatibility with the reactor coolant; (4) good thermal and radiation stability; (5) low mass (to minimize inertia effects in control-rod movement; (6) good heat-transfer characteristics; (7) ease of fabrication; and (8) reasonable cost. Table 4 lists elements commonly used or potentially useful in control rod applications. (Also see **burnable poisons, solution poisons**)

Structural Materials. Desirable properties for structural materials include: (1) mechan-

TABLE 3. NOTES ON MODERATORS

Moderator Material	*Relative Rank (1 = best)*		*Applications in Power Reactors*
	Slowing-down power	*Moderating ratio*	
Liquid			
Light water (H_2O)	1	5	See **pressurized and boiling water reactors**
Terphenyls	3	6	See **organic cooled reactors**
Heavy water (D_2O)	4	1	See **heavy water-moderated power reactors**
Solid			
Beryllium	5	4	
Beryllia (BeO)	6	2	See **Maritime Gas-Cooled Reactor Project**
Graphite	7	3	See **sodium-graphite reactors; gas-cooled reactors; molten salt reactors**
Zirconium hydride	2	7	See **SNAP Program**

TABLE 4. NOTES ON CONTROL ROD MATERIALS

Element	*Ranked by Neutron-Absorbing Capacity (1 = best)*		*Notes*
	per gram	*per cm³*	
Commonly used			
Boron	2	3	Used as boron steel (~$3.50/lb); boron carbide; boral; also as burnable poison. Boron sometimes enriched in boron-10 isotope for improved neutron absorption.
Hafnium	3	2	Hafnium metal costs ~$15–30/lb subject to availability as a by-product from the production of reactor-grade zirconium.
Cadmium	5	5	Cadmium metal costs ~$1.40/lb. Also used as silver-cadmium-indium alloy (~$13/lb).
Potentially useful [1]			
Europium	1	1	Europium oxide costs ~$600/lb.
Gadolinium	4	4	Gadolinum oxide costs ~$50/lb.

[1] Other rare earths of potential interest include dysprosium and erbium.

ical strength; (2) low thermal neutron-absorption cross section;* (3) chemical compatibility with the reactor coolant; (4) ease of fabrication; (5) good thermal and radiation stability; (6) low activation cross section; (7) good thermal conductivity; and (8) reasonable cost. Notes on the elements and materials of principal interest are given in Table 5.

* This is not an important factor in the selection of materials for use in intermediate or fast reactor systems.

REACTOR SAFEGUARDS, AEC ADVISORY COMMITTEE ON. See **Advisory Committee on Reactor Safeguards.**

TABLE 5. NOTES ON STRUCTURAL MATERIALS

Element or Material	*Ranked by Thermal Neutron-Absorption Cross Section*	*Ranked by Cost*	*Notes*
Beryllium	1	11	Unalloyed beryllium has poor mechanical properties and is incompatible with water. Beryllia (BeO) is a promising material for use in high-temperature gas-cooled power reactors.
Magnesium	2	3	Unalloyed magnesium has a low melting point and is not resistant to water corrosion. Magnox (magnesium containing 1% beryllium) is used as a fuel cladding material in low-temperature gas-cooled power reactors.
Zirconium	3	8	Alloys (zircaloy series) containing small amounts of tin, nickel and chromium have good mechanical strength and resistance to water corrosion at temperatures approaching 700°F, and are used in many water cooled power reactors.
Aluminum	4	2	Unalloyed aluminum has excellent corrosion resistance to water but its mechanical strength limits its use to low-temperature reactors—e.g., plutonium production reactors and research reactors. Alloys have been developed for use in water cooled process heat reactors at temperatures up to ~600°F. Aluminum cermets (SAP and APM alloys) are promising for use as fuel cladding in organic cooled power reactors at temperatures up to ~800°F.
Columbium[1]	5	10	Good mechanical properties but not resistant to water corrosion. Principally of interest as an alloying agent.
Molybdenum	6	7	Good mechanical properties for high-temperature applications but highly susceptible to oxidation; hence principally of interest as an alloying agent.
Carbon steel }	7	1	Corrosion properties limit use to organic cooled or low-temperature gas-cooled power reactors.
Stainless steel }		4	Excellent mechanical properties and good corrosion resistance to water at temperatures up to ~700°F. Commonly used in power reactors cooled with water or liquid sodium.
Nickel	8	5	Relatively high thermal neutron absorption cross sections preclude the use of these materials in thermal reactor systems except as minor alloying agents. This limitation does not apply to fast reactor systems.
Titanium	9	6	
Tantalum	10	9	

[1] Also known as niobium.

REACTOR SITE CRITERIA. See **nuclear power economics.**

REACTOR TYPES. See **reactor (nuclear); nuclear power development, U.S.; research and training reactors.**

REACTOR VESSEL

A **pressure vessel,** tank or other enclosure housing the core of a nuclear reactor.

REDOX PROCESS

A **solvent extraction** process used in reprocessing irradiated aluminum-clad fuel elements fabricated of normal or slightly enriched uranium. The organic solvent employed is methyl isobutyl ketone, known as "hexone." The **salting agent** is aluminum nitrate. The process recovers uranium and plutonium in the form of uranyl and plutonium nitrate solutions essentially free of fission product contamination. The intensely radioactive fission products leave the system in aqueous waste streams, which are neutralized and concentrated by evaporation and piped to large waste tanks located underground for safe storage. The Redox process was developed at Argonne National Laboratory shortly after the war and is used in a large, remotely operated and maintained reprocessing plant at the Hanford Works (see **fuel reprocessing).** The process takes its name from "*red*uction-*ox*idation," reflecting the use of valence changes in different stages of the solvent extraction operation.

REFINING. See **uranium refining and conversion.**

REFLECTOR

In a nuclear reactor, a layer of material placed around the **core** to reflect escaping neutrons and thereby reduce neutron **leakage.** Materials used for this purpose must have a low **cross section** for neutron **capture,** and a high **scattering** cross section. These properties are also shared by a good **moderator;** hence frequently the reflector is a physical extension of the moderator.

A well-designed reflector returns to the core a large percentage (sometimes as high as 90%) of the escaping neutrons, thereby permitting the reactor to operate with a smaller fuel inventory than would otherwise be required and also tending to reduce nonuniformities in **neutron density.**

REGULATING ROD

In the operation of a nuclear reactor, a type of **control rod** used for making fine adjustments in the **reactivity** of the system. Regulating rods are limited in reactivity to an amount smaller than that necessary to take the reactor from the critical to prompt-critical condition. (See **reactor control)**

REGULATIONS, AEC. See **Atomic Energy Commission—Rules and Regulations.**

RELATIVE BIOLOGICAL EFFECTIVENESS. See **radiation dose.**

RELATIVE DAMAGE FACTOR. See **radiation dose.**

RELATIVISTIC ELECTRONS

Electrons having energies in the multimillion electron-volt range. They are called relativistic electrons because in this energy range they travel at high enough speeds for the gain in mass under relativity theory to be significant. This theory states that the mass of an electron depends upon its velocity as follows:

$$m = \frac{m_0}{\sqrt{1 - \frac{v^2}{c^2}}}$$

where m_0 is the rest mass of the electron, v is its velocity, and c is the velocity of light. (See **Astron Program** of research on controlled **fusion)**

RELATIVITY

A principle that postulates the equivalence of the description of the universe, in terms of physical laws, by various observers, or for

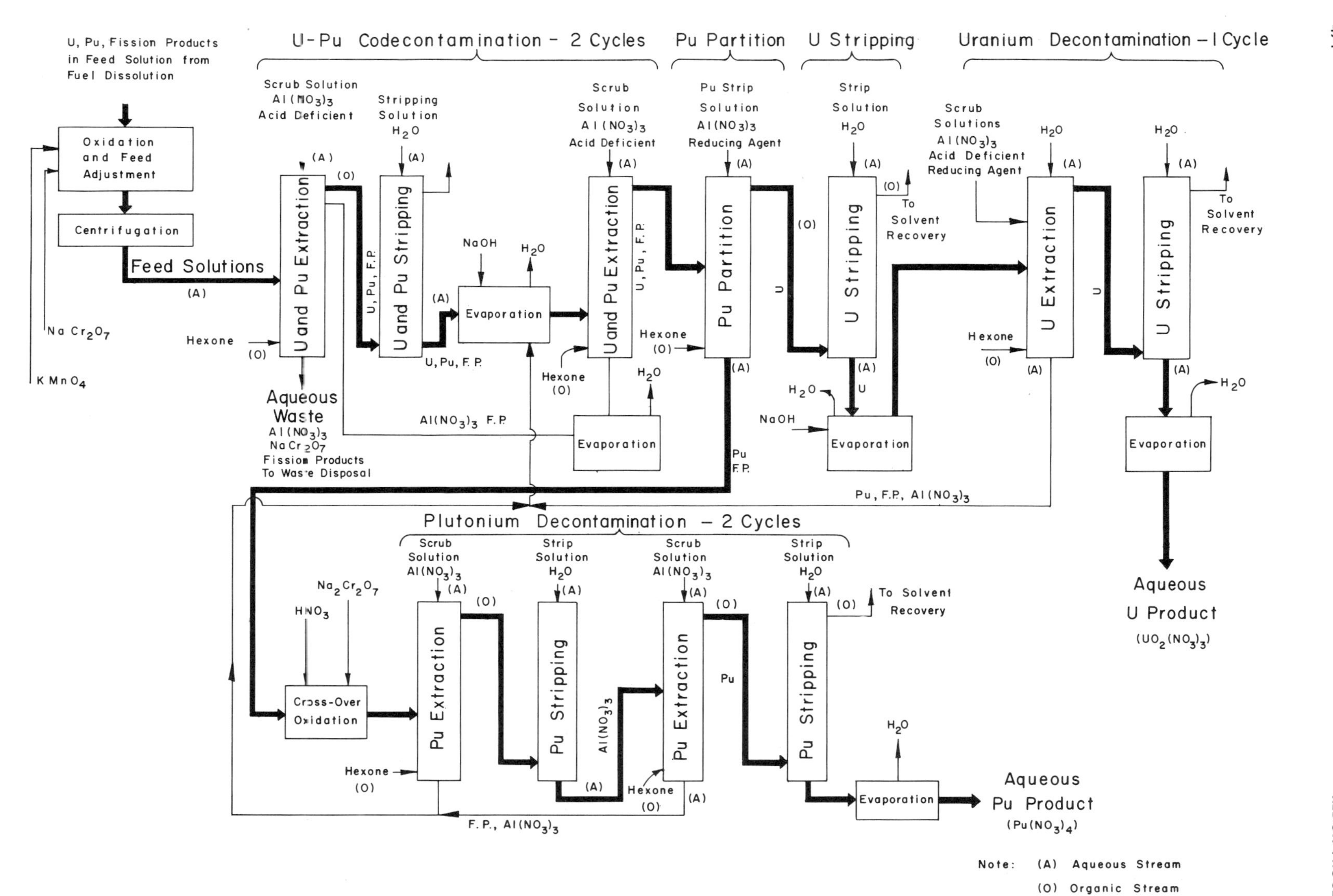

Fig. 173. Simplified flow diagram—Redox Process.

various frames of reference. Einstein's Special (or Restricted) Theory of Relativity (1905) is of great importance in atomic and nuclear physics. It is based on two postulates:

1. The laws of physical phenonema are the same when stated in terms of either of two reference systems moving at a constant velocity relative to each other.
2. The speed of light in free space is the same for all observers, and is independent of the relative velocity of the source of light and the observer.

The Special Theory of Relativity represents an improvement over classical, Newtonian physics with the differences most marked for bodies moving with speeds approaching that of light. Two very striking differences between classical and relativistic differences are:

1. The variation of mass with velocity, represented by the relation:

$$m = \frac{m_o}{\sqrt{1 - \frac{v^2}{c^2}}}$$

where m_o is the mass of a body when it is at rest ($v = 0$), m is the mass of the body when it is moving with velocity (v) and c is the velocity of light.

2. The equivalence of mass and energy expressed by the relation:

$$E = mc^2$$

(See **mass-energy equivalence**)

Apart from their profound theoretical and philosophical implications, these two results have great practical importance in nucleonics: the variation of mass with velocity plays an important role in the design and engineering of accelerators; the mass-energy equivalence is the basis for the controlled uses of nuclear energy by means of fission and fusion processes.

The General Theory of Relativity proposed by Einstein in 1915, has broader philosophical implications than the Special Theory and has an important bearing on the theory of gravitation and in cosmology. However, it has less immediate application to atomic and nuclear physics than the Special Theory.

REM

A unit of absorbed dose of **ionizing radiation** in biological matter; specifically, the absorbed dose in **rads** multiplied by a constant which takes into account the biological effectiveness of the particular radiation relative to 0.25-Mev gamma rays. The constant is known as the RBE (relative biological effectiveness) factor; values commonly used are 1 for gamma and x-rays and beta particles; 10 for alpha particles and for neutrons and protons up to 10 Mev; and 20 for heavy ions. Thus a 1-rad dose of neutrons is equivalent in its biological effects to 10 rads of gamma radiation and hence is assigned a value of 10 rems. The term rem derives from *r*oentgen *e*quivalent *m*an. For background information see **radiation dose.**

REMOTE FABRICATION OF FUEL ELEMENTS.

See **fuel element fabrication.**

REMOTE MAINTENANCE

The use of remote manipulation in performing maintenance or replacement tasks in facilities where large quantities of radioactive materials are handled. Remote maintenance is used in cases where it is not feasible for workmen to enter an equipment area once operations have started. Prime examples are the **fuel reprocessing** plants at Hanford and Savannah River. In these plants the main process equipment is located in massively shielded concrete cells with removable concrete covers. The cells are serviced by an overhead crane equipped with remotely operated manipulation devices capable of performing a variety of operations, such as repairing electrical connections, and dismantling and removing equipment. A three-dimensional periscopic viewing system permits the crane operator to see what he is doing. The operations are facilitated by a number of ingenious equipment features, such as special disconnect devices, and by an elaborate "mock-up" facility which permits the maintenance engineers to pretest equipment repair or replacement procedures under simulated conditions. The alternative to remote maintenance is a procedure involving decontamination of the trouble area and subsequent direct-contact operations. (See **direct maintenance**)

REP

An obsolete unit of absorbed dose of **ionizing radiation**; it has been superseded by the **rad.** The rep (from *r*oentgen *e*quivalent *p*hysical) derived from the **roentgen** and was defined as an absorption of 93 ergs of radiation per gram of matter. For background information see **radiation dose.**

RESEARCH AND TRAINING REACTORS

Nuclear reactors designed to supply ionizing radiation (principally neutrons) for experimental purposes and/or for use in student training programs. Examples of uses of research reactors follow:

1. Nuclear physics: Measurement of neutron **cross sections.**
2. Solid state physics: Neutron diffraction studies of crystal structure.
3. Radiation chemistry: Study of the effect of radiation on chemical reactions and properties.
4. Analytical chemistry: **Activation analysis.**
5. Biology: Study of radiation-induced mutations in plant species.
6. Medicine: **Neutron capture therapy.**
7. Reactor Development: Study of the effects of radiation on reactor materials and equipment components; radiation shielding studies; study of reactor design parameters.
8. Other: Production of radioisotopes; student training.

For information on reactors designed specifically for one or more of the purposes noted under (7), see **test reactors.**

The purposes for which a given research reactor can be considered are largely determined by its **neutron flux** and experimental capacity.

Neutron flux, i.e., the intensity of the neutron field within the reactor core or of beams emanating from the reactor, is a direct function of the power level at which a reactor operates, but also depends upon the design. The main research reactor application in which a high neutron flux is an absolute requirement is in the production of radioisotopes of high specific activity. In testing the effects of radiation on materials and equipment components for power reactors, a high flux, while not an absolute requirement, is a practical necessity. That is because radiation damage phenomena are generally a function of the integrated flux; thus, a result that takes 100 days to obtain at a neutron flux level of 1×10^{13}n/cm^{2}sec can be obtained in 10 days at a flux level of 1×10^{14}n/cm^{2}sec. Other research reactor applications do not require a high neutron flux, either because of the nature of the phenomena involved or because time is not of critical importance. Following, by way of orientation, is a rough categorization of research reactor flux levels:

Average Thermal-neutron Flux

(n/cm^{2}sec)

Low flux	Below 10^{12}
Medium flux	10^{12}-5×10^{14}
High flux	Above 5×10^{14}

The experimental capacity of a research reactor depends on the volume of irradiation space (which is largely a function of the physical size of the core) and on the experimental facilities provided. Depending on the purposes it is intended to serve, a research reactor may be equipped with any or all of the following experimental facilities:

1. One or more **thermal columns** to supply fluxes or beams of purely thermal neutrons for experiments.
2. Channels by means of which test specimens can be inserted into the reactor for irradiation. These are usually called "thimbles." When the channel extends through the entire reactor, usually passing close to the core, it is called a "through hole."
3. Pneumatic or hydraulic devices for inserting test specimens for brief exposure intervals and then dispatching them to labora-

tories in the vicinity of the reactor. These are called "rabbits."

4. Beam tubes and ports, i.e., channels and openings through which neutron beams can pass for use in experiments conducted outside the reactor shield.

5. Shield plugs to close off all channels, beam ports, etc., when not in use.

6. In-pile loops for conducting irradiation experiments under controlled conditions of temperature, pressure, and/or flow.

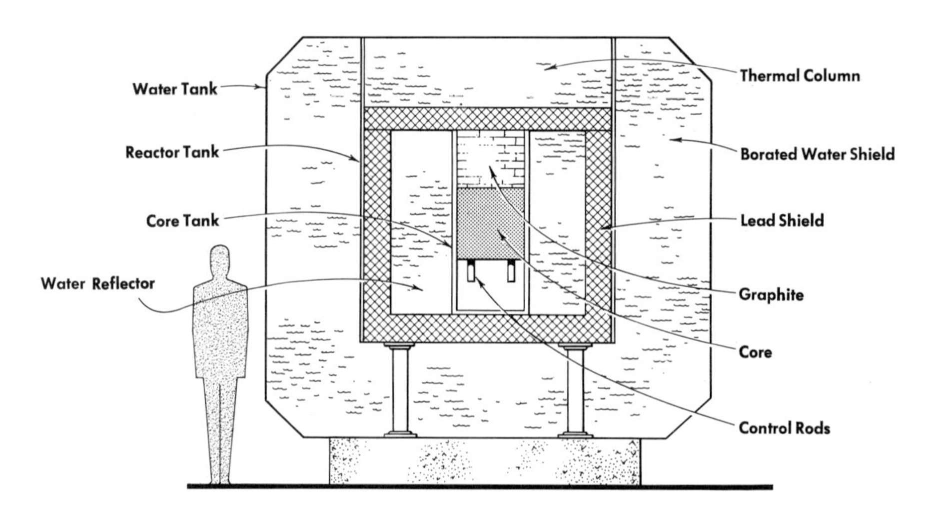

Fig. 174. Schematic diagram of solid homogeneous reactor.

Reactor Types. The principal types of research and training reactors in use in the United States can be categorized as follows:

Type	*Power Ratings* [1] *(thermal)*	*Primary Use*
Solid homogeneous		
AGN-type	negligible ($\lesssim$ watts)	Training
TRIGA-type	10–100 kilowatts	Training/research
Graphite/water	negligible—10 kilowatts	Training
Water boiler	negligible—50 kilowatts	Training/research
Pool	1000–5000 kilowatts	Research
Tank	1000–40,000 kilowatts	Research
Graphite	4000–20,000 kilowatts	Research

[1] Ranges given are representative, not all-inclusive.

These reactor types are discussed in the paragraph immediately following.

Solid Homogeneous Reactors. These are small low-power reactors developed for use in student training and/or limited research programs. Standard models are available at prices in the general range, $100,000-500,000, delivered and installed in available laboratory space.

One line of solid homogeneous reactors is manufactured by Aerojet-General Nucleonics Corporation ("AGN" series). They are fueled with a solid homogeneous mixture of enriched uranium dioxide and polyethylene, the latter material serving as moderator. Most of the AGN reactors supplied to date are compact tank-type units (see Fig. 174) designed to operate at negligible power (0.1 thermal watts). Such units provide a thermal-neutron flux of the order of $10^6 n/cm^2 sec$.

Another line of solid homogeneous reactors is manufactured by General Atomic, a division of General Dynamics Corporation ("TRIGA" series). They are fueled with a mixture of enriched uranium-zirconium hydride, the hydrogen serving as moderator. Several standardized designs of pool-type installations are available. Most of the TRIGA reactors supplied to date are designed to operate at a power level of 100 thermal kilowatts. Such units provide a thermal-neutron flux of the order of $10^{12} n/cm^2$ sec.

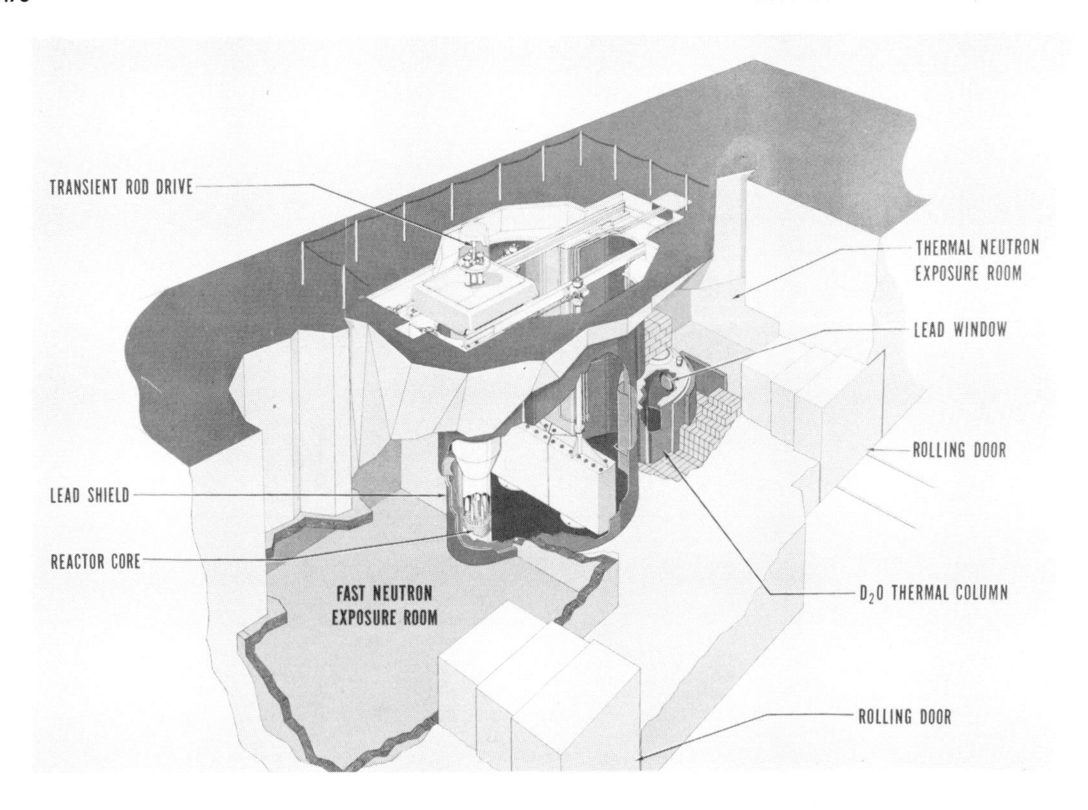

Fig. 175. Above, diagram of TRIGA Mark-F (pulsing) reactor installation at National Naval Medical Center in Bethesda, Md. Right, prototype TRIGA Mark-F reactor at General Atomic's Laboratory. (*Courtesy of General Atomic*)

Table 1 lists the solid homogeneous reactors installed in the United States or exported by U.S. manufacturers as of January, 1961.

Graphite Water Reactors. These are also small, low-power reactors for use in student training and/or limited research programs. Standard models are available at prices in the neighborhood of **$150,000-200,000**, delivered and installed in available laboratory space.

Graphite/water reactors are fueled with aluminum-clad plates containing a dispersion of enriched uranium in an aluminum matrix. They are cooled with water (H_2O), and moderated with water and graphite. Argonne National Laboratory's Argonaut Reactor (CP-11) was the first reactor of this general type

TABLE 1. SOLID HOMOGENEOUS REACTORS
(January, 1961)

Installation	*Designation*	*Location*	*Designer*	*Power Rating (thermal kilowatts)*	*Start-up* [1]
U.S. Installations:					
Aerojet-General Nucleonics Corp.	AGN-201P	San Ramon, Calif.	Aerojet-General	negl.	1957
Akron, University of	AGN-201	Akron, Ohio	Aerojet-General	negl.	1957
Argonne National Laboratory	AGN-201	Argonne, Illinois	Aerojet-General	negl.	1957
Arizona, University of	TRIGA-Mk. I	Tucson, Arizona	General Atomic	10	1958
Biomedical Radiational Research Facility (DOD)	DASA-TRIGA	Bethesda, Md.	General Atomic	100	(1961)
California, University of	AGN-201	Berkeley, Calif.	Aerojet-General	negl.	1957
Catholic University of America	AGN-201	Washington, D. C.	Aerojet-General	negl.	1957
Colorado State University	AGN-201	Fort Collins, Col.	Aerojet-General	negl.	1957
Cornell University	TRIGA-Mk. I	Ithaca, N. Y.	General Atomic	10	(1961)
Delaware, University of	AGN-201	Newark, Del.	Aerojet-General	negl.	1958
Diamond Ordnance Fuse Laboratory (USA)	TRIGA(DORF)	Washington, D. C.	General Atomic	100	(1961)
General Atomic	TRIGA-Mk. I	San Diego, Calif.	General Atomic	250	1958
General Atomic	TRIGA-Mk. F	San Diego, Calif.	General Atomic	1000 [2]	1960
Illinois, University of	TRIGA-Mk. II	Urbana-Champaign, Ill.	General Atomic	100	1960
Kansas State University	TRIGA-Mk. II	Manhattan, Kansas	General Atomic	10	(1961)
Maine, University of	AGN-201	Orono, Maine	Aerojet-General	negl.	(1961)
National Naval Medical Center (USN)	AGN-201	Bethesda, Md.	Aerojet-General	negl.	1957
Oklahoma State University	AGN-211	Norman, Okla.	Aerojet-General	negl.	1958
Oklahoma, University of	AGN-201	Stillwater, Okla.	Aerojet-General	negl.	1957
Omaha Veterans Administration Hospital	TRIGA-Mk. I	Omaha, Neb.	General Atomic	10	1959
Oregon State College	AGN-201	Corvallis, Ore.	Aerojet-General	negl.	1958
Texas Agricultural and Mechanical College	AGN-201	College Station, Tex.	Aerojet-General	negl.	1957
U.S. Naval Post Graduate School (USN)	AGN-201	Monterey, Calif.	Aerojet-General	negl.	1956
Utah, University of	AGN-201	Salt Lake City, Utah.	Aerojet-General	negl.	1957
West Virginia University	AGN-211	Morgantown, W. Va.	Aerojet-General	negl.	1959
William Marsh Rice University	AGN-211	Houston, Texas	Aerojet-General	negl.	1959
U.S. Exports:					
Austria (Vienna Polytechnic Institute)	TRIGA-Mk. II	Vienna	General Atomic	100	(1961)
Brazil (University of Minas Gerais)	TRIGA-Mk. I	Minas Gerais	General Atomic	30	1960
Congo, Republic of (University of Louvanium)	TRIGA-Mk. I	Leopoldville	General Atomic	10	1959
Finland (Institute of Technology)	TRIGA-Mk. II	Helsinki	General Atomic	100	(1961)
Germany, West (University of Mainz)	TRIGA-Mk. II	Mainz	General Atomic	100	(1961)
Indonesia (Institute of Technology)	TRIGA-Mk. II	Bandung	General Atomic	100	(1961)
Italy (CNEN)	TRIGA-Mk. II	Rome	General Atomic	100	1960
Italy (University of Palermo)	AGN-201	Palermo	Aerojet-General	negl.	1960
Japan (Rikkyo University)	TRIGA-Mk. II	Yokosuka City	General Atomic	100	(1961)
Japan (Musashi University)	TRIGA-Mk. II	Kawasaki City	General Atomic	100	(1961)
Korea (Atomic Energy Research Institute)	TRIGA-Mk. II	Seoul	General Atomic	100	(1961)
Switzerland (University of Geneva)	AGN-201	Geneva	Aerojet-General	negl.	1958
Switzerland (University of Basel)	AGN-211	Basel	Aerojet-General	negl.	1958
Vietnam (Institute of Nuclear Research)	TRIGA-Mk. II	Dalat	General Atomic	100	(1961)
Yugoslavia (Josef Stefan Nuclear Institute)	TRIGA-Mk. II	Ljubljama	General Atomic	100	(1962)

[1] Parentheses denote scheduled or planned start-up.
[2] This is a pulsing reactor so that the indicated power level represents a transient and not a steady-state condition.

to be developed. Graphite/water reactors are supplied commercially by several companies. They include the Atomic Energy Division of American Radiator and Standard Sanitary Corporation ("University Training Reactor" series) and AMF Atomics, Inc. ("Educator" series). Most of the commercial models supplied to date have a power rating of 10 thermal kilowatts and provide a thermal-neutron flux of the order of 10^{11}n/cm^2 sec.

Table 2 lists the graphite/water reactors installed in the United States or exported by U.S. manufacturers as of January, 1961.

*Water Boiler Reactors.** These are also small, low-power reactors for use in student training and/or limited research programs. Standard models are available at prices in the general range, $100,000-250,000, delivered and installed in available laboratory space.

The core of a water boiler consists of an aqueous fuel solution of enriched uranyl sulfate or nitrate contained in a stainless steel sphere about 1 foot in diameter (see Fig. 176). Cooling water flows through a coil in the sphere, which may also be penetrated by an experimental channel (known as the "glory hole"). The core is surrounded by a graphite reflector, an extension of which serves as a thermal column. Although the fuel solution does not get hot enough to boil, hydrogen and oxygen formed by the radiolytic decomposition of the water cause a boiling-like action as they bubble through the solution. Provision must be made for recombining these gases.

Water boilers have been designed to operate at power levels ranging from watts to 50 thermal kilowatts. At the latter level they provide a thermal-neutron flux of the order of 10^{12}n/cm^2 sec. This represents a high flux-to-power ratio, which is attributable to the homogeneous distribution of fuel and moderator and to the fact that the core contains a minimal amount of neutron-absorbing structural material.

The first water boiler was built at Los Alamos Scientific Laboratory (see **Los Alamos Water Boilers**). Water boilers are supplied commercially by Atomics International, a division of North American Aviation, Inc. ("Laboratory Reactor" series).

* Not to be confused with **boiling water reactors.** Water boilers are also known as "solution reactors."

TABLE 2. GRAPHITE/WATER REACTORS
(January, 1961)

Installation	*Designation*	*Location*	*Designer*	*Power Rating (thermal kilowatts)*	*Start-up* [1]
U.S. Installations:					
American Radiator & Standard Sanitary Corporation	UTR Mod. 2	Mountain View, Calif.	ARSS	negl.	1960
Argonne National Laboratory (Argonaut), AEC	CP-11	Argonne, Ill.	Argonne Nat'l Lab.	10	1957
Argonne National Laboratory (Juggernaut), AEC	—	Argonne, Ill.	Argonne Nat'l Lab.	250	(1961)
Florida, University of	UFTR	Gainesville, Fla.	General Nuclear Eng. Corp.	10	1959
Iowa State University	UTR-10	Ames, Iowa	ARSS	10	1959
North Carolina State College	—	Raleigh, N. C.	Cook	10	1960
University of California at Los Angeles	Educator	Los Angeles, Calif.	AMF Atomics	10	1960
Virginia Polytechnic Institute	UTR-10	Blacksburg, Va.	ARSS	10	1959
Washington, University of	Educator	Seattle, Wash.	AMF Atomics	10	1960
U.S. Exports:					
Australia (AAEC Research Establishment)	UTR-10	Lucas Heights, N.S.W.	ARSS	negl.	(1961)
Japan (Kinki University)	UTR-10	Osaka	ARSS	negl.	(1961)
Japan (Tokai University)	UTR-10		ARSS	negl.	Planned

[1] Parentheses denote scheduled or planned start-up.

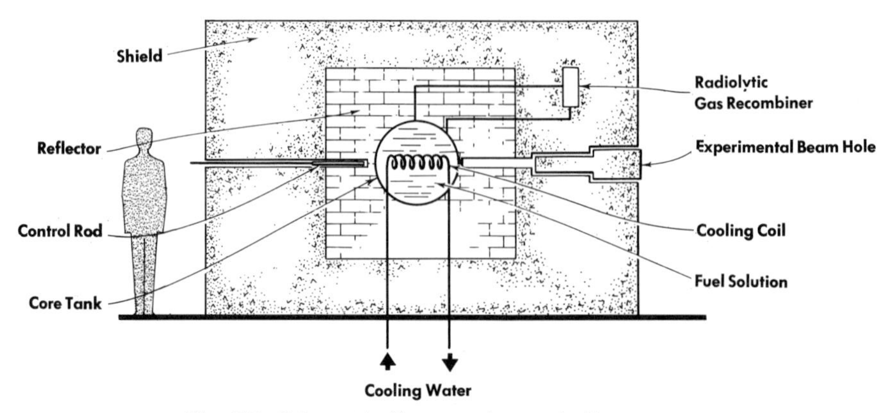

Fig. 176. Schematic diagram of water boiler reactor.

Table 3 lists the water boilers installed in the United States or exported by U.S. manufacturers as of January, 1961.

Pool Reactors. This term normally connotes heterogeneous reactor systems that operate with an open grid of fuel elements suspended in a deep pool of water.* Such reactors are widely used for general experimentation and are supplied by a number of U.S. manufacturers. The cost of a pool reactor installation, including building and supporting experimental facilities, is usually in the range, **$1-3** million.

The core of a pool reactor consists of an open assembly of aluminum-clad fuel plates (usually fabricated of an enriched uranium-aluminum alloy) suspended in a deep (~ 20 feet) pool of water (see Fig. 177). The water serves as coolant, moderator, primary or secondary reflector, and radiation shield. (In

* In some research reactor designs, an enclosed grid of fuel elements is operated in a pool. These are higher-power units and are covered herein under "tank reactors."

TABLE 3. WATER BOILER REACTORS

(January, 1961)

Installation	*Designation*	*Location*	*Designer*	*Power Rating (thermal kilowatts)*	*Start-up* [1]
U.S. Installations:					
Armour Research Foundation (Armour Research Reactor)	ARR	Chicago, Illinois	Atomics International	50	1956
E. O. Lawrence Radiation Laboratory (Livermore Water Boiler), AEC	LIWB	Livermore, Calif.	Atomics International	0.5	1953
Atomics International (NAA Water Boiler Neutron Source), AEC	WBNS	Santa Susana, Calif.	Atomics International	2	1952
Atomics International	L-77	Canoga Park, Calif.	Atomics International	negl.	1958
Los Alamos Scientific Laboratory, AEC	SUPO	Los Alamos, N. Mex.	Los Alamos Sc. Lab.	25	1950
North Carolina State College	NCSR-2	Raleigh, N. C.	University staff	0.5	1957
Puerto Rico Nuclear Center, AEC	L-77	Mayaguez, P. R.	Atomics International	negl.	1959
Walter Reed Army Institute of Research	L-54	Washington, D. C.	Atomics International	50	(1961)
Wyoming, University of	L-77	Laramie, Wyo.	Atomics International	negl.	1959
U.S. Exports:					
Denmark (Risø Research Establishment)	L-55	Risø	Atomics International	2	1957
Germany, West (Universities of Frankfurt and Darmstadt)	L-54	Frankfurt	Atomics International	50	1958
Germany, West (Interatom, Inc.)	L-77	Duisberg	Atomics International	negl.	1960
Italy (University of Milan)	L-54	Milan	Atomics International	50	1959
Japan (Japan Atomic Energy Research Institute)	L-54	Mito	Atomics International	50	1957
West Berlin, City of (Institute for Nuclear Research)	L-54	Berlin	Atomics International	50	1958

[1] Parentheses denote scheduled start-up.

some installations there is a primary reflector of beryllium.) The use of water as a radiation shield facilitates the arrangement and manipulation of experimental apparatus and affords considerable experimental flexibility, since the position of the core can readily be shifted. Also, it permits direct visual observation of the reactor.

Pool reactors designed to operate at relatively low power levels are cooled by natural convection; at power levels of 1000 kilowatts and above, forced circulation of the water is necessary. Pool reactors of the type described have been operated at power levels up to 5000 thermal kilowatts.

At a power level of 100 thermal kilowatts, pool reactors provide a thermal-neutron flux of the order of 10^{12}n/cm^2 sec; at 1000 kilowatts, the flux provided is of the order of 10^{13}n/cm^2 sec.

Table 4 lists the pool reactors installed in the United States or exported by U.S. manufacturers as of January, 1961. Also see **test reactors.**

Tank Reactors. Reference here is to heterogeneous reactor systems that operate with a grid of fuel elements enclosed in a reactor tank. The tank is usually installed in a concrete radiation shield but may be installed in a pool. The cost of a tank reactor installation, including building and supporting experimental facilities, is usually in the range, $1-5 million. (High-power installations designed for large-scale materials testing cost much more. See **test reactors.**) Tank reactors are supplied, on a custom-design basis, by several U.S. manufacturers.

The core of a tank reactor consists of an assembly of aluminum-clad fuel plates (usually fabricated of an enriched uranium-aluminum alloy) held in a fixed position in a closed reactor tank (see Fig. 178). Beryllium is often used as the primary reflector. The reactor is cooled and moderated with water. Heavy water (D_2O) is used in some installations; light water (H_2O) is used in others. The use of heavy water permits a somewhat lower fuel inventory, and provides a somewhat higher and more uniform thermal-neutron flux.

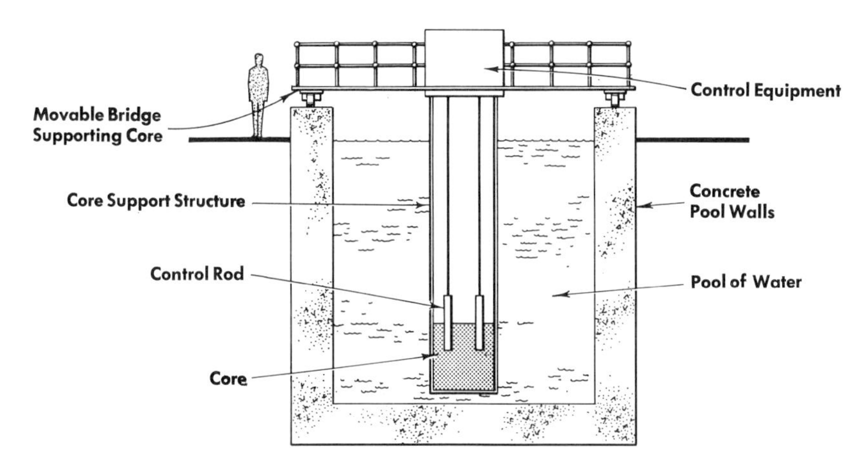

Fig. 177. Schematic diagram of pool reactor.

The power ratings of most research-type tank reactors are in the range, 1,000-40,000 thermal kilowatts. The thermal-neutron fluxes range correspondingly from on the order of 10^{13} to 10^{14} or even 10^{15}n/cm^2 sec.

Table 5 lists the tank reactors installed in the United States or exported by U.S. manufacturers as of January, 1961. Also see **test reactors.**

Graphite Reactors. There are two principal graphite-moderated, air-cooled research reactors in the United States, namely, the Oak Ridge Graphite Reactor (X-10) and the Brookhaven Graphite Research Reactor (BGRR) (see Table 6). X-10 has been in

Table 4. Pool Reactors
(January, 1961)

Installation	Designation	Location	Designer	Power Rating (thermal kilowatts)	Start-up [1]
U.S. Intallations:					
Babcock & Wilcox Co. (B. & W. Lynchburg Pool Reactor)	LPR	Lynchburg, Va.	Babcock & Wilcox	10	1958
Battelle Memorial Institute (Battelle Research Reactor)	BRR	West Jefferson, Ohio	AMF Atomics	2000	1956
Buffalo, University of	—	Buffalo, N.Y.	AMF Atomics	1000	(1961)
Industrial Reactor Laboratories, Inc.[3]	ILR	Plainsboro, N.J.	AMF Atomics	5000	1958
Kansas, University of	—	Lawrence, Kansas	Bendix Aviation	10	(1961)
Leland Stanford University	—	Palo Alto, Calif.	General Electric	10	1959
Lockheed Aircraft Corp.	—	(on loan for exhibit)	Lockheed Aircraft	negl.	1960
Maryland, University of	—	College Park, Md.	Allis-Chalmers	10	1960
Michigan, University of (Ford Nuclear Reactor)	FNR	Ann Arbor, Mich.	Babcock & Wilcox	1000	1957
Missouri, University of	—	Rolla, Mo.	Curtiss-Wright	10	(1961)
Naval Research Laboratory (Naval Research Reactor), USN	NRR	Washington, D.C.	NRL	100	1956
Ohio State University	—	Columbus, Ohio	Lockheed Aircraft	10	(1961)
Pennsylvania State University	—	University Park, Pa.	University staff	200	1955
Pennsylvania State University [2]	—	Quehenna, Pa.	Curtiss-Wright	4000	1958
Puerto Rico Nuclear Center (Puerto Rico Research Reactor), AEC	—	Mayaguez, P.R.	AMF Atomics	1000	1960
Rhode Island, University of	—	Saunderstown, R.I.	General Electric	1000	Planned
Texas A & M (Nuclear Science Center Reactor)	NSCR	College Station, Tex.	Convair	100	(1961)
Texas Technical College	—	Lubbock, Tex.	Convair	10	(1963)
Union Carbide Nuclear Corp.	—	Sterling Forest, N.Y.	AMF Atomics	5000	(1961)
Virginia, University of	—	Charlottesville, Va.	Babcock & Wilcox	1000	(1960)
Washington State University	—	Pullman, Wash.	General Electric	100	(1961)
Watertown Arsenal (Horace Hardy Lester Reactor for Materials Research), USA	—	Watertown, Mass.	WA	1000	(1961)
Wisconsin, University of	—	Madison, Wisc.	General Electric	10	1960
Worcester Polytechnic Institute	—	Worcester, Mass.	General Electric	negl.	1959
U.S. Exports:					
Austria (Austrian Research Reactor Center)	—	Seibersdorf	AMF Atomics	5000	1960
Brazil (University of Sao Paulo)	—	Sao Paulo	Babcock & Wilcox	5000	1957
Canada (McMaster University)	—	Hamilton, Ontario	AMF Atomics	1000	1959
China, Republic of (National Tsing-Hua University)	—	Hsinchu	General Electric	1000	(1961)
Germany, West (Technical University of Munich)	—	Munich	AMF Atomics	1000	1957
Germany, West (GKSS)	—	Geestacht	Babcock & Wilcox	5000	1958
Greece (Democritus Nuclear Center)	—	Mt. Hymettus	AMF Atomics	1000	(1961)
Iran (University of Teheran)	—	Teheran	AMF Atomics	5000	(1961)
Israel (Israeli Nuclear Center)	—	Nebi Rubin	AMF Atomics	1000	(1961)
Italy (SORIN Nuclear Center)	—	Saluggia	AMF Atomics	1000	1959
Italy (CAMEN)	—	San Piero	Babcock & Wilcox	5000	(1961)
Netherlands (Delft Technical University)	—	Delft	AMF Atomics	100	1957
Pakistan (Pakistan AEC)	—	Taxila	AMF Atomics	1000	Planned
Philippines (Nuclear Research Center)	—	Quezon City	General Electric	1000	(1961)
Portugal (Portuguese Nuclear Research Center)	—	Lisbon	AMF Atomics	1000	1960
Spain (Nuclear Research Center of Moncloa	—	Moncloa	General Electric	3000	1958
Switzerland (Institute for Reactor Research)	—	Wuerlingen	Oak Ridge Natl'l Lab.	1000	1955
Thailand (Chulalongkorn University)	—	Bangkok	Curtiss-Wright	1000	(1961)
Turkey (Nuclear Research Center)	—	Istanbul	AMF Atomics	1000	(1961)
Venezuela (IVIC)	—	Caracas	General Electric	3000	1960

[1] Parentheses denote scheduled or planned start-up.
[2] Built by Curtiss-Wright Corporation for its own use and later donated to the University.
[3] Operated by Columbia University.
Note: See test reactors for additional listings.

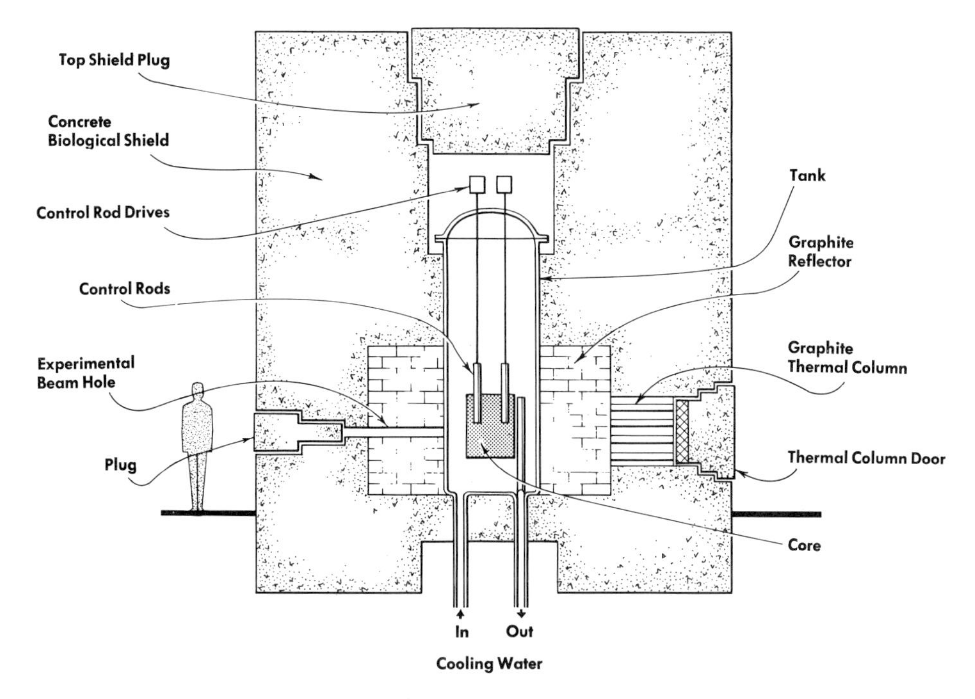

Fig. 178. Schematic diagram of tank reactor.

TABLE 5. TANK REACTORS
(January, 1961)

Installation	*Designation*	*Location*	*Designer*	*Type*	*Power Rating (thermal kilowatts)*	*Start-up* [1]
U.S. Installations:						
Ames Laboratory (Ames Laboratory Research Reactor), AEC	ALRR	Ames, Iowa	AMF Atoms	D_2O	5,000	(1962)
Argonne National Laboratory (Argonne Research Reactor), AEC	CP-5	Argonne, Ill.	ANL	D_2O	5,000	1954
Brookhaven National Laboratory (Neutron Source Reactor), AEC	—	Upton, N.Y.	BNL	H_2O	100	1958
Brookhaven National Laboratory (Medical Research Reactor), AEC	MRR	Upton, N.Y.	Daystrom, Inc.	H_2O	3,000	1959
Brookhaven National Laboratory (High Flux Beam Research Reactor), AEC	HFBR	Upton, N.Y.	BNL	D_2O	40,000	(1962)
E. O. Lawrence Radiation Laboratory (Livermore Pool Type Reactor), AEC	LPTR	Livermore, Calif.	Foster-Wheeler	H_2O	2,000	1957
Georgia Institute of Technology	GTRR	Atlanta, Ga.	General Nucl. Eng. Corp	D_2O	1,000	(1962)
Los Alamos Scientific Laboratory (Omega West Reactor), AEC	OWR	Los Alamos, N.M.	LASL	H_2O	5,000	1956
Massachusetts Institute of Technology	MITR	Cambridge, Mass.	Allis-Chalmers (ACF)	D_2O	2,000	1958
Oak Ridge National Laboratory (Low Intensity Test Reactor), AEC	LITR	Oak Ridge, Tenn.	ORNL	H_2O	3,000	1950
Oak Ridge National Laboratory (Oak Ridge Research Reactor)	ORR	Oak Ridge, Tenn.	ORNL	H_2O	20,000	1958
United Nuclear Corp. (Pawling Research Reactor)	PRP	Pawling, N.Y.	United Nuclear (NDA)	H_2O	negl.	1958
U.S. Exports:						
Denmark (Risø Research Establishment)	—	Risø	Foster-Wheeler	H_2O	5,000	1959
Italy (Center for Nuclear Studies)	—	Ispra	Allis-Chalmers (ACF)	D_2O	5,000	1959
South Africa (National Nuclear Research Center)	—		Allis-Chalmers	H_2O	6,600	Planned

[1] Parentheses denote scheduled or planned start-up
Note: See test reactors for additional listings.

TABLE 6. OTHER U.S. RESEARCH REACTORS
(January, 1961)

Installation	*Desig-nation*	*Location*	*Designer*	*Type*	*Power Rating (thermal kilo-watts)*	*Start-up* [1]
Aberdeen Proving Ground (Ordnance Pulsed Experimental Research Assembly), USA	OPERA	Aberdeen Proving Ground, Md.	Aerojet-General	Prompt burst	100	(1962)
Brookhaven National Laboratory (Brookhaven Graphite Research Reactor)	BGRR	Upton, N.Y.	BNL—H. K. Ferguson	Graphite	20,000	1950
General Electric Vallecitos Laboratory (G.E. Nuclear Test Reactor)	NTR	Pleasanton, Calif.	General Electric	TTR-Type	30	1957
Knolls Atomic Power Laboratory (Thermal Test Reactor)	TTR-1	Schenectady, N.Y.	KAPL	TTR-Type	10	1951
Oak Ridge National Laboratory (Oak Ridge Graphite Reactor)	X-10	Oak Ridge, Tenn.	(Manhattan Project)	Graphite	3,800	1943
Oak Ridge National Laboratory (High Flux Isotope Reactor)	HFIR	Oak Ridge, Tenn.	ORNL	Flux trap	100,000	(1963)
Picatinny Arsenal (USA)	—	Dover, N.J.		Prompt burst	20,000	Planned
White Sands Missile Range Nuclear Effects Facility (USA)	WSMR	White Sands, N.M.	Hughes	Prompt burst		(1963)

[1] Parentheses denote scheduled start-up.

operation since 1943; BGRR, since 1950.

As is indicated by Fig. 179, the core of these reactors consists of a large graphite structure (about 25 feet on a side) penetrated by hundreds of horizontal fuel channels. X-10 is fueled with aluminum-clad slugs of natural uranium metal, operates at a power level of 3800 thermal kilowatts, and provides a thermal-neutron flux of the order of 10^{12}n/cm^2 sec. BGRR has been converted from natural to enriched uranium fuel, operates at a power level of 20,000 thermal kilowatts, and provides a thermal-neutron flux of the order of 10^{13}n/cm^2 sec.

Because of their physical size, these reactors have greater experimental capacity than any

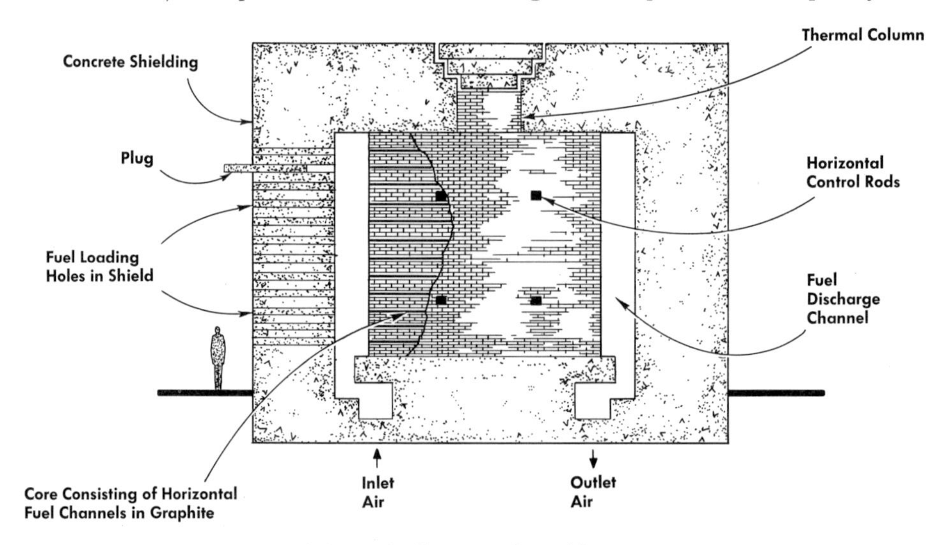

Fig. 179. Schematic diagram of graphite reactor.

of the research reactor types described above. An offsetting consideration is the fact that their flux-to-power ratio is low.

Operating Costs. The cost of operating a research reactor is partly determined by factors relating to the design of the particular installation and the power level at which it is operated, but it also depends on many "indirect" factors. These include the salaries of the operating staff, the cost of supporting services (such as health physics and radioactive waste disposal), and various overhead costs (e.g., insurance). It is difficult to generalize on operating costs since the latter factors depend to some degree on the circumstances under which the reactor is operated. In very rough terms, an annual operating cost (including fixed charges) of several hundred thousand dollars per year is the right order of magnitude for a 1000-2000 kilowatt installation; very low-power units (a few watts) cost perhaps one-tenth as much to operate. The cost of operating a research reactor can be thought of in terms of supplying neutrons and gamma rays for research. The cost of the research *per se* is an additional consideration. It has been estimated that the cost of supplying the radiation usually accounts for between 10 and 25% of the total budget of a reactor-based research program. Thus, given an operating cost of $250,000 per year, an annual research budget in the range of $1-3 million may be required for efficient use of the installation.

RESIDUAL RADIATION

With reference to nuclear weapons, the nuclear radiation emitted by the radioactive debris produced by the detonation; principally fission-product and induced radioactivity. (See **weapons phenomenology**)

RESIN-IN-PULP PROCESS (RIP)

A modified ion-exchange technique used in **uranium milling** for the recovery of uranium from unclarified acid **leach liquors** ("pulp"), eliminating the leach-liquor clarification step required in conventional ion-exchange processing. In the resin-in-pulp process, perforated stainless steel baskets containing anion-resin beads are rocked mechanically in leach-pulp tanks. A typical installation comprises multiple cascades of tanks, each consisting of a

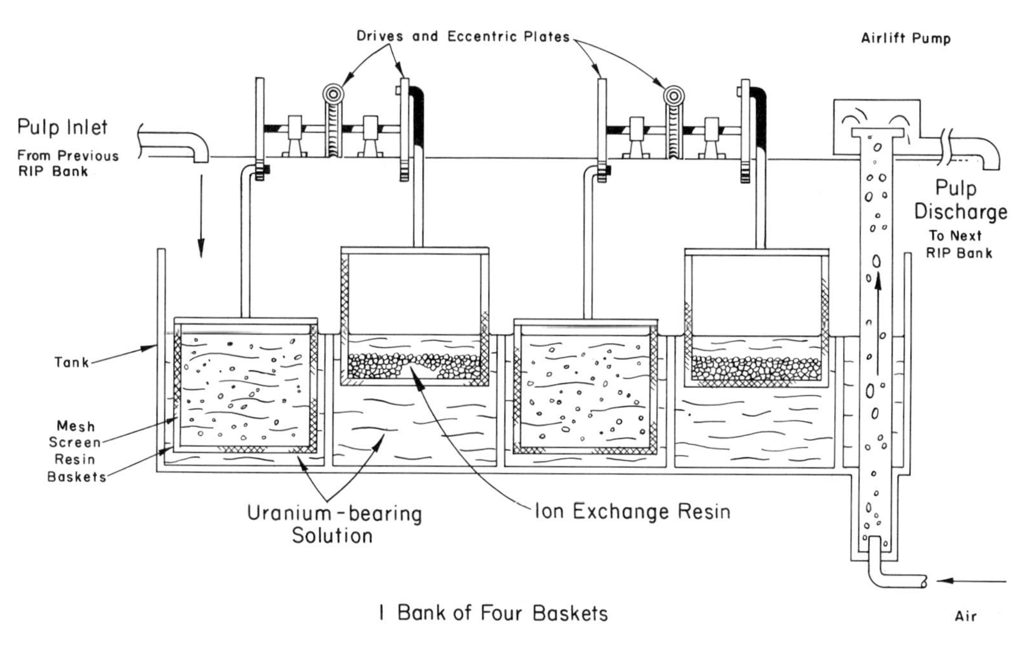

Fig. 180. Simplified diagram—basket arrangement for resin-in-pulp process.

number of units connected in series. The individual cascades are operated in cyclic fashion. During the "loading" (i.e., adsorption) cycle, desanded pulp is pumped through the cascade, emerging as a waste stream. The "unloading" cycle then follows, during which uranium is stripped from the saturated resins by elution with an ammonium nitrate stream. The resins are occasionally washed with a mild caustic solution to remove accumulated impurities.

As in the conventional **column ion-exchange process,** uranium is recovered from the elutriant stream by precipitation with ammonia or sodium hydroxide, yielding "yellow cake," containing mainly ammonium diuranate $[(NH_4)_2U_2O_7]$ or sodium diuranate $Na_2U_2O_7$. The final steps are filtration and drying of the "yellow cake." Some of the newer uranium mills employing ion exchange for product recovery use the resin-in-pulp process.

RESONANCE

A term referring to several different phenomena in physics. In reactor physics, it is that phenomenon which gives rise to very high reaction probabilities for particles incident upon a nucleus at very discrete particle energies.

RESONANCE ABSORPTION

A high rate of absorption of neutrons by materials in a nuclear reactor due to resonance effects at particular neutron energies. Resonance absorption is an important consideration in the design of **thermal reactors** fueled with normal or slightly enriched uranium, due to the fact that uranium-238 has a number of resonances for neutron absorption at neutron energies above thermal values. While such absorption is desirable in promoting the conversion of fertile to fissionable material (see **conversion ratio),** if too many neutrons are captured before they are slowed down to the energy level at which they cause fission of uranium-235 the fission chain reaction cannot be sustained. This would happen, for example, if one attempted to operate a reactor containing a homogeneous mixture of normal uranium fuel and graphite moderator. The effect of resonance absorption can be reduced by lumping the fuel in a heterogeneous fuel-moderator matrix so that the neutrons tend to be slowed to thermal energy values by the time they have traversed the moderator medium and enter the fuel medium. This explains why graphite-moderated reactors fueled with normal uranium (e.g., the Hanford plutonium production reactors) are designed as heterogeneous systems.

RESONANCE ESCAPE PROBABILITY

In reactor theory, a measure of the probability that a neutron undergoing moderation will escape capture as, in slowing down, it passes through critical energy states. (See **resonance absorption)**

RESONANT TRANSFORMER

A type of electron accelerator (see **particle accelerators)** supplied commercially for use in research and for industrial radiation applications. A resonant transformer is essentially an adaptation of a conventional x-ray machine. Electrons given off at the cathode of a continuously evacuated multi-stage tube are accelerated by an electrical potential generated by a high-voltage transformer. The name, resonant transformer, derives from the fact that the secondary circuit of the transformer (which contains the accelerator tube) is tuned to resonance, eliminating the need for an iron magnet core.

Resonant transformers are manufactured by the General Electric Company. The output characteristics are: electron energy, 1-3.5 Mev; beam power, 0.5- ~ 26 kilowatts.

RESTRICTED DATA

As defined by law, all data covering (1) the design, manufacture, or utilization of nuclear weapons, (2) the production of **special nuclear material,** or (3) the use of special nuclear material in the production of energy, exclusive of information declassified or removed from the Restricted Data category by the Atomic Energy Commission pursuant to Section 142 of the Atomic Energy Act of 1954. (See **classification—declassification**)

RETINAL BURNS

One of the biological effects of nuclear weapons. Burns on the retina of the eye are caused by concentration of direct thermal radiation through the focusing action of the lens. A burn may be produced on the retina even though the thermal intensity is not enough to cause a skin burn. Varying degrees of damage may result, ranging from temporary loss of sharp vision, to almost total blindness.

A condition known as "flash blindness" may occur upon momentary exposure to the brilliant light from the **fireball,** but this condition is only temporary and vision is not damaged.

RICHLAND, WASHINGTON

A residential center for personnel employed at the Hanford Operations Office of the Atomic Energy Commission and its contractors at the nearby atomic energy production facilities (Hanford Works). Richland is located on the Columbia River in southeastern Washington near Pasco. The 1960 Census listed the population of Richland as 23,521.

Richland was established as a government community in conjunction with the wartime **Manhattan Project.** In 1955 legislation was enacted (Public Law 84-221) authorizing the sale of government-owned houses, apartments, commercial properties and land at Richland and at **Oak Ridge, Tennessee.** By late 1960, all houses and most commercial properties listed for sale at Richland had been sold with proceeds totaling $33.7 million.

ROCKET PROPULSION (nuclear)

A rocket engine may be defined as any propulsion system that develops thrust by the high-velocity ejection of a propellant fluid and functions independently of the atmosphere in which it operates, i.e., is self-contained. Two principal types of rocket employing nuclear fuel as the energy source are currently being developed for space applications:

1. Nuclear heat-exchanger rockets in which a nuclear reactor is used to heat a propellant gas in an otherwise conventional direct-cycle rocket engine. (See **Rover Project)**

2. Electric rockets in which thrust is developed by ejecting a high-energy beam of charged particles. A nuclear reactor power generation system is believed to be the most practical means of supplying the electric power required to ionize and accelerate the propellant particles (see **SNAP Program).** The acceleration may be accomplished by applying voltage potentials to separated beams of ions and electrons (ion rocket) or by energizing a magnetically confined plasma of ions and electrons (plasma rocket).

It is estimated that nuclear heat-exchanger rockets can achieve a specific impulse in the range of 800 to 1000 pounds of thrust per pound of propellant ejected per second, which is roughly twice that achievable with the most advanced chemical fuels. This factor, combined with the compactness of nuclear fuel, means that the substitution of a nuclear engine for one or more chemical engines in a multiple-stage launching system can greatly extend the mission that can be accomplished with a given weight of fuel and propellant.

Electric rockets have extremely high specific impulse characteristics (of the order of ten thousand pounds of thrust per pound of matter ejected per second) but extremely low mass throughput capabilities (of the order of millipounds per second). They can thus generate only a very small absolute thrust (tens of pounds). For this reason they are of interest only for maneuvering or accelerating spacecraft that have been lifted out of the earth's gravitational field by other means. They are well suited to this application by virtue of the fact that they can operate for long periods of time with very low fuel and propellant consumption. Also, the jet velocities that can be achieved with electric rockets are very high relative to those achievable by chemical and nuclear heat-exchanger rockets (of the order of 200,000 mph *vs.* 10,000 and 25,000 mph, respectively).

ROCKY FLATS PLANT.

See **Atomic Energy Commission—Facilities.**

ROENTGEN

A unit of exposure dose of **ionizing radiation**; defined as the quantity of gamma or x-rays required to produce ions carrying 1 electrostatic unit of electricity in 1 cubic centimeter of dry air under standard conditions. The roentgen thus applies only to electromagnetic radiation and is not a measure of the amount of energy actually absorbed. In the older literature the amount of energy absorption (i.e., the absorbed dose) associated with 1 roentgen was given as 83.9 ergs per gram in air and 93 ergs per gram in water or soft tissue. Recent determinations indicate that these values are about 5% too low. For most present-day biological and health-physics work, the **rad,** which measures absorbed energy of any form of radiation in any medium, is frequently used. For background information, see **radiation dose.**

ROTATING PLASMA

A technique of interest in connection with the confinement and heating of fuel **plasma** in experimental controlled-**fusion** devices of the "magnetic mirror" type (see **magnetic mirror systems**). By superimposing a radial electric field on the transverse magnetic field used in magnetic mirror systems, the plasma can be caused to rotate. The resulting centrifugal force helps keep the plasma particles away from the axis of the containing tube and, since particles must approach this axis in order to leak through the "magnetic mirrors," confinement of the plasma is thereby enhanced. Also, the kinetic energy imparted to the plasma ions by rotation offers a possible means of raising plasma temperatures. Several rotating-plasma devices have been built to study these phenomena. (See **Homopolar series, Ixion,** and **Ion Magnetron**)

ROTATIONAL TRANSFORM

With reference to the magnetic field used for the confinement of fuel **plasma** in experimental controlled-**fusion** devices of the toroidal stellarator type, a deliberate twisting of the lines of magnetic force to prevent (or minimize) drift of plasma to the walls of the apparatus. Thus, instead of traveling parallel to the so-called magnetic axis, the lines of force follow a corkscrew path. (See **Stellarator Program**)

ROVER PROJECT

A program of research and development in the field of nuclear rocket propulsion. The objective is the development of nuclear reactors and related technology for open-cycle rocket engines for the propulsion of space vehicles.

Project Rover was initiated in 1957 by the U.S. Atomic Energy Commission and the U.S. Air Force. The National Aeronautics and Space Administration (NASA) subsequently replaced the Air Force as the co-sponsor and the program is currently directed by a joint group, known as the AEC-NASA Space Nuclear Propulsion Office. The division of responsibility is as follows: (1) AEC has primary responsibility for the development of reactors and their components, including units required for flight missions; and (2) NASA has primary responsibility for the development of non-nuclear components and for the integration of the nuclear and non-nuclear components into rocket engines and vehicles. NASA also has primary responsibility for flight-test plans and programs.

The planned development sequence is as follows:

1. Development of a "breadboard" engine, i.e., a system that contains all the essential components of an ultimate nuclear rocket engine but is not engineered to meet operational requirements.
2. Development of a flight-test engine.

3. Development of a flight-test vehicle.
4. Actual flight missions.

The program is currently in the breadboard engine development stage; however, contracts for the next stage were recently awarded (see below). AEC rsearch and development expenditures through mid-1961 totaled $74 million, exclusive of capital costs and commitments of approximately $29 million.

terms of the weight of fuel and propellant required for a given propulsion mission or, conversely, in terms of the mission that can be performed with a given weight of fuel and propellant. (See **rocket propulsion (nuclear)**)

As presently conceived, an open-cycle nuclear rocket system utilizing hydrogen as propellant requires the following principal functional components: (1) a liquid-hydrogen storage tank; (2) a turbopump to feed the hydrogen into the engine proper; (3) a hydrogen-cooled reactor; (4) a liquid-hydrogen cooled jet nozzle; and (5) controls. The hydrogen would be vaporized (by passing through the nozzle cooling coil) before entering the reactor, which can thus be classed as an open-cycle gas-cooled unit.

Fig. 181. Rover Project. Left, Kiwi-A3 at its test stand at the Nevada Test Site. Right, one of the Kiwi-A series of ground-based nuclear rocket propulsion experiments in progress. (*Courtesy of Los Alamos Scientific Laboratory*)

Concept. In an open-cycle nuclear rocket propulsion system, a nuclear reactor is used to heat a propellant gas, which is then ejected by expanding it through a rear nozzle, thereby developing propulsive thrust. It is estimated that the specific impulse, i.e., pounds of thrust per pound of propellant ejected per second, that can be achieved in such a system is roughly twice that achievable in a rocket using the most advanced chemical fuel. This factor, combined with the compactness of nuclear fuel, gives nuclear rocket propulsion systems inherent advantages over chemical systems in

Basic design considerations are as follows:

1. The specific impulse developed (and thus the engine efficiency) is a function of the temperature of the hydrogen exhaust jet; hence

it is desired to operate the reactor at as high a temperature as is practicable. Temperatures above 3500°F are desired. The limiting factor is the mechanical strength of reactor materials.

2. The engine must be compact and of minimum weight; hence, the reactor must be designed to operate at maximum power densities.

3. Mission requirements demand that the engine be capable of starting and stopping quickly and precisely.

The reactor outputs required for useful space missions are in the range of several to hundreds of megawatts of electrical power equivalent. For example, it is estimated that an output of 2000 thermal megawatts would be required to develop a thrust of 100,000 pounds. Fortunately, these outputs are only required for brief intervals of time and the total operating lifetime may be only a matter of minutes.

Development Program. The prime contractor for the nuclear aspects of Project Rover is Los Alamos Scientific Laboratory. Studies to determine the operational requirements for nuclear rockets, and to define the missions to which nuclear rocket power can usefully be applied, are conducted by NASA's Lewis Research Center.

As was indicated earlier, the first objective has been the development of a breadboard engine. To this end a series of ground-based experimental reactor systems—designated as the "Kiwi" series after the earth-bound Australian bird—is being built and operated at AEC's Nevada Test Site (NTS). Kiwi-A, the first of the series, was completed and successfully operated in June, 1959. Modified reactors, designated Kiwi-A Prime and Kiwi-A3, were operated in July and October of 1960, respectively. All three reactor experiments operated with gaseous hydrogen supplied from a gas storage-tank farm and used a water cooled nozzle. The tests served to check design power ratings and design temperatures and to explore performance characteristics and limitations. In each case, the experimental system was disassembled by remote manipulation for post-mortem examination of key components.

The above experiments concluded the Kiwi-A series. The Kiwi-B series, which began in December, 1961, will incorporate improved reactor systems operating with a liquid-hydrogen supply.

In mid-1961, NASA contracted with Aeroject-General Corporation to begin the development of a nuclear rocket engine, to be known as NERVA (Nuclear Engine for Rocket Vehicle Application). Under a subcontract, Westinghouse Electric Corporation has responsibility for the nuclear aspects of engine development. Relatedly, in August, 1961, the AEC and NASA jointly contracted with Vitro Engineering Company, a division of Vitro Corporation of America, for architect-engineering design of a maintenance and disassembly facility to be used in support of nuclear rocket engine test operation. This facility is to be the first component of a National Nuclear Rocket Development Station. The station is to be located in the Jackass Flats area of the Nevada Test Site. Catalytic Construction Company has been selected as the prime construction contractor.

RUMANIA

A Nuclear Energy Board has been established in Bucharest as the agency responsible for atomic energy matters.

The Nuclear Physics Institute, Bucharest, is the principal research establishment. The experimental facilities include a cyclotron and a 2000-kilowatt (thermal) pool-type research reactor, both supplied by the U.S.S.R.

Uranium deposits have been found in the western and northeastern sections, and recovery facilities are located at Petrila. The energy economy is coal-based, with extensive coal deposits in the Ploësti region. No nuclear power projects had been announced through 1960, but 500 megawatts of nuclear power capacity have been targeted for 1975.

Rumania is a member of the **International Atomic Energy Agency,** has a technical assistance agreement with the U.S.S.R., and is a participant in the **Joint Institute for Nuclear Research** at Dubna in the U.S.S.R.

RUNAWAY ELECTRONS

In experimental controlled-**fusion** devices of the **stellarator** type, a current pulse has been used for initial heating of the confined **plasma** (see **ohmic heating**). It has been found that the application of such a unidirectional field causes the faster moving electrons to "run away" from the slower moving ones, i.e., to gain energy at a divergent rate. The reason is that the faster an electron travels, the lower is the probability that it will be deflected by another particle and therefore the higher the probability that it will retain any kinetic energy imparted to it. Runaway electrons are undesirable since they absorb a disproportionate amount of the input power, resulting in nonuniform heating of the plasma and in some cases causing plasma instability. They are one of several factors that act to make ohmic heating ineffective at plasma temperatures much above one million degrees.

RUSSIA. See **Soviet Union.**

RUTHENIUM

Element No. 44 (symbol, Ru; atomic weight, 101.7), several isotopes of which are formed as fission products. The chemistry of ruthenium is extremely complex, and accordingly these fission products are a complicating factor in **fuel reprocessing.** Ruthenium forms compounds that are soluble in the organic solvents used in aqueous fuel reprocessing operations, thereby adding to the difficulty of decontaminating the product. In pyrometallurgical reprocessing techniques, the ruthenium usually remains in the irradiated fuel. In general, it is the most persistent and troublesome contaminant in any fuel reprocessing method.

S

S-50 PLANT

A plant built at Oak Ridge, Tennessee, during World War II for the partial separation of uranium isotopes by the **thermal diffusion process**; later dismantled. See **Manhattan Project** for background information.

SAFETY ROD

In the operation of a nuclear reactor, a stand-by **control rod** used to shut down the reactor in the event of failure of routine control devices (**regulating rods, shim rods** or other) or for emergency shutdowns (see **scram**). Safety rods must be capable of reducing the **reactivity** of the system extremely quickly and are usually withdrawn from the core during normal operation. (See **reactor control**)

SAFETY STATISTICS, AEC. See **radiation protection.**

SALTING AGENT

In **solvent extraction** systems, a solute added to the aqueous scrub solution which encourages the transfer of a desired component from the aqueous phase into the organic solvent, thereby increasing the recovery of that component. The effectiveness of salting agents is accounted for by common ion effects. The salting agents used in the **Redox** and **Purex** solvent extraction processes are aluminum nitrate and nitric acid, respectively.

SAMARIUM-149

A stable isotope of the rare earth element, samarium, formed as a fission product and second only to **xenon-135** in its poisoning effect in reactor systems. Samarium-149 has the unusually high thermal-neutron absorption cross section of 1.6×10^4 barns.

Natural samarium has a cross section of 5500 barns and is of interest as a possible neutron absorbing material for use in reactor control rods.

SANDIA LABORATORY

A major U.S. Atomic Energy Commission laboratory charged with development of the non-nuclear components of nuclear weapons. Sandia's operations are centered at Sandia Base, near Albuquerque, New Mexico; however, the Laboratory has a branch at Livermore, California, and it maintains test ranges and facilities at Salton Sea, California, and Tonapah, Nevada. *Operating contractor*: Sandia Corporation, a non-profit subsidiary of Western Electric Company. *President, Sandia Corporation*: S. P. Schwartz. *AEC investment in plant and equipment (all sites)*: $104 million.* *Staff (all sites)*: 7800, one-third of whom are engaged in research and development; one-third in operations and maintenance; and one-third in clerical and administrative support.

In effect, Sandia Laboratory takes nuclear devices developed and tested by Los Alamos Scientific Laboratory and the Livermore branch of the E. O. Lawrence Radiation Laboratory and performs the research and development necessary to incorporate them into operational weapons. In addition to weapons research and engineering the Laboratory con-

* Includes facilities authorized or under construction as of June 30, 1960. Not adjusted for depreciation.

ducts fundamental research in the field of radiation effects on materials and in other fields of interest to atomic energy development. As a logical outgrowth of its weapons program, it is a participant in the AEC's program to develop peaceful applications for nuclear explosives (see **Plowshare Project).** It was recently assigned primary responsibility for AEC's program of studies on the safety aspects of space applications of atomic energy (Aerospace Nuclear Safety Program).

Sandia is equipped with a variety of experimental and environmental test facilities. They include a 5000 kilowatt (thermal) **test reactor** known as the Sandia Engineering Reactor Facility, or SERF); another test reactor (the Sandia Pulsed Reactor Facility) whose function is to provide prompt neutron bursts for experimental purposes; a 2.5-Mev Van de Graaff generator; a high-speed computer facility; high temperature solar furnaces; hypersonic wind tunnels (one of which provides wind speeds up to Mach 9 and temperatures up to 2500°F); a 3000-foot rocket-sled track and other equipment for acceleration and shock studies; and ballistic test ranges.

SAP ALLOYS

A term for sintered aluminum powder materials under development for fuel element cladding applications. (See **organic cooled reactors)**

NS *SAVANNAH*

A demonstration nuclear-powered merchant ship built as a joint project of the U.S. Atomic Energy Commission and the U.S. Maritime Administration under the **Maritime Reactors Program.** Designed for passenger-cargo operations, the NS (nuclear ship) *Savannah* represents the first nonmilitary application of marine nuclear propulsion undertaken by the United States.* The propulsion system, powered by a **pressurized water reactor** with a rated output of approximately 75 megawatts (thermal) and designed to deliver 22,300 shaft horsepower, was designed and built by the Bacbcock & Wilcox Company. The ship was designed by George G. Sharp, Inc. and constructed by the New York Shipbuilding Corporation at Camden, New Jersey. Mrs. Dwight D. Eisenhower christened the vessel during launching ceremonies on July 21, 1959. The reactor began operation on December 21, 1961, and sea trials began in March of 1962. By June 1, 1962, *Savannah* had cruised nearly 6000 miles and had demonstrated excellent performance.

Upon completion of sea trials the *Savannah* is scheduled for two or three years of experimental operation. Toward the end of the experimental period limited service will be undertaken, during which the ship will visit major world ports. The *Savannah* is operated by the U.S. Maritime Administration through its general agent, States Marine Lines.

Named after the SS *Savannah* which pioneered the use of steam in a transatlantic crossing in 1819, the NS *Savannah* displaces 22,000 tons, is designed for a cruising speed of 24 knots, and is capable of traveling some 350,000 miles without refueling. The vessel measures 596 feet in length and has a 78-foot beam. It will accommodate 60 passengers and carry a crew of 110 and about 10,000 tons of cargo. The nuclear power plant is located amidship. The reactor core is housed in a massively shielded pressure vessel. The overall primary reactor system is enclosed in an airtight steel vapor containment vessel. Protection against collision damage is afforded by a laminated structure of steel plate and wood construction surrounding the containment vessel. Auxiliary and emergency power is provided by two 750-kilowatt and one 300-kilowatt diesel-electric generators.

The reactor is fueled with slightly enriched uranium (4.4% U^{235}) in the form of uranium dioxide (UO_2) pellets contained in stainless steel tubes. The operating pressure is 1750 psi; the exit coolant temperature, ~ 524°F. Steam to operate the propulsion machinery is generated in an external heat exchanger at an

* The Russian ice-breaker, ***Lenin,*** was the world's first nonmilitary nuclear ship. (See **Soviet Union)**

average pressure of 492 psi and a temperature of ~ 450°F.

The cost of the *Savannah* is estimated at $35.6 million, exclusive of research and development and support costs.* Of this figure, $19.6 million represents the cost of the power plant and related propulsion machinery, and $16 million represents the cost of the hull and fittings.

Reactor safeguard studies and environmental surveys relating to the operation of the *Savannah* have been in progress for some time. Negotiations were initiated in 1959 with foreign governments regarding the entry of the *Savannah* into major foreign ports. Public hearings on the safety of the *Savannah* were held in March, 1961.

SAVANNAH RIVER PLANT

A U.S. Atomic Energy Commission plutonium production facility, located on the Savannah River, 12 miles south of Aiken, South Carolina. *Operating contractor:* E. I. duPont de Nemours & Company. *AEC investment in plant and equipment:* ~ $1.317 billion. *Employment:* ~ 7000.

* Estimated at $11.3 million, bringing the total cost to an estimated $46.9 million.

The Savannah River Plant was built in the early fifties and represents the largest single construction project ever undertaken in the United States. Its primary function is the production of plutonium by the irradiation of natural uranium and subsequent chemical separation and decontamination of the irradiated material. The irradiation is conducted in heavy water moderated reactors, which are also used for the irradiation of lithium and to perform other irradiation services on the AEC's behalf. Another important activity is research and development (see below).

The principal production facilities of the Savannah River Plant are as follows:

1. Fuel element fabrication facilities: The SRP receives natural uranium metal in the form of short slugs which, after inspection and nickel plating are canned in aluminum and tested.

2. Production reactors: There are five production reactors, identified by letter designations (C-, K-, L-, P- and R-Reactors). These are heavy-water moderated, tank-type units designed by duPont in collaboration with Argonne National Laboratory.

3. Chemical separation plants: There are two chemical separation plants, both of which were designed to utilize the **Purex** solvent extraction process for uranium-plutonium sepa-

Fig. 182. One of five plutonium production reactor installations at the Savannah River Plant. (*Courtesy E. I. duPont de Nemours & Co.*)

ration and removal of fission-product contamination (see **fuel reprocessing**).

4. Heavy water production plant: The original heavy water (D_2O) inventory for the production reactors was produced in two plants, one located on the site of the Savannah River Plant and the other located at Newport, Indiana (see **Dana Heavy Water Plant**). The latter was shut down in 1957 but the Savannah River installation continues in operation to supply SRP make-up requirements and to provide heavy water for other AEC programs and requirements. The basic process employed is **dual-temperature chemical exchange**. (See **deuterium** for background information)

A major branch of the plant organization is the Savannah River Laboratory which conducts research in physics, chemistry, metallurgy and engineering in support of the production operations, and additionally engages in research and development projects in areas of civilian atomic energy application. A major program in the latter category is development work on heavy water moderated power reactors. (See **Heavy Water Components Test Reactor**)

The prime contractor for the design and construction of the Savannah River Plant was duPont. Acceptance of this assignment in 1950 marked the company's re-entry into the atomic energy field; during the wartime **Manhattan Project** it served as prime contractor, and until 1946, operator of the Hanford plutonium production plant. (See **Hanford Works**)

SAXTON EXPERIMENTAL NUCLEAR REACTOR

A small power reactor of the **pressurized water** type at Saxton, Pennsylvania; sometimes referred to as the "Saxton Hook-on." The owner is the Saxton Nuclear Experimental Corporation.* The reactor was supplied by Westinghouse Electric Corporation under a turn-key contract, with Gilbert Associates as architect-engineer-contractor.

The reactor installation supplies steam to an existing turbine-generator located in the Saxton Generating Station of the Pennsylvania Electric Corporation. It is operated partly as a development facility and partly as a training facility. Special emphasis is being placed on lowering fuel costs through improvements in core design and operating techniques. Also, equipment has been provided for studies of nuclear superheating. The following notes reflect the status of the project as of mid-1962:

Power: 3 megawatts (electrical). *Fuel:* Slightly enriched uranium (5.7% U^{235}) in the form of uranium dioxide (UO_2). *Fuel element design:* A single fuel element consists of an assembly of thin stainless steel tubes loaded with UO_2 pellets. *Fuel inventory:* 1000 kilograms of uranium dioxide. *Coolant:* Ordinary water at 2000 pounds pressure; inlet temperature, 494°F; outlet temperature, 540°F. *Steam conditions:* Saturated steam at 500 pounds pressure and 476°F. *Thermal conversion efficiency:* 25%. *Cost:* $6.25 million (contract price) including fuel costs for the first 5 years of operation. *Dates:* Construction started in February, 1960. Power operation began in the spring of 1962.

* The shareholders are four subsidiaries of General Public Utilities Corporation, namely, Jersey Central Power & Light Company, New Jersey Power & Light Company, Metropolitan Edison Company, and Pennsylvania Electric Company. Pennsylvania State University and Rutgers University are participating members of the Corporation and will have access to the reactor for teaching and research purposes.

SCALER

An electronic device used in counting individual pulses from a radiation-sensing instrument whenever the required counting rate exceeds the capability of a mechanical counter. The scaler is inserted between the sensing instrument and the mechanical counter and reduces the flow of signals by whatever factor is necessary to permit the counter to handle the count.** Binary scalers permit one out of every 2, 4, 8, 16, 32, etc., signals to reach the counter; decade scalers permit one out of every 10, 100, 1000, etc., signals to reach the counter. The recorded count multiplied by the scaling factor then gives the total count of photons or particles of incident radiation. Scalers may be used with pulse-type **ionization chambers,**

** In commercial models of scalers, the mechanical counter is incorporated as an integral part of the instrument.

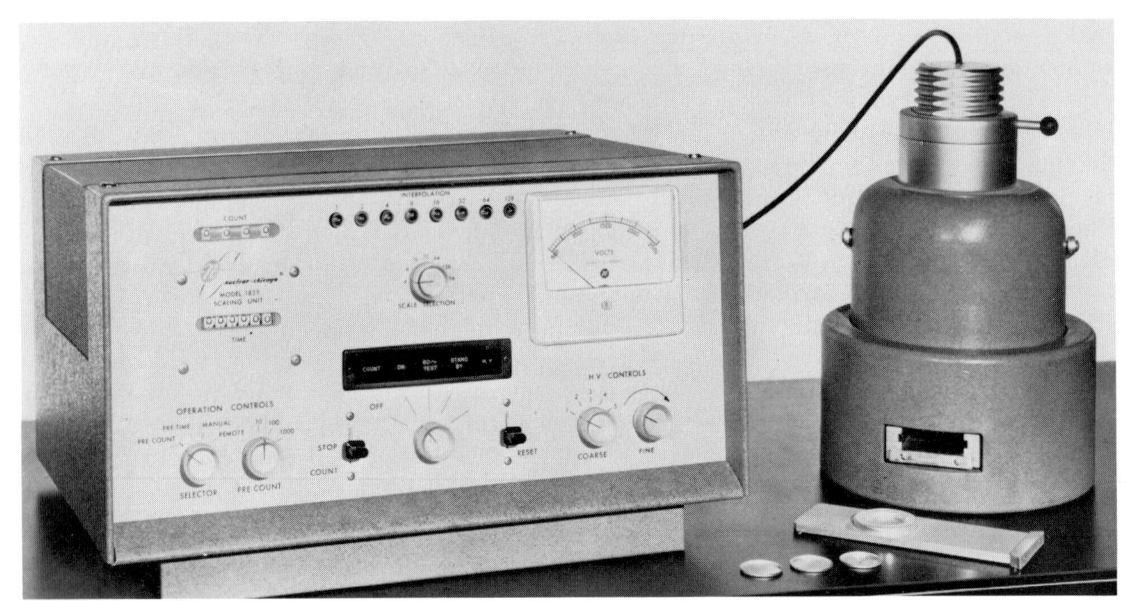

Fig. 183. Scaler (at left). (*Courtesy of Nucleonics*)

proportional counters, Geiger counters, or **scintillation counters.**

Scalers are not to be confused with **rate-meters,** which provide a continuous measure of the average pulse rate of a radiation-sensing instrument rather than a cumulative pulse count.

SCATTERING

A collision between an incident particle (neutron, proton or other) and an atomic nucleus that does not involve a **nuclear reaction** in the sense that the particle and the nucleus retain their identity. In **elastic scattering,** the particle transfers some of its kinetic energy to the nucleus but the total kinetic energy of the particle and nucleus is unchanged. In **inelastic scattering,** the total kinetic energy is decreased and the nucleus is left in an excited state.

Elastic scattering is the primary mechanism by which a **moderator** slows down neutrons below about 1 Mev in a nuclear reactor. Inelastic scattering of fast neutrons by heavy nuclei, e.g., U^{238}, has a moderating effect in reactors fueled with normal or slightly enriched uranium.

SCHROECKINGERITE

Hydrated calcium uranium carbonate—a secondary uranium mineral, yellow or greenish yellow in color, found in minor occurrences in certain gypsum-bearing clays and in the oxidized portions of some primary deposits.

SCINTILLATION COUNTER

An instrument that detects and measures **ionizing radiation** by means of light flashes induced in certain materials, called phosphors. The light flashes (scintillations) result from complex excitation phenomena. They are converted to measurable electrical impulses by means of a photomultiplier tube, the outputs from which are counted by a **scaler** or **ratemeter.**

Scintillation counters are capable of extremely rapid response and hence can achieve very high counting rates. They can detect and measure any form of ionizing radiation with high efficiency. The signals they produce bear an approximately linear relation to the energy of the incident radiation so that they can be used in combination with a **pulse height analyzer** to discriminate between photons or

Fig. 184. Assortment of phosphors used in scintillation counters. (*Courtesy of Brookhaven National Laboratory*)

TABLE 1. CHARACTERISTICS OF PHOSPHORS USED IN SCINTILLATION COUNTERS

		Order of Rank (1 = best)	
Type	*Example*	*Strength of Scintillation*	*Response Time*
Inorganic crystals [1]	Sodium iodide activated by thallium	1	4
Organic crystals	Anthracene	2	3
Organic solution [2]	Diphenyloxazole in toluene solution	3	2
Inert gas	Argon	4	1

[1] Inorganic crystals must be "activated" by a small amount (∽ 0.1% of an impurity. They are most useful for gamma measurements.
[2] The use of a liquid scintillator permits large counter sizes. See **whole body counter.**

particles of radiation of different energy, and thereby identify specific radionuclides in a radioactive mixture. They are widely used as portable survey meters for prospecting and **radiation monitoring** purposes, and also for radiation measurements in research laboratories.

Various phosphor materials are used in scintillation counters, including inorganic and organic crystals, organic solutions, and inert gases. Table 1 shows a rough comparison of the scintillation characteristics of these materials.

The principle of radiation-induced scintillation is also used in luminescent chambers, which are devices for observing and recording particle tracks in high-energy physics experiments.

SCRAM

A term for the sudden shutdown of a nuclear reactor, usually by the rapid insertion of **safety rods.** A reactor may be "scrammed" manually in an emergency or may occur automatically when a predetermined condition is reached that actuates preset controls.

SCRAM ROD

A **safety rod** used for a **scram,** or emergency shutdown of a nuclear reactor. A scram rod is fully withdrawn from the reactor core in normal operation.

SCREW-DYNAMIC PINCH EXPERIMENT

An experimental device built in 1956 at the Livermore Branch of the E. O. Lawrence Radiation Laboratory as part of the **Pinch Program** of research on controlled **fusion.** It is used for research on techniques for achieving quasi-stabilized pinch-confinement of an ionized gas, or **plasma,** in a straight-tube configuration. It differs from other stabilized linear-pinch devices in two principal respects: (1) Helical slots are cut into the surrounding conductive layer which carries the return current from the plasma. (2) As a result of the slots, an axial component of magnetic field is set up by the pinch current itself.

SCYLLA

The name of a series of experimental devices built at Los Alamos Scientific Laboratory in 1958 for research on controlled **fusion.** It is of the "magnetic mirror" type (see **magnetic mirror systems).** The experiments have involved injecting a partially ionized fuel stream into a reaction chamber wound coaxially with a single compression coil connecting to a low-inductance capacitor bank. A strong magnetic field is applied by a sudden discharge of current into the coil, the field strength in the central portion of the chamber reaching 40,000 gauss in about 1 microsecond.

The effect of so rapid a build-up of compressive force is to shock-excite the fuel to a temperature in the region of several hundred thousand degrees as a result of which the resulting **plasma** is heated still further by adiabatic compression. The emission of intense bursts of neutrons, and also of **bremsstrahlung** radiation, has been observed to occur at peak compression. These phenomena have been studied intensely to determine whether fusion reactions may actually have been achieved. The evidence accumulated to date, while not yet conclusive on this point, is largely affirmative. A similar approach is used at the Naval Research Laboratory in **magnetic compression experiments.**

Fig. 185. Scylla III. (*Courtesy of Los Alamos Scientific Laboratory*)

SEALED SOURCE

A radiation source consisting of a radioactive material hermetically sealed within a suitable thin-walled container. Radioisotopes used in industry for other than tracer applications are commonly supplied as sealed sources to minimize handling and contamination problems.

USS *SEAWOLF* (SSN-575)

The second nuclear-powered ship. An attack-class submarine with a displacement of 3260 tons, *Seawolf* was originally powered with an S2G sodium-cooled reactor plant designed by Knolls Atomic Power Laboratory.

The ship was constructed by the Electric Boat Division of General Dynamics Corporation, launched on July 21, 1954 and commissioned March 30, 1957.

As noted in the **Naval Reactors Program** entry, leaks appeared in the superheater system resulting in the requirement that the superheaters be by-passed. Additional leaks appeared in one of the steam generators and as a result of these problems, the sodium cooled reactor was replaced by a pressurized water cooled reactor (S2W-A) similar to that of the ***Nautilus*** at the time her initial core required replacement. By this time, the *Seawolf* had steamed a total of 71,611 miles of which 57,118 were fully submerged. The reactor proper operated in a trouble-free manner during this period; in fact, the reactor compartment was not entered during the nearly 2 years of operation. The only difficulties experienced were with auxiliary sodium equipment (notably the superheater) and most of these occurred before the ship was commissioned.

On December 12, 1958, the *Seawolf* entered Electric Boat Division building yard at Groton, Connecticut, for replacement of her sodium cooled plant, she commenced sea trials August 28, 1960, with her new pressured water-cooled plant and was recommissioned September 30, 1960.

SECURITY CLEARANCE

An authorization that must be obtained from the U.S. Atomic Energy Commission before an individual may be permitted access to classified information (or areas) under the AEC's jurisdiction.

An "L" clearance or access authorization permits access to **Restricted Data** classified no higher than "confidential" or Defense Information classified "confidential" or "secret" (see **classification—declassification**). An "L" clearance or access authorization may be granted to U.S. citizens after a National Agency Check (NAC) by the U.S. Civil Service Commission.

A "Q" clearance or access authorization permits access to **Restricted Data** of "secret" or "top secret" classification (see above reference) or to Defense Information classified "secret" or "top secret." Such a clearance or access authorization requires a full field investigation by the U.S. Civil Service Commission; and, in special cases (e.g., "positions of a high degree of importance or sensitivity"), requires an investigation by the Federal Bureau of Investigation.

"L" and "Q" clearances are granted to employees of the AEC and other federal agencies. "Q" and "L" access authorizations are granted to employees of contractors of the AEC and of other federal agencies. Authorizations granted under the **Access Permit** Program are termed "LX" or "QX". This distinction is purely for administrative purposes; there is no substantive distinction between "L" and "LX" access authorizations or between "Q" and "QX" access authorizations. Access to weapons data or "top secret" information is not permitted under the Access Permit Program.

SEED CORE

A special configuration of **spiked core** in which the enriched component of the core loading, referred to as the seed, is the critical region and the only region requiring control. The nonenriched component serves as **reflector** and **blanket**.

The **Shippingport Atomic Power Station** employs a seed core consisting of a square-doughnut shaped seed of enriched fuel blanketed inside and out by nonenriched fuel.

SENEGAL

Joined the **International Atomic Energy Agency** in 1960.

SEPARATION FACTOR

In isotope separation, a measure of the degree of separation accomplished in a single stage of separative work, and hence of the number of stages required for a given degree of separation. Ideal separation factors express the theoretical limit for a given process. Practical separation factors take into account inefficiencies in actual process application.

By way of illustration, the ideal separation factor for the separation of uranium isotopes by **gaseous diffusion** is:

$$\sqrt{\frac{U^{238}F_6}{U^{235}F_6}} = 1.00142$$

SHERWOOD PROJECT

A former code designation for the U.S. program of research on controlled **fusion** (see **thermonuclear power**). Work in this field started more or less spontaneously at several major U.S. laboratories over the period 1951-1953. The first of a series of informal coordination meetings was held in mid-1952 and by the fall of 1953, a decision was reached to establish formal coordination. The following year the Controlled Thermonuclear Branch of the AEC's Division of Research was set up for this purpose, and the then classified U.S. controlled-fusion effort was formally designated as "Project Sherwood." With subsequent declassification of the program, the need for a code designation was removed but the term is still in use.

SHIELD, RADIATION

A layer or mass of material used to reduce the intensity of ionizing radiation and thereby protect personnel or equipment.

SHIELD WINDOWS

Transparent radiation shields built into the walls of **hot cells** to permit direct viewing of operations conducted therein. Several types of shield windows are in common use: (1) Liquid-filled windows consisting of an aquarium-like tank containing an optical-grade zinc bromide solution. Such windows match ordinary concrete in shielding power and thus must be somewhat thicker than the cell wall when the latter is made of high-density concrete. The maximum thickness is 4½ feet, a limitation imposed by adverse radiation effects (gas generation) at radiation intensities requiring greater shield thicknesses. (2) Glass-filled shield windows consisting of a laminar array of closely placed glass plates immersed in mineral oil and contained in a rectangular tank with steel end plates. Such windows can be made to match ordinary or high-density concrete in shielding power, depending on the type of glass specified, and can be used in thicknesses up to 5 or 6 feet. The limitation in this case is gamma-induced darkening and heating of the glass at radiation intensities requiring greater thicknesses. (3) Lead-glass windows. These are plates or slabs of high-density lead glass which provide gamma shielding power equivalent to steel. The maximum usable thickness is 8 to 12 inches. (4) Composite shield windows often consisting of a lamination of lead glass plates (inside section) in combination with a liquid-filled window (outside section).

SHIELDING

The use of thicknesses of material to reduce the intensity of radiation (see **attenuation**) and thereby protect personnel or equipment from radiation injury or damage. Following are the general characteristics of the principal forms of radiation from the standpoint of shielding requirements:

1. **Alpha particles** have little penetrating power and do not present a shielding problem in the ordinary sense. They can be stopped, for example, by a sheet of writing paper. Alpha-emitting materials are safely handled in the laboratory in **glove boxes.** The principal health hazard is ingestion or inhalation. (See **radiation protection**)

2. **Beta particles** have greater penetrating power than alpha particles but cannot penetrate more than 1 centimeter or so of metal or glass. The principal shielding problem associated with beta radiation arises from what is known as the **bremsstrahlung** effect, i.e., the presence of highly penetrating rays (similar to x-rays) resulting from the deflection of fast-moving beta particles by the nuclei in the shielding medium. The bremsstrahlung effect

tends to increase with **atomic number** so that materials of high atomic weight are not satisfactory beta shields.

3. Neutrons are highly penetrating and are most effectively stopped by a combination of materials of fairly high and low **mass number.** The former act to slow down the fast neutrons to energies of the order of 100,000 ev by **inelastic scattering**; the latter then further reduce the neutron energy by **elastic scattering** to a point where they are readily absorbed. In the absorption process (see **neutron capture**), gamma radiation is emitted and this becomes a factor in the design of the shield. Concrete is commonly used to shield nuclear reactors. It contains considerable amounts of hydrogen, which answers the low mass-number requirement, and the high mass-number requirement is readily accommodated by adding iron ore or other dense matter to the formulation. (See **heavy aggregate concrete**)

4. **Gamma radiation** is also highly penetrating. The best gamma shields are high-density materials of high atomic number. Lead is an excellent gamma shield and steel (iron) is also very effective. Following is the relative thickness of material required to reduce the intensity of 1-Mev gamma radiation by a factor of 10:

Material	*Inches of Thickness (approx.)*
Water	18
Ordinary concrete	9
Barytes concrete	7
Steel-loaded concrete	4
Iron	3
Lead	2

The nature and intensity of the radiation and the attenuation characteristics of the shielding material are not the only factors that must be taken into account in the design of a radiation shield. Other factors include the geometry of the source and the allowable radiation level beyond the shield.

In laboratories where radioactive materials are handled, improvised arrangements of lead bricks are commonly used for "low-level" gamma and neutron shielding. "High-level" experiments are normally conducted in specially designed **hot cells,** or caves, constructed of thick walls of high-density concrete (sometimes lead-lined) and equipped with **shield windows.**

Lead and high-density concrete are commonly used to shield high-intensity radiation sources such as megacurie radionuclide sources (e.g., cobalt-60) and particle accelerators (e.g., Van de Graaff machines).

There are two shielding functions in many nuclear reactor installations involving an internal shield, commonly fabricated of several inches of steel plate, and an external shield, commonly consisting of 8 or more feet of heavy-aggregate concrete. The internal, or thermal, shield serves to prevent thermal and **radiation damage** to the external shield; the external, or biological, shield protects personnel from radiation exposure (see **biological effects of ionizing radiation**). Some research reactors are shielded by about 20 or so feet of water, an arrangement which lends flexibility to the positioning of the core and permits direct observation of fuel replacement and other operating and maintenance procedures (see **pool reactors**). Water shielding is also commonly used in storing irradiated fuel elements. (See **laminated shield; radiation protection**)

SHIM ROD

In the operation of a nuclear reactor, a type of **control rod** used for making occasional coarse adjustments in the **reactivity** of the system. (See **reactor control**)

SHIP PROPULSION, NUCLEAR. See Naval Reactors Program; Maritime Reactors Program.

SHIPMENT OF RADIOACTIVE MATERIALS. See transportation of radioactive materials.

SHIPPING CONTAINERS. See transportation of radioactive materials.

SHIPPINGPORT ATOMIC POWER STATION (PWR)

A large-scale nuclear power plant of the **pressurized water** type, located on the Ohio

River at Shippingport, Pennsylvania. The plant was built for development and demonstration purposes. The steam portion, i.e., the reactor and related steam generating facilities, is owned by the U.S. Atomic Energy Commission.* The electrical portion, i.e., the turbine and related electrical generating facilities, is owned by Duquesne Light Company. Duquesne operates the station, makes payment to the AEC for the steam, and distributes the power produced. Shippingport was designed by Bettis Atomic Power Laboratory, which is operated for the AEC by Westinghouse Electric Corporation. Stone and Webster Engineering Corporation served as architect-engineer. Dravo Corporation and Burns and Roe, Inc. were the construction contractors. The project was directed by the Naval Reactors Group of the AEC's Division of Reactor Development.

The Shippingport station is of historical interest as the first large-scale civilian nuclear power plant built in the United States.** Its main importance, however, is as a pressurized water reactor development facility and as the first power reactor to employ uranium dioxide (UO_2) fuel elements. It was designed and is equipped to test different core designs and explore operating variables, as well as to obtain experience in large-scale nuclear power generation. It is much more heavily instrumented and has considerable more operational flexibility than any other U.S. power reactor of comparable size.

Shippingport first achieved criticality in December, 1957, and full power operation with the first core (PWR-1), rated at 68 megawatts (gross electrical), began that same month.

The PWR-1 core is of the "seed and blanket" type (see descriptive notes below), which permits substantial amounts of the power output to be extracted from natural uranium. As of the end of 1961, the operating history of this core was as follows:

1. The reactor operated on an initial seed (Seed 1) until October, 1959, by which time it had logged approximately 5800 equivalent full-power hours—nearly twice the original design estimate. Seed 1 was then replaced with Seed 2.

2. The reactor operated on Seed 2 from May, 1960 to August, 1961, logging a total of 7900 equivalent full-power hours. Seed 2 was then replaced with Seed 3.

3. Operation with Seed 3 began early October, 1961.

4. The blanket section of the core, which reached its design lifetime of approximately 8000 equivalent full-power hours in September, 1960, was partially inspected during the Seed 3 refueling and found to have substantial residual life. (By the time Seed 3 is depleted, the blanket will have operated for approximately 20,000 equivalent full-power hours and may still be in satisfactory condition for a fourth seed cycle.)

The total gross electrical output of the Shippingport plant, as of December 31, 1961, was just over 1 billion kilowatt-hours.

A second core (PWR-2), of advanced design, is being fabricated. Just as the PWR-1 core demonstrated the use of uranium dioxide fuel elements in the form of pellets contained in zircaloy tubes, the PWR-2 core has as a main objective the demonstration of a more advanced fuel element consisting of compartmented flat plates containing wafers of uranium dioxide. The blanket elements will utilize normal uranium while the seed elements will utilize enriched uranium dioxide diluted with zirconium oxide. An improved zircaloy will be used for cladding. This new core will have a power capability of 150 megawatts (gross electrical output) and will utilize only 20 control rods compared to 32 in PWR-1. The design lifetime is 20,000 equivalent full-power hours so that the total design energy output from PWR-2 is approximately

---

* Duquesne Light Company and Westinghouse Electric Corporation contributed $5 million and $0.5 million, respectively, toward the cost of reactor construction.

** It is also the world's first large-scale installation built exclusively for civilian power purposes. The British Calder Hall reactors predated Shippingport but they were designed for military plutonium production as well as civilian electrical power generation. (See **United Kingdom.**)

Fig. 186. The Shippingport Atomic Power Station. Above, general view. Right, core seen being lowered into place in reactor vault. [*Courtesy of Duquesne Light Co.* (top), and *Westinghouse Electric Corp.* (right)]

five and a half times that of PWR-1. Since the present capacity of the Shippingport turbine-generator is only 100 megawatts (electrical), the excess thermal energy will be fed to a heat sink.

The schedule for installation of PWR-2 is indefinite at this writing, depending upon the lifetime of Seed 3 of PWR-1 and on whether or not a fourth seed is employed in PWR-1.

The following notes related to the first core (PWR-1) unless otherwise noted:

Power: 68 megawatts (gross electrical). To be increased to 100 megawatts with second core loading. *Fuel:* The reactor has a dual-region core. The seed material is fully enriched uranium in the form of a uranium-zirconium alloy. The blanket material is natural uranium in the form of uranium dioxide (UO_2). *Fuel element design:* An individual seed element consists of U-Zr alloy plates clad with zircaloy-2. A blanket element consists of an assembly of zircaloy tubes loaded with UO_2 pellets. *Fuel inventory:* 90 kilograms of fully enriched uranium and 14 tons of natural uranium. *Coolant:* Ordinary water at 2000 pounds pressure; outlet temperature: 515°F. *Steam conditions:* Saturated steam at 600 pounds pressure and 490°F. *Thermal conversion efficiency:* 29%. *Control materials:* 32 hafnium control rods. *Containment:* The reactor, steam boilers, and auxiliary equipment system are contained in steel, pressure vessels which are enclosed in a concrete radiation shield. There is no over-all containment sphere. *Cost:* The original capital investment is reported at $74 million. *Dates:* Construction started in April, 1955. Initial criticality and full-power operation were both first achieved in December, 1957. Modifications to permit higher power operation were initiated in 1961.

SHOCK HEATING

A technique used in some experimental controlled-**fusion** devices for raising the temperature of the fuel **plasma.** In shock heating, the plasma is heated by rapidly increasing the magnetic field used for plasma confinement. The rapid increase of the magnetic field causes a hydromagnetic shock wave to move through, and energize, the plasma. Shock heating is thus distinct from **adiabatic compression,** which involves a gradual increase in field strength. (See **pinch program)**

SIGMA PILE

An experimental assembly consisting of an array of a **moderator** material and a neutron source, used to study the neutron properties (elastic scattering, diffusion, etc.) of the material. A sigma pile differs from an **exponential experiment** in that the latter additionally contains fuel.

SILVER

Element No. 47 (symbol, Ag; atomic weight, 107.88), of interest in the nuclear field in two unrelated ways: (1) It shows some promise for use as a neutron-absorbing material in reactor control rods, principally because of its strong resonance capture characteristics in the middle and upper portions of the neutron energy spectrum. It is thus complementary to materials such as **cadmium** which, while having very high absorption cross sections for thermal neutrons, are not very effective in the higher energy ranges. (2) Silver is one of the metal solvents being studied in research on high-temperature **metal-to-metal extraction** techniques for certain **fuel reprocessing** applications.

SITE CRITERIA, REACTOR. See **nuclear power economics.**

USS *SKATE* (SSN-578)

First of the small attack class of nuclear-powered submarines (see **Naval Reactors Program).** *Skate* displaces 2360 tons and is powered by an S3W pressurized water reactor plant designed by Bettis Atomic Power Laboratory and developed without benefit of a land prototype. The ship was constructed by the Electric Boat Division of General Dynamics Corporation, launched on May 16, 1957, and commissioned on December 23, 1957.

Three other submarines of the *Skate* class have been built: *Swordfish, Sargo,* and *Seadragon.*

USS *SKIPJACK* (SSN-585)

First of the fast attack class of nuclear-powered submarine (see **Naval Reactors Program).** *Skipjack* has a streamlined "teardrop-shaped" hull for maximum speed and maneuverability. It displaces 2830 tons and is powered by an S5W pressurized water reactor plant designed by Bettis Atomic Power Laboratory. The ship was constructed by the Electric Boat Division of General Dynamics Corporation, launched on May 26, 1958, and commissioned April 15, 1959.

Through mid-1961, 21 additional submarines of the *Skipjack* class had been built or authorized. The seventh in this series of 22, the **USS *Thresher,*** introduced improvements that will be incorporated in subsequent ships of this class. For this reason, *Thresher* is referred to as being the "lead ship" of an improved *Skipjack* class. *Thresher,* displacing 3747 tons, was commissioned August 3, 1961.

The *Skipjack* class and the Polaris missile class (see **USS *George Washington***) constitute the two basic types of nuclear-powered submarine now being built.

SL-1 (Army Nuclear Power Plant)

Stationary Low-Powerplant-1, a small nuclear power plant of the direct-cycle **boiling water** type operated at the National Reactor Testing Station from December, 1958, until January, 1961, and now being dismantled following an explosion resulting in three fatalities (see below).

SL-1, formerly known as the Argonne Low Power Reactor (ALPR), was developed under the **Army Nuclear Power Program** as a prototype for power plants in the 0.1-1 megawatt (electrical) range for military use in remote locations. It was designed and originally operated by Argonne National Laboratory. Pioneer Service Engineering Company was the architect-engineer. In February, 1959, Combustion Engineering Company became the operating contractor.

On the evening of January 3, 1961, an explosion occurred within the SL-1 reactor vessel, causing the death of three military crew members. This was the first fatal accident in the history of U.S. reactor operation. A Board of Investigation was appointed by the U.S. Atomic Energy Commission to determine the cause of the accident, an investigation made difficult by extremely high radiation levels in the reactor room (500-1000 roentgens per hour). The Board's findings, as of June, 1961, can be partially summarized as follows:

1. The explosion involved a nuclear reaction.
2. The most likely immediate cause of the explosion appears to have been a nuclear excursion resulting from unusually rapid and extensive motion of the central control rod.
3. It is known that a variety of conditions had developed in the reactor, some having their origin in the design of the reactor and others in the cumulative effects of reactor operation, which may have contributed to the cause and extent of the incident. Among these conditions were loss from the core of burnable boron poison, and deterioration of the condition of the control rods resulting in sticking.

A positive aspect of the accident was that physical damage was confined to the reactor room and severe radioactive contamination was largely confined to the reactor building.

Particulars of the SL-1 installation are as follows: *Power:* 0.2 megawatt (electrical), plus 0.4 megawatt (thermal) for space heating. *Fuel:* Highly enriched uranium (90% U^{235}) in the form of an uranium-aluminum alloy. *Fuel element design:* Flat fuel plates clad with aluminum. *Core loading:* 14 kilograms U^{235}. *Core life:* 6.3 thermal megawatt-years. *Coolant:* Ordinary boiling water at 300 psi; outlet temperature, 422°F.

SLANT RANGE

With reference to nuclear weapons, the straight-line distance between a given location and the point of detonation.

SLOW NEUTRON

Synonymous with **thermal neutron.**

SLURRY

A homogeneous suspension of solid particles in a liquid. Slurries of enriched uranium oxide in light or heavy water have been studied as possible fuels for aqueous homogeneous reactors as an alternative to aqueous solutions of uranium salts. Also, a suspension of thorium oxide in heavy water has been studied for use as a **blanket** material in such reactors. The interest in slurries for these applications stems from the desire to avoid the severe corrosion problems associated with most aqueous fuel solutions, which are inherently acidic in nature, e.g., uranyl sulfate and uranyl nitrate solutions. In addition, slurries allow a higher concentration of uranium or thorium than can be achieved in an aqueous solution.

Slurries can be neutral or alkaline. While offering a possible solution to the problems of chemical corrosion, slurries introduce other difficulties, such as the problem of preventing erosion of equipment surfaces and that of maintaining the slurry particles in proper suspension. (See **aqueous homogeneous reactors**)

SM-1 (Army Nuclear Power Plant)

Stationary Medium-Powerplant-1, a small nuclear power plant of the **pressurized water** type located at Fort Belvoir, Virginia, SM-1, originally known as Army Package Power Reactor No. 1 (APPR-1), was developed under the **Army Nuclear Power Program** as a prototype for fixed-base power plants in the 1-10 megawatt range for use in remote locations (see **SM-1A**). It has also served as a training, and research and development facility for other Army reactor projects.

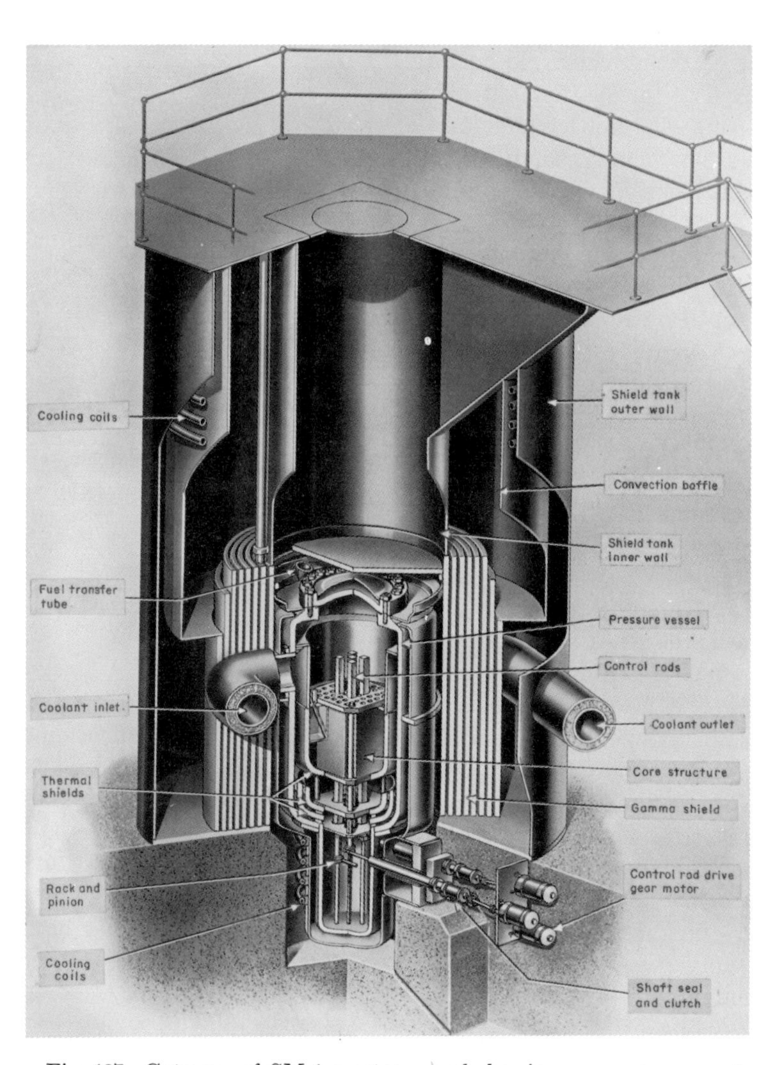

Fig. 187. Cutaway of SM-1 reactor vessel showing core arrangement. (*Courtesy of Nucleonics*)

Alco Products, Inc. was the prime contractor for SM-1, and operated the facility for 3 years. The reactor began operation in April, 1957. The first core was replenished in April, 1960, by which time it had exceeded its predicted lifetime (16.4 *vs.* 15.0 thermal megawatt-years). In July, 1960, responsibility for the SM-1 facility transferred from the U.S. Atomic Energy Commission to the Army Corps of Engineers. Particulars follow:

Power: 1.855 megawatts (electrical). No provision for space heating. *Fuel:* Highly enriched uranium ($> 90\%$ U^{235}) in the form of a dispersion of uranium dioxide (UO_2) in a stainless steel matrix. *Fuel element design:* Flat fuel plates clad with stainless steel. *Core life:* 16.4 thermal megawatt-years. *Coolant:* Ordinary water at 1200 psi; outlet temperature, 450°F. *Dates:* Start of operation, April, 1957.

SM-1A (Army Nuclear Power Plant)

Stationary Medium-Powerplant-1A, a plant similar to **SM-1** but with twice the latter's rated core heat output, located at Fort Greeley, Alaska. SM-1A, formerly known as Army Package Power Reactor No. 1A (APPR-1A), is designed to supply 1.640 megawatts of electric power and 11.15 megawatts of heat for space heating. The plant, completed in 1962, was built with Army funds and is operated by Army personnel. The prime contractor was Peter Kiewit Sons Company under contract with the Army Engineers' Alaska District; the reactor contractor was Alco Products, Inc.

SM-2 (Army Nuclear Power Plant)

Stationary Medium-Powerplant-2, the designation for a nuclear power plant design extrapolated from SM-1. The SM-2 design project was initiated to meet an anticipated requirement for a reliable 6-megawatt power supply for Nike-Zeus missile sites. The project as originally conceived was terminated in 1961, but design activity was carried forward to establish the basic features of a plant design for a twin reactor installation with a capability of 12 megawatts (electrical), for possible future requirements. The contractor for this work was Alco Products, Inc.

SNAP PROGRAM

A program of research and development on compact nuclear power systems for use as auxiliary power units in satellites and space vehicles and for other specialized applications. (The term "SNAP" is an acronym for Systems for Nuclear Auxiliary Power.) The SNAP Program was initiated in the mid-fifties, as a joint effort of the U.S. Atomic Energy Commission and the U.S. Air Force. It is now an AEC-directed effort with other agencies of government cooperating in specific development projects.

The SNAP Program is divided into two parts:

1. Development of systems utilizing the decay heat from radionuclides as the energy source. These systems carry odd-numbered designations and range in electrical power output from a few watts to several hundred watts. The prime contractors for this work (recently designated the Isotopic Power Program) are the Martin-Marietta Corporation (SNAP-1, -1A,-3,-5,-7,-9,-11,-13), Royal Research Corporation (underwater seismograph station), and General Instrument Corporation (mixed fission product generator).

2. Development of systems utilizing reactors as the energy source. These systems carry even-numbered designations and range in electrical power output from several hundred watts to the megawatt range. The prime contractors for this work are Atomics International, a division of North American Aviation, Inc. (SNAP-2,-4,-6,-8,-10A) and Pratt and Whitney Aircraft Division of United Aircraft Corporation (SNAP-50).

AEC research and development expenditures on the SNAP Program through mid-1961 totaled approximately $41 million, exclusive of capital costs.

Radionuclide Systems. Table 1 lists the radionuclide devices developed or planned for development, as of mid-1962, together with the

TABLE 1. ODD-NUMBERED SNAP DEVICES—MID-1962
(Radionuclide energy source)

Desig-nation	*Power Rating (net electrical)*	*Radionuclide*	*Energy Conversion Method*	*Notes*
SNAP-1	Several hundred watts	cerium-144	turboelectric	Development objectives redefined (see SNAP-1A) before the prototype stage was reached.
SNAP-1A	125 watts	cerium-144	thermoelectric	Prototype ground tested in 1961. No specific military requirement presently exists for this device which was originally intended for use in an Air Force satellite.
SNAP-3	3.5 watts	polonium-210	thermoelectric	Proof-of-principle device. First demonstrated in 1958. Tests of this device were completed in 1961.
SNAP-5	—	—	—	Supplied for classified application. No details available.
SNAP-7A	5 watts	strontium-90	thermoelectric	Prototype power supply for coastal light buoy (U.S. Coast Guard). Delivered in December, 1961.
SNAP-7B	30 watts	strontium-90	thermoelectric	Prototype power supply for coastal light station (U.S. Coast Guard). Delivery scheduled for 1962.
SNAP-7C	5 watts	strontium-90	thermoelectric	Prototype power supply for automatic weather station (U.S. Navy). Delivered in October, 1961.
SNAP-7D	30 watts	strontium-90	thermoelectric	Prototype power supply for automatic weather station (U.S. Navy). Delivery scheduled for 1962.
SNAP-7E	5 watts	strontium-90	thermoelectric	Prototype being developed for use on the ocean floor in powering navigational aids.
SNAP-9	14.5 watts	plutonium-238	thermoelectric	Developed for use in Navy's TRANSIT satellites, starting in 1962.
SNAP-11	18.6 watts (min)	curium-242	thermoelectric	Prototype being developed for use in NASA's SURVEYOR spacecraft in "soft" lunar impact experiment.
SNAP-13	not specified	curium-242	thermionic (cesium diode)	Being developed as an alternative to SNAP-11. Prototype scheduled for completion in 1963.
—[1]	5 watts	strontium-90	thermoelectric	Prototype power supply for automatic weather station (U.S. Weather Bureau). Placed in operation in August, 1961 at Axel Herberg Island.
—[1]	5 watts	cesium-137	thermoelectric	Prototype power supply for underwater seismograph station (Lamont Geological Observatory). Scheduled for delivery in 1962.
—	5 watts	mixed fission products	thermoelectric	Proof-of-principle device to demonstrate use of calcined mixed fission-product mixture as heat source. Feasibility study completed in 1961; development in progress.

[1] Development of these devices was conducted under the AEC's Isotope Development Program (see **radioisotopes in industry**). In 1962, these projects were integrated with the radionuclide portion of the SNAP Program under what is now known as the Isotopic Power Program.

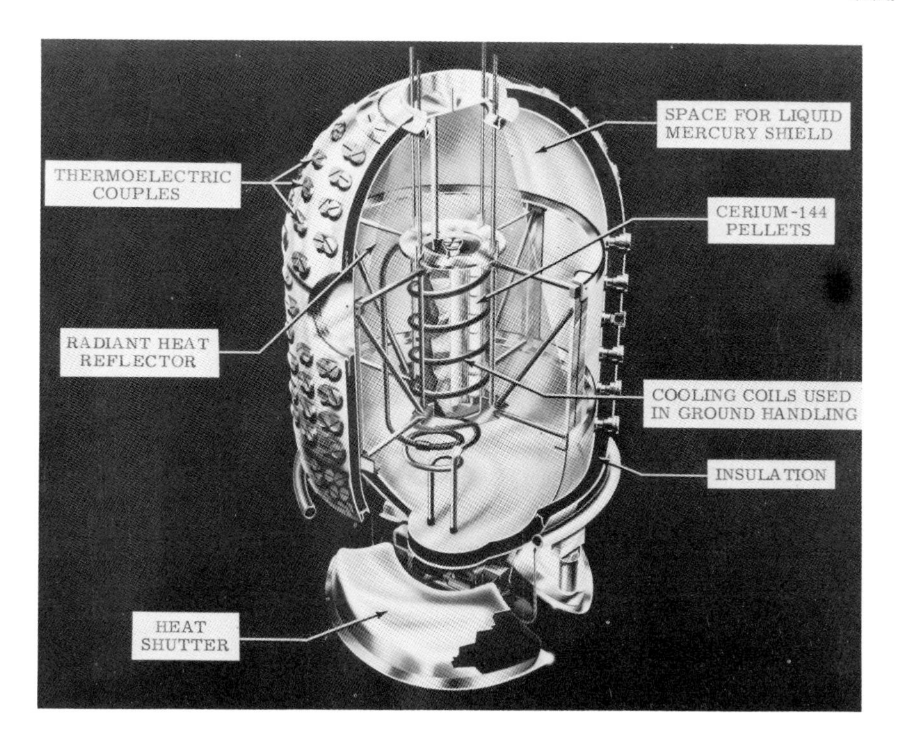

applications for which they are intended. Table 2 presents comparative data on the principal radionuclide sources used or studied for use in these devices. Following are supplementary notes on two of the several devices completed to date:

	SNAP-1A	*SNAP-3*
Size	Elongated spheroid, 34 x 24 in.	Elongated spheroid, 5½ x 4¾ in.
Weight	200 lb	4 lb
Fuel loading	~800,000 curies of cerium-144	~2200 curies of polonium-210
Thermoelectric elements	Lead telluride	Lead telluride
Performance	Designed to supply 125 watts of continuous power at 28 volts for a full year.	Designed to supply an average of ~1.75 watts over a period of 280 days.

Fuel Development. An important part of the radionuclide program is fuel development. One aspect has been the development of methods of preparing and encapsulating the several radionuclides of interest; another has been the de-

Fig. 188. SNAP-IA radionuclide power source. Top, conceptual diagram showing principal components. Above, prototype 125-watt device. (*Courtesy of The Martin Co.*)

TABLE 2. COMPARISON OF RADIONUCLIDE SOURCES

Primary Radionuclide			*Daughter Product*			*Curies of Primary Radionuclide Required per Watt of Electrical Output (at 100% energy conversion efficiency)*	*Notes*
Nuclide	*Radioactive Half-life*	*Emission*	*Nuclide*	*Radioactive Half-life*	*Emission*		
Polonium-210	138 days	5.3-Mev alpha	Lead-206	stable	—	~ 31	Produced by neutron irradiation of bismuth capsules in reactors.
Curium-242	163 days	~ 6.1-Mev alpha	Plutonium-238	90 years	5.5-Mev Alpha	~ 27	Produced by neutron irradiation of americium-241 capsules in reactors.
Cerium-144	285 days	0.3-Mev beta	Praesodymium-144	17 minutes	~ 3.0-Mev beta 0.7-Mev gamma	~ 128	Recovered in kilocurie quantities from fission product wastes.[1]
Promethium-147	2.6 years	pure ~ 0.2-Mev beta	Samarium-147	1.3×10^{11} years	2.1-Mev alpha	~ 2,700	Recovered in kilocurie quantities from fission product wastes.[1]
Strontium-90	28 years	pure ~ 0.5-Mev beta	Yttrium-90	64 hours	pure ~ 2.3-Mev beta	~ 156	Recovered in megacurie quantities from fission product wastes.[1]
Plutonium-238	90 years	5.5-Mev alpha	Uranium-234	2.5×10^{5} years	4.8-Mev alpha	~ 30	

[1] See **Multicurie Fission Products Pilot Plant.**

sign of generators (i.e., fuel assemblies and containers) rugged enough to withstand extreme service conditions and eventualities without releasing their radioactive contents to the earth's atmosphere. In the case of devices intended for use in satellites or space vehicles, the eventualities that must be taken into account include aborted launchings and burn-up on re-entry into the earth's atmosphere.

Tests conducted on SNAP-3 indicate that the devices will withstand the impact, fire and other extremes associated with a launch failure. Analyses indicate that burn-up on re-entry is not likely to cause significant contamination of the earth's atmosphere due to the fact that the particles formed would be extremely small and hence would tend to remain above the atmosphere for a long enough time for their radioactivity to decay to low levels. In the latter connection, the radionuclides which appear most suitable for short term space applications are **curium-242** and **polonium-210** which, in addition to other advantages,* have a relatively short radioactive half-life (see Table 2).

In the case of terrestrial applications, a radionuclide with a relatively long half-life is desired to permit operation for long periods of time without refueling. Here an important step has been the development of a technique for preparing **strontium-90** in a water-insolu-

* Relatively high-power output per curie; minimal shielding problems due to the fact that they are predominantly alpha emitters.

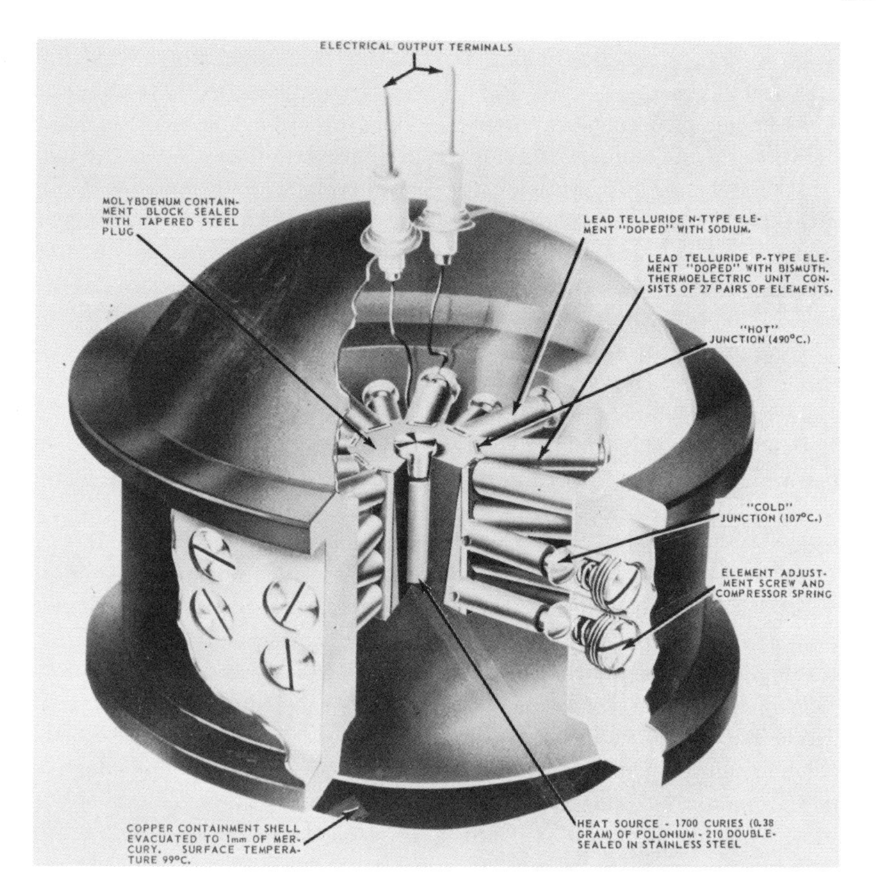

ble form (strontium titanate) which minimizes the biological hazard associated with that radionuclide. The advantages of strontium-90 for terrestrial applications, besides its long half-life, are (1) it is a pure beta emitter and hence easier to shield than gamma emitters; * (2) and it can be made available in large quantities at relatively low cost, given a large scale demand.**

Relatedly, cesium-137 has been prepared in an insoluble and unreactive form known as cesium polyglass (a calcium cesium aluminum borosilicate).

Another fuel development which should be

Fig. 189. SNAP-III radionuclide power source. Left, conceptual drawing showing principal parts. Right, 5-watt device under laboratory bell jar. (*Courtesy of The Martin Co.*)

* The principal shielding problem associated with high-energy beta emitters arises from **bremsstrahlung** radiation.

** The present price for amounts above 30,000 curies is 75¢ per curie, which is appreciably lower than the price of the other radionuclides listed in Table 2. It has been estimated that strontium-90 prices in the neighborhood of 20¢ per curie can be attained in a very large-scale production operation.

noted is the work on long-lived mixed fission product mixtures (see Table).

Electrical Conversion. Another important part of the program is the development of compact systems for converting the radioactive decay heat into electricity. The energy conversion system first studied was based on a thermodynamic (Rankin) cycle using a mercury turbine. Thompson-Ramo-Woolridge, Inc. developed a miniature turbogenerator for SNAP-1 but, as is noted in Table 1, work on that device was terminated before the prototype stage was reached. All subsequent development work on radionuclide power units has been based on **thermoelectric** and **thermionic conversion** systems, which permit the design of more compact and lighter weight power devices. The prototypes built to date use thermoelectric conversion and achieve energy conversion efficiencies in the neighborhood of 5 or 6%. Research on improved thermoelectric materials is expected to result in gains in conversion efficiency; however, present indications are that thermionic systems are likely to prove the most efficient (13 or 14%). Companies that have been engaged in research on direct-energy conversion systems include Martin-Marietta Corporation, Minnesota Mining and Manufacturing Company, Thermo Electron Engineering Company (TECO), United Electronics Company and Westinghouse Research Laboratories.

Applications. At this writing several applications of radionuclide power sources are being tested. In space, two modified SNAP-3 devices are being successfully used to power instruments carried by the Navy's navigational satellites, TRANSIT-4A (launched June 29, 1961) and TRANSIT-4B (launched November 15, 1961). These devices weigh 4.6 pounds and generate 2.7 watts of electricity. They are fueled with plutonium-238.

On land, there have been two applications to date. In August, 1961, a 5-watt device fueled with strontium-90 was placed in service at a remote weather station maintained by the U.S. Weather Bureau in cooperation with the Canadian Government on Axel Herberg Island in the Canadian Northwest Territories. The station automatically telemeters wind speed, wind direction, temperature and barometric pressure data every 3 hours to manned weather stations in Canada and the United States. In February, 1962, a similar device (SNAP-7C) began similar service at a weather station maintained by the Navy at Minna Bluff, about 50 miles south of McMurdo Sound in Antarctica.

At sea, SNAP-7A began service on December 15, 1961, in a Coast Guard light buoy in Curtis Bay, Maryland.

Reactor Systems. Table 3 lists the reactor devices that are being developed or have been studied under the SNAP Program. As indicated, active development effort has so far been largely focused on devices for space applications. SNAP-2 and 10A are intended for use strictly as auxiliary power units, i.e., to operate instruments, communication equipment, and the like. SNAP-8, which is a joint project of the AEC and the National Aeronautics and Space Administration (NASA), is intended to be used as an auxiliary power unit and also for experiments on electric propulsion systems for space vehicles (see **rocket propulsion, nuclear**). SNAP-50, also a joint AEC-NASA project, is intended for use in electric propulsion systems for space vehicles.

SNAP-2. The reactor developed for SNAP-2 is extremely compact. Unshielded, it is about the size of a 5-gallon can and weighs about 220 pounds. It is of the solid-homogeneous epithermal type and has a rated power output of 50 kilowatts (thermal). The fuel is a homogeneous mixture of fully enriched uranium, zirconium and hydrogen in the form of a U-Zr alloy hydride, the hydrogen content providing all the neutron moderation required. The fuel elements are contained in stainless steel cans. The coolant is a eutectic mixture of sodium and potassium ("NaK"), which is liquid at room temperature. The outlet coolant temperature is 1200°F. The reactor is controlled by adjusting the position of rotating segments of a beryllium reflector; there are no control rods.

TABLE 3. EVEN-NUMBERED SNAP DEVICES—MID-1962
(Reactor energy source [1])

Designation	Power Rating (electrical)	System Weight [3]	Energy Conversion		Notes
			Method	Efficiency	
SNAP-2	3 kw	1150 lb	Turboelectric	6%	Prototype reactor and turbogenerator have been individually tested. Test of integrated system scheduled for 1962. Space applications. Objective is to have a fully developed SNAP-2 device available for flight testing by 1965.
SNAP-4	1000–4000 kw	50–60 tons	Turboelectric	—	Design studies and component development in progress. Underwater or remote land applications.
(SNAP-6)	1–300 kw	1 ton	Thermoelectric	—	Parametric studies of devices ranging in output from 1 to several hundred kilowatts for underwater applications. No active development to date.
SNAP-8	30 kw [2]	300 lb [4]	Turboelectric	5%	Reactor experiment scheduled for 1962. Turbogenerator being developed by Aeroject-General Corporation under NASA contract. Space applications. Objectives are to demonstrate a system with a proven 90-day operating lifetime by 1964, and a 1-year operating lifetime by 1965.
SNAP-10A	500 watts	750 lb	Thermoelectric	2.5%	Under development for space applications. Flight demonstration targeted for 1963.
SNAP-50	1000 kw	—	Turboelectric	—	Objective is to develop power supply for electric rocket propulsion of space vehicles by late sixties.

[1] See text for notes on SNAP reactors.
[2] With one energy conversion unit. Reactor has sufficient capacity to operate with two conversion units and hence produce double the rated amount of electric power.
[3] The weights given relate to designs developed for specific applications, and, except for SNAP-8, include the weight of radiation shielding.
[4] Without shielding.

Development of the SNAP-2 reactor began in 1956. A prototype unit, known as the SNAP Experimental Reactor (SER) was placed in operation in Atomics International's laboratories at Santa Susana, California, in November, 1959 and was run continuously for one year, logging some 4200 hours at full power. Prototype mercury vapor turbogenerator equipment supplied by Thompson-Ramo-Woolridge, Inc., was tested separately. An integrated SNAP-2 system has been installed in an environmental test facility and is scheduled to begin operation in 1962. A progression of tests is planned. The first, designated SNAP-2 Developmental System (S2DS), will serve to provide basic data on system performance under design conditions. The second, designated SNAP-2 Package System (S2PS), will provide similar data for a "flight package" configuration. The third, designated SNAP-2 Flight System No. 1 (S2FS1), will be a ground demonstration of a final flight system.

SNAP-4. This will be a boiling water-cooled reactor utilizing the hydride fuel technology

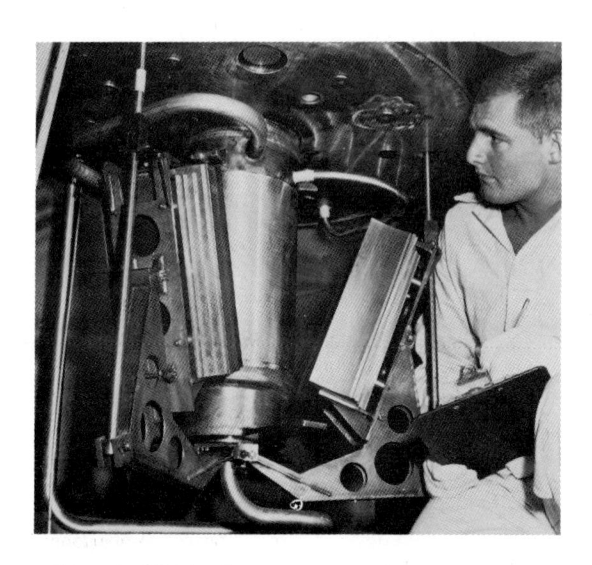

Fig. 190. SNAP-II reactor power source. Above, cylinder containing core of the SNAP-II experimental reactor (SER). Right, full-scale model of SNAP-II system mounted in nose cone of rocket. The reactor, about the size of a five-gallon can, is seen at the top of the cone. (*Courtesy of Atomics International*)

developed for SNAP-2. Design studies and component development work are now in progress as an outgrowth of feasibility studies initiated in 1959. The objective is to develop a compact system with an electrical output in the 1000-4000 kilowatt range and capable of unattended operation in an underwater or remote land environment.

SNAP-8. This is essentially a scaled-up version of SNAP-2. A reactor experiment is to be conducted in 1962, and a facility for environmental tests of an integrated SNAP-8 system is scheduled to be completed by the end of 1962.

SNAP-10A. This system will employ a SNAP-2 reactor operated at a power level of 30 kilowatts (thermal). An electromagnetic pump will circulate the coolant from the reactor core to a thermoelectric power conversion unit. The system will not require active control manipulation once in operation, and hence will have no moving parts in orbital use.

SNAP-50. This project, initiated in 1962, is based on the high temperature lithium cooled reactor concept formerly under development under the **Aircraft Nuclear Propulsion Program.** Construction of a 10-megawatt (thermal) reactor experiment at the National Reactor Testing Station is planned, subject (at this writing) to Congressional appropriation of the necessary funds. The ultimate design objectives of the SNAP-50 development are to achieve a system with a specific weight on the order of 10 pounds per kilowatt of electric power output (including the reactor, electrical conversion unit and heat dissipation radiator but excluding the radiation shield) and capable of unattended operation for 10,000 hours. It is envisioned that the fuel form will be a ceramic such as uranium monocarbide or uranium dioxide; that refractory metals such as columbium alloys will be used for the structural materials; and that the electrical conversion unit will employ a high-temperature working fluid, probably boiling potassium.

SODIUM

Element No. 11 (symbol, Na; atomic weight, 22.997) used in liquid metal form as a reactor coolant. The major advantages of liquid sodium as a reactor coolant are its excellent heat-transfer and pumping characteristics, and low vapor pressure, the latter property permitting high-temperature operation in a low-pressure system. Also it is chemically compatible with uranium. Its major disadvantages are its chemical reactivity with water in the presence of oxygen and its temporary radioactivity under neutron irradiation, due to the formation of sodium-24, a hard gamma emitter with a radioactive half-life of 15 hours. Also it should be noted that the thermal neutron absorption cross section of sodium (0.505 barn) precludes the attainment of a breeding economy in thermal reactor applications.

The use of sodium as a reactor coolant was first studied under the **Naval Reactors Program.** Two major power reactor concepts currently under development for civilian power reactors are based on sodium cooling (see **sodium-graphite reactors, fast breeder reactors**). For additional references to sodium cooling see **Advanced Epithermal Thorium Reactor Concept, Chugach Electric Association Project.** (Also see **reactor materials**)

SODIUM-GRAPHITE REACTORS

Power reactors that are cooled with liquid sodium * and moderated with graphite. The reactor coolant, which is made temporarily radioactive by neutron activation as it passes through the core, is circulated in a closed loop, referred to as the primary loop. Rather than radioactive sodium for steam generation, an intermediate heat exchange medium (nonradioactive sodium) is employed.** Two heat exchangers are thus required. In the first, referred to as the intermediate heat exchanger, the radioactive sodium transfers heat to nonradioactive sodium. In the second, referred to as the secondary heat exchanger or steam generator, the nonradioactive sodium transfers heat to water, thereby generating steam for power generation (see Fig. 191).

The feasibility of the sodium-graphite concept was first demonstrated by the successful operation of the **Sodium Reactor Experiment** (SRE) in April, 1957. A 76-megawatt (electrical) sodium-graphite power plant has been built under the U.S. Atomic Energy Commission's Power Demonstration Reactor Program (see **Hallem Nuclear Power Facility**). Both reactors were designed by Atomics International, a division of North American Aviation, Inc. Atomics International has been the major AEC contractor for research and development on sodium-graphite reactors. Of the approximately $476 million spent by the AEC for civilian reactor research and development through mid-1960, $111 million was applied to sodium-cooled reactors and, of this, about half went into the development of sodium-reactors and related materials and equipment, notably fuel materials and sodium equipment components.† Considerable use has been made in the sodium-graphite program of technology developed by other reactor programs, in particular: (1) The graphite technology developed during and after the war in the course of designing, building and operating the Hanford plutonium production reactors (see **Hanford Works**); (2) The original sodium technology developed by Knolls Atomic Power Laboratory in connection with the Sodium Intermediate Reactor (SIR)

* Sodium melts at approximately 208°F.

** This accomplishes several purposes: It avoids the problem of radiolytic decomposition of boiler feed water; it eliminates the hazard of radioactivity in the event of a sodium-water reaction in the steam generator (see text); and it avoids the need to shield the steam generator loop.

† These figures are exclusive of capital costs. Source: AEC.

Project (see **Naval Reactors Program),** and by Argonne National Laboratory in connection with Experimental Breeder Reactor No. 1 (see **fast breeder reactors)**; (3) The continuing development of sodium technology in connection with Experimental Breeder Reactor No. 2 and the Enrico Fermi Atomic Power Station (see **fast breeder reactors)**; and (4) General research and development sponsored by the AEC on sodium system components.

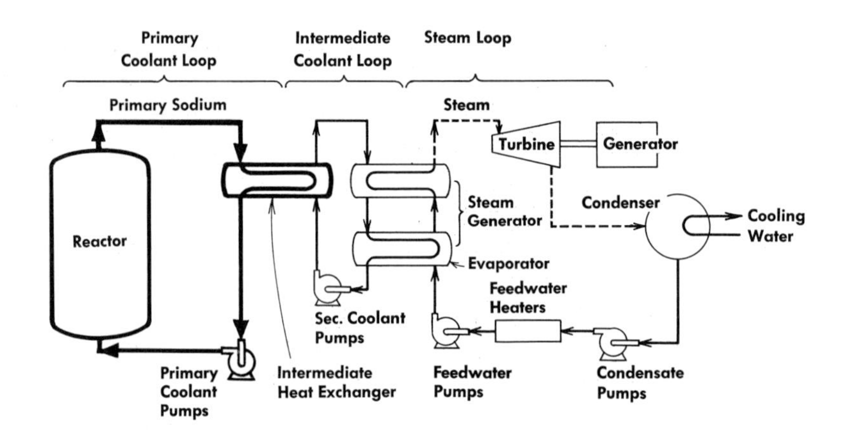

Fig. 191. Schematic diagram of sodium-graphite reactor plant.

General Considerations. The strong points usually cited for the sodium-graphite concept are:

1. Sodium has a high boiling point (1638°F), which permits operation at high temperature with a low-pressure system. Reactor overpressure is normally less than 3 psig.

2. Sodium has excellent heat-transfer properties which, combined with its high-temperature capability, permit achieving high thermal conversion efficiencies in power generation and high **specific power** in the fuel.

3. There is no problem of energy release from chemical reactions between sodium and any current or proposed fuel or structural materials.

4. Experience with the Sodium Reactor Experiment has shown this type of reactor to be extremely stable in operation.

The major limitations or problems associated with sodium-graphite reactors at the present time are:

1. Their neutron economy is such that they cannot serve as breeders.* This limitation derives from the fact that sodium absorbs an appreciable number of neutrons, its microscopic cross section for thermal-neutral capture being about two-thirds that of light water (H_2O). Unlike water-cooled systems, sodium-graphite reactors could operate with normal (nonenriched) uranium; however, over-all system economics dictate the use of slightly enriched fuel.

2. They are at an early stage of development, particularly with respect to fuel element and equipment technology (see later discussion).

3. The radioactivity induced in sodium by neutron activation ** is a disadvantage in two respects. One, noted earlier, is that it warrants the use of an an intermediate heat exchange system. The other disadvantage is the need to wait for the radioactivity to decay before

---

* Breeding is possible in sodium cooled reactors that operate with fast or intermediate neutrons. (See **fast breeder reactors, Advanced Epithermal Thorium Reactor**)

** Activation occurs by the neutron-gamma reaction, resulting in the formation of sodium-24, a gamma emitter with a radioactive half-life of 15 hours. Sodium-24 decays to magnesium-24, which is stable.

maintenance work can be done on primary sodium equipment following shutdown of a primary system loop. Normally a 10-day waiting period is required; however, in an emergency, earlier access to some primary sodium equipment is possible.

4. The design of the steam generator is complicated by the fact that sodium can undergo an exothermic chemical reaction on contact with water in the presence of air (see **metal-water reactions**). To minimize the possibility of air inleakage, both the Sodium Reactor Experiment and the Hallam Nuclear Power Facility use double-walled tube construction in the steam generator. The annular space is filled with an inert fluid which is monitored to detect leaks (see further discussion below).

5. Saturation of the graphite with sodium would substantially reduce the reactivity of the core. Therefore, the moderator material must be sheathed with a suitable cladding material or otherwise protected from contact with the coolant. An alternative to cladding the moderator is the so-called "calandria" design in which a large graphite structure is penetrated by fuel channels and coolant tubes. Other design alternatives are under investigation.

6. While not corrosive to most metals and ceramics, sodium reacts with some impurities which may be introduced into a reactor system, primarily oxygen. This is a complicating factor in the design of the reactor system and also in maintenance work since it means that equipment in which sodium is handled must be blanketed with inert gas.

7. Sodium-graphite reactors operate at low volumetric power densities and hence have large core structures. This characteristic stems from the large mass of graphite that must be built into the core, and not from heat-transfer considerations. It is not a disadvantage from a capital cost standpoint due to the use of thin wall vessels made possible by the low pressure at which sodium graphite reactors operate.

Plant Characteristics. See Table.

Development Trends. The most critical problem is the development of a fuel combining high thermal conductivity with the ability to withstand long exposure at high temperatures. The minimal development objective is an average burn-up of 17,000 MWD/ton at a surface temperature of 1200°F. Various metallic fuel alloys have been tested and of these only one—an alloy of uranium and thorium (< 10 weight % U)—appears capable of retaining dimensional stability at even moderate

SOME CHARACTERISTICS OF SODIUM GRAPHITE PLANTS

System Parameters	*Recent Design* [1]	*Projection* [2]
Pressure in primary loop	atmospheric	atmospheric
Primary coolant outlet temperature	945°F	1150°F
Intermediate coolant outlet temperature	905°F	1110°F
Steam conditions	800 psi, 825°F	2400 psi/1000°F/1000°F
Thermal conversion efficiency	31.6%	41.6%
Power density	4.4 tkw/liter	16tkw/liter
Specific power	7.3 tkw/kg U	38 tkw/kg U
Fuel		
Enrichment	2.85% U^{235}	3% U^{235}
Form	uranium-molybdenum alloy (10 wt. % Mo)	uranium carbide (UC)
Cladding material	stainless steel)	stainless steel)
Maximum central fuel temperature	1130°F	2200°F
Average burn-up	11,000 MWD/metric ton U	19,000 MWD/metric ton U

[1] Based on a design of a 76-megawatt (net electrical) plant prepared under AEC auspices in the fall of 1959. Source: TID-8516, Part I.
[2] Projected for a 300-megawatt (electrical) plant to be placed in operation in 1967-1968, assuming success of development work now in progress. Source: TID-8516, Part II.

burn-ups (~ 11,000 MWD/ton) at temperatures approaching the desired level. Uranium dioxide, which might be acceptable from a burn-up standpoint, has too low a thermal conductivity to be attractive in a high-performance sodium system. Preliminary data indicate that uranium mono-carbide (UC) has considerable promise as a fuel for sodium-graphite reactors; samples have been exposed to burn-ups as high as 25,000 MWD/ton with excellent results.

The need for high thermal conductivity and dimensional stability at high temperatures of course also applies to the fuel cladding material. Stainless steel, which is the cladding material presently used, leaves much to be desired from the standpoint of its neutron absorption and heat-transfer characteristics. Existing zirconium alloys, while excellent in most other respects, have inadequate high temperature strength. New zirconium alloys containing small amounts of molybdenum or aluminum show promise and are currently under development.

While considerable experience has been accumulated in the handling of sodium at elevated temperatures, development work needs to be done to improve and/or lower the cost of the major items of sodium equipment used in sodium-graphite reactors. Following are some of the considerations involved:

1. The use of double-wall construction in the steam generator entails excessive fabrication costs (~ $200 per square foot of heat transfer surface). Various design improvements are under investigation. For example, in the Enrico Fermi Atomic Power Plant, also a sodium-cooled system, single-wall tube construction with once-through coolant flow is employed. The Fermi steam generators cost ~ $55 per square foot (see **heat exchangers** for background information).

2. Both electromagnetic and mechanical pumps have been developed for use with sodium. Electromagnetic pumps are inherently inefficient and, in some designs, are installed directly in the coolant line, making access difficult. Centrifugal mechanical pumps of the shaft-seal type have not proved entirely reliable in high-temperature sodium service. A hybrid device has been developed which is based on mechanical rotation of a magnetic field. While such a device is no more efficient than a straight electromagnetic pump, it has the advantage that the components most likely to require maintenance are located outside the coolant line and hence are readily accessible (see **pumps** for background information).

3. Existing sodium stop valves are satisfactory in performance but very expensive, ranging from ~ $1000 per inch of valve opening for 14-inch valves to ~ $200 per inch for 2-inch valves. Various valve types are being studied in an effort to develop less expensive designs.

Economics. See **nuclear power economics.**

SODIUM-POTASSIUM ALLOY (NaK)

A low-melting **eutectic** of sodium and potassium (melting point, ~ 52°F; normal composition, 22% Na-78% K) used as the primary coolant in Experimental Breeder Reactor No. 1 (EBR-1).

SODIUM REACTOR EXPERIMENT (SRE)

A small government-owned experimental power reactor of the **sodium-graphite** type located in the Santa Susana Mountains, near Los Angeles, California. SRE was designed and is operated by Atomics International, a division of North American Aviation, Inc. It is connected to a turbine-generator owned and operated by the Southern California Edison Company.

SRE began operation in April, 1957. It has been used to demonstrate the feasibility and to study the operating characteristics of the sodium-graphite reactor concept, with particular emphasis on studying the performance of fuel elements and sodium-system components.

SRE operated for more than two years on its initial fuel loading. In July, 1959, plugged coolant channels caused overheating and failure of fuel elements and required that the reactor be shut down for core replacement. The plugging of the channels was found to have resulted from inleakage of an auxiliary cooling fluid (tetralin) used in the primary pump shaft seals. The use of this fluid has been discontinued and plant modifications have been made to avoid this problem in the future. Operation resumed in September, 1960.

Fig. 192. General view of the Sodium Reactor Experiment (SRE). (*Courtesy of Atomics International*)

SRE was initially fueled with stainless steel-clad uranium fuel elements. The present core contains stainless steel-clad uranium-thorium alloy fuel elements. It is contemplated that the third core will contain uranium-carbide fuel elements.

The following notes relate to the uranium-thorium core loading:

Power: 5 megawatts (electrical). *Fuel:* Fully enriched uranium-thorium alloy. *Fuel element design:* A single fuel element consists of a cluster of stainless steel tubes containing fuel slugs bonded with sodium-potassium. *Fuel inventory:* 87 kilograms of fully enriched uranium and 1160 kilograms of thorium. *Coolant:* Liquid sodium enters the reactor at 6 pounds pressure and 530°F, and leaves the reactor at 3 psi and 960°F. *Steam conditions:* 600 psi pressure and 825°F. (Steam temperatures as high as 1000°F have been achieved on a trial basis.) *Thermal conversion efficiency:* 29%. *Control materials:* 8 stainless steel-clad assemblies containing cylinders of a boron-nickel alloy. *Containment:* Steel-lined concrete vault in airtight building. *Cost:* The original capital investment is reported at $8.6 million, including $2.3 million for the turbine-generator and related electric facilities (owned by Southern California Edison Company) and buildings and supporting facilities contributed by Atomics International. Modifications made since the original installation have cost about $4.7 million. *Dates:* The project was initiated in July, 1954. The reactor first went critical in April, 1957. Electric power was first produced in July, 1957. Full power operation was first reached in May, 1958. Operation on the second core began in September, 1960.

SOLID-FUEL REACTOR

A nuclear reactor in which the fuel is in the solid phase, usually in the form of fabricated **fuel elements.** Usually the term is restricted to reactors having a fixed core, as distinct from fluidized bed or other designs in which the fuel is a solid but moves as a fluid.

SOLID HOMOGENEOUS REACTOR

A nuclear reactor whose core contains a solid homogeneous mixture of fuel and moderator. (See **research and training reactors**)

SOLUTION POISON

A soluble **poison** added to the coolant of a nuclear reactor for purposes of reactivity control (see **reactor control;** also see **burnable poisons).** To date, solution poisons have only been used during shutdown periods and are chemically removed from the coolant prior to resuming operation. The use of solution poisons is a means of reducing the requirement for control rods. An example of the use of solution poisons is the addition of boric acid to the coolant of the Yankee Atomic Electric Plant during shutdown periods.

SOLVENT EXTRACTION

A widely used method of accomplishing chemical separations based on preferential solubility in immiscible liquids; also called liquid-liquid extraction. Various solvent extraction processes are used in the atomic energy field, the major applications being in **uranium milling, uranium refining,** and **fuel reprocessing.**

The method can best be described within the context of a particular application. Consider, then, the separations involved in the reprocessing of irradiated uranium, as in the **Purex process.** The mixture fed to the solvent extraction portion of this process contains three basic components: uranium, plutonium, and an assortment of radioactive **fission products.** The form of the mixture is an aqueous nitrate solution in which the concentration of metallic nitrate ions has been carefully adjusted for optimum extraction conditions. Both plutonium and uranium are in the tetravalent state. As the feed enters the first extraction column, it is contacted with an upward-flowing organic solvent. Under the conditions maintained, the plutonium and uranium preferentially transfer into the organic solvent, forming what is known as the "extract" stream. Some of the fission products also transfer to the organic phase; however most of the fission product activity remains in the aqueous phase and leaves the bottom of the column as a waste stream, or "raffinate." Unavoidably traces of uranium will remain in the aqueous phase. The loss is held to a minimum by contacting the extract with a scrub solution containing a "salting agent," which enhances the effectiveness of the solvent by common ion effects. The lower part of the column in which most of the extraction takes place is known as the "extracting" section; the upper part is known as the "scrubbing" section.

The extract stream from the first column is fed into a second column in which it is contacted with a downward-flowing aqueous solution containing a reducing agent. The reducing agent serves to reduce the plutonium to the trivalent state, causing it to transfer from the organic to the aqueous phase. A separation is thus effected between the uranium, which leaves the top of the column still in the organic phase, and the plutonium, which leaves the bottom of the column in the aqueous stream.

In subsequent operations the uranium and plutonium-bearing streams are separately processed through additional solvent extraction cycles to remove residual fission product activity and are discharged as decontaminated aqueous solutions. The organic solvent employed in the process is recovered in auxiliary facilities and reused.

Considerable development work has gone into the design of the liquid-liquid contacting equipment used in solvent extraction systems, since the efficiency of the process depends on thorough mixing of the aqueous and organic phases. The three principal types of contacting equipment used in atomic energy applications are **packed columns, pulse columns,** and **mixer-settlers.**

The solvent extraction method has a number of desirable features where large amounts of metals are to be separated: (1) It lends itself to continuous, multicycle operation. (2) It is highly efficient, both in terms of the degree of separation and recovery achieved, and in terms of the use of process chemicals. (3) It is flexible and can accommodate changes in feed composition. In fuel reprocessing, these desirable features must be balanced against two undesirable features: (1) It generates large volumes of high-level radioactive wastes than

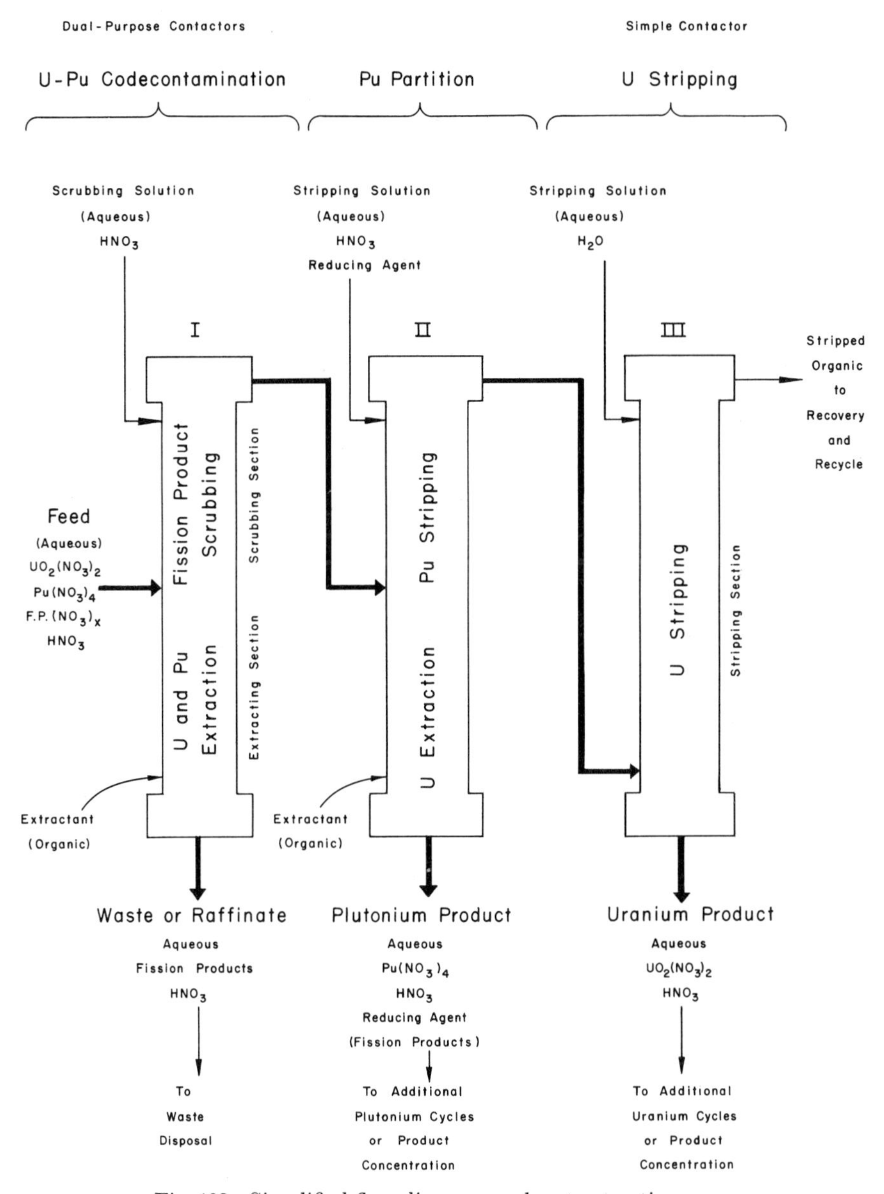

Fig. 193. Simplified flow diagram—solvent extraction process.

other reprocessing methods under development. (2) The organic solvents used are subject to **radiation damage,** which imposes limits on the radiation levels that can be permitted. (See **decay cooling)**

SOMATIC EFFECTS OF IONIZING RADIATION

A general term for all effects caused or induced by ionizing radiation which manifest themselves during the lifetime of the individual receiving the radiation dose (as opposed to genetic effects). (See **biological effects of ionizing radiation)**

SOURCE MATERIALS, NUCLEAR

A term used in federal atomic energy law and presently defined by U.S. Atomic Energy Commission regulations to mean materials, other than a **special nuclear material,** containing by weight one-twentieth of 1%

(0.05%) or more of uranium and/or thorium. The term derives from the fact that these elements constitute the source of the fissionable materials, uranium-235, uranium-233 and plutonium-239.

Source Materials	*Natural Isotopic Composition*	*Fissionable Materials*	*Means of Producing Fissionable Material*
Uranium	Fissionable component U^{235} (0.71%)	U^{235}	Isotope separation
	Fertile component U^{238} (99.28%)	Pu^{239}	Transmutation
Thorium	No fissionable component	—	—
	Fertile component Th^{232} (100%)	U^{233}	Transmutation

Under existing U.S. law, a license must be obtained from the AEC before source materials can be mined, bought or sold, imported or exported, or otherwise transferred. An exception is made for "unimportant quantities," as defined in Title 10 of the Code of Federal Regulations, Part 40.13.

Source materials are subject to AEC accountability procedures. (See **accountability for source and special nuclear materials)**

SOUTH AFRICA

Agency. The Atomic Energy Board, Pretoria, is the agency responsible for atomic energy maters.

International Relationships. Member of the **International Atomic Energy Agency.** Comprehensive **Agreement for Cooperation** with the United States.

Research Centers. A National Nuclear Research Center is being established near Pretoria and will be equipped with a high-flux research reactor supplied by Allis-Chalmers Manufacturing Company (U.S.). Research and training activity presently centers in the larger universities and in existing physical, medical, and agricultural research institutions.

The Government Metallurgy Laboratory of the University of Witwatersrand, Johannesburg, is a center of research on methods for the extraction of uranium from South African ores.

Production Activity. South Africa is a major producer of uranium (ranking third after the United States and Canada). Reserves are estimated at 370,000 tons, expressed as U_3O_8. Production is currently at a rate of about 6000 tons per year, most of which is supplied to the United States and the United Kingdom via the **Combined Development Agency.** The major producing areas are gold fields in the Transvaal and Orange Free State. There are in all some 27 producing mines and 17 ore processing facilities. The ore is usually first processed to recover gold and other precious metals. The tailings (residues) from this operation are then leached with sulfuric acid and, following an ion-exchange process, the uranium is recovered from the solution by precipitation. The precipitates (uranium diurinate) are sent to a central facility at Zuurbekom where they are filtered, dried, and calcined to form uranium trioxide, which is the form in which the uranium is shipped.

The following companies are engaged in large-scale uranium mining and processing operations: Anglo-American Corporation of South Africa Ltd.; Anglo-Transvaal Consolidated Investment Company Ltd.; New Consolidated Goldfields Ltd.; Rand Mines Ltd.; and Dominion Reefs (Klerksdork) Ltd. The central facility at Zuurbekom is operated by Calcined Products (Proprietary) Ltd.

A monazite deposit at Steekampskraal in northwest Cape Province is currently the world's largest source of thorium production.

Energy Economy. South Africa's energy economy is based on coal, of which there are ample reserves for the foreseeable future.

Nuclear Power Program. There is interest in nuclear power to serve areas remote from coal deposits; however, no projects have been announced.

Industry Notes. Transvaal and Orange Free State Chamber of Mines is a cooperative association whose membership includes most of the uranium producing companies.

Cape Nucleonic Society is an organization of prominent industrialists interested in promoting atomic energy research and development.

Fig. 194. Ion exchange columns in the uranium ore processing plant at the Welkom gold mine in the Orange Free State, an operation of the Anglo American Corporation of South Africa Ltd. (*Courtesy of Anglo American Corp.*)

Several South African companies are active in developing radioisotope applications and equipment. They include African Explosives and Chemical Industries Ltd. (Research Laboratories Division), Transvaal; Protea Holdings Ltd. (Nucleonic and Scientific Division), Johannesburg; and Electronic Development Laboratories, Johannesburg.

SOUTH ALBUQUERQUE WORKS. See **Atomic Energy Commission—Facilities.**

SOVIET UNION (USSR)

Agencies. The Ministry of Medium Machine Building, U.S.S.R., is the agency responsible for implementing Soviet policy and programs in regard to the military applications of atomic energy. The State Committee of the Council of Ministers for the Use of Atomic Energy is responsible for unclassified aspects of the Soviet program for East-West exchanges in atomic energy; for assistance to other countries; and for civil applications of atomic energy. The above two agencies work closely with other branches of the Soviet Government in discharging their responsibilities. For example, in some power reactor projects, the State Committee for the Use of Atomic Energy coordinates the necessary nuclear research and development and the supply of primary reactor components; the Ministry for Medium Machine Building supplies the nuclear fuel; the Ministry of Instruments and Automation develops and supplies the necessary instrumentation; and the Ministry of Power Plant Construction constructs and operates the station. However, there are some atomic power projects over which the State Committee has no jurisdiction.

National atomic energy policy is formulated by a complex process in which the Ministries of Defense and Medium Machine Building, the State Committee, the State Planning Commission (GOSPLAN), and the Academy of Sciences participate in formulating plans with final approval vested in the Central Committee of the Communist Party.

International Relationships. Member of the **International Atomic Energy Agency.** Organizer and principal member of the **Joint Institute for Nuclear Research** at Dubna. Various bilateral agreements for cooperation (see Table 1).

TABLE 1. BILATERAL AGREEMENTS OF THE U.S.S.R. FOR ATOMIC ENERGY COOPERATION

(as of mid-1960)

Country	*Research Agreement* [1]	*Power Agreement* [2]	*Recriprocal Exchange Agreement* [3]
Soviet Block Countries [4]			
Bulgaria	X		
Communist China	X		
Czechoslovakia	X	X	
East Germany	X	X	
Hungary	X		
North Korea	X		
Poland	X		
Rumania	X		
Other Countries			
France			X
India		Under discussion	
Indonesia	Under discussion		
Iraq	X		
United Arab Republic	X		
United Kingdom			X
United States			X
Yugoslavia	X		

[1] Covers technical assistance, usually including help in constructing a research reactor and a cyclotron together with other specialized equipment such as "hot" laboratories. The research reactors are of three types: TVR-S is a 7000-10,000 kilowatt (thermal) heavy water-moderated tank-type unit fueled with slightly enriched uranium. WWR-S is a 2000-kilowatt (thermal) pool-type unit fueled with uranium enriched up to 10%. IRT-1000 is a lower power (1000 kilowatts) version of WWR-S. The cooperating country bears the cost of the equipment, materials and service provided.

[2] Provides for Soviet assistance in carrying out an agreed nuclear power project.

[3] Provides for information exchange, increased contacts, etc.

[4] Members of the Joint Institute for Nuclear Research at Dubna in the U.S.S.R. Other members are Albania, Mongolia and North Vietnam.

Research Centers. See Table 2.

Production Activity. By Soviet law, all aspects of fissionable material production are classified; hence little information is available on raw material production or on the Soviet network of plant facilities. It has been estimated that uranium production in the Soviet Bloc as a whole is between 10,000 and 20,000 metric tons per year, expressed as uranium metal. It is clear that the U.S.S.R., like the U.S. and the U.K., has a completely integrated production complex, and that both uranium-235 and plutonium are produced in quantity. The following dates may be taken as indicative of the timetable of Soviet weapons development and underlying production capability: First detonation of a nuclear device in August, 1949; first detonation of a thermonuclear device August, 1953; successful test of deliverable thermonuclear weapon in November, 1955.

Nuclear Power Program. In June, 1954, the U.S.S.R. placed a 5-megawatt (electrical) nuclear power station in operation. While token amounts of electrical power had been produced from an experimental nuclear reactor in the U.S. prior to that date (see **Experimental Breeder Reactor No. I**), the Soviet unit represented the world's first demonstration of the operation of a reactor designed for power generation. In 1956, the Twentieth Party Congress announced that as part of the Five-Year Plan for national economic development over the period, 1956-1960, between 2000 and 2500 megawatts of nuclear power capacity would be constructed in the Soviet Union. That goal was later revised downward in the light of subsequent developments, notably rising nuclear power cost estimates. In 1957, the Five-Year Plan was abandoned in favor of a Seven-Year Plan for the period, 1959-1965. While this latter plan calls for doubling the national electrical power generating capacity (thereby bringing it up to 112,000 megawatts), and although the emphasis is placed on thermal (as opposed to hydroelectric) power plant construction, no goal for nuclear stations is mentioned. At about the same time the Seven-Year Plan was an-

TABLE 2. NUCLEAR RESEARCH CENTERS IN THE U.S.S.R. (1961)

Name	*Location*	*Major Experimental Facilities*
Joint Institute for Nuclear Research	Dubna	680-Mev synchrocyclotron; 10-Bev proton synchrotron. Pulsed neutron source reactor to operate at power levels up to 10,000 tkw is under construction
Institute for Atomic Energy	Moscow	2000-tkw pool-type research reactor (WWR-S); 15-20,000-tkw graphite-moderated test reactor (RPT); 1-Bev electron-synchrotron; OGRA high-energy injection device for controlled fusion research (similar in concept to U.S. DCX Experiment)
Thermotechnical Institute	Moscow	500-tkw heavy water-moderated research reactor (TR); 7-Bev proton synchrotron
Lebedev Physical Institute	Moscow	280-Mev electron synchrotron; 600-Mev electron synchrotron
Institute of Physical Problems	Moscow	4-6 Bev electron synchrotron in the design stage
Research Institute for Electron-Physical Instruments	Leningrad	200-Mev proton synchrotron; 50-Bev proton synchrotron in the planning stage
Institute of Physics and Technology	Leningrad	10,000-tkw pool-type research reactor (WWR-M); Alpha toroidal pinch device for controlled fusion research
Ukrainian Technical Institute	Kharkov	1-Bev electron linear accelerator
Kiev Physics Institute	Kiev	10,000-tkw pool-type research reactor (WWR-M)
Institute of the Latvian Academy of Science	Salapilis	2000-tkw pool-type research reactor
Physical Institute of the Georgian Academy of Sciences	Tbilisi	2000-tkw pool-type research reactor (IRT-2000)
Institute of Nuclear Physics	Kibrai (Uzbekistan)	(Center under construction)
Siberian Department of the U.S.S.R. Academy of Sciences	Novosibirsk (Siberia)	(Center under construction)
Polytechnical Institute	Tomsk	(Center under construction)
Institute of Physics	Krasnoyarsk	(Center under construction)

nounced, a leading Soviet scientist characterized the nuclear power program as an "experimental construction program intended to enable selection of the best methods of developing atomic power in the future."

Table 3 lists the nuclear power projects undertaken or planned by the U.S.S.R. as of mid-1960. This table, derived from various and sometimes contradictory Soviet statements, indicates that Soviet nuclear power capacity was approximately 100 megawatts as of mid-1960, and will not greatly exceed 1000 megawatts during the period of the present Seven-Year Plan.

Nuclear Ship Propulsion. The Soviet icebreaker, Lenin, a 16,000-ton vessel of 44,000 shaft horsepower, which began sea trials in September 1959, is powered by three pressurized water reactors, each rated at 90,000 kilowatts (thermal). The Lenin is reported to have assisted merchant ship convoys during the 1960 shipping season on the northern sea route.

Recent statements by Soviet officials indicate that the U.S.S.R. has constructed nuclear-powered submarines.

Nuclear Space Technology. The Soviet Union is reported to be developing a cesium-ion rocket propulsion system powered by a compact nuclear reactor.

Controlled Fusion. Research on controlled-fusion reactions, expected to lead ultimately to thermonuclear power development, is conducted on a scale comparable to that in the United States. The pattern is different, however; for example, there appears to be no Soviet effort comparable to the U.S. **Astron** and **Stellarator Programs.** Following are notes on several areas of Soviet controlled-fusion research:

OGRA. This is a very large molecular-ion injection and magnetic trapping device, similar in concept to the **DCX Experiment** at Oak Ridge National Laboratory. It is located at the Institute of Atomic Energy in Moscow and is a major focal point of the U.S.S.R. controlled-fusion effort.

Pinch Experiments. The major pinch device is Alpha, a large slow toroidal pinch apparatus, similar in concept to the United Kingdom's former Zeta apparatus. In addition, considerable work has been done on fast-pinch discharges, both stabilized and dynamic.

Other. The use of radiofrequency waves and of rotating plasmas are being studied in efforts to improve plasma confinement in magnetic

Fig. 195. The Soviet Union's nuclear-powered 16,000-ton icebreaker, *Lenin.* Top, the launching of the *Lenin* on the Neva River in Leningrad on September 12, 1959. Bottom, model showing arrangement of the power and propulsion equipment. (*Photo (top) courtesy of World Wide Photos. Photo (bottom) courtesy of USAEC*)

TABLE 3. U.S.S.R. NUCLEAR POWER PROGRAM

(Includes Projects Announced as of Mid-1960)

Reactor Type	*Installation*	*Location*	*Rated Capacity (MWe)*		*Notes*
			Per Reactor	*Total*	
Graphite-moderated, water cooled (pressure-tube design)	Demonstration Reactor (APS-1)	Obninsk (near Moscow)	5	5	Began operation in June, 1954.
"	Siberian Dual-Purpose Reactor Station (for plutonium and power production)-6 reactors	Somewhere in Siberia	100	600	First unit reported in operation September, 1958.
"	Beloyarsk Nuclear Power Station-4 reactors	Beloyarsk	100	400	Two units reported under construction, the first of which is due to begin operation in 1962. These reactors are designed to produce superheated steam.
Pressurized water	Voronezh Nuclear Power Station-2 reactors	On the Don River, 25 miles from Voronezh	210	420	First unit reported under construction and due to start operation in 1961 or 1962.
"	Leningrad Nuclear Power Station-2 reactors	Near Leningrad	210	420	To be built after experience has been gained at Voronezh.
"	Prototype Mobile Reactor	Obninsk	2	2	Prototype for military applications; believed to be in operation.
Heavy water-moderated, gas-cooled	—	—	—	—	Experimental power stations being built in Czechoslovakia and East Germany with Soviet assistance.
Fast breeder	Reactor Experiment (BN-50)	Ulyanovsk Reactor Center	50	50	Being designed; reactor to be fueled with a plutonium-uranium alloy.
"	Full-Scale Demonstration (BN-250)	(not announced)	250	250	Project awaits completion of BN-50.
Boiling water	Reactor Experiment	Ulyanovsk Reactor Center	50	50	Scheduled to be in operation in 1961.
Homogeneous suspension (uranium dioxide in heavy water)	Reactor Experiment	Ulyanovsk Reactor Center	heat only	heat only	Reported to be under construction.
		TOTALS:	107 MWe	In Operation	
			960 MWe	Under Construction	
			1130 MWe	Planned	
			2197 MWe	Grand Total	

Source: Volume 4 of Report of Robert McKinney to U.S. JCAE, October, 1960.

mirror systems. Various means of plasma heating, including the method known as ion-cyclotron resonance heating are being used.

SPACE APPLICATIONS OF ATOMIC ENERGY

While space technology is still at an early stage of development, it is the prevailing opinion that only by the exploitation of nuclear energy sources will it be possible to obtain sufficient operational independence from the earth to conduct manned interplanetary exploration. This opinion derives from the almost certain impracticability of launching and sustaining by chemical means the large spacecraft "payloads" that will be required to achieve orbital maneuverability, protection of personnel against corpuscular radiation in space, mobility on the surface of other planets, and other prerequisites of such exploration.

Apart from some brief background notes on propulsion systems (see **rocket propulsion (nuclear)**), coverage of this subject in this book is limited to the following specific nuclear development programs which relate wholly or in part to space applications: (1) **Rover Project,** which is devoted to the development of a nuclear heat-exchanger type of rocket propulsion system; and (2) **SNAP Program,** which is devoted to the development of radionuclide sources for use as small-scale auxiliary power units, and to the development of compact reactors for use as medium-scale auxiliary power units and in electric rocket propulsion systems.

SPAIN

Agency. The Junta de Energia Nuclear (JEN), Madrid, is the agency responsible for atomic energy matters.

International Relationships. Member of the **International Atomic Energy Agency,** the **European Nuclear Energy Agency,** and the European Organization for Nuclear Research **(CERN).** Comprehensive **Agreement for Cooperation** with the United States.

Research Center. The Centro Nacional de Energia Nuclear de la Moncloa, near Madrid, is JEN's principal research establishment. The diversified facilities include a uranium metal pilot-plant and fuel element fabrication facility; particle accelerators; a critical experiment facility; and a 3000-kilowatt (thermal) pool-type research reactor. The latter, supplied by General Electric Company, was constructed with the aid of a $350,000 Foreign Research Reactor Grant from the United States. An Argonaut-type research and training reactor recently built by the JEN staff is to be installed at the University of Barcelona.

Production Activity. Low-grade deposits of uranium have been found in Cordoba, Jaén, Cáceres, Badajoz, and Salamanca provinces. Mining operations produce sufficient marginal ore to supply an ore processing plant with a capacity of 200 tons of ore per day, operated by JEN at Andújar (Jaén), 200 miles south of Madrid. Up to 10 tons of uranium metal per year are produced in the Moncloa pilot plant. Heavy water is produced on a limited scale ($\sim$ ton/year) by electrolysis in a plant operated jointly by JEN and EIASA (Energia e Industrias Aragoneses, S.A.) at Sabinanigo.

Energy Economy. Spain's present electric power-generating capacity is about 6500 megawatts, three-quarters of it hydroelectric. Relatively little hydro potential remains to be developed. Coal is available but production costs are high. There is no oil.

Nuclear Power Program. Spain's long-range plans call for the installation of 1800 megawatts of nuclear power capacity by 1975. The first step planned by JEN is the construction of a 30-megawatt (thermal) power reactor for power demonstration purposes and to serve as a materials testing facility. JEN also plans to construct a large-scale nuclear power station by the mid-sixties. Several private interests have expressed interest in nuclear power projects (see below).

Industry Notes. CENUSA (Centrales Nucleares, S.A.), Madrid, is a company formed by three utilities with tentative plans for constructing a 250-megawatt (electrical) nuclear power station on the Tagus River.

CONUSA (Construcciones Nucleares, S.A.), Bilbao, is a company formed by 2 financial and 10 industrial concerns in Northern Spain to supply reactor components.

NUCLENOR (Centrales Nucleares del Norte, S.A.), Santander, is a company formed by utility and financial interests with tentative plans for the construction of a 300-megawatt (electrical) nuclear power station on the Ebro River at Tovalina.

TECNATOM, Madrid, is a company formed by utility, manufacturing, and financial interests to promote atomic energy development and participate in industrial projects. It will provide services in connection with JEN's power demonstration project (see above).

SPALLATION

A **nuclear reaction** in which the target nucleus splinters into a number of fragments. Spallation occurs when nuclei of intermediate mass number and atomic number are bombarded by elementary particles of high energy (several hundred million ev). For example, when uranium-238 is bombarded by a high-energy alpha particle, 13 or 14 neutrons may be emitted. The phenomenon was first observed by G. T. Seaborg, I. Perlman and colleagues at the E. O. Lawrence Radiation Laboratory in 1947.

SPECIAL NUCLEAR MATERIAL

A term used in federal atomic energy law and presently defined by U.S. Atomic Energy Commission regulations to mean plutonium, uranium-233, and uranium containing more than the natural abundance of the uranium-235 isotope, or any material artificially enriched by any of these substances. By definition, **source materials** are not classed as special nuclear materials.

Under existing law, the U.S. Government, through the AEC, has all rights and title to special nuclear material under U.S. jurisdiction. The AEC is authorized to issue **licenses** for the possession of special nuclear materials for approved purposes within the United States, and to make foreign distribution of such materials under **Agreements for Cooperation.**

Licensed industrial use of special nuclear material is normally subject to a use charge of 4.75% per annum applied to the value of the special materials inventory. This charge is sometimes waived in joint industry-AEC research and development projects.

Special nuclear material under U.S. jurisdiction is subject to AEC accountability procedures. (See **accountability for source and special nuclear materials)**

SPECIAL POWER EXCURSION REACTOR TEST PROGRAM (SPERT SERIES)

A program of reactor safety experiments conducted by the Phillips Petroleum Company at the National Reactor Testing Station on behalf of the U.S. Atomic Energy Commission. The program is concerned with the safety characteristics of water moderated reactor systems under transient conditions, i.e., during power excursions. The general objectives are to identify factors affecting the safety of such systems during periods of instability, and also to determine the conditions under which they become unstable. To these ends, the SPERT program has included study of the kinetics of the fission chain reaction; identification of inherent safety mechanisms; observation of reactor power surges and oscillations; measurement of **void coefficients;** and investigation of the hydrodynamic and thermodynamic characteristics of particular reactor systems. This work has led to improved understanding of the limitations of current reactor designs and is providing a basis for future design improvements.

Four special-purpose **test reactors** have been constructed under this program, identified as SPERT I, II, III and IV. Each is a flexible facility in which different cores can be installed and tested and each is equipped with a dual set of controls—one for steady-state operation and the other for transient operation.

SPERT I is an open tank reactor, used to study unpressurized light water-moderated reactor systems. First operated in 1955, it has been used for more than 750 transient tests, in some of which the power level has risen as high as 2400 megawatts (thermal) for brief intervals of time (usually less than one-tenth of a second).

SPERT II is a closed-tank reactor which can be operated with light or heavy water at pressures up to 300 psi and at temperatures up to 400°F. It was placed in operation in 1959 and is used mainly to study the effect of various moderator and reflector conditions on reactor performance.

SPERT III is a closed-tank reactor which can be operated with light water (boiling or pressurized) at pressures up to 2500 psi and temperatures up to 670°F, and with coolant flows ranging from zero to 20,000 gallons per minute. It is equipped to run transient tests and to operate at a steady-state power level of 60,000 kilowatts (thermal) for half-hour periods. It has been in use since 1958.

SPERT IV is a pool installation designed to study the kinetics of pool reactors of the type commonly used for research programs. Initial tests with this facility began in 1961.

SPECIFIC ACTIVITY

(1) With reference to a preparation of a radioisotope, the **activity** of the radioisotope per unit weight of the element present in the

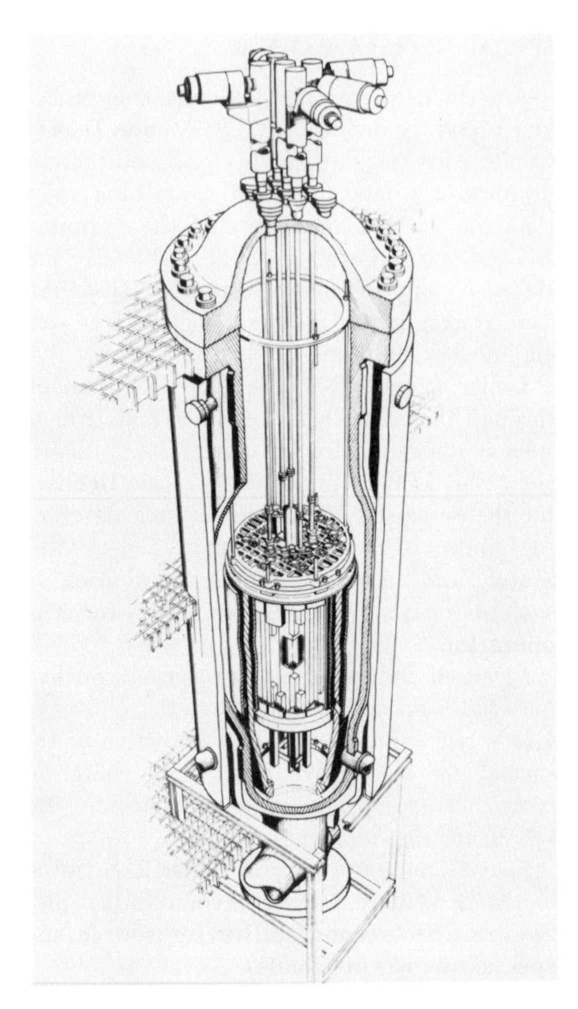

Fig. 196. Special Power Excursion Test Reactors. Above, general view of SPERT-II. Right, cutaway of SPERT-III reactor showing core arrangement. (*Courtesy of Phillips Petroleum Co.*)

sample. (2) The activity per unit mass of a pure radionuclide. (3) The activity per unit mass of any radioactive material.

SPECIFIC IONIZATION

The number of ion pairs formed per unit distance along the path of travel of a particle or photon of **ionizing radiation.**

SPECIFIC POWER

The power generated by a nuclear reactor per unit mass of fuel contained in the system. Specific power is usually expressed in kilowatts of heat per kilogram of **fissionable** plus **fertile material** contained in the reactor core, but values may sometimes be based only on the fissionable component of the fuel. In another usage, specific power is expressed in terms of the total inventory of the **fuel cycle,** i.e., the amount of fissionable plus fertile material contained in the reactor core plus that tied up in fuel reprocessing and refabrication.

The trend of power reactor development is in the direction of higher specific power in the interest of lower fuel inventory costs. A limiting factor is the rate at which heat can be removed from the core. (See **power density)**

SPECTRAL SHIFT REACTOR CONCEPT

A scheme for controlling a **pressurized water reactor** system based on adding or subtracting heavy water (D_2O) to the ordinary water (H_2O) coolant-moderator stream, thereby decreasing or increasing the reactivity of the core; sometimes referred to as the moderator control concept. By starting the freshly fueled reactor with a high ratio of D_2O to H_2O in the moderator, the system is "undermoderated" since D_2O is a poorer moderator of neutrons than is H_2O. The neutron spectrum is thereby shifted from the thermal toward the epithermal range. In the latter range, neutron resonance absorption in fertile material is relatively high, and, consequently, the need for control poisons to absorb neutrons is reduced or eliminated. As the fuel is irradiated, H_2O is added to the moderator to reduce resonance absorption in fertile material, thereby offsetting the decrease in reactivity due to fuel burn-up and fission product formation.

The use of moderator control in lieu of conventional poison control offers three advantages: (1) It reduces the amount of excess reactivity that must be built into the system, which reduction is desirable from a fuel inventory as well as a safety standpoint. (2) It reduces the number of control rods required. (3) It improves the neutron economy of the system by reducing parasitic neutron capture in control poisons.

Research on the spectral shift concept is being carried out by Babcock & Wilcox Company under an Atomic Energy Commission contract.

See **variable moderator reactor concept** for notes on another method of moderator control.

SPENT FUEL ELEMENTS AS RADIATION SOURCES.

See **radiation sources.**

SPIKED CORE

A general term for the core of a nuclear reactor containing a combination (not a mixture) of highly enriched and normal or slightly enriched fuel. Such a core is said to be "spiked" with the highly enriched component. (See **seed core)**

SS MATERIALS

Shorthand expression for **source** and **special nuclear materials** and any other high-value materials determined by the U.S. Atomic Energy Commission to require accountability measures. (See **accountability for source and special nuclear materials)**

STABILIZED LINEAR PINCH EXPERIMENTS

Experimental devices built as part of the **Pinch Program** of research on controlled **fusion.** These devices are used for research on techniques for achieving stabilized pinch-confinement of an ionized gas, or **plasma,** in a straight-tube configuration.

STABILIZED TOROIDAL PINCH EXPERIMENTS

Experimental devices built as part of the **Pinch Program** of research on controlled **fusion.** These devices are used for research on techniques for achieving stabilized pinch-confinement of an ionized gas, or **plasma,** in a toroidal (ring-shaped) tube configuration.

STABLE ISOTOPES

Nuclides which do not undergo radioactive decay. Sixty-three elements are known to have stable isotopes, many having several. (See Table in Appendix F.)

Stable isotopes are of interest to research workers as tracers in chemical experiments in which radioisotopes are not available or would introduce undesirable side effects. Other uses of stable isotopes, or elements or compounds enriched therein, include use as a starting material for the production of certain radioisotopes; use in experiments in which the differences in nuclear properties between isotopes of a given element are of interest; and use in the isotope dilution technique of chemical analysis.

Research quantities of many stable isotopes are produced at Oak Ridge National Laboratory by **electromagnetic separation** and are distributed through the Isotope Sales Department of ORNL and through various commercial firms.

STACK GAS PROBLEM WORKING GROUP

An *ad hoc* (nonstatutory) advisory body to the U.S. Atomic Energy Commission established in 1948 to consult with the AEC and its contractors on problems in the treatment and control of gaseous effluents from atomic energy facilities. Membership listed in Appendix D.

STAINLESS STEELS

Stainless steels are used extensively in the nuclear field, principally as a cladding or canning material for power reactor fuel elements, as a reactor structural material, and as a material of construction for chemical process equipment, notably in aqueous fuel reprocessing systems.

In the design of thermal reactor systems a choice must often be made between stainless steels and alloys of zirconium for use as fuel element cladding and/or the reactor core. Both materials have excellent corrosion resistance and mechanical strength up to moderate temperatures. Stainless steels are less expensive. Zirconium alloys have appreciably lower thermal neutron capture cross sections ($\sim$ 0.2 barn *vs.* 2.5 barns). The choice is therefore usually arrived at by balancing the added cost of the zirconium alloys against the savings that accrue from having a more favorable neutron economy in the reactor system. (See **reactor materials**)

STANDARD MAN

A standard description of the human body used to provide a common basis for interpreting experimental data relating to **maximum permissible concentrations** of radioactive substances in man's environment. Following is the "standard man":

Mass of Organs of the Adult Human Body

	Mass (gr)	%
Total body	70,000	100
Muscle	36,000	43
Skin and subcutaneous tissue	6,100	8.7
Fat	10,000	14
Skeleton		
Without bone marrow	7,000	10
Red marrow	1,500	2.1
Yellow marrow	1,500	2.1
Blood	5,400	7.7
Gastrointestinal tract	2,000	2.9
Contents of G.I. tract		
Lower large intestine	150	—
Stomach	250	—
Small intestine	1,100	—
Upper large intestine	135	—
Liver	1,700	2.4
Brain	1,500	2.1
Lungs [2]	1,000	1.4
Lymphoid tissue	700	1.0
Kidneys [2]	300	0.43
Heart	300	0.43
Spleen	150	0.21
Urinary bladder	150	0.21
Pancreas	70	0.10
Salivary glands [6]	50	0.071
Testes [2]	40	0.057
Spinal cord	30	0.043
Eyes [2]	30	0.043
Thyroid gland	20	0.029
Teeth	20	0.029
Prostate gland	20	0.029
Adrenal glands or suprarenal [2]	20	0.029
Thymus	10	0.014
Miscellaneous (blood vessels, cartilage, nerves, etc.)	390	0.56

Chemical Composition of the Adult Human Body

Element	*Mass (gr)*	%
Oxygen	45,500	65.0
Carbon	12,600	18.0
Hydrogen	7,000	10.0
Nitrogen	2,100	3.0
Calcium	1,050	1.5
Phosphorus	700	1.0
Sulfur	175	0.25
Potassium	140	0.2
Sodium	105	0.15
Chlorine	105	0.15
Magnesium	35	0.0511
Iron	4	0.006
Manganese	0.02	0.00003
Copper	0.1	0.0002
Iodine	0.003	0.00004

STANFORD LINEAR ELECTRON ACCELERATOR PROJECT

A U.S. Atomic Energy Commission-sponsored project involving the construction, on land owned by Stanford University, of a large linear electron accelerator (see **particle accelerator**) to operate in the 10-20 Bev range.* The accelerator, which will be approximately 2 miles in length and will cost an estimated $114 million, is scheduled to be in operation in 1967 or 1968. The project was originally proposed in 1957. In 1960, authorization was obtained for a design study, and in 1961, construction was authorized.

The accelerator will be powered by 240 klystron amplifiers each of which will initially operate at 6 megawatts, yielding a beam energy of 10 Bev. It is expected that it will prove possible to operate the klystron units at higher power and thereby achieve a beam energy of 20 Bev. Also, sufficient flexibility is being built into the design of the accelerator and klystron housing and other features of the installation to facilitate future operation at beam energies up to 45 Bev, should this be desired.

The accelerator beam will have an average current of 15 microamperes, which is substantially higher than can be achieved in circular electron machines. Also, it will have a small angular divergence, which should make possible great precision in experimental work.

STATE ACTIVITIES IN THE ATOMIC ENERGY FIELD

Passage of the **Atomic Energy Act of 1954,** which opened the way for private initiative and investment in the atomic energy field, brought to the forefront the need to define the division of responsibility between state and federal agencies in regulating atomic energy activities and also stimulated state governments to take an active interest in attracting atomic industry and promoting developments in this field.

Regulatory Responsibility. The question of federal *vs.* state regulatory responsibility was clarified by a 1959 amendment ** to the 1954 Act, which added a new section (Section 274) dealing with cooperation between the U.S. Atomic Energy Commission and the states. Basic provisions of Section 274 are essentially as follows:

1. The AEC retains authority and responsibility for granting licenses for (a) the construction and operation of all **production** and **utilization facilities;** (b) the export or import of **by-product, source** and **special nuclear material,** and of production and utilization facilities; (c) the disposal at sea of by-product, source or special nuclear waste materials; and (d) the disposal of such other by-product, source or special nuclear material as the AEC may specify as being sufficiently hazardous to require an AEC disposal license.

2. On certification of the existence of effective radiation control procedures, individual states may arrange to assume regulatory authority over the possession or transfer of (a) by-product materials, (b) source materials, and (c) special nuclear materials in quantities not sufficient to form a **critical mass.**

Also, Section 274 requires that the AEC cooperate with the states in the formulation of **radiation protection standards** to ensure "coordination and compatibility." (See **Federal Radiation Council**)

Legislative and Regulatory Actions. Prior to the passage of the above-mentioned amendment to federal law, a number of states had by legislation or executive order taken one or more of the following steps:

1. Established committees advisory to the governor or legislature to study the role of the state in atomic energy matters;

2. Appointed a state coordinator, usually reporting to the governor, to keep the state informed on atomic energy developments and to act in liaison with interested state agencies and with the federal government;

3. Passed enabling legislation for the control of radiation hazards;

4. Formulated specific radiation control codes or regulations.

Subsequent to the passage of the amendment, the Atomic Energy Commission has taken the following steps:

1. Prepared and distributed criteria for the guidance of the states and the AEC in deter-

* The most powerful electron accelerator now in operation is limited to 6-Bev (see Table in entry on **particle accelerator**).

** Public Law 86-373. (See **legislation, federal**)

mining the compatibility of state *vs.* federal regulatory programs;

2. Drafted, in cooperation with the Council of State Governments, a suggested State Radiation Control Act to serve as a model for basic enabling legislation for radiation control programs;

3. Drafted, in cooperation with the Council of State Governments, the U.S. Public Health Service, the U.S. Department of Labor, and the **National Committee on Radiation Protection and Measurements,** suggested state radiation control regulations.

4. Established training programs to prepare state and local government personnel for the assumption of regulatory responsibilities.

As the foregoing suggests, at this writing many states are currently engaged either in establishing radiation control programs or in harmonizing existing programs with recently established federal criteria; similarly, many are also preparing to assume the regulatory functions open to them under existing federal laws. The first state to assume regulatory authority under the new law was Kentucky, which, effective March 26, 1962, took over rulemaking, licensing, inspection and enforcement responsibility for the categories of radioactive materials described above in Item 2 under the heading, "Regulatory Responsibility." As of mid-1962, two other states (California and Mississippi) had signed agreements with the AEC providing for the transfer of similar responsibility.

Workmen's Compensation. Matters relating to workmen's compensation are solely within the jurisdiction of the states. Here a problem arises in connection with radiation effects caused by small amounts of radiation exposure over a long period of time. The National Industrial Council has proposed that the "statute of limitations" provisions of workmen's compensation statutes be modified to provide for actions to be filed within a reasonable period from the time of discovery of the injury or disease and not from the time of cause as is commonly the case.

Nuclear Power. State utility commissions are beginning to be faced with policy questions relating to nuclear power projects, e.g., whether or not to allow the accelerated depreciation of capital investment, as under grants of convenience and necessity; and, similarly, whether or not to allow the write-off of research and development costs as current expense. As yet there have been too few cases for a meaningful pattern to emerge.

Industrial Development. Several states have taken significant steps to attract atomic industry and/or promote local atomic energy developments. In New York, for example, a State Atomic Energy Research and Development Authority has been established and, as of mid-1962, had appropriated funds for three projects, namely, study of the feasibility of constructing a salt water desalination plant utilizing a nuclear reactor as the heat source; start of construction of a Space Technology and Atomic Radiation Center to be equipped with a pulse-type research reactor; and construction of certain facilities for a fuel reprocessing and radioactive waste storage center. (See **Nuclear Fuel Services, Inc. Project**)

AEC Advisory Committee. In 1955 an **Advisory Committee of State Officials** was appointed by the Atomic Energy Commission as a means of obtaining the views and advice of state regulatory agencies in connection with the AEC's regulatory responsibilities in the field of public health and safety. Membership of the committee was broadened in 1960 in light of the increased emphasis on federal and state cooperation in atomic energy matters.

STATE DEPARTMENT, U.S.

The U.S. Department of State is concerned with the international aspects of U.S. atomic energy activities, both in relation to peaceful and military applications. Major areas of activity relate to bilateral agreements between the United States and other countries or international organizations for cooperation in atomic energy development or mutual defense purposes (see **Agreements for Cooperation**); and negotiations bearing on **international control of atomic energy.**

Responsibility within the Department for atomic energy matters rests with (1) the Office of the Special Assistant to the Secretary for Atomic Energy and Outer Space (S/AE), which handles policy development and co-ordination relating to bilateral and multilateral arrangements in the peaceful and military uses of atomic energy and maintains liaison with the U.S. Atomic Energy Commission, the Department of Defense and other appropriate federal agencies, (2) the Disarmament Administration, which is concerned with all disarmament matters, and (3) the Department's Bureau of International Organizations Affairs, which handles operating problems relating to the **International Atomic Energy Agency (IAEA)** and the United Nations, maintaining a U.S. mission at the Vienna headquarters of the former organization. The United States is represented at the European Atomic Energy Community **(Euratom)**, the European Economic Community and the European Coal and Steel Community by an ambassador who has a deputy for Euratom affairs appointed by the AEC with the concurrence of the Department of State. The Special Assistant to the Secretary of State (see above) represents the United States at the **European Nuclear Energy Agency**. The Department maintains atomic energy officers on the staff of the embassies in London and Paris.

STATIONARY LOW-POWERPLANT. See SL-1.

STATIONARY MEDIUM-POWERPLANTS. See SM-1; -1A; -2.

STEAM COOLED REACTOR CONCEPT

Steam cooled reactors are of potential interest as a means of superheating steam produced in boiling water reactors and thereby improving the thermal conversion efficiency of a boiling water power plant. See discussion of separate *vs.* integral nuclear superheating under **boiling water reactors**.

STEAM GENERATORS. See heat exchangers.

STELLAR TEMPERATURES

Temperatures above several million degrees—so called because temperatures of this magnitude occur naturally only in the interior of the sun and other stars. Stellar temperatures are of interest in context with research on controlled **fusion** for **thermonuclear power** generation. For this purpose, temperatures of the order of 100,000,000 degrees Kelvin are believed to be required (see **ignition temperature**). Such temperatures, commonly referred to as "thermonuclear temperatures," are usually expressed in electron volt units: 1 ev corresponds to 1.16×10^4 °K.

In controlled fusion, the fuel is in the form of an ionized gas, or **plasma.** When reference is made to a "plasma temperature" of, for example, 100,000,000 degrees, what is meant is that the ions and electrons which comprise the plasma have a Maxwellian velocity distribution corresponding to that temperature. During the intervals when such a condition exists the plasma would normally be insulated from the walls of the reaction apparatus by a vacuum zone. Also, the mass of the plasma is very small relative to that of the apparatus. Thus a "stellar-hot" plasma can be achieved in a relatively cold apparatus.

STELLARATOR PROGRAM

One of several lines of U.S. research on controlled **fusion** (see **thermonuclear power**). A stellarator (the term connotes "stellar" temperatures) is a device in which an ionized fuel, or **plasma,** is magnetically confined in an endless tube by means of an externally imposed magnetic field. The program is being conducted for the U.S. Atomic Energy Commission at the Plasma Physics Laboratory, James Forrestal Research Center, Princeton University, under the direction of L. Spitzer, Jr., and has been in progress since 1951.

Concept. A strong uniform magnetic field, such as can be produced in a straight tube wound with a solenoidal coil, will confine charged particles except for losses at the tube ends. At first glance, it would appear that bending the tube and joining the ends to form a ring-shaped tube, or torus, would prevent these losses. Unfortunately, this results in a magnetic field which is stronger toward the inside of the bend and weaker toward the periphery. The nonuniformity of the field causes positive and negative particles to drift in opposite directions across the magnetic lines. The resulting charge separation in turn sets up an electric field which drives all particles to the tube walls.

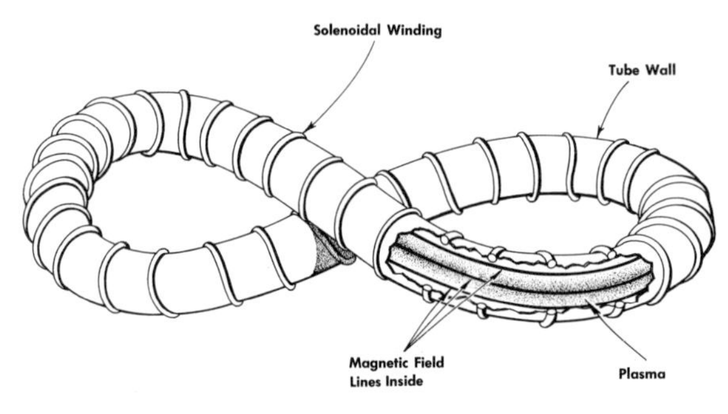

Fig. 197. Figure "8" stellarator configuration.

If the torus is twisted into a pretzel-like shape such as a figure "8" (Fig. 197), the magnetic field lines will twist correspondingly as they travel around the closed loop. Then the charged particles, in moving along field lines, will neutralize any space charge fields tending to be set up, and large-scale particle drift is thereby minimized. Similar results can be achieved in a simple, untwisted "racetrack" tube by placing several secondary helical windings around the tube with current flowing in opposite directions in adjacent helices (see Fig. 198). This serves to twist the magnetic field lines, thereby canceling particle drift. Moreover, the magnetic field is not merely twisted but twisted with "shear," which adds in an important way to the plasma stability. The use of such helical winding is now favored in the stellarator program.

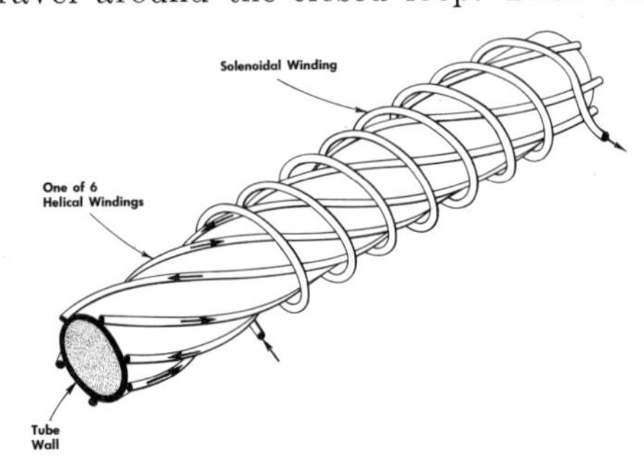

Fig. 198. "Racetrack" stellarator tube with secondary helical windings.

Several methods for heating the ionized plasma to thermonuclear temperatures have been proposed and investigated. In early models the plasma was subjected first to a radiofrequency voltage and then to a DC pulse process called **ohmic heating.** Calculations showed, however, that even in large models this method would fail to raise the plasma temperature much above a million degrees. A second method, called **magnetic pumping,** involves heating the plasma by rapidly fluctuating the applied field in successive sections around the tube. The plasma in these regions is thus successively compressed and expanded by a sort of pumping action. Theoretical studies indicated that with proper choice of pumping frequency, degree of modulation of the magnetic field, etc., magnetic pumping should result not only in rapid heating of the plasma but, more important, in the preferential heating of the positive ions. A modified version of magnetic pumping called **cyclotron resonance heating** involves compression and expansion of the plasma at a frequency close to the so-called cyclotron frequency of the ions, i.e., the natural frequency of rotation of ions in the magnetic field. Charge separation is prevented by placing two cyclotron heating units side by side operating in opposite phase. Preliminary tests of the method have proved successful.

As in all proposed controlled thermonuclear devices, impurities in the system can seriously increase the production of **bremsstrahlung** radiation and thereby depress the temperature of the plasma. The stellarator program has attempted to deal with this problem in two ways: First, by the development of a very clean vacuum system (the walls of the discharge tube are baked to remove occluded gases). Second, by use of a **divertor,** the function of which is to lead wall-originated impurities out of the system before they make their way into the plasma.

Fig. 199. Model C Stellarator. (*Courtesy of Allis-Chalmers Manufacturing Co.*)

Program. Between 1951 and the end of 1959, a total of 8 major experimental devices were built in connection with the stellarator program (see Table 1). Some of the accomplishments, prior to start-up of the Model C Stellarator (see below), can be stated as follows: It has been shown that both figure "8" and racetrack configurations have confinement capability. Plasmas have been produced for periods of several milliseconds, and ion temperatures in excess of 1,000,000°K have been achieved. It has been discovered that the quasi-DC pulse induced in the stellarator for initial ohmic heating produces **runaway electrons,** whose presence is disadvantageous to proper operation. Operation of the Model-C Stellarator will provide information on plasma stability in relatively large-scale equipment and is expected to shed considerable light on the basic feasibility of the stellarator concept. This unit, built at a cost of $24 million, was constructed by C-Stellarator Associates—a joint venture of Radio Corporation of America and Allis-Chalmers Manufacturing Company—under a subcontract to Princeton University, the prime contractor to the U.S. Atomic Energy Commission. Preliminary operation started in 1961. It is hoped that ion temperatures in the range of 1-2 $\times$ 10^8 °K may eventually be attained.

STERILIZATION, FOOD. See **food preservation.**

STERILIZATION, PHARMACEUTICALS. See **cold sterilization of pharmaceuticals.**

STORED ENERGY

Potential energy built up in a solid as a result of atom displacement by **fast neutrons** during irradiation in a nuclear reactor. The phenomenon occurs most notably in the graphite lattice of graphite-moderated reactors operating at relatively low temperatures. The potential energy in this case may exceed 500 calories per gram, enough to increase the temperature of the graphite by 1200°C if released suddenly, and hence is a potential hazard in the operation of such reactors. Stored energy

TABLE 1. STELLARATOR-TYPE EXPERIMENTAL FUSION MODELS

Model	*Operating Date*	*Purpose and Description*	*Geometry*	*Length (feet)*	*Tube Diameter (inches)*	*Method of Heating*	*Expected Ion Temperature (°K)*
A	1952	To test effectiveness of figure-8 configuration and radiofrequency voltage for initial ionization	Figure-8	6	2	Radiofrequency	—
Etude (A-2, A-3)	1957	To study confining field with quasi-continuous pulse, helical windings in A-3	Figure-8	4	2	—	—
B-1	1954	To test ohmic heating; modified in 1956 with improved mgnetic field coils	Figure-8	7	2	Radiofrequency and quasi-d-c pulse	7×10^5
B-2	1956	To test magnetic pumping	Figure-8	10	2	Radiofrequency, d-c pulse, and magnetic pumping	3×10^6
B-64, B-64-0	1955	To test operation of a divertor	Flexible distorted toroid	6	4	Radiofrequency and d-c pulse	5×10^5
B-65	1959	To test ion-cyclotron resonance heating	Race track	10	5	Radiofrequency, d-c pulse, and ion cyclotron	10^7
B-3	1958	Improved B-2 model incorporating a bakeable vacuum system, divertor, and stabilizing windings	Figure-8	10	2	Radiofrequency, d-c pulse, and ion cyclotron	—
C	1961	Large experimental model to test effective use of full-scale components	Race track	25	8	Radiofrequency, d-c pulse, and magnetic pumping	$1\text{–}2 \times 10^8$

in graphite can be "bled off" by annealing the graphite for a brief period at elevated temperatures and this is usually done periodically to maintain safe conditions.

The atom displacement causing the buildup of stored energy is known as the Wigner effect, having been predicted by E. P. Wigner.

STRANGE PARTICLES

A term applied to certain **elementary particles,** namely, **mu-mesons, K-mesons** and **hyperons** which are produced in nuclear reactions induced by charged particles from high-energy **particle accelerators.** The adjective "strange" indicates that the role of these particles in the determination of the properties and behavior of matter is not yet understood.

STRATOSPHERE

That part of the earth's atmosphere lying between the troposphere and the ionosphere. The dividing line (tropopause) between the stratosphere and the troposphere (lower part of the atmosphere) lies at different altitudes at different latitudes and fluctuates with the seasons and with atmospheric conditions, but is in the general range of 6 to 12 miles above sea level. (It is lowest at the poles and highest at the equator.) Similarly, the dividing line between stratosphere and the ionosphere is 50 or 60 miles or more above sea level. The stratosphere is characterized by an almost complete absence of weather phenomena, a factor which bears on the problem of predicting "stratospheric fallout." (See **radioactive fallout)**

STRETCH

The name given to a series of large electronic digital computer systems manufactured by the International Business Machines Corporation. The computer operates at a speed roughly 40 times that of the IBM-704 machines, and has a much larger memory capacity.

The first Stretch computer was installed at Los Alamos Scientific Laboratory in 1961. A second, and larger, Stretch system is to be installed at the Livermore Branch of the E. O. Lawrence Radiation Laboratory.

STRONG FOCUSING

In certain high-energy **particle accelerators,** the use of opposite polarity in successive sections of the stabilizing magnet to obtain a more strongly focused particle beam. See discussion under **alternating gradient synchrotron;** also see **fixed-field alternating gradient synchrotron.**

STRONTIUM-90

A beta-emitting fission product with radioactive half-life of approximately 28 years, of interest in the following applications: (1) Beta **gages** activated by strontium-90 are extensively used in industry to measure (and thereby control) the thickness or density of thin materials (paper, textiles, etc.) or coatings. (2) It is one of several radionuclides being used as energy sources for small auxiliary power units (see **SNAP Program).** (3) It is used as a source of beta radiation in medical research, notably in treatment of skin diseases and lesions of the eye.

Formerly produced exclusively and on a limited scale by the irradiation and subsequent processing of uranium capsules, strontium-90 is now being produced in amounts up to 4,000,000 curies per year by the Multicurie Fission Products Pilot Plant at Oak Ridge, which receives shipments of a strontium concentrate recovered from radioactive wastes at the AEC's Hanford Works and processes it into strontium titanate. The current price schedule (effective March 20, 1962) is $2.00 per curie for amounts up to 5000 curies; $1.00 per curie for amounts in the range of 5-30,000 curies; and $0.75 per curie for amounts above 30,000 curies.

Strontium-90 is also of interest as a potential public health hazard, being the most biologically significant constituent of **radioactive fallout** from nuclear weapon tests. Its biological significance derives from several factors: (1) It is produced in appreciable yield in the detonation of fission-type weapon devices. (2) It tends to deposit in bone tissue.* (3) It has a long **effective half-life.**

STRUCTURAL MATERIALS

In a nuclear reactor, materials used for structural purposes (as distinct from fuel, coolant, moderator or control materials, all of which have working functions). Structural materials include coolant piping, core supports, grid plates for spacing fuel elements, channels for control rods, and the like. Fuel element cladding materials are sometimes categorized as structural materials.

For information on structural materials, see **reactor materials.**

SUBCRITICAL REACTOR

A nuclear reactor whose effective **multiplication factor** is less than unity and hence cannot sustain a chain reaction, i.e., is noncritical. Subcritical reactors are primarily used for educational purposes.

SUBMARINES, NUCLEAR. See **Naval Reactors Program.**

SUDAN

Member of the **International Atomic Energy Agency** (IAEA). No active atomic energy program.

SULFEX PROCESS

A technique of **"head-end"** treatment being developed for the reprocessing of stainless

* Due to the fact that strontium is chemically similar to calcium.

steel-clad fuel elements from power reactors—specifically, a process for dissolving the cladding of such fuel elements preparatory to dissolution of the fuel proper and subsequent solvent extraction (see **fuel reprocessing**). The reagent used in the Sulfex process is sulfuric acid.

SULFUR

Element No. 16 (symbol, S; atomic weight, 32.066). Sulfur has been considered for use in fluid form as a power reactor coolant but has been found to be excessively corrosive (see **boiling sulfur reactor concept**). Interest in this element is therefore limited at the present time to applications for the radioisotope, sulfur-35, produced by neutron irradiation of chlorine:

$${}_{17}Cl^{35} + {}_{0}n^{1} \longrightarrow {}_{16}S^{35} + {}_{1}P^{1}$$

Sulfur-35 is used industrially in beta **gages** of the types that measure the thickness or density of thin coatings by back scattering techniques. It is also used extensively as a radioactive tracer, notably in animal metabolism studies and in medical research.

SUPERCRITICAL REACTOR

A nuclear reactor whose effective **multiplication factor** is greater than unity; hence a reactor with a rising reaction rate.

SUPERHEATING

Heating a vapor, especially steam, beyond its saturation point at a particular pressure. Superheating is used to improve the efficiency of thermal conversion in steam-electric power generating systems and also to minimize condensation problems in the turbines used in such systems. (See **nuclear superheating, nuclear power development, U.S.**)

SURFACE BLAST

The detonation of a nuclear weapon at a point on the earth's surface (land or water).

SURFACE BURST

The detonation of a nuclear weapon at a low enough altitude for the **fireball** to come into contact with the earth's surface (land or water). (See **weapons phenomenology**)

SURVEY METER

A portable radiation detection instrument, usually a **Geiger counter, scintillation counter,** or pulse-type **ionization chamber** in combination with a **ratemeter.** Survey meters are used in prospecting for radioactive materials, in **radiation monitoring,** and in checking radiation levels during operations involving the handling of radioactive materials.

Fig. 200. Survey meter. (*Courtesy of Nucleonics*)

SWEDEN

Agencies. The Atomic Energy Board (Delegationen för Atomenergifragor), Stockholm, an advisory body under the Department of Commerce, maintains supervision over the national atomic energy program. Aktiebolaget Atomenergi (AA), Stockholm, a quasi-official organization capitalized jointly by the government (57%) and private interests (43%), is responsible for planning and implementing the national program. The State Power Board (Kgl Vattenfallsstyrelsen), Stockholm, collaborates with AA on space heating and power reactor projects.

International Relationships. Member of **International Atomic Energy Agency,** the **European Nuclear Energy Agency,** and the European Organization for Nuclear Research **(CERN).** Research-type **Agreement for Cooperation** with the United States.

Research Centers. Studsvik Research Station at Studsvik, 60 miles south of Stockholm, is AA's principal research establishment. It has extensive experimental facilities, including a zero-energy reactor (RO) for studies of natural uranium-heavy water lattices; and a 30,000-kilowatt (thermal) tank-type research and materials testing reactor (R2). The latter, supplied by ACF Industries, was constructed with the aid of a $350,000 Foreign Research Reactor Grant from the United States. AA has additional research facilities in Stockholm, including a 1000-kilowatt (thermal) heavy water-moderated tank-type research reactor (R1) built by the laboratory staff in 1954.

Production Activity. An estimated 1 million tons of uranium are contained in low-grade ($\sim$ 0.03%) shale deposits near Billingen. An ore processing plant with a capacity of 120 tons per year is located in this area. Small-scale uranium refining and metal production facilities are operated by AA in Stockholm. AA is considering installing small-scale facilities at Studsvik for the recovery of plutonium from irradiated fuel. Consideration is also being given to the construction of heavy water production facilities.

Energy Economy. Sweden's present electrical generating capacity is about 7300 megawatts, practically all of it hydroelectric. It is estimated that hydro sources will largely satisfy the country's power requirements until the mid-seventies; at which time supplementary energy supplies will need to be provided. Sweden has no oil and very little coal of commercial grade.

Nuclear Power Program. Sweden has tentatively targeted the installation of 2000 megawatts of nuclear power capacity by 1975. Sweden is also interested in the use of reactors for space heating and estimates a potential requirement for at least 50 district heating plants, sized in the 30-60 megawatt (thermal) range. Information on specific projects is given below.

Adam (R3), Agesta (near Stockholm). This is a natural uranium heavy water-moderated and cooled reactor being built by AA in collaboration with the State Power Board. It is scheduled for completion in 1962 and will initially operate at a power level of 65 megawatts (thermal) with provision for later operation at 125 megawatts. Its primary purpose is to supply heat for central district heating of a Stockholm suburb; however, it will also produce some electrical power by means of a back-pressure turbine.

Fig. 201. The R-2 materials testing reactor installation at the Atomic Energy Board's Studsvik Research Station. (*Courtesy of Allis Chalmers Manufacturing Co.*)

Eva (4), Vickbolandet (90 miles southwest of Stockholm). This is to be a natural uranium heavy water nuclear power station (size not fixed). Now in the design stage, it is scheduled for completion in 1967. It is a joint project of

AA, the State Power Board (which will operate the station), ASEA, and NOHAB (see below).

SIMPEVARP, Kalmar County. AKK (see below) plans to contract for the installation of a 50-60 megawatt (electrical) boiling water nuclear power station on the Baltic Coast by 1965, or thereabouts.

Industry Notes. AKK (Atomkraftkonsortiet Krangede AB & Co.), Stockholm, is an organization formed by leading private and municipal electrical utilities to conduct nuclear power studies. (See SIMPEVARP Project above.)

ASEA (Allmänna Svenska Elektriska Aktiebolaget), Västeras, Sweden's largest electrical equipment concern, is interested in reactor manufacture and has license agreements with Atomic International in this field; it is also interested in the establishment of facilities for heavy water production.

The Johnson Concern, Stockholm, a family-owned industrial complex, is interested in supplying nuclear materials and marine propulsion equipment; it has license agreements with Westinghouse Electric Corporation.

NOHAB (Hydqvist & Holm AB), Trollhättan and Bofors, a manufacturing combine (heavy machinery and chemicals), is interested in reactor manufacture and nuclear materials production.

Swedish Ship Building Research Foundation (Stiftelsen för Skeppsbyggnadsteknisk Forskning), Göteborg, is an association of ship owners interested in reactors for marine propulsion.

SWITZERLAND

Agencies. The Office of the Delegate for Atomic Questions (part of the Department of Foreign Affairs of the federal government) is the agency responsible for atomic energy matters. The Federal Commission for Atomic Energy, a committee comprised of government officials and chaired by the Delegate for Atomic Questions, advises the Federal Council on questions of atomic energy policy. The Commission for Atomic Science, an arm of the Swiss National Science Foundation, coordinates the nuclear research activity of the Swiss Universities and Institutes of Technology. All three agencies are located at Berne.

International Relationships. Member of the **International Atomic Energy Agency,** the **European Nuclear Energy Agency,** and the European Organization for Nuclear Research **(CERN).** Research-type **Agreement for Cooperation** with the United States.

Research Center. The Institute for Reactor Research, Würenlingen, is the principal nuclear research center in Switzerland. Formerly the Würenlingen Laboratory of Reactor A.B. (see below), this center is now operated by the Federal Polytechnical Institute of Zurich. The specialized experimental facilities include "hot" laboratories, a critical assembly, and two reactors: SAPHIRE, a 1000-kilowatt (thermal) pool-type research reactor, was purchased from the United States after the 1955 Geneva Conference at which it had been on exhibit. DIORIT, a recently completed 12,000-kilowatt (thermal) natural uranium heavy water research and materials testing reactor, was designed and built by Reactor A.G.

The University of Geneva has a 20-watt AGN-201 research and training reactor, and the University of Basle has a 1-kilowatt AGN-211 research reactor.

Production Activity. Limited at present to uranium exploration. Deposits found to date are not of commercial grade.

Energy Economy. Switzerland's present electrical generating capacity is about 5000 megawatts, nearly all hydroelectric. There appear to be ample hydro resources for near future requirements. There is no oil and virtually no coal.

Nuclear Power Program. Long-term planning awaits the outcome of the following experimental projects:

A 16-megawatt (electrical) boiling water reactor is scheduled for installation at Villigen by 1963. This is a project of Suisatom A.G. (see below). The contractor is International

General Electric Company in collaboration with Brown, Boveri & Company.

A second small boiling water reactor (5 megawatts electrical) is planned for installation at Lucens by 1963. This unit is to be operated by ENUSA (see below).

A 30-megawatt (thermal) natural uranium heavy water reactor is planned for installation at Villigen by 1964. This unit is to be built by a consortium (see below) with General Nuclear Engineering Company (U.S.) acting as technical consultants.

Industry Notes. Consortium for the Construction of a Prototype Reactor, Winterthur, is an organization of seven Swiss industrial interests formed on the initiative of Sulzer Brothers, Ltd.

ENUSA (Energie Nucléaire S.A.), Lausanne, is an organization formed by 13 industrial interests in French-speaking Switzerland.

Reactor A.G. was a private corporation formed with the general participation of Swiss industry and with substantial government subsidies to conduct atomic energy research and development. It established the research facilities at Würenlingen and operated this center until 1960, at which time the assets of the corporation were taken over by the government.

Suisatom A.G., Zurich, is an association formed by electric utility interests with the participation of the Swiss Federal Railroads and the cities of Berne, Basle, and Zurich.

SYNCHROCYCLOTRON

A type of **particle accelerator** used to produce beams of protons, deuterons or alpha particles of high energy (hundreds of Mev); sometimes referred to as a frequency-modulated cyclotron. A synchrocyclotron differs from a conventional cyclotron in that provision is made for varying the radiofrequency of the oscillating electrical field to compensate for the relativistic increase of particle mass at increasing particle energies (see discussion under **cyclotron**). Specifically, the frequency is decreased, on a synchronized basis, as the particle velocity increases.

This means of compensating for the relativistic mass effect was independently proposed in 1945 by E. M. McMillan of the U.S. and V. Veksler of the U.S.S.R. It was first reduced to practice in a 37-inch machine, but was followed by the 184-inch synchrocyclotron at the E. O. Lawrence Radiation Laboratory. The 184-inch machine was placed into operation in the fall of 1946, and is currently capable of producing beams of 730-Mev protons, 460-Mev deuterons, or 910-Mev alpha particles.

The term synchrocyclotron should not be confused with synchrotron.

SYNCHROTRON. See **electron synchrotron; proton synchrotron.**

T

TABLE TOP (I, II AND III)

The name of a series of experimental controlled-**fusion** devices of the "magnetic mirror" type built at the Livermore Branch of the E. O. Lawrence Radiation Laboratory (see **magnetic mirror systems**). Table Top I was operated in 1954-1955. Table Top II, built in 1955, has been used to conduct single-stage high-compression experiments in which stable **plasma confinement** has been demonstrated, albeit at low ion temperatures. It has also been used for the detailed study of predicted confinement instabilities which can be achieved by adjustment of the operating conditions. Table Top III went into operation in 1961.

TAGGING. See labeling.

TANK REACTOR

A nuclear reactor in which the core is installed in a closed tank (as opposed to an open pool). The term is used to identify a general class of research or test reactors and connotes a heterogeneous (as opposed to a solid homogeneous or aqueous homogeneous) system. See **research and training reactors** for a description of a tank reactor.

TECHNETIUM

Element No. 43 (symbol, Tc; atomic weight, 99), first identified in 1937 by C. Perrier and E. Segré in Italy, working with a specimen of molybdenum that had been subjected to deuteron-neutron bombardment in a cyclotron at the University of California. The name technetium, from the Greek "technetos" (meaning artificial), was suggested by the fact that this was the first element, previously unknown on earth, to be produced artificially.

Various isotopes of technetium have since been identified. One of particular interest is technetium-99, a beta-emitter with a radioactive half-life of 2×10^5 years that is potentially useful as a beta source for industrial applications. Technetium-99 occurs as a fission product and is currently being recovered from radioactive wastes in kilocurie quantities in the Multicurie Fission Products Pilot Plant at Oak Ridge.

TELETHERAPY

Radiation therapy performed by means of an external, as oposed to an internal, source of ionizing radiation, e.g., x-ray therapy. (See **medical aspects of atomic energy**)

TEMPERATURE COEFFICIENT OF REACTIVITY

In reactor theory, the rate of change of **reactivity** per unit temperature change.

TERPHENYL

An organic compound [$(C_6H_5)_2C_6H_4$] which is the basic component of the organic mixtures used as coolant-moderator in **organic cooled reactors.** Following are approximate data for several organic mixtures marketed commercially under the name "Santowax":

	"Santowax OM"	"Santowax R"	"Santowax OMP"
Diphenyl	16%	<1%	<1%
Ortho-terphenyl	46%	10%	12%
Meta-terphenyl	32%	50%	61%
Para-terphenyl	6%	20%	25%
High-boiler impurities	<1%	20%	~ 1%
	100%	100%	100%

"Santowax OM," which is relatively rich in diphenyls, is the mixture used in the Organic Moderated Reactor Experiment (OMRE). "Santowax OMP," which is essentially a pure terphenyl mixture, or "Santowax R," which is the raw preparation from which the "OMP" product is distilled, are currently preferred. The price of these mixtures is currently in the neighborhood of 15 cents per pound.

Advantages cited for the above mixtures relative to other organic compounds that have been considered for reactor use are better stability under irradiation; a comparatively low melting-point range (70-200°F); lower vapor pressure; and the fact that they are available commercially.

The advantages of organics in general, relative to other fluids with which they can be compared for reactor use—notably water—are that they permit operation at substantially lower pressures and are essentially noncorrosive.

Organics are subject to degradation under irradiation, requiring that purification facilities be provided and fresh make-up supplied; however, the operating experience of OMRE indicates that the rate of degradation is well within acceptable limits.

See **organic cooled reactors** and **reactor materials** for further information. Also note reference to organic cooling under **heavy water-moderated power reactors.**

TEST REACTORS

Nuclear reactors used to conduct tests in support of reactor development. For information on reactors used for more varied experimental purposes, see **research and training reactors.**

Test reactors designed for general irradiation testing of reactor materials and equipment components are usually referred to as general-purpose test reactors (see Table 1, p. 544). Those designed to study the performance of particular reactor systems or for other specific purposes are usually referred to as special test reactors (see Table 2, p. 545 for partial listing).

THAILAND

The Thai Atomic Energy for Peace Commission, Bangkok, is the agency responsible for atomic energy matters. A 1000-kilowatt (thermal) pool-type research reactor is planned for Chulalongkern University. The United States has committed $350,000 toward the cost of this installation under its program of Foreign Reactor Research Grants.

Thailand's present electric power capacity is only 100 megawatts, most of which serves Bangkok and environs. A large hydroelectric development is underway at Yan Hei, which will initially supply an additional 500 megawatts, and ultimately 800 megawatts, of generating capacity. No nuclear power projects have been announced.

Thailand is a member of the **International Atomic Energy Agency** and has a research-type **Agreement for Cooperation** with the United States.

THERMAL BOND

In reactor fuel elements, provision for effective heat transfer between the fuel material and the protective cladding. The term implies "thermal conductivity bond" and means that the fuel and cladding surfaces are either physically bonded together or are otherwise thermally connected. Ways of achieving a thermal bond include: (1) fusing the cladding to the fuel material by the application of pressure and heat; and (2) use of a solid or gaseous bonding medium. (See **fuel element fabrication**)

TABLE 1. GENERAL-PURPOSE TEST REACTORS
(January 1961)

Installation	*Designation*	*Location*	*Designer*	*Type*	*Power Rating (Thermal kilowatts)*	*Neutron Flux (max. thermal in core n/cm² sec)*	*Start-up* [1]
U.S. Installations							
Materials Testing Reactor (AEC) [2]	MTR	National Reactor Testing Station	ORNL-ANL/Blaw-Knox	Tank	40,000	5×10^{14}	1952
Engineering Test Reactor (AEC) [2]	ETR	National Reactor Testing Station	General Electric/ Kaiser Eng.	Tank	175,000	7.5×10^{14}	1957
General Electric Test Reactor	GETR	Pleasanton, California	General Electric/ Bechtel	Tank	30,000	2.4×10^{14}	1958
Westinghouse Testing Reactor [3]	WTR	Waltz Mill, Pennsylvania	Westinghouse	Tank	60,000	1.1×10^{14}	1959
Plum Brook Reactor Facility (NASA)	NASA-TR	Sandusky, Ohio	NASA	Tank	60,000	$\sim 10^{15}$	1961
Advanced Engineering Test Reactor (AEC)	ETR-II	National Reactor Testing Station	Phillips Petroleum/ Ebasco	Tank	$\sim$ 250,000	$\sim 10^{15}$	(1964)
U.S. Exports							
Japan (Japan Atomic Energy Research Institute)	JRR-2	Tokai-Mura	AMF Atomics	Tank (D_2O)	10,000		1960
Netherlands (National Reactor Center)	HFR	Petten	Allis-Chalmers (ACF)	Tank	20,000		1961
Sweden (Studsvik Research Station)	R2	Studsvik	Allis-Chalmers (ACF)	Tank	30,000		1960

[1] Parentheses denote scheduled start-up.
[2] Operator: Phillips Petroleum Company.
[3] Operation terminated in 1962.

THERMAL BREEDER REACTOR

Any reactor that operates with neutrons in the thermal energy range (<1 ev) and achieves a **breeding gain,** i.e., produces more fissionable material than it consumes. The best fuel cycle for thermal breeding is the uranium-233—thorium-232—uranium-233 cycle, i.e., the use of uranium-233 as fuel and thorium as fertile material, resulting in the breeding of additional uranium-233. A uranium-235—thorium-232—uranium-233 "chain" may also be used, however U^{235} has a lower **eta** value for thermal neutrons than U^{233} (2.07 *vs.* an estimated 2.29 neutrons per fission).

Thermal breeding has not been demonstrated to date. Types of power reactor considered to have potential for thermal breeding include **molten salt reactors** and **aqueous homogeneous reactors.** (See **breeder reactors, fast breeder reactors**)

TABLE 2. SOME SPECIAL TEST REACTORS
(1961)

Installation	*Designation*	*Location*	*Contractor*	*Start-up* [1]
Civilian				
Reactor safety experiments:				
Kinetic Experiment on Water Boilers (AEC)	KEWB	Santa Susanna, Calif.	Atomics International	1956
Special Power Excursion Reactor Test No. 1 (AEC)	SPERT-1	National Reactor Testing Station	Argonne Nat'l Lab.	1955
Special Power Excursion Reactor Test No. 2 (AEC)	SPERT-2	National Reactor Testing Station	Argonne Nat'l Lab.	1960
Special Power Excursion Reactor Test No. 3 (AEC)	SPERT-3	National Reactor Testing Station	Argonne Nat'l Lab.	1958
Special Power Excursion Reactor Test No. 4 (AEC)	SPERT-4	National Reactor Testing Station	Argonne Nat'l Lab.	(1962)
Transient Test Reactor Facility (AEC)	TREAT	National Reactor Testing Station	Argonne Nat'l Lab.	1959
Reactor physics measurements:				
Argonne Fast Source Reactor (AEC)	AFSR	National Reactor Testing Station	Argonne Nat'l Lab.	1959
Special fuel-element testing facilities:				
Heavy Water Components Test Reactor (AEC)	HWCTR	Savannah River, S.C.	du Pont	(1962)
Plutonium Recycle Test Reactor (AEC)	PRTR	Hanford, Wash.	General Electric	1960
Radiation shielding studies:				
Bulk Shielding Reactor Nos. 1 & 2 (AEC) [2]	BSR-1, -2	Oak Ridge, Tenn.	Oak Ridge Nat'l Lab.	1950/ 1959
Biomedical research:				
Biological Research Reactor (AEC)	JANUS	Argonne, Illinois	Argonne Nat'l Lab.	(1962)
Fast Burst Reactor (AEC)	FBR	Oak Ridge, Tenn.	Oak Ridge Nat'l Lab.	(1962)
Military [3]				
Sandia Engineering Reactor Facility (AEC)	SERF	Sandia Base, N. Mex.	Sandia Corp.	(1962)
Sandia Pulsed Reactor Facility (AEC)	SPRF	Sandia Base, N. Mex.	Sandia Corp	1961

[1] Parentheses denote scheduled or planned start-up.
[2] BSR-1 was the first pool reactor built.
[3] Excludes test reactors built under the **Aircraft Nuclear Propulsion Program**, which was terminated in 1961.

THERMAL COLUMN

A facility incorporated in some nuclear reactors to provide **thermal neutrons** for experimental purposes. A thermal column consists of a large body of **moderator** located adjacent to the core or **reflector** of the reactor. Neutrons that leak from the core or reflector enter the thermal column and are slowed down to thermal energy. Experiments can be conducted in the neutron flux within the thermal column or with neutron beams emerging from the thermal column through ports in the reactor shield. Most **research** and **test reactors** are equipped with thermal columns. Thermal columns are commonly used as the external neutron source in exponential experiments.

THERMAL CONVERSION EFFICIENCY. See **thermal efficiency.**

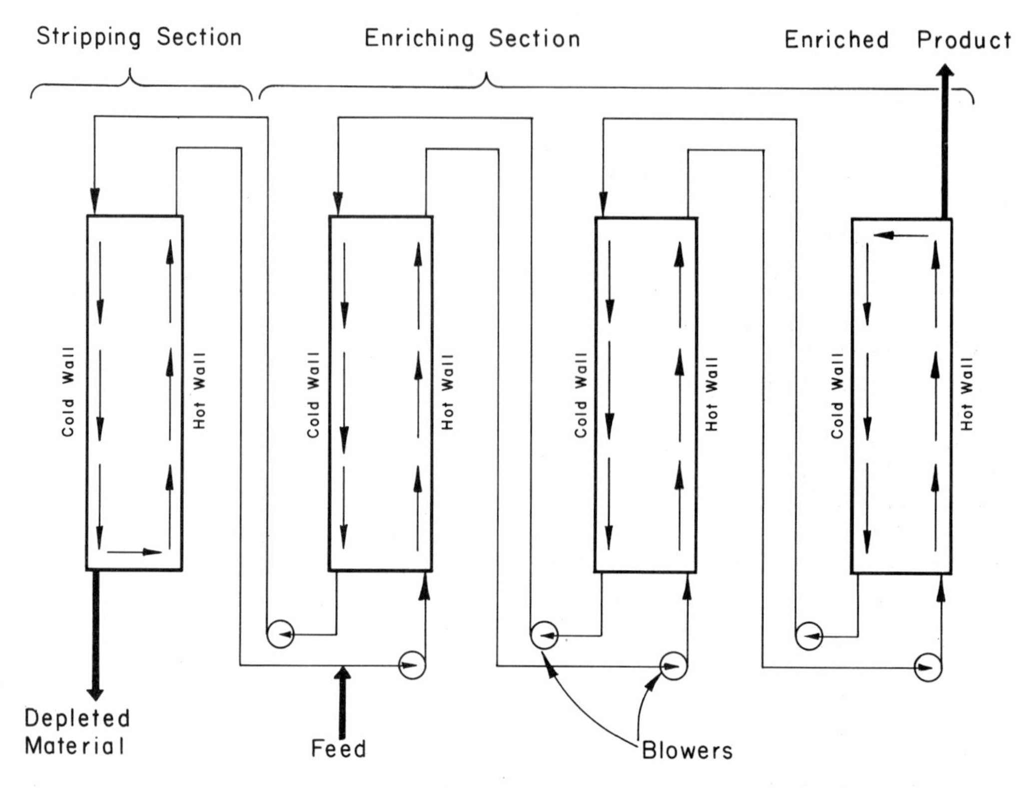

Fig. 202. Simplified diagram—thermal diffusion process.

THERMAL DIFFUSION PROCESS

A process for the separation of isotopes based on the fact that if there is a temperature gradient in a mixture of two or more fluids a concentration gradient tends to be established, with the lighter molecules tending to concentrate in regions of higher temperature. The method was used during the **Manhattan Project** on an interim basis to produce partially enriched uranium (which was then further enriched by **electromagnetic separation).** The facility built for this purpose was located at Oak Ridge and was known as the S-50 Plant. It consisted principally of a series of diffusion columns, each containing two concentric pipes, the inner of which was heated and the outer of which was cooled. A countercurrent flow of liquid-phrase uranium hexafluoride was maintained in the annular space between the pipes, the enriched stream flowing up the column adjacent to the hot wall of the annulus and the depleted stream flowing down the column adjacent to the cold wall of the annulus. The columns were connected in a cascade arrangement, the enriched stream from one column being piped to the next column "up" the cascade and the depleted stream being piped to the next column "down," etc.

THERMAL EFFICIENCY

In steam-electric power generation, a measure of the efficiency with which a given generating unit or system converts latent thermal energy to actual electrical energy; also referred to as thermal conversion efficiency. It is defined as follows:

$$\text{Thermal efficiency } (\%) = 100 \times \frac{\text{net electrical energy produced}}{\text{heat value of fuel consumed}}$$

A related term is "heat rate," which is defined as the number of Btu's of heat consumed per kilowatt-hour of net electrical power output.

In conventional, i.e., fossil fuel-fired-steam-electric plants the thermal input is taken as the heat of combustion of the fuel fed to the steam boiler. Heat losses through furnace walls and the smokestack, estimated to average 14% of the heat of combustion in modern installations, are thus taken into account. Other factors are the thermodynamic loss in the energy conversion, and the amount of the electricity produced that goes to operate plant equipment, i.e., the difference between the gross and the net electrical output. Thermodynamic loss is the principal factor and is largely a function of the temperature and pressure at which steam is generated, being less at higher operating conditions. The thermal efficiency of the best coal-fired plants in the United States has increased substantially over the years—from about 5% at the turn of the century, to about 30% in the mid-thirties, to as high as 40% today. The average thermal efficiency of all thermal power plants now in operation in the United States is estimated to be approximately 33% at the present time.

In the case of nuclear power plants, the thermal input is usually taken as the increase in energy content of the coolant as it passes through the reactor core. Certain energy losses, e.g., heat removed by the shielding cooling system, are sometimes disregarded, resulting in an overstatement of thermal efficiency. Thermal efficiencies achieved by or predicted for the several large-scale nuclear power plants presently in operation or under construction range from 26 to 30%. Reactors capable of operation at higher temperatures and methods for increasing steam temperatures by superheating are under development in an effort to achieve higher thermal efficiencies. (See **nuclear power development; nuclear power economics)**

THERMAL NEUTRON

A neutron which is in thermal (or molecular kinetic) equilibrium with its surrounding medium. Hence, the energy of a thermal neutron is dependent upon the temperature of the medium. At ordinary temperatures, this energy is approximately 0.026 ev, giving the neutron a speed of about 2.2×10^5 centimeters per second. The table below gives the average speeds and energies of thermal neutrons:

Temperature °*C*	°*F*	*Energy* (*ev*)	*Speed* (*cm/sec*)
25	77	0.026	2.2×10^5
200	392	0.041	2.8×10^5
400	752	0.058	3.4×10^5
600	1112	0.075	3.8×10^5
800	1472	0.092	4.2×10^5

Thermal neutrons are often referred to as slow neutrons. (See **fast neutrons, intermediate neutrons)**

THERMAL POWER PLANT

Any electric power plant which operates by generating heat and converting the heat to electricity; thus any steam-electric plant, whether fueled with fossil fuels (coal, oil and natural gas) or with nuclear fuels. The term is usually used in contradistinction to a hydroelectric plant.

THERMAL REACTOR

A nuclear reactor in which the fission chain reaction is propagated mainly by **thermal neutrons,** i.e., by neutrons that have been slowed down until they are in thermal equilibrium with the atoms of the **moderator.** The high end of the thermal-neutron energy range is usually taken to be 0.25 ev.

THERMAL SHIELD

In a nuclear reactor, a radiation **shield** of dense material located between the reflector and the **biological shield** to reduce the intensity of the ionizing and thermal radiation to which the latter is exposed. By reducing the radiation intensity the thermal shield reduces thermal stresses, prevents weakening of the biological shield due to **radiation damage,** and also avoids the need for cooling the biological shield. (Where the reactor core is housed in a tank or pressure vesesel, the walls thereof are also protected by the thermal shield.) Steel slabs cooled by an auxiliary cooling system comprise a common form of thermal shield.

THERMAL TEST REACTORS

Small nuclear reactors used for reactor physics measurements, such as **danger coefficients,** and for measuring neutron **cross sections.** TTR-1, at Knolls Atomic Power Laboratory, and NTR, a privately owned facility at General Electric Company's Vallecitos Laboratory in Pleasanton, California, are used for research purposes. TTR-2, at the Hanford Works, and SP, at the Savannah River Plant, are used for routine tests in support of plutonium production reactor operations. *Type*: Special design. *Power rating*: TTR-1, 10 thermal kilowatts. TTR-2, 100 watts. SP, 2-10 kilowatts. NTR, 30 kilowatts. *Fuel*: Highly enriched uranium in the form of uranium-aluminum disks mounted on rods. *Coolant*: H_2O. *Moderator*: H_2O. *Reflector*: Graphite.

THERMAL UTILIZATION FACTOR

In reactor theory, the ratio of the number of **thermal neutrons** absorbed per unit time in reactor fuel to the total number absorbed in the reactor system in the same unit time; hence a measure of the efficiency of thermal-neutron utilization. (See **neutron economy)**

THERMIONIC CONVERSION

A technique for the direct conversion of heat to direct-current electricity (see **direct energy conversion).** Thermionic conversion devices are being developed to produce small amounts (watts) of electricity from the decay heat of radioisotopes, and are being studied for ultimate application to power reactor systems (see below).

Principles. A thermionic converter is akin to an electronic vacuum tube. The simplest configuration is that of a vacuum diode tube, which consists of two metal electrodes separated by a vacuum space. Heating of the cathode serves to dislodge electrons from the lattice structure of the cathode material by increasing their kinetic energy. These electrons "boil off" and flow to the anode, which is maintained at lower temperature. By connecting the two electrodes to a load, an electrical circuit is established and current flows, the heat serving as a kind of "electron pump." Usually the material selected for use in the cathode has a higher "work function" * than that used in the anode. The latter should have as low a work function as possible in order to achieve maximum output from the system. An example of a metal commonly used as an anode material is nickel.

In contrast to **thermoelectric conversion,** little energy is lost through thermal conduction between the hot and cold terminals since heat cannot readily cross a vacuum. Partly for this reason and partly because they characteristically operate at higher temperatures, thermionic converters can achieve higher energy conversion efficiencies than thermoelectric converters. Efficiencies of 40% or higher are theoretically possible with thermionic conversion and efficiencies somewhat above 10% have been demonstrated; whereas thermoelectric conversion has a maximum efficiency somewhere between 25 and 35%, and the best performance demonstrated to date is around 5 or 6%.

A major problem in thermionic conversion is inhibition of current flow by what are known as "space charge" effects. In essence electrons crossing the vacuum space build up an effective negative space charge which, by electric repulsion, discourages further electron flow. A way to reduce space charge effects in a simple diode system is to minimize the distance between the electrodes. To be effective this requires spacings of the order of 0.0001 inch. Another way is to neutralize the space charge with positive ions, thereby creating an electrically neutral **plasma** in the space between the electrodes. Most of the research currently being conducted on thermionic systems is based on the use of plasma diodes.

In a plasma diode, the tube containing the electrodes is filled with cesium vapor or other gas with suitable ionization characteristics, usually at low absolute pressure (< 1.0 mm

* Work function is a threshold energy value, namely, the energy required to enable the most energetic electrons (so-called Fermi level electrons) to escape from a given material at a given operating temperature.

Hg). Where a source of high-intensity gamma radiation is available (as when the thermionic converter is used inside a nuclear reactor) ionization is automatically provided for. Where this is not the case, ionization must take place at the cathode, which requires that the cathode material be at an extremely high temperature (~ 2000°C). Desirable electrode spacing in the case of a plasma diode employing cesium is ~ 0.004 inch.

Thermionic converters, whether of the vacuum or plasma diode type, are intrinsically low-voltage, high-current devices; hence for practical application a number of such devices must be connected in electrical series.

Applications. Thermionic devices, principally of the cesium diode type, are being developed for use in small radionuclide power sources (sometimes referred to as nuclear batteries) with power outputs ranging from 3.5 to 125 watts. The radionuclide sources built to date employ thermoelectric conversion. (See **SNAP Program** for details)

Intensive research is being conducted, notably at Los Alamos Scientific Laboratory, on thermionic techniques for converting reactor heat to electricity. The Los Alamos work is based on the concept of a thermionic fuel cell, i.e., a combination reactor fuel element and thermionic converter. One device that has been successfully demonstrated in in-pile tests consists essentially of a cesium-filled, electrically insulated, stainless steel cylinder containing a fuel rod fabricated of a solid solution of uranium and zirconium carbides (UC-ZrC). The fuel rod, capable of operation at temperatures above 2000°C, serves as the electron emitter. The inner wall of the cylinder serves as the electron collector. A coolant is circulated through the fuel cell. A reactor core would consist of an array of hundreds of such cells immersed in a coolant-moderator fluid.

The Los Alamos work is oriented toward the development of a small, compact, lightweight power source with outputs exceeding 100 watts per equipment pound for use in ion propulsion systems for propelling spacecraft (see **rocket propulsion (nuclear)**) or for other space applications. In such applications the "low temperature" heat removed by the reactor coolant would be dissipated.

It is also envisioned that thermionic fuel cells may find application in central station nuclear power plants. In this case the primary source of energy would be the heat carried by the reactor coolant, as in a conventional nuclear power plant. The thermionic circuitry would function as a "topping" system, producing supplementary electricity from the high-temperature heat at the fuel surface and thereby enhancing the over-all thermal conversion efficiency of the system.

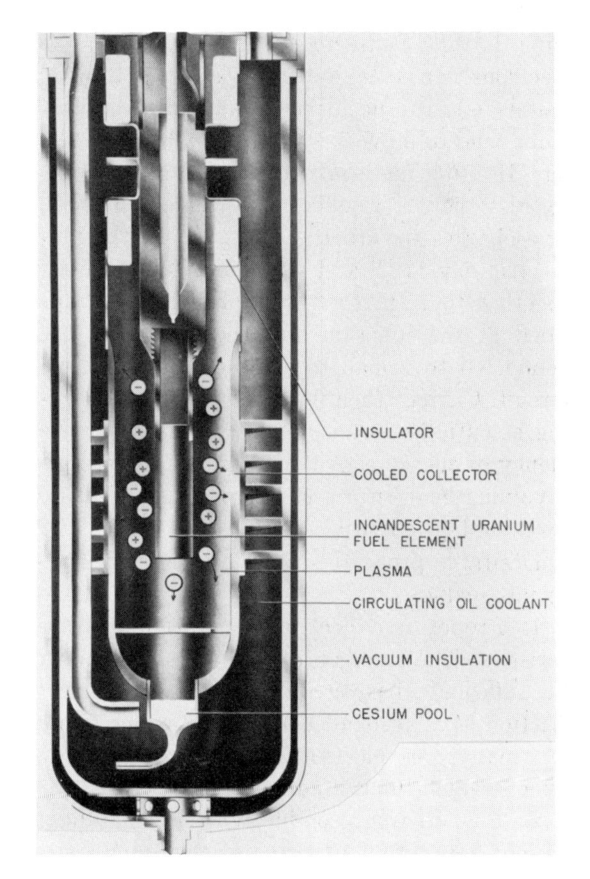

Fig. 203. Diagram of two-inch diameter thermionic fuel cell used at Los Alamos for in-pile tests. (*Courtesy of Los Alamos Scientific Laboratory*)

THERMOELECTRIC CONVERSION

A technique for the direct conversion of heat to direct-current electricity (see **direct energy conversion**). Thermoelectric conversion is used to produce small amounts (watts) of electricity from the decay heat of radioisotopes, and is under development for use in compact power reactor systems (see below).

Principles. The principle of thermoelectric conversion has been known since the early nineteenth century and has found its most important application to date in conventional temperature measurement and control.

If a temperature differential is established along a bar of electrically conductive material, an electric potential results. This is due to the fact that, under the influence of heat, some of the electrons of the constituent atoms escape lattice confinement and become "free electrons." In some materials (referred to as *N* materials), the negatively charged free electrons tend to move toward the cold end of the bar. In other materials, (referred to as *P* materials) there is in effect a movement of positive charges toward the cold end. In thermoelectric devices *P* and *N* materials are joined together to form thermocouples. Heat is applied at the junction and the cold ends are connected to a load to complete an electrical circuit. Current then flows with the heat serving essentially as an electron pump. The efficiency of energy conversion, as in all processes involving heat, increases with the temperature level and differential.

Desirable properties for thermoelectric materials include:

1. Proper free-electron generation characteristics. The number of free electrons must be sufficient to overcome internal electrical friction (i.e., resistances); on the other hand, too many free electrons introduce scattering effects which impede current flow.

2. Low thermal conductivity so that heat cannot flow through the material without performing some useful electrical work.

3. Ability to operate at high temperatures. Additional property requirements depend upon the application; for example, thermoelectric materials selected for use in a reactor environment would be required to have acceptable neutron absorption and radiation stability characteristics.

Because of (1) and (2) above, semiconductors are more efficient thermoelectric materials than ordinary metals. One such material is lead telluride (PbTe), a binary compound of lead and tellurium capable of operation at temperatures up to 600-700°C. By addition of an impurity (a process referred to as doping), the lead telluride can be made to operate as an *N* or a *P* material. (Sodium is added to form an *N* material, and potassium iodide is added to form a *P* material.) The voltage generated by a single thermocouple is between 60 and 200 millivolts, so a number of thermocouples must be connected in electrical series to achieve useful voltage outputs. Lead telluride has found application in radionuclide power sources (see below) which have achieved net conversion efficiencies of 5 or 6%.

For higher efficiencies, materials capable of operation at temperatures as high as 1500-1800°C are desired. Among the materials being studied are compounds of bismuth and tellurium, germanium and tellurium, cerium and selenium, and zirconium and antimony.

Any one thermoelectric material has optimum properties at a particular temperature, so that complex material systems are required for optimum conversion efficiency over a range of operating temperature. The maximum efficiency attainable is believed to be in the range of 25-35%.

Applications. Thermoelectric energy conversion is being applied in the atomic energy field as part of the SNAP Program, which involves the development of two types of small auxiliary power unit for a variety of specialized uses (see **SNAP Program** for details). One type is the so-called radionuclide source—sometimes referred to as a nuclear battery—in which electrical power is generated from the decay heat of a radioisotope. A family of such devices is being developed with power outputs ranging from 3.5-125 watts. Thermoelectric conversion is presently used in those devices, however **thermionic conversion** systems are also under development. The thermoelectric material presently used is lead telluride.

The other type of SNAP unit employs a compact nuclear reactor as the heat source. One such device (SNAP-10A, rated at 500 watts) is being developed with a thermoelectric conversion system, again employing lead telluride.

The use of thermoelectric conversion in large-scale power reactor systems is contingent on the development of improved thermoelectric materials and conversion efficiencies, and also depends on how thermoelectric conversion is found to compare with other direct or quasi-direct energy conversion methods (specifically, thermionic and **magnetohydrodynamic conversion**). There are essentially two ways in which thermoelectric conversion might be used in large power reactor systems. One would be to circulate the reactor coolant through an external thermoelectric converter. The other would be to incorporate thermocouples in the reactor fuel elements, thereby directly removing some of the reactor heat as electricity. The term used to describe the latter technique is "topping," since it makes use of the high-temperature heat inside the fuel element, leaving the lower-temperature heat carried by the reactor coolant to be separately processed. The two methods could be combined in an "all thermoelectric" reactor system. The largest program of research on thermoelectric materials for in-pile use is reportedly being conducted by Westinghouse Electric Corporation.

THERMONUCLEAR POWER

The controlled generation of useful power from the energy released by **fusion** reactions—an objective, not a reality. As will be discussed in subsequent paragraphs, there are three factors involved in realizing the objective of practicable thermonuclear power:

1. The feasibility of controlling the process of nuclear fusion must be demonstrated;
2. It must be shown that thermonuclear devices can be built which generate more energy than they consume;
3. The economic feasibility of thermonuclear power generation must be proven.

Research aimed at resolving the basic question of technical feasibility began informally in the United States in 1951, under U.S. Atomic Energy Commission auspices, has steadily gained momentum, and in recent years has been augmented by several industry-sponsored programs. Also, there are comparable efforts being made in other countries. The work to date has primarily been of a basic research nature, and the end of this phase of the effort is not yet in sight.

Concept. As is discussed under **fusion,** the fuel for thermonuclear power generation would either be **deuterium** (D) or a mixture of deuterium and **tritium (T).** It is hoped that it will prove feasible to use straight deuterium, a stable isotope of hydrogen whose natural abundance in the hydrogen element is one part in 6500, or 0.015%. (A gallon of ordinary sea water contains one-eighth of a gram of deuterium, which can be extracted at a cost of about four cents and is equivalent, in terms of energy content, to 300 gallons of gasoline.) Unfortunately the **ignition temperature** for deuterium-deuterium reactions is extremely high (see below), and there is some doubt that straight deuterium will prove to be a practical fuel. Deuterium-tritium mixtures, which ignite at temperatures nearly a factor of ten lower, appear at present to offer considerably more promise, and will almost certainly be used in early demonstration systems. The disadvantage of such mixtures, from a fuel logistics viewpoint, is that large supplies of tritium, a rare unstable isotope of hydrogen, would be costly to produce. It should be possible, however, to regenerate tritium *in situ,* i.e., within the thermonuclear device—by surrounding the reaction zone with a blanket of **lithium-6.** Tritium would then be formed by neutrons released by the fusion process:

$$_3Li^6 + {}_0n^1 \longrightarrow {}_1T^3 + {}_2He^4$$

Since only one neutron is released per fusion event (see **fusion**) and since some neutron losses would occur, means would have to be provided to amplify the neutron flow. This could be done by adding beryllium:

$$_0n^1 + {}_4Be^9 \longrightarrow {}_4Be^8 + 2{}_0n^1$$

Thus, from a fuel-supply standpoint, the use of deuterium-tritium mixtures would entail supplying deuterium and lithium plus just enough tritium to get the reaction started.

The basic problem in achieving controlled fusion is to create conditions in which a properly dense body of fuel is maintained for a long enough time at a high enough temperature for the desired reactions to take place. There are thus three basic process variables—density, time and temperature. Density and time are interdependent, and are conveniently treated by the expression, nt, where n is the number of fuel particles per cubic centimeter and t is the time in seconds. Following are the minimum values of nt believed to be required for a practical thermonuclear device:

Reaction	nt
Deuterium-tritium	10^{14}
Deuterium-deuterium	10^{16}

Representative values for all three variables on this basis are as follows:

Reaction	*Density (particles per cm³)*	*Time (sec)*	*Practical Ignition Temperature (°K)*
Deuterium-tritium	10^{15}	0.1	70,000,000
Deuterium-deuterium (followed by D-T)	10^{17}	0.1	600,000,000

The only type of system that has been seriously considered for controlled fusion is one in which the fuel is in the form of an ionized gas, or **plasma,** confined by **magnetic pressure** within an evacuated apparatus (see **plasma confinement).** In effect, the plasma is held in a "magnetic bottle." Confining the plasma in this fashion serves two purposes. It is a way of achieving the required particle density, and also of preventing the particles from dissipating their energy by collisions with the walls of the apparatus. Unfortunately, confinement is a very unnatural condition for plasma and is exceedingly difficult of accomplishment. (See **plasma stability)**

One approach to achieving a workable plasma system is to raise the energy of the fuel ions before injecting them into a confining magnetic field; the field then serves to trap the ions and to build up the *density* of the resulting plasma. This approach is the basis of the **Molecular Ion Ignition Program.** A basically different approach is to use a magnetic field to constrict a high-current discharge of "luke-warm" fuel ions and to confine the resulting dense plasma while its *temperature* is raised by **adiabatic compression, shock heating,** or other heating techniques. There are several major lines of effort representing alternative magnetic field configurations. (See **Astron Program, cusped geometry, magnetic mirror systems, Pinch Program** and **Stellarator Program)**

Program. AEC-sponsored research on controlled fusion has centered at the following laboratories:

Laboratory	*Program*	*Year Started*	*Approx. Costs (cumulative to June 30, 1960)*
Princeton University	Stellarator	1952	$ 38,143,719.
Lawrence Radiation Laboratory	Magnetic mirror	1952	
	Pinch	1954	30,629,084.
	Astron	1956	
	Neutral particle injection		
Los Alamos Scientific Laboratory	Pinch	1951	11,926,715.
	Magnetic compression		
	Cusp geometry		
Naval Research Laboratory	Magnetic compression	1954	823,766.
New York University	Cusped geometry	1955	1,223,562.
Oak Ridge National Laboratory	Molecular ion ignition	1954	14,250,849.
Other	(miscellaneous supporting research)		4,271,136.
	Total		$101,268,831.

In its early stages, the over-all effort was known by the code designation, "Project Sherwood" (see **Sherwood Project**). The rate of growth of the over-all program has been as follows:

Year (AEC Fiscal)		*Approx. Costs, Exclusive of Equipment ($ Thousands)*
1951		50.
1952		150.
1953		800.
1954		1,741.
1955		4,718.
1956		6,725.
1957		10,735.
1958		18,424.
1959		26,972.
1960		32,148.
1961		30,136.
	Total	133,601.

The AEC-sponsored research effort has been augmented in recent years by privately sponsored programs. The most notable example is a program of basic research initiated in 1957, at the John Jay Hopkins Laboratory of the General Atomic Division of General Dynamics Corporation under the joint sponsorship of the corporation and Texas Atomic Energy Research Foundation, representing a group of southwestern utilities. Other industrial organizations reported to be supporting research on controlled fusion include the General Electric Company and Westinghouse Electric Corporation. Research on controlled fusion began under tight security restrictions and it was not until 1955, that the United States, the United Kingdom and the U.S.S.R. publicly announced that work was in progress in this field. The occasion was the First United Nations Conference on the Peaceful Uses of Atomic Energy, held at Geneva, Switzerland in August of that year. Information on the work began to be made available to the public in the months following; however, it was not until the Second Geneva Conference in the fall of 1958, that research in this field was completely declassified.

Incentives and status. The possible advantages of thermonuclear power are as follows:

1. It offers the promise of extremely low fuel costs and virtually inexhaustible fuel supplies.

2. The radioactive waste disposal problem associated with nuclear power would be largely avoided since no unstable reaction products are formed in the fusion process. Neutron activation of equipment parts and impurities

Fig. 204. Model-C Stellarator Laboratory Facility at the James Forrestal Research Center, Princeton, N. J., one of the main centers of U.S. research on controlled fusion. (*Courtesy of Princeton University*)

Fig. 205. Left, "Torus," a toroidal pinch apparatus used in privately sponsored program of research on controlled fusion at General Atomic's laboratory near San Diego, Calif. The cables supply power from a condenser bank. Above, "Zeus," a giant capacitor bank used to supply power for controlled fusion experiments at Los Alamos Scientific Laboratory. (*Courtesy of General Atomic and Los Alamos Scientific Laboratory*)

present in the system would result in some radioactive wastes but the **half-life** of the activity would be short and hence there would be no need to provide facilities for long-term waste storage.

3. A thermonuclear power plant should be extremely safe to operate since only limited amounts of fuel would be present in the system at any given time.

4. Should it prove possible to develop thermonuclear power systems capable of operating on straight deuterium, as much as 30% of the energy generated could be converted directly into electrical power by simply expanding the hot plasma, i.e., without going through a thermal conversion cycle. If deuterium-tritium mixtures have to be used, only one-fifth of the energy generated could be directly converted. (See notes on pattern of energy distribution under **fusion.)**

There is thus ample incentive to press forward with thermonuclear research despite the many difficult problems involved and the present absence of certainty that practical solutions to these problems can be devised.

As was noted at the start of this discussion, the objective of the initial research conducted has been to demonstrate the basic feasibility of achieving controlled-fusion reactors. Whereas this objective has not yet been realized, certain accomplishments can be cited, which indicate a definite degree of success. Some of these are:

1. In the **Scylla** device, ion temperatures of the order of 23,000,000 degrees have been achieved in relatively dense ($\sim 5 \times 10^{16}$ particles per cubic centimeter) plasmas which have been stably confined for intervals of time as long as several microseconds.

2. In the multiple magnetic compression and transfer experiment **Toy Top,** a very encouraging advance has been achieved. A deuterium plasma has been heated to a temperature of about 35 million degrees and confined in a stable manner for about 90 microseconds. However, the ion density was relatively low ($\sim 2 \times 10^{13}$ particles per cubic centimeter).

3. Evidence has accumulated that controlled-fusion reactions may have already been achieved in laboratory experiments, though not on a sustained basis.

Other statements of the accomplishments of controlled-fusion experimentation will be found in the entries on the individual programs.

It should again be stressed that the work is still at a very basic stage. Even after ignition conditions have been demonstrated, as now appears reasonably certain of accomplishment, it will remain to be seen whether fusion systems can be developed which will be net producers of energy and, if that bridge is crossed, whether plants can be built which will generate power on an economic basis.

In the latter connection, no one as yet knows with any degree of certainty what the minimum size of a practical thermonuclear power plant might prove to be and hence what markets such plants, if proved feasible, might serve. At one time it appeared that, because of the large amounts of power used to energize the magnetic confinement field and to heat the plasma ions, thermonuclear power plants might have to be built in such large sizes as to limit their usefulness to large load centers. Fortunately, recent work with low-temperature magnet coils of low electrical resistivity (see **cryogenic coils)** indicates that the internal power consumption of a thermonuclear system can be kept within reasonable limits and gives hope that thermonuclear plants with generating capacities of the order of 10,000 kilowatts of electric power may prove technically feasible. There is, of course, no basis for assessing the economic feasibility of thermonuclear power generation, whether on a large or a small scale, and will not be until the technical feasibility has been proved.

THERMONUCLEAR WEAPONS. See **weapons.**

THICKNESS GAGES. See **gages.**

THOREX PROCESS

A **solvent extraction** process developed for use in reprocessing irradiated thorium core or blanket material. The organic solvent em-

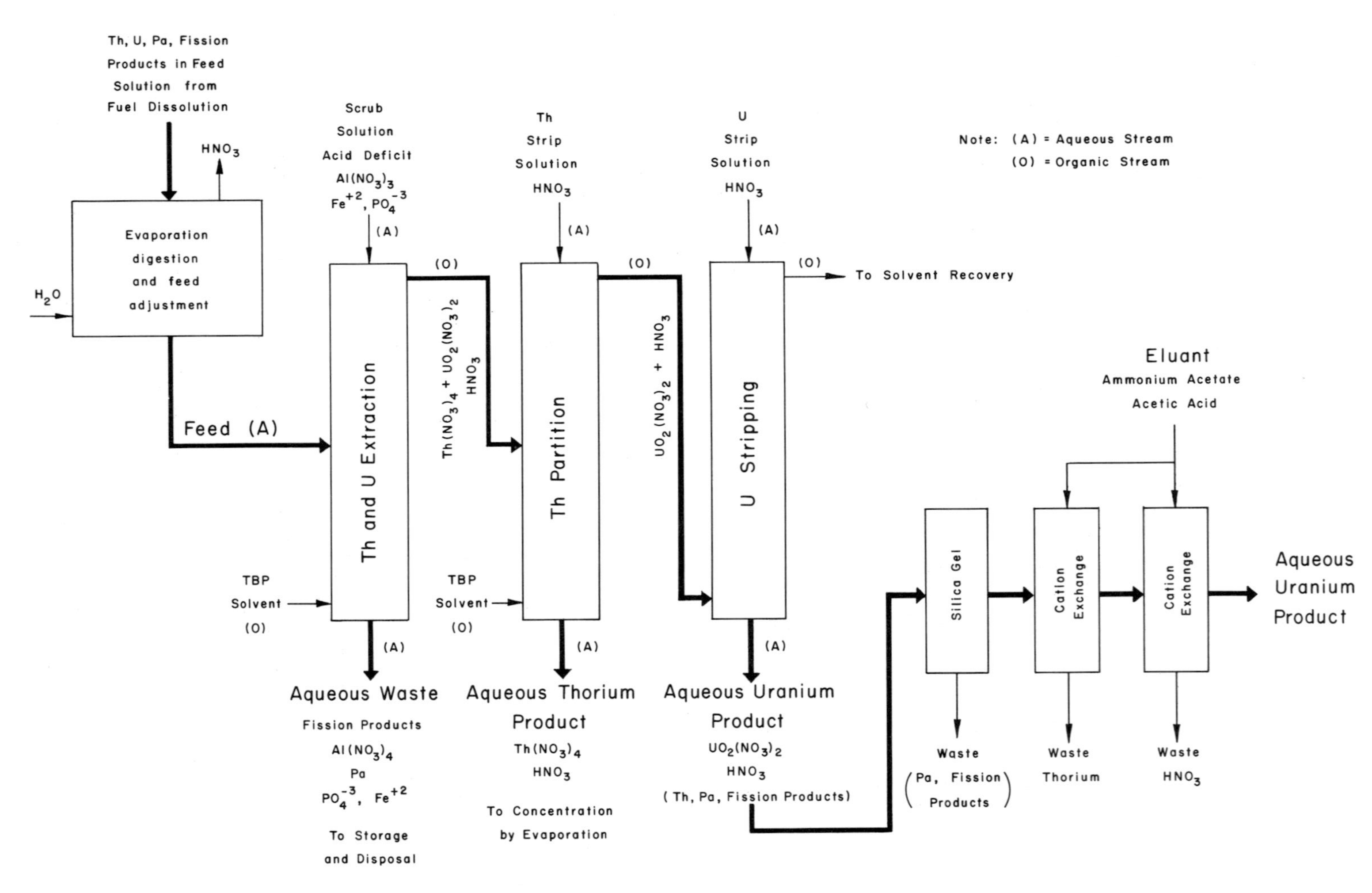

Fig. 206. Simplified flow diagram—Thorex Process.

ployed is tributyl phosphate (TBP), diluted with Amsco—an inert paraffinic hydrocarbon. Aluminum nitrate is used as a **salting agent** in the initial stage of the process in which uranium-233 and thorium are extracted from protoactinium and the bulk of the fission product contaminants. The latter components are carried away in the aqueous waste stream, or "raffinate," which is concentrated by evaporation prior to being piped to radioactive waste storage facilities. (If the economics are favorable, the protoactinium can be removed from the concentrated waste stream by precipitation-carrier technique prior to sending it to storage. Then, after allowing time for the radioactive decay of protoactinium to uranium-233, the latter can be recovered in a supplementary solvent extraction operation.)

The organic stream from the initial extraction stage contains uranium-233 and thorium plus some residual fission product activity. This stream enters a second extraction stage wherein thorium is separated from the uranium by a dilute nitric acid scrub solution, which strips it from the organic solvent. The thorium-bearing raffinate is concentrated by evaporation, yielding a uranyl nitrate product.

The organic stream from the second stage enters a third stage wherein uranium-233 is in turn transferred to the aqueous phase, thereby freeing the organic solvent for reuse. The aqueous product solution is passed over silica gel to remove trace quantities of protoactinium, zirconium and miobium, and thence through an **ion-exchange** column for final decontamination. The final steps are elution of the uranium-233 from the ion exchange resins, followed by precipitation and calcination. The final product form is uranium trioxide ($U^{233}O_3$).

The Thorex process (from *tho*rium *ex*traction) was developed at Oak Ridge National Laboratory where its feasibility was established by extensive pilot plant operations. To date there has been no occasion for the large-scale reprocessing of irradiated thorium, hence no Thorex production facility has been built.

For mention of certain complications in thorium reprocessing arising from the presence of unstable daughter products, see **fuel reprocessing.**

THORIA

Thorium oxide (ThO_2).

THORIUM

A heavy, slightly radioactive, metallic element (atomic no., 90; atomic weight, 232.12), discovered by the Swedish chemist J. J. Berzelius in 1828. Thorium is of principal interest as a potential source of uranium-233—one of the three primary fissionable materials. Uranium-233 is produced from thorium by the following reaction and decay sequence, involving the intermediate product, protoactinium:

$$_{90}Th^{232} + {_0n^1} \longrightarrow {_{90}Th^{233}} + \gamma \qquad (1)$$

$$_{90}Th^{233} \xrightarrow{23.5\text{ min}} {_{91}Pa^{233}} + {_{-1}e^{o}} \qquad (2)$$

$$_{91}Pa^{233} \xrightarrow{27.4\text{ days}} {_{92}U^{233}} + {_{-1}e^{o}} \qquad (3)$$

The average concentration of thorium in the earth's crust is estimated at 12 parts per million, making it about three times as abundant as **uranium.** As found in nature it consists entirely of the fertile isotope, thorium-232. Various other isotopes are found as short-lived decay products of other elements. Of these the most significant is thorium-228, a radioactive **daughter product** of uranium-232, which is a complicating factor in thorium-based reactor fuel cycles. (See **fuel reprocessing)**

Thorium usually reacts in the +4 valence state in forming compounds with other elements. It oxidizes readily. Thoria (ThO_2), the common oxide, is one of the most refractory substances known. Thorium metal has a high melting point ($\sim$ 1750°C) and is highly reactive. Its mechanical properties are sensitive to trace amounts of impurities; generally, however, it is a soft, ductile silvery metal.

THORIUM DEPOSITS AND RESERVES

Thorium is a relatively abundant element, occurring in numerous minerals, usually associated with uranium and the rare earths. Generally accepted estimates of the thorium content of the earth's crust range from 0.001-0.002%.

Of the thorium-bearing minerals, the most common are original constituents of granite, gneiss, and pegmatite; but the concentration in the host rock is quite low, usually not more than 0.1%. Crushing rock to recover thorium is ordinarily not feasible. However, since thorium minerals are not soluble in water, natural concentration occurs with erosion in river beds and ocean beach placers.

The most important commercial source of thorium is monazite, essentially a phosphate of cerium and lanthanum, in which thorium and yttrium earths substitute for cerium. Monazite is processed currently to recover cerium and other rare earths, the thorium being a by-product. Large deposits of monazite sands have been found in four areas: Brazil; India and Ceylon; Indonesia, Malaya and Australia; and the United States. Beach placers occur in Florida and California; stream placers in Carolina, Georgia, Idaho, Montana, and Wyoming. A typical concentrated domestic monazite will show the following analysis:

Constituent	%
Rare earth oxides	40.1
Phosphoric oxide	20.5
Ceria	19.5
Alumina	12.5
Silica	8.5
Ferric oxide	4.5
Thoria	3.5
Titanium dioxide	2.1
Zirconia	0.1–1.0
Uranium oxide (U_3O_8)	0.15
	100.00

Although monazite occurs in massive form in pegmatite and vein deposits, the only producing occurrence is from a hydrothermal vein in the Van Rhynsdorp district of the Union of South Africa. The bulk of current U.S. monazite requirements come from this vein. Present monazite production is believed to be about 10,000 tons per year, of which the Van Rhynsdorp district produces about 8000 tons. Present market value for 6% ThO_2 monazite is about $300 per short ton. Other thorium minerals of potential significance are thorite, a thorium silicate, and thorianite, a thorium-uranium oxide. There is no current domestic production of thorite, although potentially workable deposits have been found in several states. Thorianite is commercially produced in Madagascar.

By-product production of thorium concentrate from uranium operations is possible in a few instances, notably from the Blind River uranium deposits in Canada, where thorium appears in proportion to uranium of about 1 to 2. Whether or not the product would be competitive price-wise with monazite is not yet definitely known.

Although the crystal abundance of thorium is believed to be about three times that of uranium, commercially workable deposits appear to be fewer. Reserve figures are indefinite. World reserves of thorium at or near present costs probably total more than a million tons. Authorities feel confident that price incentive programs to encourage exploration and mining would reveal additional reserves. With expanded production, however, a serious problem might develop in keeping the cost of thorium materials within present limits unless expanded uses for rare earths are found.

THORIUM, ENERGY FROM. See **energy statistics, U.S.; energy statistics, world.**

THORIUM PRODUCTION TECHNOLOGY

Processes for the milling of thorium ores and for the refining and conversion of mill concentrates to metal or compounds of adequate purity for reactor use have been developed in the United States and have been operated on a pilot-plant scale. No full-scale production facilities have yet been required. Effectively, then, thorium production technology is in "stand-by" status awaiting future requirements.

Milling. The main source of thorium is **monazite** sand, also a source of rare earths and frequently associated with uranium and other valuable minerals. The separation of monazite from surrounding ore matter normally begins with rough, physical concentration, either in sluice boxes or by tabling to reject lighter sands. The heavier sands are then carefully separated by gravity concentration or by electrostatic or electromagnetic methods. Market-grade concentrates ordinarily contain at least 95% of the monazite mineral.

The treatment of monazite to extract crude thorium and rare earth fractions starts, as does **uranium milling**, with a leaching operation. In one process, developed by Ames Laboratory, the mineral concentrate is digested in sulfuric acid, yielding a solution of thorium, rare earth, and uranium sulfates and a filterable residue of phosphate and silica gangue. In an alternative caustic soda process developed by Battelle Memorial Institute the gangue goes into solution, leaving the desired elements as oxide precipitates, which are filtered, washed, and dried.

Refining. In the past, thorium was chiefly used in the manufacture of gas mantles, and commercial ("mantle-grade") thorium nitrate tetrahydrate (TNT) was obtained by fractional crystallization or selective precipitation methods. For reactor use greater purity is required and **solvent extraction** with tributyl phosphate (TBP) appears to be more effective. The process that has been developed has been satisfactorily tested on a variety of feeds, including mantle-grade TNT and Brazilian sludge (essentially monazite that has been stripped of rare earths), as well as thorium concentrates from the sulfuric acid and caustic soda milling processes noted earlier. The basic steps are: (1) Preparation of a nitric acid feed solution. (2) Transfer of thorium and uranium values from the aqueous to the organic phase by countercurrent flow of TBP. (3) Removal of residual rare earth impurities by contacting the organic stream from Step 2 with an aqueous scrub solution. (4) Extraction of thorium by contacting the purified organic stream with a slightly acidic aqueous strip solution. (5) Concentration of the aqueous product stream by evaporation.

Conversion. The purified thorium nitrate from the above refining operation is converted to thorium tetrafluoride (ThF_4) preparatory to being reduced to metal. Two processes have been developed for the conversion step:

1. Precipitation of thorium oxalate and subsequent calcination to thorium oxide, which is reacted with anhydrous hydrogen fluoride (HF) to form thorium tetrafluoride.

2. Direct treatment of the concentrated thorium nitrate solution with hydrofluoric acid, followed by calcination in an atmosphere of hydrogen fluoride gas to form thorium tetrafluoride.

Although the former process has been most thoroughly tested, it is believed that the latter process might prove more economic in large-scale production since it lends itself more readily to continuous operation.

The pilot-scale production of thorium metal from thorium tetrafluoride has been done by means of a thermite reduction process similar in basic method to that used in uranium metal reduction. The basic steps are: (1) Thorium tetrafluoride is mixed with finely divided high-purity calcium powder and anhydrous zinc fluoride in a closed dolomite-lined steel crucible. (2) The crucible is heated to the ignition temperature of the reduction process, whereupon thorium metal collects as a "biscuit" at the bottom of the crucible, covered by a slag of calcium fluoride. (3) The thorium biscuit is chipped free of slag and vacuum-distilled to remove the zinc. (4) The purified metal is arc-melted and cast into ingots.

Various alternative methods have been studied for the production of reactor-grade thorium metal, including electrolytic techniques, and the use of different reduction media in processes otherwise similar to that described above.

Facilities. Up until 1954, the U.S. Atomic Energy Commission's requirements for thorium metal were supplied by small semi-works facilities at Ames Laboratory. Since that time production has centered at a pilot plant at the Feed Materials Production Center, operated by the National Lead Company of Ohio.

THREE STAGE TOY TOP

The name of an experimental controlled-**fusion** device of the "magnetic mirror" type placed in operation in 1957, at the Livermore

Branch of the E. O. Lawrence Radiation Laboratory (see **magnetic mirror systems**). In this multiple magnetic compression and transfer experiment, a deuterium **plasma** has been heated to a temperature of about 35 million °K and confined in a stable manner for about 1 millisecond. This result was made possible by the previous development of an improved plasma source which produces plasma bursts in which the mean energy of the ions is relatively high (about 850 ev).

THULIUM-170

A radioisotope of the **rare earth element,** thulium, used to a limited extent in medical teletherapy and industrial radiography applications where a high degree of penetration is not required. Thulium-170 is a reactor-produced nuclide, formed from thulium-169 by neutron absorption. It is a strong emitter of beta and attendant **bremsstrahlung** radiation. Its radioactive half-life is 129 days.

TISSUE EQUIVALENT IONIZATION CHAMBER

A laboratory device used in simulation studies of the radiation absorption characteristics of body tissues. In its simplest form it consists of an ionization chamber whose walls are made of a plastic material chosen to simulate the particular tissue of interest, i.e., having essentially the same chemical elements in the same proportions as occur in the tissue, but not, of course, the same molecular composition.

TITANIUM

Element No. 22 (symbol, Ti; atomic weight, 47.90), of some interest as a reactor structural material because of its mechanical properties and corrosion resistance but handicapped, especially in thermal reactor applications, by its appreciable thermal neutron absorption cross section (5.6 barns). (See **reactor materials**)

TOLERANCE DOSE, OF IONIZING RADIATION

An obsolete term. The concept of a tolerance dose was based on the assumption that the human system has some degree of tolerance for ionizing radiation so that a corresponding degree of exposure could be incurred without any harmful effects. This assumption is now believed to be invalid (see reference to genetic damage under **biological effects of ionizing radiation**). Most authorities now use the term, **maximum permissible dose,** which may in the future be replaced by the term, **Radiation Protection Guide.** (See **radiation protection standards and regulations**)

TORBERNITE

Hydrated copper uranium phosphate—a secondary mineral, bright green in color, found with other uranium minerals especially where oxidation of a primary deposit has occurred. There are minor occurrences of torbernite ores in the western United States. Large amounts have been found in oxidized ores in the Republic of the Congo.

TORY IIA, IIC. See **Pluto Project.**

TOY TOP

The name of a series of experimental controlled-**fusion** devices of the **"magnetic mirror"** type at the Livermore Branch of the E. O. Lawrence Radiation Laboratory. In these ex-

Fig. 207. Above, general view of Toy Top III, a multi-stage device used for controlled-fusion research at the Livermore Branch of the E. O. Lawrence Radiation Laboratory. Below, cutaway diagram of the device. Deuterium plasma is injected into the first stage at far right by a bank of nine plasma guns. The initial force of injection is sufficient to carry the plasma through the first stage, where it is initially constricted by DC magnetic field coils, and into the second stage. The gating coils serve to prevent the plasma from returning to the first stage, while the transfer coils compress and heat the plama still further and force it into the third stage. There, the plasma is held by the stopping coil while the final compression and heating are performed by the compression coils. The compression coils create the magnetic mirrors which serve as the ends of the magnetic bottle. The ejector coil can be used to control the effective strength of the magnetic mirrors, or to force the plasma into the ion analyzer at far left. (*Courtesy of the E. O. Lawrence Radiation Lab.*)

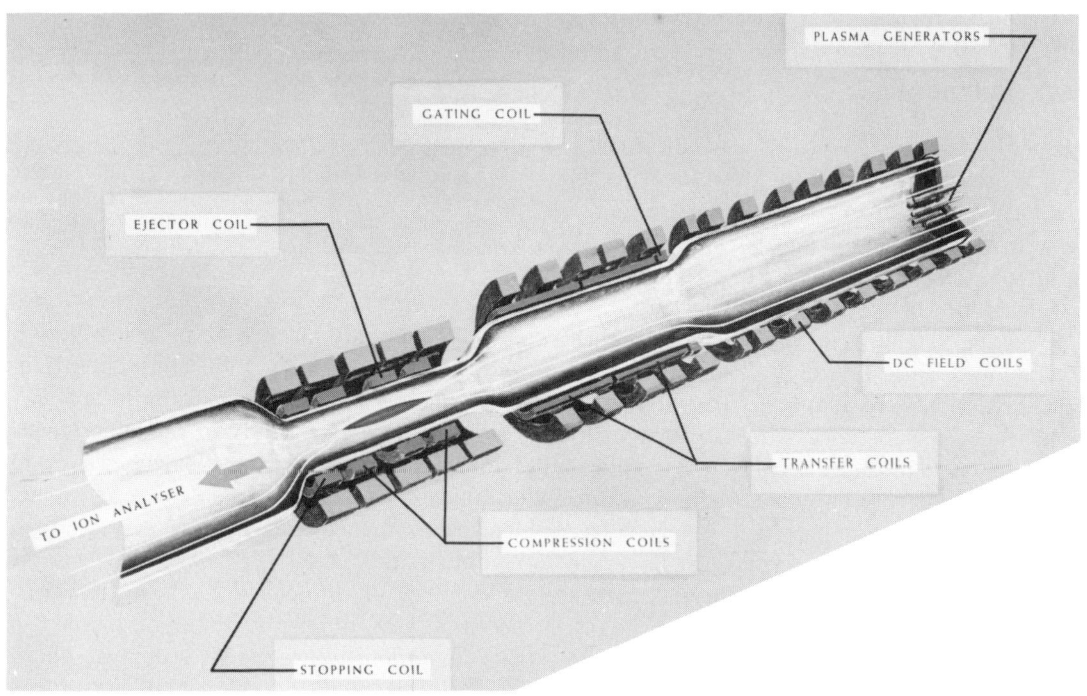

Fig. 207 (See caption on facing page)

periments, a deuterium plasma is injected into a large diameter tube with a low magnetic field, then transferred and compressed into successively smaller tubes at higher magnetic field strengths. Thus far, the plasma has been heated to a temperature of about 35 million °K and confined in a stable manner for about 90 microseconds. This result was made possible by the previous development of an improved plasma source which produces plasma bursts in which the mean energy of the ions is relatively high (about 850 ev).

TRACE ELEMENTS

Chemical elements present in plant or animal tissue in extremely small amounts. Examples of trace elements important to man are iodine, cadmium, manganese, zinc, and fluorine. The role of trace elements in plant and animal metabolism is a subject of continuing biological and biomedical research.

The term "trace elements" should not be confused with the use of stable or radioactive isotopes as "tracers." (See **tracer technique**)

TRACER TECHNIQUE

Broadly defined, the use of a small amount of a representative and readily identifiable substance as a means of following ("tracing") the flow or behavior of another substance. A distinction may be made between applications in which a physical system is being traced, as in following the flow of crude oil through a pipeline, and those in which chemical or biological reactions are involved. In the former applications, a substance with a distinguishable color or odor may satisfy the requirements; alternatively, any of various radioactive substances can be used. In the latter applications, the tracer usually must have the same chemical or biological properties as the substance being traced, which requires the use of a stable or radioactive isotope of one of the ingredient atoms (see **labeling**). In either type of application the use of a radioactive tracer usually offers the easiest and most sensitive means of following the system.

The use of radioactive tracers is not new; it dates back to 1913, when Georg de Hevesy of Sweden and Fritz Paneth of Austria jointly reported techniques for determining trace solubilities of lead salts, using a natural radionuclide (Radium D) as an indicator for lead. However, the advent of the nuclear reactor brought about a breakthrough by making radioisotopes available in unprecedented variety and at low cost. Radioactive tracing is

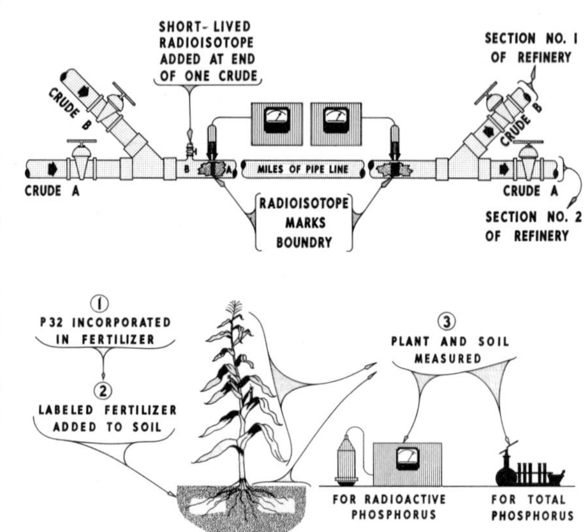

Fig. 208. Tracer techniques. Top, use of a radioactive substance to follow the flow of crude oil fractions through a pipe line. Bottom, use of a radioisotope of phosphorus to measure the uptake of phosphate fertilizer in a growing plant.

now a commonly used tool in research laboratories and in many industrial operations. Following are a few random examples:

Physical Systems. Study of the effectiveness of lubricants in preventing bearing wear; determination of leakage in gas storage systems; measuring surface area of powders; study of river currents.

Chemical or Biological Systems. Study of the uptake of nutrients by plants; study of body metabolism processes; study of photosynthesis; tracing the role of sulfur in coal combustion. (See **agricultural applications of atomic energy, medical aspects of atomic energy, oil well logging, radioisotopes)**

TRAINING COURSES. See **education and training programs, AEC.**

TRAINING REACTORS. See **research and training reactors.**

TRAINING REACTORS, TABULATIONS OF. See **research and training reactors.**

TRANSIENT REACTOR TEST EXPERIMENT (TREAT)

A special-purpose **test reactor** at the National Reactor Testing Station, used to study the effect of transient conditions (power surges) on fuel elements of interest in the development of **fast reactors,** and to study **metal-water reactions** under in-pile conditions. ***TREAT*** was designed and is operated by Argonne National Laboratory. The test program was initiated early in 1959, and has involved a series of reactor excursions with energy peaks of a few milliseconds duration. The transients are too brief to cause structural damage to the facility but the energy release is sufficient for the fuel under test to melt or be otherwise damaged. *Type:* Solid homogeneous reactor. *Power rating:* 100 kilowatts (thermal) during steady state operation. 1×10^6 kilowatt-second surges during transient operation. *Fuel:* Zircaloy-clad blocks containing fully enriched uranium dispersed in graphite. *Moderator:* Graphite. *Reflector:* Graphite. *Neutron flux:* Of the order of 10^{16}n/cm^{2}sec (maximum thermal-neutron flux during transient).

TRANSMUTATION

The process of transforming one chemical element into another, as in the transmutation of uranium-238 into plutonium-239. The term is usually used in reference to **nuclear reactions** involving one or more small step changes in **atomic number. Nuclear fission** and **spallation** are not usually regarded as transmutation processes, even though different chemical elements result, since they involve fragmentation phenomena.

TRANSPORTATION OF RADIOACTIVE MATERIALS

Regulations. Regulations governing the packaging, labeling and shipment of radioactive materials have been issued by several U.S. Government agencies as follows:

Agency	*Regulating Authority*	*Reference* [1]
Interstate Commerce Commission (ICC)	Shipments via rail, public highway and interstate waterways.	CFR Title 49, Part 71-78, 190-197
Civil Aeronautics Board (CAB)	Air shipments	CFR Title 14, Part 49
U.S. Coast Guard	Shipments via coastal waterways	CFR Title 46, Part 146
U.S. Post Office	Mail shipments (limited to materials exempt from other regulations, e.g., clock dials)	U.S. Official Postal Guide, Chapter IV, Article 37
U.S. Atomic Energy Commission	All shipments of special nuclear material	CFR Title 10, Part 70-72

[1] CFR—Code of Federal Regulations.

Many states have adopted the ICC regulations in regulating intrastate shipments; however, in some instances local authorities have imposed more restrictive rules for shipments moving through critical areas such as tunnels or ports.

In a move toward standardization, an interagency committee has drafted a standard covering the transportation of radioactive materials. The draft standard was issued for public comment in December, 1962. The agencies represented are the Interstate Commerce Commission, the Federal Aviation Agency, the Coast Guard, the Post Office Department, the Bureau of Explosives of the Association of American Railroads, and the U.S. Atomic Energy Commission.

The AEC's existing regulations covering shipment of special nuclear materials (e.g., reactor fuel elements) are concerned primarily with criticality hazards, and are designed to maintain subcritical conditions under accidental circumstances. The other regulations noted above are concerned primarily with radioactivity hazards, and are designed to prevent harmful radiation exposure under ordinary, rather than accidental circumstances. The following are illustrative of the requirements imposed by the latter regulations:

1. With certain exceptions, a single package must not contain more than 2 **curies** of radium, polonium or other members of the radium family, or more than 2.7 curies of other radioactive substances. Exception is made for cesium-137, cobalt-60 (in solid form), gold-198 and iridium-192, which are commonly used in multicurie amounts in industrial or medical applications, and may be shipped in 300-curie packages. The shipment of larger amounts of radioactivity may be done only with the approval of the Bureau of Explosives.

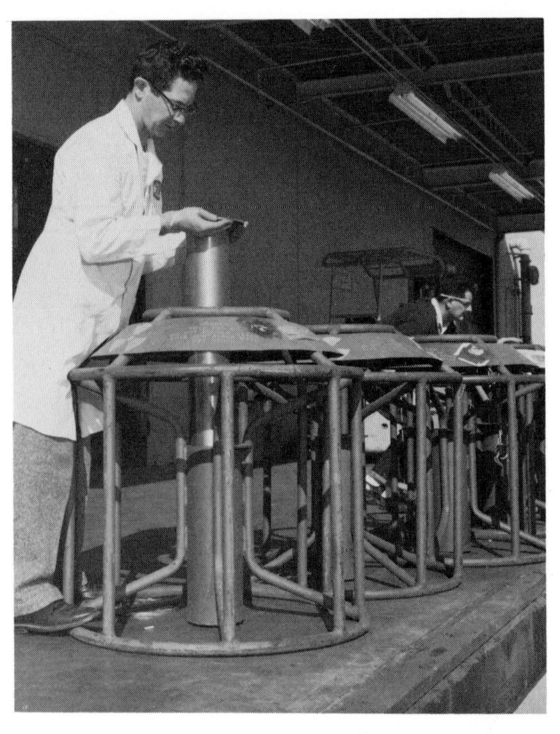

Fig. 209. "Bird cage" containers used to transport reactor fuel containing highly enriched uranium. The rib-work serves to prevent two or more containers being brought close enough together to create a critical mass. (*Courtesy of Atomics International*)

2. The outer surface of the shipping container must be essentially free of radioactive contamination. The radiation dose rate at the surface must not exceed 200 mr/hr (i.e., 200 milli-roentgens or the equivalent in milli-rems per hour), and the rate one meter from any position on the source must not exceed 10 mr/hr. (See **radiation dose** for explanation of these units.)

3. The shipping container must conform to Bureau of Explosives specifications designed to assure that it will not leak or otherwise release radioactive contamination during shipment.

4. The package must not measure less than 4 inches in any dimension—a requirement designed to discourage individuals from carrying such packages in their pockets.

Shipping Containers. Containers for shipping radioactive materials range widely in size and vary in design (see Fig. 209), depending on the amount and nature of the material being shipped. Disposable containers for small quantities of radioisotopes that do not require lead shielding (e.g., some pure beta emitters) weigh in the range, 1 to 5 pounds. Durable (reusable) containers for amounts up to, say, one curie of radioisotopes which require lead shielding may weigh anywhere from 15 to 300 pounds, depending on the thickness of lead required. Containers for special shipments of kilocurie quantities of cobalt-60 weigh as much as several thousand pounds. Containers for shipping spent fuel elements weigh as much as 125 tons. Where very large amounts (tens of kilocuries) of radioactivity are involved, the container must be equipped with a cooling system to remove the decay heat. Where fissionable material is involved, the container design must take into account the problem of accidental criticality.

TRANSURANIUM ELEMENTS

The elements beyond uranium in the periodic table, i.e., elements with atomic number Z greater than 92. All the transuranium elements are radioactive and do not occur in nature except for very small amounts of plutonium ($Z = 94$) which result from the interaction of cosmic ray neutrons with uranium. Transuranium nuclides can be prepared by means of nuclear reactions in which uranium or plutonium is the target, especially as the result of successive neutron capture reactions in a high-flux nuclear reactor. Some information on the known transuranium elements is summarized in Table 1.

TABLE 1. TRANSURANIUM ELEMENTS

Atomic Number	*Name*	*Symbol*	*Date of Discovery*	*Most Stable Observed Isotope*	
				Mass Number	*Half-life*
93	Neptunium	Np	1940	237	2.2×10^6 yr
94	Plutonium	Pu	1940	244	7.6×10^7 yr
95	Americium	Am	1944	243	8.0×10^3 yr
96	Curium	Cm	1944	246	2.0×10^3 yr
97	Berkelium	Bk	1949	249	290 days
98	Californium	Cf	1950	249	470 years
99	Einsteinium	Es	1954	253	20 days
100	Fermium	Fm	1954		
101	Mendelevium	Mv	1955		
102	(Nobelium)	—	1957		
103	(Lawrencium)	(Lw)	1961		

TRIAXIAL PINCH EXPERIMENT

An experimental device built in 1957 at the Berkeley Branch of the E. O. Lawrence Radiation Laboratory as part of the **Pinch Program** of research on controlled **fusion.** It is used for research on techniques for achieving quasi-stabilized pinch-confinement of an ion-

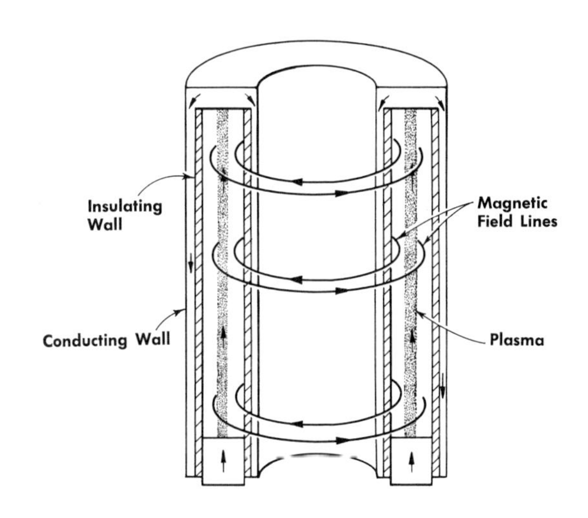

Fig. 210. Configuration of triaxial pinch device.

ized gas, or **plasma.** Unlike other pinch devices, which employ either a straight or a toroidal (ring-shaped) discharge tube, the Triaxial Pinch Experiment employs an annular discharge chamber. Thus, instead of being pinched into a narrow "filament," the plasma takes the form of a thin cylindrical sheet, which, in principle, should better resist plasma instabilities.

TRIBUTYL PHOSPHATE (TBP)

The organic solvent used in the **Purex process.** Because of its viscosity, and also to reduce its density, TBP is normally diluted with an inert paraffinic material such as kerosene or hexane.

TRIGA * REACTORS

Trade name of a line of small nuclear reactors developed and manufactured by General Atomic, a division of General Dynamics Corporation, located near San Diego, California. Through 1960, 19 TRIGA units had been supplied or were scheduled for delivery to laboratories in the United States and abroad for limited research and/or student training programs. *Type:* Solid homogeneous reactors, primarily in pool-type installations. TRIGA-Mk. I is a design in which the pool is installed below grade. TRIGA-Mk. II is a variant design in which the pool is above grade and a thermal column is provided. *Power ratings:* TRIGA-Mk. I models, from 10-250 thermal kilowatts. TRIGA-Mk. II models, 100 kilo-

* Acronym for *T*raining, *R*esearch and *I*sotope Production Reactors—*G*eneral *A*tomic.

watts. *Fuel:* Aluminum-clad rods fabricated of enriched uranium (20% U^{235})-zirconium hydride. *Coolant:* H_2O. *Moderator:* Zirconium hydride and H_2O. *Reflector:* Graphite. *Neutron flux:* Of the order of 10^{12}n/cm^{2}sec (thermal) at a power level of 100 thermal kilowatts. *Note:* A pulsing model (TRIGA-Mk. F) has been developed which, on a transient basis, attains power levels of $\sim$ 1000 kilowatts.

For a listing of TRIGA reactor installations and general background information, see **research and training reactors.**

TRIPARTITE NUCLEAR CROSS SECTIONS COMMITTEE

An advisory and coordinating group of representatives of the United States, United Kingdom, and Canada. The committee is concerned with coordination of work in the three countries with regard to the measurements of nuclear **cross sections** and basic nuclear constants, and the precommercial development of laboratory instruments and techniques.

TRITIUM

A radioactive hydrogen isotope (symbol, T; mass number, 3), sometimes referred to as "heavy heavy hydrogen." Tritium is formed from lithium-6 by the neutron-alpha reaction:

$$_3Li^6 + {}_0n^1 \longrightarrow {}_1T^3 + {}_2He^4$$

It is a soft beta emitter with a radioactive half-life of 12.26 years. Available as a reactor-produced nuclide, tritium is of interest in several ways: (1) It is used in industrial **beta gages** of the type employed to measure (and thereby control) the thickness or density of thin films. (2) It is used to label hydrogen or hydrogen-bearing compounds in tracer experiments in which distortions (as in reaction rates) that may be introduced by the appreciable mass difference between tritium and hydrogen do not bear on the results, and under circumstances in which it is feasible to detect the weak beta rays from tritium. (3) It is a possible fuel for use in the generation of power from controlled thermonuclear reactions, assuming that this method of power generation is found to be feasible. (See **thermonuclear power)**

TRITON

The nucleus of the **tritium** atom.

USS *TRITON* (SSN-586)

Originally built as a radar picket type of nuclear-powered submarine and later designated for other service, *Triton* displaces 5900 tons making it the largest underwater vessel ever built. It is powered by twin S4G pressurized water reactors designed by Knolls Atomic Power Laboratory. The ship was constructed by the Electric Boat Division of General Dynamics Corporation, launched on August 19, 1958, and commissioned November 10, 1959. On February 16, 1960, the *Triton* departed New London on a voyage to test the cruising range and endurance of a nuclear-powered submarine. It was ordered to circumnavigate the world submerged. Navigating over much the same route taken by Ferdinand Magellan in 1519, the *Triton* traveled a distance of 35,979 nautical miles in 83 days continuously submerged. (See **Naval Reactors Program)**

TROPOSPHERE

The lower part of the earth's atmosphere. The dividing line (tropopause) between the troposphere and the upper part of the atmosphere (stratosphere) lies at different altitudes at different latitudes and fluctuates with the seasons and with atmospheric conditions, but is in the general range of 6-12 miles above sea level. (It is lowest at the poles and highest at the equator.) Virtually all of the familiar weather phenomena (winds, clouds, precipitation, jet streams, etc.) occur in the troposphere, a factor which aids the prediction of "tropospheric fallout." (See **radioactive fallout)**

TUBALLOY

World War II code designation for normal uranium metal.

Fig. 211. USS *Triton* undergoing sea trials. (*Courtesy of Electric Boat Division, General Dynamics Corp.*)

USS *TULLIBEE* (SSN-597)

Originally built as a "hunter-killer" type of nuclear-powered submarine and later designated for attack service, *Tullibee* displaces 2600 tons and is powered by an S2C pressurized-water reactor plant designed and developed by Combustion Engineering, Inc. under the direction of and in technical cooperation with the USAEC. The ship was constructed by the Electric Boat Division of General Dynamics Corporation, launched April 27, 1960, and commissioned November 10, 1960. (See **Naval Reactors Program**)

Fig. 212. USS *Tullibee* returning from sea trials. (*Courtesy of Electric Boat Division, General Dynamics Corp.*)

TURKEY

The Turkish Atomic Energy Commission, Ankara, is the agency responsible for atomic energy matters. A center for nuclear research and development near Ankara is equipped with a 1000-kilowatt (thermal) pool-type research reactor supplied by AMF Atomics, Inc. (U.S.) for installation in 1961. The United States has contributed $350,000 for this installation under its Foreign Research Reactor Grant program.

Uranium exploration is in progress in Turkey; however, no deposits have been reported. A nuclear power project is tentatively targeted for the late sixties. Turkey is a member of the **International Atomic Energy Agency** and has a research-type **Agreement for Cooperation** with the United States.

25-TBP PROCESS

A **solvent extraction** process used to recover uranium from irradiated highly enriched reactor fuel elements. The 25-TBP process represents an adaptation of the **Purex process** and uses the same organic solvent, namely, a kerosene solution of tributyl phosphate (TBP). It differs from the Purex process in two principal respects: (1) No facilities are provided for plutonium recovery, the trace amounts that are present being removed solely for decontamination purposes. (2) Aluminum nitrate replaces nitric acid as the **salting agent** in the first extraction column. There is also a notable difference in the engineering design of 25-TBP facilities relative to Purex facilities. This difference stems from the problem of maintaining subcritical conditions when handling highly enriched fuel and is reflected in smaller equipment sizes, special geometries and special control features. The 25-TBP process takes its name from the fact that "25" was once a code name for $_{92}U^{235}$ and continues to be used as a popular shorthand expression for that isotope. The process is used in the Idaho Chemical Processing Plant. (See **fuel reprocessing**)

"202" HEARINGS

Annual hearings conducted by the **Joint Committee on Atomic Energy** of the U.S. Congress, as required under Section 202 of the Atomic Energy Act of 1954, to receive "information concerning the development, growth, and state of the atomic energy industry." The "202" hearings are required to be held during the first 60 days of the Congressional session. Transcripts of the proceedings are available from the Superintendent of Public Documents, U.S. Government Printing Office at nominal cost.

2W CONCEPT

A theorem that has evolved from nuclear weapons tests—namely, that the detonation of a nuclear weapon of energy yield *W* on the surface of the earth produces blast phenomena essentially identical to those produced by a device of twice the yield, or 2*W*, in free air, i.e., away from any reflecting surface.

TYUYAMINATE

Hydrated calcium uranium vanadate—a secondary mineral, greenish yellow in color, commonly associated with **carnotite.** It is particularly abundant in the Grants-Laguna area of New Mexico.

U

ULTRA HIGH-TEMPERATURE REACTOR EXPERIMENT (UHTREX)

A high-temperature gas-cooled reactor experiment under construction at Los Alamos Scientific Laboratory; formerly known as the Turret Reactor. Operation is expected to start late in 1964, or early in 1965. The project is to serve as a test of the feasibility of operating a helium cooled reactor at temperatures in the neighborhood of 2400°F, using unclad fuel elements consisting of graphite impregnated with fully enriched uranium. The application contemplated is the production of high temperature heat for industrial processes such as coal gasification. (See **process heat applications for reactors**)

UNDERGROUND BURST

The detonation of a nuclear weapon or device below the surface of the ground. (See **weapons phenomenology, Plowshare Program**)

UNDERWATER BURST

The detonation of a nuclear weapon below the surface of the water. (See **weapons phenomenology**)

UNICE

The Union of Industries of the European Community, an organization established to coordinate industrial activity within the member countries of the three European community institutions—namely, the Coal and Steel Community, the Common Market, and **Euratom.** A subcommittee for nuclear matters was formed recently to handle UNICE activity in relation to Euratom. The European community countries are Belgium, France, West Germany, Italy, Luxembourg, and the Netherlands.

UNION CARBIDE NUCLEAR COMPANY RESEARCH REACTOR

A 5000-kilowatt (thermal) pool-type research reactor operated as part of UCNC's research center at Sterling Forest, New York. It was supplied by AMF Atomics, Inc. and began operation in 1961. (See **research and training reactors**)

UNITED ARAB REPUBLIC

The UAR Atomic Energy Commission, Cairo, is the agency responsible for atomic energy matters. A nuclear research center, known as the UAR Atomic Energy Institution, has been established at Inshas, just outside Cairo. A 2000-megawatt (thermal) tank-type research reactor is being installed at this center with the assistance of the U.S.S.R. Facilities already in operation include a nuclear physics laboratory and a laboratory for research with radioisotopes.

Small reserves of monazite have been found in the Nile Delta Basin. An ore processing facility is reportedly planned for construction at Inshas. Aerial surveys are planned in an effort to locate additional deposits of radioactive minerals.

The UAR is a member of the **International Atomic Energy Agency,** and has a technical assistance agreement with the U.S.S.R.

UNITED KINGDOM

Agencies. The United Kingdom Atomic Energy Authority (AEA), London, is the agency responsible for atomic energy research and development under policy direction of the Minister of Science. All commercial nuclear power stations are built and operated by the Central Electricity Generating Board (CEGB) or the South of Scotland Electricity Board (SSEB), which are responsible to the Ministry of Power for electricity supply in England and Wales or Southern Scotland, respectively.

International Relationships. Member of the **International Atomic Energy Agency,** the **European Nuclear Energy Agency,** and the Organization for European Nuclear Research **(CERN).** Comprehensive **Agreement for Cooperation** with the United States. Agreements with **Euratom** and with various individual countries within and outside the British Commonwealth.

Research Centers. The Atomic Energy Research Establishment, Harwell, Berks, one of the world's major scientific laboratories, is operated by AEA's Research Group. It carries out basic research in all aspects of atomic energy. Its experimental facilities include several large particle accelerators and six research reactors. Three of the research reactors (GLEEP, LIDO, and DAPHNE) are low-power units. The others are used largely for materials testing and isotope production. BEPO is a natural uranium graphite-moderated reactor which operates at a power level of 6000 kilowatts (thermal). DIDO and PLUTO are high-flux tank-type reactors, fueled with enriched uranium and moderated with heavy water, which operates at 13,000 and 10,000 kilowatts (thermal), respectively.

The Atomic Energy Establishment, Winfrith Heath, Dorset, is a reactor development center operated by AEA's Reactor Group. ZENITH, a zero energy reactor primarily intended for reactor physics investigations on high-temperature gas-cooled systems has been in operation since 1959. Dragon, a 20-megawatt (thermal) experimental high-temperature gas-cooled power reactor, is under construction as a joint project of the AEA and the European Nuclear Energy Agency (see **Dragon Project).** Other reactors include NESTOR, a low-power research and training reactor of the **Argonaut** type, NERO and HECTOR, graphite-moderated reactors for reactivity measurements, DIMPLE, a zero energy facility for the study of water systems and ZEBRA for studies of fast reactors.

Dounreay Experimental Reactor Establishment, Dounreay, Caithness, is a development center also operated by AEA's Reactor Group. The principal reactor facilities are DFR, a 60-megawatt (thermal) prototype fast breeder power reactor; and DMTR, a high-flux materials testing reactor similar to Harwell's PLUTO. Other facilities include a plant for fabricating fuel elements containing plutonium or highly enriched uranium; facilities for reprocessing such fuel elements after irradiation; and "hot" cells for irradiated fuel element examination. A land-based prototype naval propulsion reactor is operated by the Royal Navy.

Culcheth Metallurgical Laboratories, Culcheth, Lancashire, is a reactor metallurgy center operated by AEA's Reactor Group and equipped with facilities for studying the corrosion resistance and other properties of reactor fuels, cladding agents and structural materials; developing fuel cladding techniques; and conducting related experimental programs.

Work on controlled-fusion research is being steadily transferred to new laboratories at Culham in Oxfordshire.

Wantage Research Laboratories, Wantage, Berks, is a center for research on new applications for radioisotopes. The facilities, which include high-level irradiation cells are an integral part of the organization of Harwell 7 miles away. A school teaches radioisotope techniques and ways of overcoming industrial problems by the use of isotopes are investigated.

The Atomic Weapons Research Establishment, Aldermaston, Berks, is the AEA's principal weapons research center.

The CEGB has established a laboratory for

reactor research and development at the Berkeley Nuclear Power Station (see below).

The Rutherford Laboratory of the National Institute for Research in Nuclear Science (NIRNS), which provides specialized facilities for use by educational and research institutions is located at Harwell. The largest single facility is a 7-Bev proton synchroton, scheduled to be completed in 1962-1963.

Fig. 213. Uranium metal production at the United Kingdom Atomic Energy Authority's Springfield Works, Salwick, Lancs. Equipment seen here is used for the reduction of "green salt" (UF_4) to massive uranium metal by a thermite-type reaction. (*Courtesy of UKAEA*)

Production Activity. The United Kingdom collaborated with the United States during the wartime Manhattan Project and later independently developed an integrated system of plants for the production of weapon and reactor-grade fissionable materials. Its atomic production capacity is today exceeded only by the United States and the U.S.S.R. Information on the major installations operated by AEA's Production Group follows:

Raw materials are imported, principally from Commonwealth sources *via* the **Combined Development Agency.**

Feed materials operations center at the Springfield Works, Salwick, Lancs. Here uranium concentrates are refined and processed into uranium hexafluoride (for uranium-235 production) and uranium metal fuel elements (for plutonium and power production).

Uranium isotope separation facilities for the production of uranium-235 (various grades) are located at the Capenhurst Works, Chester, Cheshire. The facilities include a large-scale gaseous diffusion plant and a plant for the conversion of enriched uranium hexafluoride to uranium tetrafluoride.

Plutonium is produced in eight natural-uranium, graphite-moderated, carbon dioxide cooled reactors. These are dual-purpose units in that they also produce electricity which is sold to CEGB for distribution over the national grid. (Each reactor operates at a maximum power level of 225 thermal megawatts and produces about 45 megawatts of net electrical power.) Four of the reactors are located at Calder Hall, adjoining the Windscale Works at Sellafield (see below); the other four are located at the Chapelcross Works, Annan, Dumfriesshire.

Chemical separation facilities for the recovery of plutonium from irradiated fuel are located at the Windscale Works, Sellafield, Cumberland. A solvent extraction process similar to the U.S. **Purex process** is used. Two plutonium production reactors (Windscale I and II) were formerly operated at this site but have been closed down.

Most radioisotopes are produced at Harwell. The Radiochemical Centre at Amersham markets these radioisotopes and, where necessary, carries out processing.

Energy Economy. The United Kingdom's electric power capacity is approximately 35,000 megawatts, virtually all of it coal-fired. Though there are extensive coal reserves, the mines are being operated at or near their peak capacity. Hydroelectric resources are very limited. There are no oil fields in the country.

Nuclear Power Program. The United Kingdom looks to nuclear power to stabilize her energy economy and sustain continued industrial growth without undue dependence on coal imports. Plans call for the installation of 4000-5000 megawatts of nuclear power capacity by 1966. Some 300 megawatts are now operated by AEA (see above reference to dual-purpose plants at Calder Hall and Chapelcross). Eight nuclear power stations with a total capacity of approximately 3600 megawatts electrical are under construction for CEGB and SSEB. The stations, each involving two reactors of the Calder Hall type but in this case optimized for power, rather than plutonium production,* are as follows (see below for more information on the three consortia).

Berkeley Station, Berkeley, Gloucester: The Nuclear Power Group built this 275 megawatt electrical station for the CEGB. The first reactor of this station went critical in August, 1961.

Fig. 214. Chapelcross Nuclear Power Station near Annan, Dumfriesshire, Scotland, operated by the United Kingdom Atomic Energy Authority. (*Courtesy of UKAEA*)

Bradwell Station, Bradwell, Essex: The Nuclear Power Group built this 300 megawatt station for the CEGB. The first reactor of this station went critical in August, 1961.

Hunterston Station, Ardrossen, Scotland: The United Power Company is building this 300 megawatt electrical station for the SSEB. Start-up is scheduled for 1963.

Hinkley Point Station, Somerset on the Bristol Channel: The English Electric, Babcock & Wilcox, Taylor-Woodrow Atomic Power Group is building this 500 megawatt electrical station for the CEGB. Power production is scheduled for 1963.

* Another difference is the use of magnox fuel element cladding in lieu of aluminum cladding.

Trawsfynydd Station, Trawsfynydd, Wales: The United Power Company is building this 500 megawatt electrical station for the CEGB. Completion is scheduled for 1964.

Dungeness Station in Kent on the south coast: The Nuclear Power Group is building this 550 megawatt electrical station for the CEGB. Completion is scheduled for 1964.

Sizewell Station, Suffolk: The English Electric, Babcock & Wilcox, Taylor-Woodrow Atomic Power Group is building this 580 megawatt electrical station for the CEGB. Completion is scheduled for 1966.

Oldbury Station, Gloucester: The Nuclear Power Group is building this 560 megawatt electrical station for the CEGB. Construction started in 1962.

A ninth reactor station at Wylfa, Anglesey, is to be built for the CEGB to generate 800 megawatts-electrical. The United Power Company is to build the first reactor of this station; the English Electric, Babcock & Wilcox, Taylor-Woodrow Atomic Power Group is to build the second reactor. A tenth reactor station is planned at Hinkley Point for the CEGB to generate 1000 megawatts-electrical.

An advanced graphite-moderated gas-cooled power reactor prototype, to be fueled with slightly enriched (1.25% U-235) uranium canned in stainless steel, is being constructed by the AEA at Windscale. This is known as the AGR Project. The prototype installation will have a thermal rating of 100 megawatts and is expected to start operating in 1962.

In the above connection, it should be noted that the AEA's nuclear power development philosophy has essentially been to rely on natural uranium gas-cooled systems for the short term with the expectation of ultimately building a network of fast breeder systems. Water-cooled systems fueled with enriched uranium were evaluated as an alternative short-term (or possible intermediate) solution, but were rejected—in part because of the AEA's desire to avoid the use of enriched uranium. As matters now stand, the need to reduce capital costs appears to be forcing the AEA in the direction of using some degree of enrichment (thereby reducing core size) in their short-term gas-cooled reactor program. Also, consideration is being given to the use of prestressed-concrete, in lieu of steel, for reactor pressure-vessel construction. (See **gas-cooled reactors** for background information.)

Nuclear Ship Propulsion. Two Naval nuclear propulsion projects have been undertaken. For the first, an S5W (Skipjack-type) pressurized water system was supplied by Westinghouse Electric Corporation under a U.S.-U.K. agreement. This system was installed by Rolls-Royce & Associates (see table) in the submarine, *Dreadnought,* which was launched in October, 1960, and is scheduled to be operational in 1962. The second submarine (*Valiant*) will be powered by a pressurized water system to be designed and constructed by Rolls-Royce & Associates under subcontract to Vickers-Armstrong.

Controlled Fusion. The AEA program of research on controlled-fusion reactions includes research on **stabilized pinch, hard-core pinch, magnetic mirror systems** and **cusped geometry.** Containment properties of toroidal pinch are being studied in ZETA, a ring-shaped apparatus at Harwell in which deuterium gas is heated to high temperatures by an electric discharge and in the Sceptre at Aldermaston. The Phoenix program at Aldermaston aims to build up clean dense plasma with high ion temperature by ionization of fast neutral particles in mirror geometry. Experimental work to clarify understanding of stability phenomena, now in progress at Harwell and Aldermaston, will be steadily transferred to the Culham Laboratory.

Industry notes: The three consortia active in the U.K. nuclear program are as follows:

1. The English Electric, B&W, Taylor-Woodrow Atomic Power Construction Company, Ltd. The three member companies have equal interest in this consortium. This group is responsible for construction of Hinkley Point, Sizewell, and Reactor #2 at Wylfa Head.

2. The Nuclear Power Group (TNPG) is a partnership between AEI-John Thompson Nuclear Energy Co. and the Nuclear Power Plant

Fig. 215. Dounreay Fast Reactor. This is a fast breeder reactor designed to operate at a power level of 60 megawatts (thermal), located in the extreme north of Scotland. Left, general view. Bottom, top of stainless steel pressure vessel inside reactor vault. (*Courtesy of UKAEA*)

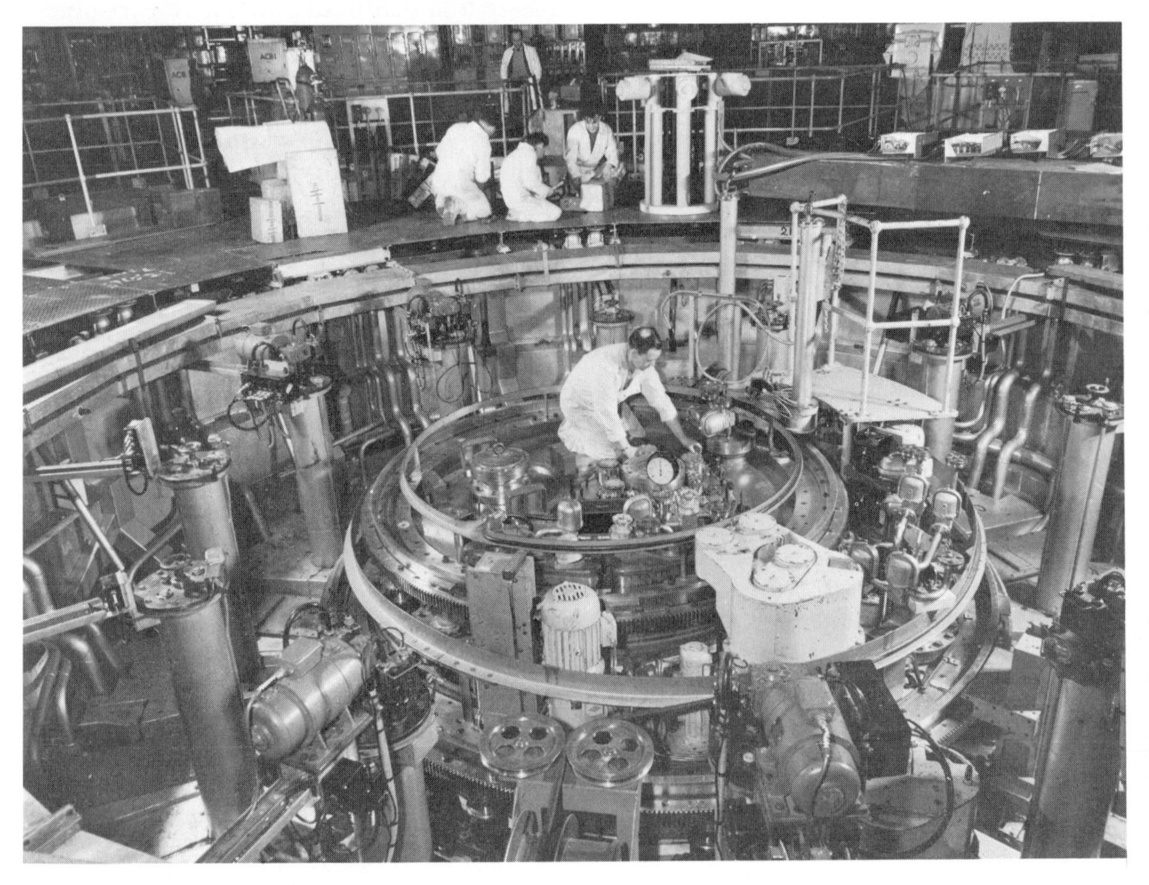

Fig. 216. Construction view of 30-megawatt (electrical) Advanced Gas-cooled Reactor (AGR) at Windscale. (*Courtesy of UKAEA*)

Company, each with a 50% share holding. TNPG is responsible for the construction of Berkeley, Bradwell, Dungeness, Oldbury, and Latina in Italy.

3. The United Power Company, Ltd. (UPC). This consortium is made up of General Electric, Simon-Carves, Ltd., International Combustion, Ltd., Fairy Engineering, Ltd., and Richardson Westgarth; each with a 20% share holding. This consortium was formed as a result of a merger of resources between the GE-Simon-Carves Atomic Energy group and Atomic Power Construction, Ltd. (APC). UPC has responsibility for Trawsfynydd, Hunterston, Reactor #1 at Wylfa Head, and the Tokai Mura Reactor in Japan.

UNITED NATIONS

The **International Atomic Energy Agency** was formed under the auspices of the United Nations in 1957, as the central international organization in the field of peaceful uses of atomic energy. The United Nations is concerned with the problems relating to the **international control of atomic energy.**

For specific activities of the United Nations in the civilian atomic energy field, see: **Food and Agriculture Organization** (FAO); **International Labor Office** (ILO); **World Health Organization** (WHO); **World Meteorological Organization** (WMO); and **United Nations Scientific Committee on the Effects of Atomic Radiation** (UNSCEAR). Also see **Geneva (Atoms for Peace) Conferences.**

UNITED NATIONS SCIENTIFIC COMMITTEE ON THE EFFECTS OF ATOMIC RADIATION (UNSCEAR)

A special committee appointed by the General Assembly of the United Nations in December, 1955, to analyze available information and advise the Secretary-General on this subject, and to prepare review reports, from time to time, for distribution to the U.N. membership.

U.S.-EURATOM JOINT PROGRAM

A joint program providing for U.S. assistance to Euratom in the construction of large power reactors and for cooperation in related research and development. The terms of the program are defined in an **Agreement for Cooperation,** signed in Washington on June 12, 1958, and ratified by the two parties later that same year. The principal points can be summarized as follows:

1. The agreement envisioned the construction in Euratom countries of six or seven nuclear power plants of "proven" U.S. design with an aggregate capacity of 1000 megawatts. These projects were to be completed by 1963, except that two projects could be deferred until 1965.

2. The United States agreed to furnish, through the **Export-Import Bank,** long-term credit up to $135 million to help finance the construction of the plants. (The total cost of construction was roughly estimated at $350 million, based on an average capital cost of $350 per kilowatt of installed capacity.)

3. The United States agreed to furnish guarantees on fuel-element performance up to a maximum commitment of $90 million over the first 10 years of plant operation.

4. The United States provided assurances of a long-term fuel supply; agreed to reprocess the fuel at prices comparable to those offered U.S. industry; and guaranteed a 10-year market for the by-product plutonium. The agreement stipulated that the fuel would be sold to Euratom on a deferred-payment basis, and that Euratom would exercise agreed safeguards procedures to prevent loss of or diversion to nonpeaceful uses of the material.

5. The United States and Euratom each agreed to contribute up to $50 million over a five-year period for research and development specifically relating to the projects undertaken, with the understanding that half of the efforts would be conducted in the United States and half in the Euratom countries.

At the time the agreement was signed there was optimism that the program would carry through as planned; but subsequent developments, notably an unexpected surplus in Western European coal supplies, acted to dampen progress. At mid-1961 the status of the program was as follows:

1. Only one project was in a position to meet the 1963 completion deadline, namely the ENSI Project of the SENN group in **Italy.** That project was planned before the Joint Program came into being but is now being carried forward under the Joint Program. It involves the construction of a 150-megawatt (electrical) boiling water plant at Punte Fiume, with provision in the design to increase the capacity at a later date to 230 megawatts (electrical).

2. Two projects appeared to be in a position to meet the 1965 deadline provided acceptable terms could be negotiated. One was the SENA Project, a joint venture of **France** and **Belgium** for the construction of a 230-megawatt (electrical) pressurized water plant near the Franco-Belgian border in the vicinity of the towns of Chooz and Givet.* The other was a project of the KBWP group in West **Germany** to build a 150-megawatt (electrical) organic moderated plant.

3. Research and development contracts authorized under the Joint Program through 1960, totaled $8 million of which $5.5 million was to be expended by Euratom in the Community.

UNIVERSITY OF CALIFORNIA AT LOS ANGELES ATOMIC ENERGY PROJECT

A U.S. Atomic Energy Commission biomedical research laboratory in Los Angeles, California. *Operating contractor:* University of California. *Director:* Joseph F. Ross. *AEC investment in plant and equipment:* ~ $1 million.

The laboratory is operated in conjunction with the UCLA Medical School and is primarily concerned with research on the biological effects of radiation, including study of methods

* Acceptance of the SENA proposal was announced by the U.S.-Euratom Joint Reactor Board in July, 1962.

for protection against and treatment of radiation injury. Another activity is the development of radiation instruments.

For a number of years the laboratory has been responsible for monitoring residual radioactivity and other environmental effects at the site of the first nuclear weapon test ("Trinity") near Almogordo, New Mexico, and at the **Nevada Test Site.**

UNIVERSITY OF ROCHESTER ATOMIC ENERGY PROJECT

A U.S. Atomic Energy Commission biomedical research laboratory in Rochester, New York. *Operating contractor:* University of Rochester. *Director:* Henry A. Blair. *AEC investment in plant and equipment:* ~ $6 million. *Staff:* ~ 50 scientists, and ~ 140 supporting personnel.

The laboratory is operated in conjunction with the Rochester Medical Center and is primarily concerned with research on the toxicity of materials of importance in atomic energy development, and with investigation of the biological effects of radiation. In the field of toxicity, through metabolic and other studies the laboratory has made important contributions to the determination of safe tolerances for the inhalation and/or ingestion of beryllium, indium, mercury, and other nonradioactive metals; and of alpha-emitting materials such as plutonium, polonium and radon. In the field of radiation effects, it has given particular attention to determining whole-body tolerances for chronic low-level radiation exposure. Other activities include cancer research; the development of radiation instruments, especially air sampling devices; and graduate training in biophysics, pharmacology, toxicology, and related fields.

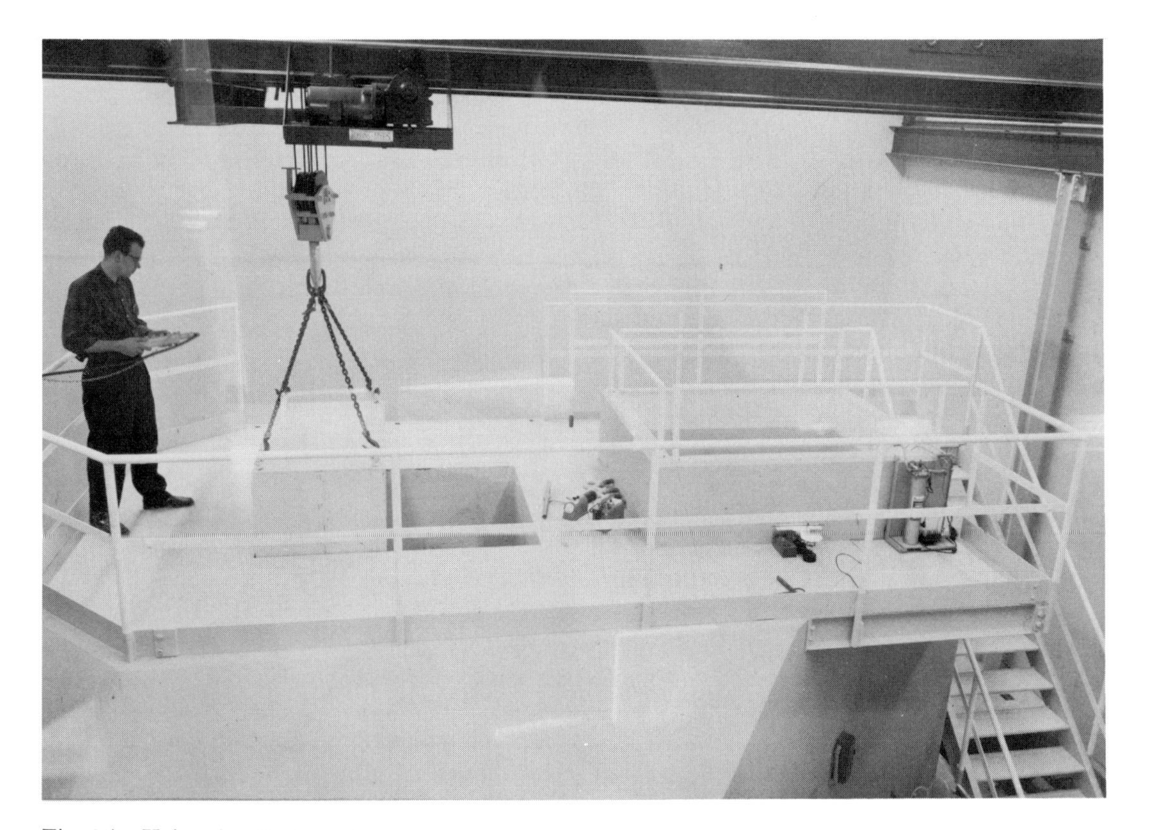

Fig. 217. University Training Reactor (UTR) at Virginia Polytechnic Institute (*Courtesy of Advanced Technology Laboratories, American Radiator and Standard Sanitary Corp.*)

UNIVERSITY TRAINING REACTORS (UTR SERIES)

Trade name of a line of small nuclear reactors manufactured by the Atomic Energy Division of American Radiator and Standard Sanitary Corporation at Mountain View, California. Through 1960, 5 UTR units had been supplied or were scheduled or planned for delivery to laboratories in the United States and abroad, mainly for student training programs. *Type:* Graphite/water reactors. *Power ratings:* Up to 10 thermal kilowatts. *Fuel:* Aluminum-clad plates containing a dispersion of an enriched uranium (20% U^{235})-aluminum alloy in an aluminum matrix. *Coolant:* H_2O. *Moderator:* H_2O. *Reflector:* Graphite. *Neutron flux:* Of the order of 10^{11}n/cm^{2}sec (maximum thermal). (See Fig. 217)

For a listing of UTR installations and general background information, see **research and training reactors.**

URANINITE

An anhydrous primary uranium mineral consisting of a mixture of uranium dioxide (UO_2) and uranium trioxide (UO_3). Uraninite is chiefly black in color and is found in massive or disseminated form in veins and sedimentary rocks. It is a common constituent of the "black ores" of the western United States, often associated with **coffinite,** and represents a major source of domestic uranium production.

URANIUM

A heavy, slightly radioactive metallic element (atomic number, 92; atomic weight, 238.07), discovered by the German chemist H. M. Klaproth in 1789. The concentration of uranium in the earth's crust is estimated at 4 parts per million; it is thus as abundant as lead or molybdenum, and more so than antimony, bismuth, mercury, or silver.

As it is found in nature uranium is a mixture of three isotopes: U^{234} (0.01%), U^{235} (0.71%), and U^{238} (99.28%). Following are notes on these naturally occurring species.

Uranium-234: A nonfissionable, nonfertile, long-lived, alpha emitter of no practical importance.

Uranium-235: Indispensable to fission-based atomic energy development, being one of the three primary fissionable materials and the only one that occurs naturally. It is an alpha emitter with a half-life of 7.13×10^8 years.

Uranium-238: Also of vital importance, being one of the two fertile materials available for fissionable material production. An alpha emitter with a half-life of 4.51×10^9 years, U-238 yields the primary fissionable material, **plutonium** by the following reaction and decay sequence, involving the intermediate product, **neptunium:**

$$_{92}U^{238} + {}_0n^1 \longrightarrow {}_{92}U^{239} + \gamma \quad (1)$$

$$_{92}U^{239} \xrightarrow{23.5\text{ min}} {}_{93}Np^{239} + {}_{-1}e^0 \quad (2)$$

$$_{93}Np^{239} \xrightarrow{2.3\text{ days}} {}_{94}Pu^{239} + {}_{-1}e^0 \quad (3)$$

Another important characteristic of U^{238} is that it will undergo fission under fast-neutron bombardment. (See **fast fission)**

Various additional isotopes of uranium are formed artificially, including:

Uranium-233: The third primary fissionable material. It is produced from the fertile material, thorium, by the following reaction and decay sequence involving the intermediate product, **protoactinium:**

$$_{90}Th^{232} + {}_0N^1 \longrightarrow {}_{90}Th^{233} + \gamma \quad (1)$$

$$_{90}Th^{233} \xrightarrow{23.5\text{ min}} {}_{91}Pa^{233} + {}_{-1}e^0 \quad (2)$$

$$_{91}Pa^{233} \xrightarrow{27.4\text{ days}} {}_{92}U^{233} + {}_{-1}e^0 \quad (3)$$

Uranium-233 is an alpha emitter with a half-life of 1.6×10^5 years. Of the three primary fissionable materials, it has the highest neutron yield in thermal fission and hence offers great promise as a fuel in thermal breeding systems.

Uranium-236: A long-lived alpha emitter (2.4×10^7 years half-life) formed by parasitic neutron capture in uranium-235 during the irradiation of uranium fuel. It is a complicating factor in nuclear power applications:

1. Where uranium recovered from reactor operations must be upgraded in isotope sepa-

ration facilities prior to reuse as fuel, the presence of U^{236} complicates the upgrading process. (See **uranium enrichment**)

2. U^{236} has an appreciable neutron capture **cross section** and therefore its presence in recycled fuel causes neutron losses in reactor use.

3. The product of neutron capture in U^{236} is U^{237}, itself an undesirable material.

Uranium-237: An energetic 6.8 day gamma emitter. Its concentration in irradiated fuel generally determines the length of time which must be allowed for **decay cooling** prior to initiating **fuel reprocessing** operations.

Uranium is highly reactive. The normal valences are +3, +4, and +6. The common oxides are uranium dioxide (UO_2), known as "brown oxide"; uranous uranyl oxide (U_3O_8), known as "black oxide"; and uranium trioxide (UO_3), known as "orange oxide." Uranium metal for reactor fuel is obtained by reduction of uranium tetrafluoride (UF_4), known as "green salt." Uranium hexafluoride (UF_6), sometimes called "hex," is a volatile compound used as the process medium in the gaseous diffusion process for the isotopic enrichment of uranium.

Uranium metal has three crystalline phases: alpha, up to 660°C; beta, between 660° and 760°C; and gamma, from 760°C up to the melting point, 1132°C. The metal is normally worked in the alpha phase. It is reasonably ductile and can be fabricated by standard metallurgical techniques; however, since uranium chips are highly pyrophoric, grinding and similar operations must be conducted in an inert atmosphere or under a flood of coolant. Uranium has very poor corrosion resistance and must be clad or otherwise protected when used in solid form as reactor fuel.

Uranium alloys may be classified as follows: (1) True intermetallic compounds as when it is alloyed with aluminum, beryllium, or silicon; (2) solid solutions as when alloyed with zirconium, titanium, or molybdenum; and (3) limited solubility mixtures as when alloyed with chromium, vanadium, or thorium.

For further information, see **uranium deposits and reserves, uranium exploration, uranium mining, uranium milling, uranium refining and conversion,** and **uranium enrichment.**

URANIUM DEPOSITS AND RESERVES

Uranium reacts with many elements, enters the structure of numerous minerals, and is deposited in a variety of igneous and sedimentary environments. The most common uranium mineral ore deposits in the United States are **carnotite, coffinite, tyuyamunite, uraninite** and **pitchblende.** Although uranium is mined from vein deposits in certain areas of the United States, the principal production of uranium is from flat-lying deposits in sedimentary rock—principally sandstones. The average uranium content for ores currently being mined is about 0.25%, expressed as U_3O_8. As of December 31, 1960, known and inferred U.S. deposits of minimal grade or higher were estimated at 82.0 million ore tons, representing a reserve of some 240,000 tons of U_3O_8.* Material not amenable by milling by established methods was excluded from this estimate. Following is a breakdown of the estimated reserves by states:

State	*Approx. % of Total*
New Mexico	57
Wyoming	20
Utah	8
Colorado	6
Arizona	3
Washington, Oregon and Nevada	3
Others [1]	3
	100

[1] North and South Dakota, California, Montana, Idaho and Alaska.

The price established by the USAEC for high-grade concentrate produced from domestic ore deposits is $8.00 per pound of U_3O_8 content. In addition to its "commercial grade" uranium ore resources, the United States has extensive low-grade uranium deposits in phosphate rock (Florida, Idaho, Utah, Wyoming and Montana) and bituminous shale (Ten-

* An additional 1.3 million tons of ore were held in government stockpiles as of this date.

nessee). An estimated several million tons of U_3O_8 is contained in these deposits in concentrations of the order of .005 to .01%. Here uranium recovery is presently uneconomic on other than a by-product basis. (Current estimates place the cost of recovery from shales on a primary basis (i.e., not as a by-product) at between **$45-55** per pound of U_3O_8.)

Uranium deposits found elsewhere in the free world include the following:

Mineral	*Major Deposits*
Uraninite (pitchblende)	Shinkolobwe, Republic of the Congo; Great Bear Lake, Northwest Territory, Canada; Lake Athabasca, Saskatchewan, Canada; Massif Central, France; Rum Jungle, Northern Territory, Australia
Davidite	Radium Hill, South Australia
Uraninite and brannerite	Blind River, Ontario, Canada; Witwatersrand, South Africa
Uraninite	Mt. Isa-Cloncurry district, Queensland, Australia

Estimates of the uranium reserves of the principal free world areas where uranium is currently produced have been reliably reported as follows:

Country	*Avg. Grade of Ore (% U_3O_8)*	*Tons of U_3O_8*
Canada	0.10	400,000
Africa	0.03	400,000
U.S.	0.28	240,000
U.K. and Western Europe	0.17	40,000
Asia and Far East	0.15	10,000
Latin America	0.30	3,000
	Total (rounded)	1,100,000

Source: Joint Committee on Atomic Energy, "Background Material For The Review of The International Policies of the United States," Vol. 4, October, 1960.

These estimates relate to deposits from which uranium concentrates can be produced at currently acceptable cost levels. These levels vary with the individual countries but are generally of the order of **$10** per pound of U_3O_8 or less. If the price is allowed to increase by a factor of 5 and if total known free world resources are taken into account, it is estimated that an additional **10** million tons of recoverable U_3O_8 would become available.

URANIUM DIOXIDE (UO_2)

"Brown oxide," commonly used as a fuel material in power reactors (see **reactor materials**); also, an intermediate product in the production of uranium tetrafluoride from uranium trioxide (see **uranium refining and conversion**)

Most power reactors fueled with uranium dioxide require slightly enriched material. This is produced commercially by what is sometimes called the ADU (ammonium diuranate) process. The starting material is uranium hexafluoride (UF_6) from one of the U.S. Atomic Energy Commission's **uranium enrichment** plants. There are 3 basic steps in the process: (1) The enriched UF_6 is hydrolyzed to a uranyl fluoride solution. (2) The fluoride solution is mixed with concentrated ammonium hydroxide to yield a precipitate of ammonium diuranate ($(NH_4)_2 U_2O_7$). (3) The precipitate is calcined to UO_3, which is in turn reduced to UO_2.

The grade of UO_2 powder produced is controlled by varying the process conditions—in particular the hydroxide concentration and speed of mixing in the precipitation step, and the temperature and atmosphere in the UO_3 reduction step. "Sintered" UO_2 is a powder of high density suitable for fabrication into fuel-element forms by hot swaging techniques. "Ceramic grade" UO_2 is a low-density powder that can be pressed and sintered into dense oxide pellets. "Pigment grade" UO_2 is an intermediate-density powder that is promising for use in dispersion-type fuel elements. For information on the fabrication of UO_2 powder into fuel elements, see **fuel element fabrication.**

Normal UO_2, used as a blanket material in some reactor systems, can be supplied direct from uranium refining operations.

URANIUM, ENERGY FROM. See **energy statistics, U.S.; energy statistics, world.**

URANIUM ENRICHMENT

The separation of uranium isotopes to obtain a product enriched in uranium-235, and resulting in "waste" depleted in that isotope.

The production of enriched uranium for weapon stockpiles and for use as reactor fuel is conducted on a large scale in the United States. During the wartime **Manhattan Project**, four principal uranium isotope separation processes were investigated:

1. **Gas centrifuge process**, the development of which was not carried beyond the pilot plant stage.
2. **Electromagnetic separation**, a batch process used for wartime production (Y-12 Plant) but thereafter limited in application to the separation of laboratory quantities of **stable isotopes** for research purposes.
3. **Thermal diffusion**, used for an interim period during the war (S-50 Plant).
4. **Gaseous diffusion**, a continuous process, used in the late stages of the war effort and for all postwar production.

The wartime gaseous diffusion facilities were located at Oak Ridge (as were Y-12 and S-50) and consisted of two production units—K-25, the original plant, and K-27, an addition thereto. Since the war, the Oak Ridge gaseous diffusion facilities have been expanded considerably, and comparable production centers have been built at Paducah, Kentucky and Portsmouth, Ohio. (See below.)

Operations. To date the gaseous diffusion plants have processed normal uranium and slightly depleted uranium—the latter recovered from plutonium production operations. It is to be expected that in the future they will additionally process uranium recovered from power reactor operations.

In the case of normal uranium the feedstock arrives at the gaseous diffusion plant site in the form of uranium trioxide (UO_3) from government-owned refineries at Fernald, Ohio and Weldon Spring, Missouri, or in the form of uranium hexafluoride (UF_6) from a privately owned plant of Allied Chemical Corporation in Metropolis, Illinois. (See **uranium refining and conversion**) When received as trioxide, the uranium is converted to the hexafluoride form. This compound, a solid at room temperatures, sublimes on heating and remains in the gaseous state at the temperatures used in the gaseous diffusion process.

Slightly depleted uranium is received in the form of concentrated solutions of decontami-

Fig. 218. The K-25 cascade, part of the Oak Ridge Gaseous Diffusion Plant. (*Courtesy Union Carbide Corp.*)

nated uranyl nitrate from the Hanford and Savannah River plutonium production centers. These solutions are calcined to uranium trioxide, which in turn is converted to the hexafluoride.

A gaseous diffusion plant consists primarily of a cascade, or series, of hundreds of stages of diffusion equipment. The hexafluoride is fed into the system at an intermediate point in the cascade. The enriched product is withdrawn from any one of various points further up the cascade depending on the uranium-235 concentration desired. The depleted or "tails" material is withdrawn from the bottom of the cascade. Removal is accomplished by means of refrigerated "cold traps."

The diffusion plants are equipped to convert the product material to metal or intermediate chemical form. It may also be shipped out as solid hexafluoride in pressurized metal cylinders.

The U-236 Problem. A complicating factor will be introduced into the operation of gaseous diffusion facilities when they are called upon to re-enrich or upgrade uranium that has been recovered from power reactors. Such uranium will contain appreciable quantities of uranium-236, an isotope that does not occur naturally but is formed in the course of irradiation. (In a thermal power reactor fueled with slightly enriched uranium, as much as one-sixth of the uranium-235 consumed may be converted to uranium-236.) The presence of uranium-236 in reactor fuel is undesirable on two counts: (1) because it is a neutron absorber and (2) because upon neutron capture it converts to uranium-237, a short-lived gamma emitter that must be allowed to decay before the irradiated fuel can be reprocessed (see **fuel reprocessing**). While it would thus be desirable to remove the uranium-236 during the re-enrichment operation, this will be difficult in practice due to the small weight difference between uranium-235 and uranium-236 relative to that between uranium-235 and uranium-238.

Facilities. As has been noted, gaseous diffusion plants are located at Oak Ridge, Paducah and Portsmouth. The facilities at the first two locations are operated on behalf of the U.S. Atomic Energy Commission by Union Carbide Nuclear Company, a division of Union Carbide Corporation. The Portsmouth plant is operated by Goodyear Atomic Corporation, a subsidiary of Goodyear Tire and Rubber Company. The total investment is approximately $2.3 billion. Some 10,000 operating personnel are employed, 1000 of them scientists or engineers. Some 5 million kilowatts of electrical power generating capacity are required to operate the three plants at full capacity.

CHARGES FOR ENRICHED URANIUM IN THE FORM OF UF_6[1]

(July 1, 1962)

Weight Fraction U^{235}	*Dollars per Kilogram of Uranium*	*Dollars per Gram of U^{235} Content*
.010	47.70	4.77
.015	95.30	6.35
.020	146.50	7.33
.030	254.30	8.48
.050	497.40	9.59
.10	1062.00	10.62
.20	2252.00	11.26
.90	10,808.00	12.01

[1] These prices reflect price reductions made on July 1, 1961 (because of reduced costs in raw uranium procurement) and July 1, 1962 (because of lowered cost of uranium enrichment).

Cost and Availability of Enriched Uranium. Title to enriched uranium remains with the government. It is leased to licensees at a use charge, f.o.b. from and to Oak Ridge, Tennessee, currently set at 4.75% of its value per year. The charge commences as of the date the material is diverted from AEC production channels and is continued until (1) the material or some part of it is returned to the AEC, at which time the licensee is credited for the value of the returned material less any processing charges to bring it to specifications; or (2) the licensee decleares that all or some part of the material has been burned, lost, or otherwise consumed, and makes payment therefor.

The AEC's prices for various grades of enriched uranium as hexafluoride are given in the accompanying table. The AEC will supply enriched uranium in other forms at additional cost but only when there is no commercial source for the particular form required.

Export Limitation. See **Agreements for Cooperation.**

URANIUM EXPLORATION

The search for uranium has involved all of the classical techniques of mineral exploration plus specialized techniques based on the radioactivity of uranium-bearing ores. It is an activity in which government, industrial and land-owning interests, and individual prospectors have all played important roles.

Techniques that have been used in the United States to locate promising localities for detailed field investigation include geologic, geophysical, geochemical and geobotanical studies and aerial radiometric surveys. The first step is the identification of favorable terrain, which is done in part by inference from geologic data. Geochemical investigations, such as the analysis of ground water for anomalous concentrations of uranium or elements associated with uranium minerals, provide supplementary information. Once favorable terrain has been selected or identified, the second step is to spot promising localities. Here one of the most effective techniques has been the use of airborne radiation detection equipment to locate anomalous concentrations of radioactivity; this is done by low-flying aircraft equipped with high-sensitivity **scintillation counters.** Helpful information may also come from geophysical investigations. Indirect techniques include the mapping of rock strata and of local lithologic, mineralogic and structural characteristics and alteration phenomena.

Actual delineation of ore bodies is principally a matter of drilling or underground development. Various drilling techniques have been developed; however, the three most commonly used are diamond core drilling, rotary air and/or water drilling, and air percussion drilling. While diamond core drilling is the most versatile, it is also the slowest and most expensive method in normal circumstances. Radiometric logging of drill holes is standard practice. Radiometric prospecting is done by hand-carried and/or jeep-mounted radioactivity detection equipment—principally **Geiger** and **scintillation counters.** The latter are

Fig. 219. Drilling rig used in uranium exploration. (*Courtesy Union Carbide Corp.*)

the more sensitive instruments; the former have the advantage of greater compactness, lighter weight, and lower cost.

Uranium exploration began in earnest in the United States in 1948, when the U.S. Atomic Energy Commission launched an intensive program of its own, aided by the U.S. Geological Survey, and at the same time established incentives for exploration by private prospectors and mining interests. The government program hit its peak in 1953-55 and tapered off sharply after 1956, by which time private exploration activity had gained full momentum. Much of the government activity centered in unexplored public lands in the Colorado Plateau area. By way of comparison, prior to 1953 less than 1 million feet of drilling had been done by private interests and most of this was for the purpose of delimiting known ore bodies. By 1957, private drilling reached a peak of 9 million feet and much of it was exploratory in nature.

In addition to its domestic uranium exploration efforts, the AEC has done a great deal to stimulate uranium exploration activity in other countries, including technical consultations on exploration techniques and participation in joint exploration programs.

URANIUM HEXAFLUORIDE (UF_6)

A compound of uranium that is solid at room temperatures but sublimes to a gas on heating (sublimation point: 56.5°C). UF_6 is the process gas used in the **gaseous diffusion** process for **uranium enrichment.** UF_6 feed for the gaseous diffusion plants is produced by the fluorination of uranium tetrafluoride (UF_4), and also by a fluoride distillation process. (See **uranium refining and conversion**)

The volatility of UF_6 is the basis for certain **fuel reprocessing** techniques. (See **fluoride volatility processes**)

URANIUM METAL REDUCTION.

See **uranium refining and conversion.**

URANIUM MILLING

The extraction of uranium from ore, accomplished by leaching followed by recovery of the uranium from the leach solution. Most ores processed commercially in the United States contain 0.4-10 pounds of U_3O_8 per ton: the average concentration is about 5 pounds per ton (0.28 weight percent). The product of milling is a crude oxide or salt concentrate assaying 70-90% U_3O_8. Since many uranium ores also contain vanadium, vanadium oxide (V_2O_5) is sometimes a by-product of mill operations.

Processes Used. There are many variations in U.S. mill practice, reflecting the wide variety of ores handled and advances in milling technology. Basically, however, all mills that process commercial-grade ore currently use one or more of the following three generic methods:

1. Alkaline leaching in combination with caustic precipitation. (See **carbonate-leach process**)
2. Acid leaching in combination with ion exchange. (See **column ion exchange process, resin-in-pulp process**)
3. Acid leaching in combination with **solvent extraction.** (See **Amex, Dapex,** and **DDPA processes**)

Alkaline leaching is generally used in treating ores with high lime content (> 15% $CaCO_3$), and is sometimes preferred for low-lime ores. The ore must be finely ground and, in some cases, roasted. While pilot-scale tests have shown it to be feasible to recover uranium from alkaline leach solutions by ion exchange, precipitation is most commonly used in production operations. Decantation and filtration, sometimes with flocculants, precede the precipitation step since a clear leach solution is required for good uranium recovery. The reagent generally used is sodium hydroxide ($NaOH$), the uranium precipitating out as sodium diuranate ($Na_2U_2O_7$).* The final steps are filtration and calcination.

Acid leaching is usually used with low-lime ores. After crushing and grinding, the ore is leached with sulfuric acid and desanded, yielding a sludge-like solution known as "pulp." Where uranium recovery is to be accomplished by conventional ion exchange or solvent extraction techniques, the pulp is put through a countercurrent decanting operation to yield a clear liquor. After recovery by ion exchange or solvent extraction, as the case may be, ammonia (NH_3), magnesia (MgO) or sodium hydroxide is added to precipitate the uranium as ammonium diuranate ($(NH_4)_2U_2O_7$) or

* Known, along with ammonium diuranate, as "yellow cake."

magnesium or sodium diuranate. The final steps are filtration and calcination.

The pulp clarification step is eliminated in the resin-in-pulp process. Here, instead of having to pass a clear solution through closely packed columns (as in conventional ion exchange), large baskets containing the ion exchange resins are moved up and down in the tanks in which the pulp is contained.

The use of ion-exchange and/or solvent extraction techniques in milling applications is a relatively recent development and has replaced the use of chemical precipitation for the recovery of uranium from acid leach solutions. As of 1960, the process "mix" of U.S. mills handling commercial-grade ores was as follows:

	Approximate % of Total U.S. Mill Capacity
Carbonate treatment process	19
Column ion exchange process	11
Resin-in-pulp process	35
Solvent extraction processes	35
	100%

Certain types of low-grade secondary ores, and some commercial-grade ores, are upgraded by physical methods prior to milling. This is generally accomplished by fine grinding followed by particle sizing, the uranium minerals tending to concentrate in the fine fractions. The residual uranium in the coarse fractions may be recovered by acid treatment without further grinding.

U.S. Uranium Mills
(December 31, 1961)

Company	*Location of Mill*	*Present Contract Terminates*	*Tons of Ore per Day*	*Estimated Cost of Mill*
Anaconda Co.	Grants, N.M.	12/31/66	3,000	$ 19,358,000
Climax Uranium Co.	Grand Junction, Colo.	12/31/66	330	3,088,000
Cotter Corp.	Canon City, Colo.	2/28/65	200	1,800,000
Dawn Mining Co.	Ford, Wash.	12/31/66	400	3,100,000
Federal-Radorock-Gas Hills Partners	Fremont Co., Wyo.	12/31/66	520	3,370,000
Globe Mining Co.	Natrona Co., Wyo.	12/31/66	490	3,100,000
Gunnison Mining Co.	Gunnison, Colo.	12/31/62	200	2,025,000
Homestake-New Mexico Partners	Grants, N.M.	12/31/66	750	5,325,000
Homestake-Sapin Partners	Grants, N.M.	12/31/66	1,500	9,000,000
Kermac Nuclear Fuels, Corp.	Grants, N.M.	12/31/66	3,300	16,000,000
Kerr-McGee Oil Industries	Shiprock, N.M.	6/30/65	300	3,161,000
Lakeview Mining Co.	Lakeview, Ore.	11/30/63	210	2,600,000
Mines Development, Inc.	Edgemont, S.D.	12/31/66	400	1,900,000
Phillips Petroleum Co.	Grants, N.M.	12/31/66	1,725	9,500,000
Rare Metals Corp. of America	Tuba City, Ariz.	3/31/62	300	3,600,000
Susquehanna-Western, Inc.	Riverton, Wyo.	12/31/66	500	3,500,000
Susquehanna-Western, Inc.	Falls City, Tex.	12/31/66	200	2,000,000
Texas-Zinc Minerals Corp.	Mexican Hat, Utah	12/31/66	1,000	7,000,000
Trace Elements Co.	Maybell, Colo.	12/31/66	300	2,208,000
Union Carbide Nuclear Co.	Rifle, Colo.	12/31/66	1,000	8,500,000
Union Carbide Nuclear Co.	Uravan, Colo.	12/31/66	1,000	5,000,000
Uranium Reduction Co.	Moab, Utah	12/31/66	1,500	11,172,000
Utah Construction & Mining Co.	Fremont Co., Wyo.	12/31/66	980	6,900,000
Vanadium Corp. of America	Durango, Colo.	12/31/66	750	813,000
Vitro Chemical Co.	Salt Lake City, Utah	3/31/62	600	5,500,000
Western Nuclear, Inc.	Jeffrey City, Wyo.	12/31/66	845	4,300,000
		TOTALS	22,300	$143,820,000

Recovery from Low-Grade Sources. At one time uranium was recovered from phosphate rock on a small scale in the United States as a by-product from the manufacture of superphosphate fertilizers. Such recovery would be economically impractical at the present time on other than a by-product basis due to the low concentration of uranium in phosphate rock (~ 0.2 pound of U_3O_8 per ton), and even as a by-product the economics are marginal in today's uranium market. At some time in the future, however, the extensive deposits of phosphate rock in the United States may well prove to be an important uranium source. The same is true of U.S. deposits of uranium-bearing shale, which are even more extensive if somewhat poorer in grade (U_3O_8 content ~ 0.1 pound per ton) (see **uranium deposits**). It has been estimated that uranium could be recovered from shale as a primary operation at costs of from $45-55 per pound of U_3O_8—a level 5 to 7 times higher than current U.S. mill prices (see below).

U.S. Mills. As of the end of 1961, 26 privately owned uranium mills were in operation on commercial-grade ores in the United States, and 1 was under construction. The only government-owned mill (at Monticello, Utah) was shut down in 1959, after nearly 10 years of operation. The mills operating or under construction have an aggregate capacity of some 22,000 tons of ore per day and represent an investment of about $140 million. (See table, p. 585.)

Production and Prices. Following are production figures and projections for the U.S. milling industry.

AEC Fiscal Year	*Tons of U_3O_8*
1956	4,200
1957	7,580
1958	10,240
1959	15,162
1960	16,570
1961	17,760
1962 (projected)	17,820
1963 "	17,300
1964 "	16,900
1965 "	16,000
1966 "	16,000
1967 " (half year)	8,000

Prior to April 1, 1962, all domestic uranium mills operated under negotiated-price contracts with the U.S. Atomic Energy Commission. The prices paid under these contracts varied with the grade of ore handled and with the cost structure of the individual mills. The 1960 average was $8.85 per pound of U_3O_8 or equivalent, and in that year sales to the AEC approximated $300 million. Starting April 1, 1962, and continuing through December 31, 1966, the AEC will purchase mill concentrates at a guaranteed base price of $8.00 per pound under contracts that will specify production rate, ore source, and related matters.

In addition to selling to the AEC, domestic mills can, under license, sell directly to commercial markets. In this case the price is set by competitive factors. To date commercial purchases of uranium concentrates have been limited; however, as the U.S. nuclear power industry gains momentum they are expected to take on major proportions.

The following data provide perspective on the importance of the domestic milling industry in the over-all U.S. uranium procurement program:

	% of AEC's Uranium Purchase Commitments	
Period	*From Domestic Sources*	*From Foreign Sources*
Manhattan Project to July 1, 1955	17	83
July 1, 1955 to June 30, 1962	47	53
June 30, 1962 through December 31, 1966	84	16

URANIUM MINING

Uranium is mined in the United States on an extensive scale. In 1960, ore production reached 8 million tons assaying on the average about 5 pounds of uranium (expressed as U_3O_8) per ton. The mining industry centers in the Colorado Plateau and in areas lying north by northeast of that region. There are more than 500 individual mines.

Three principal types of uranium deposits are being worked: (1) Extensive deep deposits, as in the lower Chinle formation of the Big Indian Wash district of Utah, and in the West Water canyon sandstones of the Grants-Ambrosia Lake districts of New Mexico. Here the ore bodies are large and highly mechanized loading and hauling equipment can be used. (2) Extensive shallow deposits, as in the Gas Hills district of Wyoming, the Grants district of New Mexico, and the Cameron area of Arizona. Here open pit methods are used. (3) Irregular shallow deposits, such as the carnotite occurrences in the Salt Wash Formation of the Uravan Mineral Belt of Colorado, and the copper-uranium ores in the White Canyon district of Utah. Here various techniques are used.

The greatest production has come in the past from deep underground mines, however open pit production is steadily gaining in importance.

Operations. The largest ore bodies mined by underground methods measure as much as half a mile in length, several hundred feet in width, and from 5 to 100 feet in thickness, and are located several hundred feet or more below ground. In most cases the ore is worked from vertical or inclined shafts.

Fig. 220. Uranium mining. Left, open pit operations; right, underground operations. (*Courtesy Nucleonics*)

Open-pit mining is characterized by more complete ore recovery than can be achieved in underground mines, and offers the additional advantage that the grade of ore can readily be controlled by selective mining and blending.

Where shallow irregular ore occurrences are involved, the mining technique is determined by the topography. Horizontal cuts and inclines are preferred, but vertical shafts are sometimes necessary. Because of the irregularity of the deposits, development and mining activities must be closely coordinated and are often conducted concurrently.

The cost of uranium mining is a function of the techniques employed and the conditions encountered. Acceptable levels are of course controlled by the value (grade) of the ore being worked. Thus, while direct mining costs ranging from $4 per ton of ore to $30 per ton of ore or higher, have been reported, the cost when expressed as $ per pound of contained U_3O_8 is probably within the range, $2.00-5.00.

AEC Procurement Policy. The U.S. Atomic Energy Commission encouraged the growth of the domestic uranium mining industry by establishing guaranteed prices for ores of various grades. The last price schedule, which expired March 31, 1962, was defined in AEC's "Domestic Uranium Program Circular No. 5 (Revised)," published in Part 60, Title 10 of the Code of Federal Regulations. Following, for historical interest, are the prices that were specified for representative grades of ore:

Grade of Ore	*Base Payment*	*Grade Premium*	*Development Allowance*	*Ore Price*	
(% U_3O_8)	*($/ton)*	*($/ton)*	*($/ton)*	*($/ton)*	*($/lb U_3O_8)*
0.15	7.50	none	1.50	9.00	3.00
0.20	14.00	none	2.00	16.00	4.00
0.25	17.50	0.75	2.50	20.75	4.15
0.50	35.00	4.50	5.00	44.50	4.45
1.00	70.00	14.50	10.00	94.50	4.73

A new procurement policy went into effect on April 1, 1962, under which AEC price guarantees are keyed to mill concentrates, rather than to ores. Effective that date the AEC made no further direct ore purchases. Ores instead are purchased by milling companies on an open market basis. (See **uranium milling**)

URANIUM REFINING AND CONVERSION

The chemical and metallurgical operations involved in purifying and converting virgin or recycled uranium to forms suitable for use in the fabrication of reactor fuel elements or as feed to uranium enrichment facilities. The principal product forms are uranium hexafluoride (UF_6), uranium metal, and uranium dioxide (UO_2). While the equipment used is fairly conventional, the quality standards that must be met are more characteristic of the pharmaceuticals industry than of normal chemical and metallurgical manufacture.

Refining. Virgin feed to the refining process includes uranium concentrates from U.S. and foreign mills and some scrap material. Formerly, rich pitchblende ore from foreign sources was also used for virgin feed. The mill concentrates constitute the main supply and are in the form of crude diuranate or oxide cake assaying 70-90% U_3O_8 or equivalent. The principal process employed is **solvent extraction,** using tributyl phosphate diluted with an inert hydrocarbon as the extraction medium. The major steps are (1) Digestion in nitric acid and adjustment of the resulting aqueous nitrate solution for proper extraction conditions. (2) Solvent extraction of the uranyl nitrate yielding a purified uranyl nitrate solution ($UO_2(NO_3)_2$). (3) Boildown and calcination, yielding uranium trioxide powder, known as "orange oxide" (UO_3).

Feed recycled from **fuel reprocessing** operations is already in the form of a concentrated uranyl nitrate solution of high purity and goes directly into the calcination step. Since this material is generally either slightly depleted or slightly enriched in uranium-235 content, it is kept separate from the flow of virgin material.

The above process sequence is used for the bulk of the uranium refining operations conducted on behalf of the U.S. Atomic Energy Commission. An alternative refining technique has recently been brought into production by Allied Chemical Corporation and is described immediately below under "uranium hexafluoride" since the removal of impurities is accomplished by UF_6 distillation.

Uranium Hexafluoride Production. The production of UF_6 from UO_3 involves the formation of an intermediate compound—namely uranium tetrafluoride (UF_4), known as "green salt." The steps taken in making this intermediate product are as follows: (1) The UO_3 is reduced by means of hydrogen to uranium dioxide (UO_2), known as "brown oxide." (2) The UO_2 is contacted with anhydrous hydrogen fluoride (HF) to convert it to UF_4. These steps are conducted in continuous fashion, either in fluidized bed equipment or in equipment containing a screw-type conveyor system. Normally uranium enters the process as UO_3 and emerges as UF_4; however, it can be withdrawn in the form of UO_2 when there are requirements for normal uranium in this form.

The UF_4 is converted to UF_6 by fluorination, using elemental fluorine gas in monel contacting equipment.

Uranium hexafluoride is also produced by the alternative refining process noted earlier. Here the following steps are involved: (1) Virgin uranium concentrates from uranium mills are put through a series of pelletizing, grinding and drying operations to obtain a fine powder. (2) The powder is moved by a screw-type conveyor through a fluidized bed reaction chamber in which it is contacted with hydrogen and thereby reduced to UO_2. Sulfur and certain other impurities are removed in this step. (3) The crude UO_2 is then screw-fed to a second chamber in which it is contacted with anhydrous hydrogen fluoride and thereby converted to UF_4. (4) The crude UF_4 is diluted with calcium fluoride (CaF_2) and contacted with elemental fluorine in a fluidized bed type of reaction system. Most of the solids are converted in this operation to volatile fluorides. Nonvolatile impurities are removed as ash. UF_6 is removed, still carrying some impurities, by refrigerated "cold-traps." (5) The UF_6, now in the solid state, is liquefied by heating under pressure and transferred to a storage tank. From there it is fed to a vaporizer and in turn to a distillation column wherein final purification takes place. High-purity UF_6 is withdrawn from a point near the top of the distillation system and is charged to pressurized shipping containers for delivery to uranium enrichment facilities, i.e., **gaseous diffusion** plants.

Uranium Metal Production. The production of normal uranium metal starts with high-purity uranium tetrafluoride (see above). The operations are: (1) The UF_4 is mixed with high-purity magnesium powder and charged to a closed dolomite-lined steel crucible. The crucible is heated in an electric furnace to the "ignition point" of the metal reduction reaction:

$$UF_4 + 2Mg \longrightarrow U + 2MgF_2$$

The reaction is strongly exothermic and the heat released plus the preheat are sufficient to melt the contents of the crucible. The uranium flows to the bottom and on cooling forms a solid mass, known as a "derby" or "dingot." The magnesium fluoride collects as a slag layer. (2) The uranium "derby" is removed from the crucible, chipped free of slag, and remelted under partial vacuum in an induction furnace. (3) The product metal is cast into ingots in an inert atmosphere.

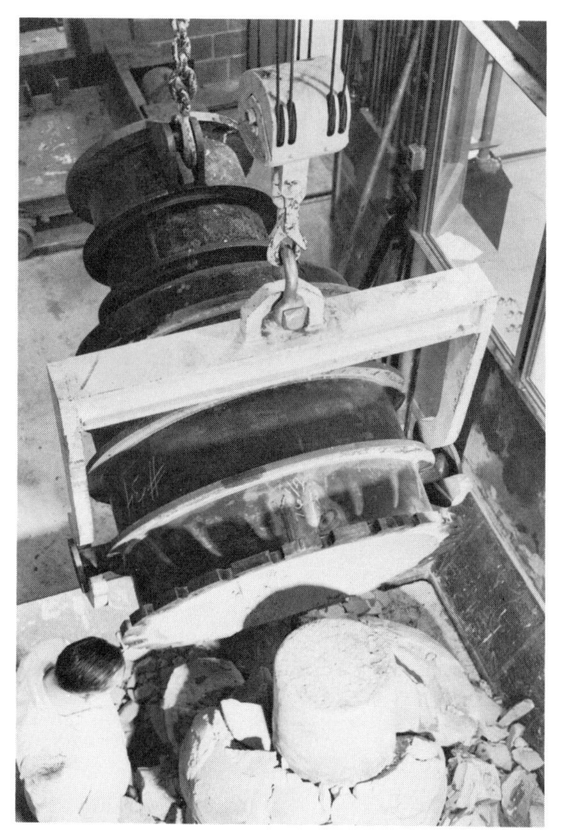

Fig. 221. Unloading 3300-lb. uranium "dingot" from crucible at Weldon Spring Plant of U.S. Atomic Energy Commission. (*Courtesy of Mallinckrodt Chemical Works*)

Powder metallurgical techniques have also been developed for the production of normal uranium metal, but have not been used in full scale operations. The method worked out involves the formation of finely divided uranium metal powder by the decomposition of uranium hydride.

The production of enriched metal starts with enriched uranium hexafluoride. Here the steps are: (1) Reduction of the UF_6 to UF_4 with hydrogen. (2) Reduction of the UF_4 to uranium metal in an operation similar to that described above, the principal difference being the substitution of calcium for magnesium as the reduction medium.

Uranium Dioxide Production. As already noted, normal uranium dioxide is available from routine UF_4 production operations. Most reactor requirements are for enriched UO_2, however, and these requirements are usually met by the conversion of enriched uranium hexafluoride using the ADU process (see **uranium dioxide**). The alternative is to start with enriched uranium metal and dissolve it in nitric acid to form uranyl nitrate, which is then calcined to UO_3 and reduced to UO_2.

Scrap Recovery. Significant amounts of uranium accumulate in the form of scrap or off-specification products in the course of conversion and subsequent **fuel element fabrication** operations. Recovery is warranted by the value of the material and/or for reasons of fissionable materials **accountability.** The recovery methods vary with the material at hand and are sometimes quite complex, especially where high-alloy scrap is involved. More often than not it is necessary to return the recovered material as feed to the refining operation for repurification; where possible, however, it is returned to a point further along the processing chain.

Facilities. Following is the AEC production network: (1) Uranium metal and uranium trioxide are produced from virgin feedstock at two large government-owned refining and conversion centers—the Feed Materials Production Center at Fernald, Ohio, operated by the National Lead Company of Ohio; and the Feed Materials Plant at Weldon Spring, near St. Louis, Missouri, operated by Mallinckrodt Chemical Works. The two plants represent an investment of ~ \$176 million. (2) The uranium trioxide from these plants, together with UO_3 recycled from fuel reprocessing operations, is converted to uranium hexafluoride in facilities located at two of the AEC's three uranium enrichment centers—namely the Oak Ridge Gaseous Diffusion Plant, Oak Ridge, Tennessee, operated by Union Carbide Nuclear Company, and the Portsmouth Gaseous Diffusion Plant, Portsmouth, Ohio, operated by Goodyear Atomic Corporation. (3) Additional uranium hexafluoride in the amount of 5000 tons per year (U_3O_8 equivalent) is produced directly from mill concentrates by Allied Chemical Corporation in a new plant at

Fig. 222. Uranium refinery of Allied Chemical Corporation's General Chemical Division at Metropolis, Ill. (*Courtesy Allied Chemical Corporation*)

Metropolis, Illinois. The plant is owned by Allied and represents an investment of ~ $11 million. The product is supplied to the AEC on a fixed-volume, fixed-price basis under a contract which permits the company to market excess production commercially.

Other companies have invested in uranium conversion facilities on a straight commercial basis, and are licensed to supply normal and enriched uranium products and/or to reclaim enriched uranium from "cold" (unirradiated) scrap. They include: Davison Chemical Company (Erwin, Tennessee), National Lead Company (Albany, N. Y.), Nuclear Materials and Equipment Corporation (Apollo, Pennsylvania), Spencer Chemial Company (Kansas City, Missouri), and United Nuclear Corporation (Hematite, Missouri).

URANIUM TETRAFLUORIDE (UF_4)

"Green salt," an intermediate product in the production of massive uranium metal, and in the production of uranium hexafluoride. It is formed by the hydrofluorination of uranium dioxide (UO_2).

URANIUM TRIOXIDE (UO_3)

"Orange oxide," an intermediate product in the refining of virgin uranium, and in the treatment of uranium recovered from fuel reprocessing operations. It is formed by the boildown and denitration of concentrated uranyl nitrate solutions from solvent extraction processes. (See **uranium refining and conversion)**

Some uranium mills produce crude uranium concentrates in the form of UO_3. In this case the UO_3 is formed by calcination of ammonium or sodium diuranate ("yellow cake").

URANOPHANE

Hydrated calcium uranium silicate—a secondary mineral, lemon or pale greenish yellow in color, found in deposits with other secondary uranium minerals. Uranophane occurs in the oxidized zones of vein deposits in the Front Range of Colorado and in the Marysvale district of Utah. It is also abundant in sedimentary deposits in the Grants-Leguna area of New Mexico.

URANOUS URANYL OXIDE (U_3O_8)

A mixed oxide of uranium ($2UO_3 \cdot UO_2$), known as "black oxide."

The uranium content of variously constituted ores and mill concentrates is usually expressed for convenience, in terms of "U_3O_8 equivalent." Values so expressed must be multiplied by $\frac{3 \times 238}{(3 \times 238) + (8 \times 16)}$ or ~ 0.85 to obtain the actual uranium content.

UTILIZATION FACILITY

In context with the Atomic Energy Commission's licensing and regulatory responsibilities (see **licenses),** a utilization facility is legally defined as "(1) any equipment or device, except an atomic weapon, determined by rule of the Commission to be capable of," or peculiarly adapted for, "making use of **special nuclear material** in such quantity as to be of significance to the common defense and security, or in such manner as to affect the health and safety of the public; . . . or (2) any important component part especially designed for such equipment or device as determined by the Commission."

V

VACUUM DISTILLATION

A pyrometallurgical **fuel reprocessing** technique that has been studied on a limited scale. It is based on volatility phenomena. After mechanical decladding, irradiated uranium is heated to the molten state at atmospheric pressure. The more volatile fission products, such as xenon, krypton, iodine and cesium, are removed in this step. The molten material is then vacuum-distilled at temperatures of about 1750°C. Plutonium and certain of the rare earth fission products become volatile at these conditions and distill off from the relatively nonvolatile uranium. Constituents which remain with the uranium include zirconium, ruthenium, niobium and molybdenum. The technique thus accomplishes plutonium separation and partial uranium decontamination.

VALLECITOS BOILING WATER REACTOR (VBWR)

A small nuclear power plant of the direct-cycle **boiling water** type located at General Electric Company's Vallecitos Atomic Laboratory near Pleasanton, California. The reactor was designed and is owned and operated by General Electric; the turbine-generator and related electrical facilities are owned and operated by Pacific Gas and Electric Company. Bechtel Corporation was the architect-engineer-constructor.

VBWR originally served as the prototype for the Dresden Nuclear Power Station and is now used for general boiling water reactor development, including studies of nuclear superheating. The following notes relate to the initial core loading:

Fig. 223. Vallecitos Boiling Water Reactor (VBWR). (*Courtesy of General Electric Co.*)

Power: The reactor has operated at power levels up to 50 megawatts (thermal); however, the electrical output of the plant is fixed by the capacity of the turbine-generator, which is 5.0 megawatts (electrical). *Fuel:* Fully enriched uranium in the form of uranium dioxide (UO_2) particles in a stainless steel matrix. *Fuel element design:* A fuel element consists of an assembly of stainless steel-clad fuel plates. *Fuel inventory:* ~ 22 kilograms of U^{235}. *Steam conditions:* Steam leaves the reactor in direct-cycle natural-circulation operation at 1000 pounds pressure and 546°F. (The reactor can also be operated as a dual-cycle system with forced circulation.) *Control materials:* 7 boron-steel control rods. *Containment:* Steel tank with hemispherically shaped top. *Cost:* The capital investment in the VBWR installation, including the electrical facilities, is reported at $3.1 million. *Dates:* Construction started in June, 1956. Reactor first critical in August, 1957. AEC Power Reactor License No. 1, i.e., the first operating license granted to a privately owned power reactor—received August 31, 1957. Full-power operation first reached in October, 1957. The reactor was shut down late in 1959 for modifications and resumed operation in September, 1960.

VALVES

Discussion of this topic will be limited to valves used in the primary coolant system of civilian power reactors. The major valve applications include stop valves, which serve to shut off coolant flow as when isolating one coolant loop in a multiple loop system; check valves, which serve to prevent backflow in the event of failure of a coolant pump; pressure relief valves; and throttling valves. Valves for these applications are required to be extremely reliable in operation and must meet stringent specifications with regard to leakage through the valve stem and, where relevant, across the valve seat. In most applications corrosion-resistant materials must be employed.

Various types of valve mechanism are employed; in general, however, gate or rotating plug valves tend to be used for stop, check, or relief valve applications, and globe or butterfly valves tend to be used for throttling applications. Stop and check valves are generally hydraulically or motor operated; relief valves are generally either self-actuated by a spring mechanism or are operated electrically by means of a solenoid system. Figure 224 shows an hydraulically operated parallel-disk-type gate valve used in the Shippingport Atomic Power Station.

Valves for large-scale water cooled reactor systems presently range in cost from $1000-3000 each for small relief valves to $40,000-60,000 each for large (up to 20-inch diameter) main stop valves.

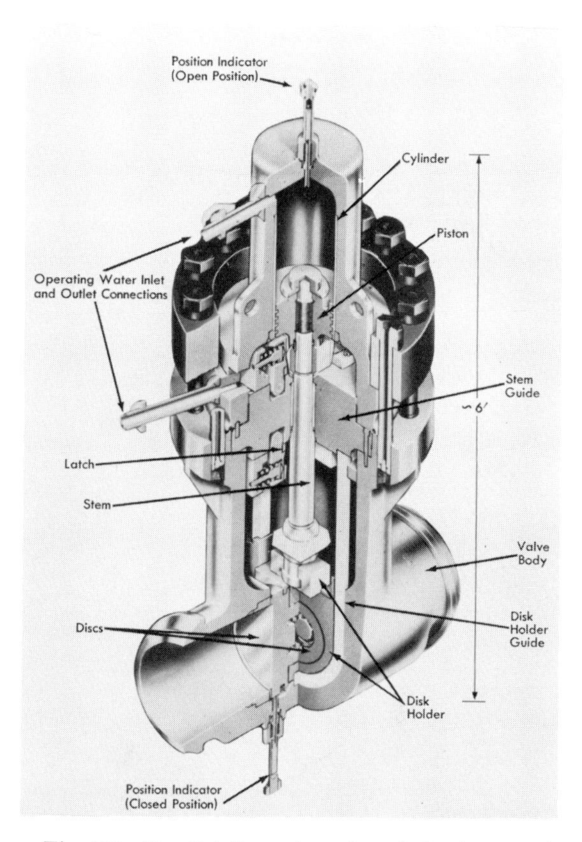

Fig. 224. Parallel-disc gate valve of the type used in the Shippingport Atomic Power Station. Reprinted from "The Shippingport Pressurized Water Reactor," Addison-Wesley Publishing Co., 1958.

VAN DE GRAAFF GENERATOR

A type of **particle accelerator** supplied commercially for use in research and for industrial radiation applications. The accompanying diagram illustrates the method of acceleration. This type of machine has excellent voltage regulation characteristics and hence can deliver essentially monoenergetic particle beams. The first Van de Graaff generator was

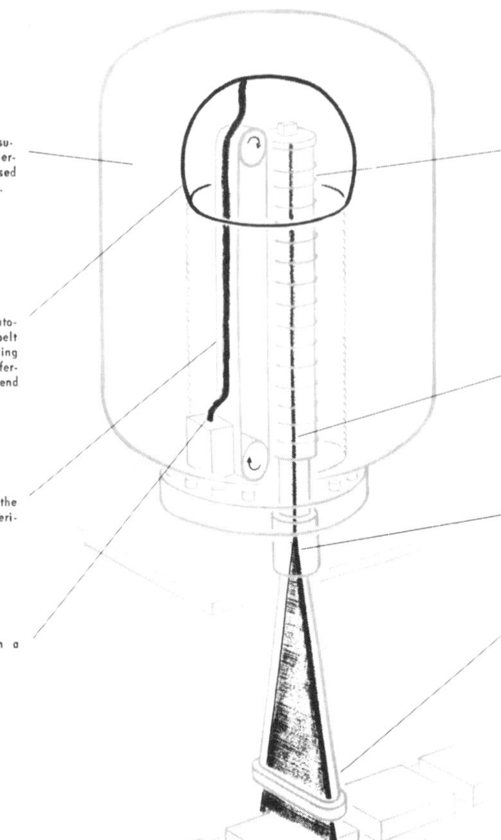

4

The high-voltage terminal is insulated from the shell of the accelerator by an atmosphere of compressed nitrogen, which prevents arc-over.

3

At the terminal, the charge is automatically transferred from the belt to the terminal, thereby establishing a high potential or voltage difference with respect to the lower end of the accelerator.

2

The belt mechanically carries the charge to an insulated, hemispherical, high-voltage terminal.

1

Electric charge is sprayed on a rapidly moving insulating belt.

5

A glass and metal tube, maintained at a very high vacuum, provides the only path for the electrons to escape from the cathode.

6

The electrons forming the high-energy beam are accelerated to extremely high velocities by the potential difference between the terminal and the lower end of the accelerator.

7

This electron beam may be scanned by magnetic coils to cover uniformly the product passing beneath.

8

The dosage received by the irradiated product depends on the speed of the conveyor belt, the energy of the beam, and the width of scan.

Fig. 225. Van de Graaff Generator. Above, diagram showing principles of operation in irradiation application. (*Courtesy of High Voltage Engineering Corporation*). Left, 6-Mev Van de Graaff at United Kingdom's Atomic Weapons Research Establishment at Aldermaston. (*Courtesy of UKAEA*)

built in 1931, by Robert J. Van de Graaff (U.S.).

Van de Graaff generators are manufactured by High Voltage Engineering Company, which has supplied several hundred machines to university and industrial laboratories in the United States and abroad. Machines for electron acceleration have beam energy range of 0.4-3.0 Mev. Machines designed for proton acceleration range in beam energy from 0.4 to 5.5 Mev with energies up to 14 Mev achieved in so-called tandem machines.

VANADIUM

Element No. 23 (symbol, V; atomic weight, 50.95), associated with uranium in many U.S. ores and in some cases produced as a by-product of **uranium milling** operations. The addition of vanadium to certain reactor fuel alloys and structural materials has been found to improve their mechanical properties at elevated temperatures; however, vanadium has an appreciable thermal neutron absorption cross section ($\sim$ 5 barns) and therefore can only be used sparingly in thermal reactor systems.

VAPOR CONTAINMENT. See **containment.**

VAPOR SUPPRESSION CONTAINMENT SCHEME. See **containment.**

VARIABLE MODERATOR REACTOR CONCEPT

A scheme for controlling water cooled power reactor systems based on raising or lowering the level of the water-steam interface in the reactor vessel, thereby increasing or decreasing the reactivity of the core. This concept, of interest as a means of minimizing excess reactivity requirements and possibly eliminating control rods, is being studied by the Atomic Energy Division of American Standard Radiator and Sanitary Corporation under a contract to the U.S. Atomic Energy Commission. For notes on another moderator control scheme, see **spectral shift reactor concept.**

VELA PROJECT. See **weapons test detection.**

VENEZUELA

Venezuela has no central atomic energy authority. Significant research and training activity is in progress, however, at the Instituto Venezolano de Investigaciones Cientificas (IVIC), Caracas. IVIC is a government-sponsored institution for general research and one of the best-equipped scientific centers in Latin America. To support its program in the atomic field, IVIC has installed extensive radioisotope laboratories and a 3000-megawatt (thermal) pool-type research reactor. The latter, supplied by International General Electric Company, was constructed with the aid of a $350,000 Foreign Research Reactor Grant from the United States.

Uranium exploration has been in progress in Venezuela for several years. Venezuela is amply endowed with energy resources, principally hydropower; but there are areas where nuclear power may be advantageous. Venezuela is a member of the **International Atomic Energy Agency** and the **Inter-American Nuclear Energy Commission,** and has a research-type **Agreement for Cooperation** with the United States.

VIETNAM

The Office of Atomic Energy, Saigon, is the agency responsible for atomic energy matters. An Institute of Nuclear Research is being established at Dalat, 180 miles north of Saigon. The facilities are to include a 100-kilowatt (thermal) Triga Mark II research and training reactor being supplied by General Atomic. The United States has committed $350,000 toward the cost of this installation under its program of Foreign Research Reactor Grants.

Vietnam's present electric power capacity is about 100 megawatts, most of it thermal. There are very substantial hydroelectric resources, 160 megawatts of which are scheduled to be developed in a 2-stage project under the Japanese reparations program.

Vietnam is a member of the **International Atomic Energy Agency** and has a research-type **Agreement for Cooperation** with the United States.

VIRGINIA, UNIVERSITY OF—RESEARCH REACTOR

A 1000-kilowatt (thermal) pool-type research reactor located just outside of Charlottesville, Virginia. It was supplied to the University by Babcock & Wilcox Co. and began operation in 1960. (See **research and training reactors)**

VOID COEFFICIENT

In a nuclear reactor employing water as **moderator** or moderator-coolant, a rate of change in the **reactivity** of the system resulting from the formation of steam bubbles (voids) as the power level and temperature increase. Void coefficients can be positive, if the material vaporized (and hence effectively removed) has an appreciable **cross section** for neutron **capture**; or they can be negative, if the material has more effect as a **moderator** than as a neutron absorber. Although the latter have the desirable effect of providing a safety factor in reactor operation, since they act to dampen **power excursions,** void coefficients are sometimes undesirable since bubble formation sets up nonuniformities in **power density** and tends to limit over-all power output. (See **boiling water reactors)**

WALTER REED MEDICAL CENTER RESEARCH REACTOR

A 50-kilowatt (thermal) water-boiler-type research reactor operated as part of the Walter Reed Army Institute of Research in Washington, D.C. The reactor was supplied by Atomics International and began operation late in 1961. It is used for biophysical research and to produce radioisotopes for medical purposes. (See **research and training reactors**)

WASTE DISPOSAL. See radioactive waste disposal.

WATER BOILER

A type of research reactor in which the core consists of a small metal sphere containing an aqueous fuel solution. Cooling water flows through a radiator-like coil in the sphere. The sphere may also be penetrated by one or more beam tubes for experiments. The term "water boiler" derives from a boiling-like action caused by bubbles of hydrogen and oxygen formed by the radiolytic dissociation of water. (See **research and training reactors**)

WATER DISTILLATION (for Deuterium Concentration)

The application of water distillation to **deuterium** concentration (i.e., heavy water production) is based on the fact that the boiling point of ordinary water (H_2O) is 1.4°F lower than that of heavy water (D_2O). In the process (see diagram), steam condensate is fed to a distillation tower wherein it is contacted with water vapor. The D_2O, because of its slightly lower volatility relative to H_2O, tends to concentrate in the liquid phase, which leaves the bottom of the tower as a somewhat enriched stream. By connecting a number of distillation stages in series, and using the bottom stream from one tower as the input to the next, a high degree of enrichment can be obtained.

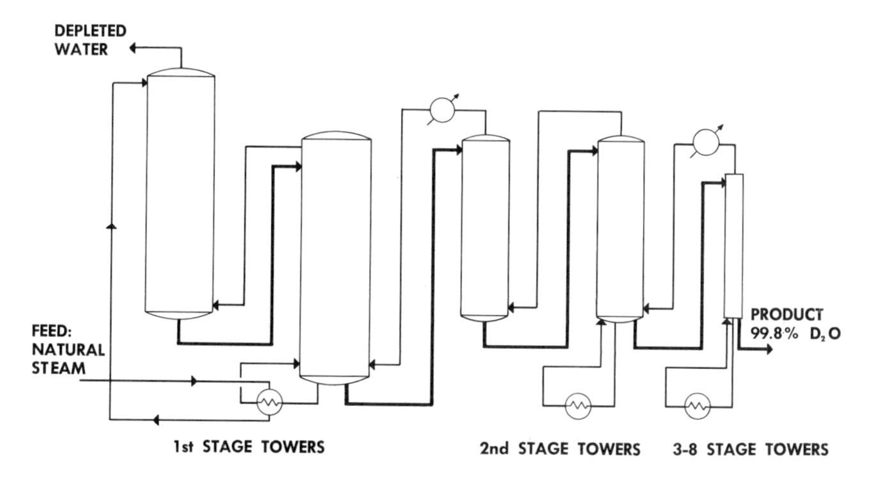

Fig. 226. Production of heavy water by water distillation.

Water distillation was used in the United States during the Manhattan Project to enrich deuterium from its natural concentration of 0.015% to concentrations in the neighborhood of 90%. (**Electrolysis** was used for the final stages of enrichment.) It has been used in postwar production operations as an intermediate process and continues to be so employed. (See **deuterium** for more details)

WEAPONS (nuclear)

Any military explosive device utilizing energy derived from nuclear **fission,** or from a combination of nuclear fission and **fusion.** Devices of the latter type are commonly referred to as thermonuclear devices ("hydrogen bombs"). The device may take the form of a bomb, a projectile fired from a cannon, or the warhead of a missile.

Principles. The basic principle underlying the design of an all-fission nuclear weapon is to bring together two or more subcritical amounts of weapon-grade **fissionable material** to form a **critical mass** and to hold the mass together long enough for the supercritical state to be reached. At least two designs have been developed for this purpose:

1. Gun-type device: In this design, a charge of conventional explosive is used to propel one subcritical piece into contact with another.
2. Implosion device: In this design, a charge of conventional explosive placed around the periphery of a subcritical sphere compresses the latter by implosion.

In either design, the speed with which the assembly is completed (and the containing pressure developed) has an important bearing on the efficiency of the device.

The basic principle underlying the design of a thermonuclear device is the use of a fissionable charge in combination with a charge of "fusionable" materials (see **fusion).** The energy from fission serves to raise the temperature of the fusionable material to the detonation point. Again there is the problem of holding the explosive mass together long enough for the desired reaction conditions to be attained.

Because of the intense field of fast neutrons generated during the fission process, it is possible to take advantage of the phenomenon known as **fast fission** as a means of readily increasing the energy release from either an all-fission or a thermonuclear device. Since uranium-238 is one of the nuclides which undergo fast fission, this means that normal or depleted uranium can be used as an added ingredient in either type of device.

Units. The energy released by a nuclear weapon is referred to as the "yield" and is expressed in terms of the quantity of TNT (trinitrotoluene) that would be needed to generate the same energy release. The usual units are kilotons (thousands of tons) or megatons (millions of tons) of TNT equivalence, abbreviated as KT and MT, respectively. Devices with yields ranging from 0.001 KT to ~ 15 MT have been tested by the United States. A so-called "nominal yield" weapon is a device with a yield of 20 KT, which was approximately the yield of the weapons used at Hiroshima and Nagasaki during World War II.

The term "fission yield" is used in reference to a thermonuclear device to define the portion of the total energy release caused by fission phenomena; it has averaged roughly 50%.

Development. The following threshold dates shed some light on the timetable of nuclear weapon development in the U.S. and elsewhere:

	First Known Test Device	
Country	*Fission-type*	*Thermonuclear*
U.S.	July 16, 1945	October 31, 1952
U.S.S.R.	August 29, 1949	August 12, 1953
United Kingdom	October 3, 1952	May 15, 1957
France	February 13, 1960	—

In the United States, the emphasis of development has shifted over the years as follows:

1. World War II: Determination of basic feasibility of fission-type nuclear weapons and development of usable devices.
2. Early postwar years: Improvement of fission-type weapon designs, both from an efficiency and an ordnance standpoint; change-

Fig. 227. World War II nuclear weapon designs. The type used at Hiroshima (top) was 28″ in diameter and 120″ in length and weighed about 7000 lbs. The type used at Nagasaki (bottom) was 60″ in diameter and 128″ in length and weighed about 10,000 lbs. (*Courtesy of Los Alamos Scientific Laboratory*)

over from improvised production methods to assembly-line techniques.

3. Early fifties: Determination of basic feasibility of thermonuclear weapons; beginning of development of a range of nuclear weapons for various military requirements.

4. Mid-fifties: Development of operational thermonuclear devices; intensification of development of a range of nuclear weapons.

5. Late fifties: Emphasis on extending the tactical, as opposed to the strategic, use of nuclear weapons, i.e., on designing a family of low-yield devices.

The major centers of the nuclear aspects of this development work have been Los Alamos Scientific Laboratory (since 1943) and the Livermore Branch of the E. O. Lawrence Radiation Laboratory (since 1952). The non-nuclear ordnance aspects have centered at the Sandia Laboratory.

Other information. For additional information on or relating to nuclear weapons, see

weapons phenomenology; weapons effects; weapons testing; weapons test detection; radioactive fallout; radiological warfare; and **international control of atomic energy.** For general orientation, see **military applications of atomic energy.** For information on peaceful uses of nuclear explosives, see **Plowshare Program.**

WEAPONS EFFECTS

The effects of nuclear weapons can be categorized as follows:

1. Blast and shock effects: Structural damage and bodily injury caused directly or indirectly by blast and/or shock phenomena. The indirect effects may take various forms, including secondary fires (as from a ruptured gas main), damage or injury caused by flying fragments, etc.
2. Thermal effects: Fires, charring and burns resulting directly from thermal radiation.
3. Initial nuclear radiation effects: Radiation injury due to exposure to **prompt radiation.**
4. Residual nuclear radiation effects: Radiation injury and/or radioactive contamination due to **residual radiation** (*via* early and/or delayed **radioactive fallout).**

The incidence and extent of these effects

A

B

C.

D

Fig. 228. High-speed photographs show sequence of events in destruction of woodframe house during Civil Effects Test Operations conducted in 1953 at the Nevada Test Site. The house was located two-thirds of a mile from ground zero of a kiloton-range nuclear weapon test. The elapsed time between photos A and D was approximately two seconds. A. Glare of light given off by detonation. B. Exposed side of house bursts into flame. C. Shock wave strikes house. D. House disintegrates.

may vary widely depending on the energy yield (i.e., size of the weapon) and on a number of other factors, including:

1. The type of detonation, i.e., high altitude burst, air burst, surface burst, underground burst, or underwater burst.
2. The elevation or, in the case of subsurface bursts, the depth of the detonation.
3. Local conditions, including the nature of the target terrain and atmospheric and meteorological conditions.
4. The types of structure in the target zone, i.e., whether reinforced concrete, brick, wood frame, etc.
5. The precautionary measures taken in the target zone, e.g., the fraction of the population in blast or fallout shelters at the time of the event.

It is thus impossible to generalize on nuclear weapon effects without defining the complete context of the event. The following brief presentation is therefore limited to indicating the nature of the effects associated with particular phenomena.

Air Blast. A distinction is made between the forces exerted by shock waves traveling through air and that exerted by winds accompanying the passage of the shock waves. The former is referred to as "overpressure" (meaning pressure above atmospheric pressure); the latter, as "dynamic pressure."

When the front of an air shock wave strikes the face of a structure, reflection occurs with the result that the overpressure builds up momentarily to at least twice (and generally several times) that in the shock front proper. This extra impact pressure quickly dissipates; meanwhile, however, the advancing shock wave bends or "diffracts" around the structure, thereby momentarily enveloping it with overpressure—a phenomenon known as "diffraction loading." In effect, therefore, the structure is subjected in one instant to an impact that tends to displace it laterally, and in the next instant to a force that tends to crush it. The dynamic wind pressure accompanying the shock wave exerts a supplementary and in this case sustained, lateral displacement force, referred to as "drag" loading.

Another but relatively minor force is exerted seconds later when, after the passage of the shock waves and accompanying winds, a momentary condition of negative pressure is created which places the structure under suction and creates strong back-gusts of wind and hence reverse drag-loading.

Table 1 indicates the composite effect of these forces on structures in the case of a one-megaton air burst. Table 2 provides some general orientation *vis-à-vis* overpressure and bodily injury.

For a given energy yield, air blast damage is most severe in the case of an air or surface burst. Subsurface bursts may or may not produce an air blast, depending on their depth and the medium in which they occur.

Ground and Water Shock. Ground shock (and crater formation) is most severe in the case of an underground burst or contact surface burst but may also accompany detonations at low altitudes in air. The shock waves are similar in some respects to those produced by an earthquake of moderate intensity but are more sharply defined and briefer in duration. Compared with an air blast, the radius of effect is relatively small. In essence, a series of surface waves moves outward from the center of the explosion, producing an oscillating effect known as "ground roll." Simultaneously, an underground shock front causes compression and shear below the surface of the ground. The effects can be categorized in terms of the following three regions:

1. The area of crater formation, which for a contact surface burst in sandy soil, is roughly as follows:

Explosion yield	*Crater radius*
20 kiloton	~ 175 ft
100 kiloton	~ 300 ft
1 megaton	~ 650 ft
10 megaton	~ 1500 ft

2. A zone extending out about 2½ times the crater radius over which the ground shock results in permanent deformation of soil structure.
3. An outlying region in which the ground

TABLE 1. EXAMPLES OF STRUCTURAL DAMAGE
DUE TO AIR BLAST EFFECTS OF A ONE-MEGATON AIR BURST[1]

Distance from Ground Zero (miles)	*Peak Overpressure (psi)*	*Peak Dynamic Pressure (psi)*	*Damage*
1	20	3.2	Moderate damage to windowless blast-resistant reinforced-concrete structures; all other above-ground structures severely damaged or destroyed
2	11	2.6	Severe damage to motor vehicles, oil storage tanks, etc.
3	7.4	1.2	Severe damage to steel-frame industrial buildings; moderate damage to highway and railroad truss bridges
4	4.7	0.55	Wood-frame houses destroyed; moderate damage to brick buildings
5	3.2	0.26	Severe damage to wood-frame houses
6	2.4	0.13	Moderate damage to steel-frame industrial buildings
7	1.8	0.08	Moderate damage to wood-frame houses
10	1.0	—	Light damage to window frames and doors
15	<1	—	Moderate damage to plaster
30	<1	—	Some glass breakage

[1] These are not "universal" examples, since the effects depend upon the height of detonation and other variables.

TABLE 2. RELATIONSHIP BETWEEN OVERPRESSURE AND BODILY INJURY
DUE TO AIR BLAST EFFECTS FROM A ONE-MEGATON SURFACE BURST

Incident Overpressure (psi)	*Distance from Ground Zero (miles)*	*Injury (or condition conducive thereto)*
15.0	1.5	Lung damage
6.0	2.6	Lung damage (assuming pressure reflection)
5.0	2.8	Eardrum rupture
4.3	3.1	Displacement of 160-lb man 10 ft/sec in 1 ft[1]
2.5	4.5	Eardrum rupture (assuming pressure reflection)
2.4	4.6	Displacement of 10-lb masonry fragments 10 ft/sec in 10 ft
2.2	4.9	Displacement of 10-gm glass splinters 115 ft/sec in 10 ft
2.1	5.1	Displacement of 160-lb man 19 ft/sec in 10 ft
1.9	5.5	Displacement of 160-lb man 10 ft/sec in 28 ft

[1] I.e., a velocity of 10 ft/sec is reached in the space of 1 ft. Impact velocities above ~15 ft/sec can cause skull fracture and when in excess of ~30 ft/sec have a 50% incidence of fatality.

shock causes transient earth movement but no permanent displacement.

In the first region, damage to structures is more or less total. In the second, the extent of damage due to ground shock depends intrinsically on the ability of the structure to "roll with the blow" and will range from collapse or severe displacement of buildings to slight cracking of building foundations, severance of utility connections, and the like. In the third region, ground shock causes no appreciable structural damage.

In the case of an underwater burst, a powerful underwater shock wave moves out rapidly, reaching a distance of 2 miles from the point of detonation in as many seconds. Except in very shallow detonations, this shock wave is the principal factor in the physical damage caused to shipping by underwater bursts. The direct impact on ship hulls is sudden and massive, tending to cause distortion of the hull below the water line, rupture of plates, etc.; and, in addition, there are indirect effects due to components being set in motion within the ship. Test experience indicates that most ships of substantial construction will sink if subjected to an overpressure of 3000 or 4000 psi; be irreparably damaged by an overpressure of 2000 psi; and be immobilized by an overpressure of 1000 psi. Following is the approximate overpressure-distance relationship for a 20-kiloton underwater burst at mid-depth in water 11 fathoms deep:

Distance from Point of Detonation (feet)	*Peak Overpressure (psi)*
1200	4000
1400	3000
2200	2000
2800	1000
4200	500
5200	300

Thermal Radiation. Damage from thermal radiation is most severe in the case of an air or surface burst but also accompanies subsurface bursts unless the detonation occurs at an appreciable depth (see **weapons phenomenology**). Thermal radiation is emitted during the first few seconds following detonation and, since it travels at the speed of light, does its damage in that brief interval of time. Upon absorption thermal radiation is immediately converted into heat and, since only a small proportion of the heat can be dissipated by conduction in the interval of time involved, exposed surfaces are briefly raised to very high temperatures. It has been estimated, for example, that transient surface temperatures at Hiroshima reached 3000-4000°F at ground zero.

The effects of ultra-high-intensity thermal radiation include scorching, charring or ignition of exposed surfaces of combustible matter such as wood, fabric or paper; and flash burns to exposed skin. The following rough data serve to illustrate the distance up to which exposed surfaces can be expected to incur severe thermal radiation damage:

	Miles from Ground Zero	
	20-kiloton Air Burst	*1-megaton Air Burst*
Ignition of such materials as newspaper, kraft paper, rayon-acetate, taffeta, coarse burlap, grass.	1–2 miles	15–35 miles
First, second or third degree skin burns.	1–2 miles	20–30 miles

The effects are influenced by atmospheric conditions; for example, fog materially reduces the effects.

Prompt Nuclear Radiation. As is brought out under **weapons phenomenology,** the period of possible exposure to the prompt (as opposed to the residual) nuclear radiation from a nuclear weapon is the first minute after detonation, and the components of this radiation are gamma rays and neutrons. Practically speaking, however, exposure to the neutron component occurs during the first second, and most of the gamma dose is delivered during the first 1-10 seconds, depending on the size of the detonation and the distance from ground zero. The following rough data indicate the distances up to which exposed persons can be expected to incur various degrees of radiation injury * in the case of an air burst:

Whole Body Dose (roentgens of gamma radiation plus rems of neutron radiation)	*Consequence*	*Range of Exposure (miles from ground zero)*	
		20-KT air burst	*1-MT air burst*
>700	Survival improbable	0.7	1.4
<300	Survival possible	0.85	1.6
<100	Survival probable	1.0	1.8
<50	No obvious somatic effect	1.15	2.0

Prompt nuclear radiation effects are most severe in the case of an air or surface burst but also accompany subsurface bursts unless detonation occurs at an appreciable depth.

Residual Nuclear Radiation. See **radioactive fallout.**

Composite Effects. As was noted earlier, it is impossible to generalize on the over-all effects to be expected from a nuclear weapon without first defining the specific circumstances. The following data on effects at Hiroshima and Nagasaki are therefore to be regarded as illustrative, rather than indicative, of the consequences of air bursts having a yield of approximately 20 kilotons:

TYPES OF INJURY AMONG SURVIVORS

Type of Injury	*Percent of Survivors*
Mechanical [1]	70
Burns	65–85
Ionizing radiation	30

[1] 11% fracture, 35% laceration, 54% contusion.

WEAPONS PHENOMENOLOGY

Energy Partition. The energy released by the detonation of a nuclear weapon of the fission-type can be described in the following terms:

1. About 84% of the energy released is accounted for by the kinetic energy of the reaction fragments (fission products). This energy is more or less instantaneously converted to heat as the fragments collide with surrounding matter. The manifestations vary, depending on whether the detonation occurs underground, at or near the earth's surface, or in the air. In an air burst, about 60% of the heat expends itself in the production of blast or shock waves, and the balance is dissipated as thermal radiation (heat and light rays).

2. About 6% of the energy released is accounted for by the instantaneous emission of gamma rays and neutrons.

3. About 10% of the energy is accounted for by the radioactive decay of fission products. The radiation emitted consists of gamma rays, beta particles and neutrinos.

Air Burst Phenomena. An air burst is defined as a detonation occurring below an altitude of 100,000 feet but at sufficient height above the earth's surface that the "fireball" (see below) does not come into contact with the ground. The following notes describe the major phenomena associated with a 1-megaton air burst.

Fireball. At the instant of detonation all components of the device as well as surrounding air are raised to temperatures approaching those of the sun, i.e., of the order of tens of millions of degrees. Within a few millionths of a second the device will have completely vaporized, however the process of vaporization starts while the casing is still intact and hence tremendous pressures (many millions of pounds per square inch) are generated by the initially confined gases. Once vaporization is complete, the resulting hot gas mass appears as a roughly spherical, rapidly expanding "fireball" whose initial luminosity greatly exceeds that of the sun. As the fireball expands, engulfing surrounding air, it rises and pales. In the case being considered, the fireball reaches a radius of several hundred feet within a millisecond of the time of detonation, and it reaches its maximum radius (~ 3600 feet) in about ten seconds. It is then rising at a velocity of several hundred miles an hour, so that it reaches an

* See **biological effects of ionizing radiation** for background information.

altitude several miles above the point of detonation within the first minute, by which time it has cooled sufficiently to be no longer visible.

Mushroom Cloud. Cooling of the fireball is accompanied by condensation of the vapors, resulting in formation of a cloud. This initially contains solid particles of bomb debris together with small drops of moisture condensed from the air. The color is at first red or reddish brown due to the formation of nitrous acid and oxides of nitrogen at the surface of the fireball. As cooling progresses the color changes to white, as in an ordinary cloud. Depending upon the height of burst and the nature of the terrain below, a strong updraft with inflowing winds (called "afterwinds") is produced which causes varying amounts of dirt and debris from the ground to be sucked up into the cloud, accounting for the stem of the familiar mushroom shape. At first the particulate matter (now consisting of dirt and ground debris as well as bomb debris) continues to be borne upward with the cloud, but in due course it begins to settle out. The heavier particles settle to the ground as "early" **radioactive fallout.** The lighter particles behave as smoke and, following the prevailing air currents, extend the base of the cloud into a drifting lateral column, from which dust-like particles gradually settle to the ground ("tropospheric" fallout). In the meantime, the top of the cloud continues its rapid rise, usually reaching an altitude within eight or ten minutes at which it begins to spread out horizontally, accounting for the head of the familiar mushroom shape. The maximum altitude (top of the mushroom) seldom exceeds 20 or 25 miles. The mushroom generally remains visible for about an hour before it is dispersed by currents in the atmosphere. The particulate matter still contained thus becomes widely distributed ("stratospheric" radioactive fallout).

Blast Wave. At the time the fireball is created a high-pressure wave develops and moves rapidly outward. The front of the wave, called the "shock front," behaves like a moving wall of highly compressed air. By the time the fireball has reached its maximum size (i.e., in about 10 seconds) the shock front will have traveled several miles. When it strikes the earth's surface it is reflected back, much as the echo from a sound wave. Interaction of the direct and reflected waves creates a so-called "Mach front," which forms near the ground at a certain radius from "ground zero" (the point directly below the detonation) and moves outward, more or less hugging the ground. The "overpressure" exerted by the Mach front, i.e.,

Fig. 229. Start of ascent of mushroom cloud from tower shot of small-scale nuclear device at the Nevada Test Site. (*Courtesy of Lookout Mountain Laboratory, USAF*)

the pressure above normal atmospheric pressure—is generally about twice that exerted by the direct shock front. In the case of a 1-megaton device, the Mach front forms 5 seconds after the detonation at a radius about 1⅓ miles out from ground zero. The overpressure at the time of formation is approximately 16 psi. As the Mach front travels outward its force diminishes: ~ 6 psi at 3 miles, ~ 1 psi at 10 miles, etc. To place these figures in some perspective, an overpressure of 6 psi is sufficient to destroy a frame dwelling (see **weapons effects**). In addition to the afterwinds caused by the rising fireball (see above), strong transient winds are generated by the shock waves. These winds have peak velocities of several hundred miles per hour in the immediate vicinity of ground zero, and may exceed 60 miles per hour 6 or 7 miles out from ground zero.

Thermal Radiation. As soon as the fireball is formed it begins to emit thermal radiation. In the first tenth of a second there is an initial pulse, principally of ultraviolet rays, which accounts for about 1% of the total heat emitted by the detonation. A second phase follows, lasting several seconds, during which the balance 99% of the heat emission occurs, principally as visible and infrared rays. This second pulse is capable of causing severe skin burns within a radius of 10 or 12 miles of ground zero (see **weapons effects**). As was brought out in the earlier analysis of energy distribution, about one-third of the total energy released in an air burst is emitted as thermal radiation. In the case of a 1-megaton device, this means that some 3.3×10^{14} calories (equivalent to 40 million kilowatt-hours of heat) are emitted within a few seconds' time.

Prompt Nuclear Radiation. The nuclear radiation emitted by the fireball and the cloud within the first minute is referred to as "prompt radiation." It includes gamma rays and neutrons released instantaneously by the fission process; gamma, beta and neutrino emission from radioactive fission products; alpha emission from any residual uranium or plutonium; and gamma and beta emission due to radioactivity induced in ambient matter by neutron capture. The alpha and beta particles are quickly absorbed by surrounding matter and are not a factor in radiation exposure at ground level, so prompt radiation can be considered as consisting essentially of gamma rays plus uncaptured neutrons. The effective range, from an exposure standpoint, depends on the energy yield of the detonation, being greater the larger the device. In the 1-megaton case, the range is several miles. As was implicit in the definition of prompt radiation, the period of exposure at ground level is approximately the first minute after detonation, by which time the cloud will have risen to a height exceeding the effective range of the radiation. (This holds roughly true for any size of detonation by reason of the fact that there is correlation between the energy release, the effective range of the radiation, and the rate of ascent of the cloud.)

Residual Nuclear Radiation. The nuclear radiation associated with the cloud after the first minute is referred to as "residual radiation." It includes gamma, beta and neutrino emission from fission products; alpha emission from any residual uranium and plutonium; and gamma and beta emission due to radioactivity induced by neutron capture during the period of prompt radiation.

Residual radiation makes itself felt primarily through the mechanism of **radioactive fallout,** which is the subject of a separate entry.

Other Types of Burst. Other types of detonation include a high altitude burst (defined as one occurring at an altitude higher than 100,000 feet); surface burst (defined as one in which the fireball contacts the ground); an underground burst; and an underwater burst. The following notes briefly describe the major differences between the latter three and the air burst described above.

Surface Burst. Here contact between the fireball and the ground causes an immense amount of rock, soil and other matter to be vaporized and sucked up into the air; hence the resulting cloud is much more heavily loaded with debris than is the case in an air burst. The amount depends on the size and elevation of the detonation but is in the range of thousands to tens or even hundreds of thousands of tons.

The principal consequence is to increase greatly the amount and seriousness of early and tropospheric fallout. Also, if the burst occurs near the ground (i.e., within several hundred feet) it usually forms an appreciable crater. In the case of a 1-megaton "contact surface burst," i.e., detonation at ground level —the crater would exceed 100 feet in depth and 1000 feet in diameter (assuming dry soil conditions). In most other respects, the phenomena attending a surface burst are similar to those attending an air burst.

Underground Burst. An underground burst involves detonation at the relatively shallow depths to which a bomb or shell might penetrate, i.e., up to 50 or 100 feet.* A notable feature of such a burst is the amount of earth displaced. For example, if a 1-megaton device were detonated at a depth of 50 feet in sandy soil, some 10 million tons of soil and rock would be hurled upward, leaving a crater nearly 200 feet deep and more than one-quarter of a mile in diameter. Depending on the depth, the fireball may be visible as it breaks through the surface, or it may be obscured by ground matter borne swiftly upward by the escaping gases. As the heavier ground matter falls back to earth it may produce an expanding "base surge" of fine soil particles which spreads outward several miles from the center of the detonation before being carried downwind. Particles settling out from this surge and from the stem of the cloud proper result in heavy early and tropospheric fallout, much of the former occurring as "local" fallout. An underground burst has at least two other distinguishing features, relative to an air burst. One is that most of the thermal and initial ionizing radiation from the fireball is absorbed by soil before the fireball breaks the surface, and hence does not constitute a major hazard. The other is that, to a degree that depends on the depth of the detonation, the predominant blast effect is a destructive underground shock similar to an earthquake (but more shallow and hence more sharply defined and shorter in duration). There is also an air blast but this is not as severe as in a comparable air burst.

Fig. 230. Underground test of small-scale nuclear device at the Nevada Test Site. Dust was stirred by the shock wave from the detonation and by rolling rocks and was raised to an altitude of several hundred feet by heat-created air currents, but was found to be free of radioactivity.

Underwater Burst. The phenomena attending an underwater burst are analogous to those attending an underground burst with the obvious difference that it is water, rather than ground matter, which is displaced and which forms the base surge, and with the difference

* As distinct from deep underground detonations of interest in peaceful applications of nuclear explosives. (See **Plowshare Program**)

also that the shock wave travels much further and more rapidly underwater than underground.

WEAPONS TEST DETECTION

Provision for the long-range detection of clandestine nuclear weapons tests is considered to be a prerequisite condition for an effective international nuclear test ban (see reference to test moratorium under **weapons testing**). The following discussion is limited to the technical aspects of this subject. For background information, see **weapons phenomenology.**

Means of Detection. Depending on the environment in which a test is conducted, one or more of the following methods could in principle be used for long-range detection purposes:

1. Collection and analysis of radioactive debris.
2. Detection and measurement of seismic (i.e., ground shock) waves.
3. Detection and measurement of sound waves.
4. Detection and measurement of electromagnetic signals resulting from gamma ray emission.
5. Detection and measurement of light emission.
6. Detection and measurement of other forms of radiation such as thermal radiation, x-rays, gamma rays or neutrons.

Of these, only the first is an established technique and it is limited in its applicability. The status of test detection is summarized in the paragraphs immediately following.

Tests Affecting the Atmosphere. These include **air bursts, surface bursts** and shallow **underground** or **underwater bursts.** All such tests result in **radioactive fallout,** the sampling and analysis of which afford a means of detecting detonations of any appreciable size. It is believed that an adequate network of air sampling stations supplemented by a pattern of aircraft sampling flights would constitute a reliable long-range detection system for "atmospheric" tests, and such a system has been proposed by the United States as a means of monitoring a ban on atmospheric tests.

High Altitude Tests. Tests conducted at a high altitude produce little or no radioactive fallout for an appreciable period of time. Adequate detection techniques for such tests do not exist at present and, once developed, will require extensive research and experimentation before they can be proven to be reliable.

Deep Underwater Tests. It is expected that detonations of moderate size carried out deep in the oceans would probably not produce radioactive fallout in sufficient amounts for long-range detection. Hydroacoustic stations could monitor the noise signals emanating from such tests and water sampling would afford a means of confirming that a test had taken place; however, it would be difficult to pinpoint the location of the test event.

Deep underground tests. Underground tests produce no radioactive fallout when completely contained below the earth's surface. There is no known way of proving that such a test has taken place other than by on-site inspection, which would entail drilling to obtain samples of radioactive debris. A world network of seismic instrumentation could provide information on significant seismic disturbances and, in some cases, could differentiate between an earthquake and an explosion, but existing instruments cannot distinguish between nuclear and conventional explosives. A further complication is the proven ability greatly to diminish the intensity of distant seismic signals from an underground explosion by what is known as "decoupling," i.e., by detonating the explosive in a large underground cavity.

At this writing, an extensive network of seismic detection stations supplemented by on-site inspection of a statistical sampling of the signals received, appears to offer the only effective means for the long-range detection of deep underground tests; and even on this basis, the detection system could only be applied at present to detonations above a certain size. The specification of minimum size and the design of the inspection sampling procedure must take into account the natural pattern of earthquake events in the particular region to be monitored. In the case of the Soviet Union, the annual number of seismic events of magnitude

TABLE 1. U.S. NUCLEAR WEAPON TESTS

Test Operation or Series	*Dates*	*Test site*	*No. of Shots*	*Remarks*
Trinity	July 16, 1945	Alamogordo, N.M.	1	First nuclear weapon test (19 KT-tower-shot)
Crossroads	June-July, 1946	Bikini	2	Included nominal-yield (~ 20 KT) underwater burst ("Baker")
Sandstone	April-May, 1948	Eniwetok	3	All tower shots; highest yield 49 KT
	January-February, 1951	Nevada Test Site	5	All air drops; yield ranged from 1.0–22 KT
Greenhouse	April-May, 1951	Eniwetok	4	All tower shots
Buster-Jangle	October-November, 1951	Nevada Test Site	7	Yield ranged from 0.1–31 KT; series included first surface and underground bursts (each 1.2 KT)
Tumbler-Snapper	April-June, 1952	Nevada Test Site	8	Yields ranged from 1–31 KT
Ivy	October-November, 1952	Pacific Proving Grounds	2	"Mike" shot on 10/31/52 was first thermonuclear weapon test
Upshot-Knothole	March-June, 1953	Nevada Test Site	11	Yield ranged from 0.2–61 KT; series included first firing of nuclear projectile from cannon (15 KT)
Castle	February-May, 1954	Pacific Proving Grounds	6	Series included 15-MT thermonuclear test ("Bravo")
Teapot	February-May, 1955	Nevada Test Site	14	Yields ranged from 1–43 KT
Wigwam	May 14, 1955	Off west coast of U.S.	1	Deep (2000′) underwater burst-30 KT
Redwing	May-July, 1956	Pacific Proving Grounds	13	First U.S. airdrop of thermonuclear device (megaton range)
Plumbbob	May-October, 1957	Nevada Test Site	24	Series included highest-yield shot fired to date in the continental U.S. ("Hood," 74 KT); first deep (790′) underground burst ("Ranier," 1.7 KT)
Hardtack-Phase I	April-August, 1958	Eniwetok Proving Grounds	31	Two shots at Johnston Island were rockets detonated at high altitudes (up to 252,000′)
Argus Project [1]	August-September, 1958	South Atlantic	3	See notes
Hardtack-Phase II	September-October, 1958	Nevada Test Site	19	Series included a number of underground bursts at depths ranging from ~ 100′ to ~ 850′

[1] This was not a weapon test as such. The Argus Project involved the detonation of 3 low-yield nuclear devices in outer space. Its purpose was to study the trapping, by the earth's magnetic field, of the electrons produced by beta decay of the fission fragments.

greater than 4.75 on the Richter scale exceeds 100; the annual number of magnitude less than 4.75 is in the thousands. In this light, the United States in 1961 proposed a treaty incorporating a ban of underground tests corresponding to a seismic intensity greater than 4.75 and providing for on-the-spot inspection of about 20% of the signals above that magnitude (specifically, 20 signals per year).

Research Program. The United States is conducting research designed to advance present capability for the long-range detection of deep underground nuclear weapons tests via seismic techniques, and also for the long-range detection of high altitude tests. The program, known as Project Vela, is directed by the Advanced Research Projects Agency (ARPA) of the Department of Defense. The U.S. Atomic Energy Commission is one of several government agencies participating in this work.

Project VELA has three parts:

1. VELA-UNIFORM: This involves basic research on seismology; development of improved seismic instruments; construction and operation of prototype seismic detection stations; and experimentation with signals from underground detonations of chemical and nuclear explosives.
2. VELA-SIERRA: This involves the development of ground-based instruments for the possible detection of high altitude tests. As part of this work, Los Alamos Scientific Laboratory is engaged in research and tests based on the detection of fluorescent light emission.
3. VELA-HOTEL: This involves the development of satellite-based instruments and systems for the possible detection of tests in space. Los Alamos Scientific Laboratory, Sandia Laboratory and the E. O. Lawrence Radiation Laboratory (Livermore Branch) are engaged in various aspects of this work.

WEAPONS TESTING

Table 1 (p. 609) summarizes available information on nuclear weapons tests conducted by the United States from the date of the historic "Trinity" experiment until the conclusion of the test moratorium in September, 1961 (see below). Table 2 shows the number of tests known to have been conducted through 1960, by other countries, namely the Soviet Union, the United Kingdom and France. Following is a breakdown of the estimated energy yield from all known tests through 1960, expressed as equivalent kilotons of TNT:

Years	*Yield from Fission*[1] *(KT)*	*Yield from Fusion*[1] *(KT)*	*Total Yield (KT)*
1945–51 incl.	760	—	760
1952–54 incl.	38,000	22,000	60,000
1955–56 incl.	13,100	14,900	28,000
1957–58 incl.	40,000	45,000	85,000
1959–60 incl.	140	—	140
TOTALS:	92,000[2]	81,900	173,900

[1] In the absence of an actual breakdown, a 50–50 split between fission and fusion has been assumed for all Soviet thermonuclear tests. (This is roughly the average for the U.S. and U.K. thermonuclear tests.)
[2] Estimated Soviet contribution: 25% of total fission yield.

The tests have been conducted for various purposes, including the obtaining of information essential to weapon design; the proving of weapons and weapon systems; and the study of weapon effects. The U.S. test program has included detonations ranging in yield from 0.001 kiloton to 15 megatons, and has en-

TABLE 2. FOREIGN NUCLEAR WEAPON TESTS

Year	*No. of Tests*		
	U.S.S.R.	*United Kingdom*	*France*
1949	1[1]	—	—
1950	—	—	—
1951	2	—	—
1952	—	1[3]	—
1953	2[2]	2	—
1954	1	—	—
1955	4	—	—
1956	7	6	—
1957	13	7[4]	—
1958	25	5	—
1959	—	—	—
1960	—	—	3[5]
	55	21	3

[1] First known Soviet test Aug. 29, 1949.
[2] First Soviet thermonuclear test Aug. 12, 1953.
[3] First U.K. test Oct. 3, 1952 (Monte Bello Islands).
[4] First U.K. thermonuclear test May 15, 1957 (Christmas Island area).
[5] First French test (~ 60 KT) Feb. 13, 1960 (Sahara Desert).

compassed bursts in the upper and lower atmosphere, surface bursts, shallow and deep underground bursts, and shallow and deep underwater bursts. The devices have been mounted on towers, floated on barges, carried by balloons, dropped by aircraft, fired by cannon and sent aloft by rockets. Each test has involved exhaustive preparations which can be grouped into two main categories:

1. Technical preparations, e.g., the installation and check-out of instrumentation used to measure weapon yield, blast and shock waves, thermal radiation, prompt and residual nuclear radiation, and other test parameters; the erection of structures and placing of equipment used to obtain information on weapon effects; the assembly of special experimental apparatus; etc.

2. Safety measures, e.g., the establishment and patrolling of exclusion areas; the making of detailed weather forecasts and analyses; the setting up of local and long-range radiation monitoring networks; the collection of environmental information prior to and after the test; arranging to track the radioactive cloud; etc.

The principal sites used by the United States for nuclear weapon tests have been the **Nevada Test Site** and the **Eniwetok Proving Grounds** in the Marshall Islands. Use of the former is restricted to devices of relatively limited yield (tens of kilotons). Another testing site which should be noted is the Tonapah Test Range in Nevada, which is used for ballistic and other tests not involving nuclear detonation. (See **Sandia Laboratory**)

Fig. 231. Underwater test of nuclear device at the Eniwetok Proving Grounds ("Baker shot," summer of 1949). (*Courtesy of Army Photographic Agency*)

Test Moratorium. In the summer of 1953, the United States proposed that the then existing nuclear-weapon powers (namely the U.S., the U.S.S.R. and the U.K.) convene a technical conference for the purpose of working out a reliable inspection system for nuclear weapon test detection. As part of the proposal, the United States offered to suspend all nuclear weapons tests for one year from the start of the conference, and stated its willingness to enter into a treaty permanently banning such tests provided the treaty contain adequate safeguards against clandestine test operations. (See **weapons test detection**) Pursuant to this proposal, an exchange of notes between the three countries led to the convening, on October 31, 1958, at Geneva, Switzerland, of the tripartite "Conference on the Discontinuance of Nuclear Weapon Tests." A 1-year test moratorium agreement became effective on that date. Insofar as is known, testing was not resumed by any of the three countries until September 1, 1961, on which date the United States announced the detection of a nuclear detonation in the atmosphere over Soviet Cen-

Fig. 232. The Weldon Spring Plant. (*Courtesy of Mallinckrodt Chemical Works*)

tral Asia. On September 15, 1961, after an unsuccessful effort to renew a moratorium, the United States resumed underground testing at the Nevada Test Site; and in the summer of 1962, the United States conducted a series of atmospheric tests in the vicinity of the Johnston and Christmas Islands in the Pacific.

WELDON SPRING PLANT

A U.S. Atomic Energy Commission production facility for the refining of uranium and preparation of **feed materials,** located on the site of the Weldon Spring Ordnance Works, 27 miles west of St. Louis, Missouri. *Operating contractor:* Mallinckrodt Chemical Works. *AEC investment in plant and equipment:* ~ $58 million.* *Employment:* ~ 1000.

The Weldon Spring Plant was completed in 1958. The architect-engineer was the Blaw-Knox Company; the construction contractors were the Fruin-Colnon and Utah Construction Companies. Many of the operations are similar to those conducted at the AEC's **Feed Materials Production Center** at Fernald, Ohio. They include: (1) The refining of uranium concentrates into "orange oxide" (UO_3); (2) the conversion of orange oxide into "green salt" (UF_4); and the reduction of green salt to high-purity uranium metal. Unlike Fernald, where the metal is cast into ingots, the Weldon Spring Plant employs an extrusion process to produce billets. These are shipped to Fernald for rolling. In 1960, a facility was added at Weldon Spring for machining rolled rods (from Fernald) into finished hollow fuel elements for the Hanford Works. For a description of the processes used in feed materials production, see **uranium refining and conversion.**

Mallinckrodt had the major responsibility for U.S. feed materials production during the wartime **Manhattan Project,** utilizing processes developed and tested on a semi-works scale by a group at Iowa State University (see **Ames Laboratory).** For this purpose govern-

* Includes facilities authorized or under construction as of June 30, 1960. Not adjusted for depreciation.

ment facilities were constructed on land made available by the company at its Destrehan Street Plant in St. Louis. These facilities were expanded after the war and continued in operation until the start-up of the Weldon Spring Plant in 1958. They have since been dismantled.

WESTINGHOUSE TESTING REACTOR (WTR)

A general-purpose **test reactor** formerly operated by Westinghouse Electric Corporation at Waltz Mill, Pennsylvania. The installation was built to serve Westinghouse's commercial power reactor development program and to provide contract irradiation services. Early in 1962, after 2 years of use, operations were terminated because of an insufficient volume of contract irradiation business. *Type:* Tank reactor. *Power rating:* 60,000 thermal kilowatts. *Fuel:* Aluminum-clad tubular fuel elements fabricated of a highly enriched uranium-aluminum alloy. *Coolant:* H_2O. *Moderator:* H_2O. *Reflector:* H_2O. *Neutron flux:* Maximum thermal neutron flux, $\sim 1.1 \times 10^{14}$ n/cm²sec. Maximum fast-neutron flux, $\sim 1.3 \times 10^{14}$n/cm²sec.

WHOLE BODY COUNTER

A device for measuring the "body burden" of natural radioactivity, used in studies of the biological effects of radiation. The measurement is made by means of a giant **scintillation counter** employing a liquid phosphor (see Fig. 233).

WOLVERINE ELECTRIC COOPERATIVE REACTOR PROJECT

A project which was to have involved the construction of a small nuclear power plant of the single-region **aqueous homogeneous** type under the "second round" of the U.S. Atomic Energy Commission's Power Demonstration Reactor Program. The project was proposed in 1956 and reached the contract negotiation stage but was cancelled in 1958, due to very substantial increases in the estimated cost of reactor construction. The organizations involved were Foster Wheeler Corporation and Worthington Corporation, who were to have supplied the reactor, and the Wolverine Electric Cooperative of Big Rapids, Michigan, which was to have operated the plant.

Fig. 233. Whole body counter at Los Alamos Scientific Laboratory. (*Courtesy of Los Alamos Scientific Laboratory*)

WORLD HEALTH ORGANIZATION (WHO)

A specialized agency of the United Nations which, through its Expert Committee on Radiation, maintains an active interest in the public health aspects of radiation exposure and protection.

WORLD METEOROLOGICAL ORGANIZATION (WMO)

A specialized agency of the United Nations whose interests in the atomic energy field include: the preparation of technical reports and bibliographies on the meteorological aspects of peaceful uses of atomic energy; study of standard instruments and measurement techniques for the collection of meteorological data required in connection with atomic energy programs; study of the use of radioisotopes and other atomic energy-based techniques in meteorological research; and coordination with the work of other international agencies such as the **International Atomic Energy Agency.**

X

X-RAYS

Short wavelength **electromagnetic radiation** normally resulting from the interaction of energetic **electrons** with a metal target, as in an x-ray tube. X-rays are similar to **gamma rays;** however, the two are differentiated on the basis of origin: x-rays derive from orbital atomic electrons; gamma rays originate in the atomic nucleus. Unlike gamma rays, which initially have discrete energy levels, x-rays from a conventional x-ray tube have a continuous energy spectrum. The "peak-value" is used to characterize both the voltage at which the tube is operated and the maximum energy of the resulting x-rays.

X-ray emission occurs spontaneously when high-energy **beta particles** undergo a sudden loss in energy in approaching a positively charged atomic nucleus—a phenomenon known as bremsstrahlung ("braking radiation").

X-10

The pilot plutonium production facility built at Oak Ridge, Tennessee during the **Manhattan Project;** now a part of Oak Ridge National Laboratory. The heart of the facility was a graphite-moderated, air cooled, natural uranium reactor which is still in operation and is now known as the **Oak Ridge Graphite Reactor** (X-10).

XENON-135

A radioisotope of the inert gaseous element, xenon, formed in high yield as a fission product. A 9.2-hour beta emitter, xenon-135 has by far the highest thermal neutron absorption cross section of any fission product (2.72×10^6 barns) and is thus the principal fission product **poison** in reactor systems. The phenomenon of xenon build-up following reactor shutdown is a complicating factor in reactor design.

XENON OVER-RIDE

In a nuclear reactor, an amount of **excess reactivity** that has been provided to compensate for the poisoning effect of xenon build-up. (See **xenon poisoning**)

XENON POISONING

The accumulation in a nuclear reactor of xenon-135, which has the highest **cross section** for thermal neutron capture of any known reactor poison—namely 2.72×10^6 **barns.** Xenon-135 is formed by beta decay of the fission product, iodine-135.

When a reactor is first placed into operation, xenon-135 begins to accumulate and reaches an equilibrium concentration in about 40 hours, provided steady-state conditions are maintained. The magnitude of the poisoning effect at equilibrium concentration is a function of the **neutron flux** of the reactor.

The equilibrium concentration reflects a balance between the rate of formation of xenon-135 and the rate at which it is consumed (by neutron absorption and subsequent radioactive decay). When the reactor is shut down, xenon-135 continues to be formed by the decay of iodine-135 and, since no neutrons are then present, its concentration rises. This phenomenon, known as "xenon build-up," continues for a period of 10 or 12 hours until a peak concentration is reached, at which time the xenon-135 decay process becomes controlling and the concentration begins gradually to decline. The peak concentration in high-flux reactors is considerably higher than the equilibrium concentration. If a reactor does not contain sufficient excess reactivity to overcome the poisoning effect of the xenon build-up, or if the reactor, once shut down, is not rapidly returned to service, operation may not be resumed until a considerable period of time has passed. (See **xenon over-ride)**

Y

Y-12 PLANT

A plant built at Oak Ridge, Tennessee during the **Manhattan Project** for the separation of uranium isotopes by the **electromagnetic separation** process. The buildings have largely been stripped of their original equipment and put to other use; however, some of the electromagnetic isotope separation units (known as Calutrons) have been retained and are used by Oak Ridge National Laboratory to separate stable isotopes for research purposes. See **Manhattan Project** for background information on the Y-12 Plant.

YANKEE ATOMIC ELECTRIC PLANT

A large-scale nuclear power plant of the **pressurized water** type, located on the Deerfield River at Rowe, Massachusetts (see Fig. 234). The plant, built for development and demonstration purposes, is owned and operated by Yankee Atomic Electric Company, an organization representing 10 investor-owned electric utilities.* Westinghouse Electric Corporation and Stone and Webster Engineering Corporation were joint contractors for the plant, the latter handling engineering design and construction.

The Yankee project is being carried out under the "first round" of the U.S. Atomic Energy Commission's Power Reactor Demonstration Program. The AEC has contributed $5 million for research and development and has waived its normal use charge on nuclear fuel material for a 5-year period (equivalent to a financial contribution of $3.7 million). The sponsoring companies are bearing the costs of construction and operation, and all costs of research and development in excess of $5 million.

The Yankee reactor first went critical in August, 1960, and first generated power in November, 1960. It was originally licensed to operate at a power output of 110 megawatts (net electrical), which it first achieved in January, 1961. It was subsequently licensed for operation at 140 megawatts, which it first achieved in June, 1961. The following notes relate to the initial core loading:

Power: 140 megawatts (net electrical). *Fuel:* Slightly enriched uranium (3.4% U^{235}) in the form of uranium dioxide (UO_2). *Fuel element design:* A single fuel element consists of an assembly of thin stainless steel tubes loaded with UO_2 pellets. *Fuel inventory:* ~ 20,900 kilograms of uranium. *Coolant:* Light water (H_2O) at 2000 pounds pressure; inlet temperature, 495°F; outlet temperature 514°F. *Steam conditions:* Saturated steam at 500 pounds pressure and 467°F. *Thermal conversion efficiency:* 29%. *Control materials:* 24 silver-cadmium-indium control rods; solution poison (boric acid) added to coolant during periods of reactor shutdown. *Containment:* Steel sphere, 125 feet in diameter. *Construction cost:* Reported at $40 million, exclusive of research and development. For other project costs, see Table 3 under **nuclear power development.** *Dates:* Provisional construction permit issued in November, 1957. Major construction work started in April, 1958. Reactor first critical in August, 1960. Full power operation at 110-megawatt rating first reached in January, 1961. Full power at 140-megawatt rating first reached in June, 1961.

* Boston Edison Company, Central Maine Power, Central Vermont Public Service Corporation, Connecticut Light and Power Company, Eastern Utilities Associates, Hartford Electric Light Company, New England Electric System, New England Gas and Electric Association, Public Service Company of New Hampshire, and Western Massachusetts Electric Company.

Fig. 234. The Yankee Atomic Electric Plant. Above left, general view. Above right, stainless steel tubes and uranium dioxide pellets from which fuel elements are assembled. Left, one of 76 fuel elements in core loading. (*Courtesy of Westinghouse Electric Corp.*)

YELLOW CAKE

A term applied to certain uranium concentrates produced by uranium mills; specifically, those in which uranium is mainly in the form of ammonium diuranate ($(NH_4)_2U_2O_7$) or sodium diuranate ($Na_2U_2O_7$). (See **uranium milling**)

YIELD (of nuclear weapons)

The amount of energy released by a nuclear explosion, including blast or shock waves, thermal radiation and nuclear radiation (see **weapons phenomenology**); thus an expression of the "size" of the device detonated. Yield is usually expressed in terms of the quantity of conventional explosive (TNT) that would be required to produce a corresponding amount of energy. The units used are equivalent kilotons (KT) or megatons (MT) of TNT. Yields reported from weapons test operations have ranged from 0.001 KT to 15 MT. (See **weapons testing**)

A related term is "fission yield," which is that part of the total yield produced by **fission** (as opposed to **fusion**). In some devices, all of the energy comes from fission; hence the fission yield and the total yield are one and the same. In the case of a thermonuclear device, however, the energy comes from a combination of fission and fusion; hence the fission yield is less than the total yield. The reason for differentiating between fission yield and total yield is that fission yield defines the amount of fission-product formation and thereby affords a better index of the **radioactive fallout** potential.

YUGOSLAVIA

The Federal Nuclear Energy Commission, Belgrade, is the agency responsible for atomic energy matters. The principal nuclear research center is the Boris Kidrič Institute at Vinča, near Belgrade. Its experimental facilities include a heavy water moderated research and materials testing reactor, supplied by the U.S.S.R., which operates at power levels up to 10,000 kilowatts (thermal). Other centers are the Rudjer Bošković Institute at Zagreb and the Jožef Stefan Institute at Ljubljana.

Uranium deposits of marginal grade and probably capable of small production have been found in Yugoslavia. An extensive exploration program is underway.

Yugoslavia is a member of the **International Atomic Energy Agency** and the European Organization for Nuclear Research **(CERN)**. The United States has made special grants to Yugoslavia of $200,000 for a research reactor and $150,000 for "hot" laboratory equipment.

Z

ZERO GRADIENT SYNCHROTRON (ZGS)

A 12.5-Bev **proton synchrotron** under construction at Argonne National Laboratory. (See **particle accelerators**)

ZERO POINT

The point at which detonation of a nuclear weapon occurs; thus, the center of the explosion. A related term is "ground zero," which is the point on the earth's surface nearest (i.e., perpendicularly below or above) the zero point. In the case of a "contact surface burst," zero point and ground zero are one and the same.

When detonation occurs in air, the zero point is sometimes referred to as "air zero."

ZIRCALOY

Any of several alloys of **zirconium** developed to improve its corrosion resistance and radiation stability and to extend the temperature range over which it can be used in reactor applications. Three formulations of zircaloy are at present available:

Alloy	*Alloying Agents in Zr*
Zircaloy-1	Tin (up to 2.5 wt. %)
Zircaloy-2	Tin (1.2–1.7 wt. %) Iron (0.07–0.2 wt. %) Chromium (0.05–0.15 wt. %) Nickel (0.03–0.06 wt. %)
Zircaloy-3	Tin (0.25 wt. %) Iron (0.25 wt. %)

Zircaloy-1 is now obsolete. Zircaloy-2 is commonly used and is implied when the number designation is omitted.

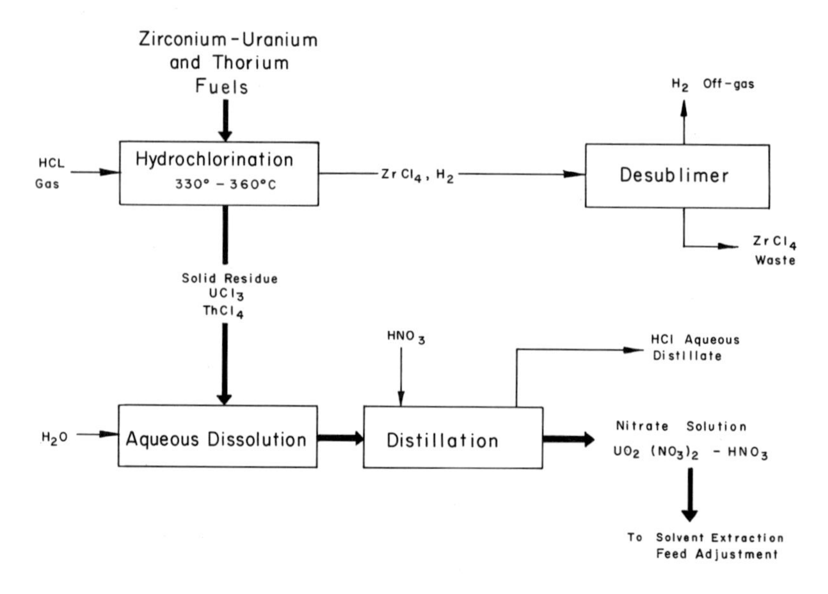

Fig. 235. Simplified flow diagram—Zircex Process (gas phase hydrochlorination).

ZIRCEX PROCESS

A technique of "**head-end**" treatment being developed for the reprocessing of zircaloy-clad, zirconium-alloy fuel elements from power reactors; specifically, a process for dissolving such fuel elements preparatory to solvent extraction (see **fuel reprocessing**). The fuel elements are contacted with anhydrous hydrogen chloride gas at elevated temperatures. Zirconium forms the volatile chloride, $ZrCl_4$, which is distilled off, leaving behind a residue of uranium and fission-product chlorides. This residue is dissolved in nitric acid and charged to a stripping column in which the chloride ions are removed by countercurrent flow of nitric acid vapor. It then goes to a feed adjustment boiler wherein sufficient nitric acid and water are removed to achieve a desired ratio of metallic nitrate ions to nitric acid. The resulting concentrated nitrate solution can then be adjusted by simple dilution to provide a suitable feed stream for solvent extraction.

A major problem in the development of this process is corrosion of container materials.

ZIRCONIUM

Element No. 40 (symbol, Zr; atomic weight, 91.22), used as a fuel-element cladding or structural material, usually in the form of **zircaloy,** in some water cooled power reactors and of interest to reactor designers generally. Reactor-grade zirconium, i.e., zirconium containing no more than 0.01% hafnium (see below), has the lowest thermal neutron cross section (0.18 barn) of any metal of comparable mechanical strength and corrosion resistance. The gain in neutron economy due to the superior nuclear properties of zirconium relative to stainless steel or other alternative materials

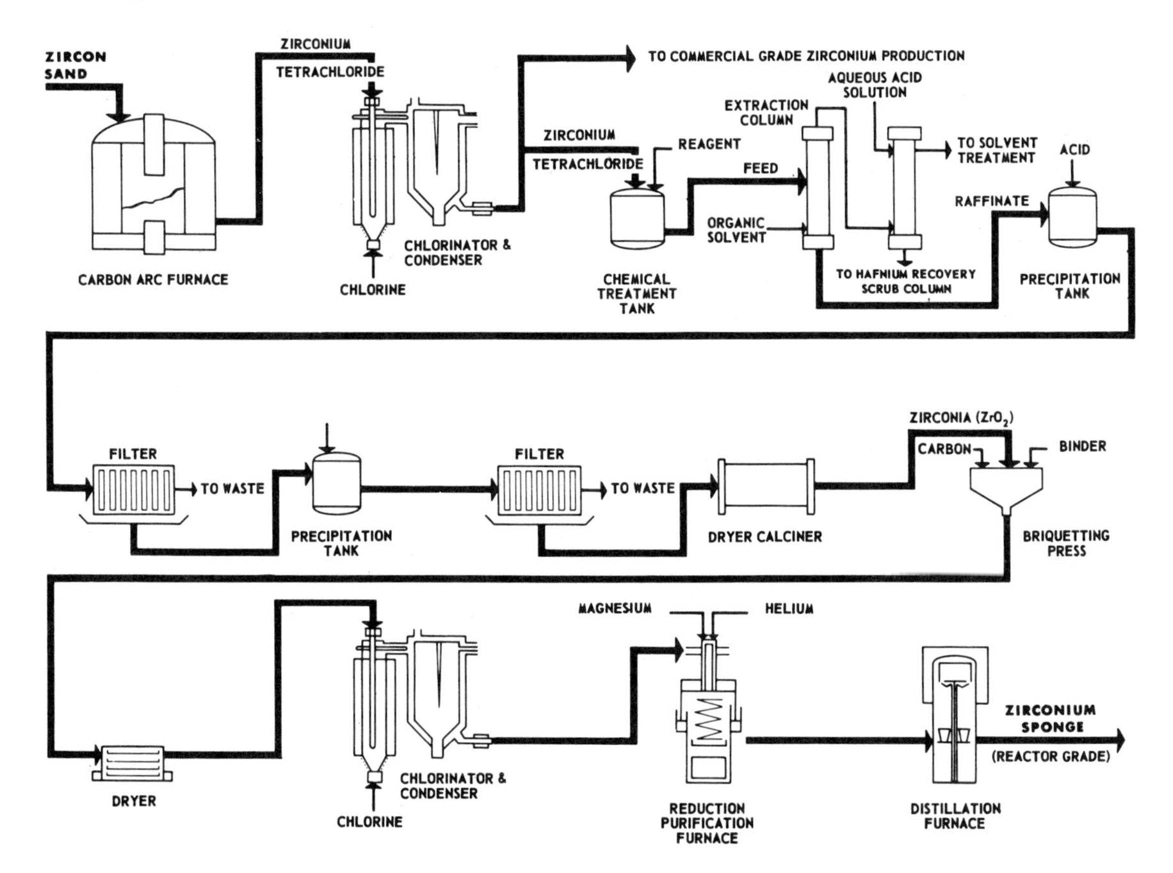

Fig. 236. Production of reactor-grade zirconium. (Reprinted from "Atomic Energy Facts.")

Fig. 237. Left, Zircaloy-2 ingot being removed from vacuum furnace. Right, machining ingot to remove surface defects. (*Courtesy of Carborundum Metals Co.*)

must be weighed against its comparatively high cost (see below).

Reactor-grade zirconium was first developed for use in naval propulsion reactors. It is now available from several commercial suppliers for general reactor use. (See **reactor materials**)

Production. Zirconium is a relatively abundant metal, U.S. reserves alone being estimated at several million tons. The principal minerals are zircon ($ZrSiO_4$), and baddeleyite (ZrO_2). As found in nature, zirconium is invariably accompanied by **hafnium,** a metal closely resembling zirconium in its chemical and metallurgical properties, but with notably different nuclear properties. (The thermal neutron absorption cross section of hafnium is 1-5 barns.) Hafnium concentrations in zirconium ore generally range between 0.5-3.0% but are sometimes higher. The removal of hafnium is the most difficult aspect of the production of reactor-grade (sometimes called "hafnium free") zirconium.

The principal steps in the production process presently used in one of the U.S. plants are as follows (see Fig. 236):

1. Zircon ore is charged to an arc furnace and reacted with carbon to form zirconium carbide, which is then chlorinated at high temperature to produce zirconium tetrachloride ($ZrCl_4$).

2. Hafnium removal is accomplished by preparing an acid solution of the zirconium tetrachloride and putting it through a **solvent extraction** process similar to that used in uranium refining, i.e., a countercurrent liquid-liquid contacting system employing an organic solvent (hexone). Hafnium is preferentially absorbed into the organic phase, zirconium remaining in the aqueous phase. The hafnium

stream leaving the extraction column passes through a scrub column, wherein the organic solvent is reclaimed for reuse, and is then processed to metal form as a by-product operation.

3. The aqueous zirconium stream from the extraction system is put through a precipitation-filtration sequence for final purification and then calcined to zirconium oxide (ZrO_2).

4. In the final stage of the process, the zirconium oxide is chlorinated to reform zirconium tetrachloride, which is reduced to zirconium metal by reaction with magnesium—an operation analogous to that used in the production of uranium metal. The zirconium metal is then freed of residual magnesium chloride first by a draining process and then by vacuum distillation to yield a final product known as "zirconium sponge."

ZIRCONIUM-NIOBIUM (Zir-nob)

A semirefined mixture of **fission products** consisting essentially of isotopes of zirconium and niobium and having an effective radioactive **half-life** of approximately 63 days. The mixture, referred to as "Zir-nob" and obtained by processing fresh high-level radioactive wastes from fuel reprocessing operations, is of interest as a possible source of gamma radiation for piloting large-scale radiation applications such as **food preservation, cold sterilization of pharmaceuticals,** and chemical manufacture. (See **radiation application in the chemical industry)**

This interest is based on estimates that, given a volume market, Zir-nob could be made available in large quantities (hundreds of thousands of curies or more) at costs of the order of 2-4 cents per curie. Availability at this level of cost suggests the possibility of using Zir-nob to test the feasibility of a proposed application without the expense of investing in longer-lived and more expensive radionuclide sources such as cobalt-60 or cesium-137. The short half-life of Zir-nob would mitigate against the use of this material in routine production operations.

ZIRFLEX PROCESS

A technique of **"head-end"** treatment being developed for the reprocessing of zircaloy-clad, zirconium-alloy fuel elements from power reactors; specifically, a process for dissolving the cladding of such fuel elements preparatory to dissolution of the fuel proper and subsequent solvent extraction (see **fuel reprocessing).** The reagent used in the Zirflex process is a mixture of ammonium fluoride and ammonium nitrate (NH_4F-NH_4NO_3).

ZONE MELTING

A technique for removing impurities from metals that has been studied for possible use in **fuel reprocessing** applications. A resistance heater or electric arc is moved along an irradiated fuel rod, causing progressive melting and recrystallization. Impurities that lower the melting point tend to concentrate in the molten zone as it travels the length of the rod. The process must be repeated a number of times and has been found to be extremely slow when applied to fission-product decontamination of uranium. Somewhat more promising results have been obtained in tests of the feasibility of using zone melting to separate uranium-233 from irradiated thorium.

Appendix A — Index

Note: The bold face type indicates where the subject is to be found in this book.

Appendix B — Selected Reading List

The basic criterion for selecting entries for any reading list such as this is the intended audience. The audience which the compiler of this reading list had in mind is the general-interest reader, as well as the technical reader with general interest who seeks information which does not gloss over technical details but at the same time is not so detailed that the major importance of what he is reading is lost. The reader interested mainly in technical detail should consult the subject area of interest in Nuclear Science Abstracts. A very extensive list of periodicals devoted solely to atomic energy or occasionally containing articles pertaining to atomic energy may be found in the semiannual and annual indexes of Nuclear Science Abstracts.

This reading list will allow the reader maximum over-all information pertaining to the many aspects of atomic energy. Each entry has a slightly different audience and need in mind, however, and where this is not evident in the title, a few words on subject matter contained in the entry is added. All selections are printed in English and are available to the general public.

Many entries contain the notation GPO or OTS. The GPO notation is to tell the reader that this reference may be purchased from the Superintendent of Documents, U.S. Government Printing Office, Washington 25, D.C. The OTS notation is to tell the reader that this reference may be purchased from the Office of Technical Services, Department of Commerce, Washington 25, D.C.

SELECTED READING LIST CATEGORIES

Periodicals
General
AEC-Information Sources
Economics
Education and Training
Energy Conversion
Energy Resources
Explosives, Peaceful Uses of
Fuel Reprocessing
Fusion, Controlled
Industrial Information Sources
International
Laws, Regulations and Insurance
Radiation Applications
Radiation Protection
Radioactive Fallout
Radioactive Waste Disposal
Radioisotopes in Agriculture and Medicine
Radioisotopes in Industry
Reactors, Civilian Power
Reactors, General
Reactors, Maritime
Reactors, Military and Space
Reactors, Process Heat
Reactors, Research and Test
Research Programs
Textbooks and Reference Works
Uranium, Thorium and Plutonium
Weapons, Nuclear

Periodicals

ANNUAL REPORT TO CONGRESS, USAEC. See MAJOR ACTIVITIES IN THE ATOMIC ENERGY PROGRAM and ATOMIC ENERGY RESEARCH below.

ATOM. Monthly Information Bulletin of the United Kingdom Atomic Energy Authority. U.K.A.E.A. Public Relations Branch, 11 Charles II Street, London, S.W.1., England. An official record of the work of the U.K.A.E.A. Contains press releases, news and patents abstracts.

ATOMIC AGE. Official publication of the Uranium Institute of America. Uranium Institute of America, Commerce Building, Grand Junction, Colorado. Nonmembers of UIA may subscribe for $10 a year. Published monthly. Contains articles of interest to the uranium mining industry.

ATOMIC ENERGY. The Editor, "Atomic Energy," Post Office, Coogee, N.S.W., Australia. Yearly subscription £1. Published quarterly. Published by the Australian Atomic Energy Commission to inform industry and commerce of progress in the field of atomic energy.

ATOMIC ENERGY CLEARING HOUSE. Congressional Information Bureau, Inc., Mills Building, 17th Street at Pennsylvania Avenue, N.W., Washington 6, D.C. Yearly subscription $100. Published weekly. A nontechnical newsletter designed for businessmen with emphasis on the regulatory and licensing aspects of atomic energy.

ATOMIC ENERGY LAW JOURNAL. Warren Publications, Inc., Publishers, 89 Beach Street, Boston 11, Massachusetts. Yearly subscription $20. Published quarterly. Contains articles, decisions or other items of interest to executives of companies engaged in the field of atomic energy and their attorneys.

ATOMIC ENERGY LAW REPORTER. Commerce Clearing House, Inc., 4025 W. Peterson Avenue, Chicago 46, Illinois. Yearly subscription $225. A loose-leaf service, arranged by subject, covering statutes, regulations, decisions and rulings, news and developments.

ATOMIC ENERGY RESEARCH. Available from the Superintendent of Documents, U.S. Government Printing Office, Washington 25, D.C. Price will vary but is usually around $2. Published annually. Life and physical sciences, reactor development and waste management research of the United States Atomic Energy Commission.

ATOMIC INDUSTRY REPORTER. The Bureau of National Affairs, Inc., 1231 24th Street, N.W., Washington 7, D.C. Yearly subscription $294. Published weekly. A loose-leaf service in three sections: (1) News and Analysis; (2) Laws and Regulations; (3) Technology Reports.

ATOMIC POWER NEWSLETTER. American Public Power Association, 919 18th Street, N.W., Washington 6, D.C. Yearly subscription $35. Published monthly.

ATOMICS. 308 E. James Street, Barrington, Illinois. Yearly subscription $5. Published bi-monthly. Contains nuclear news, nuclear literature, nuclear equipment news and current nuclear catalogs departments plus several articles of a technical nature.

ATOM INDUSTRY. Covering every phase of atomic development. Atom Industry, 400 Madison Avenue, New York 17, New York. Yearly subscription $5.

ATOMS IN JAPAN. Japan Atomic Industrial Forum, Inc., No. 1, 1-chome, Shiba-Tamuracho, Minatoku, Tokyo, Japan.

BRITISH POWER ENGINEERING. George Newnes, Ltd., Tower House, Southampton St., London, W.C.2., England. Yearly subscription $7.50. Published monthly. Contains articles on production, distribution and utilization of all forms of power: nuclear, steam, electricity, oil and gas.

BUSINESS ATOMICS REPORT. A Private Service on the Business Applications of Atomic Energy. Business Atomics Publications, Inc., 2 Sutton Place South, New York 22, New York. Yearly subscription $50. Published semimonthly. Atomic news and analyses of interest to management in the atomic energy industry.

CANADIAN NUCLEAR TECHNOLOGY. Maclean-Hunter Publishing Co., Ltd., 481 University Avenue, Toronto 2, Canada. Yearly subscription $5. Published quarterly. Contains technical information and news for nuclear industry in Canada as well as other countries.

DEVELOPMENT, GROWTH, AND STATE OF THE ATOMIC ENERGY INDUSTRY. Annual hearings held by the Joint Committee on Atomic Energy, Congress of the United States pursuant to Section 202 of the Atomic Energy Act of 1954. Available from the Superintendent of Documents, U.S. Government Printing Office, Washington 25, D.C.

FORUM MEMO. Atomic Industrial Forum, Inc., 850 Third Avenue, New York 22, New York. Yearly subscription price of $15 is included in AIF membership dues. Published monthly. Reports on political, industrial and international developments in the utilization of atomic energy for peaceful purposes.

INTERNATIONAL ATOMIC ENERGY AGENCY BULLETIN. International Atomic Energy Agency, Kaerntnerring II, Vienna 1, Austria. Available at the many AIEA sales agents throughout the world.

MAJOR ACTIVITIES IN THE ATOMIC ENERGY PROGRAMS. Available from the Superintendent of Documents, U.S. Government Printing Office, Washington 25, D.C. Price will vary but is usually around $2. Published annually, usually available in February. Annual Report of the United States Atomic Energy Commission to Congress.

NUCLEAR ENERGY. The journal of the Institution of Nuclear Engineers. A Princes Press Publication, 147 Victoria Street, London S.W.1., England. Annual subscription $10. Published monthly. Primarily directed to the United Kingdom atomic energy program with trade literature, institution news, equipment people and nuclear notes.

NUCLEAR ENGINEERING. Temple Press Limited, Bowling Green Lane, London E.C.1, England. Yearly subscription $7. Published monthly. Contains articles of interest to the nuclear power industry, with abstracts in French, German and Spanish. Primarily directed to the United Kingdom atomic energy program, with industrial notes, patents, and reviews of technical papers.

NUCLEAR NEWS. An American Nuclear Society publication. American Nuclear Society, Inc., 86 E. Randolph Street, Chicago 1, Illinois. Yearly subscription $10. Published monthly. Contains special articles and recent information on developments pertinent to nuclear energy.

NUCLEAR POWER. Rowse Muir Publications Ltd., 77-79 Charlotte Building, London W.1., England. Yearly subscription $8. Published monthly. Contains world-wide information on reactors, materials instrumentation, processes and irradiation. Often contains a large, multicolored, foldout cutaway drawing of a power reactor. Contains special feature articles and many regular features.

NUCLEAR SAFETY. A Quarterly Technical Progress Review. Superintendent of Documents, U.S. Government Printing Office, Washington 25, D.C. Yearly subscription $2. Published quarterly. This publication is prepared by Oak Ridge National Laboratory under the sponsorship of the USAEC. It reviews specific topics relevant to safety in reactor design, construction, and operation; safety considerations in reactor fuel fabrication, spent-fuel processing, nuclear-waste disposal, and related operations are also treated.

NUCLEAR SCIENCE ABSTRACTS. Superintendent of Documents, U.S. Government Printing Office, Washington 25, D.C. Yearly subscription for semimonthly issues is $22 domestic; $27.50 foreign. Yearly subscription for cumulated-index issues $15 domestic; $17.50 foreign. Published semimonthly. Cumulated indexes are published quarterly, semiannually and annually. Indexes include subject, personal and corporate author, and report number indexes. This publication is the USAEC Division of Technical Information abstracting and indexing service devoted solely to the literature of nuclear science and technology. NSA provides coverage of (1) technical reports of the USAEC and its contractors; (2) technical reports of government agencies, universities, and industrial and independent research organizations in the United States and abroad, and (3) the book, patent, and journal literature, and translations thereof, on a world-wide basis.

NUCLEONICS. McGraw-Hill Publishing Co., 330 West 42nd Street, New York 36, New York. Yearly subscription $8. Published monthly. Contains current news and articles on developments in nuclear energy. Contains articles on reactors, materials, instruments, processes and irradiation together with many regular features.

NUCLEONICS WEEK. McGraw-Hill Publishing Co., 330 West 42nd Street, New York 36, New York. Yearly subscription $75. Published weekly. Contains news of recent developments in nuclear energy.

POWER REACTOR TECHNOLOGY. A Quarterly Technical Progress Review. Superintendent of Documents, U.S. Government Printing Office, Washington 25, D.C. Yearly subscription $2. Published quarterly. This publication is prepared by General Nuclear Engineering Corp. under the sponsorship of the USAEC. It reviews selected recently published reports in the fields of civilian power-reactor research and development, power-reactor applications, design practice, and operating experiences.

REACTOR MATERIALS. A Quarterly Technical Progress Review. Superintendent of Documents, U.S. Government Printing Office, Wahington 25, D.C. Yearly subscription $2. Published quarterly. This publication is prepared by Battelle Memorial Institute under the sponsorship of the USAEC. It reviews recent developments in the field of reactor materials including fuel, fertile, moderator, cladding, and structural materials; nuclear poisons; and special fabrication techniques.

REACTOR FUEL PROCESSING. A Quarterly Technical Progress Review. Superintendent of Documents, U.S. Government Printing Office, Washington 25, D.C. Yearly subscription $2. Published quarterly. This publication is prepared by Argonne National Laboratory under the sponsorship of the USAEC. It reviews recent developments in all aspects of the fuel processing field—commercial, safety, metal preparation, waste disposal, and aqueous and nonaqueous processing.

General

Atoms for Peace, U.S.A. 1958, John F. Hogerton, Ed., GPO, 162 pp., $4.50, 1958. A pictorial survey, designed as a type of conducted tour of the growing industrial and government atomic energy installations in the United States.

Electronics and Nucleonics Dictionary, Nelson M. Cooke and John Markus, McGraw-Hill Book Company, Inc., New York, N.Y., 543 pp., $12.00, 1960.

Encyclopedic Dictionary of Electronics and Nuclear Engineering, Robert I. Sarbacher, Prentice-Hall, Inc., Englewood Cliffs, N.J., 1417 pp., $35.00, 1959.

A Glossary of Terms in Nuclear Science and Technology, The American Society of Mechanical Engineers, New York, N.Y., 195 pp., $5.00, 1957. Definitions approved by the American Standards Association.

Management of Nuclear Materials, Ralph F. Lumb, Ed., D. Van Nostrand Company, Inc., Princeton, N.J., 516 pp., $16.50, 1960. A source book that describes and discusses the acquiring, recording, evaluating, and presenting of quantity data necessary for the control of nuclear materials in all operations from mine to reactor. Processes are also described.

Modern Nuclear Technology; A Survey for Industry and Business, Mark M. Mills, Arthur T. Biehl, and Robert Mainhardt, Eds., McGraw-Hill Book Company, Inc., New York, N.Y., 336 pp., $9.50, 1960.

National Nuclear Energy Series, 51 vols., McGraw-Hill Book Company, Inc., New York, N.Y. A complete listing of the titles, availability and prices may be found in the Technical Books and Monographs booklet referenced in the AEC-INFORMATION SOURCES section below.

Pocket Encyclopedia of Atomic Energy, Frank Gaynor, Philosophical Library, New York, N.Y., 204 pp., $7.50, 1950. Brief definitions and explanations of terms used in the field of atomic energy; designed for the layman or the student with some familiarity with physics and higher mathematics.

Proceedings of the International Conference on the Peaceful Uses of Atomic Energy, Geneva, 1955, 16 vols., $130, 1956. *Proceedings of the Second International Conference on the Peaceful Uses of Atomic Energy, Geneva,* 1958, 33 vols., United Nations, New York, N.Y., $500, 1958. National Agency for International Publications, 801 Third Avenue, New York 22, N.Y. Definitive and unabridged text of the reports and proceedings. Individual volumes may be purchased separately.

Sourcebook on Atomic Energy, Samuel Glasstone, D. Van Nostrand Company, Inc., Princeton, N.J., 641 pp., $4.40, 1958. A basic text on the science and applications of atomic energy.

Who's Who in Atoms—1960 Edition, 2 Vols., A. W. Haslett, Vallancey Press, London, England £10, 10 shillings. An alphabetical listing of over 12,500 persons engaged throughout the world in atomic energy development, including biographical information on many entries.

World Nuclear Directory, A. W. Haslett, Ed., Vallancey Press, London, England, £7, 15 shillings, 1961. Lists over 2000 organizations having nuclear interests in more than 70 countries together with senior personnel. Separate sections are devoted to international bodies and nuclear periodicals.

Atomic Energy Commission—Information Sources

Proceedings of Technical Meetings, USAEC Division of Technical Information, 54 pp., no charge, 1961. Available from USAEC Division of Technical Information Extension, P.O. Box 62, Oak Ridge, Tenn.

Questions and Answers on U.S. Atomic Energy Commission Access Permits, USAEC Report TID-4558, 3rd Rev., 12 pp., no charge, 1961. Available from the USAEC Division of Technical Information Extension, P.O. Box 62, Oak Ridge, Tenn.

Special Sources of Information on Isotopes, USAEC Division of Isotopes Development, USAEC Report TID-4563, 3rd Rev., no charge, 1962. Available from the USAEC Division of Technical Information Extension, P.O. Box 62, Oak Ridge, Tenn.

Technical Books and Monographs, USAEC Division of Technical Information, 55 pp., no charge, 1962. Available from the USAEC Division of Technical Information Extension, P.O. Box 62, Oak Ridge, Tenn. Lists books and monographs published and being prepared under the sponsorship of the USAEC.

What's Available in the Atomic Energy Literature, USAEC Report TID-4550 (7th Rev.), 43 pp., no charge, 1962. Available from the USAEC Division of Technical Information Extension, P.O. Box 62, Oak Ridge, Tenn. This USAEC publication explains what unclassified atomic energy research information is available, how to locate and use this information, and how this information may be obtained.

Economics

Comments on Some Aspects of Nuclear Power Economics, L. E. Crean *et al.,* IAEA Review Series No. 9, National Agency for International Publications, New York, N.Y., 63 pp., $1.00, 1961.

Costs of Nuclear Power, AEC Office of Operations Analysis and Forecasting, USAEC Report TID-8531, Rev., 43 pp., OTS, $0.50, 1961.

Economics of Nuclear and Conventional Merchant Ships, David L. Conklin *et al.,* USAEC Report ASAE-S-5, 880 pp., GPO, $4.50, 1958.

Economics of Nuclear Power. A Bibliography of Selected Literature, William E. Bost, Comp., USAEC Report TID-3089, 89 pp., OTS, $2.00, 1960.

Introduction to Nuclear Power Costs, Arnold Rochman, Simmons-Boardman Co., New York, N.Y., 50 pp., $2.95, 1959.

Nuclear Energy and the U.S. Fuel Economy, 1955-1980, Perry D. Teitelbaum, National Planning Association, Washington, D.C., 187 pp., $3.00, 1958.

Nuclear Energy and World Fuel Prices, Cornelius J. Dwyer, National Planning Association, Washington, D.C., 74 pp., $1.25, 1958.

6th Report on Nuclear Power, in *Electrical World,* pp. 68-82, May 22, 1961, W. F. Felsen, Ed., McGraw-Hill Publishing Company, Inc., New York, N.Y., $0.50.

Status of the Application of Nuclear Reactors in the Process Industries as of 1961, AEC Division of Reactor Development, USAEC Report TID-8537, 138 pp., OTS, $2.50, 1961.

Survey of Initial Fuel Costs of Large U.S. Nuclear Power Stations, December 1958, Edison Electric Institute, New York, N.Y., 34 pp., 1959.

A Uniform Procedure for Use in the Evaluation of Nuclear Power Reactors, Atomic Industrial Forum, Inc., Report NP-10927, 44 pp., September 1959. Available from Atomic Industrial Forum, $1.50.

Education and Training

Catalogue of Courses on Nuclear Energy in OEEC Countries, European Nuclear Energy Agency and Organization for European Economic Cooperation, Paris, 138 pp., June 1960.

Education and Nuclear Energy, International Publishers Co., Inc., New York, N.Y., 62 pp., $1.00, 1960. Report of a five-day seminar jointly sponsored by IAEA and the UN's Educational, Scientific and Cultural Organization at the Nuclear Research Center, Saclay, France, concerning educational problems created by atomic energy.

Educational Programs and Facilities in Nuclear Science and Engineering, Oak Ridge Institute of Nuclear Studies, no charge, 119 pp., September 1962. Available from Oak Ridge Institute of Nuclear Studies, Oak Ridge, Tenn.

Energy Conversion

Direct Conversion of Heat to Electricity, Joseph Kaye and John A. Welsh, Ed., John Wiley & Sons, Inc., New York, N.Y., $8.75, 1960.

Direct Energy Conversion, Literature Abstracts, Naval Research Laboratory, Report AD-255294, 120 pp., OTS, $2.75, 1961.

Direct Energy Conversion Devices, A Literature Search, Henry D. Raleigh, Comp., USAEC Report TID-3561, 23 pp., OTS, $0.50, 1961.

Status of Direct Conversion Programs in the United States with Special Emphasis on Civilian Nuclear Power, William A. Robba, USAEC Report BNL-628, 13 pp., OTS, $0.50, 1960. Thermoelectric, thermionic, magnetohydrodynamic, and fuel cells are described along with the principles of each technique.

Energy Resources

An Analysis of the Current and Long-Term Availability of Uranium and Thorium Raw Materials for Atomic Energy Development, AEC Division of Raw Materials, USAEC Report TID-8201, 8 pp., OTS, $0.50, 1959.

The Atom and the Energy Revolution, Normal Lansdell, Philosophical Library, Inc., New York, N.Y., 200 pp., $6.00, 1959.

Energy from Uranium and Coal Reserves, Robert D. Nininger *et al.,* USAEC Report TID-8207, 11 pp., OTS, $0.50, 1960.

Energy in the American Economy, 1850-1975; An Economic Study of Its History and Prospects, Sam H. Schurr *et al.,* Johns Hopkins Press, Baltimore, Md., 174 pp., $12.50, 1960.

Energy Resources and Technology, Hearing before the Subcommittee on Automation and Energy Resources of the Joint Congressional Economic Committee on October 12-16, 1959, GPO, $1.25.

Fossil Fuels in the Future, Milton F. Searl, USAEC Report TID-8209, 66 pp., OTS, $0.75, 1960.

Nuclear Energy and the U.S. Fuel Economy, 1955-1980, Perry D. Teitelbaum, National Planning Association, Washington, D.C., 187 pp., $3.00, 1958.

Explosives, Peaceful Uses of

Frontiers in Atomic Energy Research, Hearings before the Subcommittee on Research and Development of the Joint Committee on Atomic Energy, 86th Congress of the United States, 382 pp., GPO, 1960.

Peaceful Uses of Nuclear Explosions, A Literature Search, Hugh E. Voress, Comp., USAEC Report TID-3522 (5th Rev.), 18 pp., OTS, $0.50, 1961.

Proceedings of the Second Plowshare Symposium, May 13-15, 1959, San Francisco, California, USAEC Reports UCRL-5675 through UCRL-5679, OTS, Part I: $3.00, Part II: $2.25, Part III: $2.25, Part IV: $2.50, Part V: $2.50. These five reports contain papers on the phenomenology of underground nuclear explosions, excavation, the recovery of power and isotopes from contained underground nuclear exploions, industrial uses of nuclear explosives in the fields of water resources, mining, chemical production, petroleum recovery and scientific applications of nuclear explosions in the fields of nuclear physics, seismology, meteorology and space.

Fuel Reprocessing

Chemical Processing of Irradiated Fuels from Power, Test and Research Reactors, Richland, Wash., October 20 and 21, 1959, USAEC Report TID-7583, 455 pp., OTS, $4.50, 1960. Contains proceedings of a 2-day symposium including papers from reprocessing sites at Hanford, Idaho Falls, Savannah River and Oak Ridge.

Chemical Processing of Nuclear Fuels, F. Martin and G. L. Miles, Academic Press, Inc., New York, N.Y., 242 pp., $7.50, 1958.

Chemical Processing of Reactor Fuels, John F. Flagg, Ed., Academic Press, Inc., New York, N.Y., 530 pp., $17.50, 1961.

Reactor Handbook (2nd Ed.), Vol. II, Fuel Reprocessing, S. M. Stoller and R. B. Richards, Eds., Interscience Publishers, Inc., New York, N.Y., 665 pp., 645 illus., $22.00, 1961.

Reprocessing of Irradiated Fission Reactor Fuel and Breeding Materials. An Annotated Bibliography of USAEC Report TID-3312, 121 pp., OTS, $2.75, 1958.

Selected Report Literature, James M. Jacobs, Comp., *Reprocessing of Irradiated Fission Reactor Fuel and Breeding Material,* James M. Jacobs, Comp., USAEC Report TID-3529, 2nd Rev., 87 pp., OTS, $2.00, 1961.

Fusion, Controlled

Controlled Thermonuclear Processes, A Literature Search, Raymond L. Scott and Sidney F. Lanier, Comps., USAEC Report TID-3557, 109 pp., OTS, $0.75, 1960.

Controlled Thermonuclear Reactions, Samuel Glasstone and Ralph H. Lovberg, D. Van Nostrand Co., Inc., Princeton, N.J., 539 pp., $5.60, 1960. An introduction to theory and experimentation for physicists and engineers who are planning to enter this field of research.

Frontiers in Atomic Energy Research, Hearings before the Subcommittee on Research and Development of the Joint Committee on Atomic Energy, 86th Congress of the United States, GPO, 1960.

Glossary of Terms Frequently Used in Plasma Physics, David R. Whitehouse, Comp., American Institute of Physics, New York, N.Y., 30 pp., May 1960.

Nuclear Fusion, William P. Allis, Ed., D. Van Nostrand Company, Inc., Princeton, N.J., 488 pp., $12.50, 1960.

Project Sherwood—The U.S. Program in Controlled Fusion, Amasa S. Bishop, Addison-Wesley Publishing Company, Inc., Reading, Mass., 216 pp., 58 illus., $7.50, 1958; Anchor Books, Doubleday & Co., Garden City, N.Y., 227 pp., 58 illus., $1.45, 1960.

Industrial Information Sources

1959 Atomic Industry Directory of Products, Equipment, and Services, Atomic Industrial Forum, Inc., New York, N.Y., 130 pp., $2.50, 1959.

Atoms for Industry World Survey, Gerald Wendt, Atomic Industrial Forum, Inc., New York, N.Y., 160 pp., 1960.

Business Statistics on the Atomic Industry, 1954-1958, Atomic Industrial Forum, Inc., New York, N.Y., 36 pp., $3.50, 1960.

A Growth Survey of the Atomic Industry, 1958-1968, Frederick H. Warren *et al.*, Atomic Industrial Forum, Inc., New York, N.Y., 84 pp., $25.00, 1958.

Handbook of the Atomic Energy Industry, Sidney Jefferson, Ed., George Newnes, Ltd., London, 178 pp., 1958.

International Nucleonics Buyers' Guide and Reference Data Issue, compiled by the staff of Nucleonics (see Periodicals section). Issued yearly as issue No. 11, $2.00. The 1962 issue includes an alphabetical listing of nucleonic products, materials and services under approximately 540 product categories, the names and addresses of more than 2000 companies manufacturing nuclear products and a 46-page manual of technical reference data.

Modern Nuclear Technology: A Survey for Industry and Business, Mark M. Mills, Arthur T. Biehl, and Robert Mainhardt, Eds., McGraw-Hill Book Company, Inc., New York, N.Y., 336 pp., $9.50, 1960.

Nuclear Frontiers—1960, proceedings of the 1960 Annual Conference of Atomic Industrial Forum held at San Francisco, December 14-16, 1960. Edwin Wiggin, Ed., Atomic Industrial Forum, Inc., New York, N.Y., 330 pp., $10.00, 1961.

International Information Sources

Atomic Energy of Canada Limited Annual Report 1959-60, The Queen's Printer and Controller of Stationery, Report AECL-1067, 37 pp., $0.25, 1960.

Atomic Energy in the Communist Bloc, G. A. Modelski, Melbourne University Press, New York, N.Y.; Cambridge University Press, New York, N.Y., 226 pp., $5.50, 1959.

Atomic Energy in the German Federal Republic, Nuclear Power, 6(59): 58-97 (March 1961).

Atomic Energy in the Soviet Union, Arnold Kramish, Stanford University Press, Stanford, Calif., 232 pp., $4.75, 1959.

Background Material for the Review of the International Atomic Policies and Programs of the United States, Robert McKinney, in Report to the Joint Committee on Atomic Energy, 86th Congress of the United States, 2nd Session, October 1960, GPO, 5 vols., 2080 pp.

Basic Assumption for Nuclear Power Estimates in Europe, European Nuclear Energy Agency of the OEEC; available from OEEC Mission Publications Office, Washington, D.C. (no charge), 32 pp., 1960.

France and the Atom. Ambassade de France Service de Presse et d'Information, 972 Fifth Avenue, New York, N.Y., no charge, 1962.

A Five-year Plan for the Development of Nuclear Research in Italy, National Committee for Nuclear Research, Rome, Italy, 101 pp., 1958.

The Industrial Challenge of Nuclear Energy, III, Stresa Conference, Paris, Organization for European Economic Cooperation, 288 pp., 1959.

The Nuclear Energy Industry of the United Kingdom, U.K. Atomic Energy Authority, London, S.W.1., 60 pp., 1958.

The Prospect for Nuclear Power in Pakistan, Maurice D. Kilbridge, National Planning Association, Washington, D.C., 59 pp., 1958.

Prospects for Nuclear Power in Finland, Joint Study by the IAEA and the Finnish Atomic Energy Commission, International Atomic Energy Agency, Kärntner Ring, Vienna 1, Austria, 96 pp., 1960 (no charge).

The Prospects of Nuclear Power in Puerto Rico, Alvin Mayne, National Planning Association, Washington, D.C., 87 pp., 1958.

United Kingdom Atomic Energy Authority Eight. Annual Report 1961-62, Her Majesty's Stationery Office. 87 pp., 6s. 6d., 1962.

Laws, Regulations, and Insurance

Atomic Energy and Law: International Symposium, Jaro Mayda, Ed., University of Puerto Rico, 258 pp., 1960.

The Atomic Energy Commission and Regulating Nuclear Facilities, William H. Berman and Lee M. Hydemann, University of Michigan Press, Ann Arbor, Mich., 336 pp., $6.00, 1961.

Atomic Energy Legislation Through 86th Congress, 2d Session, in Report to the Joint Committee on Atomic Energy, 86th Congress of the United States, 2d Session, 1961, 532 pp., GPO, $0.65.

Atoms and the Law, E. B. Stason *et al.,* University of Michigan Press, Ann Arbor, Mich., 1512 pp., $15.00, 1959. Covers tort liability and radiation injuries; workmen's compensation and radiation injuries; state regulation of atomic energy; federal regulatory and administrative limitations upon atomic activities; and international control of atomic energy.

Code of Federal Regulations, Titles 10-13, revised as of January 1, 1959, 603 pp., GPO, basic volume $5.50; pocket parts $0.75. Contains a codification of regulations issued pursuant to the Atomic Energy Act. The basic volume is supplemented annually by the Cumulative Pocket Supplement. For changes in regulations issued on or after January 1 of each year, see the daily issues of the *Federal Register.*

Convention on Third Party Liability in the Field of Nuclear Energy Held in Paris on July 29, 1960, Organization for European Economic Cooperation and European Nuclear Energy Agency, 67 pp., 1960.

Federal and State Responsibilities for Radiation Protection, the Need for Federal Legislation: A Study, William H. Berman and Lee M. Hydemann, University of Michigan Press, Ann Arbor, Mich., 120 pp., $2.00, 1959.

Improving the AEC Regulatory Process, in Report to the Joint Committee on Atomic Energy, 87th Congress of the United States, 1st Session, March 1961, GPO, Vols. 1-2, $3.50.

International Control of Nuclear Maritime Activities, Lee M. Hydemann and William H. Berman, University of Michigan Press, Ann Arbor, Mich., 384 pp., 1960.

International Problems of Financial Protection Against Nuclear Risk, R. E. Eicholz *et al.,* Atomic Industrial Forum, Inc., New York, N.Y., 95 pp., $6.00, 1959.

Law and Administration, Herbert S. Marks, Ed., in Progress in Nuclear Energy, Series X, Vol. I, Pergamon Press, New York, N.Y., 994 pp., $26.50, 1958.

Legislative History of the Atomic Energy Act of 1954 (Public Law 703, 83rd Congress), Madeleine W. Losee, Comp., GPO, 3 vols., $20.00, 1955.

Selected Materials on Federal-State Cooperation in the Atomic Energy Field, in Report to the Joint Committee on Atomic Energy, 86th Congress of the United States, 1st Session, GPO, 520 pp., $1.50, 1959.

Radiation Applications

18 Questions and Answers about Radiation, prepared by the AEC, 51 pp., GPO, $0.25, 1960.

Large Radiation Sources in Industry, Proceedings of a five-day conference sponsored by the IAEA in Warsaw on September 8-12, 1959; two volumes, International Publishers Co., Inc., N.Y.

National Food Irradiation Research Program, Hearing before the Subcommittee on Research and Development of the Joint Committee on Atomic Energy, 86th Congress of the United States, 2d Session, March 31, 1960, GPO, 2 parts.

Nuclear Radiation Engineering, An Introduction, Francis William Hutchinson, Ronald Press, New York, N.Y., 155 pp., $6.00, 1960.

Radiation: A Tool for Industry, Arthur D. Little, Inc., Comp., USAEC Report ALI-52, 414 pp., OTS, $5.50, 1959.

Radiation Preservation of Selected Fruits and Vegetables, An Analysis of R & D Programming and Market Factors, Stanford Research Institute, USAEC Report SRIA-30, 234 pp., OTS, $3.00, 1961.

Radiation Uses in Industry and Science, L. E. Brownell, 432 pp., GPO, $2.50, 1961.

Radiosterilization of Edible Fish, Mollusks, and Crustaceans, A Literature Search, Theodore F. Davis, Comp., USAEC Report TID-3565, 14 pp., OTS, $0.50, 1961.

Technology and Applications of Large Fission Product Beta Sources, Joseph Silverman *et al.,* USAEC Report NYO-2503, 110 pp., OTS, $2.50, 1961.

Utilization of Gross Fission Products. A Bibliography of Unclassified Report Literature, Gifford A. Young, Comp., USAEC Report TID-3046, 32 pp., OTS, $0.25, 1954; *Utilization of Fission Products,* Gifford A. Young and Robert E. Allen, Comps., USAEC Report TID-3046(Suppl. 1), 55 pp., OTS, $0.40, 1955; *Radiation Application and Fission Product Utilization,* Gifford A. Young, Comp., USAEC Report TID-3046 (Suppl. 2), 187 pp., OTS, $1.75, 1959.

Radiation Protection

Background Material for the Development of Radiation Protection Standards, A Staff Report of the Federal Radiation Council, GPO, $0.30, 1960.

The Biological Effects of Atomic Radiation, National Academy of Sciences, Report A/AC.82/G/L.358, 100 pp., August 18, 1960; *A Report to the Public on the Biological Effects of Atomic Radiation,* National Academy of Sciences, Report A/AC.82/G/L.358 (Add. 1), 21 pp., August 22, 1960.

18 Questions and Answers about Radiation, prepared by the AEC, 51 pp., GPO, $0.25, 1960.

General Handbook for Radiation Monitoring, Jerome E. Dummer, Jr., Ed., USAEC Report LA-1835 (3rd Ed.), 180 pp., GPO, $0.65, 1958.

Living with Radiation, Part 1, Fundamentals, Francis L. Brannigan, pp. 1-66, GPO, $0.45, 1959; *Part 2, Fire Service Problems,* Francis L. Brannigan and George S. Miles, pp. 67-199, GPO, $1.00, 1959.

Radiation Protection Criteria and Standards: Their Basis and Use, Index to Hearings and Selected Materials of May 1960, Special Subcommittee on Radiation of the Joint Committee on Atomic Energy, Congress of the United States, 97 pp., GPO, $0.30, June 1961.

Radiation Protection Standards, A Literature Search, William E. Bost, Comp., USAEC Report TID-3551 (Rev. 1), 45 pp., OTS, $1.00, 1961.

Radiological Health Handbook, Public Health Service, Report PB-121784R, 468 pp., Revised September 1960, OTS, $3.75.

Safe Handling of Radioisotopes, International Atomic Energy Agency, Vienna, Austria (available free of charge in English, French, Russian, and Spanish from the International Atomic Energy Agency).

Selected Materials on Radiation Protection Criteria and Standards: Their Basis and Use, Joint Committee on Atomic Energy, Congress of the United States, 1261 pp., GPO, May 1960.

Suggested Radiation Protection Regulations: Draft of Revision to Appendix B, Handbook 61, Health Physics, Vol. 5, Nos. 1-2, pp. 1-19, April 1961.

Radioactive Fallout

Atmospheric Radioactivity and Fallout Research, AEC Division of Biology and Medicine, USAEC Report TID-12616, 76 pp., OTS, $0.75, 1961.

Fallout from Nuclear Weapons Tests, Hearings before the Special Subcommittee on Radiation of the Joint Committee on Atomic Energy, 86th Congress of the United States, Vols. 1-3, GPO, 1959.

Radioactive Fallout—A Two-year Summary Report, Charles L. Dunham, USAEC Report TID-5550, 112 pp., OTS, $1.25, 1959.

Radioactive Fallout, A Bibliography of the World's Literature, William E. Bost *et al.,* Comps., USAEC Report TID-3086, 196 pp., OTS, $2.75, 1961.

Radioactive Waste Disposal

Disposal of Radioactive Wastes, proceedings of a conference sponsored by the IAEA in Monaco on Nov. 16-21, 1959, National Agency for International Publications, Inc., Vol. 1, 607 pp., $6.00; Vol. 2, 575 pp., $6.00, 1960.

Industrial Radioactive Waste Disposal, hearings of the Joint Committee on Atomic Energy Special Subcommittee on Radiation, January 28-30 and February 2-3, 1959, GPO, 4 vols.; Vol. 1, $3.00; Vol. 2, $2.25; Vol. 3, $2.00; Vo. 4, $1.50.

Radioactive Waste Disposal Into the Sea, Safety Series No. 5 of the IAEA, National Agency for International Publications, Inc., 174 pp., $2.50, 1961.

Radioactive Waste Handling in the Nuclear Power Industry, Pickard-Warren-Lowe Associates, EEI Publication No. 60-46, Edison Electric Institute, New York, N.Y., 90 pp., $5.00, 1960.

Radioactive Waste Processing and Disposal, A Literature Search, Theodore F. Davis, Comp., USAEC Report TID-3555, 98 pp., OTS, $2.25, 1960.

Radioisotopes in Agriculture and Medicine

Glossary of Words and Phrases used in Radiology and Nuclear Medicine, Lewis E. Etter, Charles C. Thomas Publisher, Springfield, Ill., 203 pp., 1960.

A Manual for Nuclear Medicine, Edward R. King and T. G. Mitchell, Charles C. Thomas Publisher, Springfield, Ill., 406 pp., 1961.

The Practice of Nuclear Medicine, William H. Blahd, Franz K. Bauer, and Benedict Mason, Charles C. Thomas Publisher, Springfield, Ill., 407 pp., 1958.

Radioisotope Teletherapy Equipment—International Directory, International Atomic Energy Agency, International Publishers Co., Inc., New York, N.Y., 121 pp., $2.00, 1959.

Radioisotopes at Work for Agriculture, A. Gerlof Homan and Richard R. Tarrice, USAEC Report SRIA-9, 205 pp., OTS, $3.50, 1959.

Radioisotopes in Medicine, Richard R. Tarrice and Mark S. Blumberg, USAEC Report SRIA-13, 187 pp., OTS, $3.00, 1959.

Radioisotopes in Science and Industry, AEC, Washington, D.C., 188 pp., GPO, $1.25, 1960.

Radioisotopes in Industry

Atoms for Industry World Survey, Gerald Wendt, Atomic Industrial Forum, Inc., New York, N.Y., 160 pp., 1960.

Industrial Utilization of Radioisotopes, 1946-1956, Atomic Industrial Forum, Inc., New York, N.Y., 87 pp., $2.50, 1956.

Radioisotope Applications Engineering, Jerome Kohl, Rene D. Zentner, and Herbert R. Lukens, D. Van Nostrand Co., Inc., Princeton, N.J., 562 pp., $16.50, 1961.

Radioisotopes for Industry, Robert S. Rochlin and Warner W. Schultz, Reinhold Publishing Corporation, New York, N.Y., 190 pp., $4.75, 1959.

Radioisotopes in Industry Training Program (Vols. 1 and 2), John P. Danforth and Robert P. Stapp, Eds., 835 pp., OTS, $10.00, 1959.

Radioisotopes in Science and Industry, AEC Washington, D.C., 188 pp., GPO, $1.25, 1960.

Radioisotopes in World Industry: Abstracts of Selected Foreign Literature, USAEC Report TID-6613, AEC Office of Isotopes Development, 146 pp., OTS, $2.50, 1961; USAEC Report TID-6613(Suppl. 1), Science and Technology Division, Library of Congress, 125 pp., OTS, $2.50, 1961.

Shipping, Handling and Storage of Radioactive Materials. A Literature Search, Theodore F. Davis, Comp., USAEC Report TID-3552 (Rev.), 46 pp., OTS, $1.00, 1961.

Special Sources of Information on Isotopes, AEC Office of Isotopes Development, USAEC Report TID-4563, 2nd Rev., 60 pp., 1960; available from Division of Technical Information Extension, Oak Ridge, Tenn. (no charge).

Reactors—Civilian Power

Civilian Power Reactor Program. Index to Ten-year Civilian Power Reactor Program (TID-8518 Series), AEC, Washington, D.C., 13 pp., GPO, $0.15, 1961.

Directory of Nuclear Reactors, Vol. I, Power Reactors, International Atomic Energy Agency, International Publishers Co., Inc., New York, N.Y., 214 pp., $3.50, 1959.

Fact Sheets on U.S. Nuclear Power Projects, 3rd Ed. Electric Companies Public Information Program, New York, N.Y., 52 pp., $1.00, 1961.

Handbook of the Atomic Energy Industry, Sidney Jefferson, Ed., George Newnes, Ltd., London, 278 pp., 35 shillings, 1958.

Nuclear Reactor Plant Data, Vol. 1, Power Reactors, 2nd Ed., American Society of Mechanical Engineers, New York, N.Y., 128 pp., 1959.

Nuclear Reactors Built, Being Built, or Planned in the United States as of December 31, 1961, AEC Division of Technical Information, USAEC Report TID-8200, 5th Rev., 20 pp.; available from AEC Division of Technical Information Extension, Oak Ridge, Tenn. (no charge).

Selected Reactors of the Power Reactor Demonstration Program. A Literature Search, James M. Jacobs, Comp., USAEC Report TID-3556, 35 pp., OTS, $0.75, 1960.

Reactors—General

Boiling Water Reactors, Andrew W. Kramer, Addison-Wesley Publishing Company, Inc., Reading, Mass., 572 pp., $8.50, 1958.

Breeder Reactors, Alvin M. Weinberg, *Scientific American,* 202(1): 82-94 (January 1960).

Control of Nuclear Reactors and Power Plants, Mortimer A. Schultz, McGraw-Hill Book Company, Inc., New York, N.Y., 462 pp., $12.50, 1961.

Elements of Nuclear Engineering, Glenn Murphy, John Wiley & Sons, Inc., New York, N.Y., 213 pp., $7.50, 1961.

The Engineering Design of Power Reactors, Nunzio J. Palladino and Harold L. Davis, *Nucleonics,* 18(6): 85-116 (June 1960); reprints available.

Fluid Fuel Reactors, James A. Lane, H. G. MacPherson, and Frank Maslan, Eds., Addison-Wesley Publishing Company, Inc., Reading, Mass., 979 pp., $11.50, 1958.

Gas-Cooled Reactors, proceedings of a two-day conference jointly sponsored by The Franklin Institute and the Delaware Valley Section of the American Nuclear Society in Philadelphia on February 10-11, 1960, Monograph No. 7, The Franklin Institute of the State of Pennsylvania, 20th and Parkway, Philadelphia, Pa., 349 pp., $5.00, 1960.

Handbook of Nuclear Safety, Hugh K. Clark, USAEC Report DP-532, 150 pp., OTS, $2.75, 1961.

Nuclear Reactor Containment Buildings and Pressure Vessels, proceedings of a symposium sponsored by the Royal College of Science and Technology, Glasgow, Scotland, May 17-20, Butterworth, Inc., Washington, D.C., 1960.

Nuclear Reactor Optimization, P. H. Margen, Simmons-Boardman Company, New York, N.Y., 81 pp., 1960.

Power Reactor Technology, James K. Pickard, Frederick H. Warren, and William W. Lowe, Eds., D. Van Nostrand Company, Inc., Princeton, N.J., 416 pp., $11.25, 1961.

Reactor Safety, A Literature Search, Richard J. Smith, Comp., USAEC Report TID-3525, Rev. 2, 72 pp., September 1960, OTS, $1.75.

Research and Development in Reactor Safety, B. John Garrick, Ed., USAEC Report M-7193, 69 pp., GPO, $0.65, 1959.

The Shippingport Pressurized Water Reactor, AEC Division of Reactor Development, Westinghouse Electric Corporation, and Duquesne Light Company, Addison-Wesley Publishing Company, Inc., Reading, Mass., 600 pp., $9.50, 1958.

Sodium Graphite Reactors, Chauncey Starr and Robert W. Dickinson, Addison-Wesley Publishing Company, Inc., Reading, Mass., 304 pp., $6.50, 1958.

Solid Fuel Reactors, Joseph R. Dietrich and Walter H. Zinn, Comps., Addison-Wesley Publishing Company, Inc., Reading, Mass., 864 pp., $9.50, 1958.

Reactors—Maritime

Bibliography on Nuclear Propulsion for Ships, B. Yates, Comp., Report DEG-Inf. Ser. 242, Her Majesty's Stationery Office, London, 148 pp., 10 shillings, 1960.

Economics of Nuclear and Conventional Merchant Ships, David L. Conklin *et al.,* USAEC Report ASAE-S-5, 880 pp., June 30, 1958, GPO, $4.50.

International Control of Nuclear Maritime Activities, Lee M. Hydemann and William H. Berman, University of Michigan Press, Ann Arbor, Mich., 384 pp., $6.00, 1960.

Nuclear Propulsion for Merchant Ships, A. W. Kramer, 600 pp., GPO, $2.25, 1962.

Potential Applications of Nuclear Energy in a Maritime Environment, Stanford Research Institute, USAEC Report SRIA-7, 194 pp., August 1959, OTS, $3.50.

Report of the Committee on the Safety of Nuclear-Powered Merchant Ships, Her Majesty's Stationery Office, London.

The Role of Nuclear Propulsion in Merchant Shipping, proceedings of a meeting held under the auspices of Atomic Industrial Forum, Inc., New York, N.Y.

Reactors—Military and Space

Aircraft Nuclear Propulsion Program, hearing before the Subcommittee on Research and Development of the Joint Committee on Atomic Energy, 86th Congress of the United States, 1st Session, GPO, 1959.

Nuclear Energy in Space, Nucleonics, 14(4): 53-100 (April 1961).

Nuclear-Energy Power Sources, George H. Ogburn, Jr., USAEC Report TID-6612, 18 pp., OTS, $0.50, 1961.

Nuclear Propulsion, M. W. Thiring, Ed., Butterworth & Co., Ltd., London, 300 pp., 1960.

Nuclear Rocket Propulsion, R. W. Bussard, Comp., USAEC Report LAMS-2519, 22 pp., OTS, $0.50, 1961.

The Practical Application of Space Nuclear Power in the 1960's, J. R. Wetch *et al.,* USAEC Report TID-6312, 50 pp., OTS, $1.25, 1961.

Review of Naval Reactor Program and Admiral Rickover Award, Hearings before the Joint Committee on Atomic Energy, 86th Congress of the United States, 1st Session, April 11 and 15, 1959, GPO.

Space Power System, Nathan W. Snyder, Ed., Academic Press, Inc., New York, N.Y., 632 pp., $6.00, 1961.

Reactors—Process Heat

Nuclear Process Heat in Industry, George Pearazich, National Planning Association, Washington, D.C., 44 pp., 1958.

Status of the Application of Nuclear Reactors in the Process Industries as of 1961, AEC Division of Reactor Development, USAEC Report TID-8537, 138 pp., OTS, $2.50, 1961.

Study of Conventional Process Steam Plants Capital and Steam Production Costs 125,000 Pounds Per Hour (40 Mwt) for United States Atomic Energy Commission, San Francisco Operations Office, Berkeley, California, Kaiser Engineers, Division of Henry J. Kaiser Company, USAEC Report TID-8534, 38 pp., OTS, $1.00, 1960.

Reactors—Research and Test

Directory of Nuclear Reactors, Vol. II, Research, Test and Experimental Reactors, International Atomic Energy Agency, 348 pp., 1959; available from National Agency for International Publications, New York, N.Y.

The Role of Nuclear Reactors in University Research Programs, National Science Foundation, Report NSF-60-39, 82 pp., 1960.

U.S. Research Reactor Operation and Use, Joel W. Chastain, Jr., Ed., Addison-Wesley Publishing Company, Inc., Reading, Mass., 366 pp., $7.00, 1958.

Test Reactors Meeting for Industry, Compilation of papers presented at a 3-day conference on this subject at the National Reactor Testing Station on May 13-15, 1959, USAEC Report IDO-16520, 339 pp., OTS, $5.00, 1959.

Research Programs

Applications of Radioisotopes and Radiation in the Life Sciences, Hearings before the Subcommittee on Research, Development, and Radiation of the Joint Committee on Atomic Energy, 87th Congress of the United States, 1st Session, March 27, 28, 29, and 30, 1961, GPO.

Atomic Energy Research in the Life and Physical Sciences, AEC, Washington, D.C., 175 pp., GPO, $1.25, 1961.

The Future Role of the Atomic Energy Commission Laboratories, Joint Committee on Atomic Energy, Congress of the United States, October 1960, GPO.

Genetics Research Program of the Division of Biology and Medicine, AEC Division of Biology and Medicine, USAEC Report TID-4041, 120 pp., OTS, $1.25, 1960.

Marine Sciences Research, AEC Division of Biology and Medicine, USAEC Report TID-4040, 42 pp., OTS, $0.50, 1960.

Offsite Ecological Research of the Division of Biology and Medicine—Terrestrial and Freshwater, AEC Division of Biology and Medicine, USAEC Report TID-13358, 146 pp., OTS, $2.50, 1961.

Summaries of the AEC Basic Research Programs in Metallurgy, Solid State Physics and Ceramics, R. J. Allio, Ed., USAEC Report TID-4005, Pt. 1, 6th Ed., 270 pp., OTS, $2.75, 1961.

Summaries of Fuels and Materials Development Programs, AEC Division of Reactor Development, USAEC Report TID-6506(Suppl.), 220 pp., OTS, $3.00, 1961.

Summaries of Physical Research in Physics and Mathematics, J. D. Saltzman, Ed., USAEC Report TID-4005, Pts. 3 and 4, 115 pp., OTS, $1.00, 1961.

Textbooks and Reference Works

Introduction to Nuclear Engineering, 2nd Ed., Raymond L. Murray, Prentice-Hall, Inc., Englewood Cliffs, N.J., 384 pp., 1961.

Materials for Nuclear Reactors, Bernard Kopelman, Ed., McGraw-Hill Book Company, Inc., New York, N.Y., 411 pp., $12.00, 1959.

Nuclear Engineering, Gilbert Cohen and Pierre Treille (translated by Gilbert B. Melese), Boston, Allyn & Bacon, Inc., 394 pp., 1961.

Nuclear Engineering Handbook, Harold Etherington, Ed., First Edition, McGraw-Hill Book Company, Inc., New York, N.Y., 1872 pp., $25.00, 1958.

Nuclear Safety Guide, 1961, Revised by Subcommittee 8 of the American Standards Association Sectional Committee N6 and Project 8 of the American Nuclear Society Standards Committee, Goodyear Atomic Corp., USAEC Report TID-7016, Rev. 1, 42 pp., OTS, $0.50, 1961.

Nuclear Reactor Engineering, Samuel Glasstone, D. Van Nostrand Company, Inc., New York, N.Y., 830 pp., approx. $9.00, 1963. A revision of the widely used *Principles of Nuclear Reactor Engineering.*

Radiation Hygiene Handbook, Hanson Blatz, Ed., McGraw-Hill Book Co., Inc., New York, N.Y., 947 pp., $27.50, 1959.

Reactor Handbook, 2nd Ed., Interscience Publishers, Inc., New York, N.Y., Vol. I, Materials, C. R. Tipton, Jr., Ed., 1207 pp., 1090 illus., $36.50, 1960; Vol. II, Fuel Reprocessing, S. M. Stoller and R. B. Richards, Eds., 665 pp., 645 illus., $22.00, 1961; Vol. III, Part A, Physics, H. Soodak, Ed., and Part B, Shielding, E. P. Blizard, and Lorraine S. Abbott, Eds., 1962; Vol. IV, Engineering, Stuart McLain and John H. Martens, Eds., 1963.

Uranium, Thorium, and Plutonium

Isotope Separation by Gaseous Diffusion and Centrifugation, A Literature Search, James M. Jacobs, Comp., USAEC Report TID-3554, 20 pp., OTS, $0.50, 1960.

The Metal Plutonium, A. S. Coffinberry and W. N. Miner, Eds., University of Chicago Press, Chicago, Ill., 446 pp., $9.50, 1961.

Physical Metallurgy of Uranium, A. N. Holden, Addison-Wesley Publishing Company, Inc., Reading, Mass., 272 pp., $5.75, 1958.

Potential Nonnuclear Uses of Depleted Uranium, Harlan W. Nelson and Ronald L. Carmichael, USAEC Report TID-8203, 61 pp., OTS, $0.75, 1960.

Prospecting for Uranium, revised January 1957, AEC and U.S. Geological Survey, Washington, D.C., 217 pp., GPO, $0.75, 1957.

Thorium Production Technology, F. L. Cuthbert, Addison-Wesley Publishing Company, Inc., Reading, Mass., 303 pp., $5.50, 1958.

Uranium Dioxide: Properties and Nuclear Applications, J. Belle, Ed., 739 pp., GPO, $2.50, 1961.

Uranium Ore Processing, John W. Clegg and Dennis D. Foley, Eds., Addison-Wesley Publishing Company, Inc., Reading, Mass., 448 pp., $8.50, 1958.

Uranium Production Technology, Charles D. Harrington and Archie E. Ruehle, Eds., D. Van Nostrand Company, Inc., Princeton, N.J., 579 pp., $17.50, 1959.

Weapons, Nuclear

Atomic Energy for Military Purposes, H. D. Smyth, Princeton University Press, Princeton, N.J., 182 pp., 1945.

The Effects of Nuclear Weapons, Samuel Glasstone, Ed., GPO, $3.00, 1962.

Principles of Guided Missiles and Nuclear Weapons, U.S. Navy Training Publications Center, Washington, D.C., Report NAVPERS-10784, 284 pp., GPO, $2.00, 1959.

Technical Aspects of Detection and Inspection Controls of a Nuclear Weapons Test Ban: Summary-Analysis of Hearing April 19, 20, 21, and 22, 1960, Joint Committee on Atomic Energy, Congress of the United States, Parts 1 and 2, 951 pp., GPO, 1960.

Appendix C

DEPOSITORY LIBRARIES OF UNCLASSIFIED U.S. ATOMIC ENERGY COMMISSION LITERATURE

U.S.

ALABAMA

Auburn, Auburn University
Birmingham, Birmingham Public Library

ARIZONA

Tucson, University of Arizona

ARKANSAS

Fayetteville, University of Arkansas

CALIFORNIA

Berkeley, University of California General Library
Los Angeles, University of California Library
Menlo Park, Stanford Research Institute
San Diego, San Diego Public Library

COLORADO

Boulder, the University of Colorado
Denver, The Public Library

CONNECTICUT

New Haven, Yale University Library

DELAWARE

Newark, University of Delaware Library

DISTRICT OF COLUMBIA

Washington, Library of Congress

FLORIDA

Coral Gables, University of Miami Library
Gainesville, University of Florida Library

GEORGIA

Atlanta, Georgia Institute of Technology Library

HAWAII

Honolulu, University of Hawaii

ILLINOIS

Chicago, John Crerar Library
Chicago, University of Chicago Library
Evanston, Northwestern University Library
Urbana, University of Illinois Library

INDIANA

Indianapolis, Indianapolis Public Library
Lafayette, Purdue University Library

IOWA

Ames, Iowa State University

KANSAS

Manhattan, Kansas State University

KENTUCKY

Lexington, University of Kentucky
Louisville, University of Louisville Library

LOUISIANA

Baton Rouge, Louisiana State University Library
New Orleans, Tulane University Library

MARYLAND

Baltimore, The Johns Hopkins University Library
College Park, University of Maryland Engineering and Physical Sciences Library

MASSACHUSETTS

Cambridge, Harvard University Library
Cambridge, Massachusetts Institute of Technology Library

MICHIGAN

Ann Arbor, University of Michigan Library
Detroit, Detroit Public Library

MINNESOTA

Minneapolis, University of Minnesota Library

MISSOURI

Kansas City, Linda Hall Library
Rolla, University of Missouri School of Mines and Metallurgy Library
St. Louis, Washington University Library

MONTANA

Bozeman, Montana State College Library

NEVADA

Reno, University of Nevada Library

NEW JERSEY

Princeton, Princeton University Library

NEW MEXICO

Albuquerque, University of New Mexico Library

NEW YORK

Buffalo, University of Buffalo, Lockwood Memorial Library
Ithaca, Cornell University Library
New York, Atomic Industrial Forum
New York, Columbia University Library
New York, New York Public Library
Rochester, University of Rochester Library
Schenectady, Union College Library
Syracuse, Syracuse University
Troy, Rensselaer Polytechnic Institute Library

NORTH CAROLINA

Charlotte, Charlotte and Mecklenburg County Public Library
Durham, Duke University Library
Raleigh, North Carolina State College Library

NORTH DAKOTA

Grand Forks, University of North Dakota

OHIO

Cincinnati, University of Cincinnati Library
Cleveland, Cleveland Public Library
Columbus, Ohio State University Library
Toledo, University of Toledo Library
Youngstown, Youngstown University Library

OKLAHOMA

Stillwater, Oklahoma State University Library

OREGON

Corvallis, Oregon State College Library
Portland, Reed College

PENNSYLVANIA

Philadelphia, University of Pennsylvania Library
Pittsburgh, Carnegie Library of Pittsburgh
University Park, Pennsylvania State University, Pattee Library

PUERTO RICO

Rio Piedras, University of Puerto Rico Main Library

RHODE ISLAND

Providence, Brown University

SOUTH CAROLINA

Columbia, University of South Carolina, McKissick Memorial Library

TENNESSEE

Knoxville, University of Tennessee Library
Memphis, Public Library
Nashville, Joint University Libraries
Oak Ridge, Oak Ridge Institute of Nuclear Studies

TEXAS

Austin, University of Texas Library
College Station, Agricultural and Mechanical College of Texas Library
Dallas, Southern Methodist University
Houston, Rice Institute
San Antonio, San Antonio Public Library

UTAH

Salt Lake City, University of Utah Library

VIRGINIA

Blacksburg, Virginia Polytechnic Institute
Charlottesville, University of Virginia, Alderman Library

WASHINGTON

Pullman, Washington State University Library
Seattle, University of Washington Library

WEST VIRGINIA

Morgantown, West Virginia University Library

WISCONSIN

Madison, University of Wisconsin Library
Milwaukee, Milwaukee Public Library

WYOMING

Laramie, University of Wyoming Library

Foreign

ARGENTINA

Buenos Aires, Comisión Nacional de Energía Atómica

AUSTRALIA

Canberra, Australian National Library
Sutherland, New South Wales, Australian Atomic Energy Commission

AUSTRIA

Vienna, Zentral Bibliothek der Physikalischen Institute der Universität

BELGIUM

Mol-Donk, Centre d'Etude de l'Energie Nucleaire

BOLIVIA

La Paz, Comisión National de Energía Nuclear

BRAZIL

Rio de Janeiro, Instituto Brasileiro de Bibliografia e Documentaçao
São Paulo, Instituto de Energia Atomica, Cidade Universitaria São Paulo

BURMA

Rangoon, Union of Burma Applied Research Institute, Atomic Energy Center Library

CANADA

Hamilton, McMaster University
Ottawa, National Research Council Library
Vancouver, University of British Columbia

CEYLON

Colombo, University of Ceylon

CHILE

Santiago, Instituto de Fisica y Matematicas, Universidad de Chile

CHINA

Hsinchu, Formosa, National Tsing Hua University Library

COLOMBIA

Bogotá, Instituto De Asuntos Nucleares

COSTA RICA

San Pedro, University of Costa Rica Library

DENMARK

Risö, Danish Atomic Energy Commission

DOMINICAN REPUBLIC

Santo Domingo, National Palace

ECUADOR

Quito, Escuela Politécnica Nacional

EGYPT

Cairo, Atomic Energy Commission

EL SALVADOR

San Salvador, Universidad de El Salvador, Biblioteca de Energia Nuclear

ENGLAND

Birmingham, Central Library
Bristol, Central Library
Kingston upon Hull, Central Library
Leeds, Central Library
Liverpool, Central Library
London, Central Library, Acton
London, Science Museum Library, South Kensington
Manchester, Central Library
Newcastle upon Tyne, Central Library
Nottingham, Central Library
Sheffield, Central Library

FINLAND

Helsinki, Teknillisen Korkeakoulun Kirjasto

FRANCE

Gif-sur-Yvette, Centre d'Etudes Nucléaires de Saclay
Paris, Académie des Sciences

GERMANY

Berlin, Hahn-Meitner-Institut für Kernforschung Berlin
Frankfurt/Main, Gmelin-Institut
Munich, Technische Hochschule, Bibliothek

GHANA

Accra, University College of Ghana

GREECE

Athens, Greek Atomic Energy Commission

GUATEMALA

Guatemala, Comisión Nacional de Energía Nuclear

HAITI

Port au Prince, University of Haiti

HONDURAS

Tegucicalpa, Comisión Hondureña de Energía Atómica

ICELAND

Reykjavik, University of Iceland, Atomic Energy Library

INDIA

Bombay, Department of Atomic Energy

INDONESIA

Bandung, Java, Bandung Institute of Technology
Djogjakarta, Java, Science Faculty, Gadjan Mada University

IRAN

Tehran, Tehran University Center for Nuclear Studies

IRAQ

Baghdad, Iraqi Atomic Energy Commission

IRELAND

Dublin, University College

ISRAEL

Rehovoth, Israel Atomic Energy Commission

ITALY

Rome, Centro di Studi Nucleari della Casaccia
Rome, Comitato Nazionale per l'Energia Nucleare

JAPAN

Tokyo, National Diet Library

KOREA

Seoul, Office of Atomic Energy

LEBANON

Beirut, American University

LUXEMBOURG

Luxembourg, Ministry of Transport and Electricity

MALAYA

Kuala Lumpur, University of Malaya

MEXICO

Mexico, D.F., Comisión Nacional de Energía Nuclear

NETHERLANDS

The Hague, Reactor Centrum Nederland

NEW ZEALAND

Wellington, Department of Scientific and Industrial Research

NORTHERN IRELAND

Belfast, City Library

NORWAY

Lilleström, Institutt för Atomenergi

PAKISTAN

Lahore, West Pakistan, Atomic Energy Centre

PERU

Lima, Junta de Control de Energía Atomica

PHILIPPINE REPUBLIC

Manila, Philippine Atomic Energy Commission

POLAND

Warsaw, Biura Pelnomocnika Rzadu do Spraw Wykorzystania Energii Jadrowej

PORTUGAL

Sacavem, Junta de Energía Nuclear

REPUBLIC OF SOUTH AFRICA

Pretoria, Atomic Energy Board Library

REPUBLIC OF THE CONGO

Leopoldville, Université Lovanium

SCOTLAND

Glasgow, Mitchell Library

SPAIN

Madrid, Junta de Energia Nuclear

SWEDEN

Nyköping, Artiebolaget Atomenergi

SWITZERLAND

Zurich, Institut fur Physik, Eidg. Technische Hochschule

THAILAND

Bangkok, Office of the Thai Atomic Energy Commission, Department of Science

TURKEY

Ankara, Turkish Atomic Energy Commission, Atomic Energy Library

URUGUAY

Montevideo, Comision Nacional de Energía Atomica

VENEZUELA

Caracas, Instituto Venezolano de Investigaciones Científicas

VIETNAM

Dalat, Institute of Nuclear Research, Atomic Energy Office

YUGOSLAVIA

Belgrade, Federal Commission for Nuclear Energy

International Agencies

AUSTRIA

Vienna, International Atomic Energy

BELGIUM

Brussels, La Bibliotheque EURATOM

FRANCE

Paris, European Nuclear Energy Agency, O.E.C.D.

ITALY

Ispra, EURATOM Research Center

SWITZERLAND

Geneva, United Nations Library

UNITED STATES

Washington, D.C., Inter-American Nuclear Energy Commission

Appendix D

MEMBERSHIP OF COMMITTEES U.S. ATOMIC ENERGY COMMISSION (AUGUST, 1961)

Advisory Committee for Biology and Medicine

DR. JOHN C. BUGHER, Chairman; Director, Puerto Rico Nuclear Center, Rio Piedras, Puerto Rico.

DR. H. BENTLEY GLASS, Professor of Biology, Johns Hopkins University, Baltimore, Md.

DR. FRED J. HODGES, Professor and Chairman of Radiology, Department of Radiology, University of Michigan Medical Center, Ann Arbor, Mich.

DR. JAMES G. HORSFALL, Director, Connecticut Agricultural Experiment Station, New Haven, Conn.

DR. ROBERT F. LOEB, Bard Professor of Medicine (Columbia University), 950 Park Ave., New York, N.Y.

DR. LEONIDAS D. MARINELLI, Associate Director, Radiological Physics Division, Argonne National Laboratory, Argonne, Ill.

DR. CARL V. MOORE, Professor of Medicine, Department of Internal Medicine, Washington University, Barnes & Wohl Hospital, St. Louis, Mo.

DR. JAMES H. STERNER, Medical Director, Eastman Kodak Co., Rochester, N.Y.

DR. HARLAND G. WOOD, Director, Biochemistry Department, School of Medicine, Western Reserve University, Cleveland, Ohio.

DR. HENRY I. KOHN, Scientific Secretary; Clinical Professor of Experimental Radiology, University of California Medical Center, San Francisco, Calif.

Advisory Committee for Standard Reference Materials and Methods of Measurement

DR. SAMUEL C. T. MCDOWELL, Chairman; Chief, Chemistry and Physics Branch, Division of Nuclear Materials Management, U.S. Atomic Energy Commission, Washington, D.C.

RALPH J. JONES, Division of Nuclear Materials Management, U.S. Atomic Energy Commission, Washington, D.C.

DR. CHARLES F. METZ, Group Leader, Analytical Chemistry Group, Chemistry and Metallurgical Research Division, Los Alamos Scientific Laboratory, Los Alamos, N.M.

DR. HORACE W. NORTON III, Professor of Statistical Design and Analysis, University of Illinois, Urbana, Ill.

DR. EDWIN F. ORLEMANN, Professor of Chemistry and Chemical Engineering, University of California, Berkeley, Calif.

DR. LEONARD P. PEPKOWITZ, Vice President, Nuclear Materials and Equipment Corp., Apollo, Pa.

C. J. RODDEN, Area Manager, New Brunswick Area Office, Atomic Energy Commission, New Brunswick, N.J.

CHARLES M. STEVENS, Argonne National Laboratory, Lemont, Ill.

C. D. W. THORNTON, Vice President, ITT Laboratories, International Telephone & Telegraph Corp., Fort Wayne, Ind.

DR. EDWARD WICHERS, Associate Director, National Bureau of Standards, Department of Commerce, Washington, D.C.

Advisory Committee of State Officials

WILLIAM L. BATT, JR., Secretary, Department of Labor and Industry, Harrisburg, Pa.

SALVATORE A. BONTEMPO, Commissioner, Department of Conservation and Economic Development, Trenton, N.J.

JOHN B. BRECKINRIDGE, Attorney General of Kentucky, Frankfort, Ky.

DR. BERNARD BUCOVE, Director of Health, State Department of Health, Seattle, Wash.

DR. R. L. CLEERE, Executive Director, State Department of Public Health, Denver, Colo.

NORMAN A. ERBE, Attorney General of Iowa, Des Moines, Iowa.

CURTISS M. EVERTS, JR., State Sanitary Engineer, Oregon State Board of Health, Portland, Ore.

CARL FRASURE, Department of Political Science, West Virginia University, Morgantown, W. Va.

JAMES G. FROST, Deputy Attorney General of Maine, Augusta, Me.

DR. ALEXANDER GRENDON, Coordinator of Atomic Energy Development and Radiation Protection, State of California, Sacramento, Calif.

DR. ALBERT E. HEUSTIS, Commissioner of Health, Michigan Department of Health, Lansing, Mich.

DR. HERMAN E. HILLEBOE, Commissioner of Health, State Department of Health, Albany, N.Y.

C. W. KLASSEN, Chief Sanitary Engineer, Department of Public Health, Springfield, Ill.

DR. MORRIS KLEINFELD, Director, Division of Industrial Hygiene, Department of Labor, New York, N.Y.

W. T. LINTON, Executive Director, Water Pollution Control Authority, South Carolina State Board of Health, Columbia, S.C.

HENRY M. MARX, Coordinator, Atomic Development Activities, Greenwich, Conn.

KARL M. MASON, Director, Bureau of Environmental Health, Pennsylvania Department of Health, Harrisburg, Pa.

DR. JAMES E. PEAVY, Commissioner of Health, State Department of Health, Austin, Tex.

WILLIAM J. PIERCE, University of Michigan Law School, Ann Arbor, Mich.

B. A. POOLE, Director, Bureau of Environmental Sanitation, Indiana State Board of Health, Indianapolis, Ind.

RAYMOND I. RIGNEY, Coordinator of Atomic Development, The Commonwealth of Massachusetts, Boston, Mass.

D. P. ROBERTS, Chief, Industrial Hygiene Section, Tennessee Department of Health, Nashville, Tenn.

ROBERT H. SOLOMONS, III, Executive Secretary, Regional Advisory Council on Nuclear Energy, Atlanta, Ga.

OLIVER TOWNSEND, Director, Office of Atomic Development, State of New York, Albany, N.Y.

JAMES T. VOCELLE, Chairman, Industrial Commission of Florida, Tallahassee, Fla.

Advisory Committee on Isotope and Radiation Development

DR. PAUL C. AEBERSOLD, Chairman; Director, Division of Isotopes Development, U.S. Atomic Energy Commission, Washington, D.C.

DR. JAMES F. BLACK, Products Research Division, Esso Research and Engineering Co., Linden, N.J.

DR. LAUGHLIN M. CURRIE, Vice President, Atomic Energy Division, The Babcock & Wilcox Co., New York, N.Y.

SAMUEL E. EATON, Arthur D. Little, Inc., Cambridge, Mass.

DR. HENRY J. GOMBERG, Director, Memorial-Phoenix Project, University of Michigan, Ann Arbor, Mich.

JOHN J. GREBE, Director, Basic and Nuclear Research, Dow Chemical Co., Midland, Mich.

DR. MOSES A. GREENFIELD, Dpartment of Radiology, School of Medicine, University of California Medical Center, University of California, Los Angeles, Calif.

DR. THORFIN R. HOGNESS, Director, Chicago Midway Laboratories, University of Chicago, Chicago, Ill.

JOHN L. KURANZ, Vice President, Nuclear-Chicago Corp., Des Plaines, Ill.

CLARENCE E. LARSON, Director of Research, Union Carbide Corporation, New York, N.Y.

JOHN J. MCMAHON, Manager, Marketing Research, American Machine & Foundry Atomics, Greenwich, Conn.

HOMER S. MYERS, Vice President of Marketing, Tracerlab, Inc., Waltham, Mass.

DR. LEONARD REIFFEL, Director of Physics Research, Armour Research Foundation, Illinois Institute of Technology, Chicago, Ill.

DR. LAURISTON S. TAYLOR, Chief, Atomic and Radiation Physics Division, National Bureau of Standards, Washington, D.C.

OLIVER H. TOWNSEND, Director, Office of Atomic Development, State of New York, Albany, N.Y.

Advisory Committee on Medical Uses of Isotopes

DR. WALLACE D. ARMSTRONG, Professor, University of Minnesota Medical School, Minneapolis, Minn.

DR. REYNOLDS F. BROWN, Department of Radiology, University of California Medical School, San Francisco, Calif.

DR. DONALD S. CHILDS, JR., Section of Therapeutic Radiology, Mayo Clinic, Rochester, Minn.

DR. JOHN A. D. COOPER, Assistant Dean Northwestern University Medical School, Chicago, Ill.

DR. GEORGE V. LEROY, Associate Dean, Division of Biological Sciences, University of Chicago, Chicago, Ill.

DR. EDITH H. QUIMBY, Associate Professor of Radiology, College of Physicians and Surgeons, Columbia University, New York, N.Y.

DR. RULON W. RAWSON, Memorial Hospital, New York, N.Y.

Advisory Committee on Reactor Physics

PHILIP B. HEMMIG; Chairman, Reactors Physics Branch, Division of Reactor Development, U.S. Atomic Energy Commission, Washington, D.C.

DR. ROBERT AVERY, Argonne National Laboratory, Argonne, Ill.

DR. E. RICHARD COHEN, Research Advisor, Atomics International, North American Aviation, Inc., Canoga Park, Calif.

DESLONDE DE BOISBLANC, Director, Reactor Physics and Engineering, Phillips Petroleum Co., Idaho Falls, Idaho.

JACK CHERNICK, Brookhaven National Laboratory, Upton, Long Island, N.Y.

DR. GERHARD DESSAUER, Director, Physics Section, E. I. du Pont de Nemours & Co., Inc., Aiken, S.C.

DR. MILTON EDLUND, Manager, Physics and Mathematics Department, Babcock & Wilcox Co., Lynchburg, Va.

DR. RICHARD EHRLICH, Knolls Atomic Power Laboratory, General Electric Co., Schenectady, N.Y.

DR. PAUL F. GAST, Manager, Physics and Instrument Research and Development, General Electric Co., Schenectady, N.Y.

DR. GORDON HANSEN, Los Alamos Scientific Laboratory, Los Alamos, N.M.

DR. IRVING KAPLAN, Professor of Nuclear Engineering, Massachusetts Institute of Technology, Cambridge, Mass.

DR. SIDNEY KRASIK, Astronuclear Laboratory, Westinghouse Electric Corp., Pittsburgh, Pa.

DR. F. C. MAIENSCHEIN, Oak Ridge National Laboratory, Oak Ridge, Tenn.

DR. THEODORE MERKLE, Associate Director, Pluto Project, "R" Division, Lawrence Radiation Laboratory, Livermore, Calif.

DR. THOMAS M. SNYDER, Manager, Physics—APED, Vallecitos Atomic Laboratory, General Electric Co., Pleasanton, Calif.

DR. JOHN J. TAYLOR, Westinghouse Electric Corporation, Bettis Atomic Power Division, Pittsburgh, Pa.

DR. PAUL F. ZWEIFEL, Professor of Nuclear Engineering, University of Michigan, Ann Arbor, Mich.

DR. ALVIN RAKOWSKY, Secretary; Division of Reactor Development, U.S. Atomic Energy Commission, Washington, D.C.

Advisory Committee on Reactor Safeguards (ACRS)

DR. THEOS J. THOMPSON, Chairman; Director, MIT Nuclear Reactor, Massachusetts Institute of Technology, Cambridge, Mass.

DR. HARVEY BROOKS, Dean of Engineering and Applied Physics, Harvard University, Cambridge, Mass.

DR. WILLARD P. CONNER, JR., Technical Assistant to Director of Research Center, Research Department, Hercules Powder Co., Wilmington, Del.

DR. WILLIAM K. ERGEN, Principal Physicist, Oak Ridge National Laboratory, Oak Ridge, Tenn.

DR. FRANKLIN A. GIFFORD, JR., Meteorologist in charge of the Oak Ridge Office, U.S. Weather Bureau, Oak Ridge, Tenn.

DR. DAVID B. HALL, K-Division Leader, Los Alamos Scientific Laboratory, Los Alamos, N.M.

DR. C. ROGERS MCCULLOUGH, Director of Reactor Safeguards (for foreign reactors) and Scientific Advisor to Board of Director, Nuclear Utility Services, Washington, D.C.

DR. HENRY W. NEWSON, Professor of Physics, Duke University, Durham, N.C.

KENNETH R. OSBORN, Chief Engineer, General Chemical Division, Allied Chemical Corp., New York, N.Y.

DONALD A. ROGERS, Manager of Project Analysis, Central Research Laboratory, Allied Chemical & Dye Corp., Morristown, N.J.

DR. LESLIE SILVERMAN, Professor of Engineering in Environmental Hygiene, Head of Department of Industrial Hygiene, Director of Radiological Hygiene Program, Harvard University, School of Public Health, Boston, Mass.

REUEL C. STRATTON, Consulting Engineer, Hartford, Conn.

DR. CHARLES R. WILLIAMS, Assistant Vice President, Liberty Mutual Insurance Co., Boston, Mass.

DR. ABEL WOLMAN, Consulting Engineer and Professor Emeritus, Sanitary Engineering, Johns Hopkins University, Baltimore, Md.

Advisory Committee on Technical Information

EDWARD J. BRUNENKANT, Chairman; Director, Division of Technical Information, United States Atomic Energy Commission, Washington, D.C.

HERBERT S. BAILEY, JR., Director, Princeton University Press, Princeton, N.J.

JOHN E. DOBBIN, Project Director, Educational Testing Service, St. Petersburg, Fla.

BERNARD M. FRY, Deputy Head, Office of Science Information Service, National Science Foundation, Washington, D.C.

JAMES L. GAYLORD, Senior Partner of James L. Gaylord Associates, Pacific Palisades, Calif.

DR. ALLEN G. GRAY, Editor, "Metal Progress," American Society for Metals, Metals Park, Ohio.

EUGENE J. HARDY, Assistant Vice President, National Association of Manufacturers, Washington, D.C.

NORMAN H. JACOBSON, Executive Business Editor, "Electric Light and Power," Haywood Publishing Company, Chicago, Ill.

ANDREW W. KRAMER, Editor, "Atomics," Technical Publishing Company, Barrington, Ill.

JOHN W. LANDIS, Manager, Atomic Energy Division, The Babcock and Wilcox Company, Lynchburg, Va. (representing American Nuclear Society, Chicago, Ill.).

FREDERIC A. PAWLEY, Research Secretary, American Institute of Architects, Washington, D.C.

KARL T. SCHWARTZWALDER, Director of Research, A-C Sparkplug Division, General Motors Corporation, Flint, Mich. (representing the American Ceramic Society, Inc., Columbus, Ohio)

OLIVER H. TOWNSEND, Director, Office of Atomic Development, State of New York, New York, N.Y.

STANLEY A. TUCKER, American Society of Mechanical Engineers, New York, N.Y.

JOHN W. WIGHT, Vice President, McGraw-Hill Book Company, Inc., New York, N.Y.

Atomic Energy Labor-Management Relations Panel

CYRUS S. CHING, Chairman; Industrial Relations Consultant and former Director of the Federal Mediation and Conciliation Service, Washington, D.C.

REV. LEO C. BROWN, S.J., Professor of Economics and Director of the Institute of Social Order, St. Louis University, St. Louis, Mo.

VICE ADM. O. S. COLCLOUGH, USN, Retired, Provost, the George Washington University, Washington, D.C.

ROBBEN W. FLEMING, Professor of Law, University of Illinois, Urbana, Ill.

CHARLES O. GREGORY, Professor of Law, University of Virginia, Charlottesville, Va.

RUSSELL A. SMITH, Associate Dean, University of Michigan Law School, Ann Arbor, Mich.

Committee of Senior Reviewers

DR. ALVIN C. GRAVES, Chairman; Los Alamos Scientific Laboratory, Los Alamos, N.M.

DR. JOHN P. HOWE, Nuclear Reactor Laboratory, Cornell University, Ithaca, N.Y.

DR. FRANK C. HOYT, Missile Systems Division, Lockheed Aircraft Corp., Palo Alto, Calif.

DR. WARREN C. JOHNSON, Vice President, University of Chicago, Chicago, Ill.

DR. WINSTON M. MANNING, Director, Chemistry Division, Argonne National Laboratory, Argonne, Ill.

DR. J. REGINALD RICHARDSON, Professor of Physics, University of California at Los Angeles, Calif.

General Advisory Committee (GAC)

KENNETH S. PITZER, Chairman; President, Rice University, Houston, Tex.

PHILIP H. ABELSON, Director, Geophysical Laboratory, Carnegie Institution, Washington, D.C.

MANSON BENEDICT, Professor of Nuclear Engineering, Massachusetts Institute of Technology, Cambridge, Mass.

WILLARD F. LIBBY, Professor of Chemistry, University of California, Los Angeles, Calif.

EGER V. MURPHREE, President, Esso Research & Engineering Co., Linden, N.J.

NORMAN F. RAMSEY, Professor of Physics, Harvard University, Cambridge, Mass.

J. C. WARNER, President, Carnegie Institute of Technology, Pittsburgh, Pa.

EUGENE P. WIGNER, Palmer Physical Laboratory, Princeton University, Princeton, N.J.

JOHN H. WILLIAMS, Professor of Physics, University of Minnesota, Minneapolis, Minn.

Historical Advisory Committee

DR. JAMES P. BAXTER, III, Chairman; President Emeritus, Williams College, Williamstown, Mass.

DR. JOHN M. BLUM, Department of History, Yale University, New Haven, Conn.

DR. JAMES L. CATE, Department of History, University of Chicago, Chicago, Ill.

DR. ARTHUR H. COMPTON, Washington University, St. Louis, Mo.

DR. FRANCIS T. MILES, Brookhaven National Laboratory, Upton, N.Y.

DON K. PRICE, JR., Dean, Graduate School of Public Administration, Harvard University, Cambridge, Mass.

DR. RICHARD G. HEWLETT, AEC representative; Chief Historian, U.S. Atomic Energy Commission, Washington, D.C.

Military Liaison Committee (MLC)

HON. GERALD W. JOHNSON, Chairman

MAJ. GEN. BRUCE K. HOLLOWAY, United States Air Force

REAR ADM. FRANK A. BRANDLEY, United States Navy

BRIG. GEN. RALPH L. WASSELL, United States Air Force

BRIG. GEN. DAVID C. LEWIS, United States Army

BRIG. GEN. JOHN W. KEATING, United States Army

CAPT. FRANK H. BRUMBY, JR., United States Navy

Patent Advisory Panel

JOHN A. DIENNER, Brown, Jackson, Boettcher & Dienner, Chicago, Ill.

JOHN C. STEDMAN, University of Wisconsin Law School, Madison, Wis.

Patent Compensation Board

ROBERT C. WATSON, Chairman; firm of Watson, Cole, Grindle & Watson, Washington, D.C.

DOUGLAS MCLEOD COOMBS, Simmonds Precision Products Incorporated, Tarrytown, N.Y.

MALCOLM W. FRASER, Private Practice of Patent Law, Toledo, Ohio

HERMAN I. HERSH, firm of Ooms, McDougall, Williams & Hersh, Chicago, Ill.

LAWRENCE E. KINGSLAND, firm of Kingsland, Rogers, Ezell & Robbins, St. Louis, Mo.

GEORGE SIPKIN, Private Practice of Patent Law, Washington, D.C.

Personnel Security Review Board

GANSON PURCELL, Chairman; Purcell & Nelson, Washington, D.C.

DR. PAUL E. KLOPSTEG, Special Consultant, National Science Foundation, Washington, D.C.

JOHN J. WILSON, firm of Whiteford, Hart, Carmody & Wilson, Washington, D.C.

Plowshare Advisory Committee

DR. SPOFFORD G. ENGLISH, Chairman; Assistant General Manager for Research and Development, U.S. Atomic Energy Commission, Washington, D.C.

DR. PHILIP H. ABELSON, Director, Geophysical Laboratory, Carnegie Institution, Washington, D.C.

WILLARD BASCOM, Technical Director, The AMSOC Committee, National Academy of Sciences, Washington, D.C.

LT. GEN. JAMES H. DOOLITTLE, Space Technology Laboratories, Inc., Los Angeles, Calif.

DR. LOUIS H. HEMPELMANN, School of Medicine and Dentistry, University of Rochester, Rochester, N.Y.

DR. WILLARD F. LIBBY, Department of Chemistry, University of California, Los Angeles, Calif.

DR. W. RANDOLPH LOVELACE II, Director, Lovelace Foundation, Albuquerque, N.M.

DR. DONALD H. MCLAUGHLIN, President, Homestake Mining Co., San Francisco, Calif.

DR. PHILIP C. RUTLEDGE, Partner, Moran, Proctor, Muser & Rutledge, New York, N.Y.

DR. PAUL B. SEARS, Chairman, Conservation Program, Yale University, New Haven, Conn.

DR. ABEL WOLMAN, Consulting Engineer and Professor Emeritus, Sanitary Engineering, Johns Hopkins University, Baltimore, Md.

Stack Gas Problem Working Group

DR. LYLE I. GILBERTSON, Director, Research and Engineering Department, Air Réduction Co., Inc., Murray Hill, N.J.

A. E. GORMAN, Consultant, U.S. Atomic Energy Commission, Washington, D.C.

DR. H. FRASER JOHNSTONE, Professor of Chemical Engineering, University of Illinois, Urbana, Ill.

DR. CHARLES E. LAPPLE, Stanford Research Institute, Menlo Park, Calif.

DR. J. A. LIEBERMAN, Division of Reactor Development, U.S. Atomic Energy Commission, Washington, D.C.

DR. LESLIE SILVERMAN, Professor of Industrial Hygiene, School of Public Health, Harvard University, Boston, Mass.

DR. ABEL WOLMAN, Consulting Engineer and Professor Emeritus, Sanitary Engineering, Johns Hopkins University, Baltimore, Md.

DR. WILLIAM P. YANT, Director of Research and Development, Mine Safety Appliance Co., Pittsburgh, Pa.

Appendix E

STABLE ISOTOPES AND NATURAL RADIOISOTOPES (EXCLUDING TRANSURANIUM ELEMENTS)

Atomic Number	*Element*	*Symbol*	*Mass Number*	*Natural Abundance (%)*	*Enriched Abundance* [1] *(%)*
1	Hydrogen	H	1	99.985	
	Deuterium	D	2	0.015	
2	Helium	He	3	0.00013	
			4	c. 100	
3	Lithium	Li	6	7.52	99.4
			7	92.48	99.97
4	Beryllium	Be	9	100	
5	Boron	B	10	18.98	89.9
			11	81.02	97.8
6	Carbon	C	12	98.89	99.99
			13	1.11	7.52
7	Nitrogen	N	14	99.64	
			15	0.36	
8	Oxygen	O	16	99.76	
			17	0.037	
			18	0.204	
9	Fluorine	F	19	100	
10	Neon	Ne	20	90.8	
			21	0.26	
			22	8.9	
11	Sodium	Na	23	100	
12	Magnesium	Mg	24	78.60	99.6
			25	10.11	92.3
			26	11.29	98.1
13	Aluminum	Al	27	100	
14	Silicone	Si	28	92.27	99.4
			29	4.68	68.6
			30	3.05	72.6
15	Phosphorus	P	31	100	
16	Sulfur	S	32	95.06	98.5
			33	0.74	22.1
			34	4.18	20.7
			36	0.016	0.88
17	Chlorine	Cl	35	75.4	95.7
			37	24.6	66.3
18	Argon	A	36	0.337	
			38	0.063	
			40	99.60	
19	Potassium	K	39	93.08	99.96
			40 *	0.0119	7.8
			41	6.91	99.2
20	Calcium	Ca	40	96.97	99.98
			42	0.64	82.5
			43	0.145	72.1
			44	2.06	98.0
			46	0.0033	10.2
			48	0.185	84.3
21	Scandium	Sc	45	100	
22	Titanium	Ti	46	7.95	84.4
22	Titanium	Ti	47	7.75	82.8
			48	73.45	99.2
			49	5.51	79.4
			50	5.34	84.7
			52	83.76	99.97
			53	9.55	95.2
			54	2.38	89.0
25	Manganese	Mn	55	100	
26	Iron	Fe	54	5.84	96.7
			56	91.68	99.9
			57	2.17	87.3
			58	0.31	86.0
27	Cobalt	Co	59	100	
28	Nickel	Ni	58	67.76	99.9
			60	26.16	98.5
			61	1.25	83.1
			62	3.66	96.8
			64	1.16	97.4
29	Copper	Cu	63	69.1	99.7
			65	30.9	98.2
30	Zinc	Zn	64	48.89	93.4
			66	27.82	93.4
			67	4.14	62.6
			68	18.54	95.5
			70	0.617	48.4
31	Gallium	Ga	69	60.2	98.4
			71	39.8	98.1
32	Germanium	Ge	70	20.55	91.4
			72	27.37	94.9
			73	7.61	78.0
			74	36.74	95.8
			76	7.67	81.0
33	Arsenic	As	75	100	
34	Selenium	Se	74	0.87	33.1
			76	9.02	88.5
			77	7.58	91.7
			78	23.52	98.4
			80	49.82	98.4
			82	9.19	89.9
35	Bromine	Br	79	55.2	90.5
			81	49.48	96.8
36	Krypton	Kr	78	0.35	
			81	2.27	
			82	11.6	
			83	11.5	
			84	57.0	
			86	17.3	
37	Rubidium	Rb	85	72.15	96.0
			87 *	27.85	89.6

* Radioactive.

[1] Available from the Oak Ridge National Laboratory, Oak Ridge, Tenn.

STABLE ISOTOPES AND NATURAL RADIOISOTOPES (*Cont.*)

Atomic Number	*Element*	*Symbol*	*Mass Number*	*Natural Abundance (%)*	*Enriched Abundance* [1] *(%)*
38	Strontium	Sr	84	0.56	63.7
			86	9.86	89.0
			87	7.02	73.1
			88	82.56	99.7
39	Yttrium	Y	89	100	
40	Zirconium	Zr	90	51.46	98.7
			91	11.23	88.0
			92	17.11	95.8
			94	17.40	97.9
			96	2.80	89.5
41	Columbium	Cb	93	100	
42	Molybdenum	Mo	92	15.86	95.5
			94	9.12	84.9
			95	15.70	91.3
			96	16.50	92.0
			97	9.45	89.6
			98	23.75	96.3
			100	9.62	93.0
43	Technetium	Tc	—		
44	Ruthenium	Ru	96	5.47	77.3
			98	1.84	65.05
			99	12.77	81.18
			100	12.56	88.9
			101	17.10	91.13
			102	31.70	94.2
			104	18.56	98.24
45	Rhodium	Rh	103	100	
46	Palladium	Pd	102	0.96	34.3
			104	10.97	63.2
			105	22.23	78.2
			106	27.33	82.3
			108	26.71	94.2
			110	11.81	91.4
47	Silver	Ag	107	51.35	96.1
			109	48.65	99.5
48	Cadmium	Cd	106	1.215	32.9
			108	0.875	24.8
			110	12.39	70.0
			111	12.75	64.5
			112	24.07	83.5
			113	12.26	54.1
			114	28.86	94.2
			116	7.58	71.2
49	Indium	In	113	4.23	65.4
			115 *	95.77	99.9
50	Tin	St	112	0.95	72.5
			114	0.65	50.0
			115	0.34	17.7
			116	14.24	92.6
			117	7.57	83.8
			118	24.01	96.2
			119	8.58	83.6
			120	32.97	98.2
			122	4.71	88.9
			124	5.98	95.0
51	Antimony	Sb	121	57.25	99.4
			123	42.75	96.7
52	Tellurium	Te	120	0.089	22.3
			122	2.46	86.2
			123	0.87	60.9
			124	4.61	83.9
			125	6.99	87.9
			126	18.71	95.4
			128	31.79	96.5
52	Tellurium	Te	130	97.8	
53	Iodine	I	127	100	
54	Xenon	Xe	124	0.094	
			126	0.092	
			128	1.92	
			129	26.4	
			130	0.1	
			131	21.2	
			132	26.9	
			134	10.4	
			136	8.9	
55	Cesium	Cs	133	100	
56	Barium	Ba	130	1.101	27.5
			132	0.097	12.0
			134	2.42	51.4
			135	6.59	67.3
			136	7.81	50.0
			137	11.32	43.6
			138	71.66	98.0
57	Lanthanum	La	138 *	0.089	1.7
			139	99.911	99.96
58	Cerium	Ce	136	0.193	30.0
			138	0.250	13.1
			140	88.48	99.7
			142	11.07	90.1
59	Praseodymium	Pr	141	100	
60	Neodymium	Nd	142	27.13	93.9
			143	12.20	83.9
			144 *	23.87	95.7
			145	8.30	78.6
			146	17.18	95.6
			148	5.72	89.9
			150	5.60	94.8
61	Illinium	Il	—		
62	Samarium	Sm	144	3.16	85.7
			147 *	15.07	85.1
			148	11.27	76.0
			149	13.84	81.5
			150	7.47	74.1
			152	26.63	93.9
			154	22.53	99.1
63	Europium	Eu	151	47.8	
			153	52.2	
64	Gadolinium	Gd	152	0.20	15.0
			154	2.15	33.2
			155	14.73	72.3
			156	20.47	80.2
			157	15.68	69.7
			158	24.87	92.9
			160	21.90	95.4
65	Terbium	Tb	159	100	
66	Dysprosium	Dy	156	0.052	
			158	0.090	
			160	2.29	
			161	18.9	
			162	25.5	
			163	25.0	
			164	28.2	
67	Holmium	Ho	165	100	
68	Erbium	Er	162	0.136	
			164	1.56	
			166	33.4	
			167	22.9	

Stable Isotopes and Natural Radioisotopes (*Cont.*)

Atomic Number	*Element*	*Symbol*	*Mass Number*	*Natural Abundance (%)*	*Enriched Abundance* [1] *(%)*
68	Erbium	Er	168	27.1	
			170	14.9	
69	Thulium	Tm	169	100	
70	Ytterbium	Yb	168	0.14	
			170	3.03	
			171	14.3	
			172	21.8	
			173	16.2	
			174	31.8	
			176	12.7	
71	Lutecium	Lu	175	97.40	
			176 *	2.60	
72	Hafnium	Hf	174	0.18	10.1
			176	5.15	59.5
			177	18.39	62.9
			178	27.08	84.8
			179	13.79	53.3
			180	35.44	94.0
73	Tantalum	Ta	180	0.012	0.21
			181	99.988	
74	Tungsten	W	180 *	0.135	9.0
			182	26.4	94.3
			183	14.4	86.2
			184	30.6	95.7
			186	28.4	97.9
75	Rhenium	Re	185	37.07	85.4
			187 *	62.93	98.2
76	Osmium	Os	184	0.018	
			186	1.59	
			187	1.64	
			188	13.3	
			189	16.1	
			190	26.4	
			192	41.0	

Atomic Number	*Element*	*Symbol*	*Mass Number*	*Natural Abundance (%)*	*Enriched Abundance* [1] *(%)*
77	Iridium	Ir	191	37.3	85.9
			193	62.7	89.1
78	Platinum	Pt	190 *	1.012	0.8
			192	0.78	13.9
			194	32.8	65.1
			195	33.7	60.1
			196	25.4	65.9
			198	7.23	61.0
79	Gold	Au	197	100	
80	Mercury	Hg	196	0.146	8.4
			198	10.02	79.1
			199	16.84	73.1
			200	23.13	91.3
			201	13.22	71.8
			202	29.80	98.3
			204	6.85	89.2
81	Thallium	Tl	203	29.50	86.0
			205	70.50	98.7
82	Lead	Pb	204	1.48	27.0
			206	23.6	81.0
			207	22.6	66.8
			208	52.3	96.6
83	Bismuth	Bi	209 *	100	
84	Polonium	Po	—		
85	Astatine	At	—		
86	Radon	Rn	—		
87	Francium	Fn	—		
88	Radium	Ra	226 *	100	
89	Actinium	Ac	—		
90	Thorium	Th	232 *	100	
91	Protactinium	Pa	—		
92	Uranium	U	234 *	0.0057	
			235 *	0.714	
			238 *	99.28